Who We Are

OMEGA ENGINEERING is committed to offering its customers the quality service and support that they simply won't find anywhere else in the field of process measurement and control.

Quality Products, Systems, and Custom Designs

At OMEGA our philosophy is to offer quality products as well as complete systems. Our selection of over 40,000 products is unparalleled. More impressively, most can be integrated into complete process measurement and control systems. Our skilled engineering staff is pleased to discuss your custom application requirements.

Made in USA

At OMEGA our philosophy is to offer quality products as well as complete systems. Our selection of over 40,000 products is unparalleled, but what's more impressive is how they can be integrated into complete process measurement and control SYSTEMS. Our skilled engineering staff is pleased to discuss your custom application requirements.

Exclusive Warranty Programs

Every plug-in card, software package and accessory must meet our high quality standards. At OMEGA we also have a special warranty that adds an additional month to cover shipping and handling time. . . a guarantee that you receive the maximum benefit from your warranty. Many products also feature extended warranties, beyond the industry standard.

In addition, we are proud to offer the OMEGACARE™ Extended Warranty Plan available for 1,2, or 3 years additional to the standard product warranty. Ask an OMEGA sales representative for complete details on prices and qualified products.

Customer Service That Can't Be Beat!

At OMEGA we understand that when any instrument malfunctions the results can be equipment downtime and lost productivity. If a repair is needed on any OMEGA instrumentation it will be initiated promptly. In the meantime you'll see how we can keep your process running smoothly. Call us for details!

Service from Trained Professionals

Our Sales and Engineering representatives are "product experts." A new technical training facility provides actual hands-on experience with our instrumentation, and allows simulation of many applications. One of them may be yours!

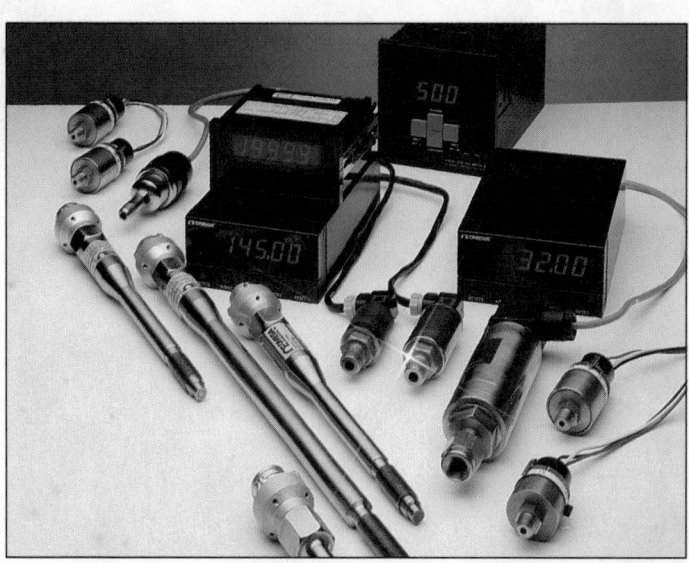

We take special care in packing and shipping every OMEGA product. Upon receipt of your order, please check each item and call us right away on our toll-free customer service line (1-800-622-BEST) if there's a problem. We'll take care of it immediately!

Custom Engineering/Customer Training

Got a Special Application?
Consider Our Custom Services!

Service Beyond the Handbooks℠

OMEGA Engineering proudly offers the most sophisticated and extensive Custom Engineering capabilities in the process measurement and control industry. Our custom manufacturing capabilities extend "beyond the handbooks," and reinforce our customer service/customer-driven philosophy. Whether you need a simple modification of a standard product or complete customized system engineering, OMEGA's degreed engineers can work with you to accommodate your special request.

GOOD NEIGHBOR POLICY

Most customers do not realize that OMEGA's support does not end with their phone call for technical assistance or their visit to OMEGA's technical center for training. If required, OMEGA Engineering also makes "house calls," as part of our Good Neighbor Policy (GNP).

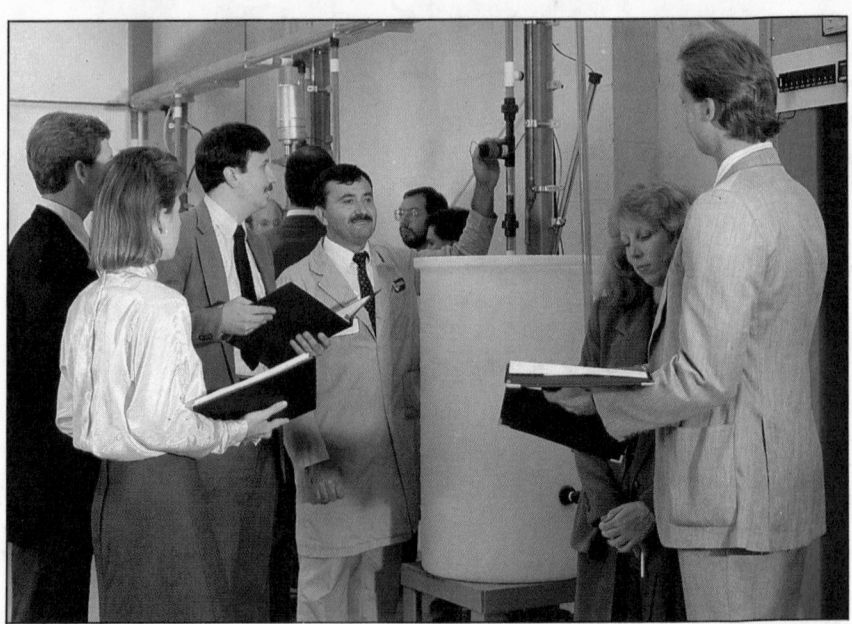

Customer Training Programs (Customer Days)

Fully Equipped 140-Seat Auditorium, Part of OMEGA's Comprehensive Training Facility

OMEGA's technical support includes more than unlimited, free engineering phone assistance. Our complimentary customer training programs allow OMEGA customers to benefit from our well-rounded expertise in industrial measurement and control. Whether you need general or product-specific training, for any level employee, from junior technicians to senior engineers, OMEGA can design a training program to meet your needs.

Individual courses, conducted by OMEGA's Engineering Group, are specialized to cover the topics you want. Depending on the level desired, we can provide basic overviews, refresher courses or in-depth training, covering theoretical and practical topics.

"Customer Days" can be arranged to include two-day sessions at our state-of-the-art Stamford Technical Center. We have a fully-equipped Conference Center, complete with a 140-seat auditorium and overhead display and projection equipment, plus a comprehensive training laboratory, where hands-on training and demonstrations are held. Customers worldwide have found their training at OMEGA to be an invaluable experience.

We welcome the opportunity to design a training program that meets your requirements! ΩΕ

REMEMBER THE OMEGA ADVANTAGES:

- ✔ Over 30 Years of Manufacturing/ Engineering Experience
- ✔ State-of-the Art Test Center Assures Quality Instrumentation and Performance
- ✔ FREE CAD Drawings Kept on File For Your Convenience
- ✔ Every Order, Large or Small, Receives the Same Care and Attention
- ✔ Unparalleled FREE Technical Support
- ✔ Request Our Current Custom Engineering Handbook
- ✔ If You Don't See What You're Looking For, Ask Us!

PHONE OR FAX WITH YOUR CUSTOM REQUESTS!
DIAL:

1-800-82-66342™
1-800-TC-OMEGA

Ask for Custom Engineering, or FAX Us Direct at:
(203) 359-7890

TABLE OF CONTENTS

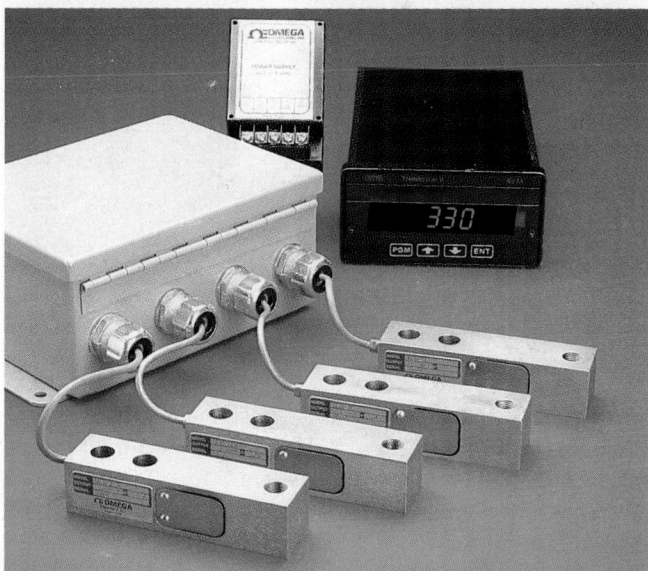

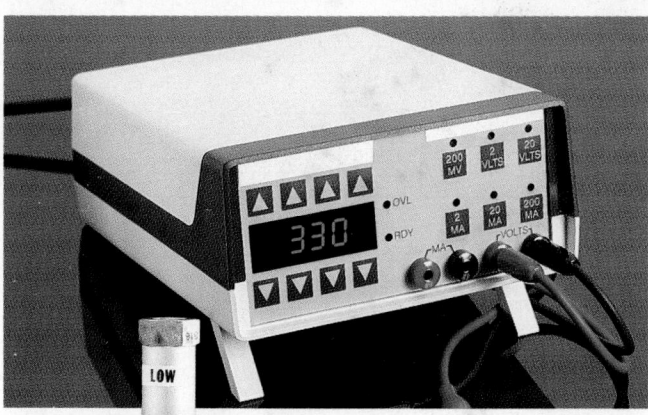

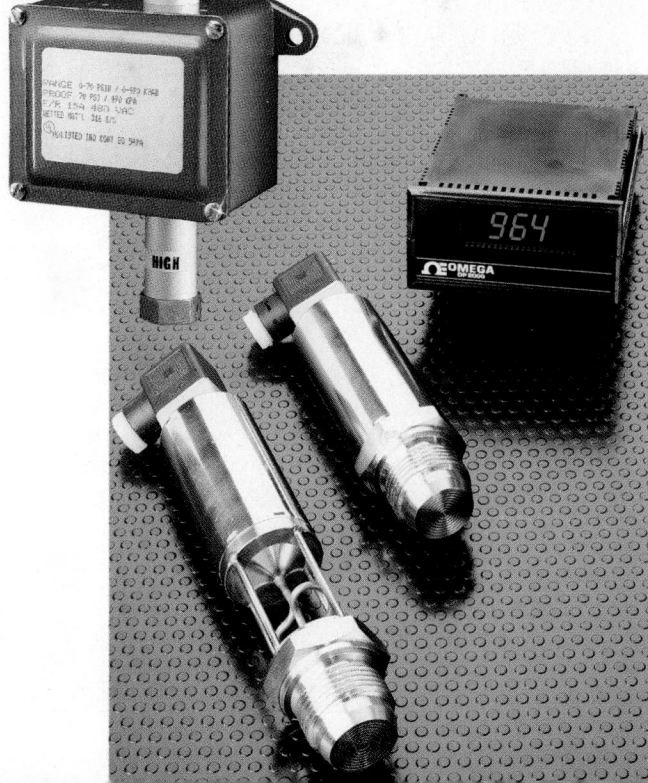

A: NEW PRODUCT SHOWCASE
A Preview of All The New and Exciting Products

B: TRANSDUCERS
An Extensive Variety of Pressure Transducers

C: ACCESSORIES
All The 'Nuts And Bolts' to Complete Your System; Control Modules, Wire, Power Supplies, Etc...

D: INSTRUMENTATION
Complete Instrumentation Packages To Turn Your Transducer Into a Measurement and Control System

E: STRAIN GAGES
A Complete Selection of Strain Gages, Accessories and Instrumentation

F: LOAD AND FORCE MEASUREMENT
A Diverse Selection of Load Cells and Torque Devices

G: PRESSURE GAUGES
Dial Gauges in All Sizes and Accuracies

H: PRESSURE SWITCHES
Miniature and Industrial Switches for General Purpose, Watertight or Hazardous Locations

J: DISPLACEMENT MEASUREMENT
LVDT Transducers and Instrumentation for Precision Displacement Measurement

Y: TECHNICAL AND SCIENTIFIC BOOKS
A Selection of Technical and Scientific Books Selected For Engineers

Z: TECHNICAL REFERENCE SECTION
A Compendium of Technical Articles, Charts and Conversion Tables

A New Product Showcase

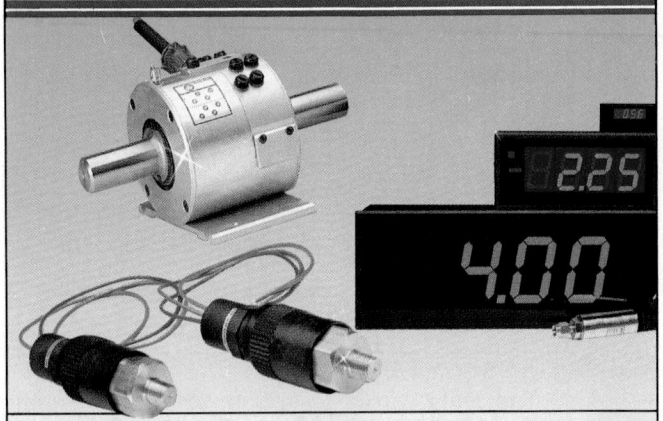

Pressure Transducers	A-1
I/P Converters	A-2
Panel and Benchtop Meters	A-3
Pressure Calibrators	A-4
Instrumentation	A-5
Strain Gages and Instrumenation	A-6
Force Measurement Products	A-7
LVDT, Dial Gages and Pressure Switches	A-8

B Pressure Transducers

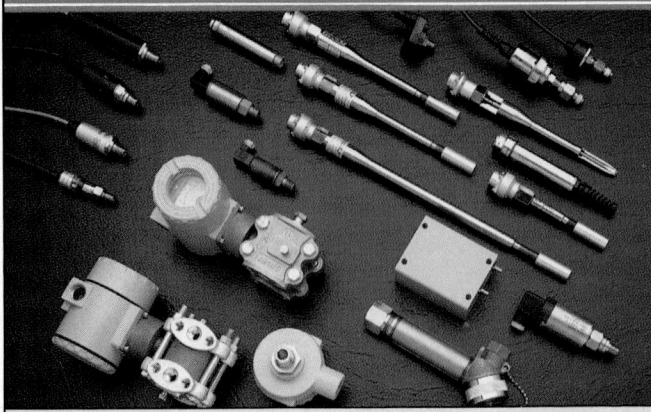

Transducer Application Guide	B-3
Custom Designed Pressure Systems	B-5
Millivolt Output Pressure Transducers	B-9 to B-30
Voltage Output Pressure Transducers	B-31 to B-48
Current Output Pressure Transducers	B-49 to B-87
Specialty Pressure Transducers	B-88 to B-102

C Accessories

Connectors and Solder Checker	C-3 to C-6
Pressure Snubbers and Digital Pressure Gage	C-7
Power Supplies	C-8 to C-12
Transmitters	C-13 to C-21
Solenoid Valves	C-22 to C-25
Batteries	C-26
I/P Current to Pneumatic Converter	C-27 to C-30
Solid State Relays, Timers, Latching Relays and Slip Rings	C-31 to C-37
Wire and Tubing	C-38 to C-41
Compression and Adaptor Fittings and Pressure/Vacuum Feedthroughs	C-42 to C-50
Intrinsic Safety	C-51

D Instrumentation

Instrumentation Article	D-3
Digital Meters	D-5 to D-36
Pressure Controllers	D-37 to D-42
Test and Calibration Equipment	D-43 to D-66
Recorders	D-67 to D-92
Computer Interfaces	D-93 to D-100

E Strain Gauges

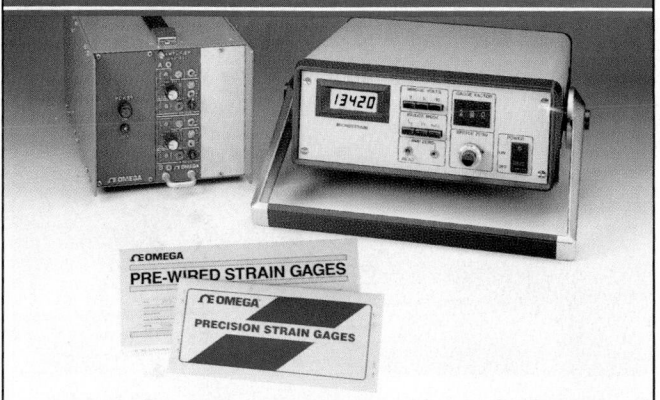

Selection Guide	E-3 to E-6
Strain Gages with 1 Measuring Grid	E-7 to E-10
Strain Gages with 2 Measuring Grids	E-11
Strain Gages with 3 Measuring Grids	E-13 to E-15
Crack and Diaphragm Strain Gages	E-16
Terminal Pads, Adhesives and Bridge Completion Resistors	E-17
Protective Coverings for Strain Gages	E-18
Application Kit and Accessories	E-19
Strain Gage Wire	E-20
Portable Strain Gage Indicators	E-21
Amplifiers, Meters, Computer Cards	E-23 to E-30
Strain Gage Principles	E-31 to E-58

F Load and Force Measurement

Technical Article and Selection Guide	F-3
Miniature Beam and Compression Load Cells	F-7 to F-10
Load Bolts and Load Washers	F-11
"S" Shaped Load Cells	F-13
Beam Type Load Cells	F-15 to F-19
Tank and Bin Weighing Assemblies	F-20
"J" Box Summing Box	F-22
Platform Load Cell	F-23
Rod Ends, Load Buttons	F-24
Thin Beam O.E.M. Load Cells	F-25 to F-28
Digital Force Gages	F-29
Stationary and Rotating Torque Cells	F-30 to F-32

G Dial Pressure Gauges

Selection Guide	G-3
2" and 2½" Commercial Grade Gauges	G-5 to G-10
2½" and 3½" Panel Mount and General Service Gauges	G-11 to G-15
General Service and Liquid Filled Gauges	G-16
4½" and 6" Process Gauges (Differential and Gauge Models)	G-17 to G-20
3½" Pocket Test and 2½" Low Pressure Diaphragm Gauges	G-21
4½" and 6" Test Gauges	G-22 to G-26
Diaphragm Pressure Seals	G-27

H Pressure Switches

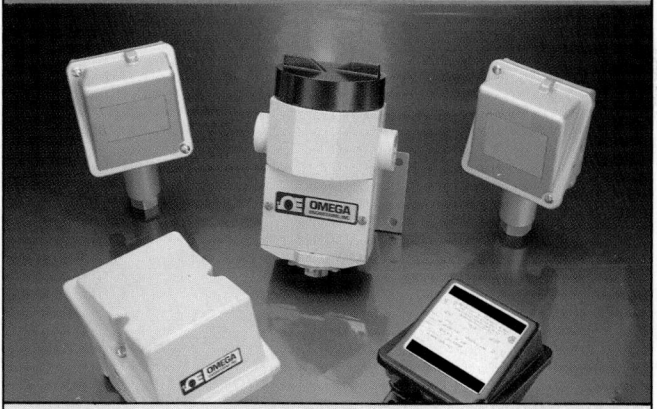

Technical Article and Selection Guide	H-3 to H-6
Miniature Pressure Switches	H-7 to H-12
Process Pressure Switches NEMA 4, 4X	H-13 to H-16
Differential Pressure Switches	H-17
Process Pressure Switches: NEMA 4X, Class I, Div. 2	H-19 to H-21
Accessories: Audible Alarm, External Relays	H-20
Process Pressure Switches for Hazardous Locations	H-22 to H-24

J Displacement

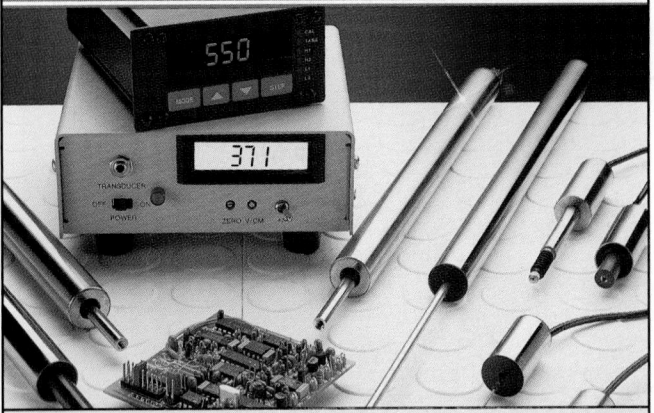

LVDT Displacement Transducers
Selection Guide   J-3
High Speed Displacement System   J-5
AC LVDT Transducers   J-7 to J-10
DC LVDT Transducers   J-11 to J-16
AC LVDT Instrumentation   J-17 to J-20

Y Technical and Scientific Books

Popular Reference Texts   Y-3 to Y-4
Mechanical Engineering Books   Y-5 to Y-9

Z Technical Reference

Pressure Reference Section (Glossary)   Z-3 to Z-6
Pressure Measurement Reference   Z-7 to Z-13
Pressure Transducer Application
Considerations   Z-14 to Z-26
Technical Data Section (Conversion Charts)   Z-27 to Z-28
Hazardous Location Classifications   Z-29 to Z-30
Pressure Transducers Installation and Use   Z-31 to Z-33
Waterhammer   Z-34 to Z-35
Mounting and Installing Load Cells   Z-36 to Z-37
Beam Diagrams and Formulas   Z-38 to Z-62

Z Technical Reference (cont'd.)

Torsional Members, Diagrams and Formulas   Z-63
Circular Flat Plates, Diagrams and Formulas   Z-64 to Z-71
LVDT Glossary   Z-72 to Z-73
LD100, A Fast Linear Displacement
Transducer   Z-74 to Z-76
The Linear Variable Displacement Transformer   Z-77 to Z-83
Chemical Resistance Chart   Z-84 to Z-95
Piping Data   Z-96
Tubing Data   Z-97
NPT and Straight Thread Data   Z-98

Trademarks

3M Co.
Nextel®

Apple Computer Co.
Apple®
Macintosh®

E.I. DuPont de Nemours
Kapton®
Mylar®
Teflon®
Viton®

General Electric Co.
Triac®

H.I. Thompson
Refrasil®

Hoskins Manufacturing Co.
Alumel®
Chromel®

Huntington Alloys
Hastelloy®

International Business Machines, Inc.
IBM®
IBM PC®
PC AT®
Personal System/2™

International Nickel Co.
Incoloy®
Inconel®
Monel®

Laboratory Technologies Corp.
Labtech Notebook®

Lotus Development Corp.
1-2-3®, Lotus®

Microsoft
MS-DOS®

Norton Co.
Neoprene®

Penwalt Corp.
Kynar®

Rosemount
Hart®

OMEGA Engineering Trademarks

ALpHA™
Book of Books®
Chart-Temp®
Chromega™
Cromega™
DialTemp ™
Digicator®
Hot News®
hot point™
ice point™
iOMEGA™
Litmustik®
New Horizons®
Omega®
Omega-Flo®

®ΩΞ MONOGRAM™

®ΩP OMEGA PRESS, INC.

®ΩΞ

ΩΞ OMEGA®

®Ωi OMEGA INTERNATIONAL CORP.

®ΩB BIOMEGA, INC.

OMEGA-N®
OMEGA-P®
OMEGA-PAD®
OMEGABASIC®
OMEGABENCH®
OMEGABOND®
OMEGABUS®
OMEGABYTE®
OMEGACLAD®
OMEGACOAT®
OMEGAETTE®
OMEGAFILM®
OMEGAFLEX®
Omegaflow Onstream®
OMEGALABEL®
OMEGALAQ®
OMEGALINE®
OMEGALLOY®
OMEGALOG®
OMEGALOK®
OMEGALUX®
OMEGAMAG®
OMEGAMARKER®
OMEGAMETER®
OMEGAMOUSE™
OMEGAMOUSE™ with Design
of Mouse
OMEGAPELLETS®
OMEGAPHONE®
OMEGAPROBE®
OMEGAROMETER®
OMEGASAYS®

OMEGASCOPE®
OMEGASEZ®
OMEGASNAP®
OMEGASOFT®
OMEGASTIK®
OMEGATEMP®
OMEGATHERM®
OMEGATITE®
Omni-Amp™
OMNICAL®
pH Solutions®
Pressure Lines®
Service Beyond the Handbook℠
TAS™
Temperature Developments®
The Acquirer®
Tools of the Trade®
μMEGA®
We Take Great Ideas and Make
Them Even Better℠
We Take Great Ideas & Make Them
Even Better®
We're More Than Just Temperature℠
WHITE BOX®
WHITE BOX & DESIGN®
WHYTE BOX®
WITE BOX®
WYTE BOX®
OMEGA Complete Handbook of
Scientific & Technical Books®
OMEGA Complete Test
Instrumentation & Tools Handbook
& Encyclopedia®
OMEGA Pressure & Strain
Measurement Handbook®
OMEGA Complete Pressure, Strain
& Force Measurement Handbook &
Encyclopedia ®
OMEGA Temperature Measurement
Handbook®
OMEGA Temperature Measurement
Handbook and Encyclopedia®
OMEGA Complete Flow and Level
Measurement Handbook &
Encyclopedia®
OMEGA Complete pH &
Conductivity Measurement
Handbook & Encyclopedia®
OMEGA Complete Data Acquisition
& Computer Interface Handbook &
Encyclopedia®

*Omega Connectors are trademarks
of Omega Engineering, Inc.

***Products in this handbook are
protected by the following
patents:***

U.S. Patents
3,914,008
3,916,691
4,133,700
4,746,298
4,735,661
4,808,241
4,830,515
D311,695
5,019,838
4,949,274
D316,053
D320,384
5,030,614
5,014,907

International Patents
1,445,741
1,418,104
1,069,337
1,531,423
1,288,142
2,193,048
2,197,533
2,200,496
2,213,232
M 88 03 842.4
1,055,583
22507
Rd, 1990, Omega Engineering, Inc.
8042
102,879
005545
1,288,818
66,767/Rd,1990, Omega
Engineering, Inc.
2,651,583
1,306,977
GB2,236,192
2,662,550
GB2,244,389A
GB2,244,474A
906,489
67,381 Rd. 1990, Omega
Engineering, Inc. 67,381
2,008,803
M9006 807.6

*Products are also covered in this
handbook that are subject to
pending patent applications in the
United States and other countries.*

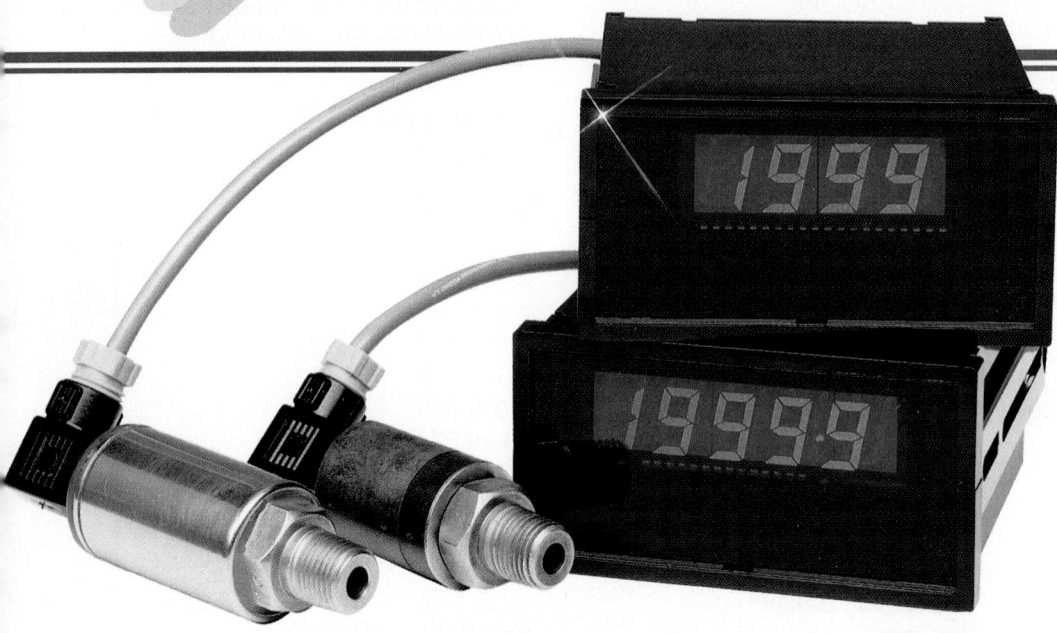

Thin Film Millivolt, Voltage and Current Loop Output Pressure Sensors—For Gage and Absolute Pressures
Models PX212/PX213/PX215 Series   From $184
OMEGA's new PX212, PX213 and PX215 Series pressure transducers are designed to provide high performance at a low cost. These unique sensors are manufactured with stainless steel wetted parts, NEMA 4 enclosures and CVD construction for stability and reliable performance under industrial conditions.
See pages B-19, B-42 and B-59.

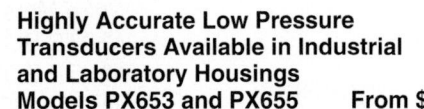

Highly Accurate Low Pressure Transducers Available in Industrial and Laboratory Housings
Models PX653 and PX655   From $342
The PX653 and PX655 Series are highly accurate, low pressure sensors. Models range in pressure from .1 to 50 in. of water column when accurate pneumatic pressures need to be monitored (such as in HVAC applications, clean rooms, etc…) These sensors are also available with an industrial enclosure and NPT fittings.
See pages B-39 and B-53.

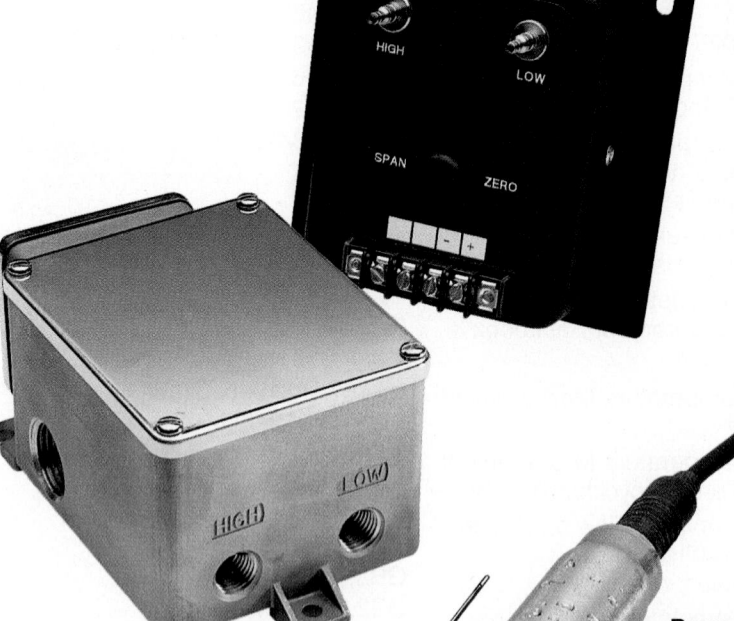

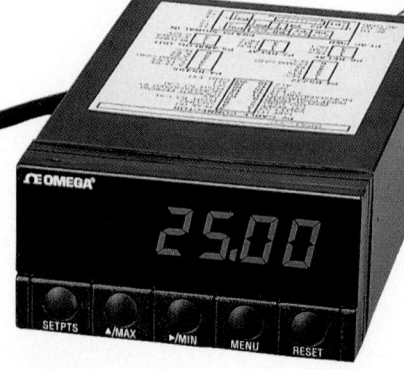

Deep Depth Submersible Pressure Transmitter
For 35 to 650 Feet of Water Ranges
Model PX428 $556
The PX428 submersible pressure transmitter is designed with all stainless steel wetted parts and CVD construction for high stability and performance while measuring static pressure under water. The unit is available in ranges operable in 0 to 650 feet of water. Standard models are available with a 4 to 20 mA output for long signal transmissions. Detachable, vented cables allow for extra quick deliveries!
See page B-90.

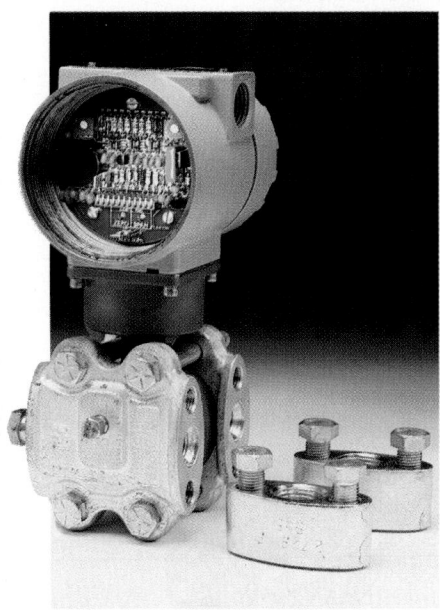

Industrial Pressure Transmitters for Rugged Environments
Model PX761 Series
From $815
The PX761 Series offers four models for gage, absolute, differential and square root differential pressure. These industrial gage transmitters offer turn down capability while providing extremely high over-pressure protection. Ranges from .5 to 4500 PSI are available.
See page B-75.

General Purpose Millivolt, Voltage and Current Output Transducers with Stainless Steel Construction
Models PX902/903/905 Series
From $180
The rugged PX900 Series pressure transducers offer state-of-the-art technology at a moderate price. These sensors are available with a millivolt (PX902), voltage (PX903) and current output (PX905); all models feature stainless steel wetted parts. The outer case is also constructed of stainless steel with pigtail termination. The sensors are available in ranges from 500 to 10,000 PSI.
See pages B-9.

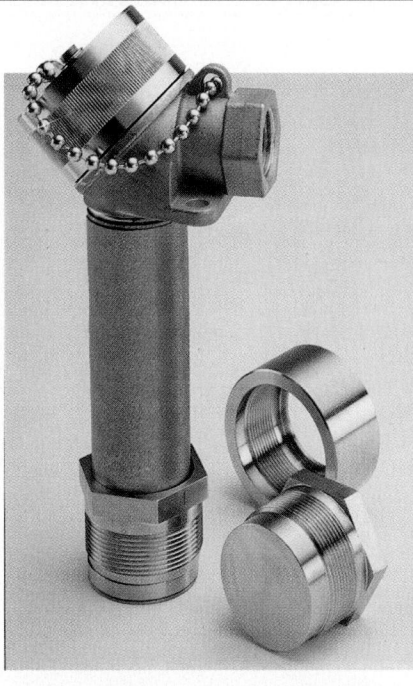

Lightweight Industrial Flush Mount Pressure Transmitter
Model PX881 $695
The PX881 is a compact, durable, accurate pressure transmitter with a flush diaphragm, built for stable performance in the toughest environments. Its flush mount design prevents against process media particles from collecting at the diaphragm. The heart of the PX881 pressure transmitter is a miniature microetched peizoresistive sensing chip. It meets FM and CSA approvals for intrinsic safety and NACE standards for offshore applications. A 4-20 mA output is standard with a 12-48 Vdc power supply.
See page B-73.

Current to Pressure (I/P) Converter
Model IP310/311 $170
The IP310/311 converts an analog signal to a proportional linear pneumatic output. Unlike other units which bleed air to maintain pressure, the IP310 and IP311 uses a silicon pressure sensor and an electropneumatic converter, to provide the desired pneumatic pressure without constant air consumption. The converter's unique design eliminates common problems such as hose chattering, air consumption from leaks, age, moisture, contamination, mounting orientation error, sticky valves, valve leakage and blockage. It provides a reliable, repeatable and accurate means of converting a current signal into a pneumatic pressure.
See page C-29.

NEW!

**High Performance
Process Indicators
Model DP41 Series   From $345**
OMEGA's DP41 Series indicators offer exceptional performance at an economical price. The DP41-E and DP41-S both have standard built-in sensor excitation, programming and scaling via a front key pad, and internal jumpers for input range selection. The DP41 accepts voltage, current and potentiometer inputs and the DP41-S accepts strain gage bridge sensors and radiometric voltage measurements. Optional RS-232 and RS-485 communications for both models allow the operator to remotely set display parameters.
See page D-7.

**Large Display
Digital Panel
Meters with 2¼
or 4" High Digits
Models LDP2
and LDP4
From $1050**
The LDP2 and LDP4 are multi-purpose large display digital meters, housed in extruded aluminum, suitable for panel mounting or free-standing installations. The LDP2 has 2¼" digits, visible from 50 feet away, and the LDP4 has 4" digits, which can be seen from 200 feet away. These panel meters are ideal for demonstration applications.
See page D-17.

**Accurate Benchtop
Pressure Standard
From 5 to 10,000 PSI
Model PCL41   From $725**
The PCL41 Series pressure standard incorporates features found in high-end standards into an affordable, portable benchtop unit. The microprocessor controller allows the user to adjust display filtering for his particular application. The front panel tare allows zeroing of the display with a single push button. All units come calibrated to NIST standards.
See page D-55.

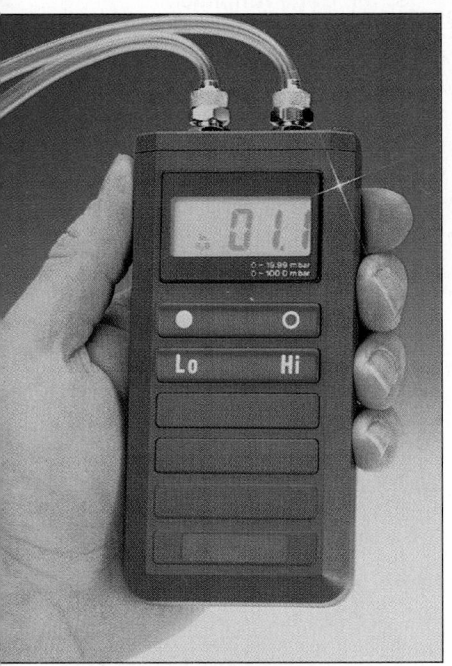

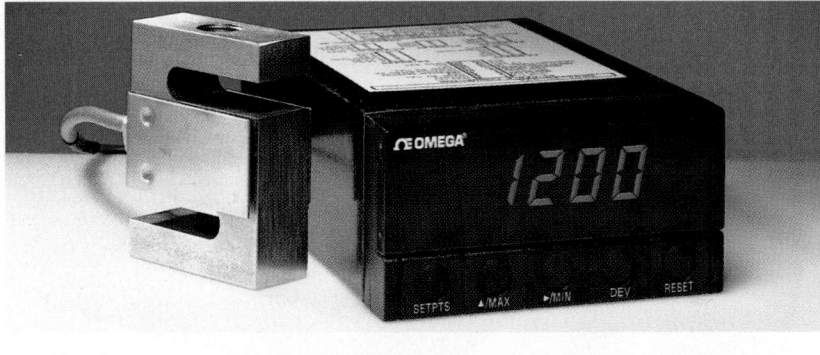

Economical Digital Indicators with Excitation and Dual Alarm Relays
Model DP205 Series $199

The DP205 Series are low-cost digital panel meters for use with voltage, current or bridge type transducers. A four digit LED display indicates from -1999 to 9999 counts. For amplified voltage and current output transducers the DP205-E has a user selectable 12 or 24 Vdc excitation supply. For strain gage bridge transducers the DP205-S has a 5 or 10 Vdc supply. Both models include analog output and dual alarm relays as standard equipment.
See page D-17.

Handheld Air Pressure Meter for Differential and Absolute Pressures
Model HHP-100   From $375

The HHP-100 Series handheld air pressure meter is designed for one handed industrial or laboratory use. The custom molded case allows this manometer to withstand continual heavy use and operation in industrial or humid conditions. Each unit has a high contrast liquid crystal display coupled with a backlight feature, allowing readings to be seen in all application environments.
See page D-48.

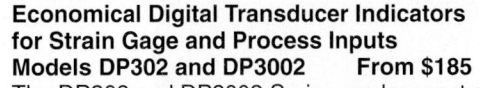

Economical Digital Transducer Indicators for Strain Gage and Process Inputs
Models DP302 and DP3002   From $185

The DP302 and DP3002 Series are low-cost digital panel meters designed for applications where indication only is required. The DP302 is a 3½ digit display capable of displaying ±1999 counts, and the DP3002 is a 4½ digit display capable of reading ±19999 counts. Both models are fully scalable to display engineering units.
See page D-19.

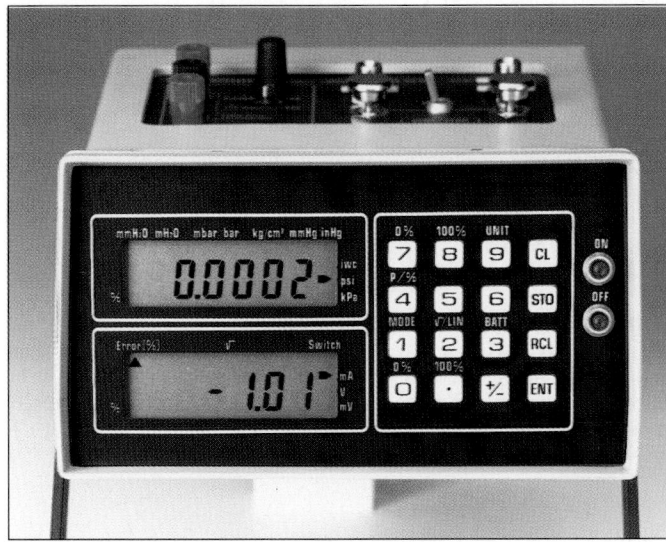

Portable, Highly Accurate Pneumatic Calibrator
Model PCL4000 Series   From $2870

The PCL4000 Series pressure calibrators are available in different pressure ranges for increased accuracy and versatility. Each unit is equipped with two displays. The top display shows the pressure in percentage of full scale or ten other engineering units. The bottom display shows the output of the sensor being tested in/or percentage of full scale. Twenty calibration points may be stored in memory for easy recall when writing calibration certificates.
See page D-53.

**Strain Gage Amplifier/
Signal Conditioner Modules for
Strain Gages, Load Cells and
Pressure Transducers
Model DMD-460 $295**
The DMD 460 Series are self-
contained, a.c. powered,
signal conditioning modules for
bridge type instrumentation. The
DMD 465 contains a precision
differential instrumentation
amplifier with filtered output. The
DMD 465WB is similar to the
DMD 465, but has a frequency response of
2khz. The DMD 466 is similar to the above units
but has a 4 to 20mA output instead of voltage.
See page C-14 or E- 25.

**Portable Pressure Calibration Kits
for Pressure or 4-20 MA Current
Model PCL425   From $599**
The OMEGA PCL425 is a handheld
calibrator capable of reading pressure or
dc current. A front panel keyboard allows
easy selection of PSI, inches of water,
milliamp scales, high or low measuring
range and adjustment of zero offset. All
readings are displayed on an LCD with 1/2"
digits. In addition to reading pressure and
current, the PCL425 can also generate
pressure and current when used together
with the optional hand pump and current
output module.
See page D-60.

US Patent 5019,838 and D311,695
Germany M88 03 842.4 Korea 102,879
UK 1,055,583 Taiwan 22507 Italy 0055451
Canada Rd Omega Engr. Inc 8042

**Microprocessor Based
Pressure/Temperature
Recorder. With Large 8"
(200 mm) Diameter Chart
Model CT585RS
From $770**
The CT585RS is a completely
self-contained
microprocessor-based
temperature/pressure
recorder, which allows
for accurate
indications, along
with the current
time and storage
of peak values
(max. and min.).
Each function of the
recorder is easily accessible
via the front panel. The user may
select 1, 7 or 32 day operation on the large, 8" (200mm) chart, in addition
to programming the digital display for PSIG, °F or °C indication.

Each CT585RS comes complete with solid state transducer, wall mount
template and hardware, a standard 110 Vac adapter, four D-cell batteries,
pressure and temperature pens and a complete operator's manual.
Optional features include: audible alarm with latching relay, 220 to 240
Vac adapter, recorder color options and a variety of replacement pens
and charts.
See page D-68.

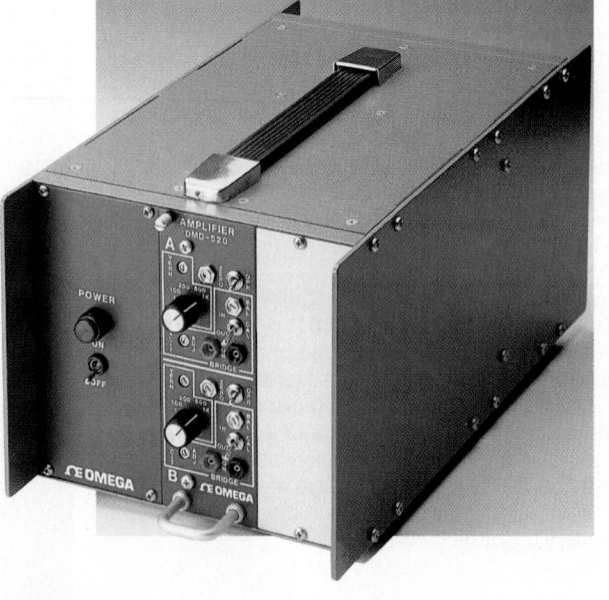

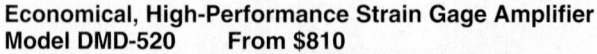

**Economical, High-Performance Strain Gage Amplifier
Model DMD-520   From $810**
The DMD-520 high performance strain gage amplifier uses cost-cutting
techniques without compromising quality engineering. Two channels per module
are housed in an eight module rack, and the result is a quality instrument at an
attractive price. Available with benchtop or rack mountable case.
See page E-24.

Hand-held Precision Calibrators for Temperature or Process Voltage and Current
Models PCL432 and CL424
From $729

The OMEGA PCL423 and CL424 are portable, handheld, microprocessor-based calibrators for process, voltage and current signals or temperature sensors. The PCL423 process signal calibrator has multiple input and output ranges for dc millivolts, volts and milliamps. The CL424 temperature calibrator can read or simulate J, K, T or E thermocouples, as well as most common RTD types. Both models utilize a large 32 character dot matrix display to simultaneously display the reading, operating mode (input or output) and range selected. For convenience three calibration points can be stored for quick recall.
See page D-47.

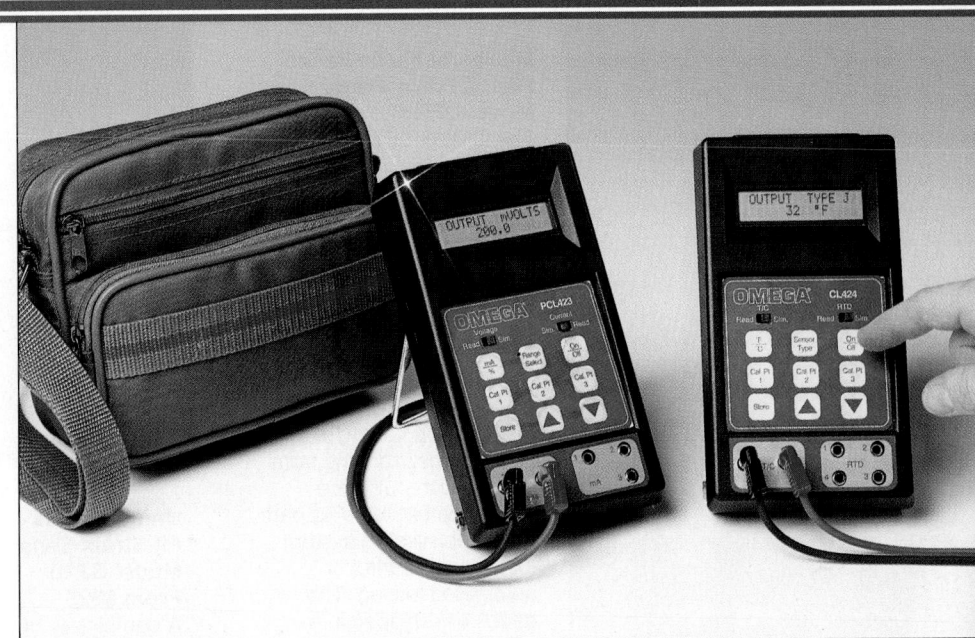

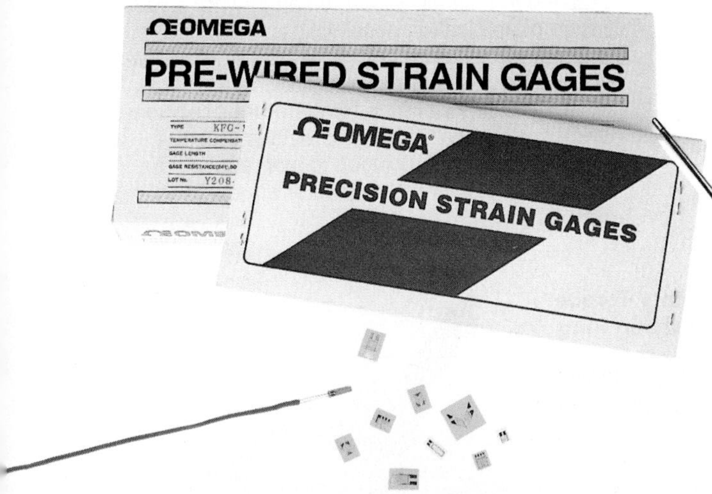

General Purpose Strain Gages
For Static and Dynamic Applications
From $47

OMEGA strain gages are available in a variety of different models to cover most strain measurement applications. Their rugged construction and flexibility make them suitable for static and dynamic measurement with a high degree of accuracy. The measuring grid is formed by etching Constantan foil which is then completely sealed in the carrier of a polymide film. A variety of different models are available with encapsulated solder pads, ribbon leads, rosettes and much, much more.
See pages E-7 to E-17.

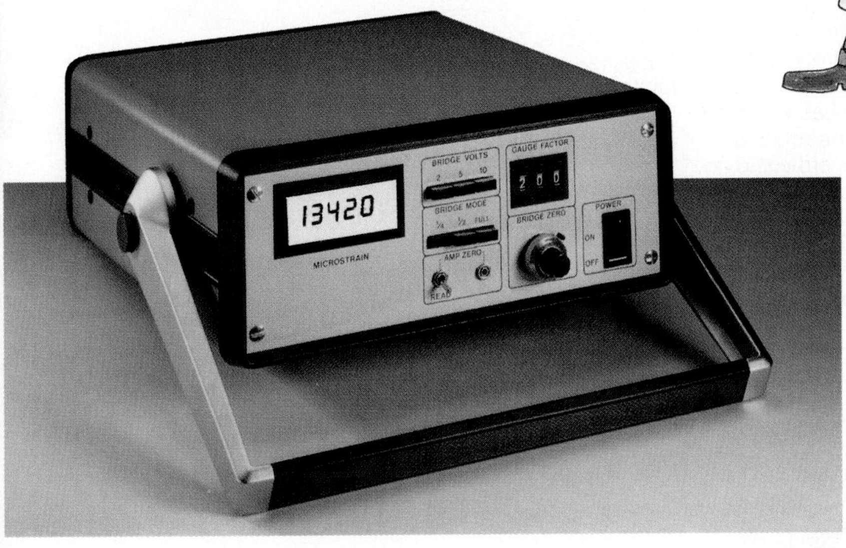

Single-Channel, Portable
Strain Gage Monitoring System
Model DMD-21 $2585

The DMD-21 makes reading strain gages simple. Since it contains bridge completion resistors, quarter and half bridges can be directly wired to the unit. The DMD-21 accepts bridge inputs, load cells and pressure transducers which can be monitored in engineering units of your choice. Static readings are displayed on the unit, while dynamic strains can be monitored via the analog output. An optional switch box(DMD-21SB) is the perfect companion for performing multiple strain gage measurements.
See page E-21.

Microprocessor-Based Digital Force Gage
Model DFG51 $1170

The OMEGA DFG51 microprocessor-based digital force gage is small, rugged and lightweight, which makes it an ideal instrument for portable handheld force measurement. It measures ranges from 2 to 100 lbs. The DFG51 has many features which allow it to be used in a variety of applications, ranging from simple push-pull force measurement to being part of a sophisticated system for process control or automated testing. The gages are shipped in a cushioned carrying case with a set of the following attachments: chisel point, V-groove cone, flat head, hook and an extension rod. An ac adapter /charger, a certificate of calibration and complete operator's manual are also included.
See page F-29.

Unique Press Fit Strain Sensor
Model GZ10
From $325

A completely new approach to sensor design, combined with proven strain gage technology, has resulted in a small, accurate sensor with a wide range of application possibilities. The GZ10 overcomes a number of current sensor problems and limitations, such as installation ease, size, load limit, location, operating temperature conditions and affordability. This unit provides a cost effective, accurate solution to load sensing for virtually any machine, device or structure.
See page F-27.

Socket Extension Reaction Torque Sensor with ¼, ⅜, ½ and ¾" Square Drives
Model TQ102 Series $420

The TQ102 Series socket extension torque sensor is easily installed between a socket and drive to measure or verify bolt torque. The sensor can measure torque in both clockwise and counterclockwise directions. This unique sensor's accuracy, compact size and cost make it ideal for a variety of industrial or laboratory applications.
See page F-30.

Rugged In-Line Rotary Torque Sensor with Integral Slip Ring Assembly
Model TQ501   From $3540

The TQ501 rotary torque sensor is ideal for measuring torque in rotating shafts. An integral slip ring assembly is used to transfer the electrical signal from rotating electronics to stationary electronics. The slip ring consists of silver graphite brushes which rub on the rotating ring, providing an electrical path for the incoming excitation and the outgoing signal voltage.
See page F-32.

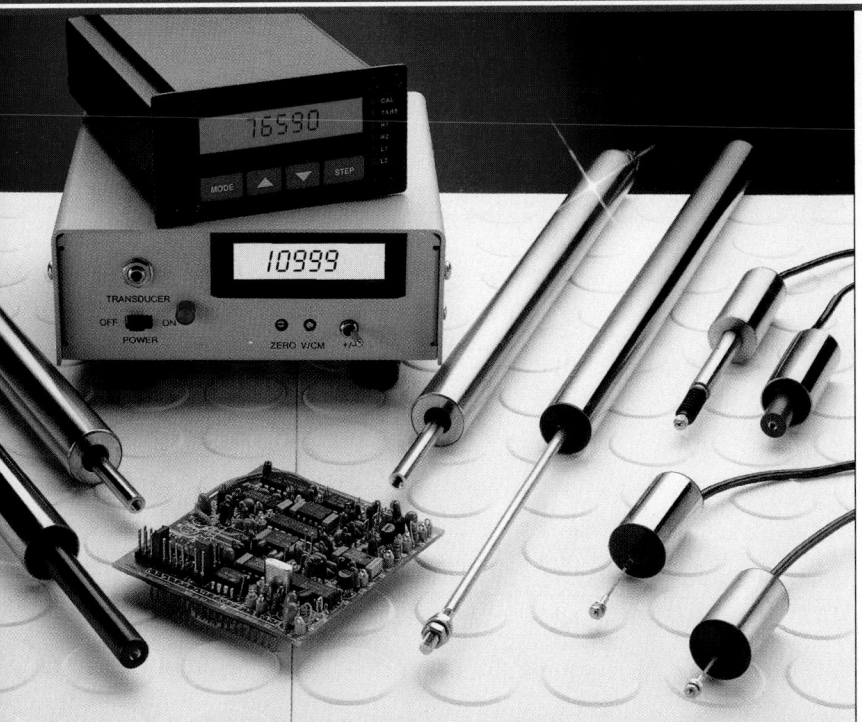

Linear Variable Displacement Transformers
Model LVDT Series   From $98
OMEGA's LVDT Series offer diverse models ideal for every application, from industrial to laboratory settings. LVDTs are available with standard ac output, or built-in dc signal conditioning for choices in instrumenting. The units are available with full stroke ranges from 1 to 600mm and with spring loaded or free-floating armature movement.

See Section J.

Differential Dial Gauges with Differential or Bi-directional Ranges
Model PGD-45 Series
From $567
The OMEGA PGD-45 Series differential pressure gauges are rugged industrial gauges which indicate the difference between the two input connections. Differential ranges provide the maximum resolution for applications where one input is always at a higher pressure than the other. In cases where one input can be higher or lower than the other, a bi-directional differential range should be used.
See page G-17.

General Purpose Pressure Switches for Vacuum to 7500 PSI
Model PSW-800 Series $77
The PSW-800 Series is an economical pressure switch which features an easy to adjust setpoint with locking set screw. It utilizes a sealed piston or diaphragm-piston design, which is ideally suited for harsh environments. All models come with 12" color coded leads and a ½" female conduit fitting for electrical connections.
See page H-10.

Miniature Pressure and Vacuum Switches
Model PSW-500 Series $74
The PSW-500 Series are compact pressure switches which provide years of trouble- free service. The adjustable pointer makes changing setpoints simple for the end-user. These reliable yet simple switches are available in a variety of ranges from 60 to 600 PSIG, and their attractive price makes the PSW-500 Series a choice switch.
See page H-7 and H-8.

A

NEW PRODUCT SHOWCASE

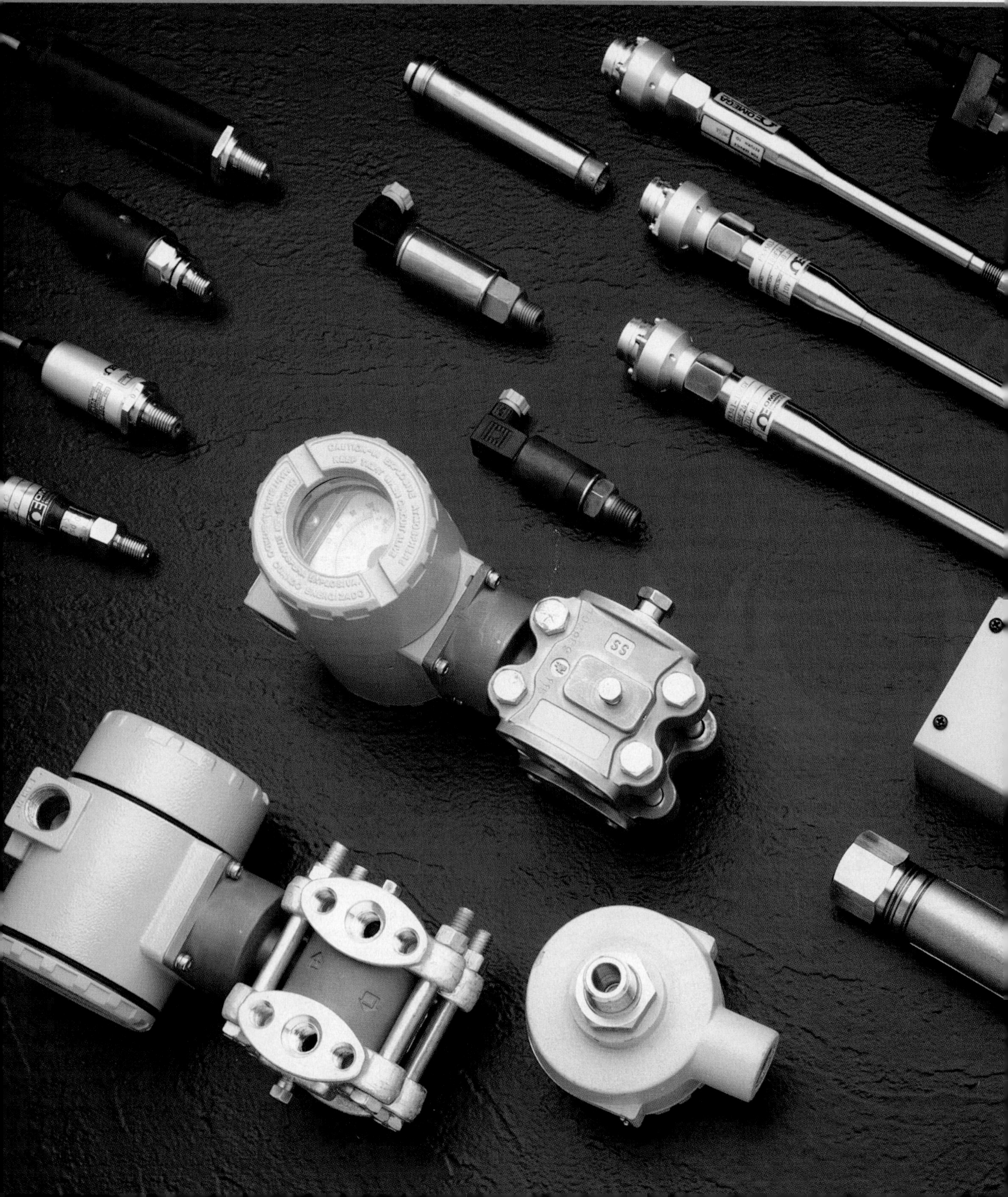

Custom Designed Pressure Systems		**B-5**
Millovolt Output Pressure Transducers		**B-9 to B-30**
Voltage Output Pressure Transducers		**B-31 to B-48**
Current Output Pressure Transducers		**B-49 to B-87**
Specialty Pressure Transducers		**B-88 to B-102**

INTRODUCTION TO PRESSURE MEASUREMENT SYSTEMS

Model DP87

How do I select a pressure measurement system for my application?

There are three main components to a pressure measurement system, they are:

1) pressure transducer
2) excitation power supply
3) signal processor (readout meter, controller, recorder)

Are there different types of pressure systems?

Yes, three distinct pressure systems are available, they include millivolt output, amplified voltage output, and current loop output transducers. A brief discussion outlining their particular characteristics and advantages follows.

Millivolt systems—are relatively lower in cost because the signal conditioning functions are remote from the actual sensor, this allows the transducer to be relatively small in size. An added advantage to these transducers is there direct compatibility with most strain gage and load cell instrumentation.

Amplified voltage systems—contain instrumentation grade amplifiers within the transducer. These systems are commonly used in laboratory applications and electrically noisy environments. Amplified voltage systems exhibit direct compatibility to most process control and computer interface systems.

Current loop systems—particularly well suited to applications where long distances and high noise immunity are required. This is achieved through the 4 to 20 mA current transmitter which is built into the transducer. This system allows wire runs of over 1,000 feet with virtually no signal degradation. This system is often selected for use in the process industry, for direct interface with most computers, data acquisition systems, and industrial process controllers.

What factors must be considered when selecting a pressure transducer?

There are three primary considerations to selecting a transducer, they are, the pressure requirements of the system, the process temperature, and the compatibility of the transducer with the working fluid.

Pressure requirements—normal working pressure should be below the maximum range of the transducer. The proof and burst pressure ratings should be sufficiently high to provide an adequate safety margin in the event of system overpressure. As a guideline, select a transducer with a range 125% of the normal working pressure.

Temperature range—normal conditions should be within the compensated temperature range of the transducer, and the maximum system temperature should not exceed the stated maximum operating temperature of the transducer.

Working fluid (media) compatibility—a very important factor when considering a pressure transducer is assuring that the transducer material is compatible with the working fluid.

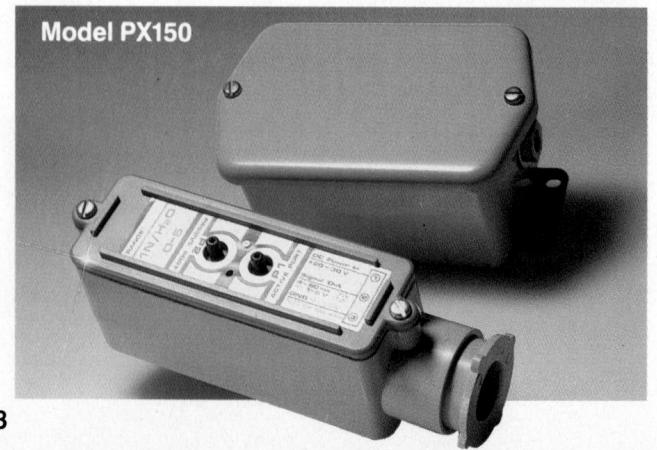

Model PX150

Should I select a transducer with a stainless steel or silicon diaphragm?

Transducers with stainless steel diaphragms are well suited for high pressures and offer superior corrosion resistance, and wide media compatibility. Silicon diaphragms typically exhibit greater accuracy, but are generally limited to lower pressures and dry gases as the working media. There are however, exceptions to this rule regarding silicon diaphragms, the individual transducer specifications will determine the full extent of its capabilities.

Model PX880

Model PX425

Are there transducers available that measure in engineering units other than PSI i.e., inches of water ?

Yes, the output signal from any transducer can be converted to the engineering units of your choice by scaling the output of the transducer via the instrument.

example: a 10 PSI pressure transducer can measure 20.4 inches of Hg (mercury) or 276.8 inches of H_2O (water)

What other factors should I consider when selecting a pressure system?

All pressure transducers require electrical excitation in order to function within the pressure system. This excitation can be provided from an independent power supply or from process instrumentation which includes excitation capabilities. The power supplies can be divided into two distinct types, regulated and unregulated. All millivolt output transducers require a regulated power supply, while current loop output transducers can use either type power supply. For voltage output transducers, the individual specifications will determine whether a regulated or unregulated power supply is required. Anytime an unregulated power supply can be used a regulated type may also be used, but the converse is not true.

An additional factor remains to be considered, and that is matching the output of the transducer with the input of the instrumentation. These specifications are provided with both components of the system.

Model PX428

What is the difference between gage pressure (PSIG), sealed gage pressure (PSIS), absolute pressure (PSIA), and differential pressure (PSID)?

Gage pressure (PSIG) transducers measure the pressure in pounds per square inch with respect to atmospheric pressure at your location i.e., 14.7 PSI at sea level, 12.2 PSI Denver Colo. This is the most common type of pressure measurement.

Sealed gage pressure (PSIS) transducers measure pressure relative to 1 atmosphere at sea level (14.7 PSI) regardless of local atmospheric pressure. For most applications gage and sealed gage pressure transducers are interchangeable.

Absolute pressure (PSIA) is a pressure measurement in pounds per square inch relative to a perfect vacuum.

PSIA = 14.7 PSI (at sea level)

Differential pressure (PSID) is pressure measurement which reflects the difference between two input pressures.

OMEGA CUSTOM PRESSURE PRODUCTS

OMEGA Engineering proudly offers the most sophisticated and extensive Custom Engineering capabilities in the process measurement and control industry. Our custom manufacturing capabilities extend beyond the handbooks, and reinforce our customer service/customer-driven philosophy. Whether you need a simple modification of a standard product or a complete customized system, OMEGA can accommodate your special request. Our pressure engineering specialists, working in conjunction with OMEGA's custom design team, can solve your custom pressure application requirements.

Calibration "Suitcase"

The portable calibration suitcase shown consists of two very accurate differential pressure transducers (model PX750), a type T test gage, three loop powered indicators (model TX82A), a 24 volt power supply (U24Y100) and a series of pressure manifolds. This custom product was designed for an OMEGA customer to perform field calibrations for a series of fluid dynamic test labs. It enabled him to measure three simultaneous pressures (two differential pressures and one gage pressure).

Portable Pressure Measurement System

This portable pressure measuring suitcase shown was specifically designed for field measurement and on-site datalogging. This unit consists of a differential pressure transducer (PX750), an industrial type-H pressure gage, a type-K thermocouple, an OM160 portable datalogging system and a U24Y100 power supply. It was designed to perform measurements on various water systems which were losing hot water pressure at certain temperatures.

The PX750 measures the differential pressure between the hot water line and the cold water line, while the type H gage allows the pressure in the hot water line to be monitored. The type K thermocouple allows the end-user to monitor temperature fluctuations in the hot water line. Datalogging in the field is accomplished via the OM160 and then later downloaded

See Pages xviii through xii of the OMEGA Temperature Measurement Handbook® for an extensive selection of OMEGA's custom products.

Benchtop Pressure System

The benchtop pressure system shown was designed for field measurements of pressure where an audible alarm was required when the pressure was too high. This custom designed benchtop device consists of a pressure transducer (model PX605), a panel meter (model DP41) and an audible alarm (model 70-1). The DP41 panel meter has easy push-button alarm programming for field set-point adjustments. The device is lightweight, rugged and accurate.

Custom Portable Case

OMEGA's custom portable measuring case shown was designed to measure pressure and temperature simultaneously. The unit consists of two digital panel meters (DP2000 series) and front mounted female plug jacks. The OMEGA sensors used with this device simply plug into the jacks for the user to perform field measurements. This unique unit also has a rear mounted analog output jacks to allow the customer to datalog measurements.

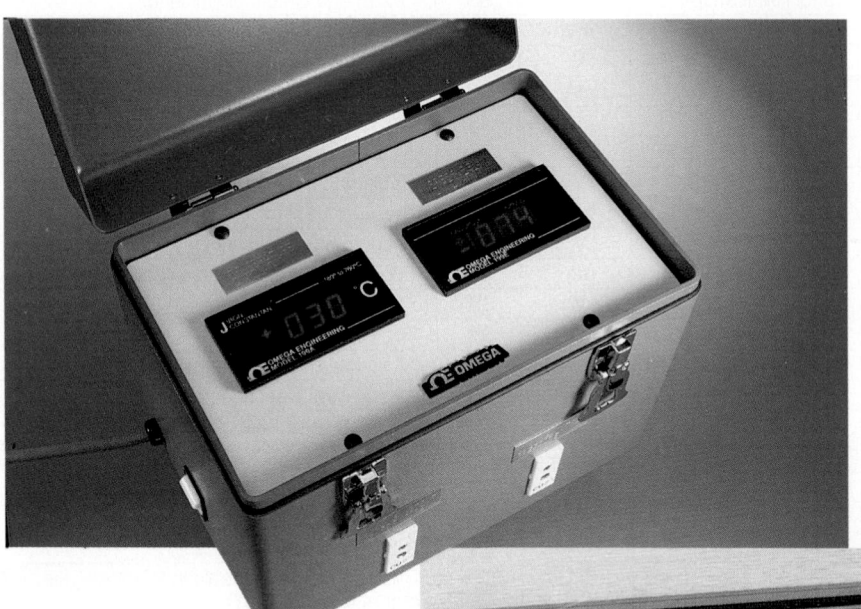

Calibration and Scaling
$75

OMEGA Engineering will scale a sensor or instrumentation set up for a charge of $75. Whether it's a pressure transducer and digital panel meter, or a load cell and chart recorder, OMEGA has the facilities to calibrate these systems, allowing the customer instant use upon receiving the equipment. A typical set up shown is a DP41 panel meter and a PX605-5KGI transducer. The meter was scaled to the transducer to read from 0 to 5000 PSI.

APPLICATION/SELECTION GUIDE FOR PRESSURE TRANSDUCERS

SERIES	PRICE	ACCURACY	PAGE	RANGE	OUTPUT	DIA.	FEATURES
GENERAL PURPOSE TRANSDUCERS							
PX105	$218	1.0%	B-36	6 to 2K PSIG	V	SS	Low Profile, connector included
PX120	158	1.0%	B-16	15 to 5K PSIG	mV	SS	Compact, weather proof boot
PX176	254	0.5%	B-37	15 to 5K PSIG/A	V	SS	Waterproof case, all sealed units
PX180	146	0.3%	B-15	15 to 500 PSIG	mV	SI	Compact, shielded pigtail leads
PX181	170	0.3%	B-35	15 to 500 PSIG	mV	SI	Compact, light weight
PX182	198	0.3%	B-56	15 to 500 PSIG	mA	SI	Compact pressure transmitter
PX212	184	0.25%	B-19	15 to 6000 PSIG/A	mV	SS	Absolute models available
PX213	226	0.25%	B-42	15 to 6000 PSIG/A	V	SS	All stainless steel NEMA-4 construction
PX215	268	0.25%	B-59	15 to 6000 PSIG/A	mA	SS	Pressure transmitter
PX236	85	1.5%	B-14	15 to 150 PSIG	mV	SI	Also measures vacuum
PX240	138	1.5%	B-34	5 to 250 PSIG/V	mV	SI	Pancake construction
PX271	130	1.0%	B-50	5 to 30 PSIG	mA	SI	Gage, vacuum, and bi-directional models
PX273	475	0.5%	B-55	20 to 300 PSID	mA	SS	Differential pressure
PX300	180	0.25%	B-17	15 to 10K PSIG/A	mV	SS	1/2 Bridge circuit, pigtail leads
PX302	180	0.25%	B-18	15 to 10K PSIG/A	mV	SS	Compact, pigtail leads
PX303	255	0.25%	B-41	15 to 10K PSIG/A	V	SS	Wide excitation range
PX305	255	0.25%	B-60	15 to 10K PSIG/A	mA	SS	Wide excitation range
PX410	390	1.0%	B-58	15 to 500 PSIG	mA	SS	1/2 Conduit connection
PX602	198	0.5%	B-20	Vac to 20,000 PSIG	mV	SS	All stainless steel case
PX603	265	0.5%	B-43	Vac to 20,000 PSIG	V	SS	Cable or connector versions
PX605	265	0.5%	B-61	Vac to 20,000 PSIG	mA	SS	Pressure transmitter
PX633	155	0.5%	B-38	5 to 300 PSIG	V	SI	Vacuum model available
PX635	155	0.5%	B-57	5 to 300 PSIG	mA	SI	Economical pressure transmitter
PX643	324	0.25%	B-38	15 to 500 PSIG	V	SS	For wet/dry media
PX645	324	0.25%	B-57	15 to 500 PSIG	mA	SS	For wet/dry media
PX902	180	0.5%	B- 9	100 to 10,000 PSIG	mV	SS	All stainless steel construction
PX903	225	0.5%	B-47	100 to 10,000 PSIG	V	SS	All stainless steel construction
PX905	255	0.5%	B-69	100 to 10,000 PSIG	mA	SS	Pressure transmitter
HIGH ACCURACY TRANSDUCERS (less than 0.25% FULL SCALE)							
PX216	512	0.15%	B-71	15 to 6000 PSIG/A	mA	SS	Stainless steel NEMA-4 construction
PX425	495	0.2%	B-22	1 to 6K PSIG/A	mV	SS	Temperature stability
PX428	556	0.2%	B-90	15 to 1500 PSIG	mA	SS	Submersible up to 650 ft.
PX620	895	0.15%	B-65	50 to 10K PSIG	V	IN	Custom ranges available in PSIG/A/V, also mA output (see pg. B-67)
PX800	485	0.1%	B-24	1 to 2K PSIG	mV	*	Quartz titanium diaphragm, acceleration
PX811	595	0.1%	B-25	2.5 to 100 PSIA	mV	SS	Absolute pressure
PX931	530	0.15%	B-23	10 to 10K PSIG	mV	SS	Wet/Wet differential, accel. & Shock specs.
PX941	670	0.15%	B-68	10 to 5K PSIG	mA	SS	Hermetically sealed
PX945	595	0.10%	B-70	10 to 10K PSIG	mA	SS	Industrial grade transmitter
PX951	675	0.15%	B-44	10 to 5K PSIG	V	SS	Hermetically sealed
PX960	995	0.15%	B-46	3 to 15 PSIG/A	V	SS	Barometer, zero and span adjustment
PC BOARD MOUNTABLE TRANSDUCERS							
PX126	49	1.5%	B-12	5 & 15 PSID	mV	SI	Plastic case
PX136	49	1.5%	B-11	1 to 150 PSIG/A/V	mV	SI	Compact plastic construction
PX140	85	0.75%	B-31	1 to 30 PSIG/D/V	V	SI	Plastic case
PX149	130	1.5%	B-49	3 to 15 PSID	mA	SI	P/I Converter
PX160	32	0.75%	B-13	5 to 30 PSID/G	mV	SI	Wet-Wet differential pressure
PX161	114	0.5%	B-32	5 to 50 H_2OG/D/V	V	SI	Low pressures, plastic case
PX170	64	1.5%	B-10	0.5 to 1 PSIG/D/V	mV	SI	Low pressures, subcompact
PX184	60	1.0%	B-33	Vac to 30 PSID	mV	SI	Amplified 5V output

SERIES	PRICE	ACCURACY	PAGE	RANGE	OUTPUT	DIA.	FEATURES
INDUSTRIAL TRANSMITTERS							
PX410	$390	1.0%	B-58	15 to 500 PSIG	mA	SS	Small Size
PX725	985	0.15%	B-72	in H_2O to 3000 PSIG	mA	SS	Rugged enclosure
PX750	955	0.25%	B-83	0.2 to 6K PSIG/D	mA	SS	6:1 Turndown, explosion proof
PX761	815	0.25%	B-75	1 in H_2O to 6000 PSI	mA	SS	Gage, absolute & differential
PX763	985	0.25%	B-79	1 in H_2O to 3600 PSI	mA	SS	Smart industrial transmitter
PX880	663	0.25%	B-73	15 to 5K PSIG	mA	SS	5:1 Turndown, 5 year warranty
SPECIAL PURPOSE TRANSDUCERS							
PX102	282	0.25%	B-28	6 to 20K PSIG/A	mV	SS	Flush mount, many process fittings available
PX149	130	1.5%	B-49	3 to 15 PSID	mA	SI	P/I Converter
PX222	184	0.25%	B-100	1 to 25 BAR	mV	SS	European style transducer
PX223	226	0.25%	B-101	1 to 25 BAR	V	SS	European style transducer
PX225	268	0.25%	B-102	1 to 25 BAR	mA	SS	European style transmitter
PX418	956	0.5%	B-89	14 to 140 IN H_2OG	mV	SS	Submersible, for low pressures
PX340	556	0.2%	B-90	1.5K to 15K PSIG	mV	SS	Plastic melt transducers
PX428	556	0.2%	B-90	6 to 650 ft H_2OG	mV	SS	Submersible, up to 650 ft.
PX440	650	1.0%	B-64	5 to 20K PSIG	mA	SS	Flush mount, zero balance connector available
PX540	489	0.3%	B-62	150 to 6000 PSIG	mA	SS	Flush diaphragm, NPT mount
PX543	1275	0.25%	B-63	Vac to 1500 PSIG	mA	SS	High temperature (570°F)
PX600	495	1.0%	B-29	200 to 7K PSIG	mV	SS	Compact, flush mount
PX610	515	1.0%	B-30	200 to 7K PSIG	mV	SS	Compact, flush mount
PX635	155	0.5%	B-57	3 to 15 PSIG	mA	SI	P/I converter
PX750	955	0.25%	B-83	0.5 H_2O to 6K PSIG	mA	SS	P/I Converter, square root output, scalability
PX761	815	0.25%	B-75	1" H_2O to 6000 PSI	mA	SS	Gage, absolute & differential
PX763	985	0.25%	B-79	1" H_2O to 3600 PSI	mA	SS	Smart industrial transmitter
PX881	695	0.25%	B-74	3 to 5000 PSIG	mA	SS	Flush mount transmitter
DP914	850	0.5%	B-88	10^{-3} to 760 TORR	–	–	Vacuum monitoring system
LOW PRESSURE TRANSDUCERS (Less than 125 in H_2O or 4.5 PSI)							
PX154	295	0.1%	B-60	1 to 25" H_2OD	mA	SI	NEMA-4, PSIG/V capability
PX161	114	0.5%	B-42	5 to 50" $H_2OG/D/V$	mV	SI	PSIG/V/D, PC board mountable
PX170	64	1.5%	B-16	14 to 28" H_2OG/D	mV	SI	PSID/G/V capability, PC board mountable
PX272	175	1.0%	B-51	0.5 to 25" H_2OD	mA	SI	Zero and span adjustments
PX653	342	0.25%	B-39	0.1 to 50" H_2OD	V	SI	Ultra-low differential pressures
PX655	528	0.25%	B-53	0.1 to 50" H_2OD	mA	SI	Ultra-low differential pressures
PX761	815	0.25%	B-75	1" H_2O to 6000 PSI	mA	SS	Gage, absolute, & differential
PX763	985	0.25%	B-79	1" H_2O to 3600 PSI	mA	SS	Smart industrial transmitter
PX750	863	0.25%	B-79	0.5 to 750" H_2OD	mA	SS	Explosion-proof, 5:1 turndown

B

GENERAL PURPOSE MILLIVOLT OUTPUT PRESSURE TRANSDUCER
ALL STAINLESS STEEL CONSTRUCTION

NEW!

PX902 Series
$180

✔ NIST Traceable
✔ NEMA 4 Enclosure
✔ CVD Construction for High Stability

SPECIFICATIONS
Excitation: 10Vdc, 15Vdc max
Output: 100mV
Accuracy: 0.5%FS
Hysteresis: 0.2%FS
Repeatability: 0.05%FS
Zero Balance: 1%FS
Stability: 1%FS/year
Operating Temp.: -55 to 195°F (-48 to 90 °C)
Compensated Temp.: -20 to 180°F (-29 to 82 °C)
Thermal Effects:
Zero 0.04% FS/°F
Span 0.04% Rdg/°F
Proof Pressure: 150% FS
Burst Pressure: 300% FS
Response Time: 1 msEC
Gage Type: Chemical vapor deposition
Enclosure: NEMA 4 stainless steel
Wetted Parts: Stainless steel
Pressure Port: ¼ NPT
Electrical Conn.: 4 cond. 22 AWG, 36", vented and shielded cable
Weight: 3 oz (85 g)

Accessories
Pressure Snubbers: *Models PS-4D (Oils), PS-4E (Water), PS-4G (Gases)* **$10 each.**
TX4-100 Wire: *100' of 4-conductor shielded copper wire,* **$28.50**

Shown with Model DP3002-S Meter ($325) and PS-4E Snubber ($10).

IN STOCK FOR FAST DELIVERY!

To Order *(Specify Model Number)*			
RANGE	**MODEL**	**PRICE**	**COMPATIBLE METER**
0-100 PSIG	**PX902-100GV**	$180	DP205-S, DP41-S, DP302-S
0-200 PSIG	**PX902-200GV**	180	DP205-S, DP41-S, DP302-S
0-300 PSIG	**PX902-300GV**	180	DP205-S, DP41-S, DP3002-S
0-500 PSIG	**PX902-500GV**	180	DP205-S, DP41-S, DP3002-S
0-1000 PSIG	**PX902-1KGV**	180	DP205-S, DP41-S, DP3002-S
0-2000 PSIG	**PX902-2KGV**	180	DP205-S, DP41-S, DP3002-S
0-3000 PSIG	**PX902-3KGV**	180	DP205-S, DP41-S, DP3002-S
0-5000 PSIG	**PX902-5KGV**	180	DP205-S, DP41-S, DP3002-S
0-7500 PSIG	**PX902-7.5KGV**	180	DP205-S, DP41-S, DP3002-S
0-10000 PSIG	**PX902-10KGV**	180	DP205-S, DP41-S, DP3002-S

Comes complete with operator's manual.
Ordering Example: *PX902-10KGV mV output pressure transducer, with 0 to 10000 PSIG range and two PS-4E pressure snubbers for water, $180 + 20 =* **$200.**

1 YEAR WARRANTY

MADE IN USA NIST

SOLID STATE SENSORS FOR LOW PRESSURES
TEMPERATURE COMPENSATED GAGE OR DIFFERENTIAL MODELS

170 Series
0-14" to 0-28" H2O

All Models
$64

✔ **Solid State Reliability**
✔ **Linear Output Proportional to Pressure**
✔ **Low Null Shift**
✔ **Integral Silicon Diaphragm**
✔ **PC Board Mount or Connector**
✔ **Ideally Suited for Clean, Dry, Non-Corrosive Gases**

SPECIFICATIONS

Excitation: 10 V dc (16 V dc max.) @ 2 mA
Output: 7" H_2O, 28 ±2 mV; 14" H_2O 35$\pm$ mV; 28" H_2O, 42 ±2 mV
Input Impedance: 6.6 K ohm

PERFORMANCE

Linearity: P2>P1 $\pm1.5\%$ FSO (Full Scale Output)
Hysteresis & Repeatability: $\pm.25\%$ FSO
Zero Balance: ±2 mV
Operable Temperature Range: −40 to 185°F (−40 to 85°C)
Compensated Temperature Range: 32 to 122°F (0 to 50°C)
Thermal Zero Effect: ±3 mV
Thermal Span Effect: $\pm3.5\%$ FSO
Operable Overpressure: 140" H_2O (5 PSI)
Stability Over 1 year: $\pm1.5\%$ FSO
Response Time: 1 ms

CONSTRUCTION

Gage Type: Solid State Piezoresistor
Diaphragm Material: .175 Inch Square Silicon Sensor Chip
Pressure Port: Tube Fitting (TY-14-100)
Electrical Connection: CX-136-4 Standard Spaced PC Board Termination
Weight: 7 grams

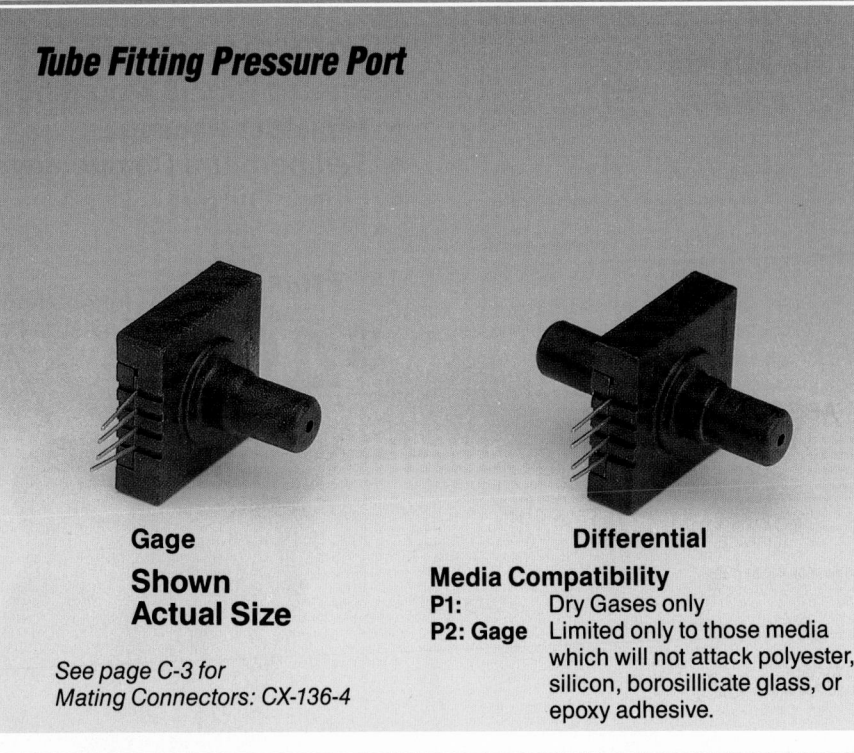

Tube Fitting Pressure Port

Gage
Shown Actual Size

See page C-3 for Mating Connectors: CX-136-4

Differential
Media Compatibility
P1: Dry Gases only
P2: Gage Limited only to those media which will not attack polyester, silicon, borosillicate glass, or epoxy adhesive.

DIMENSIONS IN INCHES

TERMINALS
1 — Vs (+)
2 — OUTPUT A (+)
3 — GROUND (−)
4 — OUTPUT B (−)

0.28 INPUT PORT
0.16 HIGH MOUNT BUSHING
0.02 X 0.015 PIN DIMENSION
0.28 MIN(4)

DIFFERENTIAL

GAGE

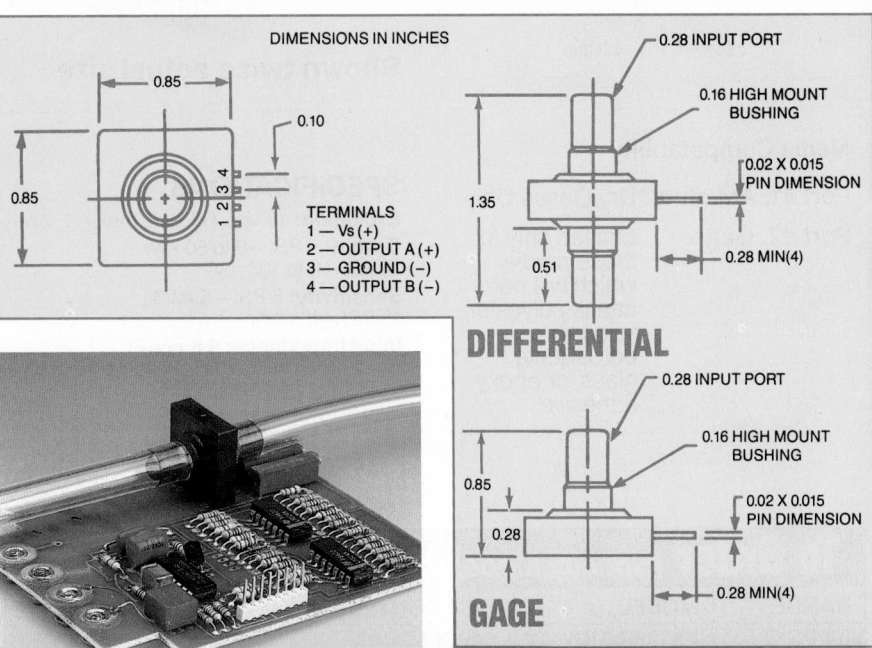

LOW COST MILLIVOLT OUTPUT TRANSDUCER
FOR GAGE, ABSOLUTE AND VACUUM MEASUREMENTS

136 Series
0-5 PSI 0-15 PSI

SILICON DIAPHRAGM
- **Printed Circuit Mounting**
- **Miniature Package**
- **Temperature Compensated**
- **Linear Output**

- **10 V dc Excitation**
- **Silicon Sensor**
- **Integral Diaphragm**

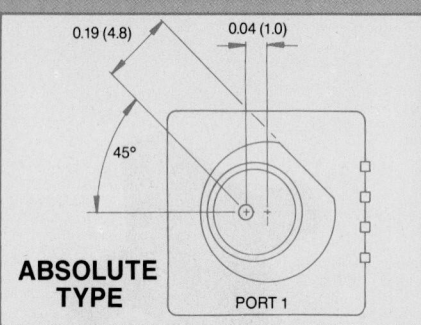

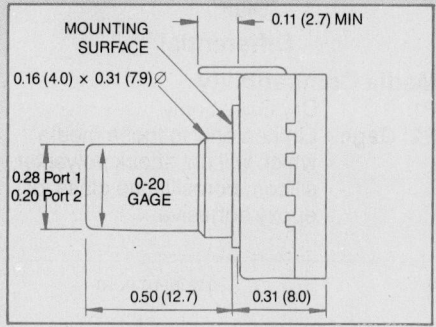

From
$49

Tube Fitting Pressure Port

Shown twice actual size

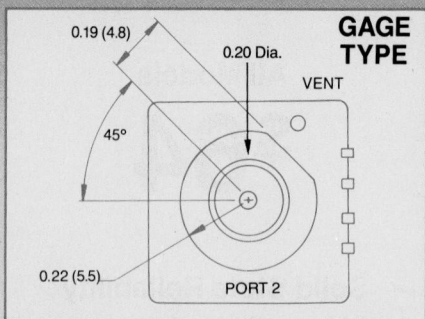

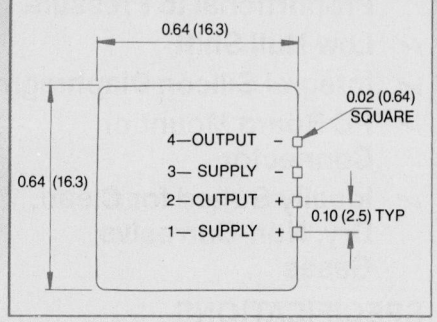

Media Compatability

Port #1, Absolute: Dry Gases Only

Port #2, Gage: Limited only to those media which will not attack polyester, silicon, borosilicate glass, or epoxy adhesive.

SPECIFICATIONS
Excitation: 10 Vdc, (16 V dc max.) @ 2 mA
Output: 5 PSI—0 to 50 mV;
15 PSI—0 to 100 mV
Sensitivity: 5 PSI—5 mV/V;
15 PSI—10 mV/V
Input Impedance: 8 K ohm

Output Impedance: 5 K ohm
Linearity: BFSL % FS
Gage: 1% max. 2.5%
Absolute: 0.5% max. 1.25%
Vacuum: 0.5% max. 1.25%
Hysteresis & Repeatability:
±0.1% full scale
Zero Balance: ±2.0 mV

To Order (Specify Model Number)
*SEE SECTION D FOR INSTRUMENT SELECTION

RANGE	MODEL	PRICE	OUTPUT	METER*
▶0-1 PSIG	PX136-001GV	$49	20 mV	DP41-S, DP2000-S4, DP302-S
▶0-5 PSIG	PX136-005GV	49	50 mV	DP41-S, DP2000-S2, DP302-S
▶0-15 PSIG	PX136-015GV	49	100 mV	DP41-S, DP2000-S2, DP302-S
▶0-30 PSIG	PX136-030GV	49	79 mV	DP41-S, DP103-R1, DP302-S
▶0-65 PSIG	PX136-065GV	49	32.5 mV	DP41-S, DP2000-S3, DP302-S
▶0-100 PSIG	PX136-100GV	49	100 mV	DP41-S, DP2000-S2, DP302-S
▶0-150 PSIG	PX136-150GV	49	60 mV	DP41-S, DP2000-S3, DP302-S
▶0-15 PSIA	PX136-015AV	56	−100 mV	DP41-S, DP2000-S2, DP302-S
▶0-30 PSIA	PX136-030AV	56	−79 mV	DP41-S, DP460-S, DP3002-S

Note: Gage models can also measure vacuum.
For tubing for gage units order model no. TY-316-100.

▶ **HIGHLIGHTED MODELS STOCKED FOR FAST DELIVERY** ◀

Operable Temperature Range: −40 to 185°F (−40 to 85°C)
Compensated Temperature Range: 32 to 122°F (0 to 50°C)
Thermal Zero Effect: ±2.0% mV typ.; ±4.0 mV max.
Thermal Sensitivity Effect: ±1.5 mV typ.; ±3.0 mV max.
Operable Overpressure: Min. 2.5 x full scale
Gage Type: Solid State Piezo-Resistive
Diaphragm Material: .10 inch Square Silicon Sensor Chip
Pressure Port: Tube Fitting (TY-316-100 for gage units)
Electrical Connections: CX 136-4 Standard Spaced PC Board Termination
Weight: 5 grams
Response Time: 1 mS

SEE PAGE C-3 FOR CONNECTORS

LOW COST MILLIVOLT OUTPUT TYPE PRESSURE TRANSDUCER
FOR DIFFERENTIAL PRESSURES UP TO 15 PSID

126 Series
0-5 PSI 0-15 PSI

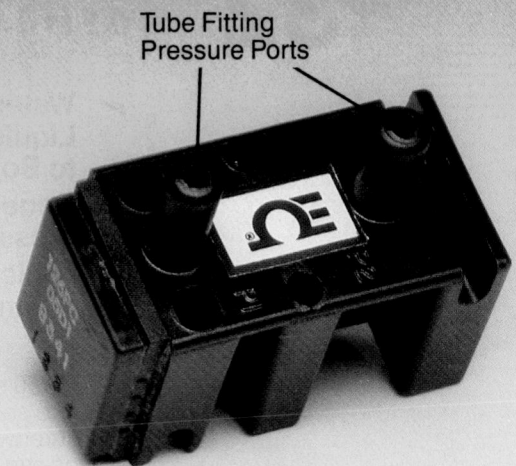

Tube Fitting Pressure Ports

$49

Shown slightly larger than actual size

SILICON DIAPHRAGM
- **Temperature Compensated**
- **Low Cost**
- **Fast Response**
- **Printed Circuit Mounting**
- **50 & 100 mV Outputs**
- **10 V dc Excitation**
- **−55 to +125°C**
- **Heavy Duty Plastic Case**
- **Vacuum or Pressure Port 1**
- **Gage Pressure Port 2**

Media Compatibility
P1: Dry Gases only
P2: Limited only to those media which will not attack polyester, silicon, borosilicate glass, or epoxy adhesive.

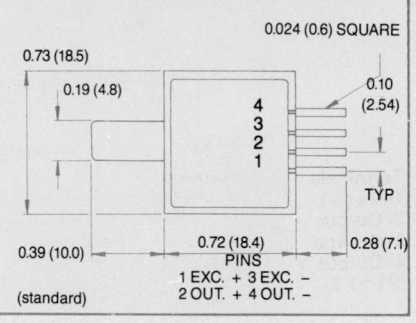

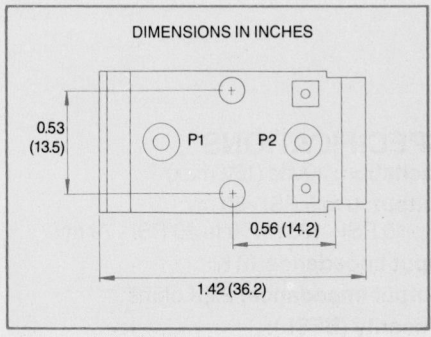

DIMENSIONS IN INCHES

0.53 (13.5)
P1 P2
0.56 (14.2)
1.42 (36.2)

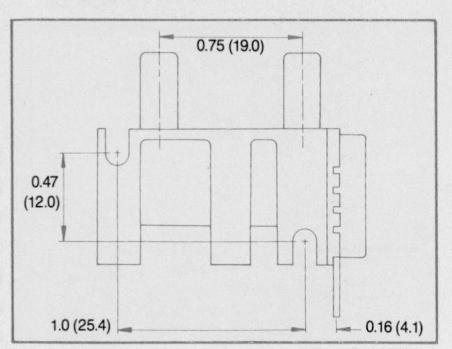

0.75 (19.0)
0.47 (12.0)
1.0 (25.4)
0.16 (4.1)

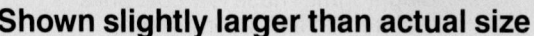

0.024 (0.6) SQUARE
0.73 (18.5)
0.19 (4.8)
0.10 (2.54)
4
3
2
1
TYP
0.39 (10.0)
(standard)
0.72 (18.4)
0.28 (7.1)
PINS
1 EXC. + 3 EXC. −
2 OUT. + 4 OUT. −

SPECIFICATIONS

Excitation: 10 V dc (16 V dc Max.) @ 2 mA
Output: 5 PSI—0 to 50 mV
Sensitivity: 5 PSI—5 mV/V; 15 PSI—10 mV/V
Input Impedance: 8 K ohm
Output Impedance: 5 K ohm

PERFORMANCE

Linearity: P2 > P1; 5 PSI–1.5% typ., 3.0% max.; 15 PSI–1.0% typ.; 2.5% max. P2 < P1; 5 PSI–0.75% typ., 1.5% max.; 15 PSI–0.5% typ., 1.25% max.
Hysteresis & Repeatability: ±0.1% full scale
Response Time: 1 mS
Zero Balance: ±2.0 mV

Operable Temperature Range: −65 to 257°F (−55 to 125°C)
Compensated Temperature Range: 32 to 122°F (0 to 50°C)
Thermal Zero Effect: ±2.0 mV typ.; ±4.0 mV Max.
Thermal Sensitivity Effect: ±1.5 mV typ.; ±3.0 mV Max.
Operable Overpressure: Min. 2.5 × full scale

CONSTRUCTION

Gage Type: Solid State Piezo-Resistive
Diaphragm Material: .10 Inch Square Silicon Sensor Chip
Pressure Port: Tube Fittings
Electrical Connection: CX 136-4 Standard Spaced PC Board Termination
Weight: 12 grams

To Order (Specify Model Number)
SEE SECTION D FOR INSTRUMENT SELECTION

RANGE	OUTPUT	MODEL	PRICE	COMPATIBLE METER*
5 PSID	50 mV	PX126-005D-V	$49	DP41-S, DP350, DP2000-S2
15 PSID	100 mV	PX126-015D-V	49	DP41-S, DP-350, DP2000-S2

▶ *HIGHLIGHTED MODELS STOCKED FOR FAST DELIVERY* ◀

LOW COST WET/WET DIFFERENTIAL PRESSURE TRANSDUCER

MADE IN USA — 1 YEAR WARRANTY

All Models
$32

PX160 Series
0-5 to 0-30 PSIG/PSID

✓ **Water and Most Industrial Liquids Can be Applied to Both Sides**

✓ **Gage and Differential Pressure Measurement**

✓ **Miniature PC Board Mountable Design**

The PX160 series solid state miniature pressure sensors are the first miniature wet/wet transducers. Liquids can be on both sides of the diaphragm. These low cost units feature thin film laser trimmed networks for close tolerances and a temperature circuit to provide low sensitivity and null shift with temperature. The sensors offer the traditional benefits of solid state design; ruggedness, small size and reliability.

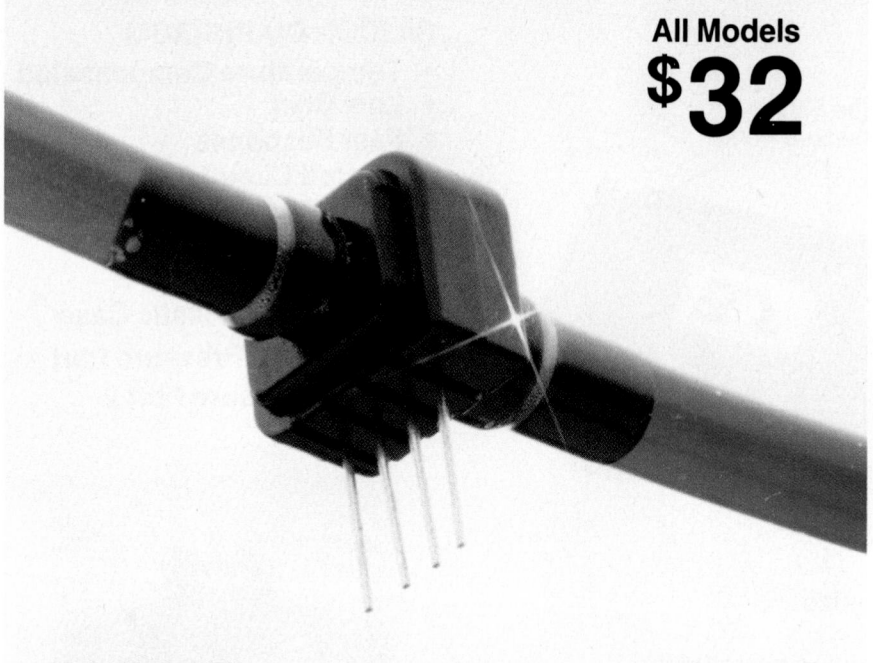

Model PX160-030DV Shown $32

Shown Larger Than Actual Size

MOUNTING DIMENSIONS: (mm/in)

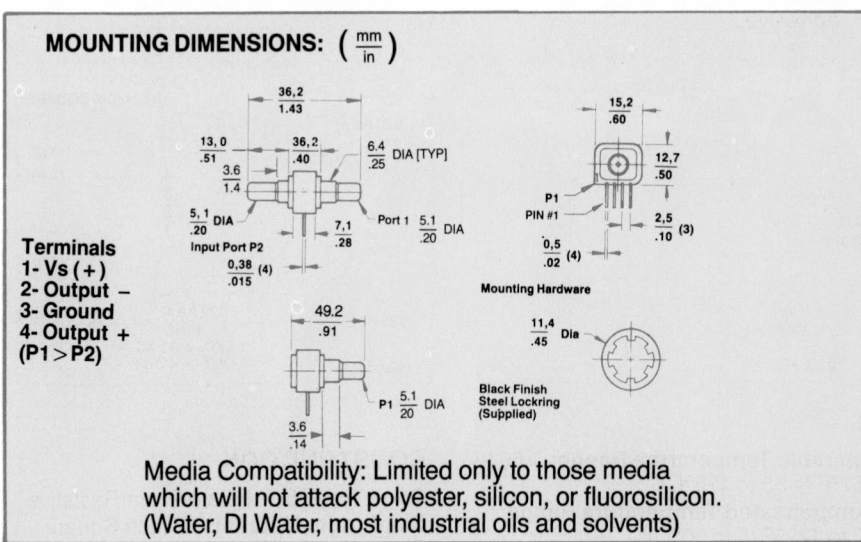

Terminals
1- Vs (+)
2- Output −
3- Ground
4- Output +
(P1 > P2)

Media Compatibility: Limited only to those media which will not attack polyester, silicon, or fluorosilicon. (Water, DI Water, most industrial oils and solvents)

▶ *HIGHLIGHTED MODELS STOCKED FOR FAST DELIVERY* ◀

To Order (Specify Model Number)

RANGE	MODEL	PRICE	COMPATIBLE METERS
0-5 PSIG	PX160-005GV	$32	DP3002-S, DP350, DP2000-S2
0-5 PSID	PX160-005DV	32	DP3002-S, DP350, DP2000-S2
0-15 PSIG	PX160-015GV	32	DP3002-S, DP350, DP2000-S2
0-15 PSID	PX160-015DV	32	DP3002-S, DP350, DP2000-S2
0-30 PSIG	PX160-030GV	32	DP3002-S, DP350, DP41-S
0-30 PSID	PX160-030DV	32	DP3002-S, DP350, DP41-S

SPECIFICATIONS

Excitation: 10Vdc (16V max)

Output: 0 to 5 PSI - 50 mV; 0 to 15 PSI - 100 mV; 0 to 30 PSI - 79 mV

Input Impedance: 10 K

Output Impedance: 2.2K ohms

Linearity (BFSL):
P1 > P2 .3% TYP .5% FS max
P2 > P1 .5% TYP 1.0% FS max

Repeatability and Hysteresis: 0.5% TYP, 0.1% FS max

Zero and Span Tolerance: ±2mV

Operating Temperature: −40 to 185°F

Compensated Temperature: 32 to 122°F

Thermal Effects: (Per 25°C Change):
Zero .5% TYP, .75% FS max
Span .5% TYP, 1.0% Rdg max

Overpressure: 0 to 5 PSI = 20 PSI; 0 to 15 PSI = 45 PSI; 0 to 30 PSI = 60 PSI

Common Mode Pressure: 60 PSI

Weight: 5 gms

Response Time: 1ms

Mating Connector: CX136-4 (for non-PC board applications)

PX236 ECONOMICAL MILLIVOLT OUTPUT TYPE PRESSURE TRANSDUCER
WITH FULL BRIDGE DESIGN FOR HIGH SENSITIVITY

236 Series New Ranges
0-15 PSIG
0-30 PSIG
0-60 PSIG
0-100 PSIG

Shown twice actual size

SILICON DIAPHRAGM
- 18″ Leads Standard
- Compensated
- ¼-18 NPT Pressure Port
- 1 Millisecond Response Time
- −30° to 70°C Operation
- 10 Vdc Excitation

$85

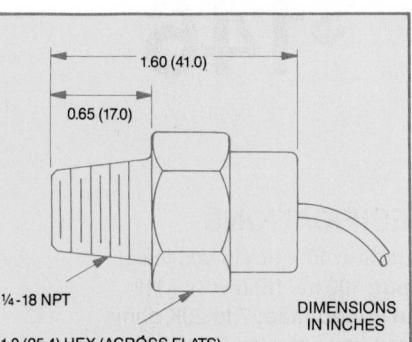

1.60 (41.0)
0.65 (17.0)
¼ - 18 NPT
1.0 (25.4) HEX (ACROSS FLATS)
DIMENSIONS IN INCHES

Can be used for vacuum applications

Media Compatability
Limited only to those media which will not attack polyester, silicon borosilicate glass, or epoxy adhesive.

LEADWIRES
1-Red	V+
2-White	Out+
3-Black	V−
4-Green	Out−

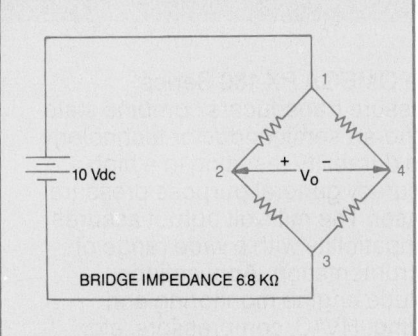

10 Vdc
BRIDGE IMPEDANCE 6.8 KΩ

Zero Balance: ±2 mV
Operable Temperature Range: −22 to 158°F (−30 to 70°C)
Compensated Temperature Range: 32 to 122°F (0 to 50°C)
Thermal Span Effect: ±1.5% full scale
Thermal Zero Effect: .022 mV/°F typ., max. .044 mV/°F
Operable Overpressure: Min. 1.5 x full scale
Response Time: 1 ms

CONSTRUCTION

Gage Type: Solid State Piezo-Resistive
Body Material: SS
Diaphragm Material: .10 inch Square Silicon Sensor Chip, .055 in³ volume
Pressure Port: ¼-18 NPT
Electrical Connections: 18″, #28 AWG; 4 Conductor Cable
Weight: 56 grams

SPECIFICATIONS

Excitation: 10 Vdc, 16 V max. @ 2 mA
Output: See Ranges
Input Impedance: 6.8 K ohm

PERFORMANCE

Linearity: Best Fit Straight Line ±1.5% full scale (±0.5% full scale 100 mV)
Hysteresis & Repeatability: ±0.25% full scale

To Order (Specify Model Number)

SEE SECTION D FOR INSTRUMENT SELECTION

RANGE	OUTPUT	MODEL	PRICE	COMPATIBLE METER*
0- 5 PSIG	50 mV	PX236-005G V	$85	DP350,DP2000S2,DP41-S
0- 15 PSIG	100 mV	PX236-015G V	85	DP2000S2,DP350,DP41-S
0- 30 PSIG	80 mV	PX236-030G V	85	DP2000P2,DP3002-S,DP41-S
0- 60 PSIG	60 mV	PX236-060G V	85	DP350,DP2000S2,DP41-S
0-100 PSIG	100 mV	PX236-100G V	85	DP350,DP2000S2,DP41-S
0-150 PSIG	60 mV	PX236-150G V	85	DP350,DP2000S3,DP41-S

◆ HIGHLIGHTED MODELS STOCKED FOR FAST DELIVERY ◆

ECONOMICAL CORROSION RESISTANT PRESSURE TRANSDUCER *WITH MILLIVOLT OUTPUT*

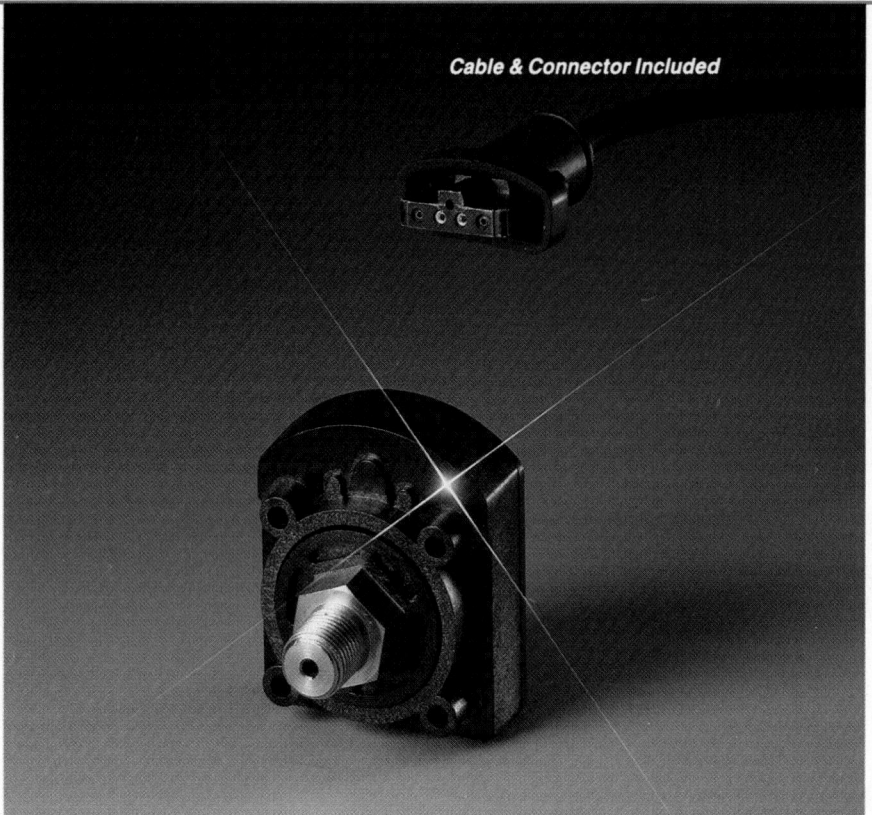

Cable & Connector Included

PX180 Series

- ✔ **Stainless Steel Pressure Port for Wide Media Compatibility**
- ✔ **Assured 0.3% Accuracy**
- ✔ **Corrosion Resistant Housing Permits Mounting In Any Environment**
- ✔ **Operating Temperature Range −55 to 110°C**
- ✔ **Extremely Compact, Weighs Only 50 Grams**

MADE IN
USA

PX180 Series

$146

The OMEGA PX-180 Series pressure transducers combine state-of-the-art semiconductor technology and durability resulting in a high accuracy general purpose pressure sensor. The millivolt output assures compatibility with a wide range of instrumentation. Applications include engine monitoring and testing, HVAC, compressors, etc. The silicon sensor is bonded on a glass pedestal to isolate it from induced stresses, provide wide media compatibility, and the stainless steel pressure port permits use with corrosive substances. These rugged, compact transducers exhibit 0.3% accuracy and excellent interchangeability.

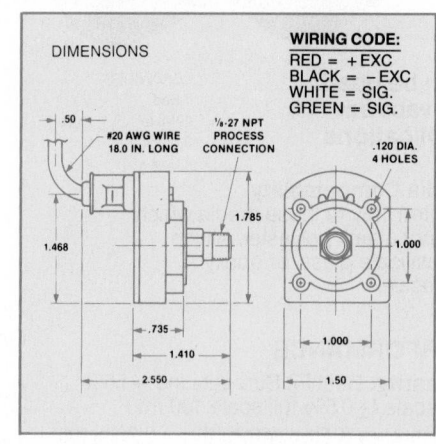

DIMENSIONS

WIRING CODE:
RED = + EXC
BLACK = − EXC
WHITE = SIG.
GREEN = SIG.

◆ *IN STOCK FOR FAST DELIVERY* ◆

SPECIFICATIONS

Excitation: 10 V dc (15 Vdc max.)
Output: 100 mV (10 mV/V) ±1%
Input Impedance: 7 to 20K ohms
Output Impedance: 5K ohms
Accuracy: ±0.3% BFSL includes linearity, repeatability, and hysteresis
Zero Balance: ±1% span
Operable Temperature Range: −55 to 110°C
Compensated Temperature Range: −55 to 75°C
Thermal Zero Effect: ±0.5% span
Thermal Span Effect: ±0.5% span
Proof Pressure: 2 x full scale
Burst Pressure: 3 x full scale
Gages: laser trimmed semiconductor
Wetted Parts: Stainless steel, glass, silicon, Fluorosilicon
Pressure Port: 1/8-27 NPT stainless steel fitting
Stability: ±1% full scale output/year
Shock: 500G
Vibration: 10G, 10 to 2000 Hz
Electrical Connection: 12″ 20 AWG, 3 conductor shielded wire with self sealing connector
Weight: 50 grams

To Order *(Specify Model Number)*

RANGE	MODEL	PRICE	COMPATIBLE METER
0 to 15 PSIG	PX180-015GV	$146	DP41-S, DP302-S, DP460-S ◆
0 to 30 PSIG	PX180-030GV	146	DP41-S, DP302-S, DP460-S
0 to 60 PSIG	PX180-060GV	146	DP41-S, DP302-S, DP460-S
0 to 100 PSIG	PX180-100GV	146	DP41-S, DP302-S, DP460-S
0 to 200 PSIG	PX180-200GV	146	DP41-S, DP302-S, DP460-S
0 to 300 PSIG	PX180-300GV	146	DP41-S, DP3002-S, DP460-S
0 to 500 PSIG	PX180-500GV	146	DP41-S, DP3002-S, DP460-S

STAINLESS STEEL TRANSDUCER FOR CORROSIVE MEDIA APPLICATIONS

PX120 Series
0-5 to 0-5000 PSIG

$158

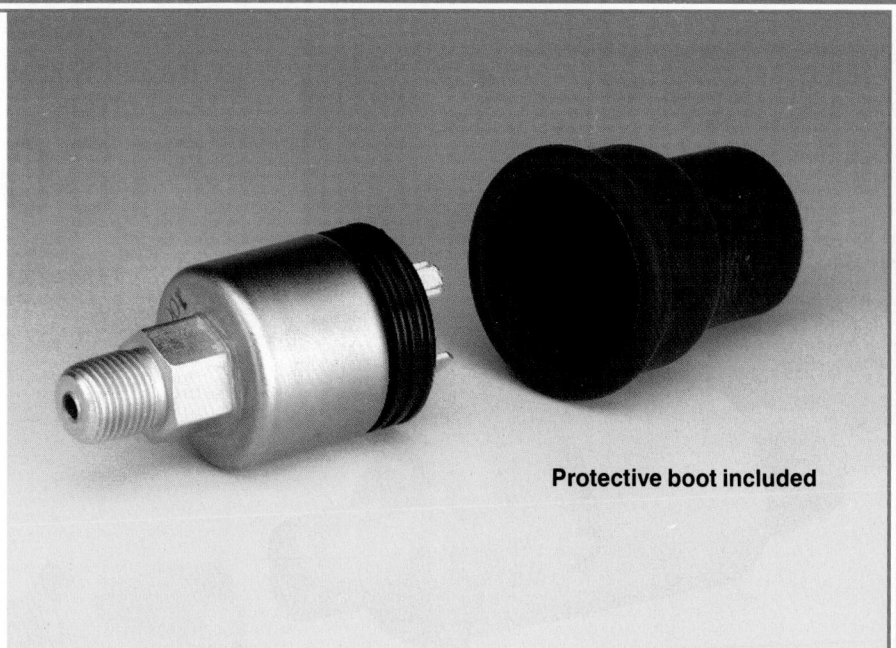

Protective boot included

- **Corrosion Resistant 300 Series Stainless Steel**
- **Rugged—100 Million Pressure Cycles**
- **Excitation 5 Vdc**
- **Compensated Temperature Range 32 to 176°F**

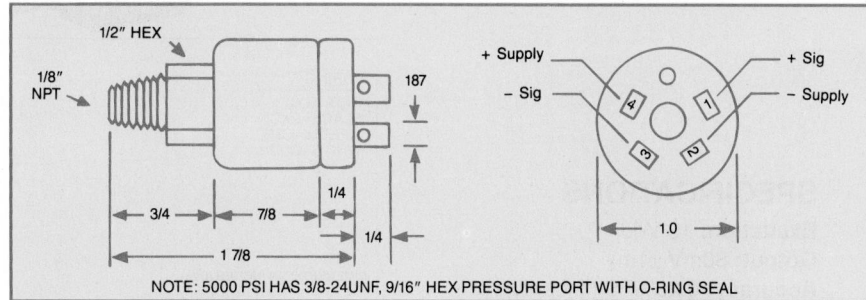

NOTE: 5000 PSI HAS 3/8-24UNF, 9/16" HEX PRESSURE PORT WITH O-RING SEAL

PERFORMANCE
Accuracy: ±1% Full Scale (BFSL includes linearity, hysteresis repeatability)
Zero Balance: ±2.5 mV @ 25°C
Operating Temperature Range: −40 to 257°F, (−40 to 125°C)
Compensated Temperature Range: 32 to 176°F, (0 to 80°C)
Thermal Zero Effect: < ±1% of FSO per 100°F
Thermal Span Effect: < ±1% of reading per 100°F
Proof Pressure: Range ≤ 200 PSI 2 x rated pressure
Range ≥ 500 PSI 1.5 x rated pressure
Burst Pressure: ≤ 200 PSI 10 x rated pressure
Range ≥ 500 PSI 5 x rated pressure
Pressure Port: 1/8 NPT
Connections: .187 push-on terminal flats
Shock: 50 G's, 5 mS
Vibration: 46.7 G's rms, 15 to 2000 Hz
Weight: 3 oz.

SPECIFICATIONS
Excitation: 5 ±.25 V dc @ 10 mA
Output: 50 ±1 mV dc
Sensitivity: 10 mV/V
Input Impedance: 500 ohms
Output Impedance: 900 ohms

MEDIA COMPATIBILITY
Wetted Parts: 300 Series Stainless Steel. Can be used with a variety of corrosive liquids and gases including freon, water, ammonia, hydraulic liquids

To Order (Specify Model Number)			*SEE SECTION D FOR INSTRUMENT SELECTION*
RANGE	**MODEL**	**PRICE**	**COMPATIBLE METER**
0 to 15 PSIG**	PX120-015GV	$158	*DP2000S3, DP350, DP41-S
0 to 25 PSIG**	PX120-025GV	158	*DP2000S1, DP350, DP41-S
0 to 50 PSIG**	PX120-050GV	158	*DP2000S2, DP350, DP41-S
0 to 100 PSIG	PX120-100GV	158	*DP2000S3, DP350, DP41-S
0 to 200 PSIG	PX120-200GV	158	*DP2000S4, DP350, DP41-S
0 to 500 PSIG	PX120-500GV	158	*DP2000S2, DP350, DP41-S
0 to 1000 PSIG	PX120-1KGV	158	*DP2000S3, DP350, DP41-S
0 to 5000 PSIG	PX120-5KGV	158	DP87, DP41-S

* Meter excitation must be adjusted by user to 5Vdc.
** User should vent boot for best accuracy

HIGHLIGHTED MODELS STOCKED FOR FAST DELIVERY

GENERAL PURPOSE 30 MILLIVOLT OUTPUT PRESSURE SENSOR
AVAILABLE IN ABSOLUTE AND GAGE MODELS

PX300 Series From

$180

3 YEAR WARRANTY | **MADE IN USA** | **NIST**

✔ **All Stainless Steel Wetted Parts**
✔ **Integral Strain Relief for Cable**
✔ **0.25% Full Scale Accuracy**

Shown With DP3002-S Meter ($325) and
PS-4 Snubber ($10). Meter and Snubber
Sold Separately.

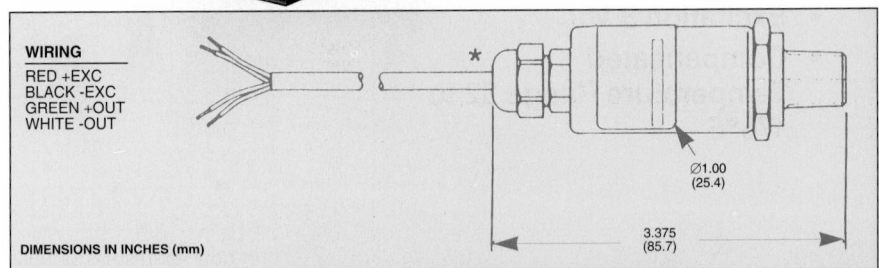

WIRING
RED +EXC
BLACK -EXC
GREEN +OUT
WHITE -OUT

*

Ø1.00 (25.4)

3.375 (85.7)

DIMENSIONS IN INCHES (mm)

SPECIFICATIONS

Excitation: 10 Vdc
Output: 30mV ±1mV
Accuracy: 0.25%FS (linearity, hysteresis, repeatability)
Zero Balance: ±2 mV
Operating Temp.: 0 to 160°F (-18 to 71°C)
Compensated Temp.: 30 to 160°F (-1 to 71°C)
Total Thermal Effects: 3% FS max
Proof Pressure: 200%, 13000 PSI max
Input/Output Resistance: 5000 ohms nominal
Response Time: 1 msec
Gage Type: Stainless steel diaphragm, silicone oil filled semiconductor sensor
Shock: 50 g @ 11msec
Wetted Parts: 300 SS series (SS and Viton ≥2000 PSI)
Pressure Port: ¼" NPT
Press. Cavity: 0.075 cubic inches
Electrical Conn.: 4 cond, 22 awg, PVC unshielded, 3 ft pigtail cable
Weight: 4.6 oz (131 grams)
Accessories: PS-4G (snubber for gaseous media), PS4E (snubber for water and light oils) and PS-4D (snubber for dense liquids/motor oils) $10 each. **Snubbers protect sensors from fluid spikes/hammers!**

HIGHLIGHTED MODELS IN STOCK FOR FAST DELIVERY!

TO ORDER (Specify Model Number)

RANGE	MODEL	PRICE	COMPATIBLE METER
GAGE MODELS			
0-15 PSIG	**PX300-015GV**	$180	DP41-S, DP2000-S4, DP460-S
0-50 PSIG	**PX300-050GV**	180	DP41-S, DP2000-S2, DP460-S
0-100 PSIG	**PX300-100GV**	180	DP41-S, DP2000-S3, DP302-S
0-200 PSIG	**PX300-200GV**	180	DP41-S, DP2000-S4, DP302-S
0-300 PSIG	**PX300-300GV**	180	DP41-S, DP3002-S, DP460-S
0-500 PSIG	**PX300-500GV**	180	DP41-S, DP3002-S, DP460-S
0-1000 PSIG	**PX300-1KGV**	180	DP41-S, DP2000-S3, DP460-S
0-2000 PSIG	**PX300-2KGV**	180	DP41-S, DP2000-S4, DP460-S
0-3000 PSIG	**PX300-3KGV**	180	DP41-S, DP3002-S, DP460-S
0-4000 PSIG	**PX300-4KGV**	180	DP41-S, DP3002-S, DP460-S
0-5000 PSIG	**PX300-5KGV**	180	DP41-S, DP3002-S, DP460-S
0-7500 PSIG	**PX300-7.5KGV**	180	DP41-S, DP3002-S, DP460-S
0-10000 PSIG	**PX300-10KGV**	180	DP41-S, DP3002-S, DP460-S

Comes with complete operator's manual.
Ordering Example: PX300-1KGV pressure transducer with 1000 PSI and 30 mV output and PS-4G pressure snubber for gasses, $180 + 10 = **$190.**

GENERAL PURPOSE 100 MILLIVOLT OUTPUT PRESSURE SENSOR
AVAILABLE IN ABSOLUTE AND GAGE MODELS

NEW!

PX302 Series
From
$180

✔ **Rugged ¼ NPT Stainless Steel Pressure Port**
✔ **Integral Strain Relief for Cable**
✔ **High Sensitivity 10 mV/V Output**

Shown with DP41-S Meter ($395) and PS-4 Snubber ($10).
Meter and Snubber Sold Separately.

SPECIFICATIONS

Excitation: 10 Vdc
Output: 100mV±1mV
Accuracy: 0.25%FS (linearity, hysteresis, repeatability)
Zero Balance: ±2 mV
Operating Temp.: 0 to 160°F (-18 to 71 °C)
Compensated Temp.: 30 to 160°F (-1 to 71 °C)
Total Thermal Effects: 1% FS max
Proof Pressure: 200%, 13000 PSI max
Input/Output Resistance: 5000 ohms nominal
Response Time: 1 msec
Gage Type: Stainless steel diaphragm, silicone oil filled semiconductor sensor
Shock: 50 g @ 11msec
Wetted Parts: 300 SS series (SS and Viton ≥ 2000 PSI)
Pressure Port: ¼" NPT
Press. Cavity: 0.075 cubic inches
Electrical Conn.: 4 cond, 22 awg, PVC unshielded, 3 ft pigtail cable
Weight: 4.6 oz (131 grams)
Accessories: PS-4G (snubber for gaseous media), **PS4E** (snubber for water and light oils) and **PS-4D** (snubber for dense liquids/motor oils) $10 each. *Snubbers protect sensors from fluid spikes/hammers!*
Dimensions: See page B-17

HIGHLIGHTED MODELS IN STOCK FOR FAST DELIVERY!

TO ORDER *(Specify Model Number)*

RANGE	MODEL	PRICE	COMPATIBLE METER
GAGE MODELS			
0-15 PSIG	PX302-015GV	$180	DP41-S, DP2000-S2, DP460-S
0-50 PSIG	PX302-050GV	180	DP41-S, DP2000-S1, DP460-S
0-100 PSIG	PX302-100GV	180	DP41-S, DP2000-S2, DP302-S
0-200 PSIG	PX302-200GV	180	DP41-S, DP2000-S3, DP302-S
0-300 PSIG	PX302-300GV	180	DP41-S, DP3002-S, DP460-S
0-500 PSIG	PX302-500GV	180	DP41-S, DP3002-S, DP460-S
0-1000 PSIG	PX302-1KGV	180	DP41-S, DP2000-S2, DP460-S
0-2000 PSIG	PX302-2KGV	180	DP41-S, DP2000-S3, DP460-S
0-3000 PSIG	PX302-3KGV	180	DP41-S, DP3002-S, DP460-S
0-4000 PSIG	PX302-4KGV	180	DP41-S, DP3002-S, DP460-S
0-5000 PSIG	PX302-5KGV	180	DP41-S, DP3002-S, DP460-S
0-7500 PSIG	PX302-7.5KGV	180	DP41-S, DP3002-S, DP460-S
0-10000 PSIG	PX302-10KGV	180	DP41-S, DP3002-S, DP460-S
ABSOLUTE MODELS			
0-15 PSIA	PX302-015AV	$180	DP41-S, DP2000-S2, DP460-S
0-50 PSIA	PX302-050AV	180	DP41-S, DP302-S1, DP460-S
0-100 PSIA	PX302-100AV	180	DP41-S, DP2000-S2, DP460-S
0-200 PSIA	PX302-200AV	180	DP41-S, DP2000-S3, DP460-S
0-300 PSIA	PX302-300AV	180	DP41-S, DP302-S, DP460-S

Comes with complete operator's manual.
Ordering Example: *PX302-050GV pressure transducer with 50 PSI full scale rating and PS-4E pressure snubber for water and light oils, $180 + 10 = **$190**.*

THIN FILM MILLIVOLT OUTPUT PRESSURE SENSOR
FOR GAGE AND ABSOLUTE PRESSURES

NEW!

3 YEAR WARRANTY

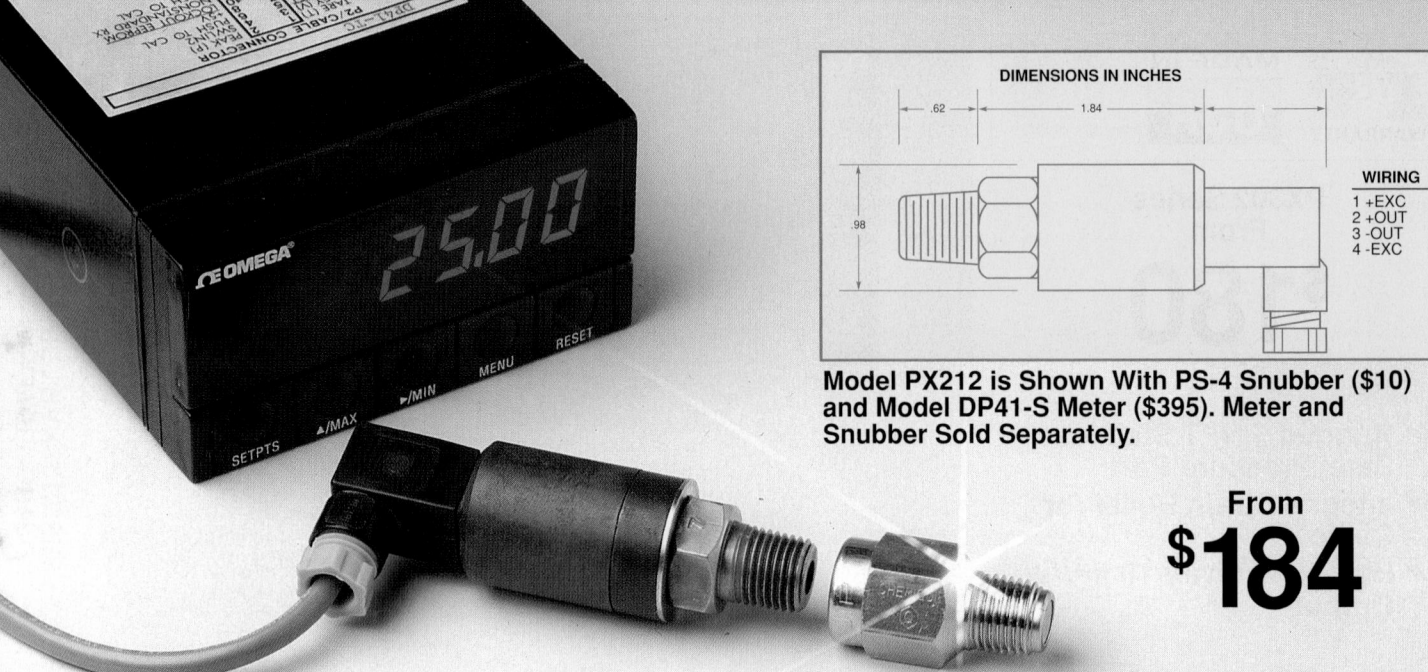

DIMENSIONS IN INCHES

.62 1.84 .98

WIRING
1 +EXC
2 +OUT
3 -OUT
4 -EXC

Model PX212 is Shown With PS-4 Snubber ($10) and Model DP41-S Meter ($395). Meter and Snubber Sold Separately.

From
$**184**

- ✔ **All Stainless Steel Wetted Parts**
- ✔ **NEMA 4 Rated**
- ✔ **CVD Construction for High Stability**

SPECIFICATIONS

Excitation: 10 Vdc, 15Vdc max.
Output: 100 mV ±1 mV
Accuracy: 0.25% (including linearity, hysteresis, and repeatability)
Zero Balance: 1% FS
Operating Temperature: -40 to 257°F (-40 to 125°C)
Compensated Temperature: -4 to 176°F (-20 to 80°C)
Thermal Effects: 1.5% FS over (-20 to 80°C)
Proof Pressure: 150%
Burst Pressure: 400%, 17000 psi max
Input Resistance: 2.5k to 6k ohms
Output Resistance: 1.2k to 4.3k ohms
Response Time: 1 ms
Gage Type: Chemical vapor deposited polysilicon strain gages
Wetted Parts: 15-7,17-4 SS, <60 PSI 17-4 SS ≥ 60 PSI
Pressure Port: ¼ -18 NPT
Case: Liquid crystal polymer (thermoplastic)
Electrical Connections: Miniature DIN connector; screw terminals
Weight: 87 grams

HIGHLIGHTED MODELS STOCKED FOR FAST DELIVERY!

To Order *(Specify Model Number)*

RANGE	MODEL	PRICE	COMPATIBLE METERS
GAGE MODELS			
0-15 PSIG	**PX212-015GV**	$184	DP41-S, DP302-S, DP2000-S2
0-30 PSIG	**PX212-030GV**	184	DP41-S, DP302-S, DP460-S
0-60 PSIG	**PX212-060GV**	184	DP41-S, DP302-S, DP460-S
0-100 PSIG	**PX212-100GV**	184	DP41-S, DP302-S, DP2000-S2
0-300 PSIG	**PX212-300GV**	184	DP41-S, DP3002-S, DP460-S
0-600 PSIG	**PX212-600GV**	184	DP41-S, DP3002-S, DP460-S
0-1000 PSIG	**PX212-1KGV**	184	DP41-S, DP302-S, DP2000-S2
0-3000 PSIG	**PX212-3KGV**	184	DP41-S, DP3002-S, DP460-S
0-6000 PSIG	**PX212-6KGV**	184	DP41-S, DP3002-S, DP460-S
ABSOLUTE MODELS			
0-15 PSIA	**PX212-015AV**	$236	DP41-S, DP302-S, DP2000-S2
0-30 PSIA	**PX212-030AV**	236	DP41-S, DP302-S, DP460-S
0-60 PSIA	**PX212-060AV**	236	DP41-S, DP302-S, DP460-S
0-100 PSIA	**PX212-100AV**	236	DP41-S, DP302-S, DP2000-S2
0-150 PSIA	**PX212-150AV**	236	DP41-S, DP302-S, DP2000-S2
0-300 PSIA	**PX212-300AV**	236	DP41-S, DP3002-S, DP460-S

ACCESSORIES	PRICE	DESCRIPTION
PS-4G	$10.00	Pressure snubber for gaseous media
PS-4E	10.00	Pressure snubber for water and light oils
PS-4D	10.00	Pressure snubber for dense liquids (motor oil)
TX4-100	28.50	100 ft of 4 conductor shielded wire

Comes with complete operator's manual.
Ordering Example: *PX212-015AV, millivolt output transducer for absolute pressure with a 0 to 15 PSIA range, two PS-4G snubbers and TX4-100 shielded wires, $236 + 20 + 28.50 = **$284.50**.*

THIN FILM PRESSURE SENSOR
100 mV OUTPUT
EXCELLENT LONG TERM STABILITY

PX602 - PX612 Series
15 PSI TO 20,000 PSI

From

$198

✔ **All Stainless Steel Case**
✔ **Small and Lightweight**
✔ **NEMA 4 Cable or Connector Models**

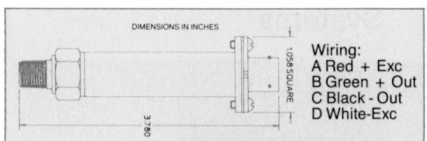

Wiring:
A Red + Exc
B Green + Out
C Black - Out
D White-Exc

Ordering Example:
DP41-S Meter $395
PX602-100GV $198
PX612-100GV $225
PT06F8-4S Connector
(not included) $24
PS-4 snubber $10

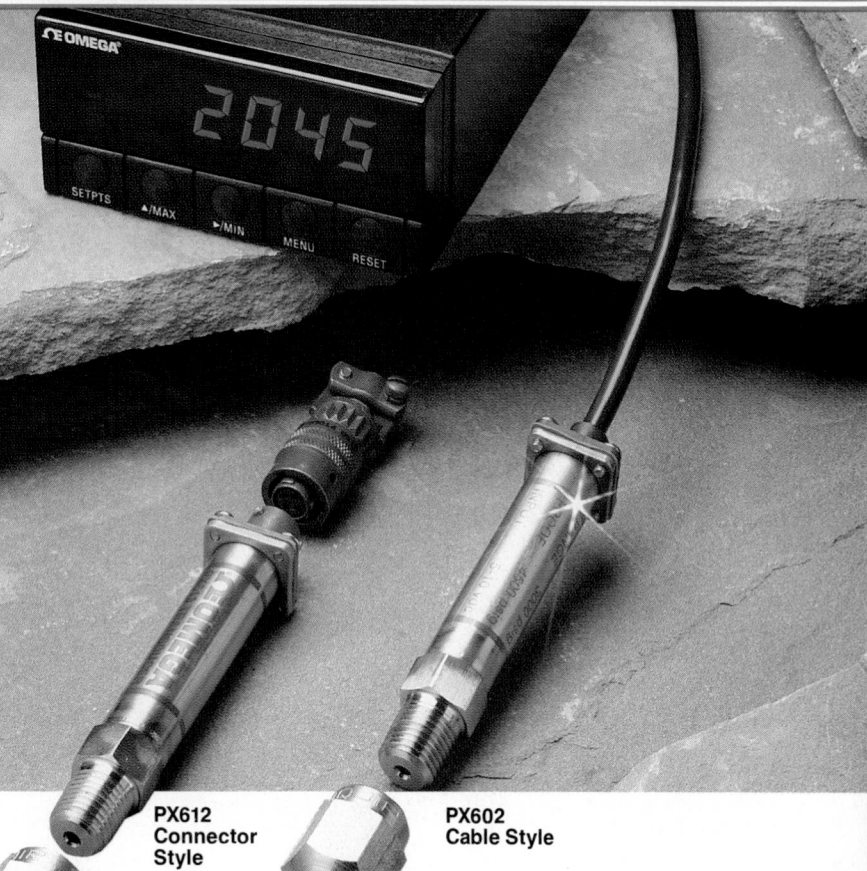

PX612
Connector
Style

PX602
Cable
Style

SPECIFICATIONS
Excitation: 10 Vdc (5 to 10 Vdc limits)
Output: 0 to 100 mV @ 10 Vdc
Sensitivity: 10 mV/V
Input Impedance: 1500Ω ohms
Output Impedance: 100Ω ohms
Insulation Resistance: 100M ohms @ 50 Vdc
Accuracy: ±0.4% BFSL
Hysteresis: ±0.2%
Repeatability: ±0.05%
Stability: ±1%/year
Zero Balance: ±1%
Durability: 100 million cycles
Operating Temp.: −55 to 195°F
Compensated Temp.: −20 to 180°F
Thermal Zero Effect: ±0.04% FS/°F
Thermal Span Effect: ±0.04% FS/°F
Proof Pressure: 15 to 2000 PSI = 200%; 3000 to 5000 = 150%; 7500 to 20000 = 120%
Burst Pressure: 15 to 2000 PSI = 800%; 3000 to 20000 = 500%
Gages: Thin film polysilicon
Diaphragm: 17-4PH stainless steel
Case: 300 Series stainless steel
Pressure Connection: 15 to 10,000 PSI: ¼ NPT; 15,000 and 20,000 PSI = 9/16-18 UNF Aminco fitting
Electrical Connection: 36″ braided shield PVC Cable or connector
Weight: 2.5 oz. without cable
Response time: 1 ms
Construction: Sealed units (except PX602 ≤ 500 PSI is vented to room)

HIGHLIGHTED MODELS IN STOCK FOR FAST DELIVERY!

To Order *(Specify PX602 for Cable or PX612 for Connector Style)*

RANGE PSIG	MODEL NO. [ ] Insert 0 or 1	PRICE PX602	PRICE PX612	COMPATIBLE METERS
0-15	PX6[ ]2-015GV	$198	$225	DP41-S, DP205-S, DP350
0-30	PX6[ ]2-030GV	198	225	DP41-S, DP205-S, DP350
0-60	PX6[ ]2-060GV	198	225	DP41-S, DP205-S, DP350
0-100	PX6[ ]2-100GV	198	225	DP41-S, DP205-S, DP350
0-150	PX6[ ]2-150GV	198	225	DP41-S, DP205-S, DP350
0-200	PX6[ ]2-200GV	198	225	DP41-S, DP205-S, DP350
0-300	PX6[ ]2-300GV	198	225	DP41-S, DP205-S, DP350
0-500	PX6[ ]2-500GV	198	225	DP41-S, DP205-S, DP350
0-1000	PX6[ ]2-1KGV	198	225	DP41-S, DP205-S, DP350
0-2000	PX6[ ]2-2KGV	198	225	DP41-S, DP205-S, DP350
0-3000	PX6[ ]2-3KGV	198	225	DP41-S, DP87, DP110-R1
0-5000	PX6[ ]2-5KGV	198	225	DP41-S, DP87, DP110-R1
0-7500	PX6[ ]2-7.5KGV	198	225	DP41-S, DP87, DP110-R1
0-10,000	PX6[ ]2-10KGV	198	225	DP41-S, DP87, DP110-R1
0-15,000	PX6[ ]2-15KGV*	198	225	DP41-S, DP87, DP110-R1
0-20,000	PX6[ ]2-20KGV*	198	225	DP41-S, DP87, DP110-R1

* 15,000 and 20,000 PSI Models Supplied With female AMINCO fitting.

MILLIVOLT OUTPUT PRESSURE TRANSDUCERS

B

ECONOMICAL MILLIVOLT OUTPUT TYPE PRESSURE TRANSDUCER
WITH FULL BRIDGE DESIGN FOR HIGH SENSITIVITY

906 Series
0-300 to 0-7500 PSIG

✓ **Stainless Steel Diaphragm for Compatibility with Most Media**
✓ **Rugged Stainless Steel Case Protects Components in Industrial Environments**

✓ **Supplied with 36″ Color Coded, Shielded Leads for Easy Connections and High Noise Immunity**
✓ **Uses a Standard 10 V dc Regulated Power Supply for Maximum Versatility**
✓ **Compact Design for Use in Restricted Areas**
✓ **¼ ″ FNPT Process Threading for Easy Installation in Piping Systems**

$219

Shown larger than actual size

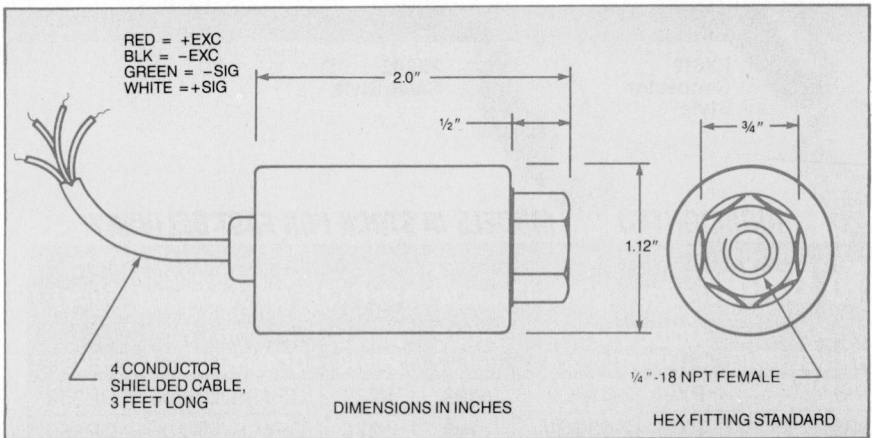

RED = +EXC
BLK = −EXC
GREEN = −SIG
WHITE = +SIG

2.0″
½″
¾″
1.12″

4 CONDUCTOR SHIELDED CABLE, 3 FEET LONG

DIMENSIONS IN INCHES

¼″-18 NPT FEMALE

HEX FITTING STANDARD

SPECIFICATIONS

Excitation: 10 V dc (12 Vdc max.) @ 30 mA
Output: 20 mV full scale
Sensitivity: 2 mV/V
Input Resistance: 350 ohms
Output Resistance: 350 ohms
Insulation Resistance: > 5 MΩ @ 75 V dc

PERFORMANCE

Accuracy: ±0.3% (Includes Linearity, Hysteresis & Repeatability)
Zero Balance: ±3%
Operable Temperature Range: −65 to 250°F
Compensated Temperature Range: 60 to 160°F
Thermal Zero Effect: ±0.01% full scale/°F
Thermal Sensitivity Effect: ±0.02% full scale/°F
Proof Pressure: 1.5 × Range
Burst Pressure: 3 x Range; 1,500 Max.

CONSTRUCTION

Body Material: 17-4 PH Stainless Steel
Diaphragm Material: 17-4 PH Stainless Steel
Pressure Port: ¼″-18 NPT Female Thread
Electrical Connection: 4 Conductor Shielded Cable, 36″
Pressure Cavity Volume: 0.122 in³
Weight: 8 ozs.

To Order: (Specify model number)

*SEE SECTION D FOR INSTRUMENT SELECTION

RANGE	MODEL	PRICE	COMPATIBLE METER*
0- 300 PSIG	PX 906-300G V	$219	DP2000S2, DP87, DP3002-S, DP41-S
0- 500 PSIG	PX 906-500G V	219	DP2000S3, DP87, DP3002-S, DP41-S
0- 750 PSIG	PX 906-750G V	219	DP2000S4, DP87, DP3002-S, DP41-S
0-1000 PSIG	PX 906-1KG V	219	DP2000S4, DP87, DP302-S, DP41-S
0-1500 PSIG	PX 906-1.5KG V	219	DP2000S5, DP302-S, DP41-S
0-2000 PSIG	PX 906-2KG V	219	DP2000S5, DP87, DP302-S, DP41-S
0-3000 PSIG	PX 906-3KG V	219	DP87, DP3002-S, DP41-S, DP460-S
0-5000 PSIG	PX 906-5KG V	219	DP87, DP3002-S, DP41-S, DP460-S
0-7500 PSIG	PX 906-7.5KG V	219	DP87, DP3002-S, DP41-S, DP460-S

HIGH STABILITY PRESSURE TRANSDUCER
COMPATIBLE WITH MOST LIQUIDS AND GASES

PX425 Series

- **Unique Molecular Bonded Strain Gage Provides Superior Temperature Stability**
- **High Accuracy ±0.2% of Span**
- **Long Term Drift is Less Than 0.1%**
- **Superior Design for Withstanding High Shock and Vibration**

The OMEGA PX-425 Series pressure transducer utilizes a sputtering technique to form a molecular bond between the silicon strain gages and the sensing steel beam. This innovative bonding method was formerly reserved for the high cost, high tech aircraft transducer industry, where long term stability is required. OMEGA now makes this technology more readily available for process monitoring applications.

From
$495

Shown larger than actual size

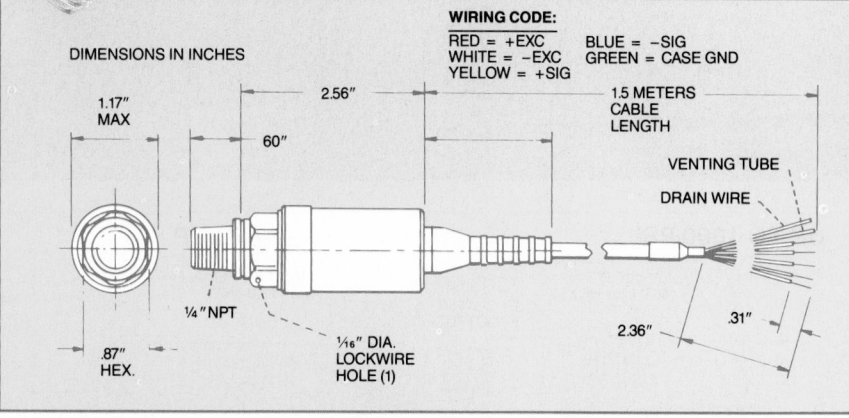

SPECIFICATIONS

Excitation: 10 Vdc (15 V max.)
Output: 30 mV ±0.3 mV
Input Impedance: 4500 ohms nominal
Output Impedance: 3000 to 5000 ohms
Insulation Resistance: 500 M ohms
Accuracy: ±0.2% span includes linearity and hysteresis
Repeatability: Maximum 0.05% span
Zero Balance: ±1.0 mV
Operable Temperature Range: −65 to 248°F (−54 to 120°C)
Compensated Temperature Range: −65 to 248°F (−54 to 120°C)
Thermal Sensitivity Effect: ±0.015% span/°C
Proof Pressure: 200% of span or 8500 PSI whichever is less
Gages: Diffused semiconductor
Cover Material: Stainless Steel
Diaphragm/Port Material: 17-4 PH SS; also 15-7 Mo SS on 15 PSI model
Pressure Port: ¼-18 NPT male
Electrical Connection: 1.5 meters (4.92 ft.) of 5 conductor shielded cable
Weight: 6 oz.
Response Time: 1 mS

◆HIGHLIGHTED MODELS STOCKED FOR FAST DELIVERY◆

To Order *(Specify Model Number)*

RANGE	MODEL	PRICE	COMPATIBLE METER
0 to 15 PSIA	PX425-015AV	$575	DP2000S4, DP350, DP41-S
0 to 30 PSIA	PX425-030AV	575	DP2000S2, DP350, DP41-S
0 to 60 PSIA	PX425-060AV	575	DP2000S3, DP350, DP41-S
0 to 100 PSIA	PX425-100AV	575	DP2000S3, DP350, DP41-S
0 to 15 PSIG	PX425-015GV	495	DP2000S4, DP350, DP41-S
0 to 30 PSIG	PX425-030GV	495	DP2000S2, DP350, DP41-S
0 to 60 PSIG	PX425-060GV	495	DP2000S3, DP350, DP41-S
0 to 100 PSIG	PX425-100GV	495	DP2000S3, DP350, DP41-S
0 to 300 PSIG	PX425-300GV	495	DP2000S2, DP350, DP41-S
0 to 600 PSIG	PX425-600GV	495	DP2000S3, DP350, DP41-S
0 to 1000 PSIG	PX425-1KGV	495	DP2000S3, DP350, DP41-S
0 to 1500 PSIG	PX425-1.5KGV	495	DP2000S4, DP350, DP41-S
0 to 3000 PSIG	PX425-3KGV	495	DP87, DP3002-S, DP41-S
0 to 6000 PSIG	PX425-6KGV	495	DP87, DP3002-S, DP41-S

HIGHLY ACCURATE MILLIVOLT OUTPUT TYPE PRESSURE TRANSDUCER

931 Series
0-10 to 0-10000 PSI

From
$530

- Rugged Stainless Steel Case Protects Components in Industrial Environments
- Connects to a PT06F-10-6S Connector for Easy Field Connections
- Stainless Steel Diaphragm Welded For Compatibility with Most Media
- Uses a Standard 10 Vdc Regulated Power Supply for Maximum Versatility
- ¼" NPT Fitting For Fast, Easy, and Secure Installation
- Excellent Temperature Stability
- Units 1000 PSIG and below Utilize Beam Mounted Strain Gages for Long Life and High Reliability

Shown slightly larger than actual size

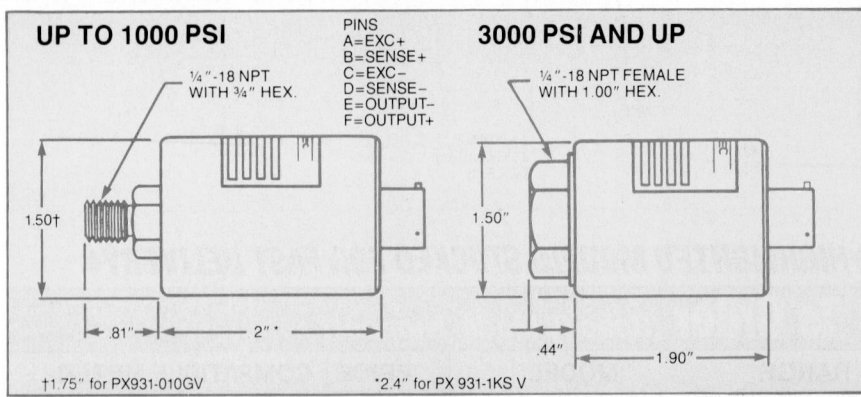

UP TO 1000 PSI

¼"-18 NPT WITH ¾" HEX.

1.50†

.81"   2"*

†1.75" for PX931-010GV

PINS
A=EXC+
B=SENSE+
C=EXC−
D=SENSE−
E=OUTPUT−
F=OUTPUT+

3000 PSI AND UP

¼"-18 NPT FEMALE WITH 1.00" HEX.

1.50"

.44"   1.90"

*2.4" for PX 931-1KS V

SPECIFICATIONS

Excitation: 10 Vdc (12 Vdc max.) @ 30 mA
Output: 30 mV ±0.25%
Sensitivity: 3 mV/V
Input Resistance: 350 ohms
Output Resistance: 350 ohms
Insulation Resistance: > 5 MΩ @ 75 V dc
Accuracy: .15%
Hysteresis: ±0.10%
Repeatability: ±0.05%
Zero Balance: ±1%
Shunt Cal: 59 KΩ
Operable Temperature Range: −100 to 325°F
Compensated Temperature Range: 60 to 160°F
Thermal Zero Effect: ±0.005% full scale/°F
Thermal Sensitivity Effect: ±0.005%/°F
Proof Pressure: 1.5 × Range
Burst Pressure: 3 ×; for 7500, 10,000 Range 2 x
Body Material: 17-4 PH Stainless Steel, hermetically sealed
Diaphragm Material: 17-4 PH Stainless Steel bonded foil gage
Pressure Port: ¼"-18 NPT (Male Thread 10 to 1,000 PSI, Female Thread 3,000 to 5,000 PSI)
Mating Connector: PT06F-10-6S (not included)
Pressure Cavity Volume: 0.171 in³
Weight: 10 ozs.

To Order (Specify model number)

RANGE	MODEL	PRICE	COMPATIBLE METER
0- 10 PSIG	PX931-010G V	$560	DP350, DP2000S4, DP3002-S
0- 25 PSIG	PX931-025G V	560	DP350, DP2000S2, DP3002-S ◄
0- 50 PSIG	PX931-050G V	530	DP350, DP2000S3, DP87
0- 100 PSIS	PX931-100S V	530	DP350, DP2000S4, DP87 ◄
0- 200 PSIS	PX931-200S V	530	DP350, DP2000S5, DP3002-S
0- 500 PSIS	PX931-500S V	530	DP350, DP2000S3, DP87
0- 1000 PSIS	PX931-1KS V	530	DP350, DP2000S4, DP87
0- 3000 PSIS	PX931-3KS V	530	DP87, DP3002-S, DP41-S
0- 5000 PSIS	PX931-5KS V	530	DP87, DP3002-S, DP41-S ◄
0- 7500 PSIS	PX931-7.5KS V	530	DP87, DP3002-S, DP41-S
0-10,000 PSIS	PX931-10KS V	530	DP87, DP3002-S, DP41-S

Absolute ranges available. Change "G" to "A" in part number. Add $25 to list price/3 piece minimum.

◄ **HIGHLIGHTED MODELS STOCKED FOR FAST DELIVERY** ◄

HIGH ACCURACY GAGE PRESSURE
TRANSDUCER RUGGED TITANIUM/QUARTZ CONSTRUCTION

PX800 Series
0-1 to 0-2000 PSIG

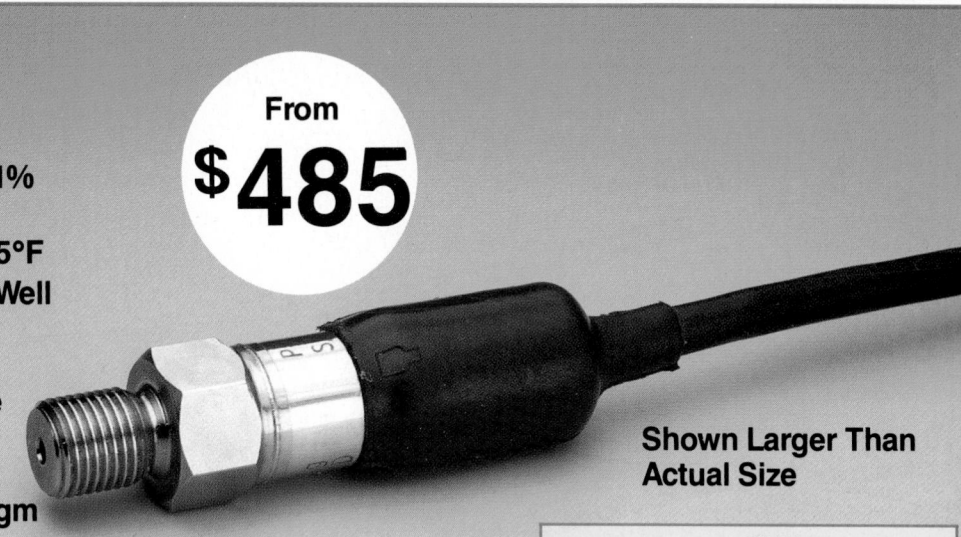

From
$485

- **High Accuracy Up to 0.1%**
- **Temperature Compensated −5 to 175°F**
- **Rugged Construction, Well Suited for Shock and Vibration**
- **Excellent Overpressure Rating 4X Full Scale Depending on Range**
- **Crystal Silicon Diaphragm for Fast Response Time**

Supplied With 3 ft Integral Vented 4 Wire Shielded Cable

Shown Larger Than Actual Size

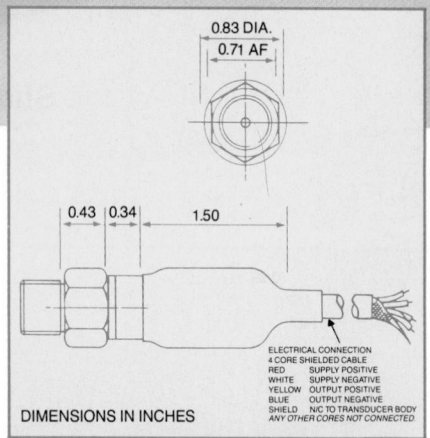

The PX800 is an extremely high accuracy rugged solid state transducer. Excellent for use in adverse environments, the PX800's fully encapsulated sensing element consists of a four arm strain gage bridge diffused into the surface of a single crystal silicon diaphragm. The silicon diaphragm has excellent mechanical and electrical properties; combined linearity and hysteresis accuracy less than 0.1% BFSL, fast response and maximum acceleration sensitivity.

SPECIFICATIONS

Excitation: 10 V dc @ 1.5 mA
Output: 1000 ohms nominal
Load Impedance: > 100K ohms for rated performance

PERFORMANCE

Accuracy: ±0.1% BFSL for 1 to 900 PSI ranges; ±0.2% BFSL for 2K PSI range (combined non-linearity and hysteresis)
Zero Balance: ±3 mV
Compensated Temperature Range: −5 to 175°F (−20 to 80°C)
Temperature Effects: ±0.5% total error 32 to 122°F; ±1.5% total error −5 to 175°F 1 PSI range ±00.5% total error band 50 to 150°F
Overpressure Rating: 10 x for 1 and 2.5 PSI ranges; 6 x for 5 PSI ranges; 4 x for 10 PSI to 2K PSI ranges, 2X for 2K PSI
Natural Frequency: 28 KHz for 5 PSI range; 360 KHz for 500 PSI range

Mechanical Shock: 1000g for 1 mS
Acceleration: 0.006% FSO/G for 5 PSI decreasing to 0.0002% FSO/G for 500 PSI
Pressure Media: Fluids compatible with quartz and titanium
Pressure Port: ¼-18 NPT
Electrical Connection: 36″ 4 wire shielded cable
Weight: 1.8 oz.

RANGE PSIG	MODEL	PRICE	COMPATIBLE METER
0 to 1	PX800-001GV	$745	DP41-S, DP2000S1, DP3002-S
0 to 2.5	PX800-002GV	610	DP350, DP2000S2, DP87
0 to 5	PX800-005GV	485	DP350, DP2000S2, DP87
0 to 10	PX800-010GV	485	DP350, DP2000S2, DP87
0 to 15	PX800-015GV	485	DP41-S, DP2000S2, DP350
0 to 20	PX800-020GV	485	DP41-S, DP2000S3, DP350
0 to 30	PX800-030GV	485	DP41-S, DP2000P2, DP3002-S
0 to 50	PX800-050GV	485	DP41-S, DP2000S1, DP350
0 to 100	PX800-100GV	485	DP350, DP2000S2, DP87
0 to 150	PX800-150GV	485	DP41-S, DP2000S2, DP350
0 to 200	PX800-200GV	485	DP41-S, DP2000S2, DP350
0 to 300	PX800-300GV	485	DP41-S, DP2000P2, DP3002-S
0 to 500	PX800-500GV	485	DP41-S, DP2000S1, DP350
0 to 900	PX800-900GV	485	DP350, DP2000S2, DP87
0 to 2K	PX800-2KSV*	595	DP41-S, DP2000S2, DP350

To Order *(Specify Model Number)* *SEE SECTION D FOR INSTRUMENT SELECTION*

* 2000 PSI range is sealed gage.

HIGHLIGHTED MODELS STOCKED FOR FAST DELIVERY

HIGH ACCURACY WET ABSOLUTE PRESSURE TRANSDUCER
RUGGED STAINLESS STEEL CONSTRUCTION

PX811 RANGES 0 TO 5 PSIA UP TO 900 PSIA

Shown Actual Size

- High Accuracy 0.1% BFSL
- Excellent Overpressure Rating 4X Full Scale or Greater Depending on Range
- Wide Compensated Range −5 to 175°F (−20 to 80°C)

From

$595

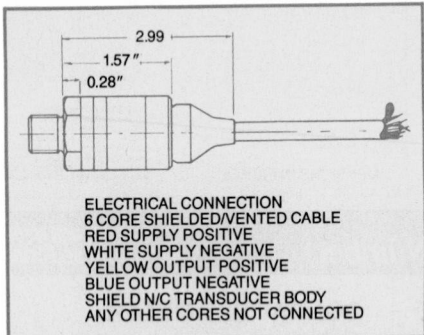

```
        2.99
     1.57"
   0.28"
```

ELECTRICAL CONNECTION
6 CORE SHIELDED/VENTED CABLE
RED SUPPLY POSITIVE
WHITE SUPPLY NEGATIVE
YELLOW OUTPUT POSITIVE
BLUE OUTPUT NEGATIVE
SHIELD N/C TRANSDUCER BODY
ANY OTHER CORES NOT CONNECTED

The PX811 is a rugged solid state transducer that measures true absolute pressure of fluids and gases. For fast response and high accuracy, the PX811 utilizes a four arm strain gage embedded in a silicon crystal. The transducer is free from hysteresis with high output at low strain. A stainless steel isolating diaphragm assures compatibility with a wide variety of liquid media.

SPECIFICATIONS
Excitation: 10 V dc regulated at 5 mA
Output: 50 mV for 5 PSI range; 100 mV for 10 mV for 10 PSI and above
Output Impedance: 2000 ohms nominal
Load Impedance: >100K ohms for rated performance
Performance Accuracy: Combined non-linearity and hysteresis ±0.1% BFSL
Zero Balance: ±3 mV
Compensated Temperature Range: −5 to 175°F (−20 to 80°C)
Temperature Effects: ±1.5% total error −5 to 175°F
Overpressure: The rated pressure can be exceeded by the following multiples causing negligible calibration change: 4 x (up to 2000 PSI max)
Natural Frequency: 10.5 kHz for 5 PSI range, 210 kHz for 900 PSI range
Mechanical Shock: 1000g for 1 ms
Acceleration: 0.044% FSO/g for 5 PSI decreasing to 0.003% FSO/g for 500 PSI
Construction Pressure Media: All media compatible with 316L and Hastelloy
Pressure Port: ¼"-18 NPT thread
Electrical Connections: 3 feet 4 wire shielded cable
Weight: 4.2 oz nominal

To Order (Specify Model Number)

RANGE	MODEL	PRICE	COMPATIBLE METER
0 to 5 PSIA	PX811-005AV	$655	DP87, DP2000S2, DP350
0 to 10 PSIA	PX811-010AV	595	DP87, DP2000S2, DP350
0 to 15 PSIA	PX811-015AV	595	DP87, DP2000S2, DP350
0 to 20 PSIA	PX811-020AV	595	DP87, DP2000S2, DP350
0 to 30 PSIA	PX811-030AV	595	DP87, DP2000P2, DP3002-S
0 to 50 PSIA	PX811-050AV	595	DP87, DP2000S1, DP350
0 to 100 PSIA	PX811-100AV	595	DP87, DP2000S2, DP350
0 to 150 PSIA	PX811-150AV	595	DP41-S, DP2000S2, DP350
0 to 200 PSIA	PX811-200AV	595	DP41-S, DP2000S3, DP350
0 to 300 PSIA	PX811-300AV	595	DP41-S, DP2000P2, DP3002-S
0 to 500 PSIA	PX811-500AV	595	DP41-S, DP2000S1, DP350
0 to 900 PSIA	PX811-900AV	595	DP41-S, DP2000S1, DP350

RUGGED WET/WET DIFFERENTIAL PRESSURE TRANSDUCER
MEDIA COMPATIBLE STAINLESS STEEL/QUARTZ CONSTRUCTION

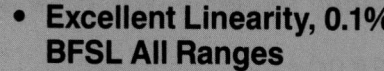

PX820 Differential Pressure Ranges From 2.5 PSID to 100 PSID

The OMEGA PX820 is a high linearity wet/wet differential pressure transducer. For compatibility with a number of different liquid and gaseous media, the positive pressure port employs a stainless steel diaphragm and the negative port's wetted components are quartz and stainless steel. Advanced construction techniques assure excellent resistance to shock, vibration and overload.

- Excellent Linearity, 0.1% BFSL All Ranges
- High Static Line Pressure, 100 PSI Maximum
- Wide Compensated Range −5 to 175°F (−20 to 80°C)
- High Overload Capacity

All Models $1050

Shown Actual Size

MILLIVOLT OUTPUT PRESSURE TRANSDUCERS

B

SPECIFICATIONS

Excitation: 10 V dc regulated at 1.5 mA
Output: 25 mV for 2.5 PSI range; 50 mV for 5 PSI range; 100 mV for ≥ 10 PSI
Output Impedance: 1000 ohms nominal
Load Impedance: >100 K ohms for rated performance
Performance Accuracy: Combined non-linearity and hysteresis—±0.1% BFSL each side considered separately
Zero Offset: ±3 mV
Side to Side Error (change of slope): ∿0.5%
Compensated Temperature Range: −5 to 175°F (−20 to 80°C)/2.5 PSI (50 to 105°F)
Temperature Effects: ±0.5% total error 32 to 122°F; ±1.5% total error −5 to 175°F
Maximum Line Pressure: 100 PSI
Overpressure: The rated pressure can be exceeded by the following multiples causing negligible calibration changes: Positive side; 10× for 2.5 PSI range, 6× for 5 PSI range, 4× for 10 PSI and above. Negative side; 6× for 2.5 PSI range, 4× for 5 PSI range, 2× for 10 PSI to 50 PSI ranges, 1.5× for 100 PSI range.
Natural Frequency: 10.5 kHz for 5 PSI range increasing to 210 kHz for 500 PSI range
Mechanical Shock: 1000 G for 1 ms
Acceleration: 0.44% FSO/G for 5 PSI decreasing to 0.0005% FSO/G for 500 PSI

Construction Positive Pressure Media: Fluids compatible with 316 stainless steel
Construction Negative Pressure Media: Fluids compatible with quartz and 316 stainless steel
Pressure Ports: ¼″-18 NPT
Electrical Connections: 3 feet 4-wire PTFE shielded cable
Weight: 11 oz.

▶ *HIGHLIGHTED MODELS STOCKED FOR FAST DELIVERY* ◀

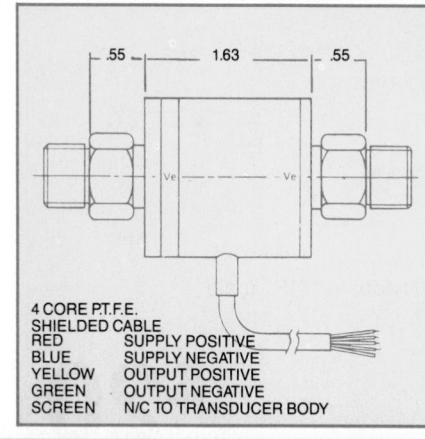

4 CORE P.T.F.E.
SHIELDED CABLE
RED — SUPPLY POSITIVE
BLUE — SUPPLY NEGATIVE
YELLOW — OUTPUT POSITIVE
GREEN — OUTPUT NEGATIVE
SCREEN — N/C TO TRANSDUCER BODY

To Order *(Specify Model Number)*

MODEL	PRICE	RANGE		COMPATIBLE METER
		PSID	BAR	
PX820-002DV	$1050	0-2.5	.175	DP350,DP87,DP2000S2
PX820-005DV	1050	0-5	.350	DP350,DP87,DP2000S2
PX820-010DV	1050	0-10	.700	DP350,DP87,DP2000S2
PX820-015DV	1050	0-14.5	1.0	DP41-S,DP350,DP2000S2
PX820-020DV	1050	0-21.7	1.5	DP41-S,DP350,DP2000S3
PX820-030DV	1050	0-29	2.0	DP41-S,DP3002-S,DP2000P2
PX820-050DV	1050	0-50.7	3.5	DP41-S,DP350,DP2000S1
PX820-070DV	1050	0-72.5	5.0	DP41-S,DP350,DP2000S1
PX820-100DV	1050	0-101.5	7.0	DP350,DP87,DP2000S2

100 PSI maximum line pressure

FLUSH MOUNT ADAPTORS
FOR SERIES 102, 440 AND 510 TRANSDUCERS

"O" Ring Included with each Adaptor

TO 20,000 PSI — DIMENSIONS IN INCHES

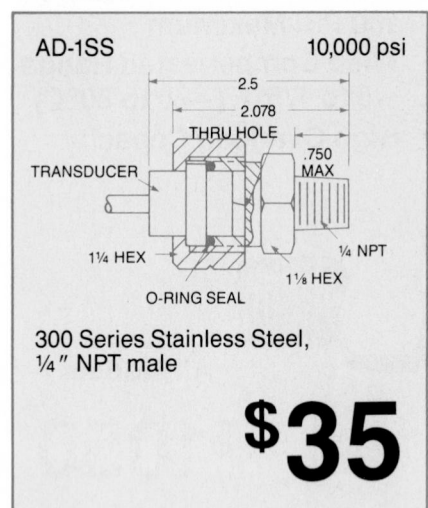

AD-1SS — 10,000 psi

300 Series Stainless Steel,
¼" NPT male

$35

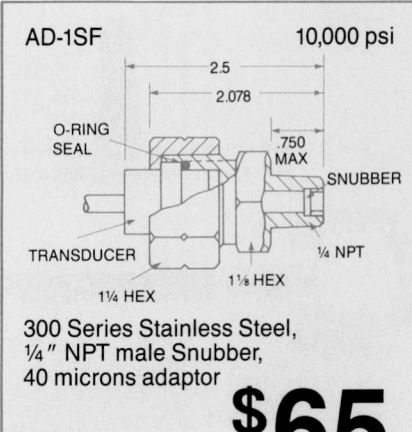

AD-1SF — 10,000 psi

300 Series Stainless Steel,
¼" NPT male Snubber,
40 microns adaptor

$65

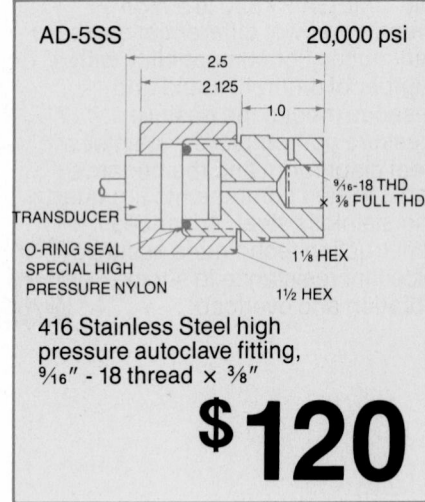

AD-5SS — 20,000 psi

416 Stainless Steel high
pressure autoclave fitting,
⁹⁄₁₆" - 18 thread × ⅜"

$120

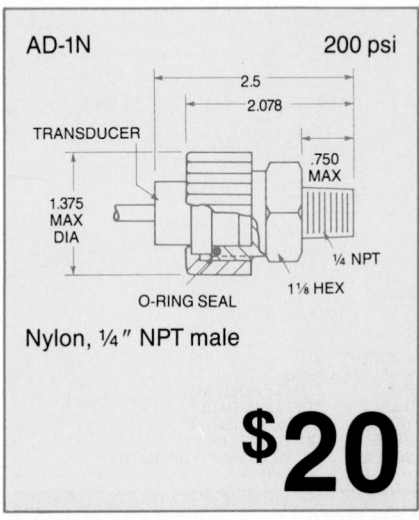

AD-1N — 200 psi

Nylon, ¼" NPT male

$20

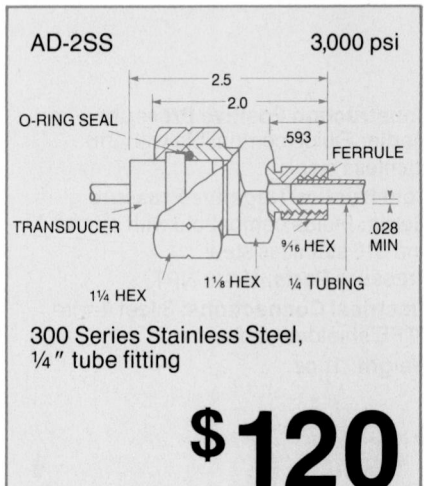

AD-2SS — 3,000 psi

300 Series Stainless Steel,
¼" tube fitting

$120

AD-6SS — 10,000 psi

300 Series Stainless Steel,
MS-33656-4 male thread

$100

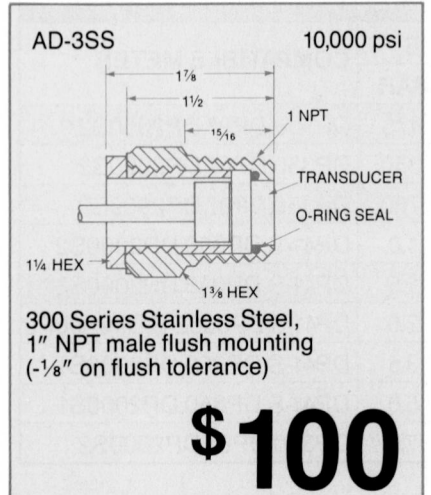

AD-3SS — 10,000 psi

300 Series Stainless Steel,
1" NPT male flush mounting
(-⅛" on flush tolerance)

$100

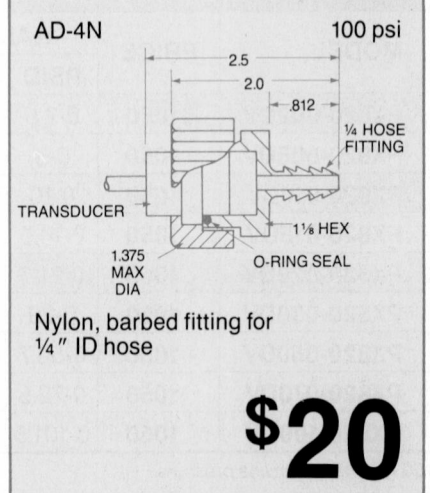

AD-4N — 100 psi

Nylon, barbed fitting for
¼" ID hose

$20

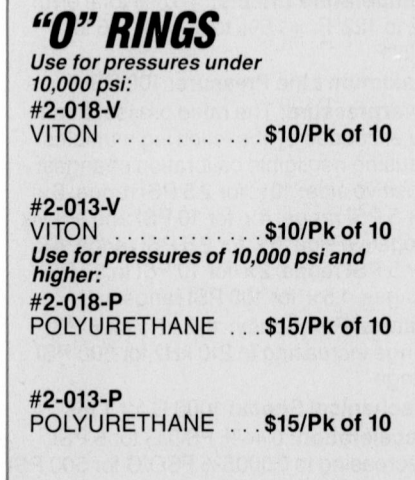

"O" RINGS
Use for pressures under 10,000 psi:
#2-018-V
VITON . . . . **$10/Pk of 10**

#2-013-V
VITON . . . . **$10/Pk of 10**
Use for pressures of 10,000 psi and higher:
#2-018-P
POLYURETHANE . . . **$15/Pk of 10**

#2-013-P
POLYURETHANE . . . **$15/Pk of 10**

FLUSH DIAPHRAGM MILLIVOLT OUTPUT TYPE PRESSURE TRANSDUCER

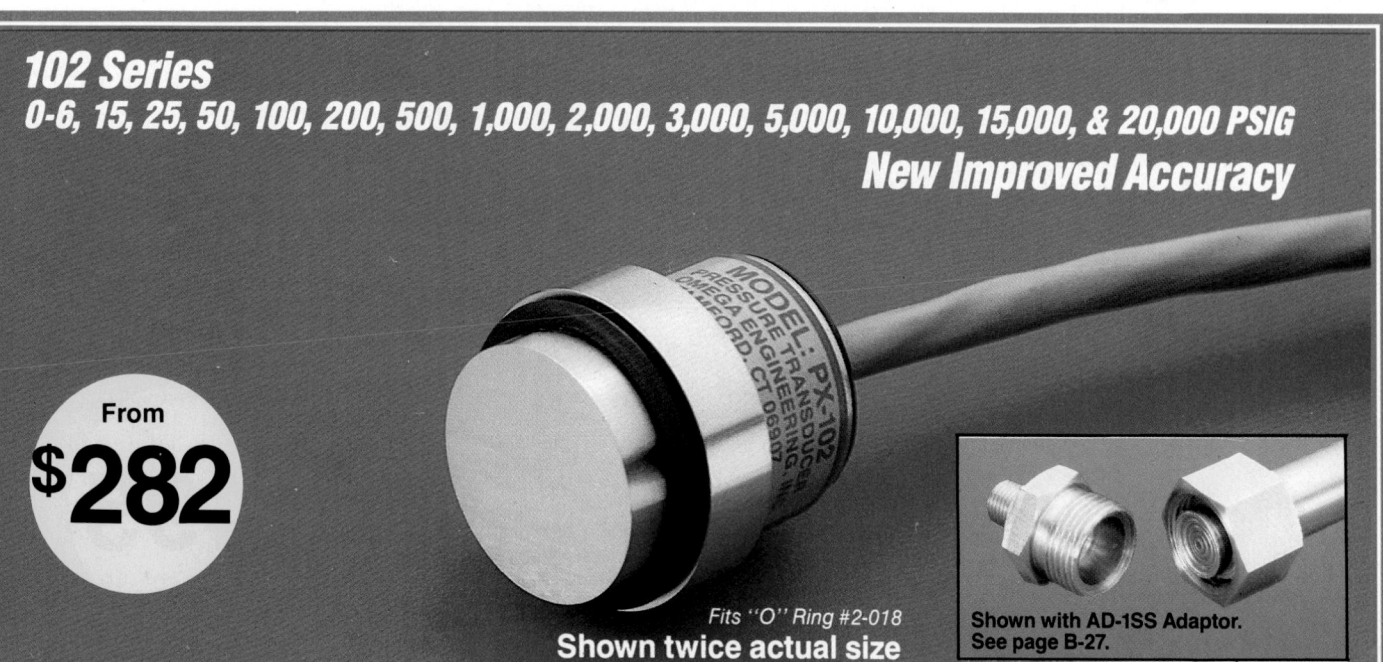

102 Series
0-6, 15, 25, 50, 100, 200, 500, 1,000, 2,000, 3,000, 5,000, 10,000, 15,000, & 20,000 PSIG
New Improved Accuracy

From
$282

Fits "O" Ring #2-018
Shown twice actual size

Shown with AD-1SS Adaptor.
See page B-27.

SPECIFICATIONS

Excitation: 5 Vdc 35 mA (6 Vdc max.)
Output: 0 to 100 mV ±1%
Input Impedance: 150 ±50 ohms
Output Impedance: 115 ±25 ohms
Insulation Resistance: 20 k M ohm at 50 Vdc

PERFORMANCE

Accuracy: 100 to 5000 PSI = .25% BFSL
All other ranges = 1% BFSL
Zero Balance: ±5 mV
Operable Temperature Range: −60 to 200°F
Compensated Temperature Range:
30 to 160°F
Thermal Zero Effect: ±0.05% RDG/°F
(0.1%/°C)
Thermal Sensitivity Effect: ±0.01% RDG/°F
(0.02%/°C)
Proof Pressure: 2 x full scale
Burst Pressure: 5 x full scale minimum
Fatigue: >160 million cycles

CONSTRUCTION

Gages: Semiconductors on Bending Beam
Body/Diaphragm Material: 316 L SS ≤50
PSI; −15-5 PH SS >50 PSI
Pressure Port: Flush
Electrical Connection: 36″ Shielded PVC
Cable, 4 Leads
Weight: 2 ozs.

*Units 100 PSI and above have cases sealed
from the surrounding atmosphere, providing
maximum reliability in humid or corrosive environment (PSIS). Ranges below 100 psi are
vented to the atmosphere and read gage
pressure.*

HIGHLIGHTED MODELS
STOCKED FOR FAST DELIVERY ◄

*Requires PST-5A, **$114** power supply.

See Selection Guide For Compatible Instrumentation

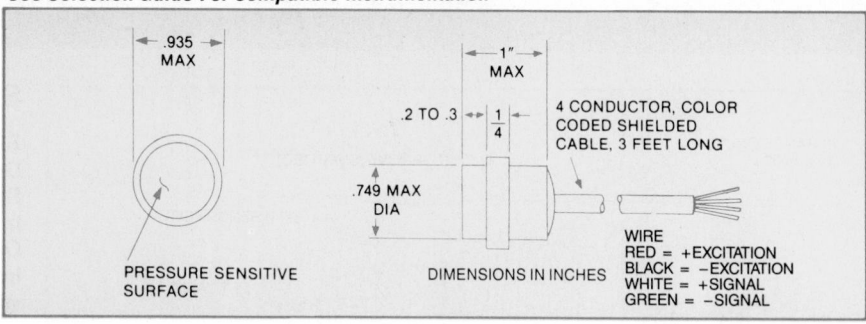

.935 MAX

1″ MAX

.2 TO .3

1/4

4 CONDUCTOR, COLOR CODED SHIELDED CABLE, 3 FEET LONG

.749 MAX DIA

DIMENSIONS IN INCHES

PRESSURE SENSITIVE SURFACE

WIRE
RED = +EXCITATION
BLACK = −EXCITATION
WHITE = +SIGNAL
GREEN = −SIGNAL

To Order (Specify Model Number)

* SEE SECTION D FOR INSTRUMENT SELECTION

RANGE	MODEL	PRICE	COMPATIBLE METER*
0- 6 PSIG	PX102-006G V	$282	DP-350, DP41-S, DP3800*
0- 15 PSIG	PX102-015G V	282	DP-350, DP41-S, DP3800*
0- 15 PSIA	PX102-015A V	356	DP-350, DP41-S, DP3800*
0- 25 PSIG	PX102-025G V	282	DP41-S, DP3800*, DP87
0- 25 PSIA	PX102-025A V	356	DP41-S, DP3800*, DP87
0- 50 PSIG	PX102-050G V	282	DP-350, DP41-S, DP3800*
0- 50 PSIA	PX102-050A V	356	DP-350, DP41-S, DP3800*
0- 100 PSIS	PX102-100S V	324	DP-350, DP41-S, DP3800*
0- 200 PSIS	PX102-200S V	324	DP-350, DP41-S, DP3800*
0- 500 PSIS	PX102-500S V	324	DP-350, DP41-S, DP3800*
0- 1000 PSIS	PX102- 1KS V	324	DP-350, DP41-S, DP3800*
0- 2000 PSIS	PX102- 2KS V	324	DP-350, DP41-S, DP3800*
0- 3000 PSIS	PX102- 3KS V	324	DP41-S, DP87, DP3800*
0- 5000 PSIS	PX102- 5KS V	324	DP41-S, DP87, DP3800*
0-10000 PSIS	PX102-10KS V	324	DP41-S, DP87, DP3800*
0-15000 PSIS	PX102-15KS V	324	DP41-S, DP87, DP3800*
0-20000 PSIS	PX102-20KS V	324	DP41-S, DP87, DP3800*

SUBMINIATURE MILLIVOLT OUTPUT TYPE PRESSURE TRANSDUCER WITH FLUSH MOUNT DIAPHRAGM

600 Series
0-200 to 0-10 K PSIG

- **Stainless Steel Diaphragm Epoxied in Place for Compatibility with Most Non-conductive Media**
- **Rugged Stainless Steel Case Protects Components in a Variety of Environments**
- **Uses a Standard 5 V dc Regulated Power Supply for Maximum Versatility**
- **Custom Subminiature Design Techniques Provide Small Size and Preserve Accuracy**

$495

Shown actual size

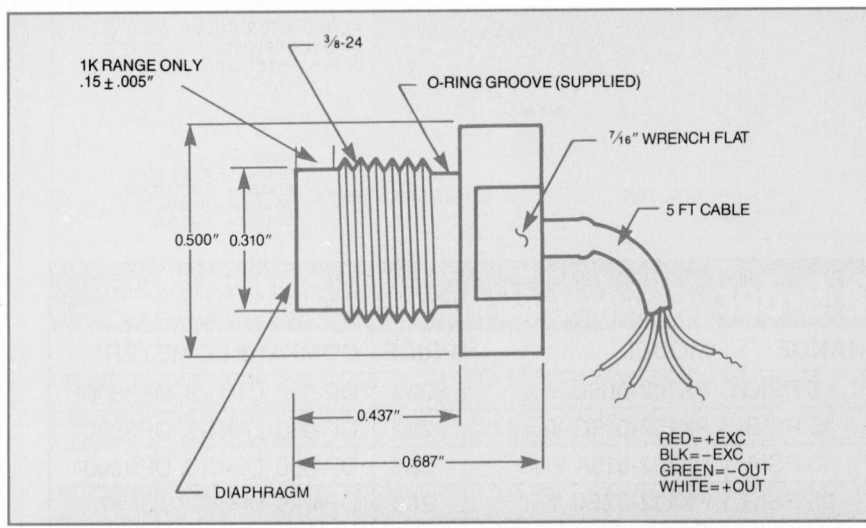

SPECIFICATIONS

Excitation: 5 V dc @ 15 mA
Output: 10 mV (200 PSI and Higher)
Sensitivity: 2 mV/V Nominal
Input Resistance: 350 ohms
Output Resistance: 350 ohms
Insulation Resistance: $> 5\ M\Omega$ @ 75 V dc

PERFORMANCE

Accuracy: $\pm 1\%$
Linearity and Hysteresis: $\pm 1\%$ full scale B.F.S.L.
Repeatability: ± 0.02 mV; $\pm 0.1\%$ full scale
Zero Balance: $\pm 3\%$
Operable Temperature Range: -65 to 300°F
Compensated Temperature Range: 60 to 160°F
Thermal Zero Effect: $\pm 0.01\%$ full scale/°F
Thermal Sensitivity Effect: $\pm 0.02\%$ full scale/°F
Proof Pressure: 1.5 x Range
Burst Pressure: 4 x Range or Unit's Maximum Range

CONSTRUCTION

Body Material: 17-4 PH Stainless Steel
Diaphragm Material: 17-4 PH Stainless Steel bonded foil gage
O-Ring Size: 011
Polyvinyl: 2-011-P **$15**/10 pack
Viton®: 2-011-V **$10**/10 pack
Electrical Connection: 4 Cond. Cable
Weight: 0.5 ozs.

To Order (Specify model number)

RANGE	MODEL	PRICE	COMPATIBLE METER
0- 200 PSIG	PX 600-200G V	$495	DP41-S**,DP2000S6**
0- 500 PSIG	PX 600-500G V	495	DP41-S**,DP2000S4**
0- 1000 PSIG	PX 600-1KG V	495	DP41-S**,DP2000S5**
0- 2000 PSIG	PX 600-2KG V	495	DP41-S**,DP2000S6**
0- 3000 PSIG	PX 600-3KG V	495	DP41-S**, DP87**
0- 5000 PSIG	PX 600-5KG V	495	DP41-S**, DP87**
0-10000 PSIG	PX 600-10KG V	495	DP41-S**, DP87**

**Meter Excitation Voltage requires field adjustment by customer to 5 Vdc.

▶ *HIGHLIGHTED MODELS STOCKED FOR FAST DELIVERY* ◀

SUBMINIATURE MILLIVOLT OUTPUT TYPE PRESSURE TRANSDUCER FOR ACCURATE
MEASUREMENTS IN RESTRICTED LOCATIONS

610 Series
0-200 to 0-10K PSIG

$515

- **Stainless Steel Diaphragm for Compatibility with Most Media**
- **Rugged Stainless Steel Case Protects Components in a Variety of Environments**
- **Uses a Standard 5 V dc Regulated Power Supply for Maximum Versatility**

- **Custom Subminiature Design Techniques Provide Small Size and Preserve Accuracy**
- **7/16" UNF Process Threading for Fast, Easy, and Secure Connections**
- **Connects to a PT06F-10-6S Quick Disconnect Connector for Easy Field Connections**

Shown actual size

See page C-4 for Mating Connectors (Sold Separately).

SPECIFICATIONS

Excitation: 5 V @ 15 mA
Output: 10 mV (200 PSI and Above)
Sensitivity: 2 mV/V Nominal
Input Resistance: 350 ohms
Output Resistance: 350 ohms
Insulation Resistance: > 5 MΩ @ 75 V dc

PERFORMANCE

Accuracy: ±1% full scale
Linearity and Hysteresis: ±1% full scale B.F.S.L.
Repeatability: ±0.02 mV; ±0.1% full scale
Zero Balance: ±3%
Operable Temperature Range: −65 to 300°F
Compensated Temperature Range: 60 to 160°F
Thermal Zero Effect: ±0.01% full scale/°F
Thermal Sensitivity Effect: ±0.02% full scale/°F
Proof Pressure: 1.5 x Range
Burst Pressure: 4 x Range; 20,000

CONSTRUCTION

Body Material: 17-4 PH Stainless Steel
Diaphragm Material: 17-4 PH Stainless Steel
O-Ring Size: 012
Mating Connector: PT06F-10-6S (not included)
Weight: 1.5 ozs.

All Units Hermetically Sealed

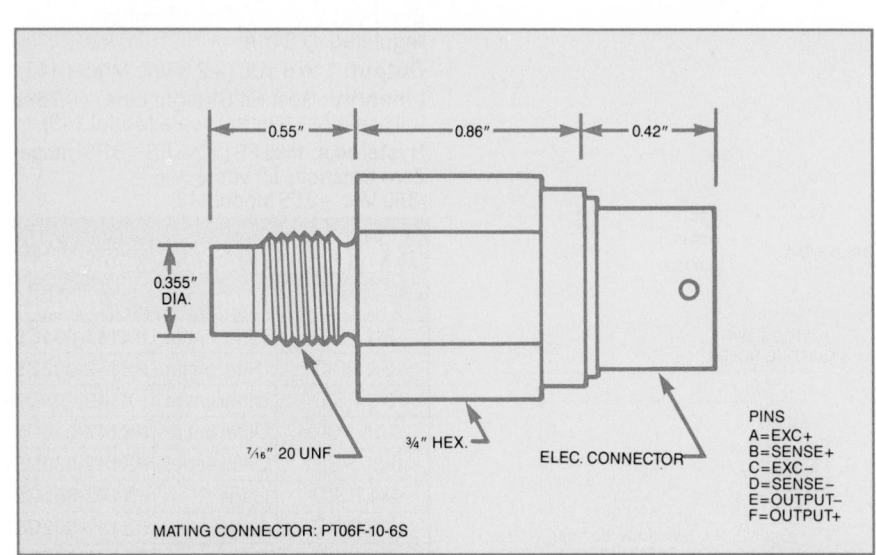

0.55" — 0.86" — 0.42"

0.355" DIA.

7/16" 20 UNF   3/4" HEX.   ELEC. CONNECTOR

PINS
A = EXC+
B = SENSE+
C = EXC−
D = SENSE−
E = OUTPUT−
F = OUTPUT+

MATING CONNECTOR: PT06F-10-6S

To Order: (Specify model number)

RANGE	MODEL	PRICE	COMPATIBLE METER
0- 200 PSIG	PX610-200G V	$515	DP41-S**,DP2000-S6**
0- 500 PSIG	PX610-500G V	515	DP41-S**,DP2000-S4**
0- 1000 PSIG	PX610-1KG V	515	DP41-S**,DP2000-S5**
0- 2000 PSIG	PX610-2KG V	515	DP41-S**,DP2000-S6**
0- 3000 PSIG	PX610-3KG V	515	DP87**, DP41-S**
0- 5000 PSIG	PX610-5KG V	515	DP87**, DP41-S**
0-10000 PSIG	PX610-10KG V	515	DP87**, DP41-S**

**Meter excitation voltage *must* be adjusted by user to 5 Vdc.

► **HIGHLIGHTED MODELS STOCKED FOR FAST DELIVERY** ◄

LOW COST TRANSDUCERS FOR VACUUM / ABSOLUTE / DIFFERENTIAL GAGE MEASUREMENTS FOR CLEAN GASES

140 Series
± 2.5 PSI to 0-30 PSI

From
$85

Shown slightly larger than actual size

See Selection Guide For Compatible Instrumentation

SILICON DIAPHRAGM
- ✔ High Level Output
- ✔ 1-6 Vdc with 8 Vdc Excitation
- ✔ Positive Pressure Measurement, Differential Gage and Absolute Types
- ✔ Positive and Negative Pressure Measurement Differential and Gage Types
- ✔ Printed Circuit Board Terminals...Exit on Opposite Side from the Ports
- ✔ Rugged-Printed Circuit Board Construction
- ✔ High Impact Plastic Case
- ✔ Accurate: All Models Temperature Compensated

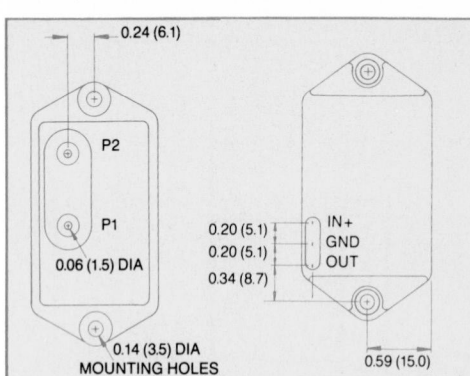

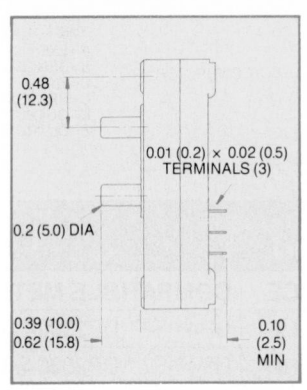

► **HIGHLIGHTED MODELS STOCKED FOR FAST DELIVERY** ◄
SEE PAGE C-3 FOR CONNECTORS

SPECIFICATIONS

Excitation: 8 Vdc (7 to 16 limits) regulated @ 8 mA

Output: 1 to 6 Vdc (±2.5 Vdc Model 143)

Linearity: Best Fit Straight Line ±0.75% full scale (+1.5% full scale Model 143)

Hysteresis: 15% FS (.30% FS ≤ 5 PSI range)

Zero Balance: 1.0 Vdc ±0.05 (3.50 Vdc ±0.05 Model 143)

Operable Overpressure: 3XFS (60 PSI for 30 PSI range, 20 PSI for ≤ 5 PSI)

Response Time: 1 mS

MEDIA COMPATIBILITY

ABS & P1: Dry gases only

Gage & P2: Limited only to those media which will not attack polyester, silicon, borosilicate glass, or epoxy adhesive

To Order *(Specify model number)*

* SEE SECTION D FOR ADDITIONAL INSTRUMENT SELECTION

RANGE	TYPE	MODEL	PRICE	COMPATIBLE METER*
0-1 PSID	Differential	PX142-001D5V	$94	DP41-S, DP354, DP460-V
0-2 PSID	Differential	PX142-002D5V	94	DP41-S, DP354, DP460-V
0-5 PSID	Differential	PX142-005D 5V	85	DP41-S, DP354, DP2000-P4
0-15 PSID	Differential	PX142-015D5V	85	DP41-S, DP354, DP2000-P5
0-30 PSID	Differential	PX142-030D5V	85	DP41-S, DP354, DP460-V
0-1 PSIG	Gage	PX142-001G5V	94	DP41-S, DP354, DP460-V
0-2 PSIG	Gage	PX142-002G5V	94	DP41-S, DP354, DP460-V
0-5 PSIG	Gage	PX142-005G5V	85	DP41-S, DP354, DP2000-P4
0-15 PSIG	Gage	PX142-015G5V	85	DP41-S, DP354, DP2000-P5
0-30 PSIG	Gage	PX142-030G5V	85	DP41-S, DP354, DP460-V
0-15 PSIA	Absolute	PX142-015A5V	94	DP41-S, DP354, DP2000-P5
0-30 PSIA	Absolute	PX142-030A5V	94	DP41-S, DP354, DP460-V
– 1 to 0 PSIV	Vacuum	PX141-001D5V	94	DP41-S, DP354, DP460-V
– 5 to 0 PSIV	Vacuum	PX141-005V5V	94	DP41-S, DP354, DP2000-P4
– 15 to 0 PSIV	Vacuum	PX141-015V5V	94	DP41-S, DP354, DP2000-P5
± 1 PSID	Differential	PX143-01BD5V	85	DP41-S, DP354, DP460-V
± 2.5 PSID	Differential	PX143-2.5BD5V	85	DP41-S, DP354, DP2000-P4
± 5 PSID	Differential	PX143-05BD5V	85	DP41-S, DP354, DP2000-P4
± 5 PSIG	Gage	PX143-05BG5V	85	DP41-S, DP354, DP2000-P4
± 15 PSID	Differential	PX143-15BD5V	85	DP41-S, DP354, DP2000-P5
± 15 PSIG	Gage	PX143-15BG5V	85	DP41-S, DP354, DP2000-P5

LOW PRESSURE TRANSDUCER FOR VACUUM/DIFFERENTIAL/GAGE
FOR MEASUREMENTS OF CLEAN GASES

PX160 Series

0-27.68″ H₂O
±5″ H₂O
0-10″ H₂O

New Range
−20 to +120 cm H₂O

From $114

See Selection Guide For Compatible Instrumentation

SILICON DIAPHRAGM
- 1 to 6 V Output Span
- Differential
- Gage
- High Level Output
- 8 V dc Excitation
- High Impact Plastic Case
- Temperature Compensated

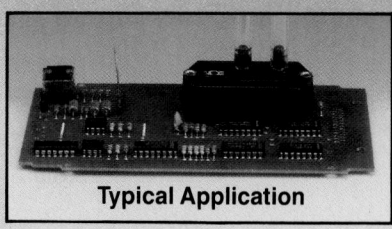

Typical Application

Shown slightly larger than actual size

Media Compatibility

P1: Dry Gases Only

P2 GAGE & VACUUM: Limited only to those media which will not attack polyester, silicon, borosilicate glass, or epoxy adhesive

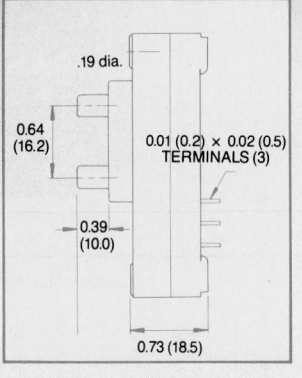

2.35 (59.8) 2.06 (52.4)

IN+
GND
OUT

0.50 (12.6)

.19 dia.

0.64 (16.2)

0.01 (0.2) × 0.02 (0.5) TERMINALS (3)

0.39 (10.0)

0.73 (18.5)

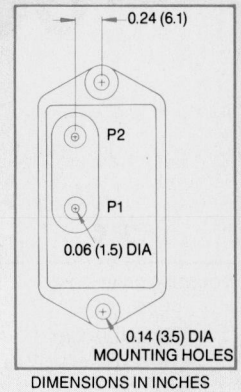

0.24 (6.1)

P2

P1

0.06 (1.5) DIA

0.14 (3.5) DIA MOUNTING HOLES

DIMENSIONS IN INCHES

SPECIFICATIONS

Excitation: 8 Vdc Regulated (6 to 12 Vdc at 20 mA)(PX163-120D5V use 10 Vdc)
Output: 1 to 6 Vdc

PERFORMANCE

Linearity: Best Fit Straight Line ± 1.0% full scale at specified voltage
Hysteresis & Repeatability: ± .25% full scale
Zero Balance: 1 Vdc ± 0.05 (3.5 ± 0.05 Vdc PX163 series)
Operable Temperature Range: − 40 to 185°F (− 40 to 85°C)
Compensated Temperature Range: PX161 and 162, 0 to 145°F; PX163 and 164, 41 to 113°F
Operable Overpressure: 5 PSI
Response Time: 1 ms

To Order (Specify model number)

SEE SECTION D FOR INSTRUMENT SELECTION

RANGE	TYPE	MODEL	PRICE	COMPATIBLE METERS
(Inches H₂O)				
± 2.5	Differential	PX163-2.5BD5V	$114	DP41-S, DP354, DP460-V*
± 5.0	Differential	PX163-005BD5V	114	DP41-S, DP354, DP460-V*
0-5	Differential	PX164-005D5V	114	DP41-S, DP354, DP460-V*
0-10	Differential	PX164-010D5V	114	DP41-S, DP354, DP460-V*
0-27.68	Differential	PX162-027D5V	114	DP41-S, DP354, DP460-V*
0-27.68	Gage	PX162-027G5V	114	DP41-S, DP354, DP460-V*
− 27.68-0	Vacuum	PX161-027D5V	114	DP41-S, DP354, DP460-V*
cm H₂O (− 50.8 to 304.8 in H₂O/ − 1.8 to 11 PSI)				
− 20 to + 120	Differential	PX163-120D5V	114	DP41-S, DP354, DP460-V*

*Use PST-8 for 8 Vdc excitation
Connectors are available - See page C-3.

MINIATURE PLASTIC CASE TRANSDUCER
WITH 1 TO 6 VOLT OUTPUT

1 YEAR WARRANTY

MADE IN USA

PX184 Vacuum Series
PX185 Pressure Series
RANGE VACUUM TO 30 PSI

✔ **Gages, Vacuum, Differential Pressure**

✔ **Linear Signal With Pressure**

✔ **Amplified Fully Signal Conditioned Output**

For Non PC Board Use
Mating Connector
CX136-4 Price $3.00

All Models

$60

▶ *HIGHLIGHTED MODELS STOCKED FOR FAST DELIVERY!* ◀

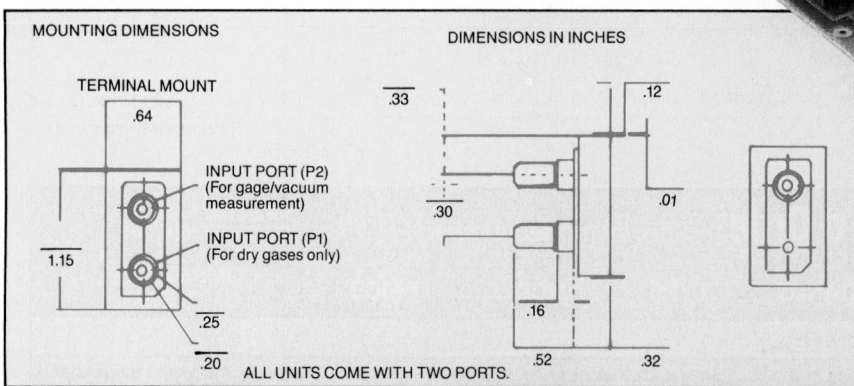

MOUNTING DIMENSIONS   DIMENSIONS IN INCHES

TERMINAL MOUNT
.64
INPUT PORT (P2)
(For gage/vacuum measurement)
INPUT PORT (P1)
(For dry gases only)
1.15
.25
.20
ALL UNITS COME WITH TWO PORTS.

.33   .12
.30   .01
.16
.52   .32

APPLICATIONS

✔ **Environmental Control Systems**
✔ **Process Control**
✔ **Lab Test Equipment**
✔ **Computer Periphals**
✔ **R & D Laboratories**

SPECIFICATIONS

Excitation: 8 Vdc (7 to 16 maximum)
Output: 1 to 6 Vdc
Supply Current: 6 mA maximum
Linearity: P2 > P1 = ±2%
Repeatability & Hysteresis: ±0.15% FS
Zero: 1V ±.05V
Span: 5V ±.05V
Overpressure: 5 PSI = 20 PSI; 15 PSI = 45 PSI; 30 PSI = 60 PSI
Operating Temperature: −40 to +185°F
Compensated Temperature: 32 to 122°F
Port: 0.20″ tube fitting
Mounting: printed circuit board
Response Time: 1 ms
Mating Connector: CX136-4 (not included)

To Order *(Specify Model Number)*

SEE SECTION D FOR INSTRUMENT SELECTION

RANGE	MODEL	PRICE	COMPATIBLE METER
−5 to 0 PSIV	PX184-005V5V	$60	DP41-S, DP-354, DP460-V*
−15 to 0 PSIV	PX184-015V5V	60	DP41-S, DP-354, DP460-V*
0 to 5 PSID	PX185-005D5V	60	DP41-S, DP-354, DP460-V*
0 to 15 PSID	PX185-015D5V	60	DP41-S, DP-354, DP460-V*
0 to 30 PSID	PX185-030D5V	60	DP41-S, DP-354, DP460-V*
±2.5 PSID	PX186-2.5 BD5V	60	DP41-S, DP-354, DP460-V*
±5 PSID	PX186-005BD5V	60	DP41-S, DP-354, DP460-V*
±15 PSID	PX186-015BD5V	60	DP41-S, DP-354, DP460-V*

* Requires PST-8 external power supply.

METAL CASE TRANSDUCER FOR MEASURING
LOW PRESSURE AND VACUUMS

240 Series
5-250 PSIG

$138

SILICON DIAPHRAGM
- Buna-N Seals
- 8.0 Vdc Excitation
- 12 Inch Leadwires
- −40 to +85°C
- 1 to 6 Vdc Output
- Temperature Compensated
- Rugged Low Profile Easy-to-Mount

Supplied with 12" Leads

OMEGA ENGINEERING, INC.

Shown larger than actual size

Media compatibility limited only to those non-caustic media which will not attack die-cast aluminum; silica borosilicate; glass; or Buna-n seal.

RED = +EX
BLK = GND
GN = +OUT

12" LEADS

2.2" (56) MAX
1.81" (46)
1.18"
2.28" (58) MAX

#10 (M5)
FASTENER CLEARANCE (4)
DIMENSIONS IN INCHES

1/8-27 NPT
19/32 (15.0) ACROSS FLATS
1.57" (40) MAX
0.59" (15) MAX

12" LEADS

SPECIFICATIONS

Excitation: 8 Vdc regulated (16 V max.)

Output: 1 to 6 Vdc

Linearity: Best Fit Straight Line ±1.5% full scale (±0.5% full scale for 60 to 100 PSI)

Hysteresis & Repeatability: ±0.25% full scale

Zero Balance: 1.0 Vdc ±0.05; PX243 3.5 Vdc ±0.05

Compensated Temperature Range: 0 to 145°F (−18 to 63°C)

Operable Overpressure: Minimum 2 x full scale

Response Time: 1 ms

Gage Type: Solid State Piezo-Resistive

Body Material: Die-Cast Aluminum Epoxied Finish

Diaphragm Material: .10 Inch Square Silicon Sensor Chip with Buna-N "O" Ring

Pressure Port: 1/8-27 NPT

To Order (Specify Model Number)

RANGE	MODEL	PRICE	COMPATIBLE METER
−5 to 0 PSIG	PX241-05NG 5V	$138	DP3002-E,DP2000P4,DP354
−15 to 5 PSIG	PX241-15NG 5V	138	DP3002-E,DP2000P5,DP354
0 to 5 PSIG	PX242-005G 5V	138	DP3002-E,DP2000P4,DP354
0 to 15 PSIG	PX242-015G 5V	138	DP3002-E,DP2000P5,DP354
0 to 30 PSIG	PX242-030G 5V	138	DP3002-E,DP2000P4,DP354
0 to 60 PSIG	PX242-060G 5V	138	DP3002-E,DP2000P4,DP354
0 to 100 PSIG	PX242-100G 5V	138	DP3002-E,DP2000P4,DP354
0 to 150 PSIG	PX242-150G 5V	138	DP3002-E,DP2000P5,DP354
0 to 250 PSIG	PX242-250G 5V	138	DP3002-E,DP2000P4,DP354
±2.5 PSIG	PX243-2.5BG 5V	138	DP3002-E,DP2000P4,DP354
±5.0 PSIG	PX243-05BG 5V	138	DP3002-E,DP2000P4,DP354
±15 PSIG	PX243-15BG 5V	138	DP3002-E,DP2000P4,DP354

HIGHLIGHTED MODELS STOCKED FOR FAST DELIVERY

External Power Supply Required

ECONOMICAL CORROSION RESISTANT PRESSURE TRANSDUCER WITH VOLTAGE OUTPUT

CABLE AND CONNECTOR INCLUDED

PX181 Series

- ✔ **Stainless Steel Pressure Port for Wide Media Compatibility**
- ✔ **Assured 0.3% Accuracy**
- ✔ **Corrosion Resistant Housing Permits Mounting In Any Environment**
- ✔ **Operating Temperature Range −55 to 105°C**
- ✔ **Extremely Compact, Weighs Only 50 Grams**

All Models

$170

MADE IN **USA**

The OMEGA PX181 Series pressure transducers combine state-of-the-art semiconductor technology and durability resulting in a high accuracy general purpose pressure sensor. The 1 to 5 volt output assures compatibility with most process controllers and computer interface equipment. Applications include engine monitoring and testing, HVAC, compressors, etc. The silicon sensor is bonded on a glass pedestal to isolate it from induced stresses, provide wide media compatibility, and the stainless steel pressure port permits use with corrosive substances. These rugged, compact transducers exhibit 0.3% accuracy and excellent interchangeability.

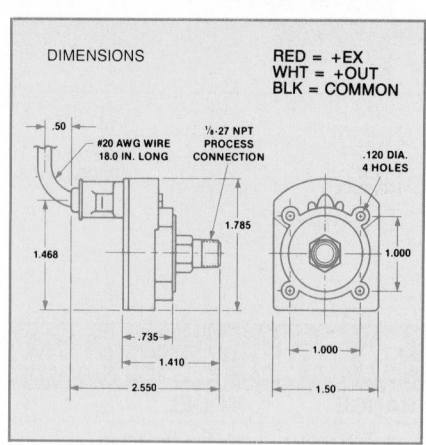

DIMENSIONS

RED = +EX
WHT = +OUT
BLK = COMMON

▶ *IN STOCK FOR FAST DELIVERY* ◀

SPECIFICATIONS

Excitation: 12 to 25 V dc
Output: 1 to 5 V dc (20 mA max)
Accuracy: ±0.3% BFSL includes linearity, repeatability, and hysteresis
Zero Balance: ±1% span
Operable Temperature Range: −55 to 105°C
Compensated Temperature Range: −25 to 75°C
Thermal Zero Effect: ±0.5% span
Thermal Span Effect: ±0.5% span
Proof Pressure: 2 x full scale (750 PSI max)
Burst Pressure: 3 x full scale (750 PSI max)
Gages: laser trimmed semiconductor
Wetted Parts: Stainless steel, glass, silicon, Flurosilicon
Pressure Port: 1/8-27 stainless steel fitting
Stability: ±1% full scale output/year
Shock: 500G
Vibration: 10G, 10 to 2000 Hz
Electrical Connection: 12″ 20 AWG, 3 conductor shielded wire with self sealing connector
Weight: 50 grams

To Order *(Specify Model Number)*

RANGE	MODEL	PRICE	COMPATIBLE METER
0 to 15 PSIG	PX181-015G5V	$170	DP3002-E, DP460-E, DP2000P4 ◀
0 to 30 PSIG	PX181-030G5V	170	DP3002-E, DP460-E, DP2000P4 ◀
0 to 60 PSIG	PX181-060G5V	170	DP3002-E, DP460-E, DP2000P4 ◀
0 to 100 PSIG	PX181-100G5V	170	DP3002-E, DP460-E, DP2000P4 ◀
0 to 200 PSIG	PX181-200G5V	170	DP3002-E, DP460-E, DP2000P4 ◀
0 to 300 PSIG	PX181-300G5V	170	DP3002-E, DP460-E, DP2000P4 ◀
0 to 500 PSIG	PX181-500G5V	170	DP3002-E, DP460-E, DP354 ◀

FAST RESPONSE VOLTAGE TYPE PRESSURE TRANSDUCER
PRESSURE RANGES FROM 5 to 2000 PSIG

105 Series
0-6 to 0-2,000 PSIG

From $218

- ✔ Voltage Output 1 to 6 Vdc
- ✔ 8-20 Vdc Excitation
- ✔ Accuracy: ±0.5% Typ
- ✔ Fully Calibrated and Temperature Compensated
- ✔ Internal Voltage Regulation
- ✔ Interchangeable: Unit to Unit ±1%
- ✔ Computer Trimmed to Insure Accuracy and Repeatability
- ✔ Long-Term Stability: ±1%
- ✔ Operating Temperature Range: −55°C to 125°C
- ✔ Rugged Temperature-Resistant Valox Case and Connector

Shown Actual Size

100 to 2000 PSIG Screw Connection

6 to 50 PSIG Tubing Connecting See Page C-29

Wire Not Included

Connector included

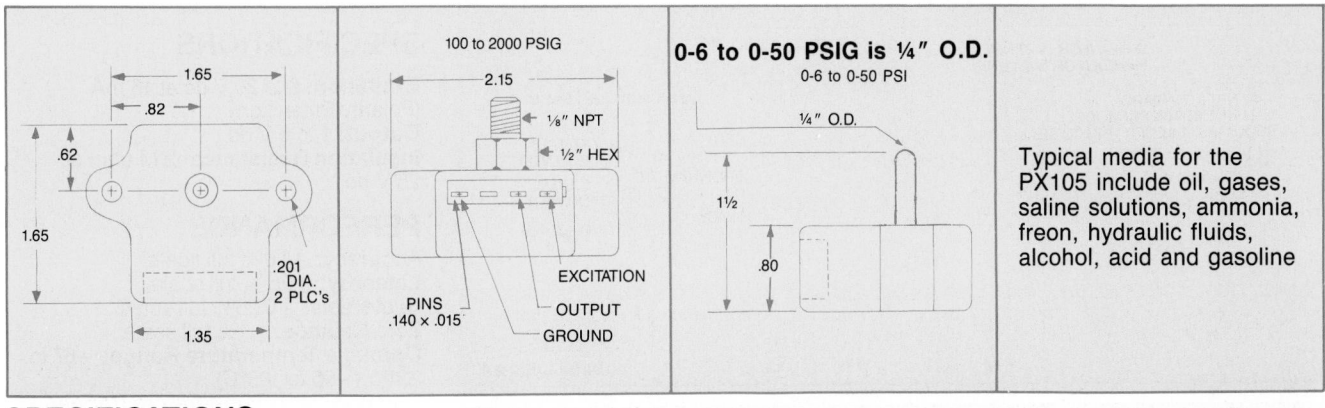

100 to 2000 PSIG
2.15
⅛" NPT
½" HEX

PINS .140 × .015
EXCITATION
OUTPUT
GROUND

0-6 to 0-50 PSIG is ¼" O.D.
0-6 to 0-50 PSI
¼" O.D.
1½
.80

Typical media for the PX105 include oil, gases, saline solutions, ammonia, freon, hydraulic fluids, alcohol, acid and gasoline

1.65 / .82 / .62 / 1.65 / 1.35 / .201 DIA. 2 PLC's

SPECIFICATIONS

Excitation: 8 to 20 V dc at 15 mA
Output: 1 to 6 V dc
Accuracy: ±1% full scale maximum
Linearity: <50 PSI ±.5%
  ≥50 PSI ±2% FS
Hysteresis: ±.25% full scale
Zero Balance: ±1% full scale Typ.,
±3% full scale max.
Frequency Response: 3 db at 1.5 kHz
Compensated Temperature Range: 32 to 185°F (0 to 85°C)
Thermal Zero Effect: ±0.01% RDG/°F (±0.02%/°C)
Proof Pressure: 2 x full scale
Burst Pressure: 5 x full scale Minimum (6, 15, 25, PSIG; 20 x FS)
Gages: Piezo-Resistive
Diaphragm/Port Material: 300 Series SS (Silver, Copper, Nickel, Cadmium Brazed)
Electrical Connection: CX-106-4
Weight: 4 ozs.

To Order (Specify model number)

RANGE	MODEL	PRICE	COMPATIBLE METER
0- 6 PSIG	PX105-006G5V	$242	DP354, DP2000P4, DP3002-E
0- 15 PSIG	PX105-015G5V	218	DP354, DP2000P5, DP3002-E
0- 25 PSIG	PX105-025G5V	218	DP354, DP2000P4, DP3002-E
0- 50 PSIG	PX105-050G5V	218	DP354, DP2000P4, DP3002-E
0- 100 PSIG	PX105-100G5V	218	DP354, DP2000P4, DP3002-E
0- 200 PSIG	PX105-200G5V	218	DP354, DP2000P5, DP3002-E
0- 500 PSIG	PX105-500G5V	218	DP354, DP2000P4, DP3002-E
0-1000 PSIG	PX105-1KG5V	218	DP354, DP2000P4, DP3002-E
0-2000 PSIG	PX105-2KG5V	218	DP354, DP2000P5, DP3002-E

HIGHLIGHTED MODELS STOCKED FOR FAST DELIVERY

AMPLIFIED VOLTAGE OUTPUT TRANSDUCER
FOR ABSOLUTE & SEALED PRESSURE
WATERPROOF CASE HARSH ENVIRONMENTS

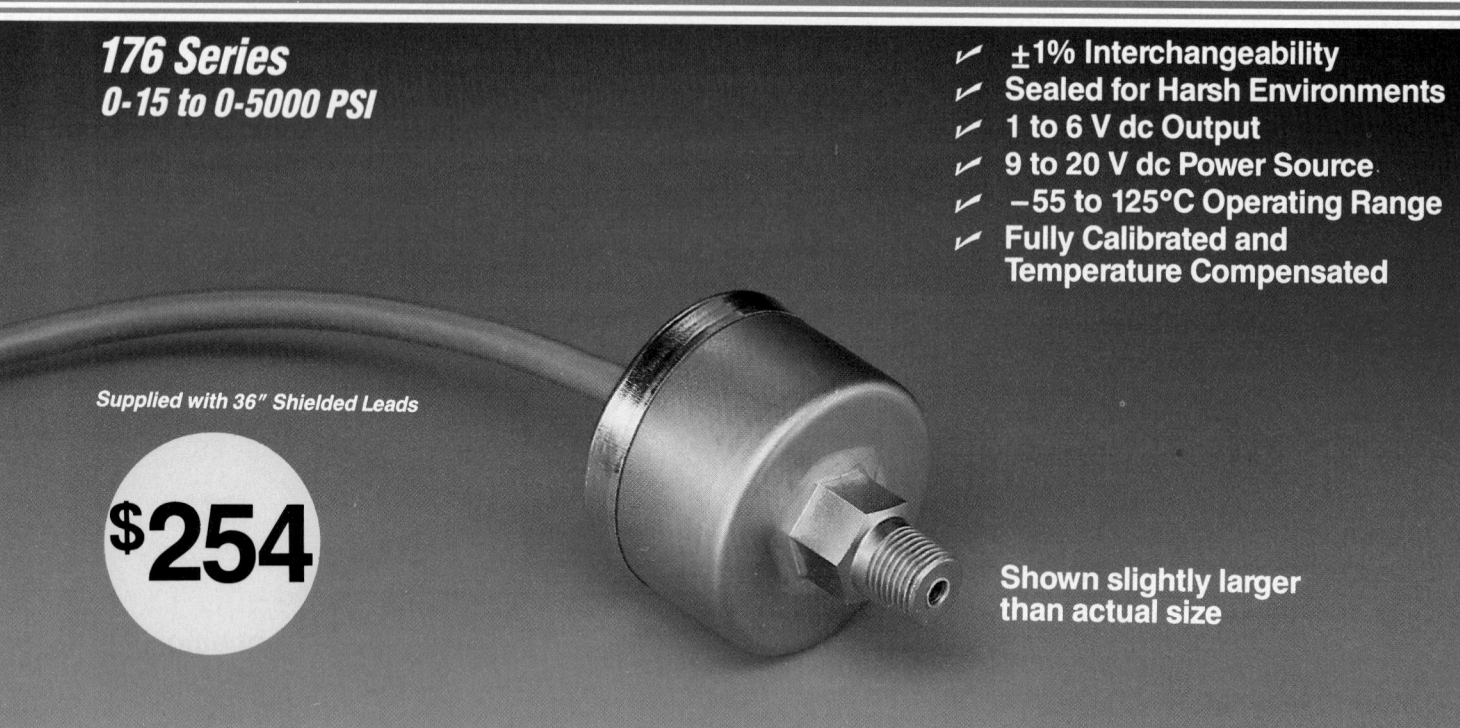

176 Series
0-15 to 0-5000 PSI

- ✓ ±1% Interchangeability
- ✓ Sealed for Harsh Environments
- ✓ 1 to 6 V dc Output
- ✓ 9 to 20 V dc Power Source
- ✓ −55 to 125°C Operating Range
- ✓ Fully Calibrated and Temperature Compensated

Supplied with 36″ Shielded Leads

$254

Shown slightly larger than actual size

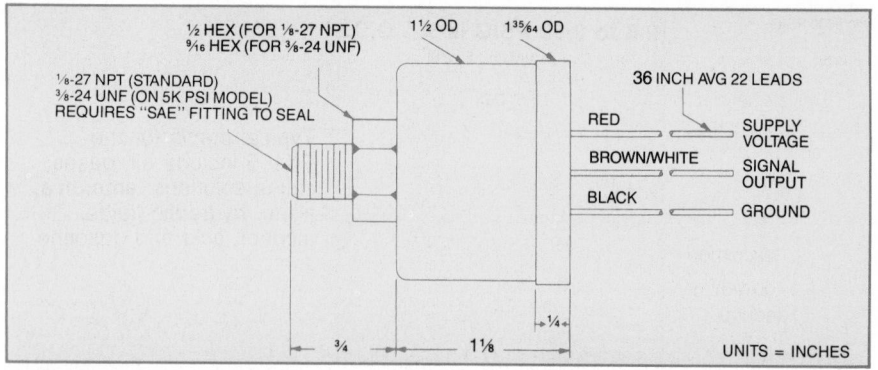

SPECIFICATIONS

Excitation: 9 to 20 V dc at 15 mA (Polarity Protection)
Output: 1 to 6 V dc
Insulation Resistance: 2 M ohm at 25 V dc

PERFORMANCE

Accuracy: ±1.0% full scale
Linearity: ±0.5% full scale
Hysteresis: ±0.25% full scale
Zero Balance: ±1% full scale
Operable Temperature Range: −67 to 221°F (−55 to 105°C)
Compensated Temperature Range: 32 to 185°F (0-85°C)
Thermal Zero Effect: ±0.01% RDG/°F (±0.02%/°C)
Thermal Sensitivity Effect: ±0.01% RDG/°F (±0.02%/°C)
Proof Pressure: 2 x full scale; 1.5 x over 200 PSI
Burst Pressure: 20 x full scale; 10x: 50-200 PSI; 5x: 500 PSI and up

CONSTRUCTION

Gages: Piezo-Resistive on Bending Beam
Body/Diaphragm Material: 300 Series SS (Silver, Copper, Nickel, Cadmium Brazed)
Pressure Port: ⅛-27 NPT; ⅜-24 UNF over 5K PSI
Electrical Connection: 36″ Shielded PVC Cable, 3 Leads
Pressure Cavity Volume: .091 in³
Weight: 4 ozs.
Frequency Response: 10 KHz

To Order *(Specify model number)*

RANGE	MODEL	PRICE	COMPATIBLE METER
0- 15 PSIA	PX176-015A5V	$262	DP302-E,DP2000P4,DP354
0- 25 PSIA	PX176-025A5V	262	DP302-E,DP2000P4,DP354
0- 50 PSIA	PX176-050A5V	262	DP302-E,DP2000P4,DP354
0- 100 PSIS*	PX176-100S5V	254	DP302-E,DP2000P4,DP354
0- 200 PSIS*	PX176-200S5V	254	DP302-E,DP2000P5,DP354
0- 500 PSIS*	PX176-500S5V	254	DP3002-E,DP2000P4,DP354
0-1000 PSIS*	PX176-1KS5V	254	DP3002-E,DP2000P4,DP354
0-5000 PSIS*	PX176-5KS5V	254	DP3002-E,DP41-E

* Measured with respect to a standard atmosphere (14.7 PSIA).
** ⅛″ NPT fitting available as special order.
Typical media include: oil, gases, saline solutions, hydraulic fluids, alcohols, freon, ammonia, acids and gasoline.

HIGHLIGHTED MODELS STOCKED FOR FAST DELIVERY

NEW! VOLTAGE OUTPUT PRESSURE TRANSDUCERS
FOR DRY AND WET APPLICATIONS

PX633 and PX643 Series From
$155

✔ PX663 for Dry Gas Media
✔ PX643 for Accurate Liquid or Gaseous Media

Models PX633 Series and PX644 Series Transducers are Shown With a DP41-E Meter ($345) and PS-4 and PS-8 Snubbers ($10 each).

SPECIFICATIONS

Excitation: PX633 6-32 Vdc; PX643 10-30 Vdc

Output: 1-5 Vdc

Accuracy: PX633 0.5% FS, (linearity, hysteresis and repeatability); PX643 0.25% FS (linearity 0.25% FS; hysteresis 0.1% FS, rep 0.05% FS)

Zero Balance: 1% FS

Operating Temp.: -20 to 160°F (-29 to 72°C)

Compensated Temp.: PX633 0 to 160°F (-18 to 72°C), PX643 -20 to 160°F (-29 to 72°C)

Thermal Effects: Zero 0.02 % FS/°F Span 0.02 % Rdg/°F

Proof Pressure: 200% FS

Burst Pressure: 300% FS

Min. Load Resistance: 2000 ohms

Gage Type: PX633 Diffused silicon; PX643 SS diaphragm with oil fill

Wetted Parts: PX633 Clean dry gases; PX643 316L SS

Pressure Port: PX633 1/8 NPT, PX643 1/4 NPT

Electrical Conn.: 24 AWG, PVC, shielded, 36" vented pigtail

Enclosure: NEMA 4

Size: PX633 1.7" L x 1.5" dia. (43 x 38 mm); PX643 4.5"L x 2" dia.(114 x 56 mm)

Weight: PX633 5 oz.(140g); PX643 7 oz.(195 g)

Accessories: PS-8G snubber for Model PX633. PS-4D (for dense oils), PS-4E (for water) and PS-4G (for gases) for Model PX643. All snubbers **$10** each.

HIGHLIGHTED MODELS STOCKED FOR FAST DELIVERY!

To Order *(Specify Model Number)*

RANGE	MODEL	PRICE	COMPATIBLE METER
PX633 DRY MEDIA			
30" Hg Vacuum	PX633-30VAC5V	$178	DP205-E, DP3002-E, DP460-E
0-5 PSIG	PX633-005G5V	178	DP205-E, DP3002-E, DP460-E
0-15 PSIG	PX633-015G5V	178	DP205-E, DP302-E, DP460-E
0-30 PSIG	PX633-030G5V	178	DP205-E, DP3002-E, DP460-E
0-50 PSIG	PX633-050G5V	155	DP205-E, DP3002-E, DP460-E
0-100 PSIG	PX633-100G5V	155	DP205-E, DP302-E, DP460-E
0-200 PSIG	PX633-200G5V	155	DP205-E, DP302-E, DP460-E
0-300 PSIG	PX633-300G5V	155	DP205-E, DP3002-E, DP460-E
PX643 WET OR DRY MEDIA			
0-15 PSIG	PX643-015G5V	$324	DP205-E, DP302-E, DP460-E
0-30 PSIG	PX643-030G5V	324	DP205-E, DP3002-E, DP460-E
0-50 PSIG	PX643-050GV	324	DP205-E, DP3002-E, DP460-E
0-100 PSIG	PX643-100G5V	324	DP205-E, DP302-E, DP460-E
0-200 PSIG	PX643-200G5V	324	DP205-E, DP302-E, DP460-E
0-300 PSIG	PX643-300G5V	324	DP205-E, DP3002-E, DP460-E
0-500 PSIG	PX643-500G5V	324	DP205-E, DP3002-E, DP460-E

All models come with a complete operator's manual.
Ordering Example: *PX633-050G5V is a voltage output transducer for dry media with 0 to 50 PSIG range, $155.*

HIGHLY ACCURATE, LOW PRESSURE LABORATORY TRANSDUCER

NEW!

Shown With Model DP3002-E Meter, $271.

PX653 Series
From
$342

1 YEAR WARRANTY · MADE IN USA · NIST

Ideal Applications:
- ✔ Clean Rooms
- ✔ HVAC
- ✔ Laboratory Fume Hoods

SPECIFICATIONS

Excitation: 12-36 Vdc
Output: 1-5 Vdc
Accuracy: 0.25% FS
Linearity: 0.25% FS (BFSL)
Hysteresis: 0.02% FS
Repeatability: 0.05% FS
Operating Temp: -20 to 160°F (-29 to 72°C)
Compensated Temp: 35 to 135°F (2 to 57°C)
Thermal Effects:
Zero 0.015% FS/°F
Span 0.015% Rdg/°F
Proof Pressure: 10 PSI
Burst Pressure: 50 PSI
Static Pressure: 10 PSI
Gage Type: Capacitance
Supply Current: <5 mA
Calibration Report: NIST cal at 25, 50, 75 and 100% FS upscale and down scale provided
Response Time: 250 msec
Wetted Parts: Dry, clean non-corrosive gases only
Enclosure: NEMA 2; 4.2"H x 4.6"W x 2.1"D (107 x 117 x 53 mm)
Pressure Port: ⅛ and ¼ barbed fittings (tubing TY-316-100)
Electrical Connections.: Screw terminal
Weight: 13 oz (368 g)

HIGHLIGHTED MODELS IN STOCK FOR FAST DELIVERY!

To Order *(Specify Model Number)*

RANGE Inches H_2O	MODEL	PRICE	COMPATIBLE METER
0-0.1	PX653-0.1D5V	$444	DP205-E, DP41-E, DP460-E
0-0.25	PX653-0.25D5V	392	DP205-E, DP41 E, DP460-E
0-0.50	PX653-0.5D5V	342	DP205-E, DP41-E, DP460-E
0-1	PX653-01D5V	342	DP205-E, DP41-E, DP3002-E
0-2	PX653-02D5V	342	DP205-E, DP41-E, DP460-E
0-3	PX653-03D5V	342	DP205-E, DP41-E, DP460-E
0-5	PX653-05D5V	342	DP205-E, DP41-E, DP460-E
0-10	PX653-10D5V	342	DP205-E, DP41-E, DP3002-E
0-25	PX653-25D5V	342	DP205-E, DP41-E, DP460-E
BI-DIRECTIONAL RANGES			
±0.25	PX653-0.25BD5V	$342	DP205-E, DP41-E, DP460-E
±0.50	PX653-0.5BD5V	342	DP205-E, DP41-E, DP460-E
±1	PX653-01BD5V	342	DP205-E, DP41-E, DP460-E
±2.5	PX653-2.5BD5V	342	DP205-E, DP41-E, DP460-E
±5	PX653-05BD5V	342	DP205-E, DP41-E, DP460-E
±10	PX653-10BD5V	342	DP205-E, DP41-E, DP460-E
±25	PX653-25BD5V	342	DP205-E, DP41-E, DP460-E

Comes complete with operator's manual.
Ordering Example: *PX653-01D5V high accuracy, low pressure transducer, with a 0 to 1" H_2O range, **$342.***

B-39

HIGHLY ACCURATE, LOW PRESSURE INDUSTRIAL TRANSDUCER

**PX654 Series
From**

$528

Ideal Applications:
- ✓ Use With Boiler Inlet Air
- ✓ HVAC
- ✓ Fume Hoods
- ✓ Level Control

HIGHLIGHTED MODELS IN STOCK FOR FAST DELIVERY!

To Order *(Specify Model Number)*

RANGE Inches H$_2$O	MODEL	PRICE	COMPATIBLE METER
0-0.1	PX654-0.1D5V	$630	DP205-E, DP41-E, DP460-E
0-0.25	PX654-0.25D5V	578	DP205-E, DP41-E, DP460-E
0-0.50	PX654-0.5D5V	528	DP205-E, DP41-E, DP460-E
0-1	PX654-01D5V	528	DP205-E, DP41-E, DP460-E
0-2	PX654-02D5V	528	DP205-E, DP41-E, DP460-E
0-3	PX654-03D5V	528	DP205-E, DP41-E, DP460-E
0-5	PX654-05D5V	528	DP205-E, DP41-E, DP460-E
0-10	PX654-10D5V	528	DP205-E, DP41-E, DP460-E
0-25	PX654-25D5V	528	DP205-E, DP41-E, DP460-E
0-50	PX654-50D5V	528	DP205-E, DP41-E, DP460-E
BI-DIRECTIONAL RANGES			
±.05	PX654-0.05BD5V	$630	DP205-E, DP41-E, DP460-E
±.25	PX654-0.25BD5V	528	DP205-E, DP41-E, DP460-E
±.50	PX654-0.5BD5V	528	DP205-E, DP41-E, DP460-E
±1	PX654-01BD5V	528	DP205-E, DP41-E, DP460-E
±2.5	PX654-2.5BD5V	528	DP205-E, DP41-E, DP460-E
±5	PX654-05BD5V	528	DP205-E, DP41-E, DP460-E
±10	PX654-10BD5V	528	DP205-E, DP41-E, DP460-E
±25	PX654-25BD5V	528	DP205-E, DP41-E, DP460-E

Comes with complete operator's manual.
Ordering Example: *PX654-01D5V is a 1-inch of water differential sensor, $528.*

SPECIFICATIONS

Excitation: 12-36 Vdc
Output: 1-5 Vdc
Accuracy: 0.25% FS
Linearity: 0.25% FS (BFSL)
Hysteresis: 0.02% FS
Repeatability: 0.05% FS
Operating Temp: -20 to 185°F (-29 to 85°C)
Compensated Temp: 35 to 160°F (-18 to 72°C)
Thermal Effects:
Zero 0.015% FS/°F
Span 0.015% FS/°F
Proof Pressure: 10 PSI
Burst Pressure: 50 PSI
Static Pressure: 100 PSI
Gage Type: Capacitance
Supply Current: <5mA
Calibration Report: NIST cal at 25, 50, 75 and 100% FS upscale and downscale provided
Response Time: 250 msec
Wetted Parts: Dry, clean non-gases only
Enclosure: NEMA 4X; 5.4"L x 3"W x 2.5"D (137 x 76 x 64 mm)
Pressure Port: ¼ NPTF
Electrical Connections.: Screw terminal (two ½ NPTF conduit)
Weight: 2.1 lbs (955 g)

 **NEW!**

GENERAL PURPOSE 5 OR 10 VOLT OUTPUT PRESSURE SENSORS

3 YEAR WARRANTY · **MADE IN USA** · **NIST**

PX303 Series

$255

Shown with PS-4 Snubber ($10)
and DP302-E Meter ($271);
See Page D-19 for Details.

WIRING
RED +EXC
WHITE +OUT
BLACK COMMON

5.438 (138.1)
1.125 (26.6)

DIMENSIONS IN INCHES (mm)

HIGHLIGHTED MODELS IN STOCK FOR FAST DELIVERY!

SPECIFICATIONS

Excitation: 12-32/14-32 Vdc
Output: 0.5-5.5/1-11 Vdc
Accuracy: 0.25%FS (linearity, hysteresis, repeatability)
Zero Balance: ± 2 %FS
Span Tolerance: ±1 %FS
Operating Temp.: 0 to 160°F (-18 to 71°C)
Compensated Temp.: 30 to 130 °F (-1 to 54°C)
Total Thermal Effects: 1% FS max
Proof Pressure: 200%, 13000 PSI max
Quiescent Exc.: 16 mA Typical
Min Load Resistance: 2000 ohms
Response Time: 1 msec
Gage Type: Stainless steel diaphragm, silicone oil filled semiconductor sensor
Shock: 50 g @ 11msec
Wetted Parts: 300 SS series (SS and Viton ≥2000 PSI)
Pressure Port: ¼" NPT
Press. Cavity: 0.075 cubic inches
Electrical Conn.: 3 cond, 22 awg, PVC unshielded, 3 ft pigtail cable
Weight: 5.8 oz (166 grams)
Accessories: PS-4G (pressure snubber for gaseous media), **PS4E** (pressure snubber for water and light oils) and **PS-4D** (pressure snubber for dense liquids/ motor oils) **$10 each.** *Snubbers protect sensors from fluid spikes/hammers!*

TO ORDER *(Specify Model Number)*

RANGE	5 VOLT OUPUT MODELS	PRICE	COMPATIBLE METER
GAGE MODELS			
0-15 PSIG	**PX303-015G5V**	$255	DP41-E, DP302-E, DP460-E
0-50 PSIG	**PX303-050G5V**	255	DP41-E, DP302-E, DP460-E
0-100 PSIG	**PX303-100G5V**	255	DP41-E, DP302-E, DP460-E
0-200 PSIG	**PX303-200G5V**	255	DP41-E, DP302-E, DP460-E
0-300 PSIG	**PX303-300G5V**	255	DP41-E, DP3002-E, DP460-E
0-500 PSIG	**PX303-500G5V**	255	DP41-E, DP3002-E, DP460-E
0-1000 PSIG	**PX303-1KG5V**	255	DP41-E, DP302-E, DP460-E
0-2000 PSIG	**PX303-2KG5V**	255	DP41-E, DP302-E, DP460-E
0-3000 PSIG	**PX303-3KG5V**	255	DP41-E, DP3002-E, DP460-E
0-4000 PSIG	**PX303-4KG5V**	255	DP41-E, DP3002-E, DP460-E
0-5000 PSIG	**PX303-5KG5V**	255	DP41-E, DP3002-E, DP460-
0-7500 PSIG	**PX303-7.5KG5V**	255	DP41-E, DP3002-E, DP460-E
0-10000 PSIG	**PX303-10KG5V**	255	DP41-E, DP3002-E, DP460-E
ABSOLUTE MODELS			
0-15 PSIA	**PX303-015A5V**	$255	DP41-E, DP3002-E, DP460-E
0-50 PSIA	**PX303-050A5V**	255	DP41-E, DP302-E, DP460-E
0-100 PSIA	**PX303-100A5V**	255	DP41-E, DP302-E, DP460-E
0-200 PSIA	**PX303-200A5V**	255	DP41-E, DP302-E, DP460-E
0-300 PSIA	**PX303-300A5V**	255	DP41-E, DP3002-E, DP460-E

To order models with 1-11 Vdc output replace 5V with 10V in model number.
Comes with complete operator's manual.

Ordering Example: *PX303-050G10V and PS-4E is a 1-11 Vdc output pressure sensor and snubber, $180 + 10 = **$190.***

THIN FILM VOLTAGE OUTPUT PRESSURE SENSOR
FOR GAGE AND ABSOLUTE PRESSURES

3 YEAR WARRANTY

NEW!

From
$226

Shown with DP41-E Meter ($345),
See Page D-7, and PS-4 Snubber ($10).

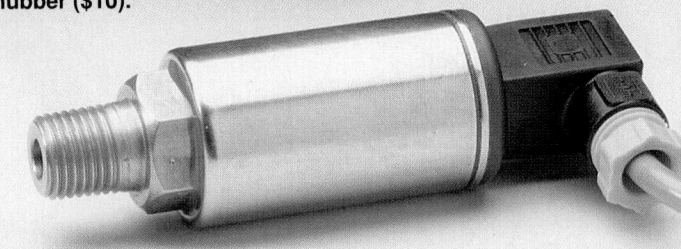

- ✔ All Stainless Steel Wetted Parts
- ✔ NEMA 4 Rated
- ✔ CVD Construction for High Stability

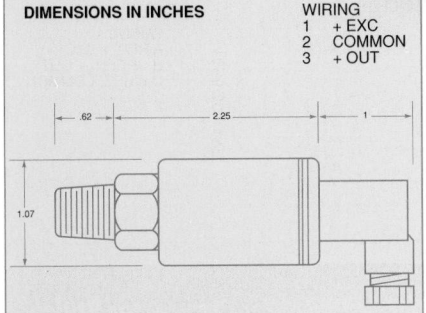

DIMENSIONS IN INCHES

WIRING
1   + EXC
2   COMMON
3   + OUT

.62 — 2.25 — 1 — 1.07

SPECIFICATIONS
Excitation: 24Vdc @15mA (12-36 Vdc)
Output: 0.5 to 5.5 Vdc
Accuracy: 0.25% FS (including linearity, hysteresis and repeatability)
Zero Balance: 0.5 Vdc ± 75 mV
Span: 5 Vdc ± 75 mV
Operating Temperature: -4 to 185°F (-20 to 85°C)
Compensated Temperature: -4 to 176 °F (-20 to 80°C)
Thermal Effects: 0.017% FS/°F
Proof Pressure: 150%
Burst Pressure: 400%, 17000 PSI max.
Response Time: 1 msec
Gage Type: Chemical vapor deposited polysilicon strain gages
Wetted Parts: 15-7,17-4 SS, <60 PSI 17-4 SS ≥60 PSI
Pressure Port: ¼-18 NPT
Electrical Connection: Miniature DIN connector; screw terminals
Weight: 4 oz (100 g)

HIGHLIGHTED MODELS STOCKED FOR FAST DELIVERY!

To Order *(Specify Model Number)*

RANGE	MODEL	PRICE	COMPATIBLE METERS
GAGE MODELS			
0-15 PSIG	**PX213-015G5V**	$226	DP41-E, DP302-E, DP460-E
0-30 PSIG	**PX213-030G5V**	226	DP41-E, DP302-E, DP460-E
0-60 PSIG	**PX213-060G5V**	226	DP41-E, DP302-E, DP460-E
0-100 PSIG	**PX213-100G5V**	226	DP41-E, DP302-E, DP460-E
0-300 PSIG	**PX213-300G5V**	226	DP41-E, DP3002-E, DP460-E
0-600 PSIG	**PX213-600G5V**	226	DP41-E, DP3002-E, DP460-E
0-1000 PSIG	**PX213-1KG5V**	226	DP41-E, DP302-E, DP460-E
0-3000 PSIG	**PX213-3KG5V**	226	DP41-E, DP3002-E, DP460-E
*0-6000 PSIG	**PX213-6KG5V**	226	DP41-E, DP3002-E, DP460-E
ABSOLUTE MODELS			
0-15PSIA	**PX213-015A5V**	$278	DP41-E, DP302-E, DP460-E
0-30PSIA	**PX213-030A5V**	278	DP41-E, DP302-E, DP460-E
0-60PSIA	**PX213-060A5V**	278	DP41-E, DP302-E, DP460-E
0-100 PSIA	**PX213-100A5V**	278	DP41-E, DP302-E, DP460-E
0-150 PSIA	**PX213-150A5V**	278	DP41-E, DP3002-E, DP460-E
0-300 PSIA	**PX213-300A5V**	278	DP41-E, DP3002-E, DP460-E

ACCESSORIES	PRICE	DESCRIPTION
PS-4G	$10.00	Pressure snubber for gaseous media
PS-4E	10.00	Pressure snubber for water and light oils
PS-4D	10.00	Pressure snubber for dense liquids (motor oil)
TX4-100	28.50	100 ft of 4 conductor shielded copper wire

Come with complete operator's manual.
Ordering Example: *PX213-015G5V is a thin film voltage output pressure sensor with a 0-15 PSIG range, **$226**.*

THIN FILM PRESSURE TRANSDUCER FOR GAGE AND VACUUM MEASUREMENTS
RUGGED STAINLESS STEEL CONSTRUCTION

PX603-PX613 Series
VACUUM TO 20,000 PSI

- ✔ **Rugged Stainless Steel Construction**
- ✔ **Fully Conditioned 1-5V Output**
- ✔ **NEMA 4 Cable or Connector Models**
- ✔ **0.4% Accuracy**
- ✔ **Calibration Certificate Supplied**
- ✔ **Zero and Span Adjustments ±15%**
- ✔ **Rugged Vibration Resistant Design**

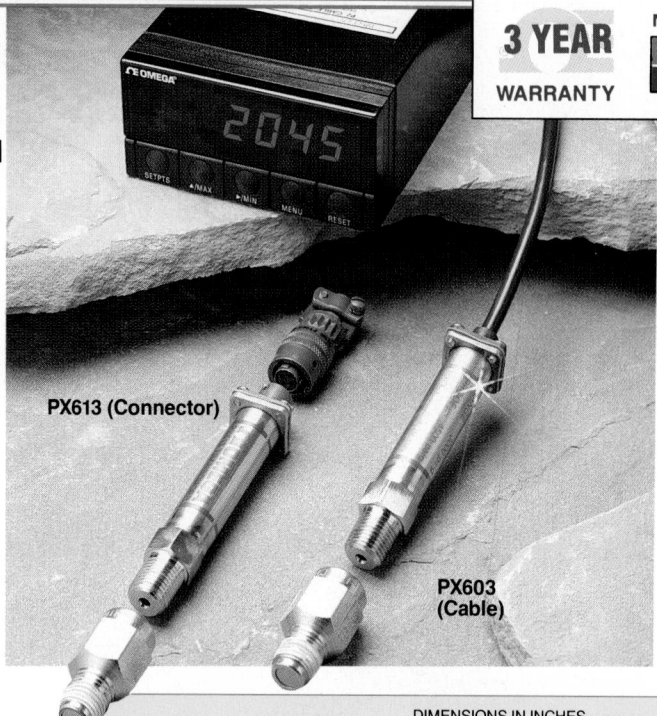

PX613 (Connector)

PX603 (Cable)

3 YEAR WARRANTY **MADE IN USA** **NIST**

From
$265

Ordering Example
DP41-E meter shown $345
PX603-100G5V shown $265
PX613-150G5V shown $289
PT06F-8-4S Connector
(not included) $24

DIMENSIONS IN INCHES

WIRING:
A RED + EXC
B GREEN + OUT
D WHITE COMMON

1.058 SQUARE

3.780

SPECIFICATIONS

Excitation: 10 to 30 Vdc unregulated
Output: 1 to 5 Vdc (3-wire)
Supply Current: < 3.0 mA
Output Impedance: 100 ohms
Insulation Resistance: 100M ohms @ 50V
Accuracy: ±0.4% BFSL
Hysteresis: ±0.2% Full Scale
Repeatability: ±0.05% Full Scale
Stability: ±1.0%/year
Durability: 100 million cycles
Operating Temp.: −55 to 195°F
Compensated Temp.: −20 to 180°F
Thermal Zero Effect: ±0.04% FS/°F
Thermal Span Effect: ±0.04% FS/°F
Proof Pressure: 15 to 2000 PSI = 200%; 3000 to 5000 = 150%; 7500 to 20000 = 120%
Burst Pressure: 15 to 2000 PSI = 800%; 3000 to 20000 = 500%
Gages: Thin film polysilicon
Diaphragm: 17-4PH Stainless Steel
Case: 300 Series Stainless Steel
Pressure Connection: 15 to 10,000 PSI: ¼ NPT; 15,000 and 20,000 PSI = Female AMINCO fitting
Electrical Connection: 36″ braided shield PVC Cable or connector
Mating Connector: PTO6F-8-4S
Weight: 4.5 oz. without cable
Response time: 1 ms
Construction: PX603 is vented to room in ≤ 500 PSI sealed above 500 PSI PX613 is sealed

To Order (Specify PX603 for Cable or PX613 for Connector Style)

RANGE PSIG	MODEL [*]=Insert 0 or 1	PRICE PX603	PRICE PX613	COMPATIBLE METERS
30″ Hg-0 vacuum	PX6[*]3-30VAC5V	$295	$320	DP3002-E,DP41-E,DP460-E
30″ Hg-30 PSI	PX6[*]3-30V305V	295	320	DP3002-E,DP41-E,DP460-E
0-15	PX6[*]3-015G5V	265	289	DP354,DP41-E, DP3002-E
0-30	PX6[*]3-030G5V	265	289	DP354,DP41-E, DP3002-E
0-60	PX6[*]3-060G5V	265	289	DP354,DP41-E, DP3002-E
0-100	PX6[*]3-100G5V	265	289	DP354,DP41-E, DP3002-E
0-150	PX6[*]3-150G5V	265	289	DP354,DP41-E, DP3002-E
0-200	PX6[*]3-200G5V	265	289	DP354,DP41-E, DP3002-E
0-300	PX6[*]3-300G5V	265	289	DP354,DP41-E, DP3002-E
0-500	PX6[*]3-500G5V	265	289	DP354,DP41-E, DP3002-E
0-1000	PX6[*]3-1KG5V	265	289	DP354,DP41-E, DP3002-E
0-2000	PX6[*]3-2KG5V	265	289	DP354,DP41-E, DP3002-E
0-3000	PX6[*]3-3KG5V	265	289	DP41-E, DP3002-E, DP110R3
0-5000	PX6[*]3-5KG5V	265	289	DP41-E, DP3002-E, DP110R3
0-7500	PX6[*]3-7.5KG5V	265	289	DP41-E, DP3002-E, DP110R3
0-10,000	PX6[*]3-10KG5V	265	289	DP41-E, DP3002-E, DP110R3
0-15,000	PX6[*]3-15KG5V†	265	289	DP41-E, DP3002-E, DP460-E
0-20,000	PX6[*]3-20KG5V†	265	289	DP41-E, DP3002-E, DP460-E

†15,000 and 20,000 PSI Models Supplied with female AMINCO fitting.
* [ ] Fill in "0" for cable style [ ] Fill in "1" for connector style

HIGHLY ACCURATE AMPLIFIED VOLTAGE TYPE PRESSURE TRANSDUCER WITH INTEGRAL SHUNT CALIBRATOR FOR QUICK CALIBRATION CHECKS

951 Series
0-10 to 0-5000 PSI

From $675

- ✔ Stainless Steel Diaphragm for Compatibility with Most Media
- ✔ Rugged Stainless Steel Case Protects Components in Industrial Environments
- ✔ Connects to a PTO6F-10-6S Connector for Easy Field Connections
- ✔ 0-5 V Amplified Output for Good Noise Immunity and Interfacing to Voltage Measuring Instrumentation
- ✔ 26 to 32 Vdc Power Supply for Maximum Versatility in Any Application
- ✔ ¼" NPT Fitting for Fast, Easy, and Secure Installation
- ✔ Units 1000 PSIG and Below Utilize Beam Mounted Strain Gages for Long Life and High Reliability

Shown larger than actual size

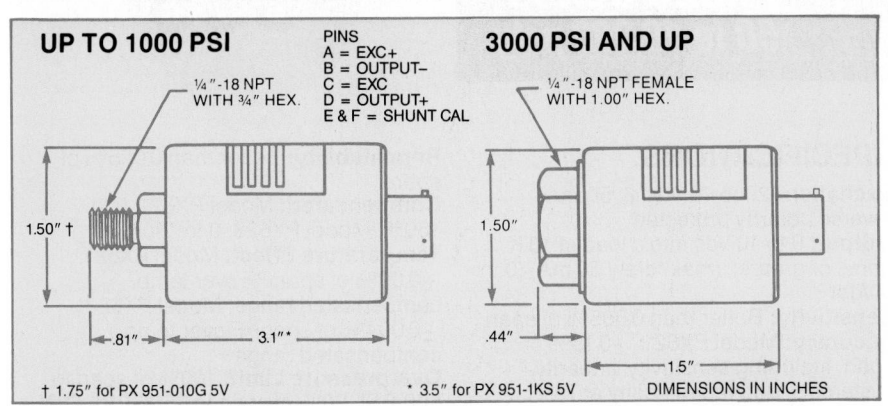

UP TO 1000 PSI

¼"-18 NPT WITH ¾" HEX.

PINS
A = EXC+
B = OUTPUT−
C = EXC
D = OUTPUT+
E & F = SHUNT CAL

1.50" †

← .81" → ← 3.1" * →

† 1.75" for PX 951-010G 5V

3000 PSI AND UP

¼"-18 NPT FEMALE WITH 1.00" HEX.

1.50"

.44"

← 1.5" →

DIMENSIONS IN INCHES

* 3.5" for PX 951-1KS 5V

SPECIFICATIONS

Excitation: 26 to 32 Vdc @ 45 mA

Output: 0-5 Vdc

Insulation Resistance: > 5 MΩ @ 75 Vdc

Accuracy: ±0.15%

Hysteresis: ±0.10%

Repeatability: ±0.05%

Zero Balance: ±1%

Built-in Span and Zero Adjusts: ±20%

Operable Temperature Range: −100 to 325°F; electronics 0 to 185°F

Compensated Temperature Range: 60 to 160°F

Thermal Zero Effect: ±0.005% full scale/°F

Thermal Sensitivity Effect: ±0.005% full scale/°F

Proof Pressure: 1.5 x Range

Burst Pressure: 5 x 100-1,000 PSI; 3.5 x 1,500 PSI; 2.5 x > 1,500 PSI

Shunt Cal: 59K Ω

Frequency Resposne: 3000 Hz

Body Material: 17-4 Stainless Steel, hermetically sealed

Diaphragm Material: 17-4 Stainless Steel, bonded foil gage

Pressure Port: ¼"-18 NPT (Male Thread 10 to 1,000 PSI, Female Thread 3,000 to 5,000 PSI)

Mating Connector: PT06F-10-6S (not included)

Pressure Cavity Volume: 0.171 in³

Weight: 10 ozs.

To Order (Specify Model Number)

SEE SECTION D FOR INSTRUMENT SELECTION

RANGE		MODEL	PRICE	COMPATIBLE METER*
0-10	PSIG	PX951-010G 5V	$695	DP3002-P, DP2000P4, DP460-V
0-25	PSIG	PX951-025G 5V	695	DP3002-P, DP2000P4, DP460-V
0-50	PSIG	PX951-050G 5V	675	DP3002-P, DP2000P4, DP460-V
0-100	PSIS	PX951-100S 5V	675	DP3002-P, DP2000P4, DP460-V
0-200	PSIS	PX951-200S 5V	675	DP3002-P, DP2000P5, DP460-V
0-500	PSIS	PX951-500S 5V	675	DP3002-P, DP2000P4, DP460-V
0-1000	PSIS	PX951-1KS 5V	675	DP3002-P, DP2000P4, DP460-V
0-3000	PSIS	PX951-3KS 5V	675	DP3002-P, DP460-V
0-5000	PSIS	PX951-5KS 5V	675	DP3002-P, DP460-V

◆ HIGHLIGHTED MODELS STOCKED FOR FAST DELIVERY ◆

*Absolute ranges available change "G" to "A" in model number. Requires external power supply PSS-D15B, **$114**. Add **$75** to base price, (3 piece minimum).*

HIGH ACCURACY PRESSURE TRANSDUCERS
WITH AMPLIFIED VOLTAGE OUTPUT
GAGE OR ABSOLUTE MODELS

PX620 Series
50 to 10,000 psig

- ✔ **Connector Included**
- ✔ **Non Contacting Optical Sensor for High Accuracy Model 621 — 0.15%, Model 623 — 0.10%**
- ✔ **Repeatability to 0.005%**
- ✔ **Corrosion Resistant Materials of Sensor**
- ✔ **Internal Zero and Span Adjustments**
- ✔ **DC Output Isolated from Input**
- ✔ **10 Vdc Output Standard for Highest Resolution**
- ✔ **Certificate of Calibration Supplied**

From
$895

The OMEGA® PX620 Series High Accuracy Pressure Sensors incorporate an optical means of detecting the effective pressure of an elastic member, so there is no physical contact between the strained member and the portion that produces the electrical signal. This unique pressure sensor offers extreme accuracy and repeatability.

SPECIFICATIONS

Excitation: 20 to 40 Vdc @ 50 mA, reverse polarity protected
Output: 0 to 10 Vdc into a load of 10 K ohms or greater. (max. draw 50 mA) (0 to 5 Vdc)
Sensitivity: Better than 0.005% of span
Accuracy: Model PX621: ±0.15% of span, including sensitivity, linearity, hysteresis, and repeatability at 73°F, Model PX623: ±0.10% of span

Repeatability: Better than 0.005% of span
Compensated: Model PX621: 0 to 150°F, Model PX623: 0 to 180°F
Temperature Effect: Model PX621: ±0.02% of span/°F over temp. compensated range; Model PX623: ±0.004% of span/°F over temp. compensated range
Overpressure Limit: 100% of span to 500 PSI, 30% of span to 7500 PSI, 20% of span to 10,000 PSI
Pressure Sensor: Non-contacting optical pressure sensor measuring motion of diaphragm or Bourdon tube element. (Diaphragm to 200 PSI, Bourdon tube for higher pressures)
Process Connection: ¼" NPT female — ½" NPT male combination for pressure ranges through 5000 psi. AUTOCLAVE and AMINCO 45-11310 for ranges over 5000 psi.
Electronic housing: Aluminum cover, epoxy finish with circular electrical connector, Mating connector included.
Wetted Parts: Element — Inconel/718; optional — 403 SS or 410 SS other wetted parts: 316 SS

To Order *(Standard Models)*

Range PSIG	Model	Price	Compatible Meter
0- 50	PX621-050G 10V	$895	DP41-E, DP3002-E, DP354
0- 100	PX621-100G 10V	895	DP41-E, DP3002-E, DP354
0- 200	PX621-200G 10V	895	DP41-E, DP3002-E, DP354
0- 500	PX621-500G 10V	895	DP41-E, DP3002-E, DP354
0- 1000	PX621-1KG 10V	895	DP41-E, DP3002-E, DP354
0- 3000	PX621-3KG 10V	895	DP41-E, DP3002-E, DP205-E
0-10000	PX621-10KG 10V	895	DP41-E, DP3002-E, DP205-E

Standard Ranges, ±0.15% span accuracy, 10 V Models in Stock
To select 5 V output model, change 10 V to 5 V, no additional cost
To select high accuracy model, change PX621 to PX623, see following page for pricing.
To select absolute pressure, change "G" to "A" add $200 to price shown.

◆ *HIGHLIGHTED MODELS STOCKED FOR FAST DELIVERY* ◆

RUGGED ELECTRONIC BAROMETERS AND MANOMETERS
WITH VOLTAGE OUTPUT

PX960 Series
16-32" HgA Barometer; 0-100" H₂O Manometer

- **Hermetically Sealed Stainless Steel Construction**
- **Fully Adjustable Zero and Span settings**

Typical Applications

- Meteorology
- Avionics
- Geophysics

$995

MADE IN USA

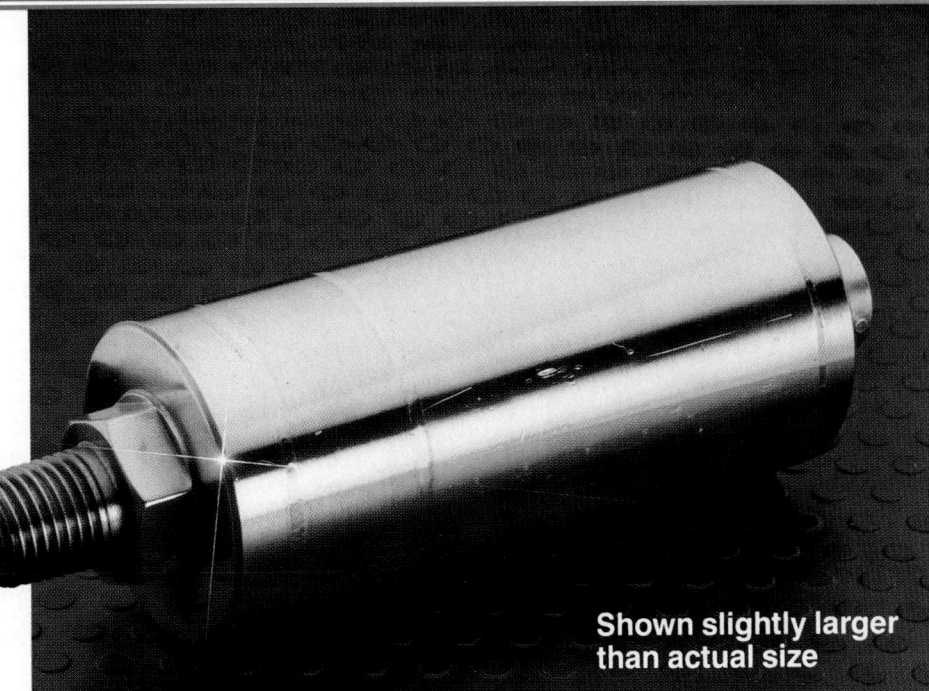

Shown slightly larger than actual size

The OMEGA PX960 electronic barometer/manometer Series is available in the barometric pressure ranges of 16 to 32" Hg and the manometric ranges from 100" H₂O to 30" Hg. These industrial transducers achieve minimum accuracies of 0.1% full scale. Hermetically sealed, stainless steel construction provides superior performance even under the most demanding applications which require high measurement stability.

SPECIFICATIONS

Excitation: 26 to 32 Vdc

Output: 0-5 Vdc (PX961), 0-2 Vdc (PX962)

Accuracy: PX961 ±0.1% of span; PX962 ±0.15%

Operating Temperature: 0°F to 185°F

Compensated Temperature: 60°F to 160°F

Temperature Effect: Zero PX961 = 0.0025%, PX962 = 0.005% full scale/°F Span PX961 = 0.0025%, PX962 = 0.005% reading/°F

Mating Connector: PTO6F-10-6S (not included)

Construction: Hermetically sealed stainless steel

Pressure Port: ¼-18 NPT male

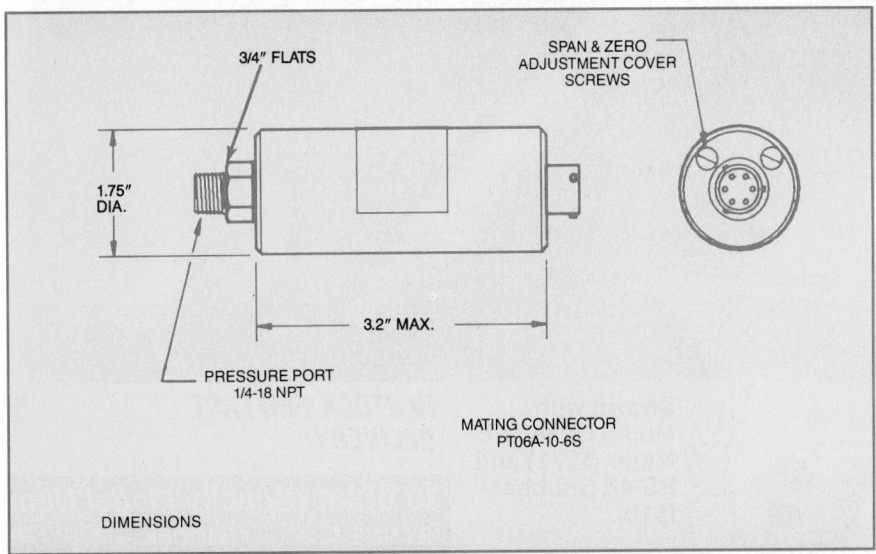

3/4" FLATS

SPAN & ZERO ADJUSTMENT COVER SCREWS

1.75" DIA.

3.2" MAX.

PRESSURE PORT 1/4-18 NPT

MATING CONNECTOR PT06A-10-6S

DIMENSIONS

To Order (Specify Model Number)

MODEL	RANGE		PRICE	COMPATIBLE METER*
Barometer	**in. HgA**	**PSIA**		
PX961-16A5V	16 to 32	7.9 to 15.7	**$995**	DP2000-P4, DP3002-P, DP460-V
Manometer	**in. H₂O**	**in. Hg**		
PX962-100G2V	0 to 100	—	995	DP2000-P4, DP3002-P, DP460-V
PX962-200G2V	0 to 200	—	995	DP2000-P4, DP3002-P, DP460-V
PX962-15G2V	—	0 to 15	995	DP2000-P4, DP3002-P, DP460-V
PX962-30G2V	—	0 to 30	995	DP2000-P4, DP3002-P, DP460-V

Requires external power supply PSS-D15B, $114.

▶ *HIGHLIGHTED MODEL IN STOCK FOR FAST DELIVERY* ◀

GENERAL PURPOSE VOLTAGE OUTPUT PRESSURE TRANSDUCER
ALL STAINLESS STEEL CONSTRUCTION

PX903 Series
$255

✔ NIST Traceable
✔ NEMA 4 Enclosure
✔ CVD Construction for High Stability

SPECIFICATIONS
Excitation: 12-30 Vdc
Output: 1-5 Vdc
Accuracy: 0.5%FS
Hysteresis: 0.2%FS
Repeatability: 0.05%FS
Zero Balance: 1%FS
Stability: 1%FS/year
Operating Temp.: -55 to 195°F (-48 to 90 °C)
Compensated Temp.: -20 to 180°F (-29 to 82 °C)
Thermal Effects:
Zero 0.04% FS/°F
Span 0.04% Rdg/°F
Proof Pressure: 150% FS
Burst Pressure: 300% FS
Response Time: 1 ms
Gage Type: Chemical vapor deposition
Enclosure: NEMA 4 stainless steel
Wetted Parts: Stainless steel
Pressure Port: ¼ NPT
Electrical Conn.: 22 AWG, 36", vented and shielded cable
Weight: 3 oz (85 g)

Accessories
Pressure Snubbers: Models PS-4D (Oils), PS-4E (Water), PS-4G (Gases)
$10 each.
*TX4-100 Wire: 100' of 4-conductor shielded copper wire, **$28.50***

Shown with Model DP3002-E Meter ($271) and PS-4E Snubber ($10).

IN STOCK FOR FAST DELIVERY!

To Order	*(Specify Model Number)*		
RANGE	**MODEL**	**PRICE**	**COMPATIBLE METER**
0-100 PSIG	**PX903-100G5V**	$255	DP205-E, DP41-E, DP302-E
0-200 PSIG	**PX903-200G5V**	255	DP205-E, DP460-E, DP302-E
0-300 PSIG	**PX903-300G5V**	255	DP205-E, DP460-E, DP3002-E
0-500 PSIG	**PX903-500G5V**	255	DP205-E, DP41-E, DP3002-E
0-1000 PSIG	**PX903-1KG5V**	255	DP205-E, DP41-E, DP3002-E
0-2000 PSIG	**PX903-2KG5V**	255	DP205-E, DP41-E, DP3002-E
0-3000 PSIG	**PX903-3KG5V**	255	DP205-E, DP41-E, DP3002-E
0-5000 PSIG	**PX903-5KG5V**	255	DP205-E, DP41-E, DP3002-E
0-7500 PSIG	**PX903-7.5KG5V**	255	DP205-E, DP41-E, DP3002-E
0-10000 PSIG	**PX903-10KG5V**	255	DP205-E, DP41-E, DP3002-E

Comes complete with operator's manual.
Ordering Example: *PX903-1KG5V voltage output pressure transducer, with 0 to 1000 PSIG range and two PS-4G snubbers for gas applications, $255 + 20 = **$275.***

B-47

RUGGED AMPLIFIED VOLTAGE TYPE PRESSURE TRANSDUCER
STAINLESS STEEL PROTECTION FOR INDUSTRIAL APPLICATIONS

510 Series
0-5 to 0-10,000 PSIG

**Shown with AD-ISS Adaptor.
See page B-27**

- ✔ **Stainless Steel Construction for Corrosion Resistance**
- ✔ **Quick Disconnect Feature**
  See Page C-4 for Mating Connectors: PT06F-10-6S
- ✔ **Broad Line of Mounting Adaptors**
  (See page B-27)

All Models $785

Fits "O" Ring #2-018

Shown actual size

VOLTAGE OUTPUT PRESSURE TRANSDUCERS

B

SPECIFICATIONS

Excitation: 12 to 20 Vdc at 30 mA max.

Output: 0 to 5 Vdc

Insulation Resistance: 1 k M ohm at 12 Vdc

Response Frequency: 3 dB @ 3 k Hz

Accuracy: ±1.0% full scale (B.F.S.L. Linearity, Hysteresis, & Repeatability)

Zero Balance: ±2% full scale

Operable Temperature Range: −50 to 200°F; (−45 to 93°C)

Compensated Temperature Range: 30 to 130°F (−1 to 55°C)

Thermal Zero Effect: ±0.02% full scale/°F (±0.04%/°C)

Thermal Sensitivity Effect: ±0.01% full scale/°F (±0.02%/°C)

Proof Pressure: 2 x full scale or 30,000 PSI whichever is less

Burst Pressure: 5 x full scale or 50,000 PSI whichever is less

Gages: Semiconductor on Bending Beam

Body/Diaphragm Material: 316 L SS ≤ 50 PSI; 15-5 PH ≥ 100 PSI

Pressure Port: Flush

Weight: 4 ozs.

Mating Connector: PT06F-10-6S (not included)

ZB-510 $75

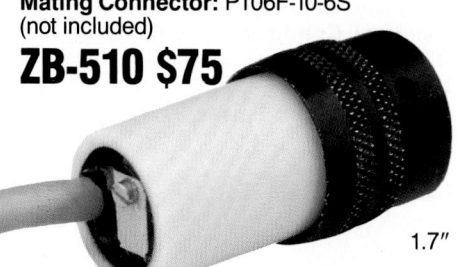

1.7"

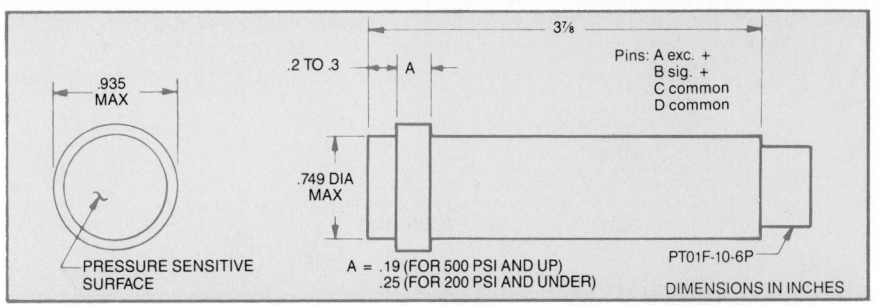

.935 MAX

.2 TO .3 — A

3⅞

Pins: A exc. +
B sig. +
C common
D common

.749 DIA MAX

PRESSURE SENSITIVE SURFACE

A = .19 (FOR 500 PSI AND UP)
.25 (FOR 200 PSI AND UNDER)

PT01F-10-6P

DIMENSIONS IN INCHES

To Order *(Specify Model Number)*

***SEE SECTION D FOR INSTRUMENT SELECTION**

RANGE	MODEL	PRICE	COMPATIBLE METER*
0- 5 PSIG	PX510-005G 5V	$785	DP41-E,DP2000P4,DP354
0- 15 PSIG	PX510-015G 5V	785	DP41-E,DP2000P5,DP354
0- 25 PSIG	PX510-025G 5V	785	DP41-E,DP2000P4,DP354
0- 50 PSIG	PX510-050G 5V	785	DP41-E,DP2000P4,DP354
0- 100 PSIG	PX510-100S 5V	785	DP41-E,DP2000P4,DP354
0- 200 PSIG	PX510-200S 5V	785	Broad-E,DP2000P5,DP354
0- 500 PSIG	PX510-500S 5V	785	DP41-E,DP2000P4,DP354
0- 1000 PSIG	PX510-1KS 5V	785	DP41-E,DP2000P4,DP354
0- 2000 PSIG	PX510-2KS 5V	785	DP41-E,DP2000P5,DP354
0- 3000 PSIG	PX510-3KS 5V	785	DP41-E,DP354,DP3002-E
0- 5000 PSIG	PX510-5KS 5V	785	DP41-E,DP354,DP3002-E
0-10000 PSIG	PX510-10KS 5V	785	DP41-E,DP354,DP3002-E

**Zero Balance Circuitry in a Mating Connector.
Adjusts Zero ±10% complete with 20" lead wire.**

See page B-27 for Flush Mount Adaptors

LOW COST CURRENT OUTPUT TYPE PRESSURE TRANSDUCER
FOR PROCESS CONTROL LOOPS

MADE IN USA

149 Series
3-15 PSID

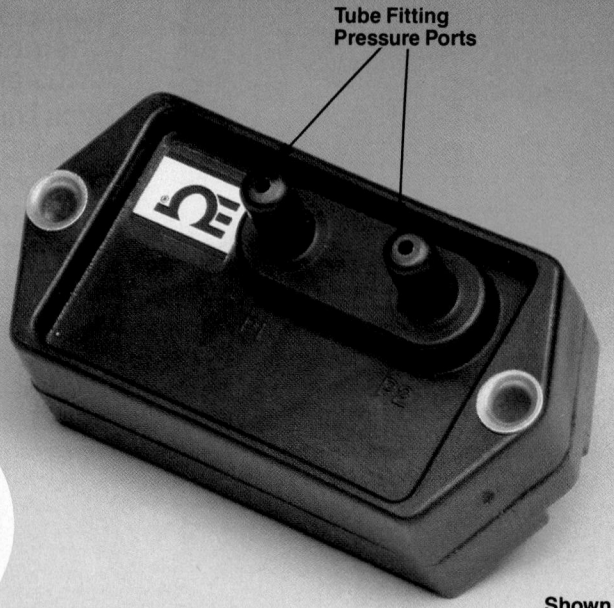

Tube Fitting Pressure Ports

Media Compatability
P1: Dry Gases only
P2: Limited only to those media which will not attack polyester, silicon, borosilicate glass, or epoxy adhesive.

$130

To Order: Specify **PX-149-015D**
(STOCKED FOR FAST DELIVERY)

- ✔ **Unidirectional Differential Pressure Measurement**
- ✔ **2-wire, 4-20 mA Current Linearity Proportional to Pressure**
- ✔ **Terminal Pins Provided for Optional External Null and F.S.O. Adjustment**
- ✔ **10-40 Vdc Input Voltage**
- ✔ **Industry Standard Pressure and Current Range**
- ✔ **Silicon Diaphragm**

Shown larger than actual size

COMPATIBLE METERS: DP2000P9, DP205-E, DPF64

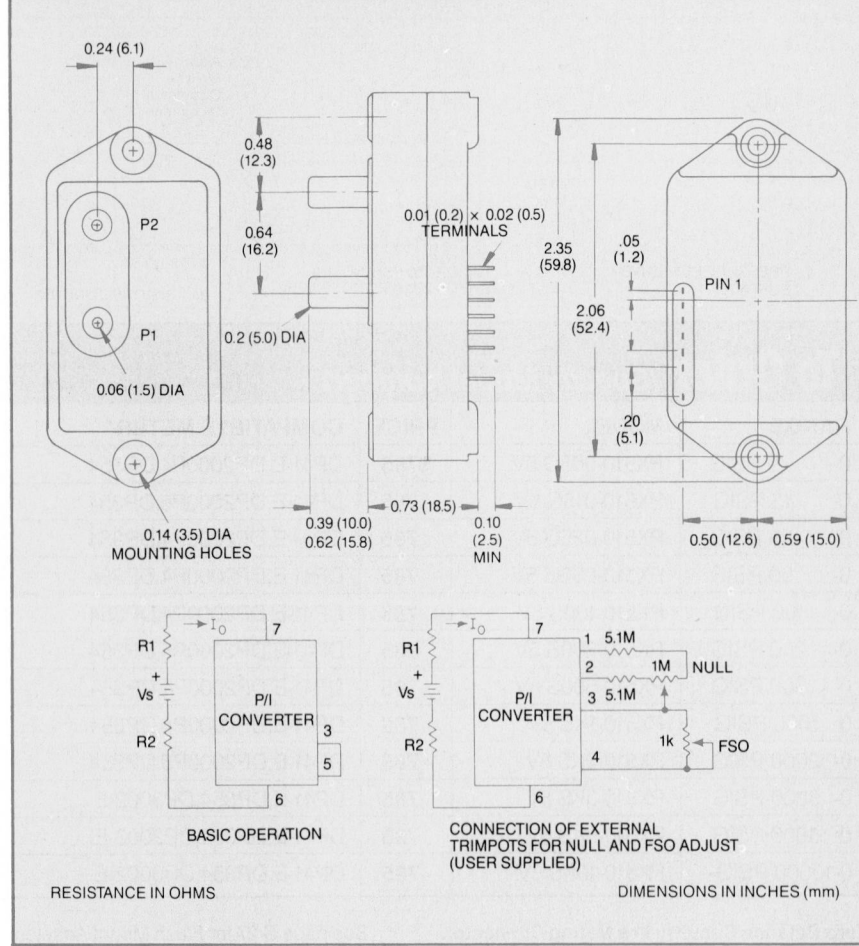

RESISTANCE IN OHMS

BASIC OPERATION

CONNECTION OF EXTERNAL TRIMPOTS FOR NULL AND FSO ADJUST (USER SUPPLIED)

DIMENSIONS IN INCHES (mm)

TUBING PAGE C-41

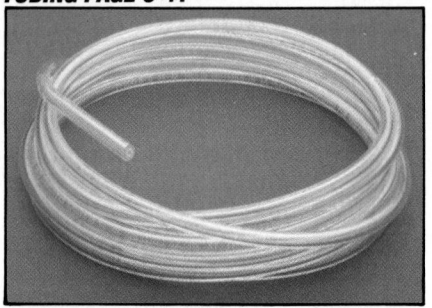

SPECIFICATIONS
Excitation: 24 Vdc (10 to 40 Vdc limit)
Output: 4 to 20 mA
PERFORMANCE
Linearity: Best Fit Straight Line ±1.5% full scale typ.; ±0.15% full scale Max.
Hysteresis & Repeatability: ±0.15% full scale
Zero Balance: Externally Adjustable
Compensated Temperature Range: 32 to 122°F (0 to 50°C)
Total Thermal Effect: ±1.0% full scale
Operable Overpressure: 50 PSI
CONSTRUCTION
Gage Type: Solid State Piezo-Resistive
Diaphragm Material: .10 Inch Square Silicon Sensor Chip
Electrical Connection: CX 136-8 Standard Spaced PC Board Terminals
Weight: 28 grams
Response Time: 1 msec
Installation: P1 > P2

COMPATIBLE METER DP 2000-P9

Absolute versions also available. Consult Sales for price and delivery.

LOW COST CURRENT OUTPUT PNEUMATIC PRESSURE TRANSMITTER
FOR GAGE PRESSURE AND VACUUM MEASUREMENT

NEW!

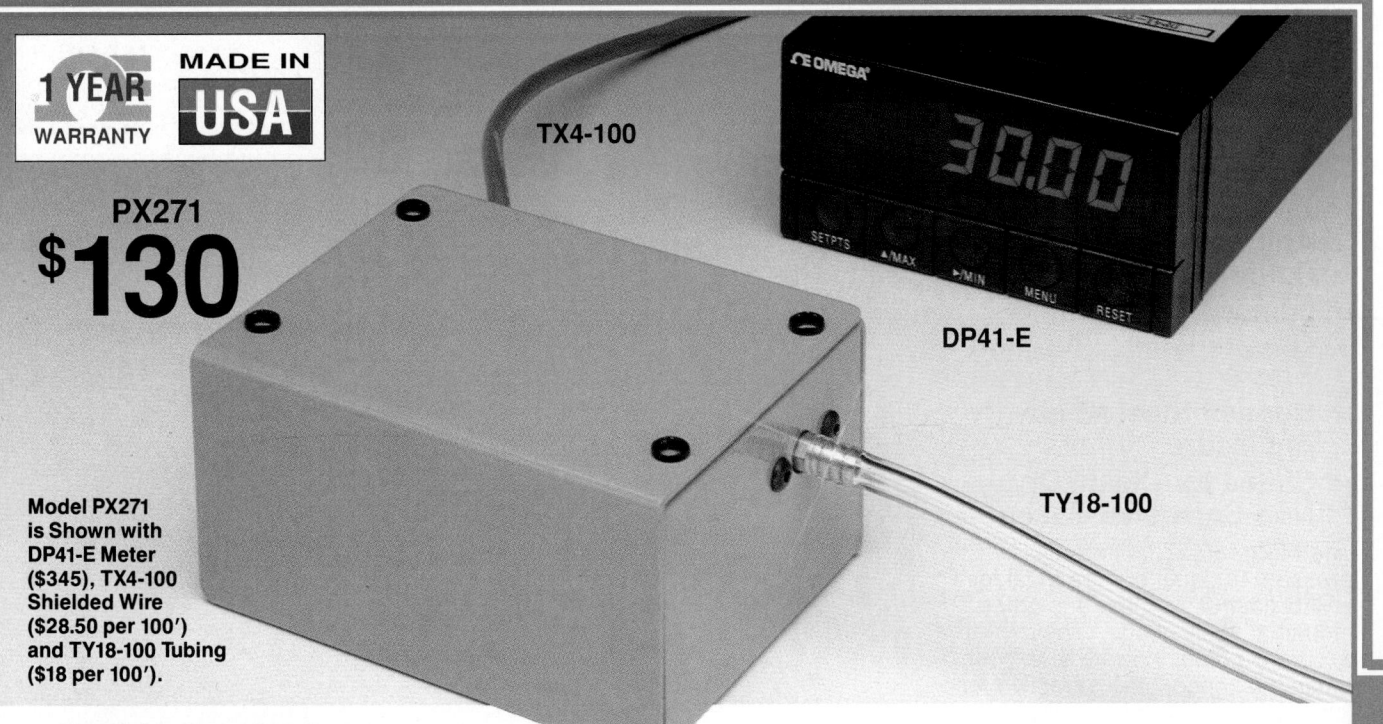

TX4-100

DP41-E

TY18-100

PX271
$130

Model PX271 is Shown with DP41-E Meter ($345), TX4-100 Shielded Wire ($28.50 per 100') and TY18-100 Tubing ($18 per 100').

- ✔ **Ideal for Monitoring Pneumatic Pressure**
- ✔ **Zero and Span Adjustment for Field Calibration**
- ✔ **Suited For Clean, Dry, Non-Corrosive Gases**
- ✔ **Rugged Steel NEMA-1 Enclosure**
- ✔ **Solid State Reliability**

The OMEGA PX271 pressure transmitter is ideal for use in pneumatic control systems and other industrial applications. The sensing element is a 100% solid state piezoresistive silicon chip featuring low hysteresis, excellent repeatability, and long term stability. The signal conditioning and temperature compensation are performed by industrial quality integrated circuits to provide an accurate, linear, 4-20 mA output that requires no additional signal conditioning.

SPECIFICATIONS

Excitation: 24 Vdc (14-28)
Output: 4-20 mA (2-wire)
Accuracy: ±1 % FS
Zero Adjustment: ±50 % FS
Span Adjustment: ±25 % FS

Operating Temp.: -20 to 150°F (-29 to 65°C)
Compensated Temp.: 32 to 125°F (0° to 50°C)
Thermal Effects:
    Zero ±0.025 % FS/°F
    Span ±0.01 % FS/°F
Proof Pressure: 40 PSIG
Burst Pressure: 100 PSIG
Max. Loop Resistance: 50 x (supply voltage -14)

Response Time: 400 ms
Media Compatibililty: Dry non-corrosive gases only
Pressure Port: ¼" hose barb
Electrical Connection: Screw terminals
Weight: 1 lb (0.45 kg)
Case: 14/16 gage steel, painted gray
Dimensions: 2" H x 3.5" W x 3" D (50 x 90 x 76 mm)

HIGHLIGHTED MODELS STOCKED FOR FAST DELIVERY!

To Order (Specify Model Number)

RANGE	MODEL	PRICE	COMPATIBLE METERS
0-20 PSIG	**PX271-020GI**	$130	DP41-E, DP302-E, DP2000-P9*
0-30 PSIG	**PX271-030GI**	130	DP41-E, DP3002-E, DP460-E
3-15 PSIG	**PX271-X15GI**	130	DP41-E, DP302-E, DP2000-P9*
±5 PSIG	**PX271-005BGI**	130	DP41-E, DP302-E, DP2000-P8*
±15PSIG	**PX271-015BGI**	130	DP41-E, DP3002-E, DP460-E
15"HG-0 VACUUM	**PX271-15VACI**	130	DP41-E, DP302-E, DP2000-P9*
30"HG-0 VACUUM	**PX271-30VACI**	130	DP41-E, DP3002-E, DP460-E

*Requires an external power supply, model U24Y101 (see page C-11).
Comes with complete operator's manual.
Ordering Example: PX271-020GI and TY18-100 is an industrial transmitter with 0 to 20 PSIG range, and 100' of flexible plastic tubing, $130 + 18 = **$148.**

ACCESSORIES

MODEL	PRICE	DESCRIPTION
TX4-100	$28.50	100 ft of 4 conductor shielded wire
TY18-100	18.00	100 ft of flexible plastic tubing

LOW PRESSURE CURRENT OUTPUT DIFFERENTIAL PRESSURE TRANSMITTER
HIGH ACCURACY AND LOW COST

- ✔ Ranges From 0-0.5" to ±25" H₂O
- ✔ Ideal for HVAC Control Systems
- ✔ Zero and Span Adjustment for Field Calibration
- ✔ Immune to Mounting Orientation or Vibration Errors
- ✔ Rugged Steel NEMA-1 Enclosure
- ✔ Suited for Clean, Dry, Non-Corrosive Gases

The Model PX272 differential pressure transmitters are ideal for HVAC control systems and other industrial applications. Their accuracy combined with their cost, make the sensor very attractive for low pressure differential or gauge pressure measurement.

The PX270-PROBE is an ideal accessory for duct pressure measurement, where air flow in the duct can affect the accuracy of the pressure measurement. The probe has two orifices, vertically opposite each other to cancel out any airflow induced errors.

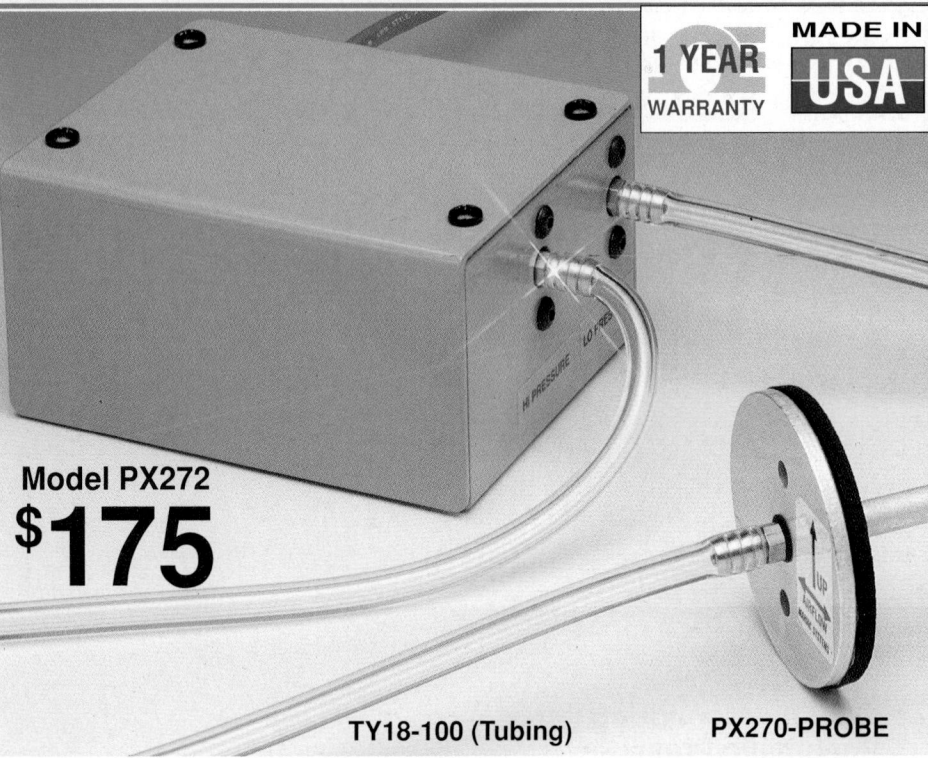

Model PX272
$175

TY18-100 (Tubing)   PX270-PROBE

1 YEAR WARRANTY   MADE IN USA

Model PX272 is Shown with PX270-PROBE Accessory ($10) and TY18-100 Tubing ($18 per 100').

HIGHLIGHTED MODELS STOCKED FOR FAST DELIVERY!

SPECIFICATIONS

Excitation: 24 Vdc (14-28)
Output: 4-20 mA
Accuracy: ±1% FS
Zero Adjustment: ±50% FS
Span Adjustment: ±25% FS
Operating Temp.: -20 to 150°F (-29 C to 65°C)
Compensated Temp.: 50 to 105°F (10 C to 40°C)
Thermal Effects:
   Zero ±0.025 FS/°F
   Span ±0.01 FS/°F
Max. Static Line Pressure: 10 PSIG
Differential Proof Pressure: 10 PSIG
Burst Pressure: 30 PSIG
Max. Loop Res.: 50 x (voltage supply -14)
Response Time: 400 ms
Media Compatibility: Dry non-corrosive gases only
Pressure Port: ¼" hose barb
Electrical Conn.: Screw terminals
Weight: 1.0 lbs (0.45 kg)
Case: 14/16 gage steel, painted gray
Dimensions: 2.5" H x 4.5" W x 4"D (63.5 x 115 x 102 mm)

To Order *(Specify Model Number)*

RANGES	MODEL	PRICE	COMPATIBLE METERS
0-0.50" H₂O	**PX272-0.5DI**	$175	DP41-E, DP302-E, DP2000-P8*
0-1" H₂O	**PX272-01DI**	175	DP41-E, DP302-E, DP2000-P8*
0-3" H₂O	**PX272-03DI**	175	DP41-E, DP3002-E, DP460-E
0-5" H₂O	**PX272-05DI**	175	DP41-E, DP3002-E, DP460-E
0-10" H₂O	**PX272-10DI**	175	DP41-E, DP302-E, DP2000-P8*
0-20" H₂O	**PX272-20DI**	175	DP41-E, DP302-E, DP2000-P8*
0-25" H₂O	**PX272-25DI**	175	DP41-E, DP3002-E, DP460-E
BI-DIRECTIONAL			
±0.25" H₂O	**PX272-0.25BDI**	$175	DP41-C, DP302-E, DP2000-P8*
±0.5" H₂O	**PX272-0.5BDI**	175	DP41-C, DP302-E, DP2000-P8*
±1" H₂O	**PX272-01BDI**	175	DP41-C, DP302-E, DP2000-P8*
±3" H₂O	**PX272-03BDI**	175	DP41-C, DP3002-E, DP460-E

Requires transducer power supply, model U24Y101 (see page C-11).
*Add suffix **-SQ** to model number for square root output option, and **$75** to price.*

ACCESSORIES

MODEL	PRICE	DESCRIPTION
PX270-PROBE	$10.00	Static Pressure Probe
TX4-100	28.50	100 ft. of 4 conductor shielded wire
TY18-100	18.00	100 ft. of flexible plastic tubing

Comes with complete operator's manual.
Ordering Example: *PX272-01DI is a low pressure transmitter with 0 to 1" H₂O range, **$175**.*

WET/WET LOW PRESSURE DIFFERENTIAL TRANSMITTER AVAILABLE IN SQUARE ROOT OUTPUT

NEW!

MADE IN USA

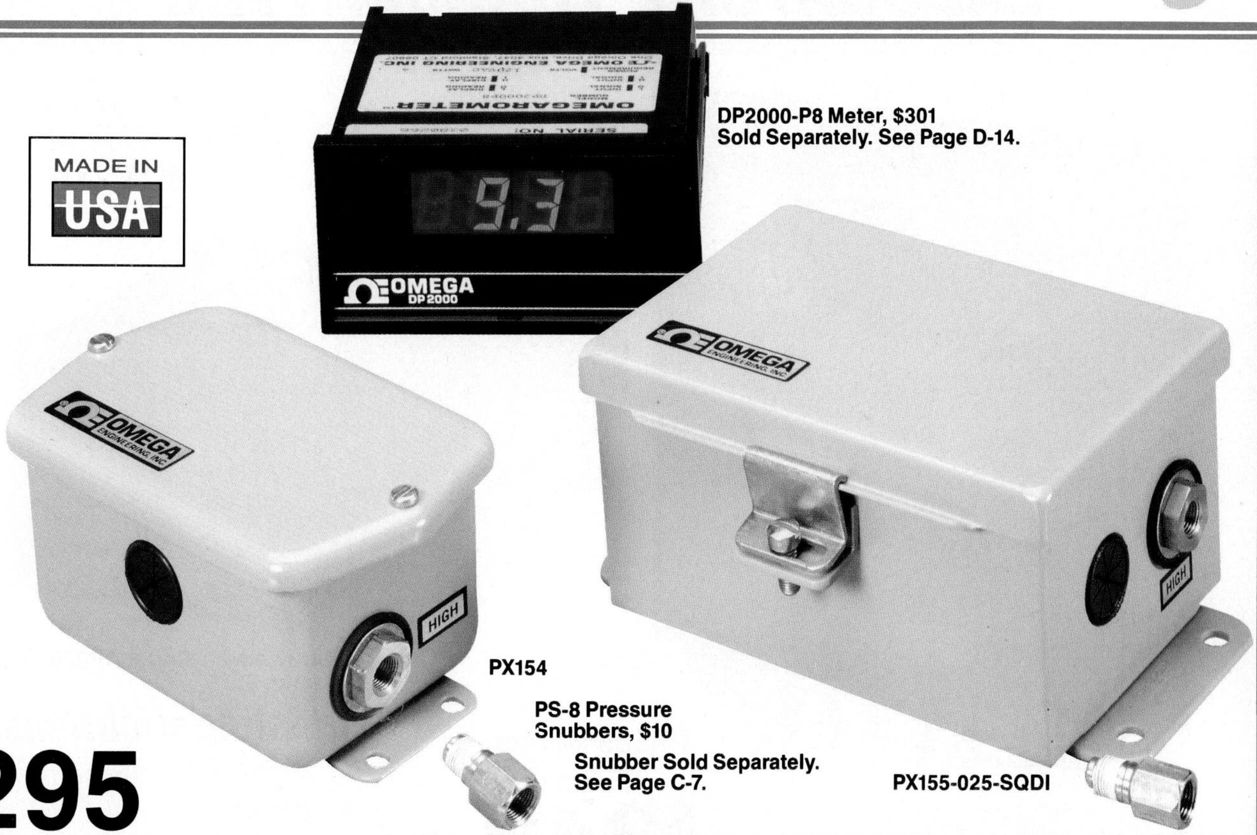

**DP2000-P8 Meter, $301
Sold Separately. See Page D-14.**

PX154

PS-8 Pressure Snubbers, $10

Snubber Sold Separately. See Page C-7.

PX155-025-SQDI

From
$295

- ✔ **Weatherproof NEMA-4 Enclosure or Electrical Conduit Enclosure**
- ✔ **Zero and Span Controls Are Provided For Easy Field Adjustment**

SPECIFICATIONS

Excitation: 24 Vdc (18 to 30 Vdc)

Output: 4 to 20 mA 2-wire
(Square Root 4-wire @ 60 mA)

Max. Loop Resistance: 400Ω @ 18 Vdc;
600Ω @ 24 Vdc, 1000Ω @ 30 Vdc

Accuracy: 1.0% FS

Linearity: .75% FS

Repeatability and Hysteresis: 0.50% FS

Zero Balance: 1%

Zero and Span Adjustment: 10%

Compensated Temperature:
32 to 122°F

Thermal Effects: zero, .05% FS/°F;
span, .05%RDG/°F

Proof Pressure: 20 PSI

Common Line Pressure: 60 PSI

Pressure Port: 1/8" NPTF

Media Compatibility: Liquids or gases
compatible with brass, vinyl, polyester,
silica, and florosilicon

Case: Gasketed steel epoxy painted

Electrical Connections: Screw terminals

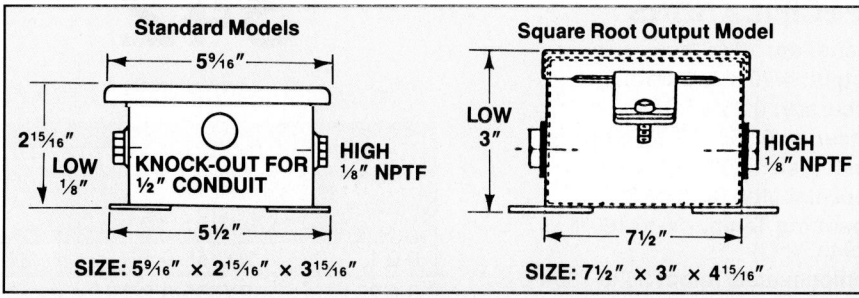

Standard Models

5⁹⁄₁₆"
2¹⁵⁄₁₆"
LOW ⅛"
KNOCK-OUT FOR ½" CONDUIT
HIGH ⅛" NPTF
5½"

SIZE: 5⁹⁄₁₆" × 2¹⁵⁄₁₆" × 3¹⁵⁄₁₆"

Square Root Output Model

LOW 3"
HIGH ⅛" NPTF
7½"

SIZE: 7½" × 3" × 4¹⁵⁄₁₆"

To Order *(Specify Model Number)* *HIGHLIGHTED MODELS STOCKED FOR FAST DELIVERY!*

Range Inches of H₂O	Model No.	Price	Compatible Meters
0 to 1"	**PX154-001DI**	$295	DP2000-P8*, DP460-E, DP3002-E
0 to 3"	**PX154-003DI**	295	DP2000-P8*, DP460-E, DP3002-E
0 to 5"	**PX154-005DI**	295	DP2000-P8*, DP460-E, DP3002-E
0 to 10"	**PX154-010DI**	295	DP2000-P8*, DP460-E, DP3002-E
0 to 25"	**PX154-025DI**	295	DP2000-P8*, DP460-E, DP3002-E
Square Root Output Transmitters			
0 to 1"	**PX155-001SQDI**	$505	DP2000-P8*, DP460-E, DP3600*
0 to 3"	**PX155-003SQDI**	505	DP2000-P8*, DP460-E, DP100-R8*
0 to 5"	**PX155-005SQDI**	505	DP2000-P8*, DP460-E, DP3600*
0 to 10"	**PX155-010SQDI**	505	DP2000-P8*, DP460-E, DP100-R8*
0 to 25"	**PX155-025SQDI**	505	DP2000-P8*, DP460-E, DP3600*

Comes with complete operator's manual.
*Transducer power supply U24Y101 (not shown) required to complete system. Pressure snubbers PS-8G (gas), PS-8E (liquids), or PS-8D (dense liquids) should be installed on transmitters, $10 each.

Ordering Example: *PX154-005DI transmitter (0-5" H₂O range) plus U24Y101 power supply, plus two PS-8G pressure snubbers (gas), plus DP2000-P8 indicator, $295 + 99 + 20 + 301 = $715.*

NEW! HIGHLY ACCURATE, LOW PRESSURE LABORATORY TRANSMITTER

Shown with Model DP3002-E Meter, $271.

PX655 Series
From
$342

Ideal Applications:
- ✔ Clean Rooms
- ✔ HVAC
- ✔ Fume Hoods
- ✔ Laboratory Monitoring

SPECIFICATIONS

Excitation: 12-36 Vdc
Output: 4-20 mA (2 wire)
Accuracy: 0.25% FS
Linearity: 0.25% FS (BFSL)
Hysteresis: 0.02% FS
Repeatability: 0.05% FS
Operating Temp: -20 to 160°F (-29 to 72°C)
Compensated Temp: 35 to 135°F (2 to 57°C)
Thermal Effects:
Zero 0.015% FS/°F
Span 0.015% Rdg/°F
Proof Pressure: 10 PSI
Burst Pressure: 50 PSI
Static Pressure: 10 PSI
Gage Type: Capacitance
Max Loop Resistance:
(supply voltage-12) x 50 ohms
Calibration Report: NIST cal at 25, 50, 75 and 100% upscale and downscale provided
Response Time: 250 msec
Wetted Parts: Dry, clean non-corrosive gases only
Enclosure: NEMA 2; 4.2"H x 4.6"W x 2.1"D (107 x 117 x 53 mm)
Pressure Port: ⅛ and ¼ barbed fittings (tubing TY-316-100)
Electrical Conn.: Screw terminal (PX656 two ½ NPTF conduit)
Weight: 13 oz (368 g)

HIGHLIGHTED MODELS IN STOCK FOR FAST DELIVERY!

To Order (Specify Model Number)

RANGE Inches H_2O	MODEL	PRICE	COMPATIBLE METER
0-0.1	PX655-0.1DI	$444	DP205-E, DP41-E, DP460-E
0-0.25	PX655-0.25DI	392	DP205-E, DP41-E, DP460-E
0-0.50	PX655-0.5DI	342	DP205-E, DP41-E, DP460-E
0-1	PX655-01DI	342	DP205-E, DP41-E, DP3002-E
0-2	PX655-02DI	342	DP205-E, DP41-E, DP460-E
0-3	PX655-03DI	342	DP205-E, DP41-E, DP460-E
0-5	PX655-05DI	342	DP205-E, DP41-E, DP460-E
0-10	PX655-10DI	342	DP205-E, DP41-E, DP3002-E
0-25	PX655-25DI	342	DP205-E, DP41-E, DP460-E
BI-DIRECTIONAL RANGES			
±0.25	PX655-0.25BDI	$342	DP205-E, DP41-E, DP460-E
±0.50	PX655-0.50BDI	342	DP205-E, DP41-E, DP460-E
±1	PX655-01BDI	342	DP205-E, DP41-E, DP460-E
±2.5	PX655-2.5BDI	342	DP205-E, DP41-E, DP460-E
±5	PX655-05BDI	342	DP205-E, DP41-E, DP460-E
±10	PX655-10BDI	342	DP205-E, DP41-E, DP460-E
±25	PX655-25BDI	342	DP205-E, DP41-E, DP460-E

Comes with complete operator's manual.
Ordering Example: *PX655-01DI is a low pressure, laboratory transmitter, **$342**.*

HIGHLY ACCURATE, LOW PRESSURE INDUSTRIAL TRANSMITTER

 **NEW!**

PX656 Series
From
$528

Ideal Applications:
✔ **Boiler Inlet Air**
✔ **HVAC**
✔ **Industrial Fume Hoods**
✔ **Level Control**

SPECIFICATIONS

Excitation: 12-36 Vdc
Output: 4-20 mA (2 wire)
Accuracy: 0.25% FS
Linearity: 0.25% FS (BFSL)
Hysteresis: 0.02% FS
Repeatability: 0.05% FS
Operating Temp: -20 to 185°F
(-29 to 85°C)
Compensated Temp.: 0 to 160°F
(-18 to 72°C)
Thermal Effects:
Zero 0.015% FS/°F
Span 0.015% FS/°F
Proof Pressure: 10 PSI
Burst Pressure: 50 PSI
Static Pressure: 100 PSI
Gage Type: Capacitance
Max Loop Resistance:
(supply voltage-12) x 50 ohms
Calibration Report: NIST cal. at 25, 50, 75 and 100% upscale and down scale provided
Response Time: 250 msec
Wetted Parts: Dry, clean non-corrosive gases only
Enclosure: NEMA 4X; 5"L x 3"W x 2.5"D (127 x76 x 64 mm)
Pressure Port: ¼ NPTF
Electrical Conn.: Screw terminal (two ½ NPTF conduit)
Weight: 2.1 lbs (955 g)

HIGHLIGHTED MODELS IN STOCK FOR FAST DELIVERY!

To Order *(Specify Model Number)*

RANGE Inches H₂O	MODEL	PRICE	COMPATIBLE METER
0-0.1	PX656-0.1DI	$630	DP205-E, DP41-E, DP460-E
0-0.25	PX656-0.25DI	578	DP205-E, DP41-E, DP460-E
0-0.5	PX656-0.5DI	528	DP205-E, DP41-E, DP460-E
0-1	PX656-01DI	528	DP205-E, DP41-E, DP3002-E
0-2	PX656-02DI	528	DP205-E, DP41-E, DP460-E
0-3	PX656-03DI	528	DP205-E, DP41-E, DP460-E
0-5	PX656-05DI	528	DP205-E, DP41-E, DP460-E
0-10	PX656-10DI	528	DP205-E, DP41-E, DP3002-E
0-25	PX656-25DI	528	DP205-E, DP41-E, DP460-E
0-50	PX656-50DI	528	DP205-E, DP41-E, DP460-E
BI-DIRECTIONAL RANGES			
± 0.05	PX656-0.05BDI	$630	DP205-E, DP41-E, DP460-E
± 0.25	PX656-0.25BDI	528	DP205-E, DP41-E, DP460-E
± 50	PX656-0.50BDI	528	DP205-E, DP41-E, DP460-E
±1	PX656-01BDI	528	DP205-E, DP41-E, DP460-E
± 2.5	PX656-2.5BDI	528	DP205-E, DP41-E, DP460-E
±5	PX656-05BDI	528	DP205-E, DP41-E, DP460-E
±10	PX656-10BDI	528	DP205-E, DP41-E, DP460-E
± 25	PX656-25BDI	528	DP205-E, DP41-E, DP460-E

Comes with complete operator's manual.
Ordering Example: *PX656-01DI is a low pressure transmitter, **$528**.*

WET/WET CURRENT OUTPUT DIFFERENTIAL PRESSURE TRANSMITTER
ALL STAINLESS STEEL WETTED PARTS

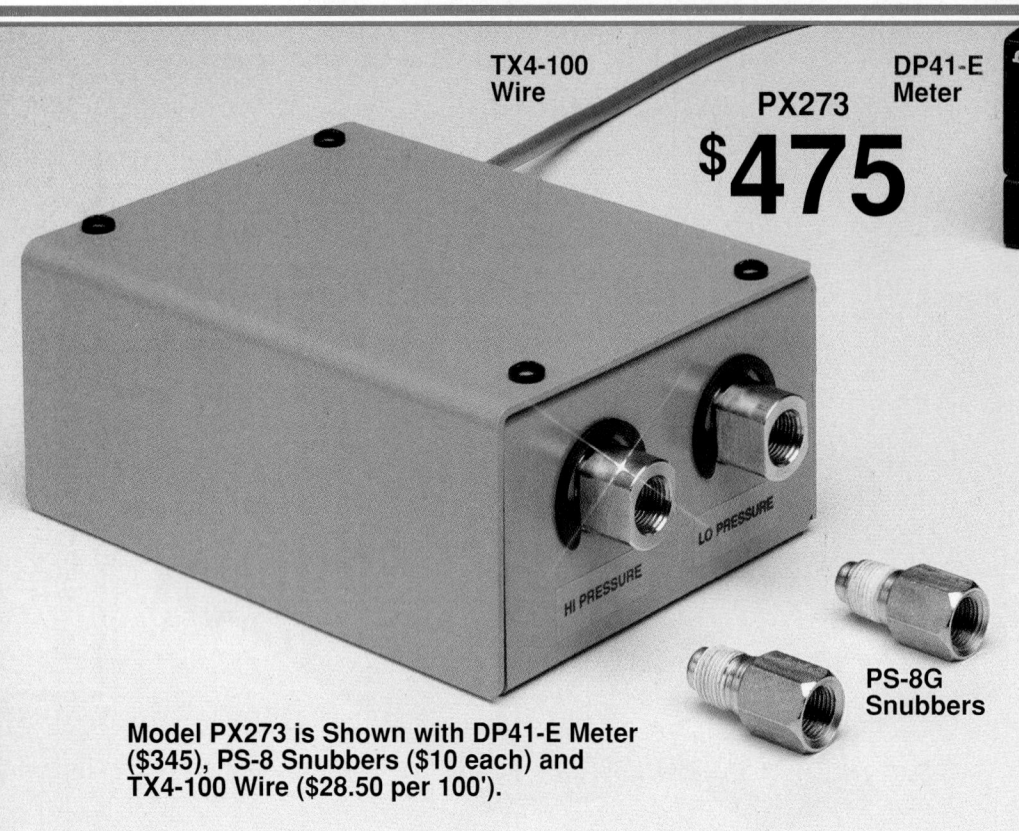

TX4-100 Wire

PX273

$475

DP41-E Meter

30.00

SETPTS ▲/MAX ▶/MIN MENU RESET

1 YEAR WARRANTY · **MADE IN USA**

Model PX273 is Shown with DP41-E Meter ($345), PS-8 Snubbers ($10 each) and TX4-100 Wire ($28.50 per 100').

PS-8G Snubbers

✔ **Liquids Can Be Applied to Both Ports**
✔ **Zero And Span Adjustments for Field Calibration**
✔ **Immune to Mounting Orientation or Vibration Errors**
✔ **Rugged Steel NEMA-1 Enclosure**
✔ **Solid State Reliability**

The OMEGA PX273 is an all stainless steel wet/wet differential pressure transmitter, incorporating dual diffused piezoresistive sensing elements with stainless steel media isolation. The unit is compatible to all media encountered in industrial applications including freon, ammonia, treated water and steam. The PX273 is ideal for monitoring and controlling pump differential pressure, CW/HW system differential pressure, chiller/boiler differential pressure drop and many other industrial applications.

SPECIFICATIONS

Excitation: 24 Vdc
Output: 4-20 mA
Accuracy: ±0.75 % FS
Zero Adjustment: ±50 % FS
Span Adjustment: ±25 % FS
Operating Temp.: 0 to 180°F (−18 to 82°C)
Compensated Temp.: 0 to 150°F (−18 to 65°C)
Thermal Effects:
　Zero ±0.025% FS/°F
　Span ±0.01 % FS/°F
Max Static Pressure: 100 %FS (each port)

Proof Pressure: 200 % FS (each port)
Burst Pressure: 500 %FS
Max. Loop Res.: 50 x (Voltage supply -14)
Response Time: 400 ms
Gage Type: Chemical vapor deposition
Wetted Parts: 316 stainless steel
Pressure Port: ⅛" NPTF

Electrical Conn.: Screw terminals
Weight: 1.5 lb (.68 kg)
Case: 16 gage steel
Dimensions: 2" H x 5" W x 3.5"D (51 x 127 x 89 mm)

HIGHLIGHTED MODELS STOCKED FOR FAST DELIVERY!

TO ORDER (Specify Model Number)

RANGE	MODEL NO.	PRICE	COMPATIBLE METERS
0-20 PSID	**PX273-020DI**	**$475**	DP41-E, DP302-E, DP2000-P9*
0-30 PSID	**PX273-030DI**	475	DP41-E, DP3002-E, DP460-V
0-50 PSID	**PX273-050DI**	475	DP41-E, DP3002-E, DP460-V
0-100 PSID	**PX273-100DI**	475	DP41-E, DP302-E, DP2000-P8*
0-200 PSID	**PX273-200DI**	475	DP41-E, DP302-E, DP2000-P8*
0-300 PSID	**PX273-300DI**	475	DP41-E, DP3002-E, DP460-V

Requires an external power supply, model U24Y101 (see page C-11).

ACCESSORIES

MODEL	PRICE	DESCRIPTION
TX4-100	**$28.50**	100 ft. of 4 conductor shielded wire
PS-8G	10.00	Pressure snubber for gaseous media
PS-8E	10.00	Pressure snubber for liquids and light oils
PS-8D	10.00	Pressure snubber for dense liquids (motor oils)

Comes with complete operator's manual.
Ordering Example: *PX273-020D1 wet/wet differential transmitter with a 0 to 20 PSID range, two PS-8 snubbers and TX4-100 shielded wire, $475 + 20+ 28.50 = **$523.50.***

ECONOMICAL CORROSION RESISTANT PRESSURE TRANSDUCER WITH CURRENT OUTPUT

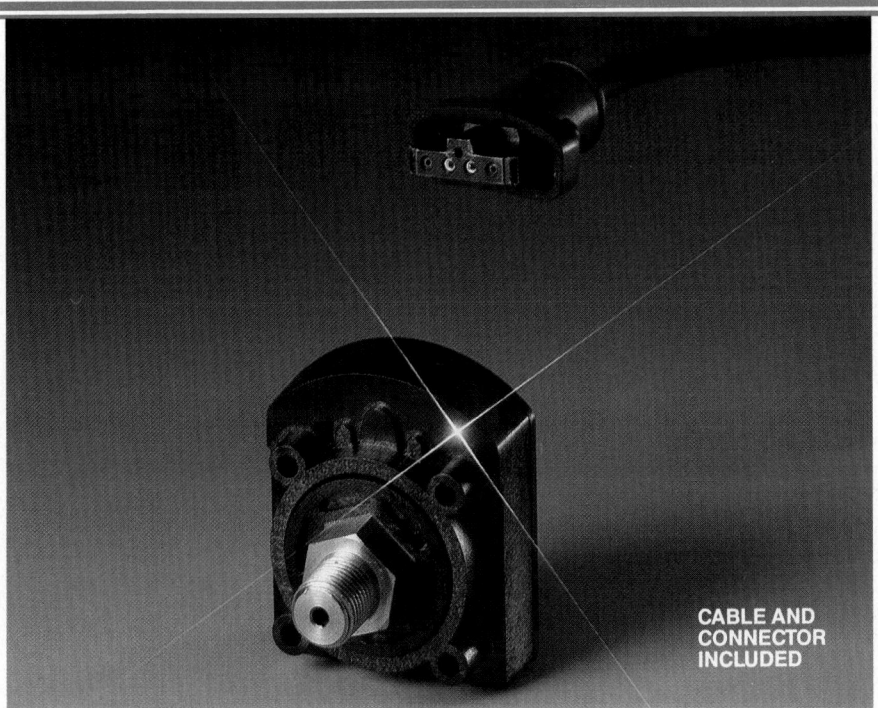

CABLE AND CONNECTOR INCLUDED

PX182 Series
$198

- ✓ Stainless Steel Pressure Port for Wide Media Compatibility
- ✓ Assured 0.3% Accuracy
- ✓ Corrosion Resistant Housing Permits Mounting In Any Environment
- ✓ Operating Temperature Range −55 to 105°C
- ✓ Extremely Compact, Weighs Only 50 Grams

The OMEGA PX182 Series pressure transducers combine state-of-the-art semiconductor technology and durability resulting in a high accuracy general purpose pressure sensor. The 4 to 20 mA output assures compatibility with most process controllers and computer interface equipment. Applications include engine monitoring and testing, HVAC, compressors, etc. The silicon sensor is bonded on a glass pedestal to isolate it from induced stresses, provide wide media compatibility, and the stainless steel pressure port permits use with corrosive substances. These rugged, compact transducers exhibit 0.3% accuracy and excellent interchangeability.

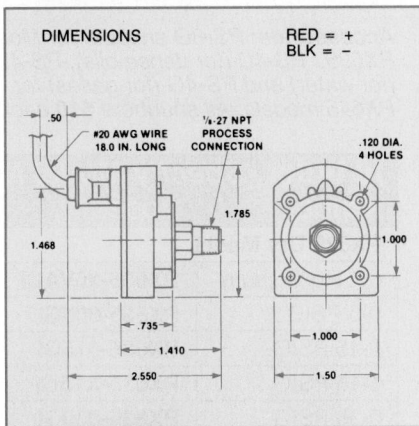

DIMENSIONS

RED = +
BLK = −

MADE IN

USA

HIGHLIGHTED MODELS STOCKED FOR FAST DELIVERY

To Order (Specify Model Number)

RANGE	MODEL	PRICE	COMPATIBLE METER
0 to 15 PSIG	PX182-015GI	$198	DP2000-P9*, DP205-E, DP103-R8
0 to 30 PSIG	PX182-030GI	198	DP2000-P8*, DP205-E, DP41-E
0 to 60 PSIG	PX182-060GI	198	DP2000-P8*, DP205-E, DP41-E
0 to 100 PSIG	PX182-100GI	198	DP2000-P8*, DP205-E, DP103-R8
0 to 200 PSIG	PX182-200GI	198	DP2000-P9*, DP205-E, DP103-R8
0 to 300 PSIG	PX182-300GI	198	DP2000-P8*, DP205-E, DP3002-E
0 to 500 PSIG	PX182-500GI	198	DP2000-P8*, DP205-E, DP3002-E

*Requires transducer power supply U24Y101, $99.
All models come with complete operator's manual.
Ordering Example: PX182-200GI is a 0-200 PSIG current output transducer, $198.

SPECIFICATIONS

Excitation: 12 to 25 Vdc
Output: 4 to 20 mA (2-wire)
Accuracy: ±0.3% BFSL includes linearity, repeatability, and hysteresis
Zero Balance: ±1% span
Operable Temperature Range: −55 to 105°C
Compensated Temperature Range: −25 to 75°C
Thermal Zero Effect: ±0.5% span
Thermal Span Effect: ±0.5% span
Proof Pressure: 2 x FS (750 PSI max)
Burst Pressure: 3 x FS (750 PSI max)
Max. Loop Resistance: 50 $(V_S$-12)
Gages: laser trimmed semiconductor
Wetted Parts: Stainless steel, glass, silicon, Flurosilicon
Pressure Port: 1/8-27 stainless steel fitting
Stability: ±1% full scale output/year
Shock: 500G
Vibration: 10G, 10 to 2000 Hz
Electrical Connection: 12" 20 AWG, 3 conductor shielded wire with self sealing connector
Weight: 50 grams

NEW! CURRENT OUTPUT PRESSURE TRANSDUCERS
FOR DRY AND WET APPLICATIONS

1 YEAR WARRANTY

MADE IN USA

PX635 and PX645 Series From $155

- ✔ PX665 for Dry Gas Media
- ✔ PX645 for Accurate Liquid or Gaseous Media

Models PX635 Series and PX645 Series Transducers are Shown With a DP41-E Meter ($345) and PS-4 and PS-8 Snubbers ($10 each).

SPECIFICATIONS

Excitation: 10-32 Vdc

Output: 4-20 mA (2 wire)

Accuracy: PX635 0.5% FS, (linearity, hysteresis and repeatability); PX645 0.25% FS (linearity 0.25% FS, hysteresis 0.1% FS, Rep .05% FS)

Zero Balance: 1% FS

Operating Temp.: -20 to 160°F (-29 to 72°C)

Compensated Temp.: PX635 0 to 160°F (-18 to 72°C); PX645 -20 to 160°F (-29 to 72°C)

Thermal Effects: Zero 0.02% FS/°F Span 0.02% Rdg/°F

Proof Pressure: 200% FS

Burst Pressure: 300% FS

Max. Loop Resistance: (voltage supply-10) x 50 ohms

Gage Type: PX635 diffused silicon; PX645 SS diaphragm oil filled

Wetted Parts: PX635 clean dry gases; PX645 316L SS

Pressure Port: PX635 ⅛ NPT; PX645 ¼ NPT

Electrical Conn.: 24 awg, PVC, shielded, 36" vented pigtail

Size: PX635 1.7" long x 1.5" dia. (43 x 38 mm); PX645 4.5"L x 2" dia. (114 x 56 mm)

Enclosure: NEMA 4

Weight: PX635 5 oz. (141 g); PX645 7 oz. (198 g)

Accessories: PS-8G snubber for Model PX635. PS-4D (for dense oils), PS-4E (for water) and PS-4G (for gases) for PX645 models. All snubbers **$10** each.

HIGHLIGHTED MODELS STOCKED FOR FAST DELIVERY!

To Order *(Specify Model Number)*

RANGE	MODEL	PRICE	COMPATIBLE METER
PX635 Dry Media			
30" Hg Vacuum	PX635-30VACI	$178	DP205-E, DP3002-E, DP460-E
0-5 PSIG	PX635-005GI	178	DP205-E, DP3002-E, DP460-E
0-15 PSIG	PX635-015GI	178	DP205-E, DP302-E, DP460-E
3-15 PSIG	PX635-X15GI	197	DP205-E, DP302-E, DP460-E
0-30 PSIG	PX635-030GI	178	DP205-E, DP3002-E, DP460-E
0-50 PSIG	PX635-050GI	155	DP205-E, DP3002-E, DP460-E
0-100 PSIG	PX635-100GI	155	DP205-E, DP302-E, DP460-E
0-200 PSIG	PX635-200GI	155	DP205-E, DP302-E, DP460-E
0-300 PSIG	PX635-300GI	155	DP205-E, DP3002-E, DP460-E
PX645 Wet or Dry Media			
0-15 PSIG	PX645-015GI	$324	DP205-E, DP302-E, DP460-E
0-30 PSIG	PX645-030GI	324	DP205-E, DP3002-E, DP460-E
0-50 PSIG	PX645-050GI	324	DP205-E, DP3002-E, DP460-E
0-100 PSIG	PX645-100GI	324	DP205-E, DP302-E, DP460-E
0-200 PSIG	PX645-200GI	324	DP205-E, DP302-E, DP460-E
0-300 PSIG	PX645-300GI	324	DP205-E, DP3002-E, DP460-E
0-500 PSIG	PX645-500GI	324	DP205-E, DP3002-E, DP460-E

All models come with a complete operator's manual.
Ordering Example: PX635-X15GI and PS-8G, is a P/I pneumatic transmitter and snubber for gas media, $197 + 10=**$207.**

COMPACT STAINLESS STEEL 4 to 20 mA PRESSURE TRANSMITTER

410 Series
0-15 to 0-500 PSI

$390

- **Well Suited for Corrosive Media**
- **Rugged All Stainless Steel Construction**
- **½″ NPT Conduit Wire Port**
- **Reverse Supply Voltage Protection**
- **Ideal for Monitoring Remote Applications**

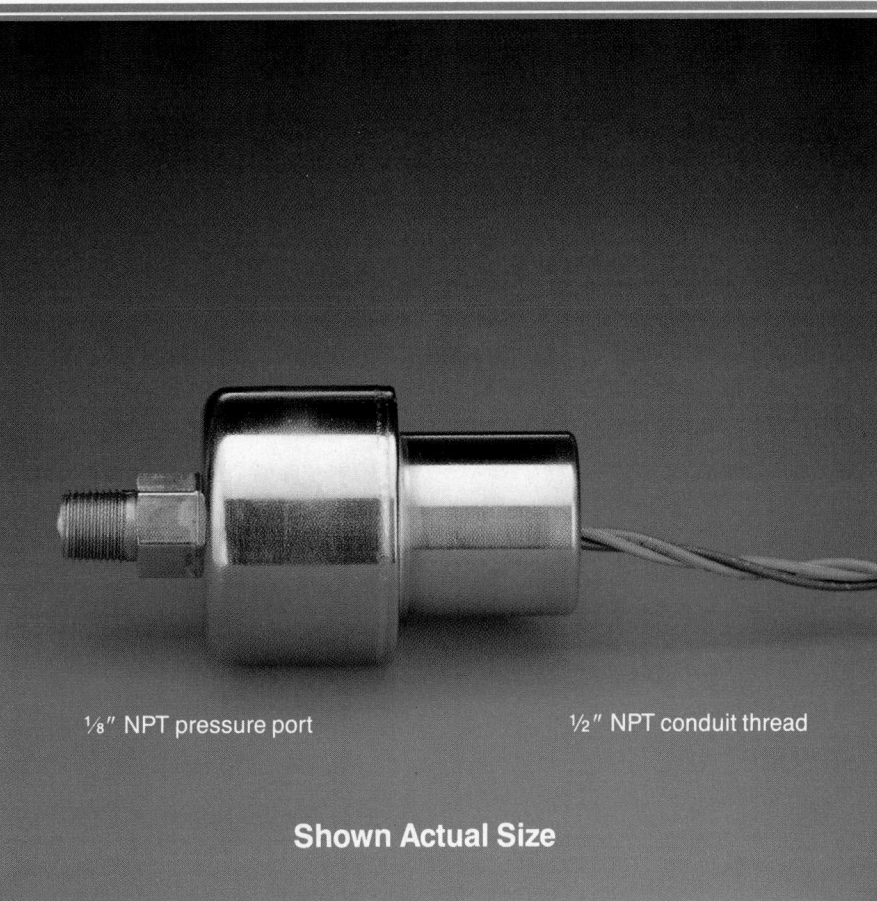

⅛″ NPT pressure port   ½″ NPT conduit thread

Shown Actual Size

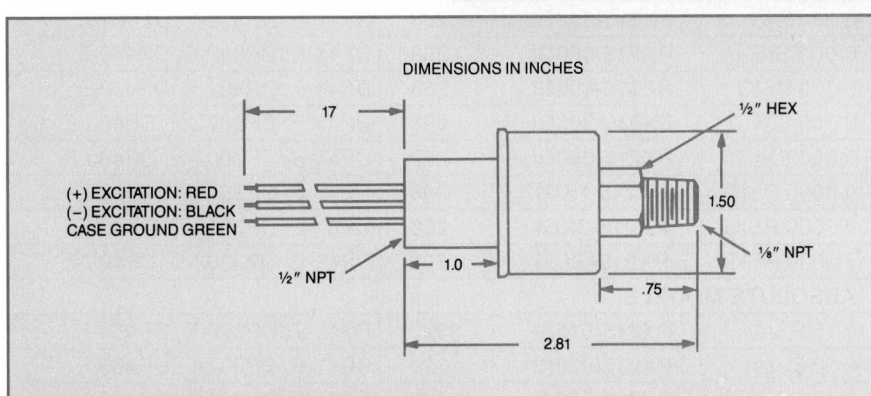

DIMENSIONS IN INCHES

(+) EXCITATION: RED
(–) EXCITATION: BLACK
CASE GROUND GREEN

17   ½″ HEX   1.50   ⅛″ NPT   ½″ NPT   1.0   .75   2.81

To Order (Specify Model Number)

SEE SECTION D FOR INSTRUMENT SELECTION

RANGE	MODEL	PRICE	COMPATIBLE METER
0 to 15 PSIG	PX410-015GI	$390	DP2000P9, DP3002-E, TX81
0 to 25 PSIG	PX410-025GI	390	DP2000P8, DP3002-E, TX81
0 to 50 PSIG	PX410-050GI	390	DP2000P8, DP3002-E, TX81
0 to 100 PSIS*	PX410-100SI	390	DP2000P8, DP3002-E, TX81
0 to 200 PSIS*	PX410-200SI	390	DP2000P9, DP3002-E, TX81
0 to 500 PSIS*	PX410-500SI	390	DP2000P8, DP3002-E, TX81

* Measured with respect to a standard atmosphere (14.7 PSIA)

◀ **HIGHLIGHTED MODELS STOCKED FOR FAST DELIVERY** ◀

SPECIFICATIONS:

Excitation: 12 to 45 V dc (linear derating to 35 V dc from 77°F to 212°F

Output: 4 to 20 mA

Insulation Resistance: 1000 M ohm @ 50 V dc

Accuracy: 1% BFSL (includes non-linearity, repeatability, and hysteresis)

Zero Balance: $\pm$0.4 mA

Operable Temperature Range: 0 to 212°F (−18 to 100°C)

Compensated Temperature Range: 30 to 150°F (−1 to 55°C)

Thermal Zero Effect: Within $\pm$1% of full scale over Comp. Temp. Range

Thermal Span Effect: Within $\pm$1% of reading over Comp. Temp. Range

Proof Pressure: 2 x rated pressure (750 psi max.)

Burst Pressure: 10 x rated pressure (2500 psi max.)

Body/Diaphragm Material: Brazed Assembly of 300 series Stainless Steel

Shock: 50 G's; 2.5 mS

Vibration: 20.7 G's rms, 20-2000 Hz

Pressure Port: 1/8″ NPT

Wire Port: 1/2″ NPT

Weight: 6 oz.

THIN FILM 4-20 mA OUTPUT PRESSURE TRANSMITTER
FOR GAGE AND ABSOLUTE PRESSURES

3 YEAR WARRANTY

Shown With DP41-E Meter ($395), PS-4 Snubber ($10) and TX4-100 Shielded Wire ($28.50 per 100').

✔ **All Stainless Steel Wetted Parts**
✔ **NEMA 4 Rated**
✔ **CVD Construction for High Stability**

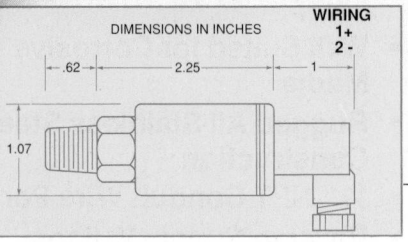

SPECIFICATIONS

Excitation: 24Vdc (12-36 Vdc) reverse polarity protected
Output: 4-20 mA (2 wire)
Accuracy: 0.25% (including linearity, hysteresis and repeatability)
Zero Balance: 2% FS
Span Tolerance: 1% FS
Max Loop Resistance: 50 x (supply voltage -12) ohms
Operating Temperature: -4 to 248°F (-20 to 120°C)
Compensated Temperature: -4 to 176°F (-20 to 80°C)
Thermal Effects: 1.5% FS over -20 to 80°C
Proof Pressure: 150%
Burst Pressure: 400%, 17000 PSI max
Response Time: 1 ms
Gage Type: Chemical vapor deposited polysilicon strain gages
Wetted Parts: 15-7,17-4 SS, <60 PSI 17-4 SS ≥60 PSI
Pressure Port: 1/4-18 NPT
Electrical Connection: Miniature DIN connector; screw terminals
Weight: 3.5 oz. (100 g)

HIGHLIGHTED MODELS STOCKED FOR FAST DELIVERY!

To Order (Specify Model Number)

RANGE	MODEL	PRICE	COMPATIBLE METERS
GAGE MODELS			
0-15 PSIG	PX215-015GI	$268	DP41-E, DP302-E, DP460-E
0-30 PSIG	PX215-030GI	268	DP41-E, DP302-E, DP460-E
0-60 PSIG	PX215-060GI	268	DP41-E, DP302-E, DP460-E
0-100 PSIG	PX215-100GI	268	DP41-E, DP302-E, DP460-E
0-300 PSIG	PX215-300GI	268	DP41-E, DP3002-E, DP460-E
0-600 PSIG	PX215-600GI	268	DP41-E, DP3002-E, DP460-E
0-1000 PSIG	PX215-1KGI	268	DP41-E, DP302-E, DP460-E
0-3000 PSIG	PX215-3KGI	268	DP41-E, DP3002-E, DP460-E
0-6000 PSIG	PX215-6KGI	268	DP41-E, DP3002-E, DP460-E
ABSOLUTE MODELS			
0-15 PSIA	PX215-015AI	$320	DP41-E, DP302-E, DP460-E
0-30 PSIA	PX215-030AI	320	DP41-E, DP302-E, DP460-E
0-60 PSIA	PX215-060AI	320	DP41-E, DP302-E, DP460-E
0-100 PSIA	PX215-100AI	320	DP41-E, DP302-E, DP460-E
0-150 PSIA	PX215-150AI	320	DP41-E, DP302-E, DP460-E
0-300 PSIA	PX215-300AI	320	DP41-E, DP3002-E, DP460-E

ACCESSORIES

MODEL	PRICE	DESCRIPTION
PS-4G	$10	Pressure snubber for gaseous media
PS-4E	10	Pressure snubber for water and light oils
PS-4D	10	Pressure snubber for dense liquids (motor oil)

Comes with complete operator's manual.
Ordering Example: *PX215-015AI, is an absolute 4 to 20 mA output transmitter with 0-15 PSIA range, and two PS-4G snubbers, $320 + 20 =* **$340.**

GENERAL PURPOSE CURRENT OUTPUT PRESSURE TRANSMITTER
AVAILABLE IN ABSOLUTE AND GAGE MODELS

NEW!

3 YEAR WARRANTY

MADE IN USA

NIST

PX305 Series From
$255

✔ **All Stainless Steel Wetted Parts**
✔ **Integral Strain Relief for Cable**
✔ **0.25% Full Scale Accuracy**

Shown with DP41-E Meter ($345) and PS-4 Snubber ($10). Meter and Snubber Sold Separately.

WIRING
RED +
BLACK -
1.125
5.438
DIMENSIONS IN INCHES

HIGHLIGHTED MODELS IN STOCK FOR FAST DELIVERY!

SPECIFICATIONS

Output: 4-20 mA (2 wire reverse polarity protected)
Accuracy: 0.25%FS (linearity, hysteresis, repeatability)
Zero Balance: ±2 %FS
Span: 16 mA ±1%FS
Max Loop Res.:
50 x (supply voltage-12) ohms
Operating Temp.: 0 to 160°F (-18 to 71°C)
Compensated Temp.: 30 to 130°F (-1 to 54°C)
Total Thermal Effects: 1% FS max
Proof Pressure: 200%, 13000 PSI max
Response Time: 1 msec
Gage Type: Stainless steel diaphragm, silicone oil filled semiconductor sensor
Shock: 50 g @ 11msec
Wetted Parts: 300 SS series (SS and viton ≥2000 PSI)
Pressure Port: ¼" NPT
Press. Cavity: 0.075 cubic inches
Electrical Conn.: 2 cond, 22 awg, PVC unshielded, 3 ft pigtail cable
Weight: 5.9 oz (168 grams)
Accessories: PS-4G (pressure snubber for gaseous media), **PS4E** (pressure snubber for water and light oils) and **PS-4D** (pressure snubber for dense liquids/motor oils) **$10** each. **Snubbers protect sensors from fluid spikes/hammers!**

RANGE	MODEL	PRICE	COMPATIBLE METER		
GAGE MODELS					
0-15 PSIG	PX305-015GI	$255	DP41-E,	DP302-E,	DP460-E
0-50 PSIG	PX305-050GI	255	DP41-E,	DP302-E,	DP460-E
0-100 PSIG	PX305-100GI	255	DP41-E,	DP302-E,	DP460-E
0-200 PSIG	PX305-200GI	255	DP41-E,	DP302-E,	DP460-E
0-300 PSIG	PX305-300GI	255	DP41-E,	DP3002-E,	DP460-E
0-500 PSIG	PX305-500GI	255	DP41-E,	DP3002-E,	DP460-E
0-1000 PSIG	PX305-1KGI	255	DP41-E,	DP302-E,	DP460-E
0-2000 PSIG	PX305-2KGI	255	DP41-E,	DP302-E,	DP460-E
0-3000 PSIG	PX305-3KGI	255	DP41-E,	DP3002-E,	DP460-E
0-4000 PSIG	PX305-4KGI	255	DP41-E,	DP3002-E,	DP460-E
0-5000 PSIG	PX305-5KGI	255	DP41-E,	DP3002-E,	DP460-E
0-7500 PSIG	PX305-7.5KGI	255	DP41-E,	DP3002-E,	DP460-E
0-10000 PSIG	PX305-10KGI	255	DP41-E,	DP3002-E,	DP460-E
ABSOLUTE MODELS					
0-15 PSIA	PX305-015AI	$255	DP41-E,	DP3002-E,	DP460-E
0-50 PSIA	PX305-050AI	255	DP41-E,	DP302-E,	DP460-E
0-100 PSIA	PX305-100AI	255	DP41-E,	DP302-E,	DP460-E
0-200 PSIA	PX305-200AI	255	DP41-E,	DP302-E,	DP460-E
0-300 PSIA	PX305-300AI	255	DP41-E,	DP3002-E,	DP460-E

Comes with complete operator's manual.
Ordering Example: PX305-015GI, with 15 PSIG full scale rating and 4 to 20 mA dc at the full scale level, and PS-4D pressure snubber, designed for use with motor oils, $255 + 10 = **$265.**

THIN FILM PRESSURE TRANSMITTERS
STAINLESS STEEL CONSTRUCTION

3 YEAR WARRANTY · **MADE IN USA** · **NIST**

PX605 - PX615 Series
VACUUM TO 20,000 PSI

From
$265

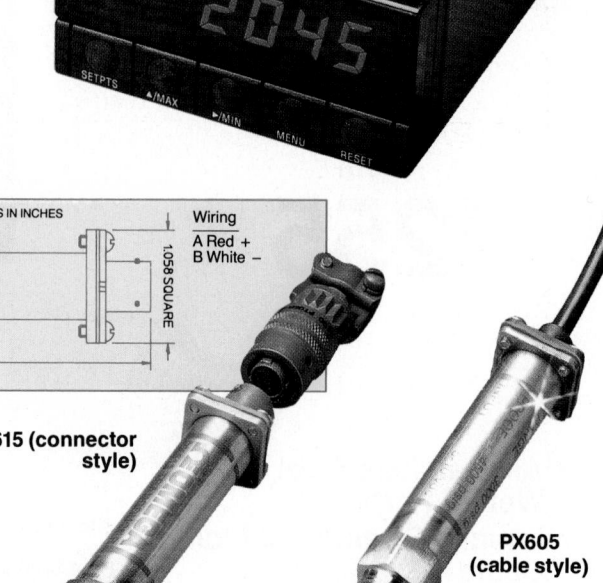

- ✔ **Excellent Long Term Stability**
- ✔ **NEMA 4 Cable or Connector Models**
- ✔ **0.4% Accuracy**
- ✔ **N.I.S.T. Calibration Certificate Supplied***
- ✔ **Thin Film Design For High Reliability**
- ✔ **Ideal for Liquid and Gas Applications**

DIMENSIONS IN INCHES

Wiring
A Red +
B White −

1.058 SQUARE

PX6[*]5   3.780

PX615 (connector style)

PX605 (cable style)

HIGHLIGHTED MODELS STOCKED FOR FAST DELIVERY

PS-4 Snubber Sold Separately

Ordering Example:
PX605-100GI shown $265
PX615-150GI shown $289
DP41-E Meter shown $345
PT06F8-4S Connector
(not included) $24

SPECIFICATIONS

Excitation: 10 to 30 Vdc unregulated
Output: 4 to 20 mA (2-wire)
Supply Current: 20 mA
Insulation Resistance: 100M ohms @ 50 V
Accuracy: $\pm$0.4% BFSL
Hysteresis: $\pm$0.2%
Repeatability: $\pm$0.05%
Stability: $\pm$1.0%/year
Durability: 100 million cycles
Operating Temperature: −55 to 195°F
Compensated Temperature: −20 to 180°F
Thermal Zero Effect: $\pm$0.04% FS/°F
Thermal Span Effect: $\pm$0.04% FS/°F
Proof Pressure: 15 to 2000 PSI = 200% Full Scale; 3000 to 5000 = 150% FS; 7500 to 20000 = 120% FS
Burst Pressure: 15 to 2000 PSI = 800% FS; 3000 to 5000 = 500% FS; 7500 to 20000 = 500% FS
Gages: Thin film polysilicon
Diaphragm: 17-4PH Stainless Steel
Case: 300 Series Stainless Steel
Pressure Connection: 15 to 10,000 PSI: 1/4 NPT; 15,000 and 20,000 PSI = female AMINCO fitting
Electrical Connection: 36" braided shield PVC Cable or connector
Weight: 4.5 oz. without cable
Response time: 1 ms
Construction: Sealed units, except PX605 ≤ 500 PSI is vented to room

To Order (Specify PX605 for Cable or PX615 for Connector Style)

RANGE PSIG	MODEL [ ] = Insert 0 or 1	PRICE PX605	PRICE PX615	COMPATIBLE METERS
30" Hg-0 vacuum	PX6[*]5-30VACI	$295	$320	DP3002-E,DP41-E,DP460-E
30" Hg-30 psi	PX6[*]5-30V30I	295	320	DP3002-E,DP41-E,DP460-E
0-15	PX6[*]5-015GI	265	289	DP3002-E,DP41-E,DP460-E
0-30	PX6[*]5-030GI	265	289	DP3002-E,DP41-E,DP460-E
0-60	PX6[*]5-060GI	265	289	DP3002-E,DP41-E,DP460-E
0-100	PX6[*]5-100GI	265	289	DP3002-E,DP41-E,DP460-E
0-150	PX6[*]5-150GI	265	289	DP3002-E,DP41-E,DP460-E
0-200	PX6[*]5-200GI	265	289	DP3002-E,DP41-E,DP460-E
0-300	PX6[*]5-300GI	265	289	DP3002-E,DP41-E,DP460-E
0-500	PX6[*]5-500GI	265	289	DP3002-E,DP41-E,DP460-E
0-1000	PX6[*]5-1KGI	265	289	DP3002-E,DP41-E,DP460-E
0-2000	PX6[*]5-2KGI	265	289	DP3002-E,DP41-E,DP460-E
0-3000	PX6[*]5-3KGI	265	289	DP3002-E,DP41-E,DP460-E
0-5000	PX6[*]5-5KGI	265	289	DP3002-E,DP41-E,DP460-E
0-7500	PX6[*]5-7.5KGI	265	289	DP3002-E,DP41-E,DP460-E
0-10,000	PX6[*]5-10KGI	265	289	DP3002-E,DP41-E,DP460-E
0-15,000	PX6[*]5-15KGI†	265	289	DP3002-E,DP41-E,DP460-E
0-20,000	PX6[*]5-20KGI†	265	289	DP3002-E,DP41-E,DP460-E

†15,000 and 20,000 PSI models supplied with female AMINCO fitting.
*[ ] insert "0" for cable style [ ] insert "1" for connector style.

INDUSTRIAL PRESSURE TRANSMITTER
ALL STAINLESS STEEL CONSTRUCTION

PX540 Series
RANGES FROM 150 TO 6000 PSIG

✓ Flush "Non-Plugging" Diaphragm
✓ Weather Resistant Connector for Wet Environment

All Models
$489

Shown with
Model DP41-E
Price $345.

Meter Sold Separately,
See Page D-7.

DIN Connector Included

DIMENSIONS IN INCHES

½ NPT

1.20

.67

4.33 (≤ 150 PSI)
3.38 (≥ 300 PSI)

Typical Applications

✓ Chemical/Petrochemical
✓ Hydraulic Equipment
✓ Machine Tools

SPECIFICATIONS

Excitation: 10 to 30 Vdc
Output: 4-20 mA two wire
Maximum Loop Impedance: 1000 ohms (see chart)
Insulation Resistance: 500 Vac

PERFORMANCE

Accuracy: 0.5% FS
Hysteresis & Repeatability: 0.1% FS
Compensated Temperature Range: 32 to 122°F (0 to 50°C)
Operating Range: −4 to 175°F (−20 to 80°C)
Thermal Zero Effect: 0.03% FS/°C
Thermal Sensitivity Effect: 0.03% FS/°C
Maximum Pressure: 150% FS

CONSTRUCTION

Body Material: Stainless Steel
Wetted Parts: ANSI 316L SS
Fill Fluid: Silicone oil
Process Connection: ½ NPT male
Electrical Connection: DIN connector with screw terminals included
Weight: 0.35 lbs
Response Time: 2 ms

HIGHLIGHTED MODELS STOCKED FOR FAST DELIVERY!

To Order (Specify Model Number)

RANGE PSIG	MODEL	PRICE	COMPATIBLE METERS
0-15	PX540-015GI	$489	DP3002-E, DP460-E, DP41-E
0-30	PX540-030GI	489	DP3002-E, DP460-E, DP41-E
0-75	PX540-075GI	489	DP3002-E, DP460-E, DP41-E
0-150	PX540-150GI	489	DP3002-E, DP460-E, DP100R8, DP41-E
0-300	PX540-300GI	489	DP3002-E, DP460-E, DP100R8, DP41-E
0-750	PX540-750GI	489	DP3002-E, DP460-E, DP100R8, DP41-E
0-1500	PX540-1.5KGI	489	DP3002-E, DP460-E, DP100R8, DP41-E
0-3000	PX540-3KGI	489	DP3002-E, DP460-E, DP110R8, DP41-E
0-6000	PX540-6KGI	489	DP3002-E, DP460-E, DP110R8, DP41-E

SPECIAL PURPOSE TRANSMITTERS FLUSH DIAPHRAGM DESIGN
MOUNT IN RF FLANGE, TRI-CLOVER FITTING, OR WELD RING

Model DP2000-P8 Shown

Model PX542

Model PX543

PX542 Series
1.5 PSI to 1500 PSI

PX543 Series
High Temperature Model

✔ **Flush Diaphragm For Viscous and Percipitating Fluids**
✔ **All Stainless Steel Construction**
✔ **Requires Installation Fitting**
✔ **PX543 Process Temperature up to 570°F**

From
$1275

SPECIFICATIONS

Excitation: 10 to 30 Vdc
Output: 4 to 20 mA two wire
Maximum Loop Impedance: 1000 ohms
Insulation Resistance: 500 Vac
Power Supply Effect: .0001 mA/V

PERFORMANCE

Accuracy: 0.5% FS
Zero Adjustment (Balance): 2% FS
Span Adjustment (Balance): 5% FS
Compensated Temperature Range: PX542: 32 to 120°F (0 to 50°C); PX543: Process fluid: 32 to 570°F (0 to 300°C)
Ambient: 32 to 120°F (0 to 50°C)

Thermal Zero Effect: 0.025% FS/°C
Thermal Sensitivity Effect: 0.026% FS/°C
Maximum Pressure: 150% FS

CONSTRUCTION

Body Material: Stainless Steel
Wetted Parts: ANSI 316L SS
Process Connection: G1 (1″ DIN std)(NPT adapter available below)
Electrical Connection: DIN connector with screw terminals
Fill Fluid: Silcone oil
Weight: 1.1 lbs
Response Time: 10ms

Dimensions (upper diagram)

G1 THD
∅ 40 (1.57)
27(1.06)
120 (4.75)
h₁
Screw in torque (85 Nm for 15,000 psi)

zero point adjustment
Z
Span adjustment

Mating Connector Supplied

DIMENSIONS: MM(INCH)

Dimensions (lower diagram)

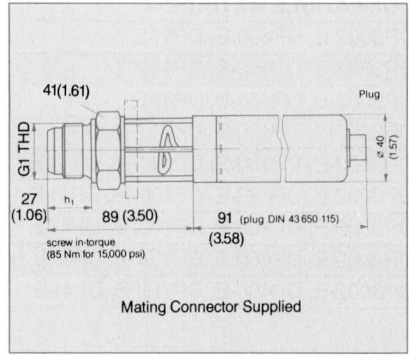

41(1.61)
Plug
G1 THD
∅ 40 (1.57)
27 (1.06)
h₁
89 (3.50)
91 (plug DIN 43 650 115)
(3.58)
screw in-torque (85 Nm for 15,000 psi)

Mating Connector Supplied

To Order *(Specify Model Number)*

RANGE	MODEL [ ] = INSERT 2 or 3	PRICE PX542 STD	PRICE PX543 HI-TEMP	COMPATIBLE METERS
0-30″ Hg Vac.	PX54[ ]-30 VACI	$1415	$1859	DP2000-P8, DP41-E, DP460-E
0 to 1.5 PSIG	PX54[ ]-1.5GI	1349	1285	DP2000-P8, DP41-E, DP460-E
0 to 3.0 PSIG	PX54[ ]-003GI	1349	1285	DP2000-P8, DP41-E, DP460-E
0 to 7.5 PSIG	PX54[ ]-7.5GI	1295	1650	DP2000-P8, DP41-E, DP460-E
0 to 15 PSIG	PX54[ ]-015GI	1275	1650	DP2000-P8, DP41-E, DP460-E
0 to 30 PSIG	PX54[ ]-030GI	1275	1650	DP2000-P8, DP41-E, DP460-E
0 to 75 PSIG	PX54[ ]-075GI	1275	1650	DP2000-P8, DP41-E, DP460-E
0 to 150 PSIG	PX54[ ]-150GI	1275	1650	DP2000-P8, DP41-E, DP460-E
0 to 300 PSIG	PX54[ ]-300GI	1275	1650	DP2000-P8, DP41-E, DP460-E
0 to 750 PSIG	PX54[ ]-750GI	1275	1650	DP2000-P8, DP41-E, DP460-E
0 to 1500 PSIG	PX54[ ]-1.5KGI	1275	1650	DP2000-P8, DP41-E, DP460-E

ACCESSORIES — WITH G1 THREAD FOR USE WITH PX542/PX543

MODEL	DESCRIPTION	PRICE
U24Y101	Loop power supply 24V @ 1000 mA	$99
PX543RF	150 pound raised face flange	144
PX543WR	Weld ring	59
PX543TC1	1½″ Tri-clamp	129
PX543TC2	2″ Tri-clamp	135
PX543AD1	G1 to 1″ NPT adaptor	129
PX543AD2	G1 to ½″ NPT adaptor	109
PX543PG	Plug for G1 thread	49

Ordering Example:
PX542-015GI is a 0-15 PSI transducer $1275
PX543-300 GI is a 0-300 PSI "high temp" transducer $1650
DP2000-P8 meter sold separately $301

FLUSH MOUNT CURRENT OUTPUT TYPE PRESSURE TRANSDUCER
DESIGNED FOR FLUSH MOUNT ADAPTORS

440 Series
0-6 TO 0-20,000 PSIG
INTERNAL VOLTAGE REGULATOR

New Improved Accuracy

- Unregulated 14 to 50 V dc Excitation
- 316SS on Ranges 50 PSI and Under
- 15-5 pH Stainless Steel on 100 and Over/PSI/Ranges
- Ranges 100/PSI and Over are Sealed (PSIS)
- 2,000 Ohms Maximum

Shown with AD-1SS Adaptor. See page B-27.

From $650

Shown actual size
See Page C-4 for Mating Connectors: PT06F-10-6S

CURRENT OUTPUT PRESSURE TRANSDUCERS B

See Selection Guide For Compatible Instrumentation

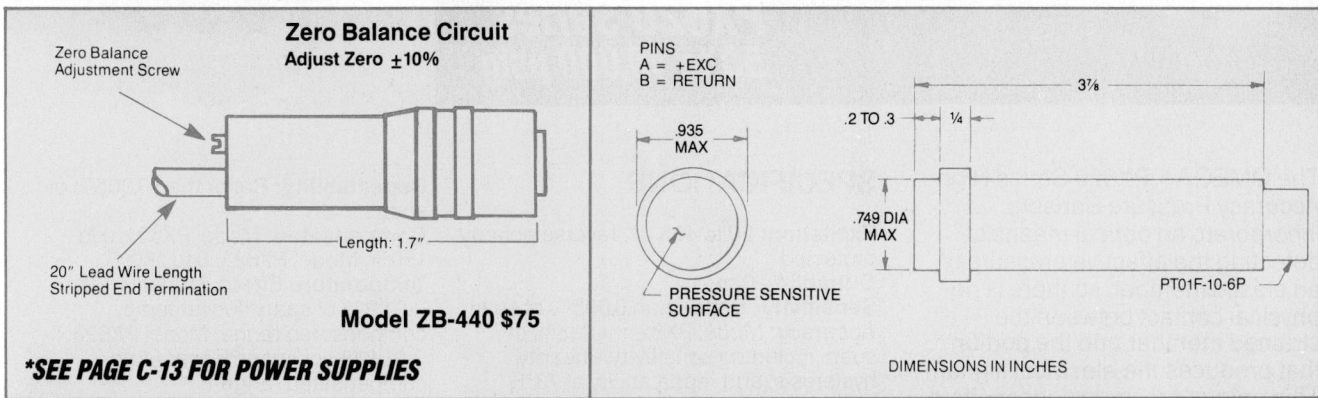

Zero Balance Circuit
Adjust Zero ±10%

Zero Balance Adjustment Screw

Length: 1.7"

20" Lead Wire Length Stripped End Termination

Model ZB-440 $75

SEE PAGE C-13 FOR POWER SUPPLIES

PINS
A = +EXC
B = RETURN

.935 MAX

PRESSURE SENSITIVE SURFACE

.2 TO .3   ¼   3⅞

.749 DIA MAX

PT01F-10-6P

DIMENSIONS IN INCHES

SPECIFICATIONS

Excitation: 12 to 36 Vdc
Output: 4-20 mA
Accuracy: ±1.0% full scale (B.F.S.L. Linearity, Hysteresis & Repeatability)
Zero Balance: ±0.4 mA
Operable Temperature Range: −40 to 180°F (−40 to 82°C)
Compensated Temperature Range: 30 to 130°F (−1 to 55°C)
Thermal Zero Effect: ±0.02% full scale/°F (±0.04%/°C)
Frequency Response: 300 Hz
Proof Pressure: 2 × full scale or 30,000 PSI whichever is less
Burst Pressure: 5 × full scale or 50,000 PSI whichever is less
Gages: Semiconductor on Bending Beam
Body/Diaphragm Material: 316 L SS ≤ 50 PSI; 15-5 PH SS ≥ 100 PSI
Weight: 4 ozs.

To Order (Specify model number)

PRESSURE RANGE	MODEL NUMBER	PRICE	COMPATIBLE METER*
0- 5 PSIG	PX 440-005G I	$650	DP41-E,DP2000P8,TX81
0- 15 PSIG	PX 440-015G I	650	DP41-E,DP2000P9,TX81
0- 25 PSIG	PX 440-025G I	650	DP41-E,DP2000P8,TX81
0- 50 PSIG	PX 440-050G I	650	DP41-E,DP2000P8,TX81
0- 100 PSIS	PX 440-100S I	650	DP41-E,DP2000P8,TX81
0- 200 PSIS	PX 440-200S I	650	DP41-E,DP2000P9,TX81
0- 500 PSIS	PX 440-500S I	650	DP41-E,DP2000P8,TX81
0- 1000 PSIS	PX 440- 1KS I	650	DP41-E,DP2000P8,TX81
0- 5000 PSIS	PX 440- 5KS I	650	DP460-E, DP3002-E
0-10000 PSIS	PX 440-10KS I	650	DP460-E, DP3002-E
0-20000 PSIS	PX 440-20KS I	650	DP460-E, DP3002-E

◆ *HIGHLIGHTED MODELS STOCKED FOR FAST DELIVERY* ◆

HIGH ACCURACY PRESSURE TRANSDUCERS
WITH 4 to 20 mA CURRENT OUTPUT

PX620 Series
50 to 10,000 psig

✔ **Non Contacting Optical Sensor for High Accuracy Model 621 — 0.15%, Model 623 — 0.10%**
✔ **Repeatability to 0.005%**
✔ **Corrosion Resistant Materials of Sensor**
✔ **Internal Zero and Span Adjustments**

From
$895

The OMEGA® PX620 Series High Accuracy Pressure Sensors incorporate an optical means of detecting the effective pressure of an elastic member, so there is no physical contact between the strained member and the portion that produces the electrical signal. This unique pressure sensor offers extreme accuracy and repeatability.

SPECIFICATIONS

Excitation: 20 to 40 Vdc, reverse polarity protected
Output: 4-20 mA
Sensitivity: Better than 0.005% of span
Accuracy: Model PX621: ±0.15% of span, including sensitivity, linearity, hysteresis, and repeatability at 73°F, Model PX623: ±0.10% of span
Response Time: 250 ms

Repeatability: Better than 0.005% of span
Compensated: Model PX621: 0 to 150°F, Model PX623: 0 to 180°F
Temperature Effect: Model PX621: ±0.02% of span/°F over temp. compensated range; Model PX623: ±0.004% of span/°F over temp. compensated range
Overpressure Limit: 100% of span to 500 PSI, 30% of span to 7500 PSI, 20% of span to 10,000 PSI
Pressure Sensor: Non-contacting optical pressure sensor measuring motion of diaphragm or Bourdon tube element. (Diaphragm to 200 PSI, Bourdon tube for higher pressures)
Process Connection: ¼" NPT female — ½" NPT male combination for pressure ranges through 5000 psi. AUTOCLAVE and AMINCO 45-11310 for ranges over 5000 psi.
Electronic housing: Aluminum cover, epoxy finish with circular electrical connector, mating connector included.
Wetted Parts: Element-Inconel 718 Optional- 403 SS or 410 SS
Other Wetted Parts: 316 SS
Typical Cavity Vol: 8.5 cc (varies with range)

To Order (Standard Models)

RANGE PSIG	MODEL	PRICE	COMPATIBLE METER
0- 100	PX621-100G I	$895	DP41-E, TX81, DP3002-E
▶ 0- 200	PX621-200G I	895	DP41-E, TX81, DP3002-E ◀
▶ 0- 300	PX621-300G I	895	DP41-E, TX81, DP3002-E ◀
0- 500	PX621-500G I	895	DP41-E, TX81, DP3002-E
0- 1000	PX621-1KG I	895	DP41-E, TX81, DP3002-E
▶ 0- 3000	PX621-3KG I	895	DP41-E, DP460-E, DP3002-E
0-10000	PX621-10KG I	895	DP41-E, DP460-E, DP3002-E

Standard Ranges, ±0.15% span accuracy, in Stock
To select 5 V output model, see page B-45
To select high accuracy model, change PX621 to PX623, see page B-66 for pricing

▶ *HIGHLIGHTED MODELS STOCKED FOR FAST DELIVERY* ◀

HIGH ACCURACY PRESSURE TRANSDUCERS
WITH AMPLIFIED VOLTAGE OR CURRENT OUTPUT
PX620 Series

Ordering Optional Ranges

```
PX  _  _  _  _  _
                    5 V (0 to 5 V)
                    10 V (0 to 10 V)
                    OUTPUT I (4 to 20 mA)
                    G—gage
                    A—absolute (add $100)
                    V—vacuum
                    Range plus scale
                    ie. 2 PSI or 50 inches of water
         621/623
```

OPTIONAL FEATURES (All Models)	ADD TO BASE PRICE
Absolute Pressure — All ranges from 5 PSIA through 30,000 PSIA	$200

Connector Included

3.0

3.20 max.

4.82

1.25

DIMENSIONS IN INCHES

PRESSURE PORT

Optional Pressure Ranges (Consult Sales for availability)

								Base Price	
PX620 SERIES Gage and Absolute Pressure Standard Ranges[1]									
psi	(in H₂O) Inches Water	(in HG) Inches Mercury	(mm HG) millimeters Mercury or Torr	Pascal	kg/cm² kp/cm² or bar	millibar or centimeters Water	(mm H₂O) millimeters Water	Model PX621	PX623
2	50	5	100	kPa20		100	2,000		
3	100		150	30		200	3,000		
	150		200			300			
5	200	10	300	50	1.0	500	5,000	$910	$1160
10	300	20	500	60	1.6	1,000	10,000		
15	400	30	600	100	2.5	2,000			
20	500	32	760	160	4.0	3,000			
30	600	36	1,000	250	5.0	5,000			
50	1,000	50	1,500	400	6.0	6,000			
60	2,000	60	2,000	500	10	10,000			
100	3,000	100	3,000	600	16			895	1135
150		200	5,000	1,000	25				
200		300	6,000	1,600	40				
300			10,000	2,500	60				
500				4,000	100				
600				6,000	160				
800				10,000	250				
1,000				16,000	400				
1,500				MPa	600				
2,000				25					
2,500				40					
3,000				60					
4,000									
5,000									
6,000									
10,000									
15,000				100	1,000			1085	1205
20,000				160	1,600				
25,000								1240	1550
30,000									
15		5	100	kPa	0.1	1000[2]		1185	1170
		10	200	20	0.2				
		20	300	30	0.3				
		30	500	50	0.5				
				200	1.0				

Gage Pressure Ranges / *Absolute Pressure Ranges[3]* / *Vacuum Ranges*

(1) — Non-standard ranges. (2) — Available in millibar only.
(3) — Evacuated reference side for barometric compensation.

INDUSTRIAL/SCIENTIFIC FLUSH PRESSURE TRANSMITTER
FOR VACUUM, BI-DIRECTIONAL AND GAGE PRESSURE

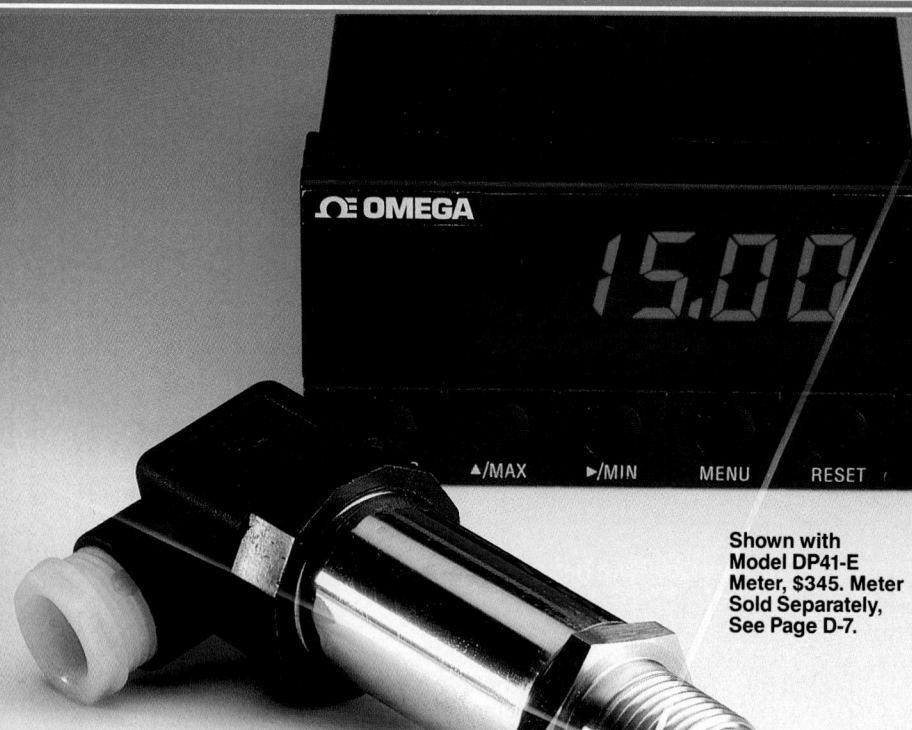

PX541 Series

Vacuum Ranges: 15 PSI
Bi-Directional: ±15, −15 to 30 PSI
Gage Pressure: to 3000 PSI

- ✔ All Stainless Steel Construction
- ✔ Weather Resistant Connection
- ✔ High Accuracy up to 0.3% Full Scale
- ✔ Flush "Non-Plugging" Diaphragm

Shown with Model DP41-E Meter, $345. Meter Sold Separately, See Page D-7.

From
$575

SPECIFICATIONS

Excitation: 10 to 30 Vdc
Output: 4-20 mA two wire
Maximum Loop Impedance: 1000 ohms (see chart)
Insulation Resistance: 500 Vac
Power Supply Effect: .0001 mA/V

PERFORMANCE

Accuracy: 0.3% FS
Zero Adjustment (Balance): 2% FS
Span Adjustment (Balance): 5% FS
Compensated Temperature Range: 32 to 120°F (0 to 50°C)
Thermal Zero Effect: 0.03% FS/°C
Thermal Sensitivity Effect: 0.026% FS/°C
Maximum Pressure: 150% FS

CONSTRUCTION

Body Material: Stainless Steel
Wetted Parts: ANSI 316L SS, Silicone O-rings
Fill Fluid: Silicone oil
Process Connection: 1/2 NPT male
Electrical Connection: DIN connector with screw terminals included
Weight: 6 oz
Response Time: 2 ms

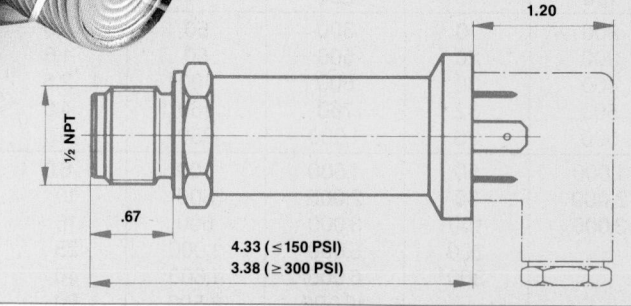
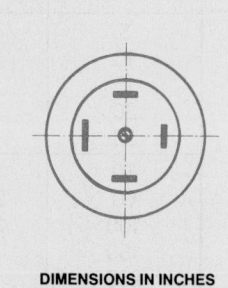

1.20
½ NPT
.67
4.33 (≤ 150 PSI)
3.38 (≥ 300 PSI)

DIMENSIONS IN INCHES

To Order (Specify Model Number)

RANGE PSI	MODEL	PRICE	COMPATIBLE METERS
−15 to 30	PX541-15V30GI	$685	DP460-E, DP41-E
−15 to 15	PX541-15V15GI	685	DP460-E, DP41-E
−15 to 0	PX541-30VACI	685	DP41-E, DP460-E, DP302-E
0 to 1.5	PX541-1.5GI	685	DP41-E, DP460-E, DP302-E
0 to 3	PX541-003GI	685	DP41-E, DP460-E, DP3002-E
0 to 7.5	PX541-7.5GI	575	DP41-E, DP460-E, DP3002-E
0 to 15	PX541-015GI	575	DP41-E, DP460-E, DP302-E
0 to 30	PX541-030GI	575	DP41-E, DP460-E, DP3002-E
0 to 75	PX541-075GI	575	DP41-E, DP460-E, DP3002-E
0 to 150	PX541-150GI	575	DP41-E, DP460-E, DP302-E
0 to 300	PX541-300GI	575	DP41-E, DP460-E, DP3002-E
0 to 750	PX541-750GI	575	DP41-E, DP460-E, DP3002-E
0 to 1500	PX541-1.5KGI	575	DP41-E, DP460-E, DP302-E
0 to 3000	PX541-3KGI	575	DP41-E, DP460-E, DP3002-E

For absolute ranges, change "G" in model no. to "A" and add $100 to price.

HIGHLY ACCURATE CURRENT LOOP OUTPUT TYPE TRANSDUCER
WITH SHUNT CALIBRATOR FOR QUICK CALIBRATION CHECKS

941 Series
0-10 to 0-10,000 PSI

From
$670

- ✓ **Stainless Steel Diaphragm** for Compatibility with Most Media
- ✓ **¼" NPT Fitting for Fast, Easy, and Secure Installation**
- ✓ **3 Wire Transmitter**
- ✓ **Rugged Stainless Steel Case Protects Components in Industrial Environments**
- ✓ **Connects to a PT06F-10-6S Connector for Easy Field Connections**
- ✓ **4-20 mA Output Provides Excellent Noise Immunity for Long Lead Lengths**
- ✓ **Compatible with 26 to 32 Vdc Unregulated Power Supply for Maximum Versatility in Any Application**
- ✓ **±20% Zero and Span Adjustments**
- ✓ **Units 1000 PSIG and Below Utilize Beam Mounted Strain Gages for Long Life and High Reliability**

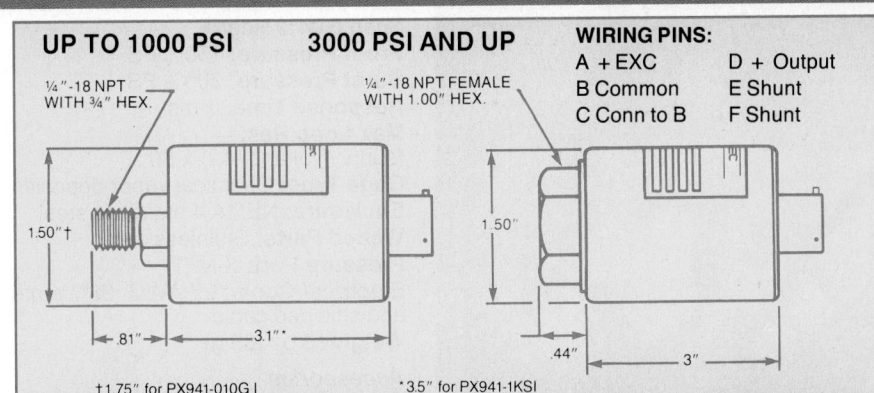

WIRING PINS:

A + EXC	D + Output
B Common	E Shunt
C Conn to B	F Shunt

UP TO 1000 PSI — ¼"-18 NPT WITH ¾" HEX. — 1.50"† — .81" — 3.1"*
†1.75" for PX941-010G I

3000 PSI AND UP — ¼"-18 NPT FEMALE WITH 1.00" HEX. — 1.50" — .44" — 3"
*3.5" for PX941-1KSI

To Order *(Specify model number)*

*SEE SECTION D FOR INSTRUMENT SELECTION

RANGE	MODEL	PRICE	COMPATIBLE METER*
0- 10 PSIG	PX941-010GI	$695	DP3002-P,DP2000P8,DP460-V
0- 25 PSIG	PX941-025GI	695	DP3002-P,DP2000P8,DP460-V
0- 50 PSIG	PX941-050GI	670	DP3002-P,DP2000P8,DP460-V
0- 100 PSIS	PX941-100SI	670	DP3002-P,DP2000P8,DP460-V
0- 200 PSIS	PX941-200SI	670	DP3002-P,DP2000P8,DP460-V
0- 500 PSIS	PX941-500SI	670	DP3002-P,DP2000P8,DP460-V
0-1000 PSIS	PX941-1KSI	670	DP3002-P,DP2000P8,DP460-V
0-3000 PSIS	PX941-3KSI	670	DP3002-P, DP460-V
0-5000 PSIS	PX941-5KSI	670	DP3002-P, DP460-V
0-7500 PSIS	PX941-7.5KSI	670	DP3002-P, DP460-V
0-10K PSIS	PX941-10KSI	670	DP3002-P, DP460-V

Absolute ranges available. Change "G" to "A" in part number. Add $75 to list price (3 piece minimum).
**Requires U24Y101 power supply, $99.*

Shown Slightly Larger than Actual Size

SPECIFICATIONS
Excitation: 22 to 32 Vdc @ 65 mA
Output: 4-20 mA dc (3 wire)
Insulation Resistance: > 5 MΩ @ 75 Vdc

PERFORMANCE
Accuracy: ±0.15%
Hysteresis: ±0.10%
Repeatability: ±0.05%
Zero Balance: ±1%
Operable Temperature Range: 0 to 185°F
Compensated Temperature Range: 60°F to 160°F
Thermal Zero Effect: ±0.005% full scale/°F
Thermal Sensitivity Effect: ±0.005%/°F
Proof Pressure: 1.5 x Range
Burst Pressure: 5 x 100-1,000 PSI; 3.5 x 1,500 PSI; 2.5 x >1,500 PSI

CONSTRUCTION
Body Material: 17-4 PH Stainless Steel
Diaphragm Material: 17-4 PH Stainless Steel
Pressure Port: ¼"-18 NPT (Male Thread 10 to 1,000 PSI, Female Thread 3,000 to 5,000 PSI)
Mating Connector: PT06F-10-6S (not included)
Pressure Cavity Volume: 0.171 in³
Weight: 13.5 ozs.

HIGHLIGHTED MODEL STOCKED FOR FAST DELIVERY

GENERAL PURPOSE CURRENT OUTPUT PRESSURE TRANSMITTER
ALL STAINLESS STEEL CONSTRUCTION

PX905 Series
$255

✔ **NIST Traceable**
✔ **NEMA 4 Enclosure**
✔ **CVD Construction for High Stability**

SPECIFICATIONS
Excitation: 10-30 Vdc
Output: 4-20 mA (2 wire)
Accuracy: 0.5%FS
Hysteresis: 0.2%FS
Repeatability: 0.05%FS
Zero Balance: 1%FS
Stability: 1%FS/year
Operating Temp.: -55 to 195°F (-48 to 90 °C)
Compensated Temp.: -20 to 180°F (-29 to 82 °C)
Thermal Effects:
Zero 0.04% FS/°F
Span 0.04% Rdg/°F
Proof Pressure: 150% FS
Burst Pressure: 300% FS
Response Time: 1 ms
Max Loop Res:
(supply voltage -12) x 50
Gage Type: Chemical vapor deposition
Enclosure: NEMA 4 stainless steel
Wetted Parts: Stainless steel
Pressure Port: ¼ NPT
Electrical Conn.: 22 AWG, 36", vented and shielded cable
Weight: 3 oz (85 g)

Accessories
Pressure Snubbers: Models PS-4D (Oils), PS-4E (Water), PS-4G (Gases) $10 each.
TX4-100 Wire: 100' of 4-conductor shielded copper wire, $28.50

Shown with Model DP3002-E Meter ($271) and PS-4E Snubber ($10).

IN STOCK FOR FAST DELIVERY!

To Order *(Specify Model Number)*

RANGE	MODEL	PRICE	COMPATIBLE METER
0-100 PSIG	**PX905-100GI**	$255	DP205-E, DP41-E, DP3002-E
0-200 PSIG	**PX905-200GI**	255	DP205-E, DP41-E, DP3002-E
0-300 PSIG	**PX905-300GI**	255	DP205-E, DP41-E, DP3002-E
0-500 PSIG	**PX905-500GI**	255	DP205-E, DP41-E, DP3002-E
0-1000 PSIG	**PX905-1KGI**	255	DP205-E, DP41-E, DP3002-E
0-2000 PSIG	**PX905-2KGI**	255	DP205-E, DP41-E, DP3002-E
0-3000 PSIG	**PX905-3KGI**	255	DP205-E, DP41-E, DP3002-E
0-5000 PSIG	**PX905-5KGI**	255	DP205-E, DP41-E, DP3002-E
0-7500 PSIG	**PX905-7.5KGI**	255	DP205-E, DP41-E, DP3002-E
0-10000 PSIG	**PX905-10KGI**	255	DP205-E, DP41-E, DP3002-E

Comes complete with operator's manual.
Ordering Example:** PX905-2KGI current output cressure transducer, with 0 to 2000 PSIG range and two PS-4D snubbers for oil media, $255 + 20 = **$275.

INDUSTRIAL GRADE TRANSMITTER WITH LABORATORY ACCURACY
AVAILABLE IN RANGES FROM 50 TO 10000 PSI

1 YEAR WARRANTY | **MADE IN USA** | **NIST**

- ✔ NIST Traceable with FS Value Listed
- ✔ High 0.1 % Accuracy
- ✔ Stainless Steel Wetted Parts

PX945
$595

Shown Slightly Smaller Than Actual Size

Shown With DP41-E Meter, $345 and PS-4 Snubber. See Page D-7 for Details on this Versatile Meter.

CURRENT OUTPUT PRESSURE TRANSDUCERS

B

SPECIFICATIONS

Excitation: 15 to 40 Vdc
Output: 4-20 mA (2 wire) (NIST tracable calibration, full scale output given)
Accuracy: .1% FS (linearity, repeatability and hysteresis)
Zero Balance: 4 ±0.015 mA
Operating Temp.: 0 to 185°F (-18 to 85°C)
Compensated Temp.: 30 to 130°F (0 to 55°C)
Thermal Effects:
  Zero .015% FS/°F
  Span .015% rdg/°F
Proof Pressure: 150% FS
Burst Pressure: 200% FS
Max. Loop Res.: (supply voltage - 15) x 50 ohms
Response Time: 2500 Hz
Gage Type: Bonded foil
Zero & Span: 15% adj
Wetted Parts: 17-4 PH SS
Pressure Port: ¼-18 NPTF

Electrical Conn.: DIN connector screw terminals (supplied with 3 ft, 29 awg , 2 cond. shielded, pigtail leads)

Dimensions: 1½" dia x 5¹⁵⁄₁₆" L (38 x 150 mm)
Weight: 13 oz (365 g)

HIGHLIGHTED MODELS STOCKED FOR FAST DELIVERY!

To Order *(Specify Model Number)*

RANGE	MODEL NO.	PRICE	COMPATIBLE METERS
0-50 PSIG	PX945-050GI	$595	DP41-E, DP3002-E, DP460-E
0-100 PSIG	PX945-100GI	595	DP41-E, DP302-E, DP460-E
0-200 PSIG	PX945-200GI	595	DP41-E, DP302-E, DP460-E
0-500 PSIG	PX945-500GI	595	DP41-E, DP3002-E, DP460-E
0-1000 PSIG	PX945-1KGI	595	DP41-E, DP302-E, DP113-R8
0-3000 PSIG	PX945-3KGI	595	DP41-E, DP3002-E, DP113-R8
0-5000 PSIG	PX945-5KGI	595	DP41-E, DP3002-E, DP460-E
0-10000 PSIG	PX945-10KGI	595	DP41-E, DP3002-E, DP460-E

ACCESSORIES	PRICE	DESCRIPTION
PS-4G	$10	Pressure snubber for gaseous media
PS-4E	10	Pressure snubber for water and light oils
PS-4D	10	Pressure snubber for dense liquids (motor oil)

Comes with complete operator's manual.

Ordering Example: *PX945-050GI, industrial transmitter with 0 to 100 PSIG range, PS-4G snubber and DP41-E process indicator (all pictured above), $595 + 10 + 345 = **$950**.*

HIGH ACCURACY 4-20 mA OUTPUT PRESSURE TRANSMITTER
WITH THIN FILM CONSTRUCTION

3 YEAR WARRANTY

✔ **All Stainless Steel Wetted Parts**
✔ **NEMA 4 Rated**
✔ **CVD Construction for High Stability**
✔ **Tamper-Proof Zero and Span Adjustments**

From
$512

Model PX216 is Shown With a PS4 Snubber and a DP41-E Meter. Model DP41-E ($345), See Page D-7 for Details.

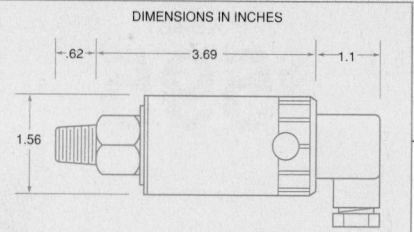

DIMENSIONS IN INCHES

The PX216 pressure transmitter utilizes the high technology chemical vapor desposited (CVD) batch manufacturing process. These stable sensors are packaged in a rugged stainless steel outer case, ideally suited for industrial applications. The transmitters include tamper-proof zero and span adjustments, and come with a complete operator's manual.

SPECIFICATIONS

Excitation: 24 Vdc, (12-36 Vdc) Reverse polarity protected
Output: 4-20 mA (2 wire)
Accuracy: 0.15% (including linearity, hystersis and repeatability)
Zero Balance: 0.03 mA
Span Tolerance: 16 ±0.03 mA
Max. Loop Resistance: 50 x (supply voltage -12) ohms
Storage Temp.: -40 to 257°F (-40 to 125°C)
Operating Temp.: -22 to 248°F (-30 to 120°C)
Compensated Temperature: -4 to 176°F (-20 to 80°C)
Thermal Effects: 1.2% FS over (-20 to 80°C)
Proof Pressure: 150%
Burst Pressure: 400%, 17000 PSI max
Zero and Span Adj.: 10% FS
Response Time: 1 ms
Gage Type: Chemical vapor deposited polysilicon strain gages
Wetted Parts: 15-7,17-4 SS,<60 PSI 17-4 SS ≥60 PSI
Pressure Port: ¼-18 NPT
Electrical Connections: Std. DIN connector screw terminals
Weight: 8 oz (230 g)

HIGHLIGHTED MODELS STOCKED FOR FAST DELIVERY

To Order (Specify Model Number)

RANGE	MODEL	PRICE	COMPATIBLE METERS
GAGE MODELS			
0-15 PSIG	PX216-015GI	$512	DP41-E, DP302-E, DP460-E
0-30 PSIG	PX216-030GI	512	DP41-E, DP302-E, DP460-E
0-60 PSIG	PX216-060GI	512	DP41-E, DP302-E, DP460-E
0-100 PSIG	PX216-100GI	512	DP41-E, DP302-E, DP460-E
0-300 PSIG	PX216-300GI	512	DP41-E, DP3002-E, DP460-E
0-600 PSIG	PX216-600GI	512	DP41-E, DP3002-E, DP460-E
0-1000 PSIG	PX216-1KGI	512	DP41-E, DP302-E, DP460-E
0-3000 PSIG	PX216-3KGI	512	DP41-E, DP3002-E, DP460-E
0-6000 PSIG	PX216-6KGI	512	DP41-E, DP3002-E, DP460-E
ABSOLUTE MODELS			
0-15 PSIA	PX216-015AI	$595	DP41-E, DP302-E, DP460-E
0-30 PSIA	PX216-030AI	595	DP41-E, DP302-E, DP460-E
0-60 PSIA	PX216-060AI	595	DP41-E, DP302-E, DP460-E
0-100 PSIA	PX216-100AI	595	DP41-E, DP302-E, DP460-E
0-300 PSIA	PX216-300AI	595	DP41-E, DP3002-E, DP460-E

ACCESSORIES	PRICE	DESCRIPTION
PS-4G	$10	Pressure snubber for gaseous media
PS-4E	10	Pressure snubber for water and light oils
PS-4D	10	Pressure snubber for dense liquids (motor oil)

Comes with complete operator's manual.

Ordering Example: *PX216-3KGI is a high accuracy pressure transmitter with 4-20 mA output and a 0 to 3000 PSIG range, **$512**.*

INDUSTRIAL PRESSURE TRANSMITTERS
RUGGED WEATHER-PROOF NEMA-4 ENCLOSURE

1 YEAR WARRANTY

MADE IN USA

CURRENT OUTPUT PRESSURE TRANSDUCERS

B

PX725 Series
50″ H₂O to 5000 PSI

All Models
$630

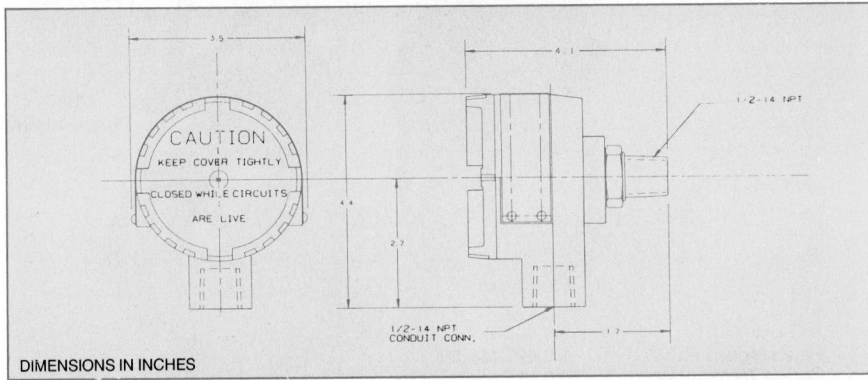

DIMENSIONS IN INCHES

- ✔ **High ±0.15% Accuracy For Precise Measurements In Hazardous Locations**
- ✔ **All 316SS Wetted Parts For Compatibility With Corrosive Media**
- ✔ **Zero and Span Adjustments**
- ✔ **Electrical Surge Protected**
- ✔ **EMI Shielded**

SPECIFICATIONS

Excitation: 15 to 42Vdc
Output: 4-20mA (2-wire)
Loop Resistance: 500ohms at 24Vdc

PERFORMANCE

Accuracy: ±0.15% of calibrated span (includes linearity, repeatability, and hysteresis). Typical values: Linearity = 0.1%; repeatability = 0.05%; hysteresis = 0.05%

Stability: ±0.25% of upper range limit for 6 months

Surge protection: 1000 watts for 1mS

Zero Adjust: ±15%

Span Adjust: ±10%

Operating Temperature limit:
   Process Temp: −40 to 220°F (−40 to 104°C)
   Electronics Temp: −25 to 185°F (−32 to 85°C)
   Storage Temperature: −40 to 212°F (−40 to 100°C)

Thermal Effect: ±0.02% of FS per °F (Includes Zero and Span)

Humidity Limits: 0-95% RH −40 to 185°F

Proof Pressure: 3 X Full Scale

CONSTRUCTION

Gages: micro-machined silicon

Electronics Enclosure: Low Copper Aluminum with epoxy coating. Designed to meet FM Explosion Proof Certification for Hazardous Areas and NEMA-4 Weatherproof

Wetted Parts: 316 Stainless Steel
Pressure Port: ½″ NPT male
Electrical Connection: ½″ NPT conduit fitting with internal screw connections
Fill Fluid: DC 200 Silicone Oil

To Order (Specify Model Number)

RANGE	MODEL	PRICE	COMPATIBLE METERS
0-100 in H₂O	PX725-100WCGI	$630	DP2000P8, DP3002-E, DP41-E
0-200 in H₂O	PX725-007GI	630	DP2000P8, DP3002-E, DP41-E
0-15 PSIG	PX725-015GI	630	DP2000P8, DP3002-E, DP41-E
0-25 PSIG	PX725-025GI	630	DP2000P8, DP3002-E, DP41-E
0-50 PSIG	PX725-050GI	630	DP2000P8, DP3002-E, DP41-E
0-100 PSIG	PX725-100GI	630	DP2000P8, DP3002-E, DP41-E
0-300 PSIG	PX725-300GI	630	DP2000P8, DP3002-E, DP41-E
0-500 PSIG	PX725-500GI	630	DP2000P8, DP3002-E, DP41-E
0-1000 PSIG	PX725-1KGI	630	DP2000P8, DP3002-E, DP41-E
0-3000 PSIG	PX725-3KGI	630	DP205-E, DP3002-E, DP41-E
0-5000 PSIG	PX725-5KGI	630	DP205-E, DP3002-E, DP41-E

HIGHLIGHTED MODELS STOCKED FOR FAST DELIVERY

LIGHTWEIGHT INDUSTRIAL PRESSURE TRANSMITTER

From

$663

- ✔ **Miniature Size**
- ✔ **±0.25% Accuracy**
- ✔ **All Welded 316 Stainless Steel Construction**
- ✔ **Zero & Span Adjustability**
- ✔ **Full 5:1 Range Turndown**
- ✔ **4-20 mA Output**
- ✔ **FM & CSA Ratings**

The PX880 Series are the most compact, durable, accurate cost-effective full featured pressure transmitters available. The 4-20 mA output is standard, with a 12-48 Vdc power supply.

Designed for stable performance in the toughest environments, with 316 stainless steel welded construction, the PX880 Series are ideal for use with corrosive media and in hazardous environments.

Both models have FM and CSA approvals for intrinsic safety and meet NACE standards for offshore applications. With the cover retained by a stainless steel chain and no internal jumpers for span turndown, losses due to misplaced or dropped parts are eliminated.

The small size and light weight of both models eliminate any complicated mounting hardware or mechanical supports, which reduces installation time substantially. The integral junction box permits simple field wiring without the need for additional hardware, and adds to the speed and ease of installation.

OPERATION

The heart of the PX880 pressure transmitter is a silicon piezoresistive sensing chip. This miniature microetched semiconductor gives a voltage output proportional to the applied pressure. The chip is isolated from the process media by a stainless steel diaphragm. Silicone oil is used to transmit the process pressure to the sensor.

An amplifier PCB enclosed in a sealed chamber is used to convert the millivolt signal from the sensor to

Flush Mount PX881 Series Transmitter Shown

½″ NPT Model PX880 Series is also Available See C-68.

1½″ Pipe Coupling

Plug

a calibrated 4-20 mA transmitter output. Feed-throughs for EMI and RF protection are used between the amplifier board and the terminal housing.

Each transmitter is tested over both pressure and temperature ranges. A compensator circuit is used to bring the output of the sensor into specification. After compensation, every transmitter is tested a second time for pressure and temperature effects to ensure that it meets performance specifications. The transmitters are calibrated to

the upper ranges listed in the order box, but end users can recalibrate them to different ranges. Recalibration is done via 3 screw potentiometers located inside the transmitter's head. Recalibrating to any range between the two listed for a particular sensor can be accomplished with a known pressure source.

The PX881 is flush diaphragm pressure transmitter, designed to mount flush against process media and to prevent any media particles from collecting at the diaphragm.

PX880 ½" NPT SERIES AND PX881 FLUSH MOUNT SERIES

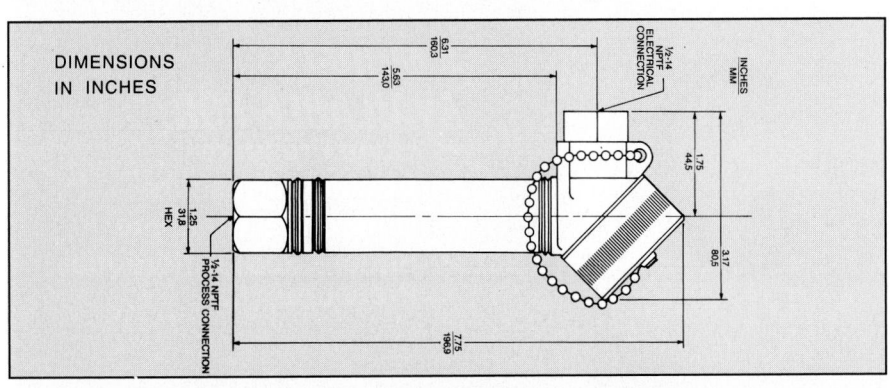

PX880 Series ½" NPT Female Connection Transmitter

OMEGACARE™ Extended Warranty Plan: not available for this product.

To Order (Specify Model Number)

RANGE, PSIG 5:1 TURNDOWN	PX880 ½" NPT FEMALE CONNECTION		
	MODEL NO.	PRICE	COMPATIBLE METER
0-3 to 0-15	PX880-015GI	$663	DP2000-P9*, DP3002-E, DP460-E
0-6 to 0-30	PX880-030GI	663	DP2000-P8*, DP3002-E, DP460-E
0-20 to 0-100	PX880-100GI	663	DP2000-P8*, DP3002-E, DP460-E
0-60 to 0-300	PX880-300GI	663	DP2000-P8*, DP3002-E, DP460-E
0-200 to 0-1000	PX880-1KGI	695	DP2000-P8*, DP3002-E, DP460-E
0-600 to 0-3000	PX880-3KGI	695	DP3002-E, DP113-R8, DP460-E
0-1000 to 0-5000	PX880-5KGI	695	DP3002-E, DP113-R8, DP460-E
3-15	PX880-X15GI	695	DP2000-P9*, DP3002-E, DP460-E

(Note: Units are shipped calibrated to highest range)
*Require transmitter power supply U24Y101 **$99**. A pressure snubber should be used with all PX880 series transmitters, to supress destructive water hammer shock waves. Snubbers are chosen by the pressure media. PS-2G for gaseous media, air, steam, etc., **$20**. PS-2E for water and light oils, **$20**. PS-2D for dense liquid, motor oil, **$20**.

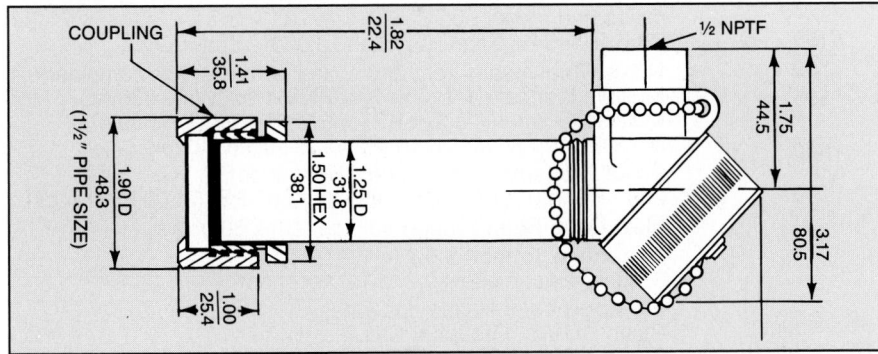

PX881 Series Flush Mount Transmitter

To Order (Specify Model Number)

RANGE, PSIG 5:1 TURNDOWN	PX881 FLUSH MOUNT TRANSMITTER		
	MODEL NO.	PRICE	COMPATIBLE METER
0-3 to 0-15	PX881-015GI	$695	DP2000-P9*, DP282-P24-C8, DP203
0-6 to 0-30	PX881-030GI	695	DP2000-P8*, DP282-P24-C8, DP203
0-20 to 0-100	PX881-100GI	695	DP2000-P8*, DP282-P24-C8, DP203
0-60 to 0-300	PX881-300GI	695	DP2000-P8*, DP282-P24-C8, DP3600*

*Requires transmitter power supply U24Y101 **$99**.
Comes with 1½" pipe coupling, plug and complete operator's manual.

Ordering Example: PX881-030GI is a flush mount transmitter with a 0-6 to 0-30 PSIG range **$695**.

SPECIFICATIONS

Excitation: 12 to 48 Vdc with reverse polarity protection

Output: 4 to 20 mA (2 wire)

Accuracy: .2% of calibrated span including linearity, hysteresis, and repeatability

Max. Loop Resistance: 600 ohms @ 24 Vdc
max ohms = (supply voltage-12) × 50

Storage Temperature: −40 to 212°F (−40 to 100°C)

Operating Temperature: −40 to 212°F (−40 to 100°C)

Compensated Temperature: −20 to 180°F (−29 to 82°C)

Thermal Effects: Zero and span combined .02% upper range/F (30 to 130°F) .032% (upper range/F (−20 to 180°F)

Proof Pressure: 200% upper range

Stability: .5% of upper range for 6 months

Vibration: .1% upper limit for 3 g @ 200 Hz

Approvals: FM (Intrinsic safety for Class 1, 2, 3, Div 1, Groups A, B, C, D, E,G: Explosion resistant for Class 1, 2, 3, Div 1, Groups B, C, D, E, G: NEMA 4 enclosure) CSA (Intrinsic safety for Class 1, 2, 3, Div 1 Groups A, B, C, D, E, F, G: Explosion resistant for Class 1, 2, 3, Div 1, Groups B, C, D, E, F, G,: enclosure 4)

Wetted Parts: 316 SS PX880; 316 SS, Teflon Gasket and Hastelloy diaphram PX881

Pressure Port: ½" NPTF PX880 Weldolet pipe coupling PX881

Electrical Conn: ½" NPTF

Body Material: 316 SS

Cast Head: CF-8M (316 Cast SS) with Buna N O-ring

Fluid Fill: DC 200 silicone oil

Response Time: 20 ms

Weight: 1.6 lbs (725 gr)

INDUSTRIAL PRESSURE TRANSMITTERS FOR RUGGED ENVIRONMENTS

PX761 Series From

$815

4 MODELS AVAILABLE FOR:
- ✔ Gage Pressure
- ✔ Absolute Pressure
- ✔ Differential Pressure
- ✔ Square Root Differential Pressure

Ω OMEGA

15.00

MAX ▶/MIN MENU RESET

Shown with Model DP41-E Meter, $345 and Optional Linear Meter PX761-M1.

ACCESSORIES:

PX761-M1 Linear Meter Kit 0-100%	**$195**
PX761-M2 Square Root Meter Kit 0-10	**$195**
PX761-B3 Mounting Bracket for 2" Piping	**$30**
PX761-FL One Stainless Steel Flange	**$95**
PX761-AD One Stainless Steel ½" NPT Process Adapter	**$60**

COMMON SPECIFICATIONS:

Excitation: 24 Vdc (12-45 Vdc)

Output: 4-20 mA (2-wire)

Accuracy: 0.25 % calibrated span (linearity, hysteresis and repeatability)

Zero Adjustment: Fully adjustable so long as transducer operates within ± max. range (PX761-XXXSQDI series is ±1% MR)

Span Adj: 6 to 1 turndown

Compensated Temp.:
Ambient: -13 to 158°F (-25 to 70°C)
Process: -22 to 212°F (-30 to 100°C)

Thermal Effects:
Calibrated at max. Span:
Zero: ±0.009 % Span/°C
Total: ±0.018 % Span/°C
(±0.06% Span/°C, PX750-030SQDI;
±0.036% Span/°C, PX761-150SQDI,-750 SQDI)
Calibrated at Mid Span:
Zero: ±0.027% Span/°C   Total: ±0.036% Span/°C

Calibrated at Min Span:
Zero: ±0.054% Span/°C Total: ±0.063% Span/°C
Notes: Total means zero and span thermal effects combined
Multiple thermal effects by 4 for PX761-006WDI,-006WGI
Multiple thermal effects by 2 for PX761-030WDI,-030WGI
Multiple thermal effects by 1.5 for absolute models

Proof Pressure: 1000 PSI (6" H₂O range)
2000 PSI (30" to 720 PSI ranges) 4500 PSI (3600 PSI range)

Max. Loop Res.: (Supply voltage -12) x 50 ohms

Response Time: Adj 0.2 to 1.7 seconds
(Square Root models 0.2 to 1.0 seconds)

FM Approvals: Hazardous areas
Class I, Div. 1, Groups B,C,D,
Class II, Div. 1, Groups E,F,G,
Class III Div. 1;
Nonincendiary Class I, Div. 2, Groups A,B,C,D;
Intrinsically safe Class I,II,III,
Div. 1, Groups A,B,C,D,E,F,G.

PHYSICAL SPECIFICATIONS:

Gage Type: Capacitance sensor, using 316SS isolation diaphragm with silicone oil fill

Wetted Parts: Cadmium plated carbon steel flanges (SS optional), 316 SS diaphragm and Viton O-ring

Pressure Port: ¼" NPTF

Electrical Conn.: ½" NPT

Electrical Housing: Epoxy painted low copper aluminum

Weight: 7 lbs (3.1 kg)

HEAVY DUTY INDUSTRIAL GAGE AND ABSOLUTE PRESSURE TRANSMITTERS

NEW!

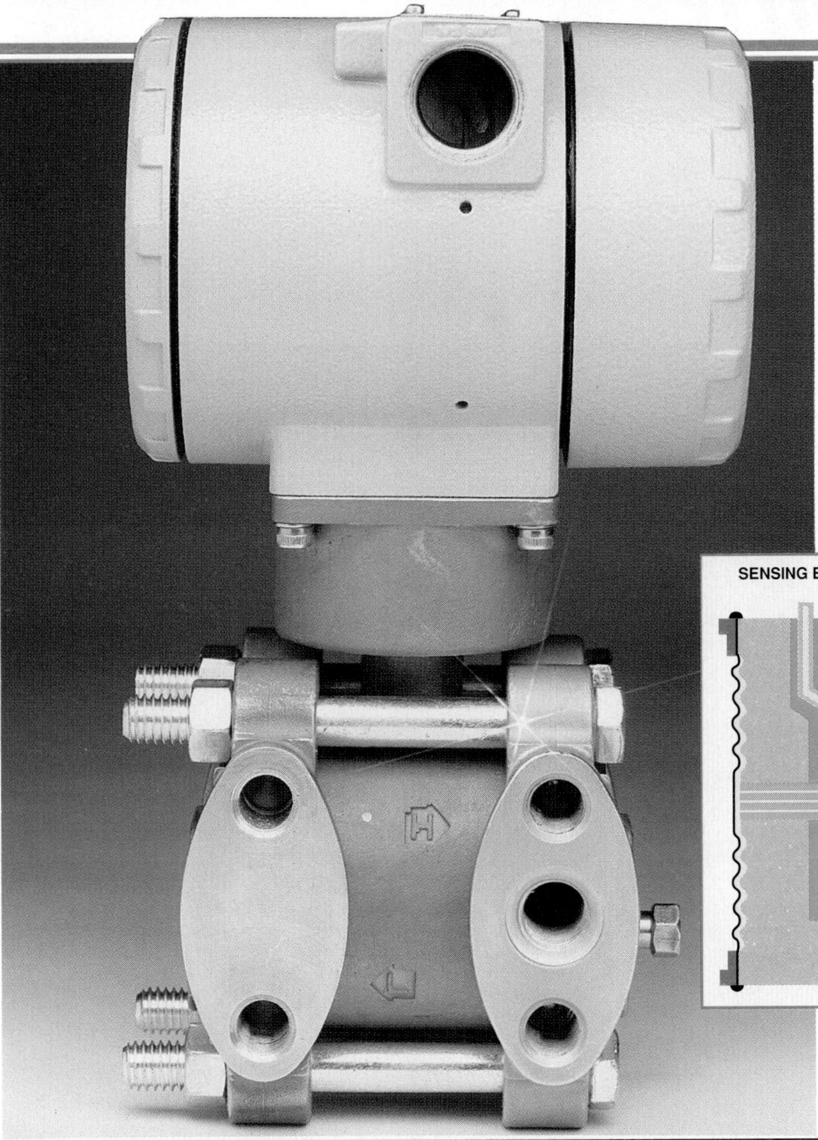

1 YEAR WARRANTY

- ✔ Compatible With Any 2-Wire System
- ✔ 6:1 Turndown Capability
- ✔ Zero Suppression and Elevation
- ✔ NEMA-4X Enclosure

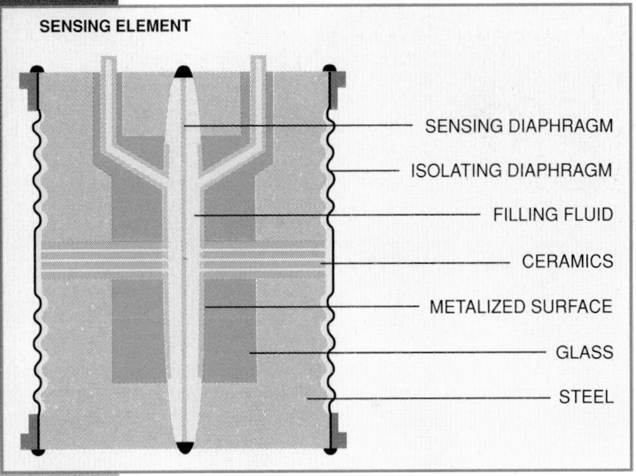

SENSING ELEMENT

- SENSING DIAPHRAGM
- ISOLATING DIAPHRAGM
- FILLING FLUID
- CERAMICS
- METALIZED SURFACE
- GLASS
- STEEL

HIGHLIGHTED MODELS IN STOCK FOR FAST DELIVERY

To Order (Specify Model Number)

RANGE	MODEL	PRICE	COMPATIBLE METER
Gage Models			
0-1" to 0-6" H_2O	**PX761-006WGI**	$895	DP41-E, DP302-E, DP460-E
0-5" to 0-30" H_2O	**PX761-030WGI**	815	DP41-E, DP3002-E, DP460-E
0-25" to 0-150" H_2O	**PX761-150WGI**	815	DP41-E, DP302-E, DP460-E
0-125" to 0-750" H_2O	**PX761-750WGI**	815	DP41-E, DP3002-E, DP460-E
0-24 to 0-144 PSIG	**PX761-144GI**	895	DP41-E, DP302-E, DP460-E
0-120 to 0-720 PSIG	**PX761-720GI**	895	DP41-E, DP3002-E, DP460-E
0-600 to 0-3600 PSIG	**PX761-3600GI**	895	DP41-E, DP3002-E, DP460-E
ABSOLUTE MODELS			
0-25" to 0-150" H_2O	**PX761-150WAI**	995	DP41-E, DP302-E, DP460-E
0-125" to 0-750" H_2O	**PX761-750WAI**	995	DP41-E, DP3002-E, DP460-E
0-24 to 0-144 PSIA	**PX761-144AI**	1115	DP41-E, DP302-E, DP460-E
0-120 to 0-720 PSIA	**PX761-720AI**	1115	DP41-E, DP3002-E, DP460-E
0-600 to 0-3600 PSIA	**PX761-3600A**	1115	DP41-E, DP3002-E, DP460-E

All models come with complete operator's manual.
Ordering Example: *PX761-030WGI is 30" of H_2O industrial gage transmitter, **$815**.*

NEW!

HEAVY DUTY INDUSTRIAL DIFFERENTIAL PRESSURE TRANSMITTER

✔ **316 Stainless Steel Isolation Diaphragm**
✔ **Accommodates High Static Line Pressures While Sensing Low Delta Pressures**
✔ **Uses Capacitance Sensing Element**

Shown with Two PX761-AD Adaptors ($60 each).

ALL MODELS IN STOCK FOR FAST DELIVERY

SPECIFICATIONS:
Static Pressure: 2000 PSI
(1000 PSI 6" H_2O Range)
Static Zero Effects:
1.0 % of max. range 6" H_2O range
0.5 % of max. range 30" H_2O range
0.25% of max. range 150 & 750" H_2O range

To Order *(Specify Model Number)*			
RANGE	MODEL	PRICE	COMPATIBLE METER
0-1 to 0-6" H_2O	PX761-006WDI	$985	DP41-E,DP302-E, DP460-E
0-5 to 0-30" H_2O	PX761-030WDI	885	DP41-E,DP3002-E, DP460-E
0-25 to 0-150" H_2O	PX761-150WDI	885	DP41-E,DP302-E, DP460-E
0-125 to 0-750" H_2O	PX761-750WDI	885	DP41-E,DP3002-E, DP460-E

All models come with complete operator's manual.
Ordering Example: *PX761-030WDI is 30" of H_2O industrial differential gage transmitter, **$885**.*

INDUSTRIAL SQUARE ROOT OUTPUT PRESSURE TRANSMITTER
FOR FLOW APPLICATIONS

1 YEAR WARRANTY

- ✔ Works with Pitot Tubes, Venturis, and Orifice Plates for Measuring Flow Rates/Totals
- ✔ Adjustable Damping
- ✔ High Static Pressure Ratings
- ✔ Compatible with Most Liquids and Gases

Works with Pitot Tube Shown in Photo. See Section G of OMEGA's Flow and Level Handbook.

Shown with Two PX761-AD Adaptors ($60 each).

SPECIFICATIONS:
Static Pressure: 2000 PSI
Static Zero Effects:
1.0% of max. range 30" H$_2$O range
0.5% of max. range 150 & 750" H$_2$O range

To Order *(Specify Model Number)*

RANGE	MODEL	PRICE	COMPATIBLE METER
0-5 to 0-30" H$_2$O	**PX761-030SQDI**	$1055	DP41-E, DP3002-E, DP460-E
0-25 to 0-150" H$_2$O	**PX761-150SQDI**	1055	DP41-E, DP302-E, DP460-E
0-125 to 0-750" H$_2$O	**PX761-750SQDI**	1055	DP41-E, DP3002-E, DP460-E

"SMART" INDUSTRIAL PRESSURE TRANSMITTERS

TX300
Smart Temperature
Transmitter, $650. See
Temperature Handbook,
Page N-5.

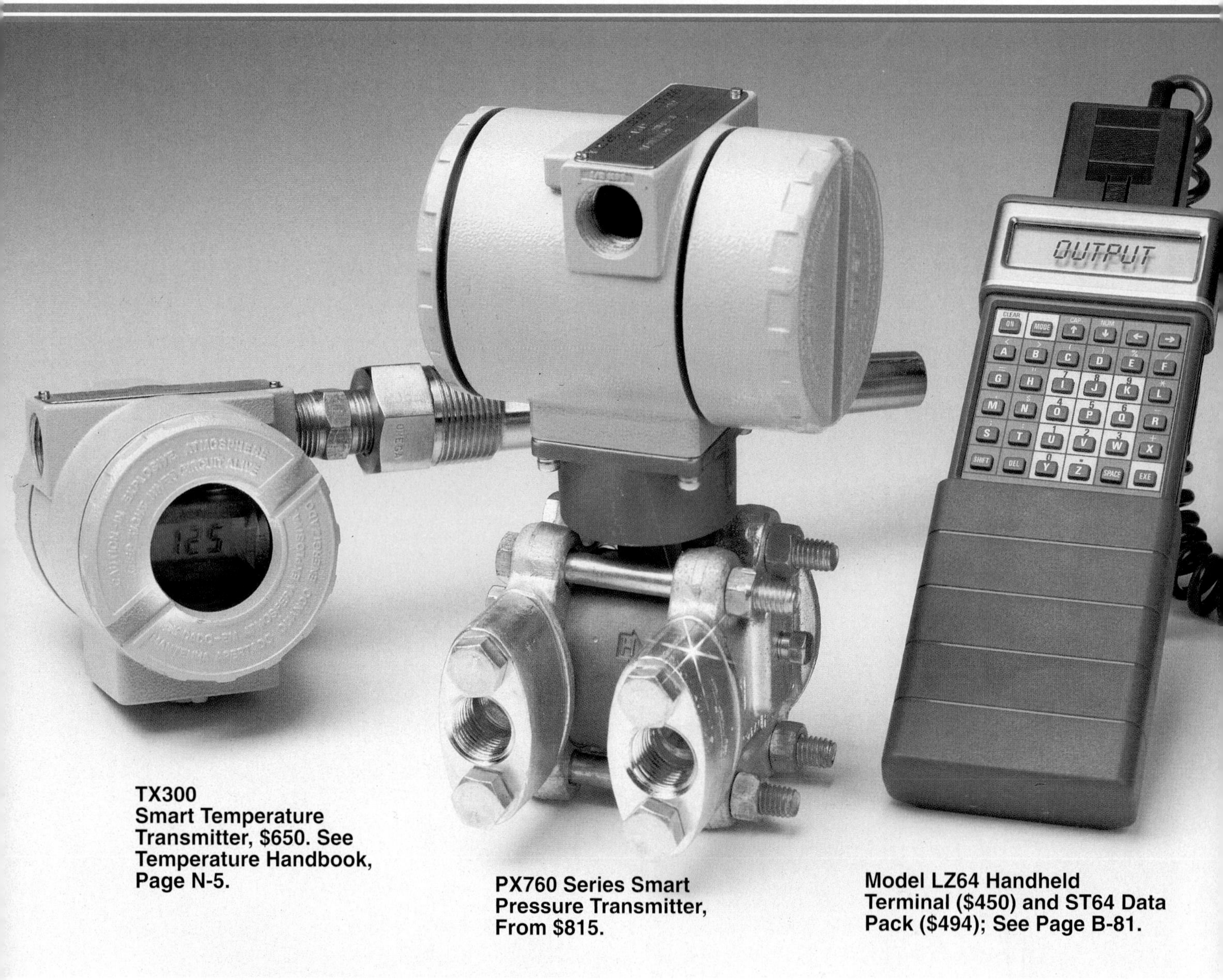

PX760 Series Smart
Pressure Transmitter,
From $815.

Model LZ64 Handheld
Terminal ($450) and ST64 Data
Pack ($494); See Page B-81.

ACCESSORIES:
PX763-M3, *Local 4 digit LCD display,*
$195
PX761-B3, *Mounting bracket for 2"*
piping, **$30**
PX761-AD, *One stainless steel*
½" NPT process adaptor, **$60**

OMEGA' s "Smart" PX763 Series sensors can be reprogrammed by a handheld terminal (HHT), a Personal Computer (PC) or by any human or machine interface featuring HART protocol [such as several Data Communication Systems (DCS)]. Reprogramming includes rescaling the transmitter to different pressure ranges, changing the transmitter into a controller, changing setpoints and other PID control funtions, logging all calibration information such as time and date of prior calibrations and adjusting transmitter specifications (such as damping time and square root output). The PX763 Series are microprocessor based sensors which offer the user unmatched accuracy and versatility.

These "Smart" sensors output both a 4-20 mA current signal and a digital signal across the same two wires. The transmitter signal can also operate as a combination of transmitter plus controller. (The 4-20 mA signal is used as the output of a PID control function, while the digital signal is used for remote monitoring of the process.)

The PX763 Series sensors can be wired in a multi-drop arrangement. The multi-drop configurations utilize one handheld terminal to monitor and reprogram several "Smart" sensors without leaving the control room. The 40:1 turndown capability and independent zero and span adjustments make replacing sensors an easy assignment with minimum spare units.

"SMART" HEAVY DUTY INDUSTRIAL PRESSURE TRANSMITTER

 NEW!

From
$985

Shown with Two PX761-AD Adaptors ($60 each).

PX763 SERIES AVAILABLE FOR:
- ✔ Gage Pressure
- ✔ Absolute Pressure
- ✔ Differential Pressure
- ✔ Square Root Differential Pressure
- ✔ Direct Digital Communications Using HART Protocol
- ✔ All Units can be Reprogrammed Via a Handheld Communicator
- ✔ Choice of PID Control or Retransmission of Pressure Signal

COMMON SPECIFICATIONS:
Excitation: 24 Vdc (12-45 Vdc)

Output: 4-20 mA (2 wire) and a superimposed digital signal (BELL 202 - HART protocol)

Accuracy: 0.1% calibrated span (linearity, hysteresis and repeatability) $(.05 \times (1 + .1 \times UR/Span)$ % cal span for cal span <10% of upper range)

Zero Adjustment: Fully adjustable so long as transmitter operates within ± upper range (UR)

Span Adj: 40 to 1 Turndown

Storage Temp: -40 to 212°F (-40 to 100°C)

COMPENSATED TEMP.:
Ambient: -13 to 167°F (-25 to 75°C)

Process: -40 to 212°F (-40 to 100°C)

Display: -14 to 167°F (-10 to 75°C)

THERMAL EFFECTS:
Zero and Span combined (% Span /°C): (.050% x UR + 0.15% x Span)/20°C [For 20" H_2O range (0.075% x UR + 0.20% Span)/20 C]

Stability: 0.1% UR for 6 months (0.2% UR/6 months for 20" H_2O)

Static Pressure: 1000 PSI (20" H_2O range) 2000 PSI (200"H_2O to 360 PSI ranges) 4500 PSI (3600 PSI range)

Burst Pressure: 8570 PSI

Max. Loop Res.: (Supply voltage - 12) x 50 ohms

Response Time: Adj. 0.2 to 32 seconds

PHYSICAL SPECIFICATIONS:
Gage Type: Capacitance sensor, using 316L SS isolation diaphragm with silicone oil fill

Wetted Parts: Cadmium plated carbon steel flanges (SS optional), 316L SS diaphragm, 316 SS vents/drains and Viton O-ring

Pressure Port: ¼" NPTF

Electrical Conn.: ½" NPTF

Electrical Housing: Epoxy painted low copper aluminum

Weight: 7 lbs (3.1 kg)

COMMUNICATOR:
RAM Memory: 32 K bytes

EPROM Memory: 64 K bytes expandable

Display: 80 characters, 4 lines

Power Supply : 9 Vdc battery

Dimensions: 5.6"H x 3.1"W x 1.2"D (142mm x 78mm x 29mm D)

"SMART" INDUSTRIAL GAGE AND ABSOLUTE PRESSURE TRANSMITTERS

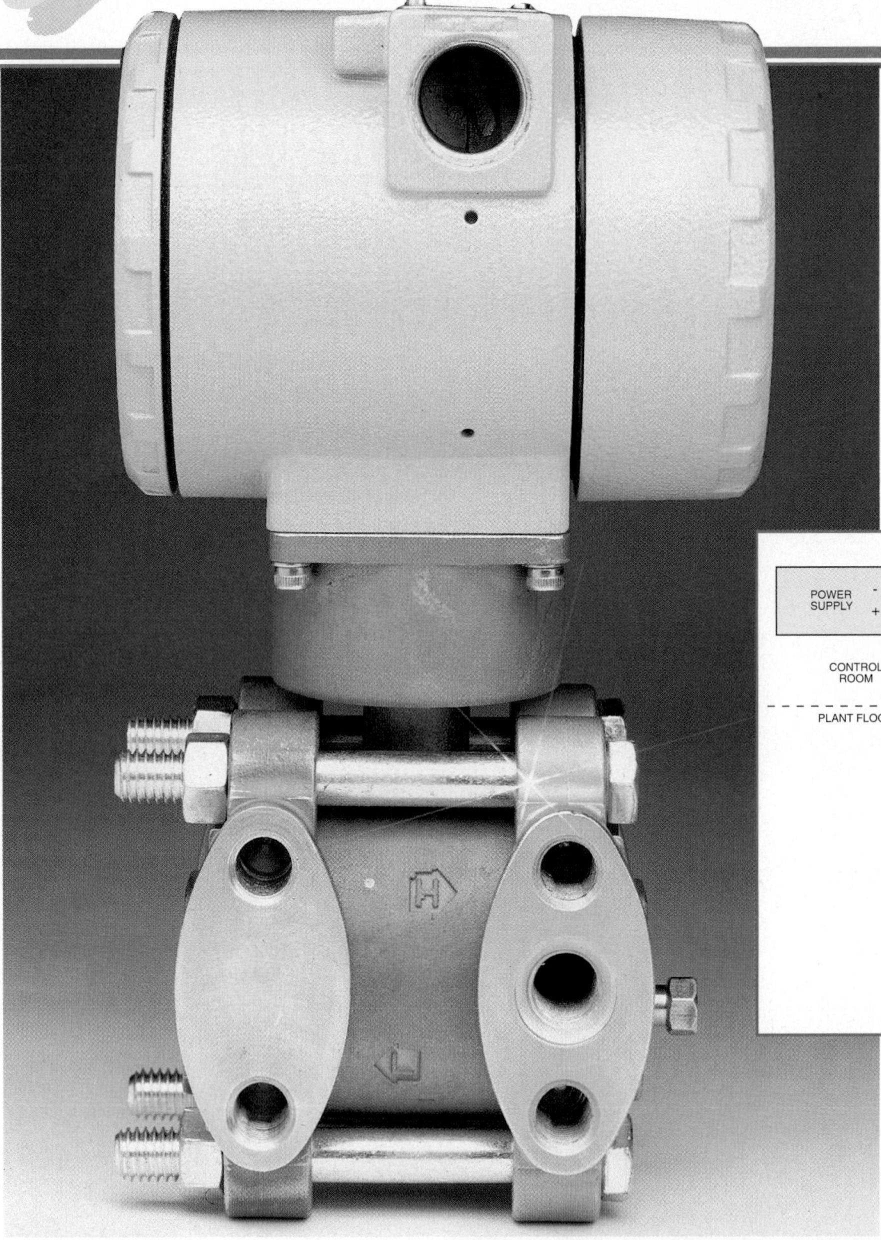

1 YEAR WARRANTY

- ✔ Digital HART Protocol
- ✔ 40:1 Turndown Capability
- ✔ True Non Interactive Zero and Span Adjustments
- ✔ 0.1% Accuracy

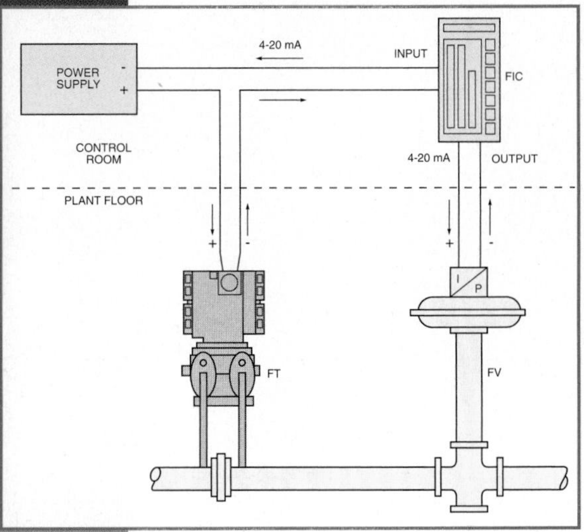

ACCESSORIES

MODEL	PRICE	DESCRIPTION
LZ64	$450	Communicator, handheld computer terminal (requires ST64)
ST64	494	Data pack for LZ64, interface cabling, and alligator clips

To Order (Specify Model Number)

RANGE	MODEL	PRICE	COMPATIBLE METER
GAGE MODELS			
0-0.5 to 0-20" H_2O	**PX763-020WGI**	$1085	DP41-E,DP3002-E, DP460-E
0-5 to 0-200" H_2O	**PX763-200WGI**	985	DP41-E,DP3002-E, DP460-E
0-1 to 0-36 PSIG	**PX763-036GI**	985	DP41-E,DP3002-E, DP460-E
0-9 to 0-360 PSIG	**PX763-360GI**	1085	DP41-E,DP3002-E, DP460-E
0-90 to 0-3600 PSIG	**PX763-3600KGI**	1085	DP41-E,DP3002-E, DP460-E
ABSOLUTE MODELS			
0-0.4 to 0-7.2 PSIA	**PX763-007AI**	$1185	DP41-E,DP3002-E, DP460-E
0-1 to 0-36 PSIA	**PX763-036AI**	1185	DP41-E,DP3002-E, DP460-E
0-9 to 0-360 PSIA	**PX763-360AI**	1290	DP41-E,DP3002-E, DP460-E
0-90 to 0-3600 PSIA	**PX763-3600AI**	1290	DP41-E,DP3002-E, DP460-E

*Ordering Example: PX763-200WGI, LZ64, and ST64 is a smart transmitter, a programmable handheld unit, and mating hardware, $985 + 450 + 494 = **$1929**.*

"SMART" INDUSTRIAL DIFFERENTIAL PRESSURE TRANSMITTER

NEW!

- ✔ Configurable for Delta Pressure or Square Root Delta Pressure Outputs for Flow Applications
- ✔ High Static Pressure Ratings
- ✔ NEMA 4 Weatherproof Enclosure

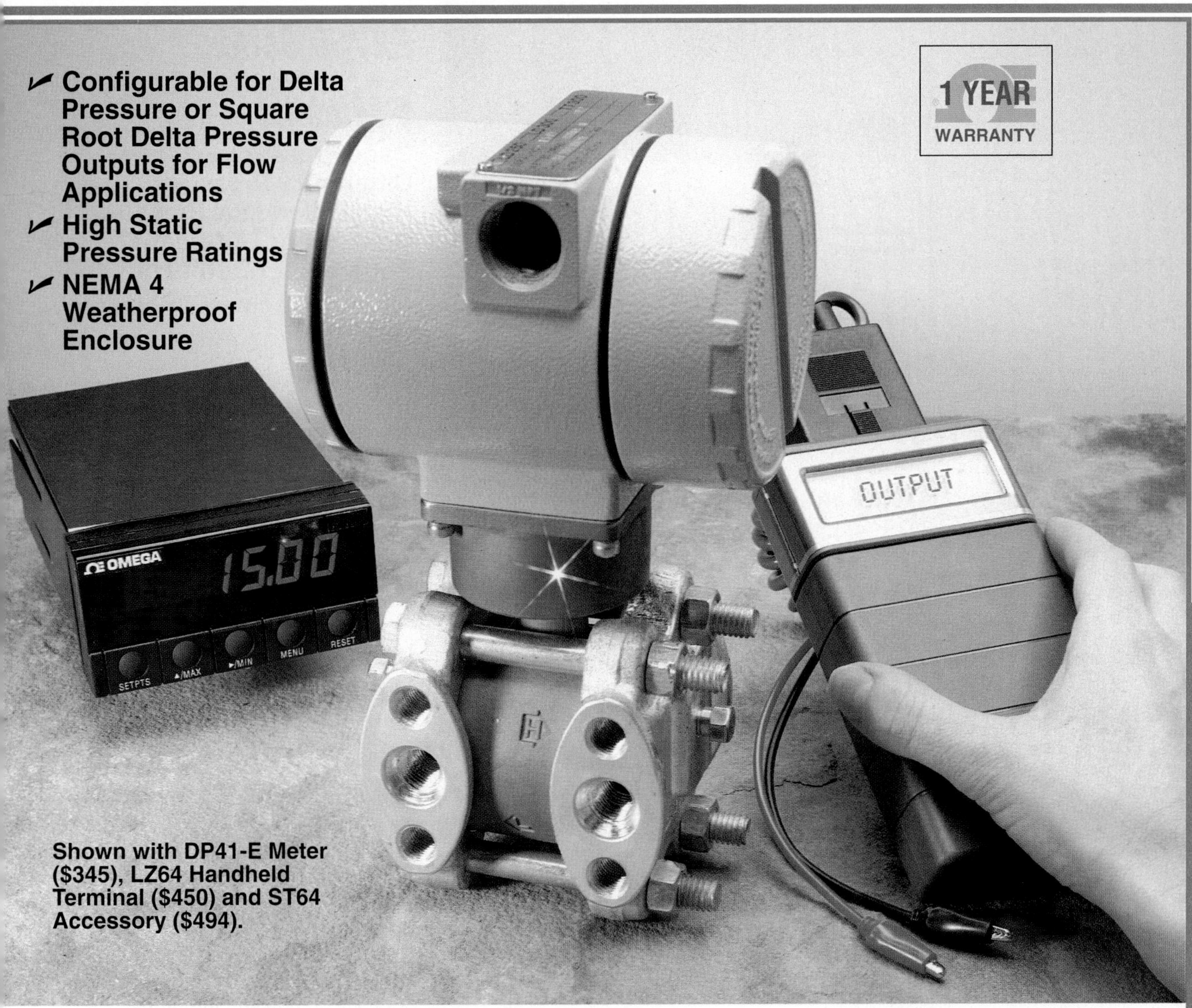

1 YEAR WARRANTY

OUTPUT

Shown with DP41-E Meter ($345), LZ64 Handheld Terminal ($450) and ST64 Accessory ($494).

The PX963 Series pressure transmitters offer the flexibility of a single differential pressure transmitter that can be reprogrammed via a handheld terminal to a square root output transmitter for flow measurements. Reprogramming via the HHT for different pressure ranges, along with high accuracy specifications, make this product ideal for most industrial applications.

SPECIFICATIONS:
Static Pressure: 2000 PSI
(1000 PSI for 20" H_2O range)

STATIC PRESSURE EFFECTS:
Zero: 0.1% Upper Range/1000 PSI
(0.1% UR/500 PSI for 20" H_2O range)
Span: 0.2% Upper Range/1000 PSI
(0.2% UR/500 PSI for 20" H_2O range)

ACCESSORIES

MODEL	PRICE	DESCRIPTION
LZ64	$450	Communicator, handheld computer terminal (requires ST64)
ST64	494	Data pack for LZ64, interface cabling and alligator clips

To Order (Specify Model Number)

RANGE	MODEL	PRICE	COMPATIBLE METER
0-0.5 to 0-20 H_2OD	**PX763-020WDI**	$1165	DP41-E, DP3002-E, DP460-E
0-5 to 0-200 H_2OD	**PX763-200WDI**	1055	DP41-E, DP3002-E, DP460-E
0-1 to 0-36 PSID	**PX763-036DI**	1055	DP41-E, DP3002-E, DP460-E
0-9 to 0-360 PSID	**PX763-360DI**	1165	DP41-E, DP3002-E, DP460-E

***Ordering Example:** PX763-200WDI, LZ64 and ST64 is a smart transmitter, a programmable handheld unit and mating hardware, $1055 + 450 + 494 = **$1999**.*

HEAVY DUTY INDUSTRIAL PROCESS TRANSMITTERS
GAGE AND DIFFERENTIAL PRESSURE

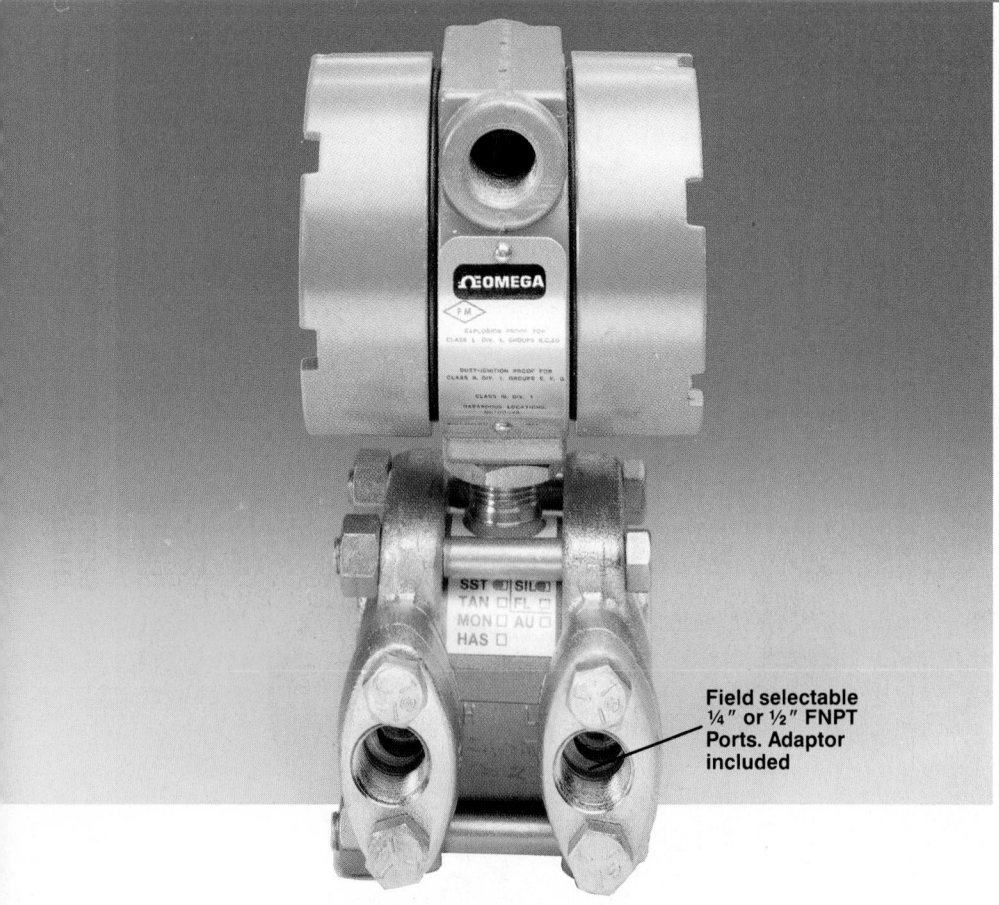

Field selectable ¼" or ½" FNPT Ports. Adaptor included

PX750 Series

5 Models:

Gage Pressure
Differential Pressure
High Differential Pressure
Draft Range Differential
Square Root Output

For ordering information, see pages B-84 through B-87

From
$955

Shown smaller than actual size

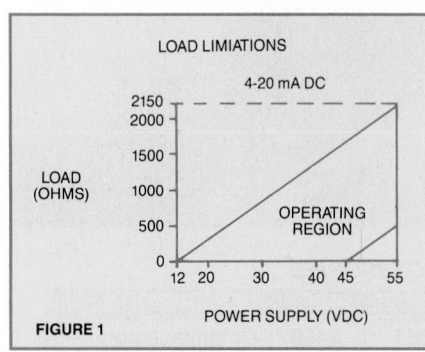

FIGURE 1

ACCESSORIES

PX750-M1 Linear Meter Kit 0 to 100% Scale **$198**
PX750-M2 Square Root Meter Kit 0 to 10% Scale **$198**
PX750-B3 Mounting Bracket Kit for Flush Panel Mounting or 2" Pipe **$40**

SPECIFICATIONS *(For All Models)*
Service: Liquid, Gas, Vapor
Outputs: 4-20 mA dc
Power Supplies: 12 to 45 V dc with no load. See chart for loop resistance (Figure 1).

Indication: Optional meter with 1¾", 0-100% scale; accuracy is 2% of span
Hazardous Locations: Factory mutual (FM) approvals: Class 1 Division 1 and 2, Groups B, C, and D.
Dust-ignition proof: Class 2, Divisions 1 and 2, Groups E, F, & G.
Suitable for use in: Class 3, Divisions 1 and 2. Indoor and outdoor use. NEMA 4X.
Zero and Span: Continuously adjustable externally
Zero Elevation and Suppression:
Regardless of output specified, zero elevation and suppression must be such that neither the span nor the upper or lower range value, exceed 100% of th eupper range limit. Maximum zero elevation: 600% of calibrated span. Maximum zero suppression: 500% of calibrated span
Temperature Limits: Amplifier: – 20 to + 200°F (– 29 to – 93°C)
Square Root Amplifier: – 20 to 150°F (– 29 to 66°C)
Element: – 40 to 220°F (– 40 to 104°C)
Humidity Limits: 0 to 100% Relative Humidity

Volumetric Displacement: Less than .01 cubic inches (.16cm^3)
Turn On Time: 2 seconds—no warm up required
PHYSICAL SPECIFICATIONS
Isolating Diaphragm: 316 Stainless Steel
Drain/Vent Valves: 316 Stainless Steel
Process Flange and Adaptor: Cadmium plated carbon steel std. (316 Stainless Steel Optional)
Wetted O-Rings: Viton® A (Floro-Polymer)
Fill Fluid: Silicon Oil
Bolts: Cadmium Plated Carbon Steel
Electronic Housing: Low Copper Aluminum
Paint: Epoxy-Polyester
Electrical Connections: ½" conduit with screw terminals and integral test jacks compatible with miniature banana plugs
Weight: 12 pounds (5.44 kg) excluding options
Vibration Effect: .05% of upper range limit per G to 200 Hz in any axis
Power Supply Effect: < .005% of shift up to 1" H_2O which can be calibrated out

HEAVY DUTY GAGE PRESSURE TRANSMITTER
RUGGED NEMA 4X ENCLOSURE

PX750 Series
0-5" H₂0 to 6000 PSIG

- ✔ **Stainless Steel Diaphragm**
- ✔ **High Accuracy 0.25% of Span**
- ✔ **FM Explosion Proof Rating; NEMA 4X Enclosure**
- ✔ **4 to 20 mA Current Output**
- ✔ **External Zero and Span Adjustments**
- ✔ **Compatible With Any 2-Wire System**

The OMEGA PX750 Gage Pressure Transmitter brings true precision and reliability to industrial pressure monitoring applications. Process pressure is transmitted through an isolating diaphragm and an oil fill fluid to a central sensing diaphragm. The atmospheric reference pressure is transmitted similarly to the other side of the sensing diaphragm. The displacement of the sensing diaphragm is proportional to the pressure differential across it. In addition to gage pressure, the PX750 can also measure vacuums by simply reversing the process connection to the sensing element.

SPECIFICATIONS

Accuracy: ±0.25% of calibrated span (includes linearity, hysteresis, and repeatability
Stability: ±0.25%
Temperature Effect: At Maximum Span: (e.g. 0 to 100 PSIG for 0 to 17/100 PSIG

range); Zero error = ±0.5% of span per 100°F (55°C). Total effect including span and zero errors = ±1.0% of span per 100°F (55°C)
Temperature Effect: At Minimum Span: (e.g. 0 to 17 PSIG for 0 to 17/100 PSIG range) Zero error = ±3.0% of span per 100°F (55°C). Total effect including span

and zero errors = ±3.5% of span per 100°F (55°C) (double the specified effects for 30" H₂O range)
Mounting: ½ NPT on adaptor, ¼ NPT with adaptor removed
Damping: Time constant continuously adjustable between 0.2 (0.4 for 30" H₂O range) to 1.67 seconds for silicone fill

To Order *(Specify Model Number)*

SEE SECTION D FOR INSTRUMENT SELECTION

MODEL	PRICE	LOWER RANGE GAGE PRESSURE	UPPER RANGE GAGE PRESSURE	COMPATIBLE METER
PX750-30GI	$1065	0 to 5" H₂0	0 to 30" H₂0	DP2000P8, TX81, DP3002-E
PX750-150GI	955	0 to 25" H₂0	0 to 150" H₂0	DP460-E, TX81, DP3002-E
PX750-750GI	955	0 to 125" H₂0	0 to 750" H₂0	DP2000P8, TX81, DP3002-E
PX750-100GI	955	0 to 17 PSI	0 to 100 PSI	DP2000P8, TX81, DP3002-E
PX750-300GI	955	0 to 50 PSI	0 to 300 PSI	DP2000P8, TX81, DP3002-E
PX750-1KGI	955	0 to 170 PSI	0 to 1000 PSI	DP2000P8, TX81, DP3002-E
PX750-3KGI	1065	0 to 500 PSI	0 to 3000 PSI	DP460-E, DP41-E, DP3002-E
PX750-6KGI	1065	0 to 1000 PSI	0 to 6000 PSI	DP460-E, DP41-E, DP3002-E

For 316SS stainless steel flanges and adaptors add suffix ''SS'' to model number and $41 to base price.

HEAVY DUTY DIFFERENTIAL PRESSURE TRANSMITTER
RANGES FROM 0 TO 5" H2O TO 750" H2O DIFFERENTIAL

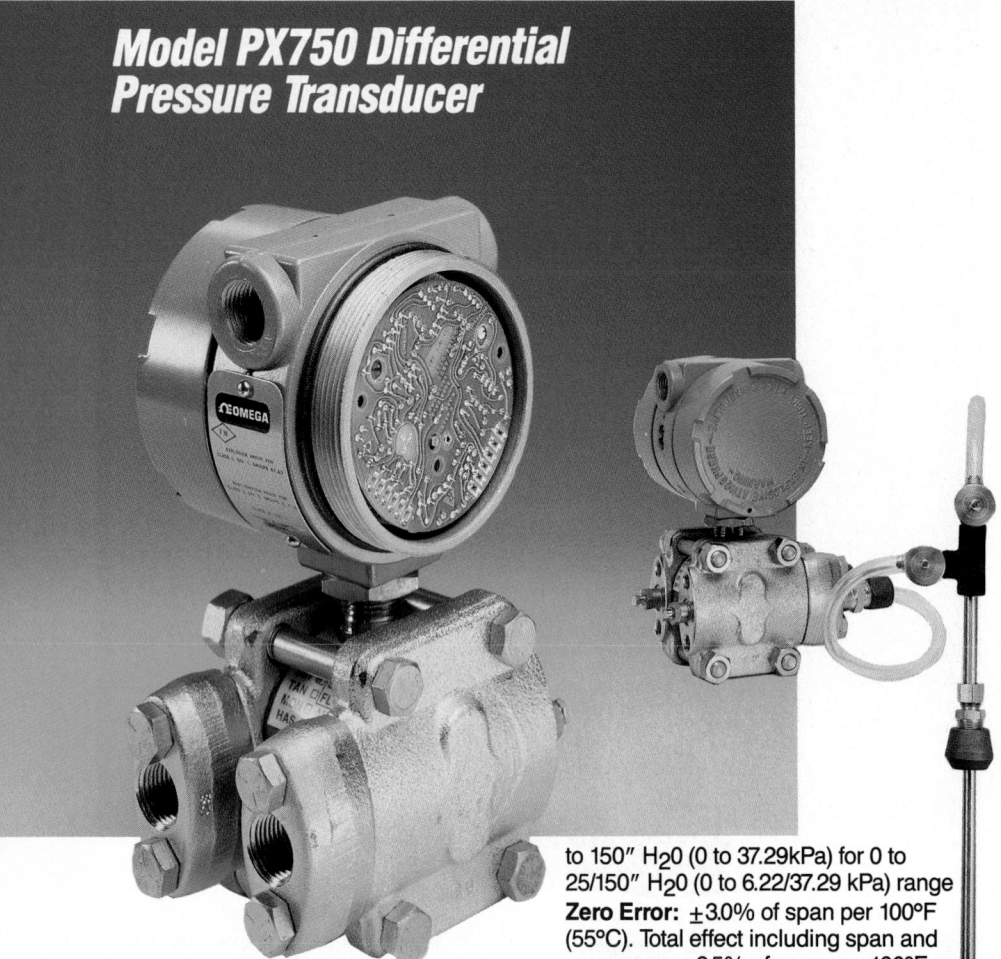

Model PX750 Differential Pressure Transducer

- ✔ **High Accuracy — 0.2% of Span**
- ✔ **External Zero and Span Adjustments Up to 600% Elevation or 500% Suppression**
- ✔ **Stainless Steel Diaphragm**
- ✔ **NEMA 4X Enclosure**
- ✔ **Compatible With Any Two Wire System**

The PX750 Pressure Transmitter is designed for accurate differential measurements in higher pressure ranges such as level measurements on towers and pressure drop across compressors. Full overpressure protection to 2000 PSI permits confident application in high pressure systems. Installation is simplified by compact design, 2-wire compatibility, external span and zero adjustments all in an explosion and weather proof NEMA 4X enclosure.

between static line pressures of 0.5 PSIA and 2000 PSIG (3.44kPa to 13.79 MPa). 10,000 PSIG (68.95 MPa) proof pressure on the flanges.

High Differential Models: Zero error: $\pm 0.5\%$ of upper range limit for 2000 PSI. Span error: $-1 \pm 0.25\%$ of reading per 1000 PSI. This is a systematic error which can be calibrated out for a particular pressure before installation.

Damping: Time constant continuously adjustable between 0.2 and 1.67 s with silicone fill.

Process Connections: ¼ NPT on 2 1/8" centers on flanges. ½ NPT on 2", 2 1/8" or 2¼" centers with adapters

SPECIFICATIONS

Accuracy: $\pm 0.2\%$ of calibrated span. Includes combined effects of linearity, hysteresis and repeatability

Linearity: $\pm 0.1\%$ of calibrated design

Hysteresis: 0.05% of calibrated span

Dead Band: None

Stability: $\pm 0.2\%$ of upper range limit for 6 months

Temperature Effect: At maximum span 0

to 150" H2O (0 to 37.29kPa) for 0 to 25/150" H2O (0 to 6.22/37.29 kPa) range

Zero Error: $\pm 3.0\%$ of span per 100°F (55°C). Total effect including span and zero errors $\pm 3.5\%$ of span per 100°F (55°C). Note: Double the specified effect for range 30" H2O.

Static Pressure Effect: Zero error: $\pm 0.25\%$ of upper range limit for 2000 PSI (13.79MPa) $\pm 0.5\%$ for 30" H2O range. Span error: correctable to 0.25% of the reading or to $\pm 0.5\%$ for 30" H2O range.

Static pressure and Overpressure Limits: 0 PSIA to 2000 PSIG (0 to 13.79 MPa) on either side without damage to the transmitter. Operates within specifications

To Order (Specify Model Number)		HIGHLIGHTED MODELS STOCKED FOR FAST DELIVERY		*SEE SECTION D FOR INSTRUMENT SELECTION
MODEL	**PRICE**	**LOWER RANGE DIFFERENTIAL**	**UPPER RANGE DIFFERENTIAL**	**COMPATIBLE METER**
PX750-30DI	$1145	0 to 5" H2O	0 to 30" H2O	DP2000P8, TX81, DP3002-E
PX750-150DI	1035	0 to 25" H2O	0 to 150" H2O	DP2000P8, TX81, DP3002-E
PX750-750DI	1035	0 to 125" H2O	0 to 750" H2O	DP2000P8, TX81, DP3002-E
HIGH DIFFERENTIAL PRESSURES				
PX750-100HDI	1185	0 to 17 PSI	0 to 100 PSI	DP2000P8, TX81, DP3002-E
PX750-300HDI	1185	0 to 50 PSI	0 to 300 PSI	DP2000P8, TX81, DP3002-E
PX750-1KHDI	1185	0 to 170 PSI	0 to 1000 PSI	DP2000P8, TX81, DP3002-E

DRAFT RANGE DIFFERENTIAL PRESSURE TRANSMITTER
RANGES FROM 0 TO ½″ H₂O TO 6″ H₂O

- ✔ **Compact Size for Easy Mounting**
- ✔ **1000 PSI Static Pressure Capability**
- ✔ **NEMA 4X Enclosure**
- ✔ **High Accuracy — 0.5% Span**
- ✔ **FM Explosion Proof Rating**

Designed for monitoring low pressure flow rates, the PX750 draft range pressure transmitter will measure extremely low pressure differentials with both positive and/or negative static pressure capabilities. Ideal for use in many types of combustion processes, the unit will measure furnace pressure, gas flow to low pressure burners, total, primary and secondary air flow, draft loss and other parameters. Housing construction is explosion proof and weather proof and plug in printed circuit cards simplify inspection, troubleshooting and maintenance.

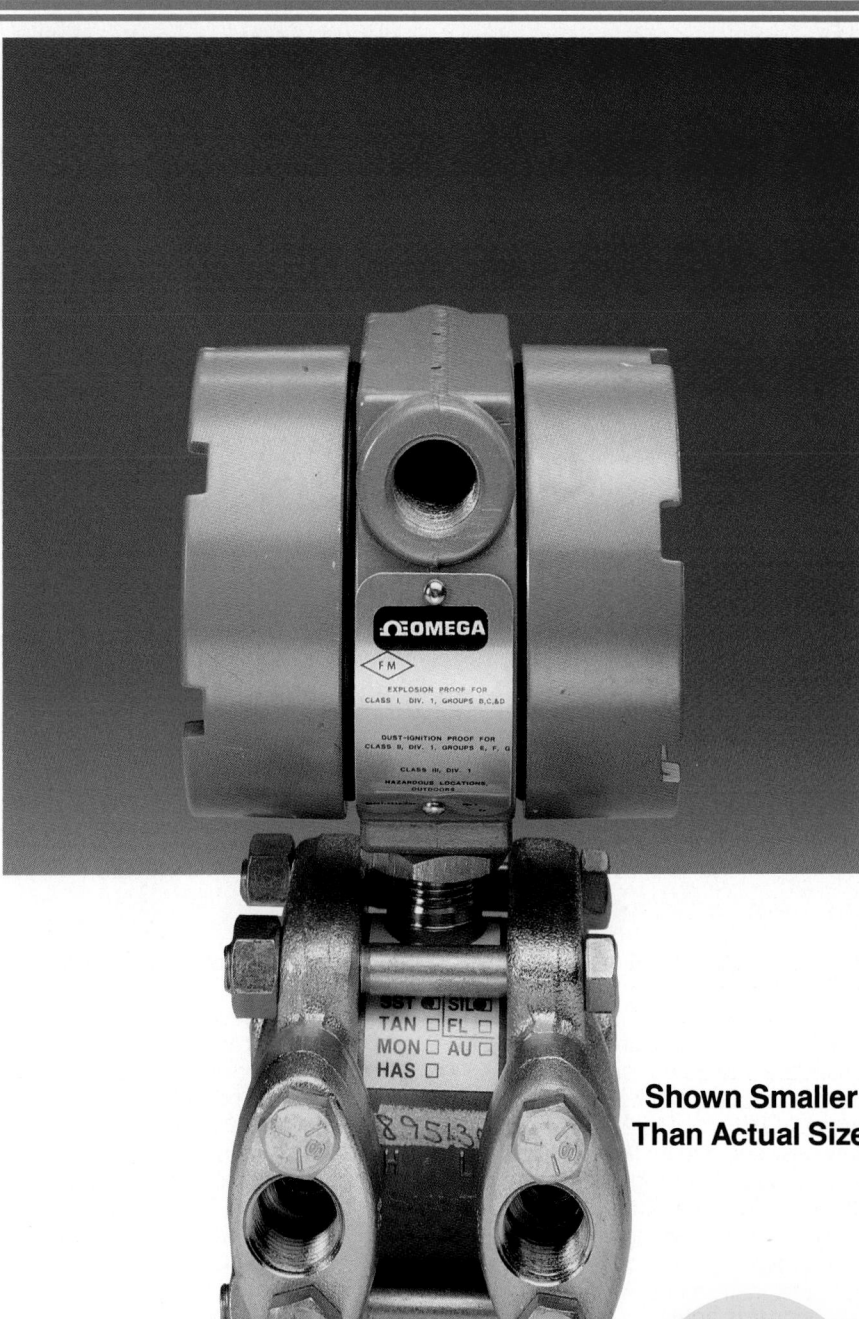

Shown Smaller Than Actual Size

$1495

SPECIFICATIONS

Accuracy: ±0.5% of calibrated span. Includes combined effects of hysteresis, linearity and repeatability

Dead Band: None

Stability: ±5% of upper range limit for 6 months

Temperature Effect at Maximum span 0 to 6″ H₂0: Zero error ±1% of span per 50°F. Total error ±1.5% of span per 50°F

Static Pressure and Overpressure Limits: 0 PSIA to 1000 PSIG on either or both sides without damage to the transmitter. Operates within specification for static pressure from 1″ Hg absolute to 1000 PSIG.

Static Pressure Effect: Zero effect: ±1% of upper range limit for 1000 PSI. Span error: −1.75 ±0.75% of reading for 1000 PSI. This is a systematic error which can be calibrated out prior to installation.

Damping: Time constant continuously adjustable between 0.4 and 4.0 seconds

See page B-83 for options and dimensions.

HIGHLIGHTED MODELS STOCKED FOR FAST DELIVERY

To Order *(Specify Model Number)*

SEE SECTION D FOR INSTRUMENT SELECTION

MODEL	LOWER RANGE DIFFERENTIAL	UPPER RANGE DIFFERENTIAL	COMPATIBLE METER
PX750-06DI	0 to ½″ H₂O	0 to 6″ H₂O	DP2000P8, DP3002-E

Add "SS" suffix for 316 stainless steel flanges and adapters. Add $41 to price.

SQUARE ROOT PRESSURE TRANSMITTER FOR FLOW MEASUREMENT
MODEL PX750 FLOW TRANSMITTER RANGES FOR 5″ TO 750″ H2O

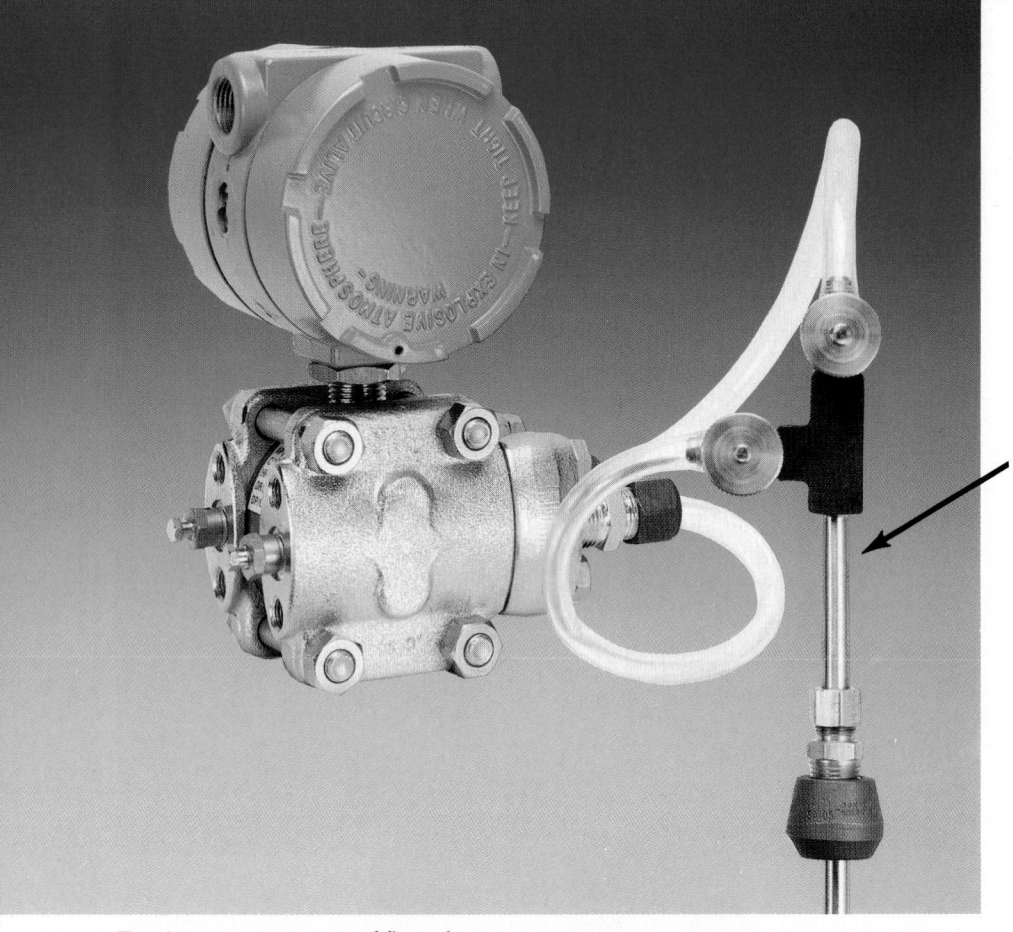

- **Output Linear with Flow**
- **High Accuracy — 0.25%**
- **Adjustable Damping**
- **Linear Zero Functions for High Stability**
- **Rugged NEMA 4X Industrial Enclosure**

Shown in typical installation with a Pitot tube sensor. See the OMEGA Flow Handbook for a complete selection of Flow Products.

From
$1295

For the measurement of flow, the PX750 transmitter combines the square root extraction function within the differential pressure transmitter to provide a 4 to 20 mA signal directly proportional to flow. It is compatible with all OMEGA 4 to 20 mA readout devices. The PX750 flow transmitter has an operable range from 20 to 100% of flow rate. No additional power supplies, wiring or additional "block boxes" are required for use with this instrument. A stable zero flow signal is achieved by electronically switching from a square root to a linear function at 20% of flow.

SPECIFICATIONS

Accuracy: ±0.25% of calibrated span for a range of 20% to 100% of flow (4% to 100% of input pressure). Includes combined effects of hysteresis, repeatability, and conformity of the square root function. Output linear with input pressure for the range of 0 to 20% of flow (0 to 4% of input pressure).
Dead Band: None

Stability: ±0.25% of upper range limit for six months
Temperature Effect: The total output effect, whether at zero or full scale, including zero and span errors: ±1.5% of upper range limit per 100°F (55°C) (±0.25% for PX750-30 model)
Static Pressure Effect: Zero error: ±0.25% of differential pressure upper range limit for 2000 PSI (13.79 MPa) (±0.5% for PX750-30 model. Span error: correctable to ±0.125% of reading per 1000 PSI (6.89 MPa) (±0.25% for PX750-30 model) This is a systematic error which can be calibrated out for a particular pressure before installation.

Damping: Time constant continuously adjustable between 0.2 and 1.0 seconds.
Static Pressure and Overpressure Limits: 0 PSIA to 2000 PSIG (to 13.79 MPa) on either side without damage to the transmitter. Operates within specifications between static line pressure of ½ PSIA and 2000 PSIG (3.44kPa to 13.79 MPa), for silicone oil transmitters, and 10,000 PSIG (68.95 MPa) proof pressure on the flanges.

To Order (Specify Model Number)				SEE SECTION D FOR INSTRUMENT SELECTION
MODEL	**PRICE**	**LOWER RANGE DIFFERENTIAL**	**UPPER RANGE DIFFERENTIAL**	**COMPATIBLE METER**
PX750-30 SQDI	**$1395**	0 to 5″ H2O	0 to 30″ H2O	DP2000P8,TX81,DP3002-E
PX750-150 SQDI	1295	0 to 25″ H2O	0 to 150″ H2O	DP281C6,TX81,DP3002-E
PX750-750 SQDI	1295	0 to 125″ H2O	0 to 750″ H2O	DP2000P8,TX81,DP3002-E

VACUUM MEASURING AND CONTROL SYSTEM

  **1 YEAR WARRANTY** **MADE IN USA**

 **NEW!**

Model DP914

$850

✓ **Wide Measuring Range from 10-3 to 1000 torr**

✓ **Complete Pre-Calibrated Vacuum System**

✓ **Push Button Recalibration**

✓ **Dual Alarms or Control Relays**

The DP914 thermocouple gage controller displays vacuum pressure as measured from a thermocouple gage tube. Thermocouple gages utilize a small thermocouple attached to a thin heated wire. Constant voltage is applied to the thin wire and as air molecules strike the wire they carry heat away from it. The amount of air molecules is directly related to the vacuum pressure and the amount of cooling. The thermocouple measures the wire temperature, which is then used to calculate the vacuum reading.

The DP914 features ease of operation and two standard independent set points for vacuum control. The controller can be panel mounted or used as a benchtop. The unit comes complete and ready to use with controller, sensor, sensor cabling, power cord and complete operator's manual.

Model DP914 Comes Complete and Ready to Use with Controller, Display Alarms, Vacuum Sensor, 10' Sensor Cord with Mating Connectors, 8' Power Cord and Operator's Manual.

SPECIFICATIONS

VACUUM RANGE	RESOLUTION
0-50 mtorr	1 mtorr
50-300 mtorr	2 mtorr
300-990 mtorr	10 mtorr
1-9.95 torr	.05 torr
10-30 torr	2 torr
30-100 torr	5 torr
100-1000 torr	10 torr

Typical System Accuracy: 5%Rdg over 0-50 mtorr range, accuracy degrades with higher ranges

METER SPECIFICATIONS

Read Rate: 2 per second
Response Time: 1.5 seconds
Gas Calibration: Air Std (Argon is a special)
Storage Temperature: 14 to 140°F (-10 to 60°C)
Operating Temperature: 50 to 122°F (10 to 50°C)
Display: 3 digit LED, .56" high, back-lit legend for mtorr or torr
Output: 2 SPDT 3 amps @ 240 Vac (Both are low alarms/stronger vacuum)
Power: 95-120 Vac or 190-240 Vac, (50-60Hz)10Vac power
Bezel: 3.8"x 3.8" (97 X 97 mm)
Panel Cutout: 1/4 DIN (3.62 x 3.62") (92 x 92mm)(Depth: 6.5", 195 mm)
Weight: 2 lbs (0.9 kgs)

THERMOCOUPLE VACUUM SENSOR

Output: 10 mV @ 1 mtorr (Output is nonlinear, algorithm in controller used)
Hysteresis: Negligible
Repeatability: 2% @ 1 mtorr, 5% @ 760 torr (highly dependent on contamination of sensor)
Operating Temperature: 50 to 212°F (10 to 100°C)
Thermal Effects: Negligible to 100°C
Burst Pressure: 50 PSI
Pressure Port: 1/8" NPT
Electrical Connection: Octal connector
Weight: 55 grams

To Order *(Specify Model No.)*

MODEL NO.	PRICE	DESCRIPTION
DP914	$850	Vacuum Measuring Control System

Comes complete and ready to use with controller, display alarms, vacuum sensor, 10' sensor cord with mating connectors, 8' power cord and operator's manual.

LOW DEPTH SUBMERSIBLE PRESSURE SENSOR
FROM 12 INCHES TO 12 FOOT DEPTHS

PX418
$956

1 YEAR WARRANTY

✔ **All Stainless Steel Wetted Parts**
✔ **Completely Immersible**
✔ **CVD Construction for High Stability**

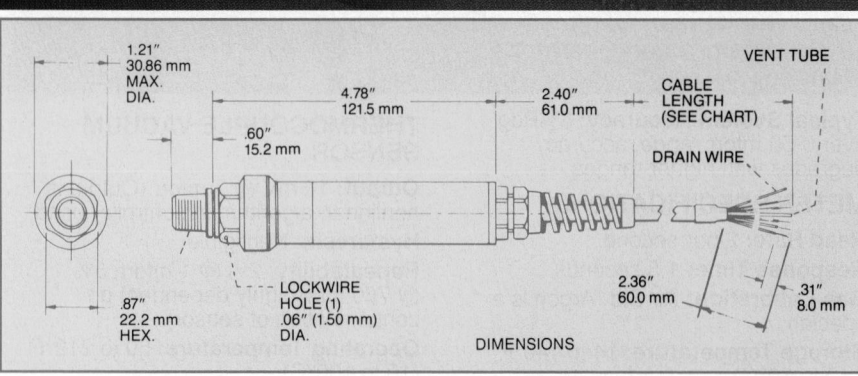

DIMENSIONS

SPECIFICATIONS
Excitation: 10 Vdc, 15 Vdc max.
Output: (actual output supplied with each unit)
Accuracy: 0.50% (including linearity, hysteresis and repeatability)
Zero Balance: 5% FS
Operating Temp.: -4 to 122°F (-20 to 50°C)
Compensated Temp.: 14 to 122°F (-10 to 50°C)
Thermal Effects: Zero, 0.03% FS/°C Span, 0.03% FS/°C
Proof Pressure: 90" for ≤ 60"H_2O 210" H_2O for >60" H_2O ranges
Burst Pressure: 72 PSI
Input Resistance: 2.5k ohms min.
Output Resistance: 1.2k to 4.3k ohms
Response Time: 1 ms
Gage Type: Chemical vapor deposited polysilicon strain gages
Wetted Parts: 15-7,17-4 SS
Pressure Port: ¼ -18 NPT
Electrical Conn.: 4 cond. shielded and vented 30 ft of cable (10 meters)
Weight: 1 lb (28 g)

◆ *HIGHLIGHTED MODEL STOCKED FOR FAST DELIVERY!* ◆

To Order *(Specify Model Number)*

TYPICAL

RANGE			MODEL	PRICE	OUTPUT (mV)	COMPATIBLE METERS
PSIG	IN H₂0	FT H₂0				
0.4	12	1.0	PX418-012GV	$956	20	DP41-S, DP3002-S, DP2000-S4
1.1	30	2.5	PX418-030GV	956	50	DP41-S, DP3002-S, DP460-S ◄
2.2	60	5.0	PX418-060GV	956	100	DP41-S, DP3002-S, DP460-S
2.9	80	6.7	PX418-080GV	956	40	DP41-S, DP3002-S, DP460-S
3.6	100	8.3	PX418-100GV	956	50	DP41-S, DP3002-S, DP460-S
5.1	140	11.7	PX418-140GV	956	70	DP41-S, DP3002-S, DP2000-S2

Comes with complete operator's manual
Ordering example: *PX418-030GV, completely immersible in 2.5' of water with 1.1 PSIG range, **$956**.*

DEEP DEPTH SUBMERSIBLE PRESSURE TRANSMITTER
35 TO 650 FEET OF WATER RANGES

1 YEAR WARRANTY

NEW!

PX428
$556

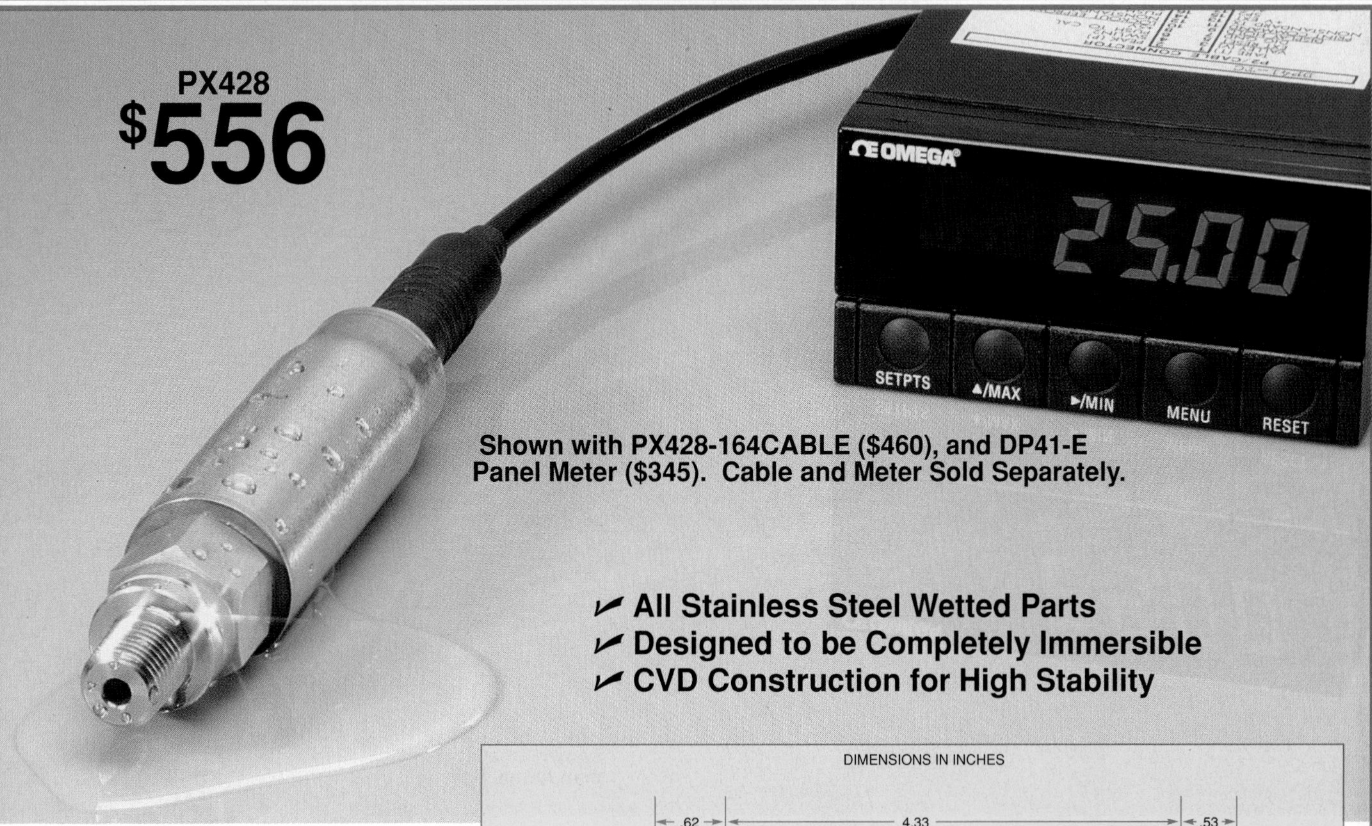

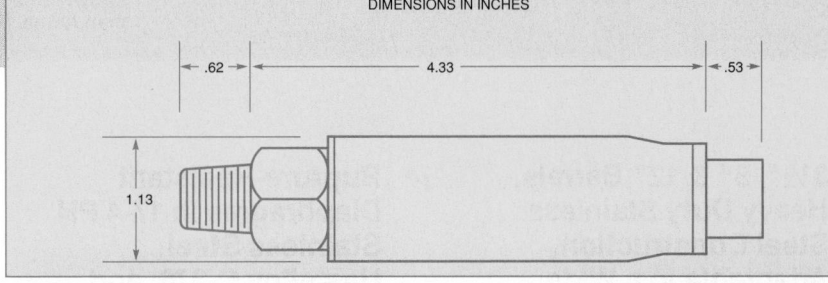

Shown with PX428-164CABLE ($460), and DP41-E
Panel Meter ($345). Cable and Meter Sold Separately.

SPECIALTY PRESSURE TRANSDUCERS

B

✔ **All Stainless Steel Wetted Parts**
✔ **Designed to be Completely Immersible**
✔ **CVD Construction for High Stability**

DIMENSIONS IN INCHES

.62 — 4.33 — .53

1.13

SPECIFICATIONS

Excitation: 24 Vdc (12-36 Vdc) reverse polarity protected

Output: 4-20 mA (2 wire)

Accuracy: 0.2% (including linearity, hysteresis and repeatability)

Zero Balance: 2% FS

Span Tolerance: 1% FS

Max Loop Resistance: 50 x (supply voltage -12)

Operating Temp.: -4 to 248°F (-20 to 120°C)

Compensated Temp.: -4 to 176°F (-20 to 80°C)

Thermal Effects: 1.5% FS over (-20 to 80°C)

Proof Pressure: 150%

Burst Pressure: 400%

Max. Immersion: 650 feet

Response Time: 1 ms

Gage Type: Chemical vapor deposited polysilicon strain gages

Wetted Parts: 15-7,17-4 SS, <60 PSI 17-4 SS ≥60 PSI

Pressure Port: 1/4-18 NPT

Electrical Conn.: IP67, mating cable sold separately

Weight: 3.5 oz (100 grams)

To Order (Specify Model Number)

RANGE		MODEL	PRICE	COMPATIBLE METERS
PSIG	FT H₂0			
0-15	34.6	**PX428-015GI**	$556	DP41-E, DP302-E, DP460-E
0-30	69.2	**PX428-030GI**	556	DP41-E, DP302-E, DP460-E
0-60	139	**PX428-060GI**	556	DP41-E, DP302-E, DP460-E
0-100	230	**PX428-100GI**	556	DP41-E, DP3002-E, DP460-E
0-300	695*	**PX428-300GI**	556	DP41-E, DP3002-E, DP460-E

PX428 transducers require cabling sold below.   * 650 ft is the maximum immersion.
Comes with complete operator's manual.

Ordering Example: *PX428-060GI transducer and PX428-164CABLE has a 0 to 60 PSIG range and operates in up to 139 feet of water with 164' of cable, $556 + 460 = **$1016**.*

MATING CABLE AND CONNECTOR ASSEMBLIES

MODEL	PRICE	WEIGHT	DESCRIPTION
PX428-33CABLE	$120	1 lb	33 feet (10 meters) of cable assembly
PX428-66CABLE	290	1.3 lbs	66 feet (20 meters) of cable assembly
PX428-164CABLE	460	3.2 lbs	164 feet (50 meters) of cable assembly
PX428-328CABLE	795	6.3 lbs	328 feet (100 meters) of cable assembly
PX428-820CABLE	1955	16 lbs	820 feet (250 meters) of cable assembly

HIGH ACCURACY MELT PRESSURE TRANSDUCERS

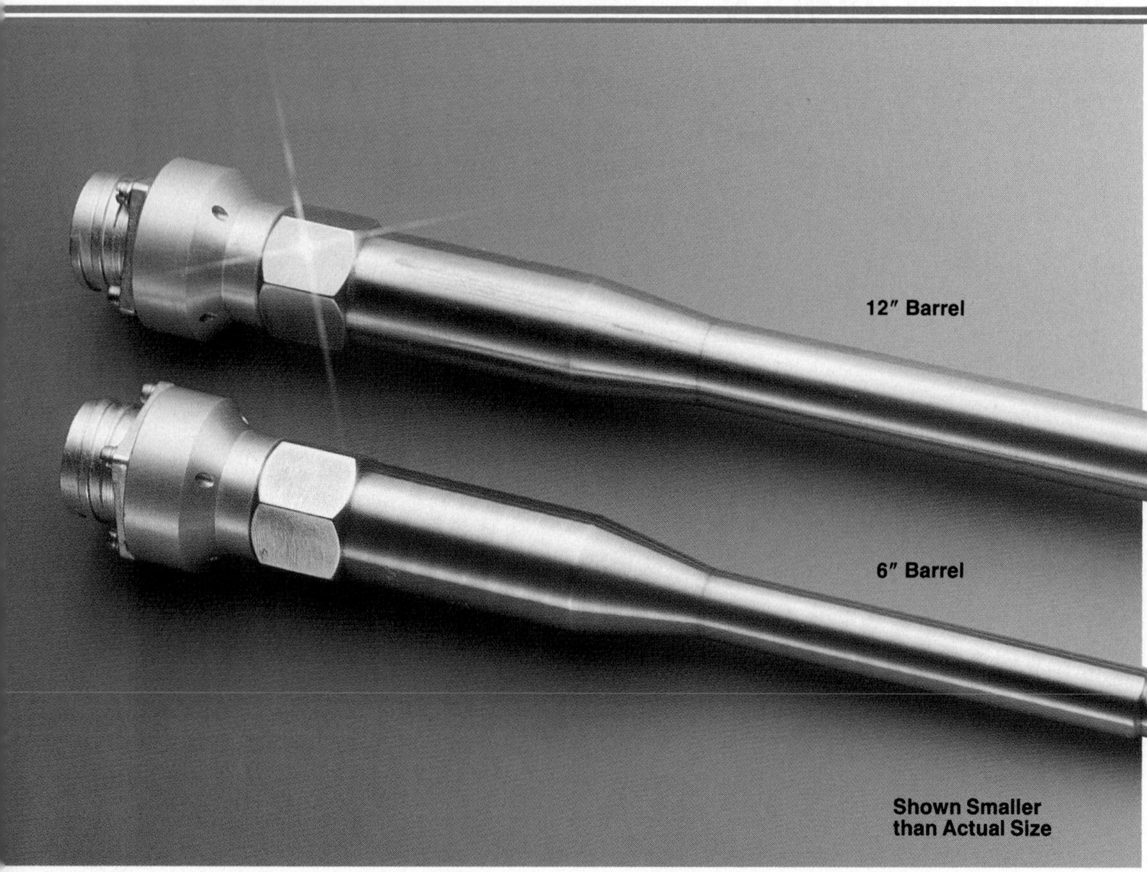

Priced from

$635

12" Barrel

6" Barrel

Shown Smaller than Actual Size

- ✔ 3½", 6" & 12" Barrels, Heavy Duty Stainless Steel Construction, Adaptable to a Wide Range of Space Requirements
- ✔ 1% FS and 0.5% FS Accuracy Models
- ✔ Force Rod Construction—No Fill-Fluid to Contaminate System
- ✔ High Temperature Design—750°F at the Diaphragm to Work with Today's Higher Extrusion Temperatures
- ✔ Fits Standard Sensor Wells
- ✔ Calibration Sheet Supplied with Each Transducer

- ✔ Rupture-Resistant Diaphragms in 17-4 PH Stainless Steel, Hastelloy C-276, and Hard Chrome Plate

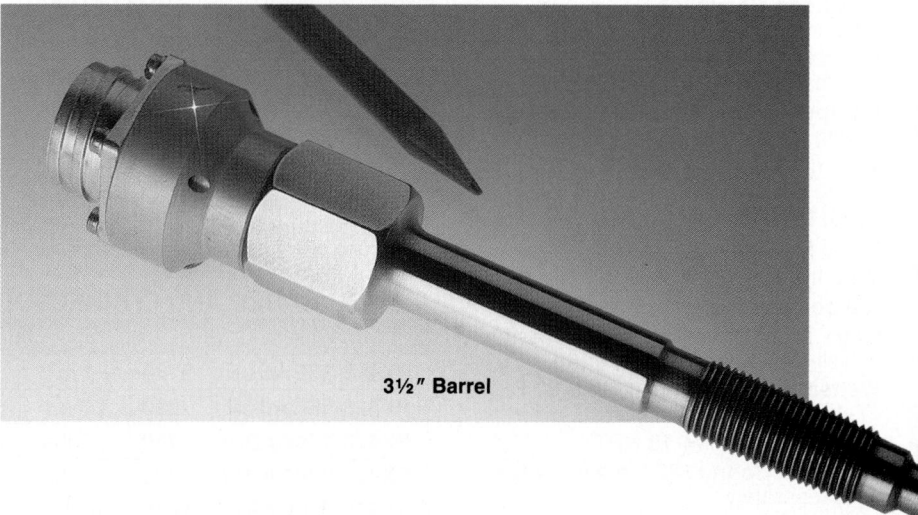

3½" Barrel

FOR ABRASIVE, NON-ABRASIVE, CORROSIVE AND NON-CORROSIVE MATERIALS

MADE IN USA

OMEGA is proud to feature state-of-the-art melt pressure transducers for general purpose and precision requirements…as well as digital indicator/controllers, thermocouples, accessory cables, and connectors for plastic extrusion.

Our transducers have been selected for applications with abrasive, non-abrasive, corrosive, or non-corrosive material; they offer a choice of 1% or 0.5% accuracy; and they feature stainless steel barrels in three lengths to meet the space requirements imposed by complex machinery, piping, and insulation.

Models 330, 335, 340, 341, 370, 371. Offered in 3½″, 6″, and 12″ barrel lengths, these transducers feature a 17-4 PH stainless steel diaphragm for melt pressure usage with non-corrosive and non-abrasive materials; ±1% FS non-linearity (models 330, 340, 341) for general purpose applications; ±0.5% FS non-linearity (models 335, 370, 371) for high accuracy; and 0 to 750°F operating range.

Models 350, 351, 380, 381. Offered in 6″ and 12″ units with Hastelloy C-276 diaphragm for melt pressure usage with corrosive materials such as Teflon®, Kynar®, and fluorocarbon polymers. These transducers also feature ±1% FS non-linearity (models 350, 351) for general purpose applications; ±0.5% FS non-linearity (models 380, 381) for high accuracy; and 0 to 750°F operating range.

Models 360, 361, 390, 391. Offered in 6″ and 12″ units with Hard Chrome Plate diaphragm for melt pressure usage with abrasive materials such as fiberglass, aluminum, and cereal. These transducers also feature ±1% FS non-linearity (models 360, 361) for general purpose applications; ±0.5% FS non-linearity (models 390, 391) for high accuracy; and 0 to 750°F operating range.

Built-in Thermocouples. Models with OMEGA's type J (Iron-Constantan®) or K (Chromega™-Alomega™)* high accuracy thermocouples enable simultaneous temperature/pressure measurements up to 750°F.

These transducers are designed for applications in which precision control is critical or in which space for only one sensor is available.

Immediate Delivery. There's no need to wait weeks and weeks for the order you need right away. Contact OMEGA now; most of the transducers shown are stocked for fast delivery.

Chromega-Alomega is a pending trademark of OMEGA Engineering, Inc.

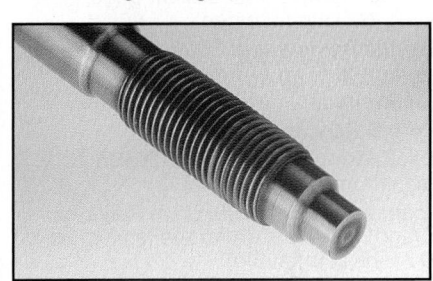

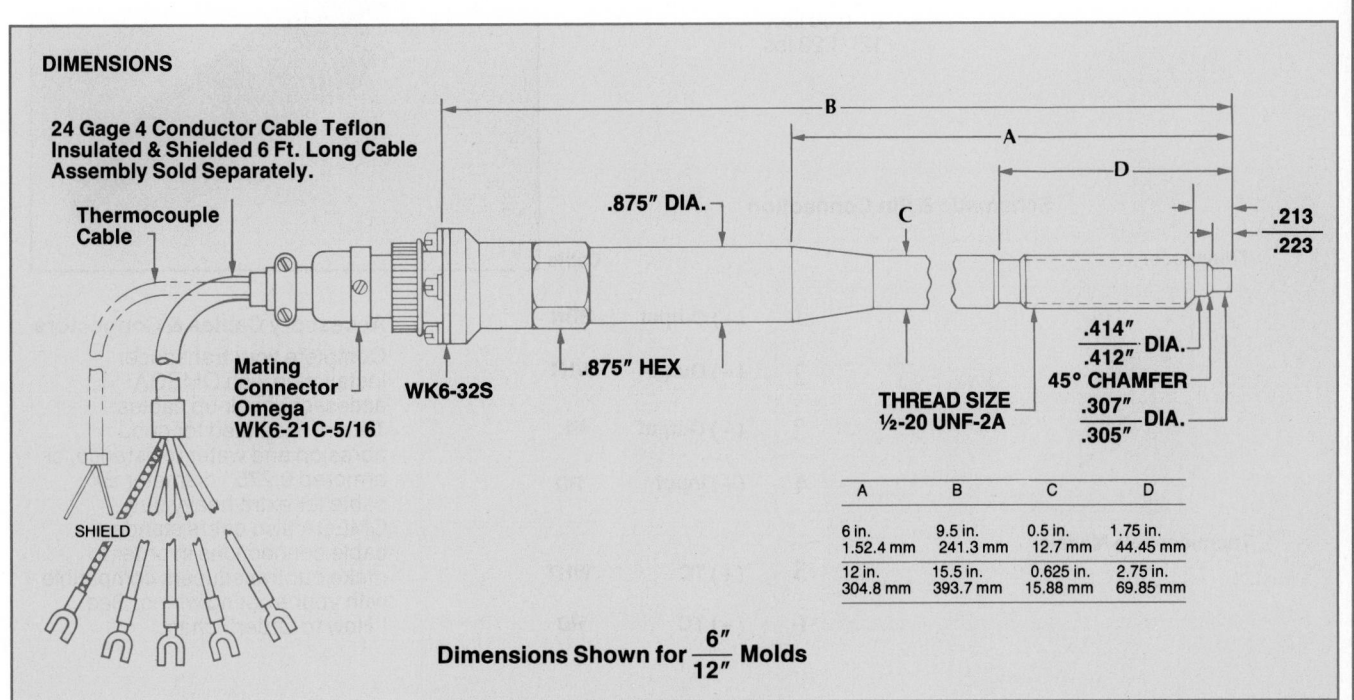

DIMENSIONS

24 Gage 4 Conductor Cable Teflon Insulated & Shielded 6 Ft. Long Cable Assembly Sold Separately.

Thermocouple Cable

Mating Connector Omega WK6-21C-5/16

WK6-32S

.875″ HEX

.875″ DIA.

THREAD SIZE ½-20 UNF-2A

SHIELD

.414″ .412″ DIA.
45° CHAMFER
.307″ .305″ DIA.

.213 .223

	A	B	C	D
	6 in.	9.5 in.	0.5 in.	1.75 in.
	1.52.4 mm	241.3 mm	12.7 mm	44.45 mm
	12 in.	15.5 in.	0.625 in.	2.75 in.
	304.8 mm	393.7 mm	15.88 mm	69.85 mm

Dimensions Shown for 6″/12″ Molds

MADE IN **USA**

SPECIFICATIONS

PERFORMANCE CHARACTERISTICS

Accuracy: ±0.5% or ±1.0% FS

Repeatability: Within ±0.1% FS maximum

Resolution: Infinite

Overload Pressure: 150% of rated range, no damage

ELECTRICAL CHARACTERISTICS

Sensor Type: Bonded Stain-gage, 4 leg Weatstone bridge

Bridge Resistance: 350Ω, ±5.0%

Sensitivity: 3.0 mV/V nominal (open circuit)

Zero Balance: ±10.0%

Excitation: 5-12 Vdc or ac (RMS), maximum 15 volts

External Shunt Calibration Resistor: Standard feature. (Also available to be Dynisco compatible)

Insulation Resistance: 100 mΩ @ 50 Vdc

Thermocouple: Types J & K available as indicated

TEMPERATURE CHARACTERISTICS

Diaphragm: 0-750°F (−18 to 400°C)

Electrical Connector: 0-250°F (−18 to 121°C)

Zero Drift: ±0.01% FS/°F ±0.02% FS/°C

Sensitivity Drift: ±0.01% FS/°F ±0.02% FS/°C

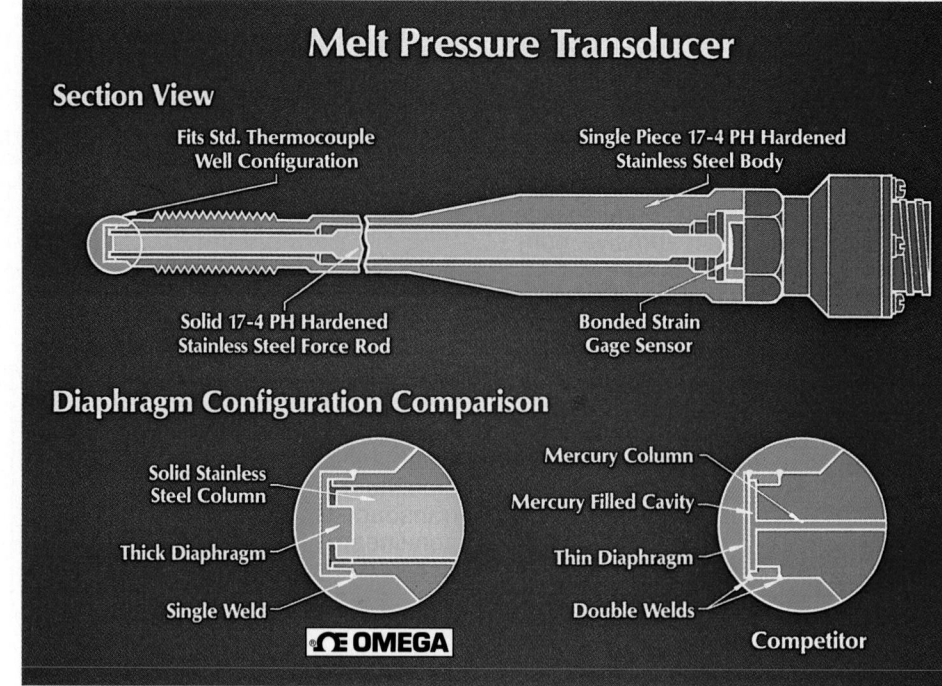

Melt Pressure Transducer

Section View

Fits Std. Thermocouple Well Configuration

Single Piece 17-4 PH Hardened Stainless Steel Body

Solid 17-4 PH Hardened Stainless Steel Force Rod

Bonded Strain Gage Sensor

Diaphragm Configuration Comparison

Solid Stainless Steel Column

Thick Diaphragm

Single Weld

OMEGA

Mercury Column

Mercury Filled Cavity

Thin Diaphragm

Double Welds

Competitor

MECHANICAL CHARACTERISTICS

Diaphragm Material: Standard 17-4 PH Stainless Steel. Others include Hard Chrome Plate, Hastelloy C-276

Pressure Fitting: ½ inch-20 UNF-2 A

Mounting Torque: 10 foot-pounds min, 20 foot-pounds max

Electrical Connector: WK6-325

Mating Connector: WK6-21C-5/16 (not included)

Weight: 3½"-0.32 lbs 6"-0.68 lbs. 12"-1.23 lbs

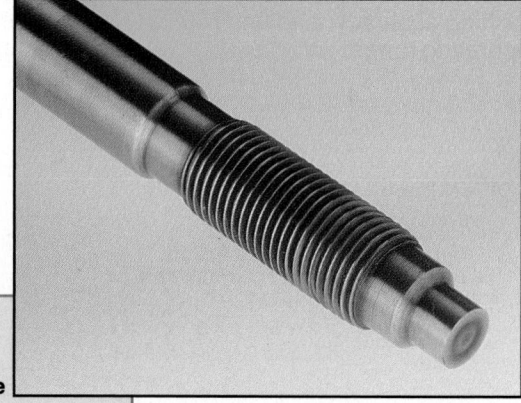

Schematic & Pin Connection

Transducer

		Cable
1	(+) Output	GRN
2	(−) Output	WHT
3	(−) Output	BL
4	(+) Input	RD

Thermocouple Models

5	(+) TC	WHT
6	(−) TC	RD

Accessory Cables & Connectors

Complete your transducer installation with OMEGA accessory hook-up cables: Teflon® insulated for good abrasion and water resistance, or armored 0.275″ diameter BX cable for extra heavy duty. OMEGA also offers standard cable connections in order to make our transducers compatible with your existing wiring. See "How to Order" chart.

MELT PRESSURE TRANSDUCERS, CABLES AND CONNECTORS

1. Select the barrel length (3½″, 6″, 12″), diaphragm material (Stainless Steel, Hastelloy, Hard Chrome), and accuracy (1%, 0.5%) as shown below.

3. Thermocouple option: add J (Iron-Constantan) or K (Chromel-Alumel) to the transducer part number. Add $125 to price (see Ordering Examples below).

3. Add range suffix to transducer part number as follows:

Range	Ordering Suffix
0 to 500 PSI	– 500 GV*
0 to 1000 PSI	– 1000 GV*
0 to 1,500 PSI	– 1500GV
0 to 3,000 PSI	– 3KGV
0 to 5,000 PSI	– 5KGV
0 to 10,000 PSI	– 10KGV
0 to 15,000 PSI	– 15KGV

Add $125 to price for these ranges.

4. **Ordering Examples:**

PX351-10KGV indicates Hastelloy diaphragm, 12″ barrel and 1% accuracy with a range of 0 to 10,000 PSI.
Price: **$870.**

PX351J-10KGV indicates same as above with optional J thermocouple.
Price: **$870 + 125 = $995.**

To Order (Specify Model Number)

Barrel Length	Diaphragm Material	Accuracy FS (non-linearity BFSL)	Model Number	Price
3½″	Stainless Steel	1%	PX330-(*)	$650
3½″	Stainless Steel	0.5%	PX335-(*)	750
6″	Stainless Steel	1%	PX340-(*)	635
12″	Stainless Steel	1%	PX341-(*)	720
6″	Hastelloy	1%	PX350-(*)	785
12″	Hastelloy	1%	PX351-(*)	870
6″	Hard Chrome	1%	PX360-(*)	705
12″	Hard Chrome	1%	PX361-(*)	790
6″	Stainless Steel	0.5%	PX370-(*)	780
12″	Stainless Steel	0.5%	PX371-(*)	845
6″	Hastelloy	0.5%	PX380-(*)	930
12″	Hastelloy	0.5%	PX381-(*)	995
6″	Hard Chrome	0.5%	PX390-(*)	850
12″	Hard Chrome	0.5%	PX391-(*)	915

*Specify range; see item 2 above

Series CX340 Cables

SPECIFICATIONS

Wire: 24 gage shielded
Number of conductors: 4 plus shield

Insulation: Teflon®
Thermocouple: 24 gage with fiberglass insulation (standard limits of error)
Armored: 0.275″ dia BX covering

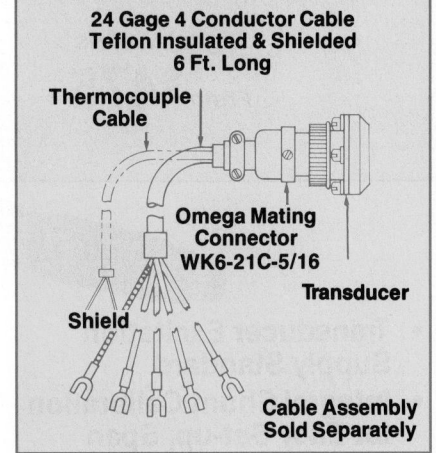

24 Gage 4 Conductor Cable Teflon Insulated & Shielded 6 Ft. Long
Thermocouple Cable
Omega Mating Connector WK6-21C-5/16
Transducer
Shield
Cable Assembly Sold Separately

To Order (Specify Model Number)

Model No.	Length	Thermocouple	Price
Teflon Cable—Mating Connector/Spade Lugs			
CX340-10	10 ft	NONE	$60
CX340-10J	10 ft	TYPE J	90
CX340-10K	10 ft	TYPE K	90
Armored Cable—Mating Connector/Spade Lugs			
CX340A-10	10 ft	NONE	$90
CX340A-10J	10 ft	TYPE J	130
CX340A-10K	10 ft	TYPE K	130
Mating Connector: WK6-21C-5/16 $25			

Mating Connector

INDICATORS FOR MELT PRESSURE CONTROL
MODELS DP434 DIGITAL & DP409 ANALOG CONTROLLERS

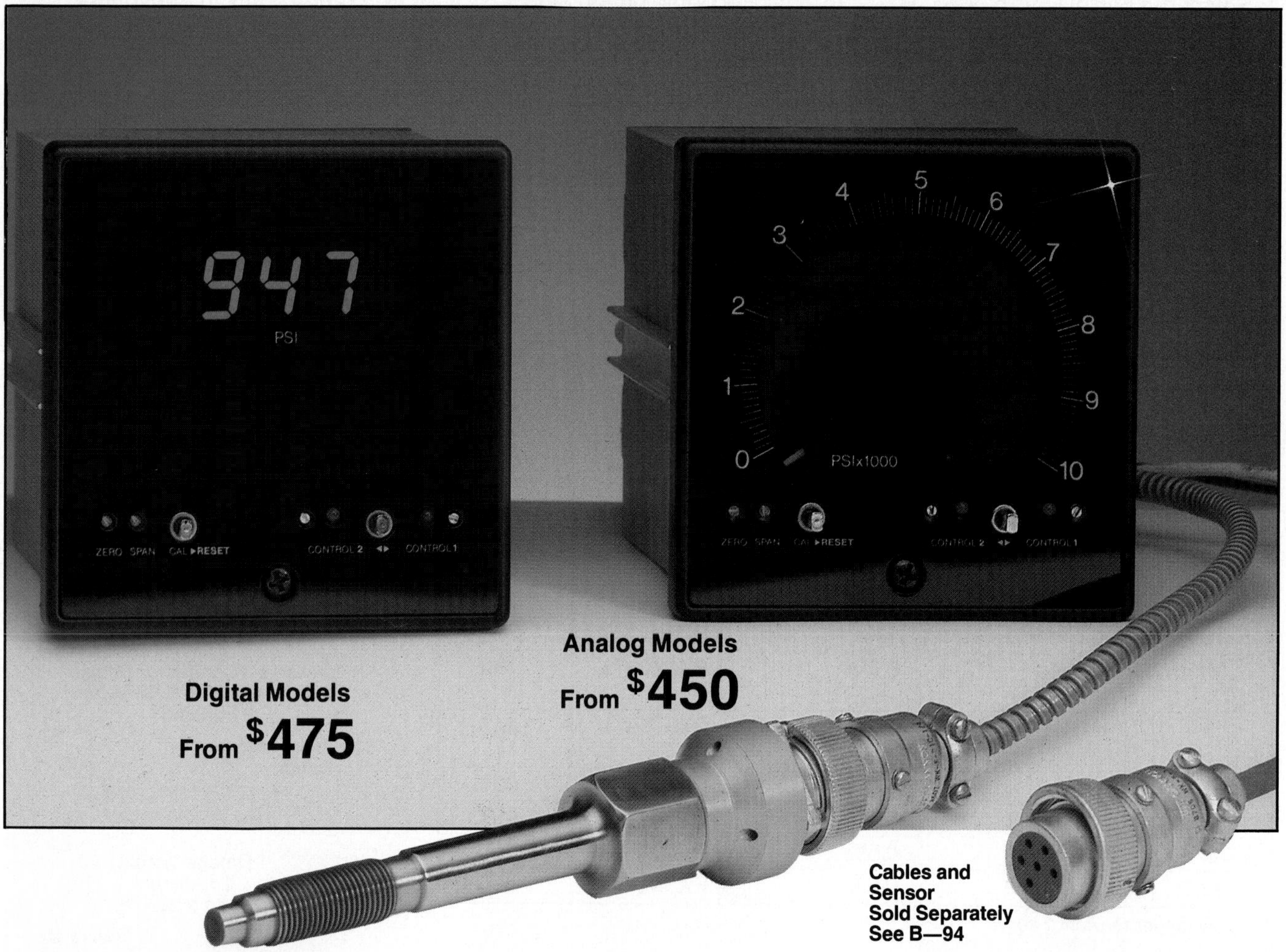

Digital Models
From **$475**

Analog Models
From **$450**

Cables and Sensor Sold Separately See B—94

- **Transducer Excitation Supply Standard**
- **Integral Shunt Calibration for Easy Set-up, Span Check and Adjustment**
- **Recorder Outputs Standard**

- **DP434 Features 3½ Digital LED Display with Fixed Zero for 19990 Display**
- **DP409 Features Easy-to-Read Analog Display with 240° Dial Indication**

- **Adjustable Damping, Response Time Selectable at 0.3 or 5.0 s**
- **Dual Alarm Setpoints HI/HI, LO/LO, LO/HI, HI/LO**

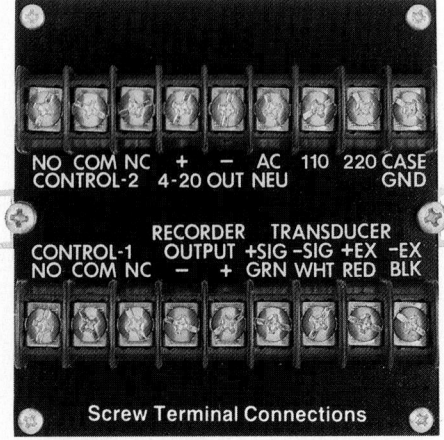

Screw Terminal Connections

OMEGA melt pressure indicators also function as transducer power supplies and signal conditioners. The DP434 Digital Model has a large 3½ digit LED display which is easy to read, even from a distance, while the DP409 Analog Model has a 6″, 240 degree arc (international scale) for easy viewing. Both units are housed in a standard ¼ DIN case.

The DP434 and DP409 are designed for use with OMEGA melt pressure transducers or any 4-leg, 350Ω Wheatstone bridge strain-gage transducer. A calibration switch allows for a quick span check and adjustment for zero at zero pressure. The complete electronic assembly can be removed and replaced from the front without disturbing the wiring in back.

Dual setpoint models can be used to give a preliminary warning before an actual shutdown sequence is initiated. HI/HI, LO/LO, LO/HI, or HI/LO alarm modes can be programmed, and the relays are isolated during a setpoint change or calibration check to prevent accidental emergency shutdown.

SPECIFICATIONS— DP434 DIGITAL & DP409 ANALOG METERS

PERFORMANCE CHARACTERISTICS

Standard Ranges: 0-1500, 0-3000, 0-5000, 0-10,000 & 0-15,000 psig

Accuracy: ±0.1% of full scale or one digit (DP434), ±2.0% of full scale (DP409)

Recorder Output: Accuracy: ±0.1% of full scale, Repeatability: ±0.1% of full scale, Linearity: ±0.1% of full scale, Stability: ±0.1% of full scale (or one digit)

ELECTRICAL CHARACTERISTICS

Power: 106-125 or 200-250 Vac 50/60 hz, 1/8 Amp maximum

Zero Adjustment: ±35% with panel pot

Sensitivity Adjustment (Span): 1-2.5 mV/V or 2.5-5.0 mV/V switch selectable and fully adjustable.

Shunt Resistance Calibration: Internal 30.1 kΩ Shunt Resistor

Response Time (Damping): Selectable at 0.3 or 5.0 seconds

Recorder Outputs: Standard: 0-1 Vdc; 0-2 Vdc, 0-5 Vdc & 0-10 Vdc; Optional: 4-20 mA, load from 15-400 ohms (add suffix R to model number and $100 to price)

Transducer Power Supply: 8.2 Vdc ±5%

CONTROL CHARACTERISTICS

Dual Relays: 2 SPDT (Single pole double throw)(Shipped 1 Hi, 2 Lo)

Relay Rating: 8 Amp @ 125/250 Vac, 5 Amp @ 30 Vdc

Set Point Range: 1-100% of full scale

Accuracy: ±0.3% of full scale

Hysteresis: ±0.5% of full scale

Alarm Indication: Front panel LED

Mode: Above or below set point

Reset: Automatic or manual

Peak Hold: Optional

PHYSICAL CHARACTERISTICS

Size: 1/4 DIN

Cutout Dimensions: See drawing

Display: For DP434—3-1/2 active digits, LED, 0.3″ height, plus last digit fixed zero and selectable decimal point. For DP409—6″ scale, 240° arc.

Operating Temperature: 0-140°F

Weight: 2.5 lbs.

Note: Range changes for the DP434 can be made in the field.

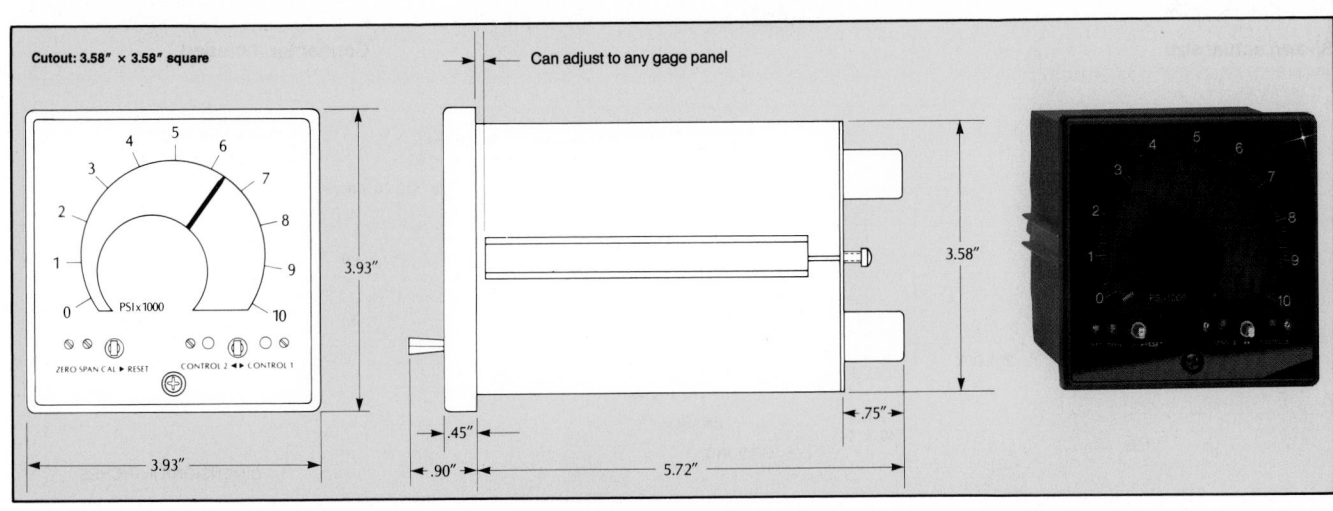

Cutout: 3.58″ × 3.58″ square

Can adjust to any gage panel

PSI x 1000

ZERO SPAN CAL ▶ RESET   CONTROL 2 ◀▶ CONTROL 1

3.93″   3.93″   .45″   .90″   5.72″   .75″   3.58″

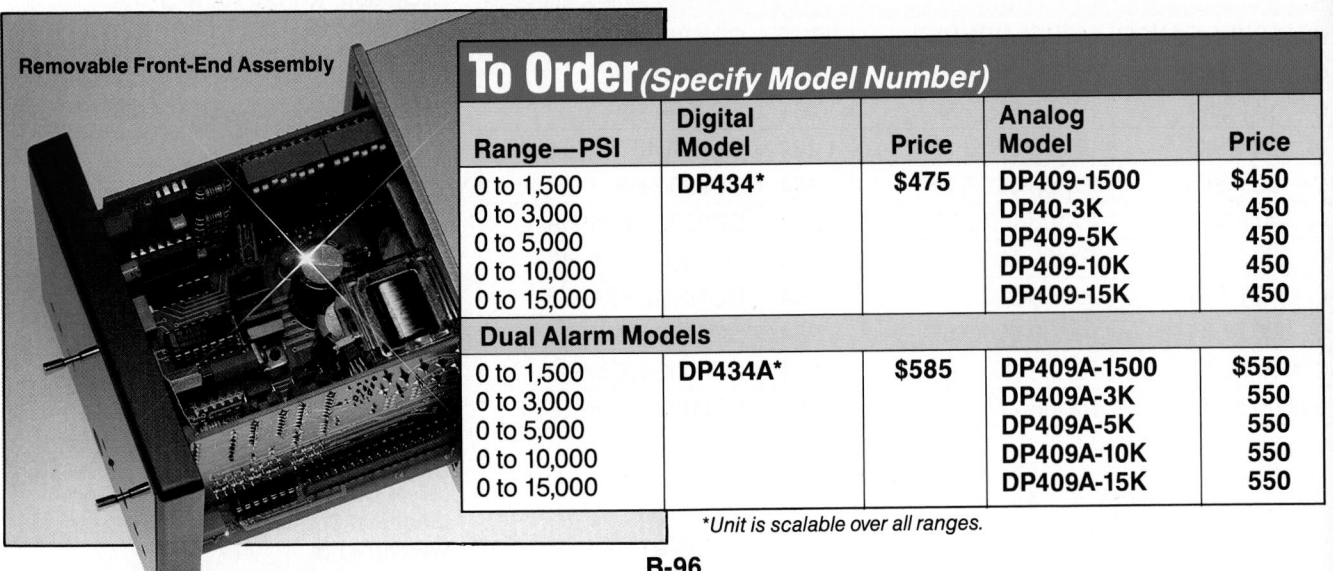

Removable Front-End Assembly

FREQUENCY OUTPUT TYPE PRESSURE TRANSDUCERS USE ON TRANSMISSION LINES OR INTERFACING WITH MICROPROCESSORS

106 Series
0-6 to 0-2,000 PSIG

Media Compatibility: Typical media include oil, gases, saline solutions, ammonia, freon, hydraulic fluids, alcohol, acids and gasoline.

Shown actual size

Connector Included

- ✔ **10-20 Vdc Excitation**
- ✔ **0.5% Linearity**
- ✔ **−40° to +85°C Operation**
- ✔ **Valox Outer Case**
- ✔ **Stainless Steel Chamber**
- ✔ **±1% FS Accuracy**

From
$254

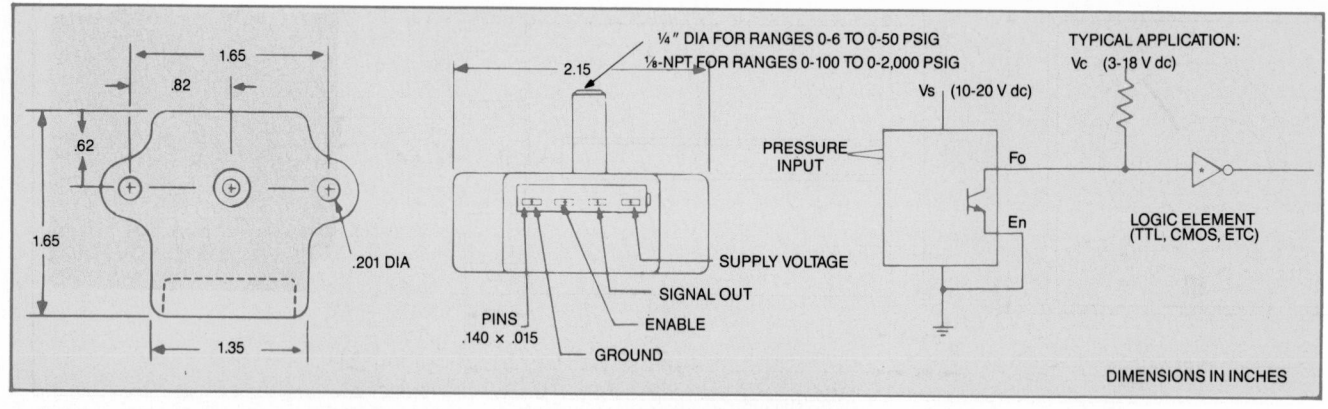

DIMENSIONS IN INCHES

To Order (Specify Model Number)

*SEE SECTION D FOR INSTRUMENT SELECTION

PRESSURE RANGE	MODEL NUMBER	PRICE	COMPATIBLE METER*
0- 6 PSIG	PX106-006G 5F	$280	DP2000-H9
0- 15 PSIG	PX106-015G 5F	254	DP2000-H8
0- 25 PSIG	PX106-025G 5F	254	CONSULT SALES
0- 50 PSIG	PX106-050G 5F	254	DP2000-H9
0- 100 PSIG	PX106-100G 5F	254	DP2000-H8 or H9
0- 200 PSIG	PX106-200G 5F	254	DP2000-H7 or H8
0- 300 PSIG	PX106-300G 5F	254	CONSULT SALES
0- 500 PSIG	PX106-500G 5F	254	DP2000-H9
0-1000 PSIG	PX106-1KG 5F	254	DP2000-H8 or H9
0-2000 PSIG	PX106-2KG 5F	254	DP2000-H7 or H8

SPECIFICATIONS

Excitation: 10 to 20 Vdc at 30 mA

Output: 1 to 6 kHz

Accuracy: ±1% full scale typ., ±2% full scale max.

Linearity: < 50 PSI ±.50%: ≥ 50 PSI ±.2% FS

Hysteresis: ±0.25% full scale

Zero Balance: ±1% typ., ±2% max.

Compensated Temperature Range: 32 to 185°F (0 to 85°C)

Thermal Zero Effect: ±0.01% RDG/°F (±0.02%/°C)

Thermal Sensitivity Effect: ±0.01% RDG/°F (±0.02%/°C)

Proof Pressure: 2 x full scale

Burst Pressure: 5 x full scale min.

Gages: Piezo-Resistive on Bending Beam

Diaphragm/Port Material: 300 Series SS (Silver, Copper, Nickel, Cadmium Brazed)

Electrical Connection: CX-106-4

Weight: 4 ozs.

RUGGED ELECTRONIC BAROMETERS AND MANOMETERS
WITH VOLTAGE OUTPUT

PX960 Series
16-32″ HgA Barometer; 0-100″ H₂O Manometer

- **Hermetically Sealed Stainless Steel Construction**
- **Fully Adjustable Zero and Span settings**

Typical Applications

- Meteorology
- Avionics
- Geophysics

$995

MADE IN USA

Shown slightly larger than actual size

The OMEGA PX960 electronic barometer/manometer Series is available in the barometric pressure ranges of 16 to 32″ Hg and the manometric ranges from 100″ H₂O to 30″ Hg. These industrial transducers achieve minimum accuracies of 0.1% full scale. Hermetically sealed, stainless steel construction provides superior performance even under the most demanding applications which require high measurement stability.

SPECIFICATIONS

Excitation: 26 to 32 Vdc

Output: 0-5 Vdc (PX961), 0-2 Vdc (PX962)

Accuracy: PX961 ±0.1% of span; PX962 ±0.15%

Operating Temperature: 0°F to 185°F

Compensated Temperature: 60°F to 160°F

Temperature Effect: Zero PX961 = 0.0025%, PX962 = 0.005% full scale/°F Span PX961 = 0.0025%, PX962 = 0.005% reading/°F

Mating Connector: PTO6F-10-6S (not included)

Construction: Hermetically sealed stainless steel

Pressure Port: ¼-18 NPT male

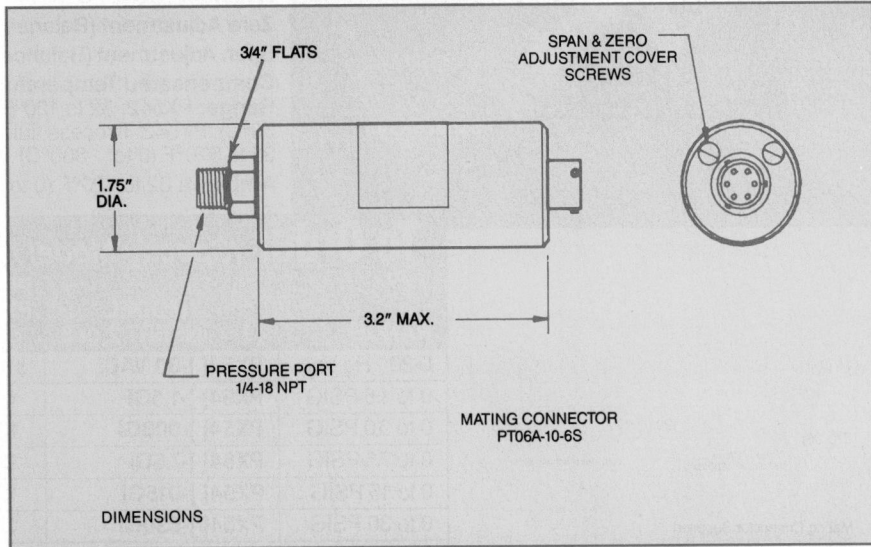

3/4″ FLATS

SPAN & ZERO ADJUSTMENT COVER SCREWS

1.75″ DIA.

3.2″ MAX.

PRESSURE PORT 1/4-18 NPT

MATING CONNECTOR PT06A-10-6S

DIMENSIONS

To Order (Specify Model Number)

MODEL	RANGE		PRICE	COMPATIBLE METER*
Barometer	in. HgA	PSIA		
▶PX961-16A5V	16 to 32	7.9 to 15.7	**$995**	DP2000-P4, DP3002-P, DP460-V ◀
Manometer	in. H₂O	in. Hg		
PX962-100G2V	0 to 100	—	995	DP2000-P4, DP3002-P, DP460-V
PX962-200G2V	0 to 200	—	995	DP2000-P4, DP3002-P, DP460-V
PX962-15G2V	—	0 to 15	995	DP2000-P4, DP3002-P, DP460-V
PX962-30G2V	—	0 to 30	995	DP2000-P4, DP3002-P, DP460-V

Requires external power supply PSS-D15B, $114.

▶ **HIGHLIGHTED MODEL IN STOCK FOR FAST DELIVERY** ◀

SPECIAL PURPOSE TRANSMITTERS FLUSH DIAPHRAGM DESIGN
MOUNT IN RF FLANGE, TRI-CLOVER FITTING, OR WELD RING

Model DP2000-P8 Shown

Model PX542

Model PX543

PX542 Series
1.5 PSI to 1500 PSI

PX543 Series
High Temperature Model

- ✔ Flush Diaphragm For Viscous and Percipitating Fluids
- ✔ All Stainless Steel Construction
- ✔ Requires Installation Fitting
- ✔ PX543 Process Temperature up to 570°F

From
$1275

SPECIFICATIONS

Excitation: 10 to 30 Vdc
Output: 4 to 20 mA two wire
Maximum Loop Impedance: 1000 ohms
Insulation Resistance: 500 Vac
Power Supply Effect: .0001 mA/V

PERFORMANCE

Accuracy: 0.5% FS
Zero Adjustment (Balance): 2% FS
Span Adjustment (Balance): 5% FS
Compensated Temperature Range: PX542: 32 to 120°F (0 to 50°C); PX543: Process fluid: 32 to 570°F (0 to 300°C)
Ambient: 32 to 120°F (0 to 50°C)

Thermal Zero Effect: 0.025% FS/°C
Thermal Sensitivity Effect: 0.026% FS/°C
Maximum Pressure: 150% FS

CONSTRUCTION

Body Material: Stainless Steel
Wetted Parts: ANSI 316L SS
Process Connection: G1 (1″ DIN std)(NPT adapter available below)
Electrical Connection: DIN connector with screw terminals
Fill Fluid: Silcone oil
Weight: 1.1 lbs
Response Time: 10ms

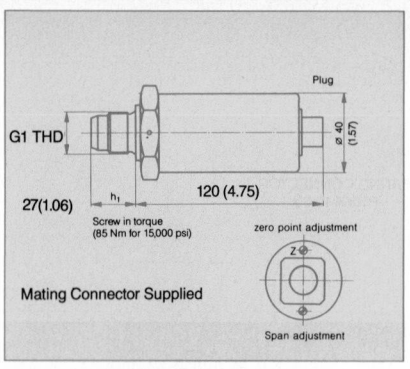

G1 THD

Plug

ø 40 (1.57)

120 (4.75)

27(1.06)

h₁

Screw in torque (85 Nm for 15,000 psi)

zero point adjustment

Z

Span adjustment

Mating Connector Supplied

DIMENSIONS: MM(INCH)

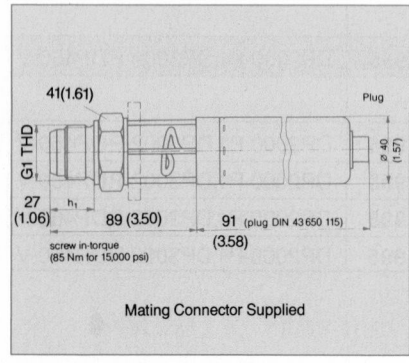

41(1.61)

Plug

G1 THD

ø 40 (1.57)

27 (1.06)

h₁

89 (3.50)

91 (plug DIN 43 650 115) (3.58)

screw in-torque (85 Nm for 15,000 psi)

Mating Connector Supplied

To Order (Specify Model Number)

RANGE	MODEL [ ] = INSERT 2 or 3	PRICE PX542 STD	PRICE PX543 HI-TEMP	COMPATIBLE METERS
0-30″ Hg Vac.	PX54[ ]-30 VACI	$1415	$1859	DP2000-P8, DP41-E, DP460-E
0 to 1.5 PSIG	PX54[ ]-1.5GI	1349	1285	DP2000-P8, DP41-E, DP460-E
0 to 3.0 PSIG	PX54[ ]-003GI	1349	1285	DP2000-P8, DP41-E, DP460-E
0 to 7.5 PSIG	PX54[ ]-7.5GI	1295	1650	DP2000-P8, DP41-E, DP460-E
0 to 15 PSIG	PX54[ ]-015GI	1275	1650	DP2000-P8, DP41-E, DP460-E
0 to 30 PSIG	PX54[ ]-030GI	1275	1650	DP2000-P8, DP41-E, DP460-E
0 to 75 PSIG	PX54[ ]-075GI	1275	1650	DP2000-P8, DP41-E, DP460-E
0 to 150 PSIG	PX54[ ]-150GI	1275	1650	DP2000-P8, DP41-E, DP460-E
0 to 300 PSIG	PX54[ ]-300GI	1275	1650	DP2000-P8, DP41-E, DP460-E
0 to 750 PSIG	PX54[ ]-750GI	1275	1650	DP2000-P8, DP41-E, DP460-E
0 to 1500 PSIG	PX54[ ]-1.5KGI	1275	1650	DP2000-P8, DP41-E, DP460-E

ACCESSORIES — WITH G1 THREAD FOR USE WITH PX542/PX543

MODEL	DESCRIPTION	PRICE
U24Y101	Loop power supply 24V @ 1000 mA	$99
PX543RF	150 pound raised face flange	144
PX543WR	Weld ring	59
PX543TC1	1½″ Tri-clamp	129
PX543TC2	2″ Tri-clamp	135
PX543AD1	G1 to 1″ NPT adaptor	129
PX543AD2	G1 to ½″ NPT adaptor	109
PX543PG	Plug for G1 thread	49

Ordering Example:
PX542-015GI is a 0-15 PSI transducer $1275

PX543-300 GI is a 0-300 PSI "high temp" transducer $1650

DP2000-P8 meter sold separately $301

EUROPEAN STYLE MILLIVOLT OUTPUT PRESSURE SENSOR
FOR GAGE AND ABSOLUTE MEASUREMENTS

3 YEAR WARRANTY

NEW!

From
$184

- ✔ Calibrated Per NPL (National Physics Laboratory)
- ✔ IP65 to BS5490(IEC 529) Protected Enclosure
- ✔ CVD Construction for High Stability

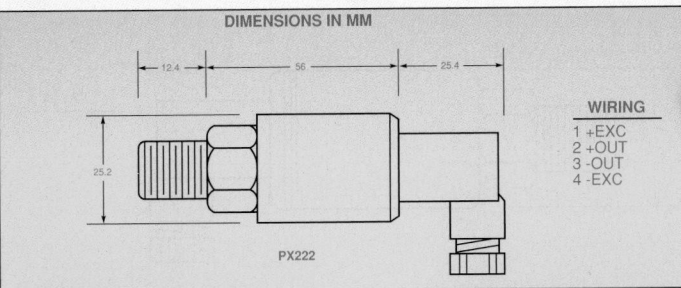

DIMENSIONS IN MM

WIRING
1 +EXC
2 +OUT
3 -OUT
4 -EXC

PX222

Shown with Model DP41-S Meter ($395); See Page D-7 for Details.

SPECIFICATIONS

Excitation: 10 Vdc, 15 Vdc max.

Output: 100 mV ±1 mV

Accuracy: 0.25% (including linearity, hysteresis and repeatability)

Zero Balance: 1% FS

Operating Temp.: -40 to 125°C (-40 to 257°F)

Compensated Temp.: -20 to 80°C (-4 to 176°F)

Thermal Effects: 1.5% FS over -20 to 80°C

Proof Pressure: 150%

Burst Pressure: 400%, 1200 bar max.

Input Resistance: 2.5k to 6k ohms

Output Resistance: 1.2k to 4.3k ohms

Response Time: 1 ms

Gage Type: Chemical vapor deposited polysilicon strain gages

Wetted Parts: 15-7,17-4 SS,<2.5 bar 17-4 SS ≥2.5 bar

Pressure Port: G ¼ male BSP compatible with ISO 228

Case: Liquid crystal polymer (thermoplastic)

Electrical Conn.: Miniature DIN connector screw terminals

Weight: 3 oz (87 g)

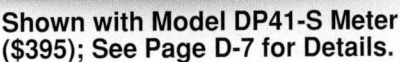

To Order (Specify Model Number)

RANGE	MODEL	PRICE	COMPATIBLE METERS
GAGE SENSORS			
0 to 1 bar	PX222-001GV	$184	DP41-S, DP460-S, DP205-S
0 to 2.5 bar	PX222-2.5GV	184	DP41-S, DP460-S, DP205-S
0 to 4 bar	PX222-004GV	184	DP41-S, DP460-S, DP205-S
0 to 10 bar	PX222-010GV	184	DP41-S, DP460-S, DP205-S
0 to 25 bar	PX222-025GV	184	DP41-S, DP460-S, DP205-S
0 to 40 bar	PX222-040GV	184	DP41-S, DP460-S, DP205-S
0 to 100 bar	PX222-100GV	184	DP41-S, DP460-S, DP205-S
0 to 250 bar	PX222-250GV	184	DP41-S, DP460-S, DP205-S
0 to 400 bar	PX222-400GV	184	DP41-S, DP460-S, DP205-S
ABSOLUTE SENSORS			
0 to 1 bar abs	PX222-001AV	$236	DP41-S, DP460-S, DP205-S
0 to 1.6 bar abs	PX222-1.6AV	236	DP41-S, DP460-S, DP205-S
0 to 2.5 bar abs	PX222-2.5AV	236	DP41-S, DP460-S, DP205-S
0 to 4 bar abs	PX222-004AV	236	DP41-S, DP460-S, DP205-S
0 to 10 bar abs	PX222-010AV	236	DP41-S, DP460-S, DP205-S
0 to 25 bar abs	PX222-025AV	236	DP41-S, DP460-S, DP205-S

Comes with complete operator's manual.

Ordering Example: *PX222-004GV is a gage model, millivolt output pressure transducer with European threads and a 0 to 4 bar range, $184.*

EUROPEAN STYLE VOLTAGE OUTPUT PRESSURE SENSOR
FOR GAGE AND ABSOLUTE MEASUREMENTS

3 YEAR WARRANTY

NEW!

From
$226

✔ **Calibrated Per NPL (National Physics Laboratory)**

✔ **IP65 to BS5490 (IEC 529) Protected Enclosure**

✔ **CVD Construction for High Stability**

The PX223 is Shown with Model DP41-E Meter ($345). Meter Sold Separately, See Page D-7 for Details.

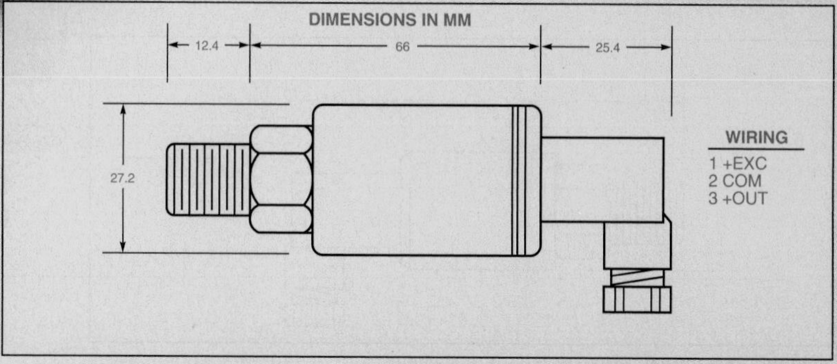

DIMENSIONS IN MM

12.4 | 66 | 25.4
27.2

WIRING
1 +EXC
2 COM
3 +OUT

SPECIFICATIONS

Excitation: 24 Vdc @ 15 mA (12-36 Vdc)

Output: 1-6 Vdc

Accuracy: 0.25% (including linearity, hysteresis and repeatability)

Zero Balance: ±75 mV

Span: 5 Vdc ±75 mV

Operating Temp.: -20 to 85°C (-48 to 185°F)

Compensated Temp.: -20 to 80°C (-4 to 176°F)

Thermal Effects: 1.5% FS over -4 to 176°C

Thermal Effects: 1.5% FS over -20 to 80°C

Proof Pressure: 150%

Burst Pressure: 400%, 1200 bar max.

Response Time: 1 ms

Gage Type: Chemical vapor deposited polysilicon strain gages

Wetted Parts: 15-7, 17-4 SS, <2.5 bar 17-4 SS ≥2.5 bar

Pressure Port: G ¼ male BSP compatible with ISO 228

Electrical Conn.: Miniature DIN connector, screw terminals

Weight: 3.5 oz (100 g)

To Order *(Specify Model Number)*

RANGE	MODEL	PRICE	COMPATIBLE METERS
GAGE SENSORS			
0 to 1 bar	PX223-001G5V	$226	DP41-E, DP460-E, DP205-E
0 to 2.5 bar	PX223-2.5G5V	226	DP41-E, DP460-E, DP205-E
0 to 4 bar	PX223-004G5V	226	DP41-E, DP460-E, DP205-E
0 to 10 bar	PX223-010G5V	226	DP41-E, DP460-E, DP205-E
0 to 25 bar	PX223-025G5V	226	DP41-E, DP460-E, DP205-E
0 to 40 bar	PX223-040G5V	226	DP41-E, DP460-E, DP205-E
0 to 100 bar	PX223-100G5V	226	DP41-E, DP460-E, DP205-E
0 to 250 bar	PX223-250G5V	226	DP41-E, DP460-E, DP205-E
0 to 400 bar	PX223-400G5V	226	DP41-E, DP460-E, DP205-E
ABSOLUTE SENSORS			
0 to 1 bar abs	PX223-001A5V	$278	DP41-E, DP460-E, DP205-E
0 to 1.6 bar abs	PX223-1.6A5V	278	DP41-E, DP460-E, DP205-E
0 to 2.5 bar abs	PX223-2.5A5V	278	DP41-E, DP460-E, DP205-E
0 to 4 bar abs	PX223-004A5V	278	DP41-E, DP460-E, DP205-E
0 to 10 bar abs	PX223-010A5V	278	DP41-E, DP460-E, DP205-E
0 to 25 bar abs	PX223-025A5V	278	DP41-E, DP460-E, DP205-E

Comes with complete operator's manual.

Ordering Example: *PX223-2.5GV is a gage model, voltage output pressure sensor with European threads and a 0 to 2.5 bar range, **$226**.*

EUROPEAN STYLE CURRENT OUTPUT PRESSURE SENSOR
FOR GAGE AND ABSOLUTE MEASUREMENTS

3 YEAR WARRANTY

NEW!

From
$268

✔ **Calibrated Per NPL (National Physics Laboratory)**
✔ **IP65 to BS5490 (IEC 529) Protected Enclosure**
✔ **CVD Construction for High Stability**

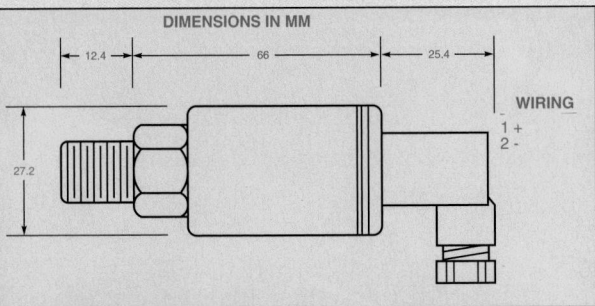

DIMENSIONS IN MM

12.4 — 66 — 25.4

27.2

WIRING
1 +
2 −

Shown with DP41-E Meter ($345). Meter Sold Separately, See Page D-7 for Details.

SPECIFICATIONS

Excitation: 24 Vdc (12-36 Vdc) Reverse polarity protected
Output: 4-20 mA (2 wire)
Accuracy: 0.25% (including linearity, hysteresis and repeatability)
Zero Balance: 2% FS
Span Tolerance: 1% FS
Max Loop Resistance: 50 x (supply voltage -12)
Operating Temp.: -20 to 120°C (-4 to 248°F)
Compensated Temp.: -20 to 80°C (-4 to 176°F)
Thermal Effects: 1.5% FS over -20 to 80°C
Thermal Effects: 1.5% FS over -20 to 80°C
Proof Pressure: 150%
Burst Pressure: 400%, 1200 bar max.
Response Time: 1 ms
Gage Type: Chemical vapor deposited polysilicon strain gages
Wetted Parts: 15-7, 17-4 SS, <2.5 bar 17-4 SS ≥2.5 bar
Pressure Port: G ¼ male BSP compatible with ISO 228
Electrical Conn.: Miniature DIN connector, screw terminals
Weight: 3/5 oz (100 g)

To Order *(Specify Model Number)*

RANGE	MODEL	PRICE	COMPATIBLE METERS
GAGE SENSORS			
0 to 1 bar	**PX225-001GI**	$268	DP41-E, DP460-E, DP205-E
0 to 2.5 bar	**PX225-2.5GI**	268	DP41-E, DP460-E, DP205-E
0 to 4 bar	**PX225-004GI**	268	DP41-E, DP460-E, DP205-E
0 to 10 bar	**PX225-010GI**	268	DP41-E, DP460-E, DP205-E
0 to 25 bar	**PX225-025GI**	268	DP41-E, DP460-E, DP205-E
0 to 40 bar	**PX225-040GI**	268	DP41-E, DP460-E, DP205-E
0 to 100 bar	**PX225-100GI**	268	DP41-E, DP460-E, DP205-E
0 to 250 bar	**PX225-250GI**	268	DP41-E, DP460-E, DP205-E
0 to 400 bar	**PX225-400GI**	268	DP41-E, DP460-E, DP205-E
ABSOLUTE SENSORS			
0 to 1 bar abs	**PX225-001AI**	$320	DP41-E, DP460-E, DP205-E
0 to 1.6 bar abs	**PX225-1.6AI**	320	DP41-E, DP460-E, DP205-E
0 to 2.5 bar abs	**PX225-2.5AI**	320	DP41-E, DP460-E, DP205-E
0 to 4 bar abs	**PX225-004AI**	320	DP41-E, DP460-E, DP205-E
0 to 10 bar abs	**PX225-010AI**	320	DP41-E, DP460-E, DP205-E
0 to 25 bar abs	**PX225-025AI**	320	DP41-E, DP460-E, DP205-E

Comes with complete operator's manual.
Ordering Example: *PX225-001AI is an absolute model, current output pressure transducer with European threading and a 0 to 1 bar abs range, **$320**.*

C ACCESSORIES

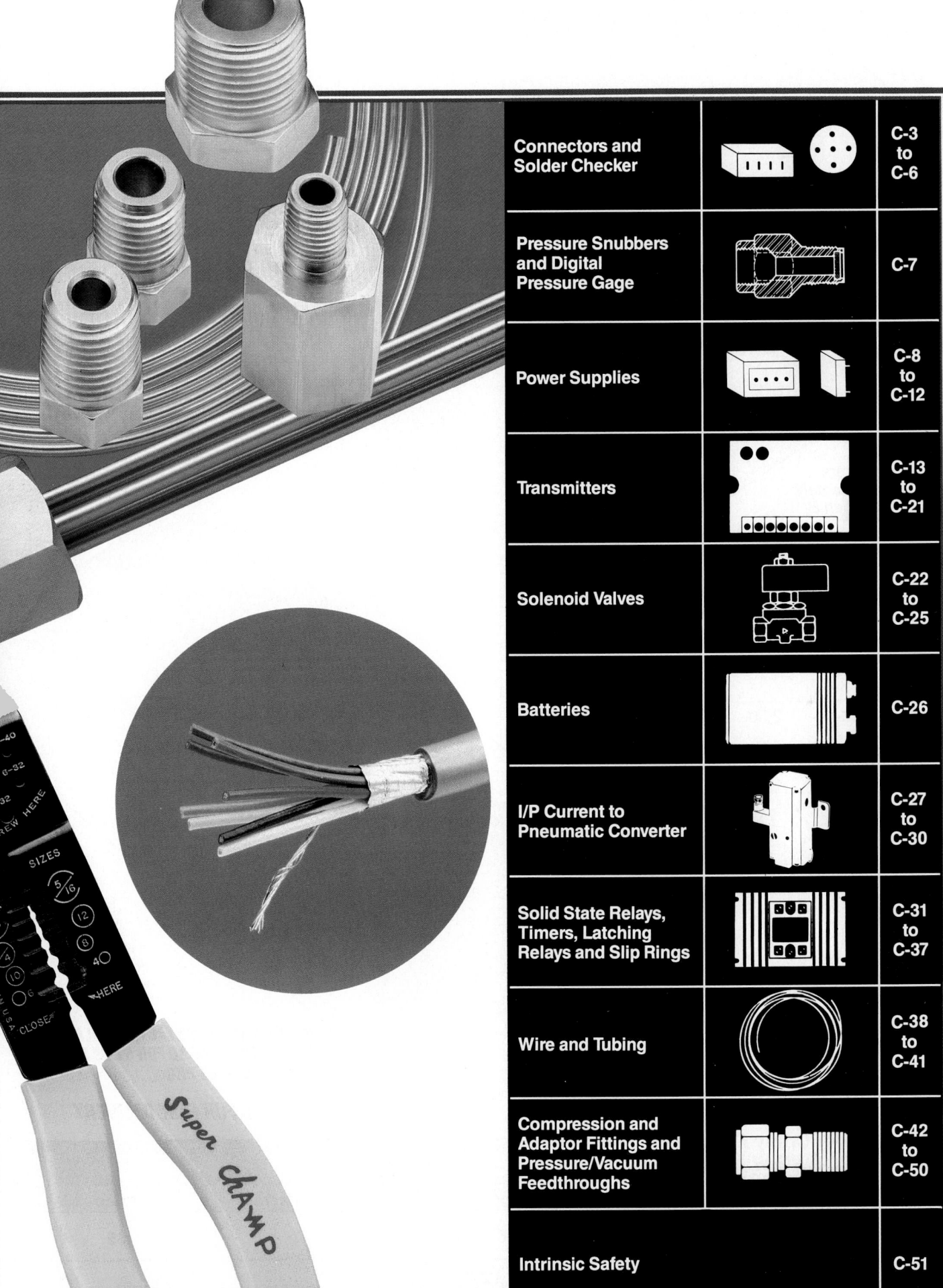

Connectors and Solder Checker		C-3 to C-6
Pressure Snubbers and Digital Pressure Gage		C-7
Power Supplies		C-8 to C-12
Transmitters		C-13 to C-21
Solenoid Valves		C-22 to C-25
Batteries		C-26
I/P Current to Pneumatic Converter		C-27 to C-30
Solid State Relays, Timers, Latching Relays and Slip Rings		C-31 to C-37
Wire and Tubing		C-38 to C-41
Compression and Adaptor Fittings and Pressure/Vacuum Feedthroughs		C-42 to C-50
Intrinsic Safety		C-51

ACCESSORIES C

CONNECTORS
PUSH-ON STYLE, CRIMP CONTACT

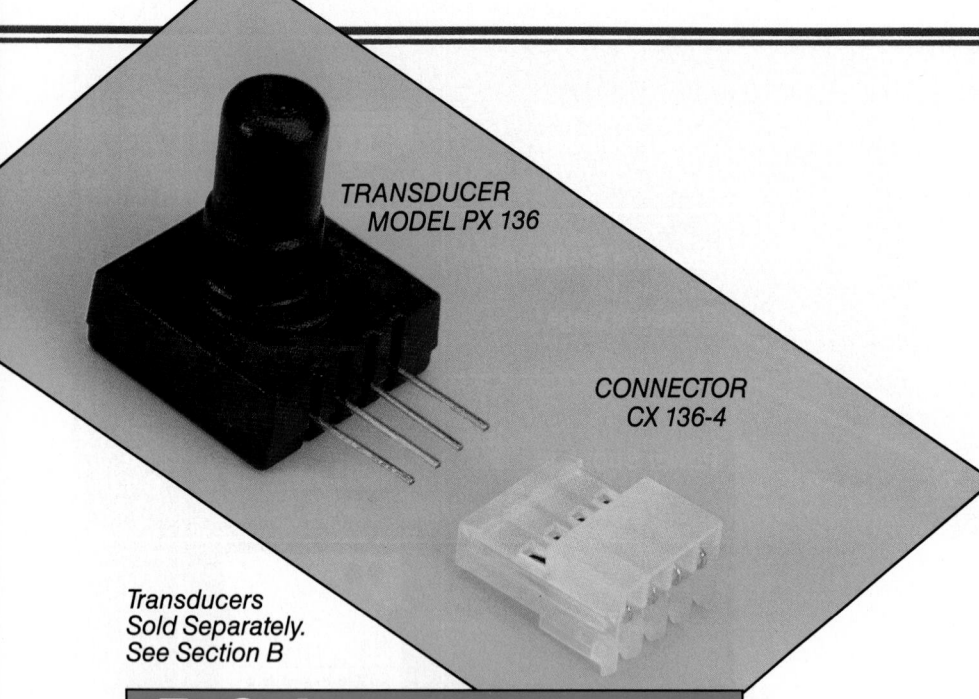

TRANSDUCER MODEL PX 136

CONNECTOR CX 136-4

Transducers Sold Separately. See Section B

NO SPECIAL TOOLS REQUIRED!

- ✔ **Heavy Duty Construction**
- ✔ **Rated to 215°F (105°C)**
- ✔ **Solder/Crimp Contacts**
- ✔ **22-26 AWG Wire Size**
- ✔ **Flame Retardant Thermoplastic Shells**
- ✔ **High Conductivity Gold Plated over Nickel Plated Contacts**

To Order *(Specify model number)*

Model No.	Price	No. of contacts	Compatible Sensors
CX-136-3	$2.50	5	Px141, PX142, PX143, PX161, PX162, PX163, PX164
CX-136-4	2.50	4	PX136, PX160, PX170, PX126, PX184, PX185
CX-136-8	2.50	8	PX149

CX-136 has spacing of .1" between pins.

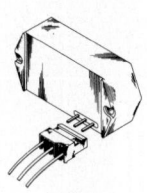

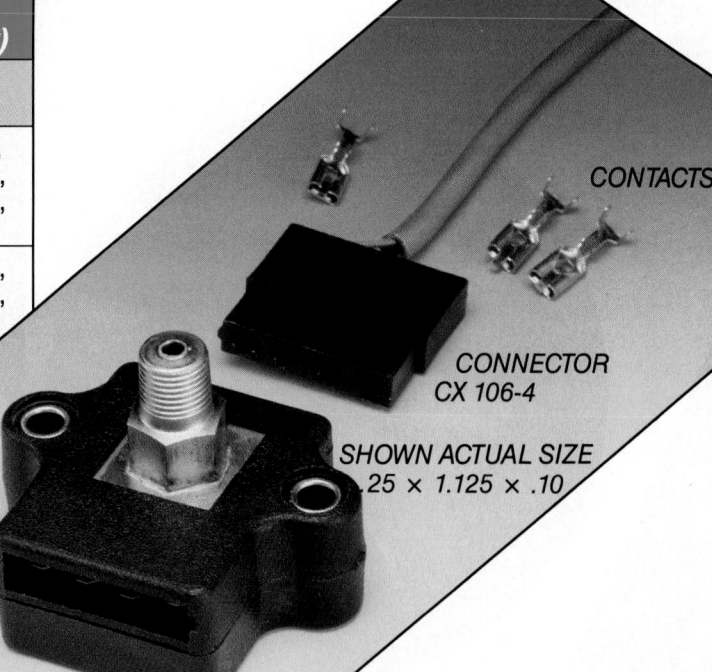

CONTACTS

CONNECTOR CX 106-4

SHOWN ACTUAL SIZE .25 × 1.125 × .10

TRANSDUCER MODEL PX 105

OEM STYLE CONNECTORS FOR PX-105 AND PX-106 PRESSURE TRANSDUCERS

- ✔ **Durable Valox Shell**
- ✔ **Rated to 257°F (125°C)**
- ✔ **Solder/Crimp Contacts**
- ✔ **16-20 AWG Wire Size**
- ✔ **High Conductivity Tin Plated over Brass Contacts**
- ✔ **Contacts Included**

REPLACEMENT CONTACTS AVAILABLE IN A PACKAGE OF 10 FOR $1.25 PKG SPECIFY CX-105-PKG

IN STOCK FOR FAST DELIVERY

To Order *(Specify part number)*

Part No.	No. of Contacts	Price
CX-106-4	4	$5

CONNECTORS
TWIST LOCK TYPE

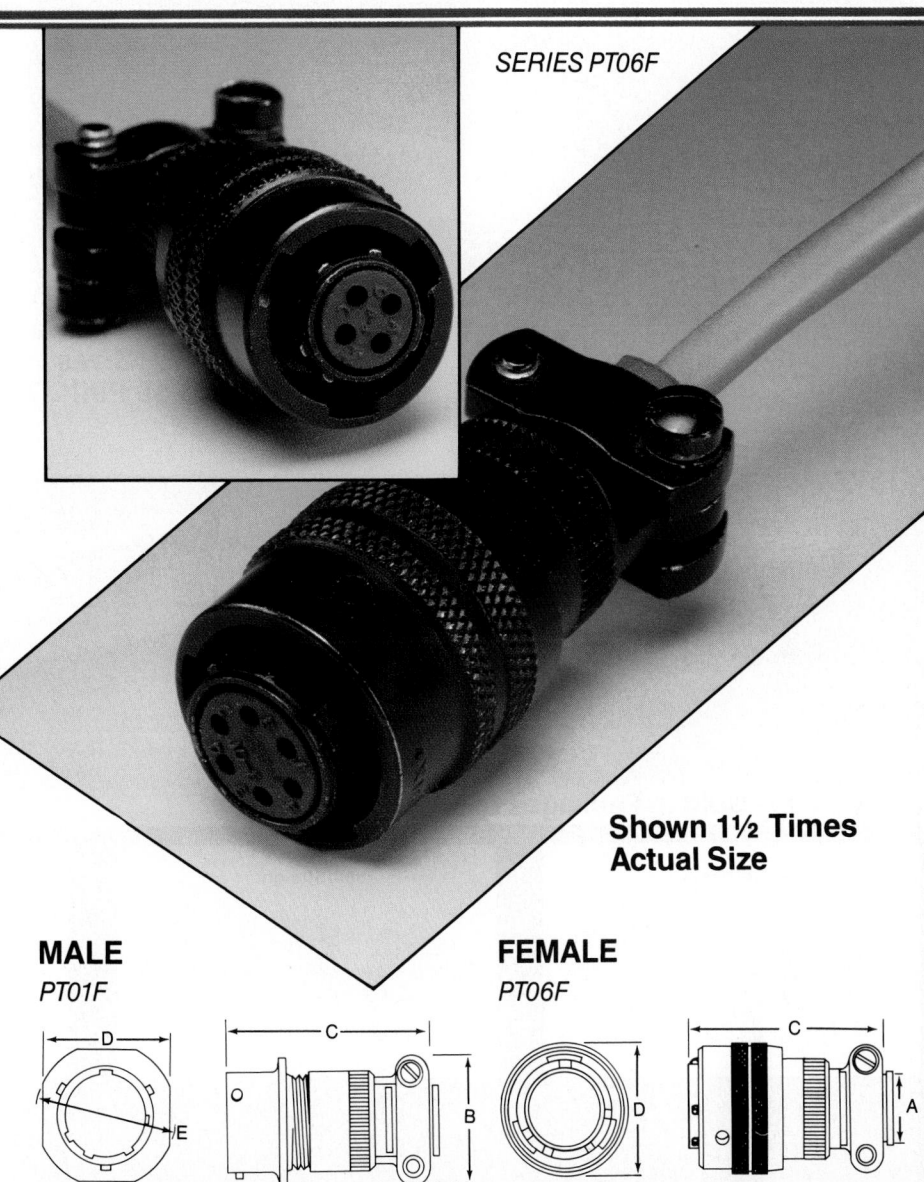

SERIES PT06F

- **Rugged Aluminum Shells**
- **Rated to 257°F (125°C)**
- **Strain Relief Cable Clamp**
- **Secure Solder Contacts**
- **#20 AWG Wire Size**
- **High Conductivity Gold Plated Contacts**

OMEGA PT Series Connectors provide an efficient method of connecting Pressure Transducers to associated instrumentation with the Multi-Conductor cable on page C-38. The solder contacts are designed to provide positive connections for signal or power circuitry. The connectors are rated for operation −67°F (−55°C) to 257°F (125°C).

INTEGRAL SOLDER CONTACTS INCLUDED

Shown 1½ Times Actual Size

IN STOCK FOR FAST DELIVERY

SPECIFICATIONS

Insulation Resistance at 77°F: 5000 megohms min.
Voltage Drop: #20 contact, #20 wire, at 7.5 A, 55 mV max.
Air Pressure: 30 psi at −55°C
Water Immersion: 6 ft., 48 hours
Durability: 500 cycles of coupling and uncoupling
Shells: Aluminum alloy, .0003 cadmium plate with olive drab chromate
Insulators: Neoprene
Contacts: High conductivity copper alloy, .000050 gold over copper.

NOTE: "P" suffix denotes male pins
"S" suffix denotes female sockets
i.e.: PT01F-8-4P mates with PT06F-8-4S

MALE
PT01F

FEMALE
PT06F

To Order (Specify part number)

Part No.	No. of Contacts	Price
PT01F- 8-4P	4–Male	$18.00
PT01F-10-6P	6–Male	24.50
PT06F- 8-4S	4–Female	24.00
PT06F-10-6S	6 Female	26.50

DIMENSIONS

	A Min. Dia.	B Max.	C Max.	D Max.	E ±.020
PT01F- 8-4P	.234	.828	1.922	.828	.938
PT01F-10-6P	.297	.891	1.922	.954	1.062
PT06F- 8-4S	.234	.828	1.828	.750	—
PT06F-10-6S	.297	.891	1.828	.859	—

INCREDIBLY LOW COST CRIMP TYPE
FOR SUB-D TYPE CONNECTORS

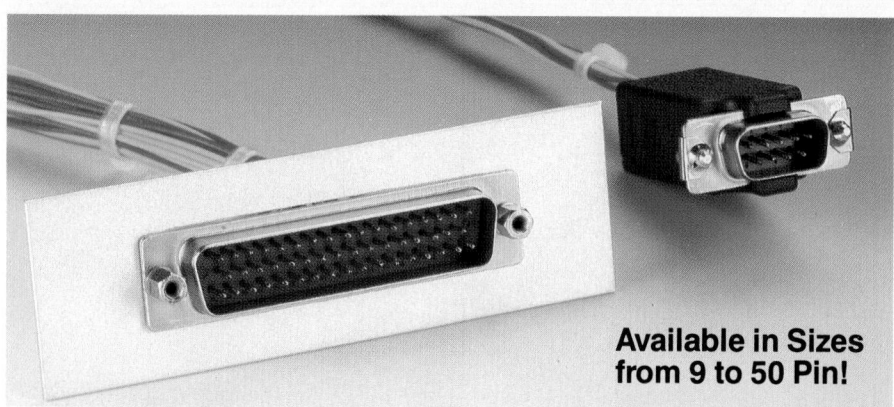

Applications Include:
- ✓ **Test Labs**
- ✓ **Automotive Testing**
- ✓ **Quality Control Stations**
- ✓ **Profile Probes**
- ✓ **High Density Applications**

Available in Sizes from 9 to 50 Pin!

Connector Bodies

9 Pin	15 Pin	25 Pin	37 Pin	50 Pin
SMTC-9MF	SMTC-15MF	SMTC-25MF	SMTC-37MF	SMTC-50MF
$15	$17.50	$20	$22.50	$25

Backshells - Sold in Packages of 5

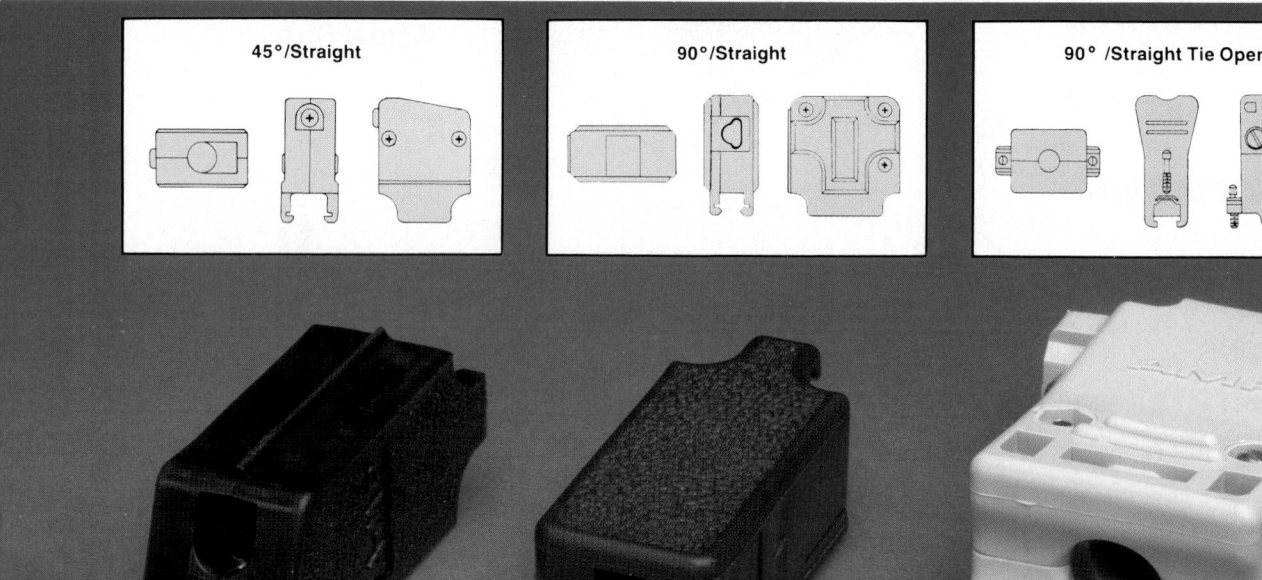

45°/Straight

90°/Straight

90°/Straight Tie Open

45°/Straight

Model No.	Price Pkg. of 5	Description	No. of Contacts
SM4-9	$17.50		9
SM4-15	17.50	45°/Straight Sub-D Backshell	15
SM4-25	17.50		25
SM4-37	17.50		37
SM4-50	17.50		50

90°/Straight

Model No.	Price Pkg. of 5	Description	No. of Contacts
SM9-9	$15		9
SM9-15	15	90°/Straight Sub-D Backshell	15
SM9-25	15		25
SM9-37	15		37
SM9-50	15		50

90°/Straight-Tie Open

Model No.	Price Pkg. of 5	Description	No. of Contacts
SMT-15	$17.50		15
SMT-25S*	17.50	90°/Straight Tie Open Sub-D Backshell	25
SMT-25L†	17.50		25
SMT-37	17.50		37
SMT-50	17.50		50

*Max Cable Dia. 0.335"   †Max Cable Dia. 0.460"

THERMOCOUPLE MULTIPINS

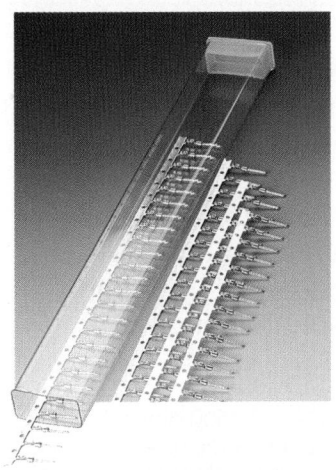

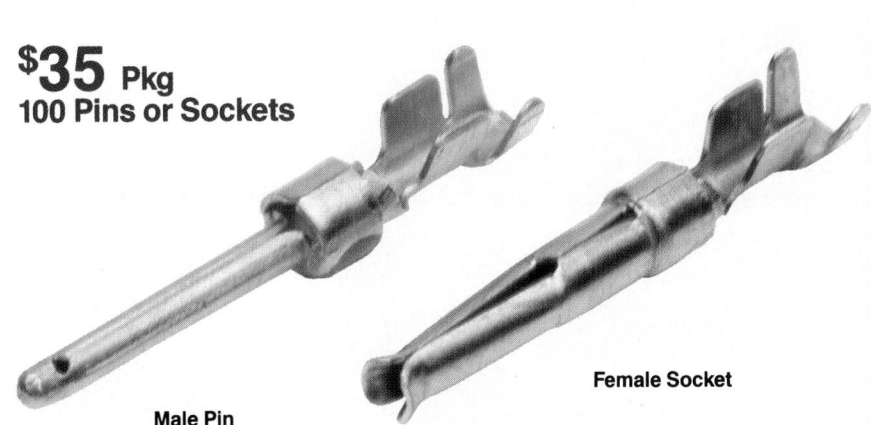

$35 Pkg
100 Pins or Sockets

Male Pin

Female Socket

Shown 7 Times Actual Size

OMEGA's exclusive low cost, crimp style thermocouple alloy pins and sockets set a new industry standard for cost and performance. These contacts are available in a number of thermocouple alloys including Chromega™, Alomega™, gold-plated Iron, Constantan and Copper. In addition, uncompensated pins and sockets are available from stock. All thermocouple contacts are color-coded for easy identification, and are sold in convenient packages of 100 (four strips of 25).

All pins and sockets can be easily wired using OMEGA Thermocouple wire in either solid or stranded construction, 20 or 24 gage. Stranded wire is recommended as electrical connections will have higher reliability.

These precision Sub-D connectors are sold in sets of five, package consisting of 5 male connector bodies and 5 female connector bodies. Sets are available in 9, 15, 25, 37 and 50 pin configurations.

Thermocouple Alloy Pins & Sockets

Alloy type	Model No. Male Pins	Price	Model No. Female Sockets	Price
Chromega	SMTC-CH-P	$35 Package of 100 Male Pins	SMTC-CH-S	$35 Package of 100 Female Sockets
Alomega	SMTC-AL-P		SMTC-AL-S	
Constantan	SMTC-CO-P		SMTC-CO-S	
Copper	SMTC-CU-P		SMTC-CU-S	
Iron*	SMTC-IR-P		SMTC-IR-S	

* Gold plated iron

Uncompensated Pins & Sockets

Model No. Male Pins	Price	Model No. Female Sockets	Price
SMTC-BR-P Gold Plated Brass	$27.50 Package of 100 Male Pins	SMTC-PBRZ-S Gold Plated Phosphorus Bronze	$27.50 Package of 100 Female Sockets

Connecting Hardware (not shown)

Model No.	Price	Description
SMFR	$10	Female screwlock set, 5 sets/pkg.
SMMR	10	Male screw retainer set, 20 sets/pkg.

To Order
Specify contacts (pins & sockets), connector bodies, backshells, connecting hardware and accessories

Ordering Example
Male and female connectors, for 25 type K thermocouples

Model No.	Price	Description
SMTC-CH-P	$ 35	Chromega (+) pins, pkg of 100 (25 req'd)
SMTC-AL-P	35	Alomega (−) pins, pkg of 100 (25 req'd)
SMTC-CH-S	35	Chromega (+) sockets, pkg of 100 (25 req'd)
SMTC-AL-S	35	Alomega (−) sockets, pkg of 100 (25 req'd)
SMTC-50MF	25	connector bodies, 50 pin (25 pos/25 neg)
SM9-50	15	90/straight backshells, pkg of 5 (2 req'd)
SMFR	10	Female screwlock set, pkg of 5 (2 req'd)
SMMR	10	Male screw retainer set, pkg of 20 (2 req'd)
SM-CTHD	185	Heavy duty crimp tool
SM-EX	4.75	Insertion/extraction tool

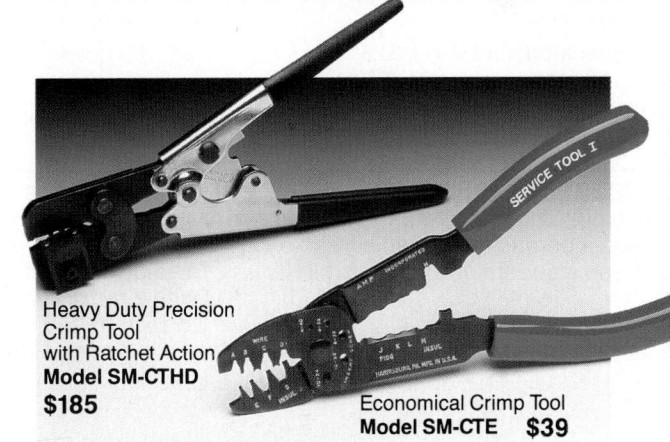

Heavy Duty Precision Crimp Tool with Ratchet Action
Model SM-CTHD
$185

Economical Crimp Tool
Model SM-CTE **$39**

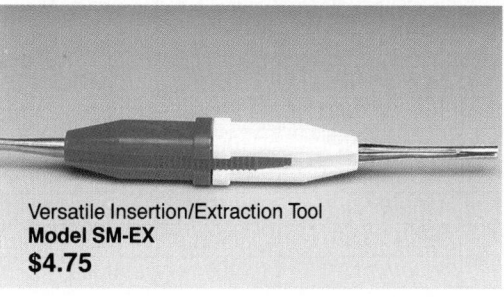

Versatile Insertion/Extraction Tool
Model SM-EX
$4.75

DIGITAL PRESSURE GAUGE
MEASURING RANGE FROM −14 to 500 PSIG

MADE IN
USA

Model DPG500

$139

✔ **Large ½″ High LCD Display**
✔ **Provided With 9 Volt Battery**
✔ **AC Power Adapter for Operation Anywhere**
✔ **Accuracy of ±1% and Resolution of 1 PSI**

The OMEGA DPG500 digital pressure gauge combines the features of a general purpose pressure transducer and a digital meter offering an attractive alternative to conventional bourdon tube gauges. A large ½ inch LCD display is exceptionally easy to read eliminating the possibility of parallax error which is commonly found while using dial gauges. The unit has a broad range of −14 to 500 PSI making it ideal for many applications. A 9 volt lithium battery and AC power adapter are included enabling both portable and stationary use.

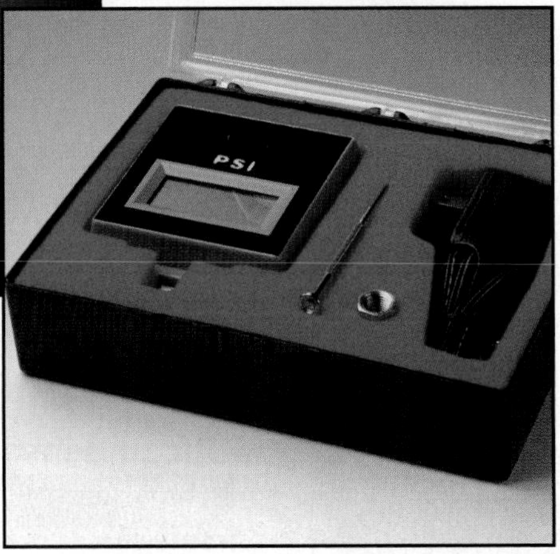

SPECIFICATIONS

Accuracy: ± 1% full scale
Operable Temperature Range: 32 to 120°F
Display: 0.5″ LCD
Diaphragm/Port Material: Brass
Pressure Port: ⅛ NPT male
Power: 9 volt lithium battery or 120 Vac with adapter
Dimensions: 3.25″ H x 3.25″ W x 1.50″ D
Weight: 8 oz.
Proof Pressure: 2× full scale

Each DPG500 includes:
✔ ⅛″NPT to ¼″ flare brass adapter fitting
✔ AC power adapter with 5 foot cord
✔ Calibration Screwdriver
✔ 9 Volt Battery

To Order *(Specify Model Number)*

RANGE	MODEL	PRICE
▶ −14 to 500 PSIG	DPG500	**$139** ◀

▶ *STOCKED FOR FAST DELIVERY* ◀

PRESSURE SNUBBER—for dampening and filtering. The snubber has a porous metal disc available in three standard grades of porosity.

Due to the large filter surface, the snubber has less tendency to clog than orifice type devices. The housing is 303SS and the filter disc is 316SS with a maximum PSI rating of 10,000 at 25°C. (PS-8 series 5000 PSI)

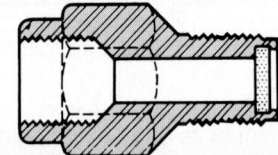

To Order *(Specify Model Number)*

Model No.	Description	Pore Opening (in.) Mean	Max.	Cap. CFH at 1-PSI-Diff. Pressure	For use with	Price
PS-8D	⅛ x ⅛″ NPT	.0025	.005	6.5	Oil (22540 500 S.S.U.)	$10
PS-8E	⅛ x ⅛″ NPT	.0013	.0025	3.0	Water & light Oils (30 to 225)	10
PS-8G	⅛ x ⅛″ NPT	.0004	.0001	1.1	Air Steam & Gases	10
PS-4D	¼ x ¼″ NPT	.0025	.005	6.5	Oil (225 to 500 S.S.U.)	10
PS-4E	¼ x ¼″ NPT	.0013	.0025	3.0	Water & Light Oils (30 to 225 S.S.U.)	10
PS-4G	¼ x ¼″ NPT	.0004	.0009	1.1	Air Steam & Gases	10
PS-2D	½ x ½″ NPT	.0025	.005	6.5	Oil (225 to 500 S.S.U.)	24
PS-2E	½ x ½″ NPT	.0013	.0025	3.0	Water & Light Oils (30 to 225 S.S.U.)	24
PS-2G	½ x ½″ NPT	.0004	.0009	1.1	Air Steam & Gases	24

Comes with operator's manual.
(Note: 225 to 500 SSU is 10 to 50 SAE motor oil at room temperature)   C-7

REGULATED POWER SUPPLY FOR TRANSDUCERS AND BRIDGES
ADJUSTABLE 4 TO 15 V DC OUTPUT

- **Adjustable 4 to 15 V dc Output**
- **Up to 150 mA Current**
- **Well Suited for 120 ohm and 350 ohm Strain Gages**
- **Can Power Multiple Pressure Transducers**
- **Screw Terminal Connections**

The PST-4130 is an AC line powered adjustable output power source designed for strain gages and pressure transducers. It can also be used as a high quality voltage source or reference in many applications. The PST-4130 has a split bobbin transformer for high line isolation. It has remote sensing to eliminate line drop errors, and features excellent regulation, stability, and very low noise.

Model PST-4130

$132

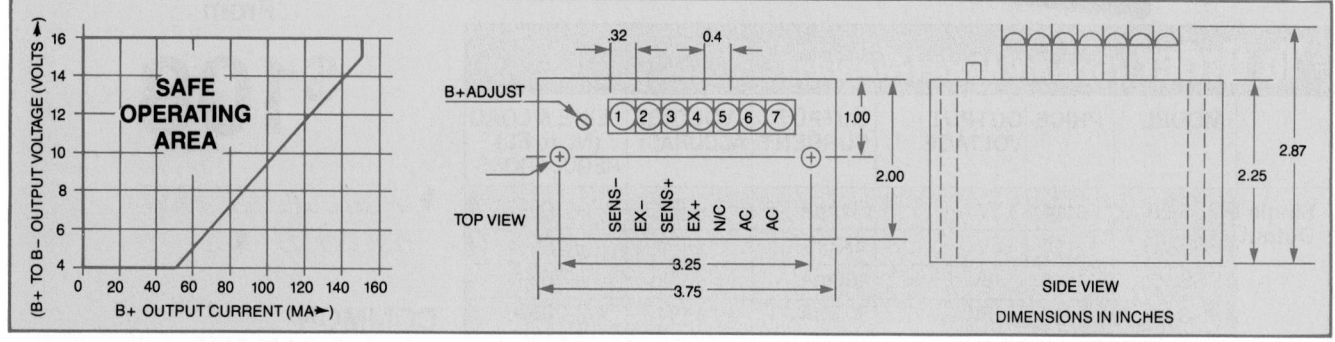

SPECIFICATIONS

Input: 115 V ac ±10% 50 to 60 Hz
Output Voltage: Adjustable 4 to 15 Vdc
Output Current: 150 mA max. (see graph)
Line and Load Regulation: 0.005%
Noise: 0.5 mV rms
Operating Temperature: 0 to 70°C
Temperature Effect: 50 ppm/°C
Storage Temperature: −25 to 85°C
Line Isolation: 1500 V dc
Weight: 18 oz. (510 grams)

— Compatible With:
- All mV output type transducers in Section B.
- All amplified voltage output type transducers requiring less than 15 V

— dc output in Section B.
- All current loop output type transducers requiring less than 15 V dc output in Section B.

◆ *HIGHLIGHTED MODELS STOCKED FOR FAST DELIVERY* **◆**

To Order (Specify Model Number)

MODEL	PRICE	OUTPUT
PST-4130	$132	4 to 15 V dc
Power Cord-Stripped End	7	—

BARRIER STRIP STYLE POWER SUPPLY
PROVIDES REGULATED STRAIN GAGE AND TRANSDUCER EXCITATION

MADE IN USA

PSS Series

- **Recessed Barrier Strip Secures Wire Without Twisting**
- **Compact Design Allows Mounting Where Space is Restricted**
- **Ideally Suited for Use With Strain Gages, Transducers, Microprocessor Systems, and Test Equipment**

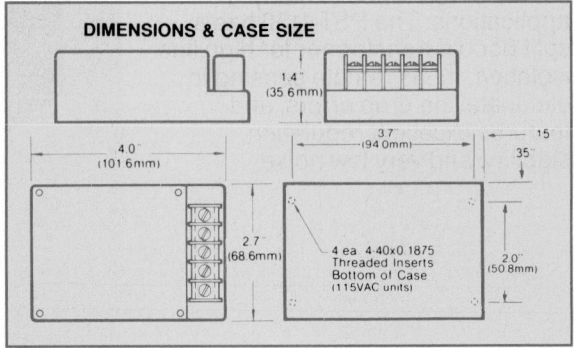

DIMENSIONS & CASE SIZE

To Order *(Specify Model Number)*

	MODEL	PRICE	OUTPUT VOLTAGE	OUTPUT CURRENT	VOLTAGE ACCURACY	LINE & LOAD (NL to FL) REGULATIONS
Single Output	PSS-5A	$114	+5V	500mA	±1%	±0.05%
	PSS-5B	150	+5V	1000mA	±1%	±0.05%
	PSS-10	150	+10V	400mA	±1%	±0.05%
	PSS-12	150	+12V	500mA	±1%	±0.05%
	PSS-15	150	+15V	400mA	±1%	±0.05%
Dual Output	PSS-D12A	114	±12V or 24V	±120mA	±0.5%	±0.02%
	PSS-D12B	150	±12V or 24V	±240mA	±0.5%	±0.02%
	PSS-D15A	108	±15V or 30V	±50mA	±0.5%	±0.02%
	PSS-D15B	114	±15V or 30V	±100mA	±0.5%	±0.02%
	PSS-D15C	150	±15V or 30V	±200mA	±0.5%	±0.02%
Triple Output	PSS-T12	174	±12V & 5V	±12V @ 100mA; +5V @ 600mA	±1%	±0.05%
	PSS-T15	174	±15V & 5V	±15V @ 100mA; +5V @500mA	±1%	±0.05%

From
$108

▶ *IN STOCK FOR FAST DELIVERY!* ◀

COMMON SPECIFICATIONS

Input Voltage: 115 Vac ± 10 volts
Input Frequency Range: 50 to 60 Hz
Isolation
> **Resistance:** 50M min.
> **Capacitance:** 250pF
> **Voltage:** 1500 Vrms

Temperature Coefficient: ± 0.01%
Noise and Ripple: 1 mVrms Single and Dual Output; 2 mVrms Triple Output
Storage Temperature: −25 to 85°C
Maximum Case Operating Temperature Without Derating: +50°C
Short Circuit Protection: Foldback current limiting

PC BOARD MOUNTABLE POWER SUPPLIES
WITH INDUSTRY STANDARD PIN CONFIGURATIONS

PSC Series

- Regulated Power Supplies With Rugged Dependability
- Two Types of Mounting Kits Available for Easy Installation
- Foldback Current Limiting Provides Outstanding Short Circuit protection

PSC-022

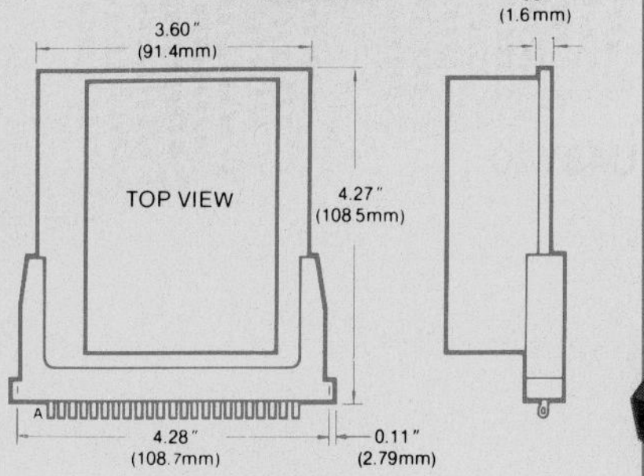

PSC-08B

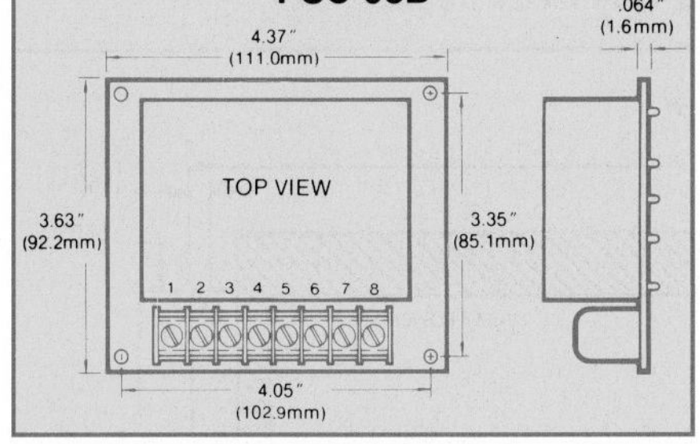

PIN CONFIGURATIONS

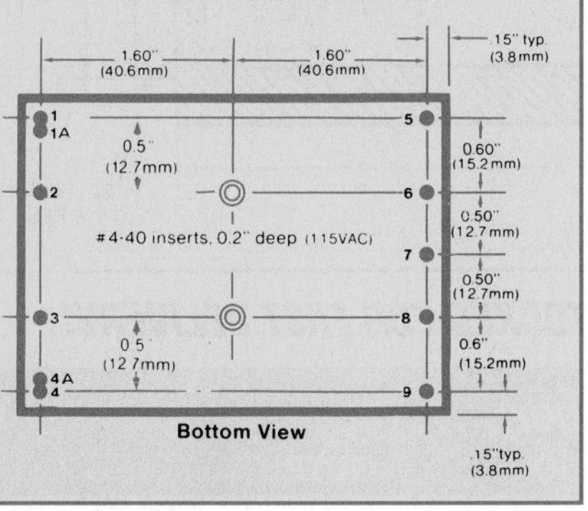

Mounting Kits

Model	Price	Description
PSC-022	$40	PC card with 22-pin connector
PSC-08B	36	barrier strip style connector

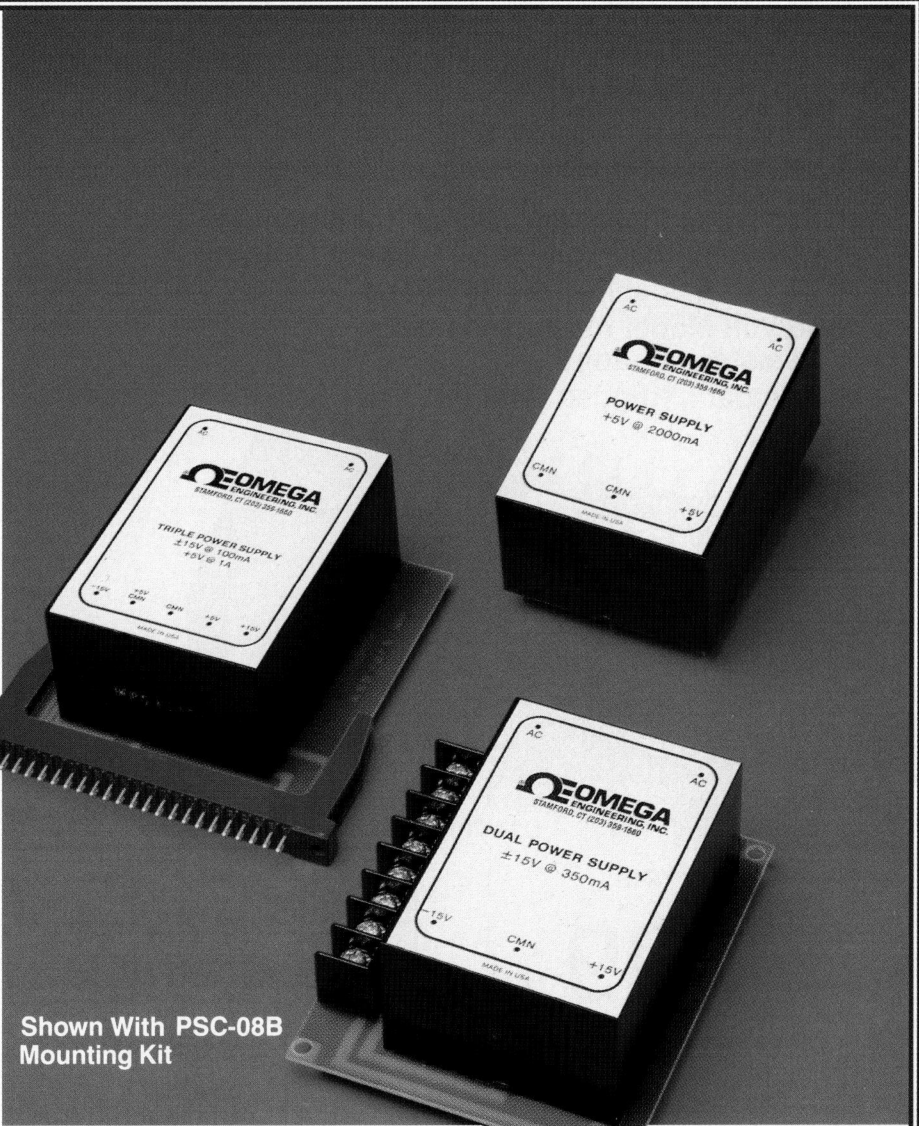

Shown With PSC-08B Mounting Kit

From **$98**, IN STOCK FOR FAST DELIVERY!

MADE IN USA

To Order (Specify Model Number)

	MODEL	PRICE	OUTPUT VOLTAGE	OUTPUT CURRENT	VOLTAGE ACCURACY	LINE & LOAD (NL to FL) REGULATIONS
Single Output	PSC-5	$ 98	+5V	500mA	±1%	±0.05%
	PSC-9	150	+9V	1000mA	±0.5%	±0.05%
	PSC-12	145	+12V	480mA	±0.5%	±0.02%
	PSC-15	126	+15V	400mA	±0.5%	±0.02%
	PSC-18	150	±18V	500mA	±0.5%	±0.02%
	PSC-24	156	+24V	375mA	±0.5%	±0.02%
Dual Output	PSC-D5	156	±5V or 10V	±750mA	±0.5%	±0.05%
	PSC-D12	98	±12V or 24V	±120mA	±0.5%	±0.02%
	PSC-D15	98	±15V or 30V	±100mA	±0.5%	±0.02%

UNREGULATED POWER SUPPLIES

- ✔ **For Transducers and Signal Conditioners with Amplified Voltage or 4-20 mA Outputs**
- ✔ **24 Volt Model Powers 50 Loops**
- ✔ **48 Volt Model Available for High Resistance Loops**
- ✔ **Compact, Rugged Design**

U48Y40

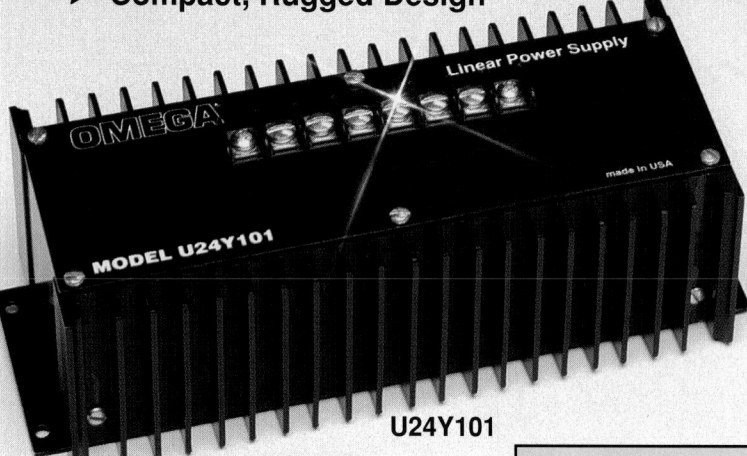

U24Y101

From

$99

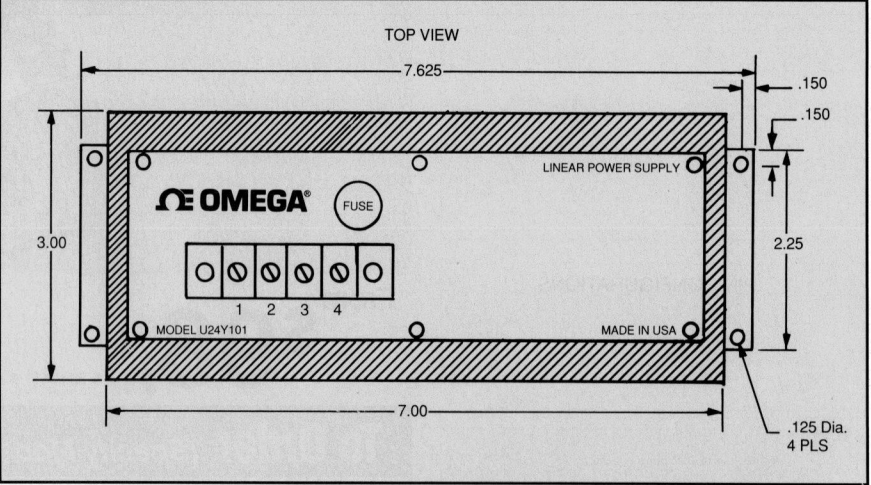

Dimensions U24Y101

OMEGA's unregulated power supplies provide a low-cost solution to excitation problems. These power supplies will work with any pressure transducer that requires 24 Vdc or 48 Vdc excitation.

SPECIFICATIONS

Input:
U24Y101: 110 Vac
U24Y101-220: 220 Vac
U48Y40: 110 Vac

Operating Range: 14 to 150°F
(-10 to 65°C)

Output:
U24Y101: 24 Vdc, @ 1000 mA
U48Y40: 48 Vdc, @ 400 mA

Dimensions:
U24Y101: 3.0" H X 7.28" W X 2.94" D
(76 x 185 x 75 mm)
U48Y40: 4.49" H X 5.12" W X 3.44" D
(114 x 130 x 87 mm)

STOCKED FOR FAST DELIVERY!

To Order *(Specify Model Number)*			
MODEL	PRICE	DESCRIPTION	OUTPUT
U24Y101	**$99**	Accommodates 50 Current Loops	24 Vdc @ 1000 mA
U24Y101-220	99	Same as U24Y101 but 220 Vac powered	24 Vdc @ 1000 mA
U48Y40	130	For Long Loops (High Resistance)	48 Vdc @ 400 mA

Each unit comes with complete operator's manual.
Ordering Example: *U24Y101 is a 24 Vdc unregulated power supply,* **$99.**

EXCITATION FOR STRAIN GAGES BRIDGES AND PRESSURE TRANSDUCERS
SCREW TERMINAL STYLE

For Easy Field Termination without Soldering

- ✔ **4-40 Screw Terminations and Mounting Inserts**
- ✔ **Floating Output**
- ✔ **Efficient**
- ✔ **Rugged**
- ✔ **15 oz.**

OMEGA ENGINEERING, INC. STAMFORD, CONN.

AC AC OUT T/C OUT

From
$165
MODEL PST-5

Works With Most Transducers

Shown actual size

ACCESSORIES C

Encapsulated Power Supplies provide a versatile excitation source for transducers and bridges. Two case styles are available for your installation needs. The pin terminal style can either be soldered into a printed circuit board or plugged into a phenolic accessory socket board with gold plated Teflon insulated contacts. A 4-40 threaded insert is molded into the power supply case to provide a means of securing the module without stressing the connection pins. The barrier strip type case is designed to be mounted to a bulkhead or chassis using four 4-40 screws. Screw terminals are provided for connection using either crimp lugs or stripped wires.

These regulated power supplies are designed to be a modular solution for your excitation needs. The stable output allows drift-free performance even if the input power source is noisy or unstable. Long term measurements can then be meaningfully compared with confidence. Short circuit protection prevents failure due to excessive current drain and the conservative design assures long term reliability.

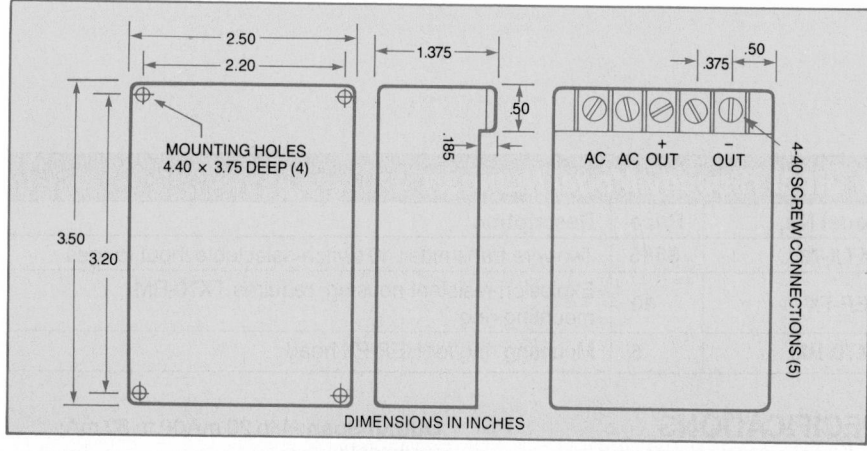

2.50
2.20
1.375
.375 .50
.50
.185
3.50
3.20

MOUNTING HOLES
4.40 × 3.75 DEEP (4)

AC   AC OUT   +OUT   −OUT
4-40 SCREW CONNECTIONS (5)

DIMENSIONS IN INCHES

To Order *(Specify model number)*

OUTPUT		MODEL	PRICE	OUTPUT		MODEL	PRICE
V	mA			V	mA		
5	500	PST-5	$165	± 15	300	PST-A15	$245
8	300	PST-8	165	± 15	500	PST-B15	295
10	240	PST-10	165	18	270	PST-18	199
15	200	PST-15	165	28	150	PST-28	199

◆ *HIGHLIGHTED MODELS STOCKED FOR FAST DELIVERY* ◆

2-WIRE TRANSMITTER FOR USE WITH OMEGA PRESSURE TRANSDUCERS
CONVERTS mV, V, OR mA INPUT TO 4 TO 20 mA OUTPUT

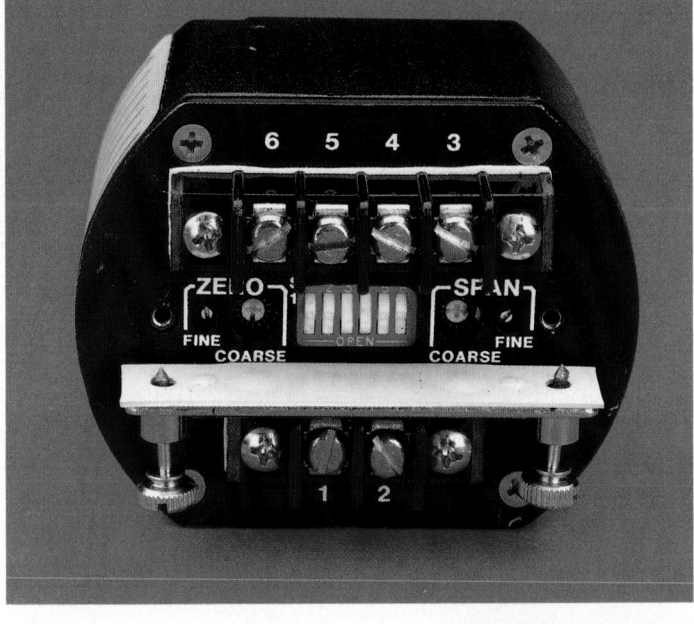

Model PXTX-703

- ✔ Provides 600V/120dB Isolation
- ✔ 10 Switch-Selectable Input Ranges
- ✔ 80% Zero and Span Adjustability within Each Input Range
- ✔ 4 to 20 mA or 10 to 50 mA Switch Selectable Output Ranges
- ✔ Rugged, EMI/RFI-Shielded Housing

$385

10 Switch-Selectable Ranges

Range No.	Range
1	0 to 10V
2	±10V
3	0 to 1V
4	±1V
5	0 to 100 mV
6	±100 mV
7	0 to 20 mA
8	±20 mA
9	0 to 60 mA
10	±50 mA

To Order (Specify Model Number)

Model No.	Price	Description
PXTX-703	$385	Two-wire transmitter, 10 switch-selectable input ranges
HEP-TX	40	Explosion-resistant housing, requires TX70-RM mounting ring
TX70-RM	5	Mounting ring for HEP-PX head

SPECIFICATIONS

Input Span: 10 Ranges Switch-Selectable, See Range Chart

Supply Voltage Range: 4 to 20 mA; 12 to 80 Vdc, 10 to 50 mA; 12 to 60 Vdc

Zero & Span Adjustability: 80% of any selected range

Accuracy: (includes linearity, hysteresis, stability) 0.5% of any adjusted span

Repeatability: 0.05% of span

Response Time: 50 ms, maximum

Stability: Zero: within 0.02% of span/°C or 2 μV, whichever is greater. Span: within 0.01% of span/°C.

Max. Leadwire Resistance Effect: Less than 0.25μV per ohm

Input Impedance: Ranges 1 and 2: > 200 KΩ; Ranges 3 through 6: 5MΩ, typical; ranges 7 through 10: equivalent to a 1V drop, max.

Output Span: 4 to 20 mA/10 to 50 mA; switchable

Min. Output Current: 3.3 mA typical

Max. Output Current: 4 to 20 mA range: 24 mA typical; 10 to 50 mA: range 58 mA typical

Max. Change-in-Supply Voltage Effect: 0.05% of span

Output Ripple: Less than 0.1% of span, rms

RFI Effect (5W, 470 MHz at 3 feet): Error less than 1% of span

Isolation: 600 Vdc or peak ac max, input to output

Operating Temperature Range (Ambient): –40 to 80°C

Explosion-Resistant Housing Model HEP-TX $40 for PXTX-703 Pressure Transmitter

TX70-RM Mounting Ring $5 for HEP-TX Protection Head

STRAIN GAGE AMPLIFIER/SIGNAL CONDITIONER MODULES
FOR STRAIN GAGES, LOAD CELLS AND TRANSDUCERS

1 YEAR WARRANTY · **MADE IN USA** · **CARE**

DMD 460 SERIES
$295

✔ **Bridge Excitation 4 to 16V dc; Up to 150 mA**

✔ **Works with 120, 350, 500 ohm and Greater Bridge Circuits**

✔ **Adjustable Gain and Offset**

✔ **6 Wire Bridge Connections**

✔ **Voltage and Current Output Versions Available**

✔ **Rugged Self Contained Module**

ACCESSORIES C

The DMD 460 Series units are self contained, AC powered, signal conditioning modules for bridge type instrumentation. The DMD 465 contains a precision differential instrumentation amplifier with filtered output. The DMD 465WB is similar to the DMD 465, but has a frequency response of 2KHZ. The DMD 466 is similar to the above units but has a 4 to 20mA output instead of voltage.

To Order *(Specify Model No)*		
MODEL NO.	**PRICE**	**DESCRIPTION**
DMD-465	$295	Amplifier
DMD-465WB	295	High Frequency Amplifier
DMD-466	295	Transmitter (4-20mA)
DMD-465-220V	295	220 Vac powered DMD-465
DMD-465WB-220V	295	220 Vac powered DMD-455WB
DMD-466-220V	295	220 Vac powered DMD-466

Comes with complete operator's manual.

Ordering Example: *DMD-465WB is high frequency amplifier/signal conditioner module, $295.*

MECHANICAL SPECIFICATIONS:
Operating Temperature: 0 to 70°C
Storage Temperature: -25 to +85°C
Weight: 18 oz.(510 grams)
Size: 3.75" L x 2" W x 3" H

BRIDGE SUPPLY SPECIFICATIONS:
Voltage Range Adjustment: 4 to 15 Vdc
Current Output: 100 mA
Line and Load Regulation: (0 to 100 mA) 0.05% max.
Output Noise: 0.5 mV RMS
Power Input: 115 Vac ±10% 50 to 60 Hz

AMPLIFIER SPECIFICATIONS: DMD 465 AND DMD 465WB
Gain Range: 40-250, (up to 1000 with external gain on DMD 465 only)
Dynamic Response: DMD 465, DC to -6 dB=5 Hz
DMD 465WB, DC to -3 dB=2 KHz
Max Output(2K Load): ±10V
Output Impedance: 0.01 ohms to 1 ohm
Output Offset: -5V to +2V (only for DMD 465WB only)
Gain Temp. Coef.: DMD 465 3ppm/C, DMD 465WB 200ppm/C

Input Bias Current: 30nA
Input Impedance: 3000 Megohms
Output Noise(RTO): 2 mV pp @ gain = 100, 1Hz to 2KHz
Input Noise Line Frequency: 15 µV pp
Common Mode Rejection: 90 dB @ gain 40, 100 dB @ gain 250
Common Mode Input Voltage: ±10V

TRANSMITTER SPECIFICATIONS: DMD 466
Output: 4 to 20 mA,0 to 20 mA (25mA max, @ 10 Ac)
Zero Adjust: 0 to +12 mA
Accuracy: ±0.05% FS
Gain Range: 0.084 to 3.2 mA/mV
Input for 4-20 mA Output: 5 to 190 mV
Temperature Stability: 200 ppm/C @ GAIN 0.084 mA/mV 135 ppm/C @ gain 2.0 mA/mV
Input Impedance: 1000 megaohms
Common Mode Rejection: 90 dB @ gain 0.084 mA/mV 100 dB @ gain 2.0 mA/mV
Common Mode Input: ±10volts
Output Noise: 1µA RMS @ gain 0.2 mA/mV, 1 to 100 Hz
Dynamic Response: DC to -6dB=5 Hz, to 1% of final value 200 mS, typical, to 0.1% of final value 300 mS, typical

PROGRAMMABLE SMART TRANSMITTER

NEW!

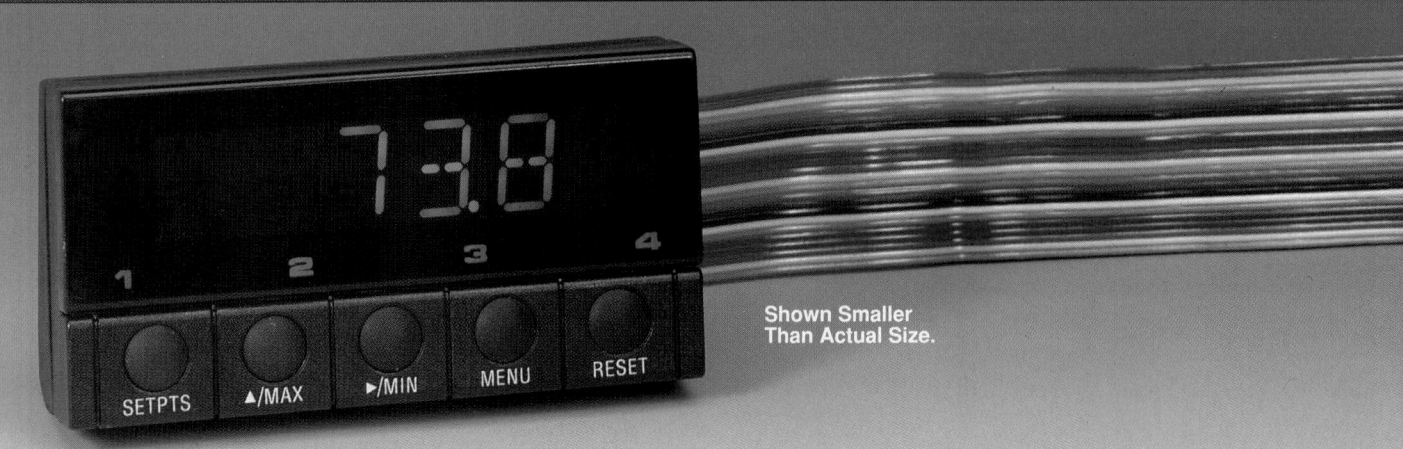

73.8

1 2 3 4

SETPTS ▲/MAX ►/MIN MENU RESET

Shown Smaller Than Actual Size.

- ✔ **Accepts Process Voltages, Curents, Strain Gages, 9 Thermocouples and RTD**
- ✔ **Programmable Via Remote Display or Serial Communications**
- ✔ **Can Provides Either 4-20 mA, 0-10 Vdc or Serial Communications Output**
- ✔ **Highly Accurate**

The TX41 Series offers a combination of flexibility and power in a single unit. These smart transmitters can be equipped with the following communication options: RS-232 or RS-485; analog, current or voltage output; mechanical relays and remote display. The unit in its standard configuration offers four open collector outputs, adjustable filtering, tracking peak or valley variables, external reset and a host of field installable options.

The TX41 can be scaled via the remote display or by serial communication. After being programmed the unit can be left to stand alone and carry out its preprogrammed function.

The units can be used in a wide variety of applications. Normally the unit is used to convert a process signal to a 4- 20 mA signal or a digital serial communication signal. In some instances, the unit serves

as a blind controller using the standard open collectors or the optional mechanical relays.

The TX41-RM will also display the actual input, minimum and maximum readings. When behind the panel depth is a concern, use the TX41-RM as a remote display.

To Order *(Specify Model Number)*

MODEL NO.	PRICE	DESCRIPTION
TX41-E-(*)	$335	Process input (voltage or current)
TX41-S-(*)	385	Strain gage input (millivolt or voltage)
TX41-TC-(*)	335	Temperature input (thermocouple)
TX41-RTD-(*)	335	Temperature input (RTD)
TX41-U-(*)	415	Universal input (accepts all inputs above)
TX41-RM	150	Red remote display
TX41-RM-GN	150	Green remote display

* Specify options below.

Outputs/Communications

ORDERING SUFFIX	PRICE	ANALOG OUTPUT
-A	$60	Analog output
-R	60	2 mechanical relays
-S2	60	RS-232 serial output (need conn. below)
-S4	80	RS485 Serial Output (need conn. below)
-B	60	BCD output

All option combinations are possible; however, options -R, -B, -S2 and -S4 are mutuall exclusive.

Accessories

MODEL NO.	PRICE	DESCRIPTION
DP40-9SC2	$30	9 pin DB serial conn. for RS232
DP40-9SC4	30	9 pin DB serial conn. for RS485
DP40-25SC2	30	25 pin DB serial conn. for RS232
DP40-25SC4	30	25 pin DB serial conn. for RS485

Each unit supplied with complete operator's manual. Units with RS-232 and RS-485 communications supplied with setup/programming disks (3.5" and 5.25") and 6' communications cable with phone plug termination. See accessories for 9- and 25-pin sub-D connector adaptors.

Ordering Example: *TX41-E -A programmable transmitter with current input, scalable analog output, with TX41-RM remote display/programmer, $335 + 150 =* **$485.**

FOR PROCESS VOLTAGE, CURRENT, STRAIN GAGE AND TEMPERATURE INPUTS

Shown with Model PX302, Millivolt
Output Pressure Transducer ($302)
See Page B-18.

Specifications

Thermocouple Input: J, K, T, E, R, S, B, N, J DIN

RTD Input: 100Ω Pt (385 or 392 curve) any 6 to 6K Ω NIST or DIN Pt and any linear RTD (10Ω Cu, etc); 2, 3 or 4 wire

Voltage Input: 0-100mV/0-1V/ 0-5V/1-5V/0-10V/1-10V/ ± 50mV/± 500mV/± 5V/± 50V

Current Input: 0-20mA/4-20mA

Excitation (E and S models only): DP41-S 1.25-10 Vdc or 24 Vdc; DP41-E 10 Vdc or 24 Vdc

Break Protection: Up or downscale, programmable

Resolution: 15-bit

Accuracy: ±0.005% of reading for voltage/current inputs

Span Temperature Coefficient: ±20 ppm

Warmup to Rated Accuracy: 50 min.

Operating Ambient Range: 32 to 122˚F (0 to 50˚C); 95% RH, non-condensing

Span Adjustment: 1 to 999,999 cts

Offset Adjustment: -99,999 to +999,999

TTL Outputs (std): 4, isolated open collector, 150mA at 1V sink; 30V open

BCD Output: Tri-state, TTL/CMOS compatible; internal 5V supply for non-isolated, external 5V supply for isolated.

Dual Relays: Form C, 7A at 30 Vdc or 230Vac

Analog Output: 0-5V/1-5V/0-10V/0-20 mA/4-20 mA; compliance, 12V at 20 mA; 15 bit resolution, 0.1% accuracy, programmable zero and span; turndown ratio (max offset-min. span): 1000 with 0.1% or 100 with 0.01% resolution

RS-232 Communications (optional): 300/1200/2400/4800/9600/19.2k baud; RJ11 4-wire connection; complete program setup and message display capability; programmable to transmit current display, alarm status, min./max, actual measured input value and status

Power: 115 or 230 Vac, 49-440Hz

Power Consumption: 6 watts nominal, 10 watts max.

RS-485 Communications (optional): 300/1200/2400/4800/9600/19.2k300/1200/2400/4800/9600/19.2k baud; RJ11 6-wire connection; addressable from 0 to 199

Isolation: 354 V

NMRR: 60 dB

CMRR: 120 dB

Common Mode Voltage: 1500V peak per Hv test

Dimensions: 1.89"H x 3.78"W x 6.5"D (48 x 96 x 165 mm)

Mounting: DIN rail mounted

TX41-RM Panel Cutout: 1.772" H x 3.622" W (45 x 92 mm) 1/8 DIN; 0.6" (15 mm) depth behind panel

Weight: 1.27 lb (574 g)

TX41-RM Display: 6-digit, 14 segment LED, red or green; 0.56" H (14.2mm); indicator lights for alarms and status modes.

INPUT TYPE		RANGE	ACCURACY
J	Iron Constantan	-346 to 1400°F -210 to 760°C	0.3°F 0.2°C
K	Chromega™ - Alomega™	-454 to 2500°F -270 to 1372°C	0.3°F 0.2°C
T	Copper-Constantan	-454 to 752°F -270 to 400°C	0.3°F 0.2°C
E	Chromega-Constantan	-454 to 1832°F -270 to 1000°C	0.3°F 0.2°C
R S	Pt/Rh	-58 to 3214°F -50 to 1768°C	0.3°F 0.2°C
B	Pt/30%Rh-Pt/6%Rh	+212 to 3300°F +100 to 1820°C	0.5°F 0.3°C
N	Omegalloy® Nicrosil-Nisil	-454 to 2372°F -270 to 1300°C	0.3°F 0.2°C
J DIN	Iron-Constantan	-328 to 1652°F -200 to 900°C	1°F 0.6°C
RTD	All Curves	-328 to 1562°F -200 to 850°C	0.3°F 0.2°C

MODULAR SIGNAL CONDITIONERS
OM3 Series

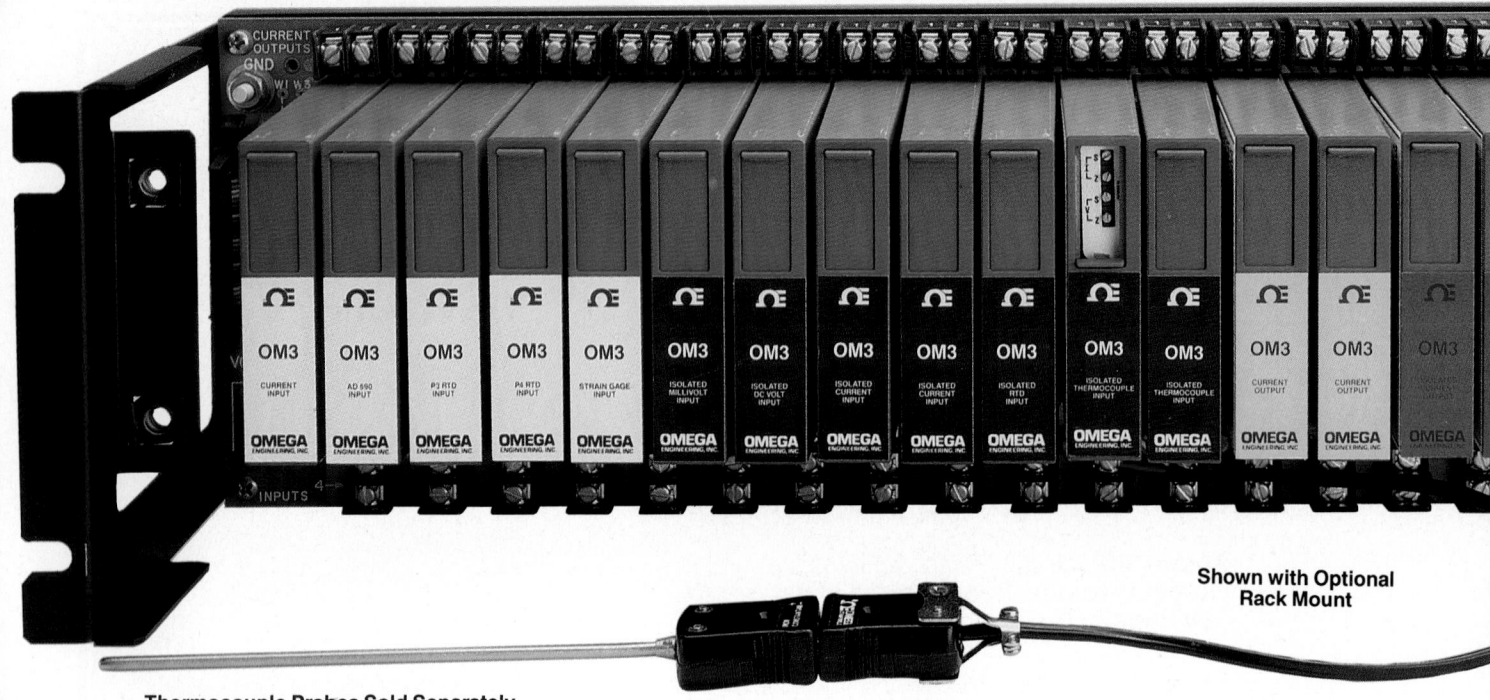

Thermocouple Probes Sold Separately.
See the OMEGA Temperature
Measurement Handbook, Section A.

Shown with Optional
Rack Mount

SPECIFICATIONS

INPUT MODULES

Input Types: Thermocouple (linearized or nonlinearized), RTD (linearized), strain gage, AD590, ac/dc voltage, ac/dc current, frequency, LVDT

Outputs (simultaneous): 0 to +10 Vdc or −10 to +10 Vdc and 4 to 20 mA or 0 to 20 mA

Accuracy: ±0.1% of span Nonlinearity: ±0.01% of span

Isolated Modules—

Common Mode Voltage, Input to Output: ±1500 V peak continuous

Transient Protection: Meets IEEE−Std 472 (SWC)

Normal Mode Protection: 220 Vrms continuous

Current Output Protection: 130 Vrms continuous

Common Mode Rejection @ 50 or 60 Hz: 160 dB

Normal Mode Rejection @ 50 or 60 Hz: 60 dB

Nonisolated Modules—

Common Mode Voltage: ±6.5 V

Normal Mode Protection: 130 Vrms continuous

Current Output Protection: 130 Vrms continuous

Common Mode Rejection @ 50 or 60 Hz: 90 dB

Normal Mode Rejection @ 50 or 60 Hz: 60 dB

MECHANICAL AND ENVIRONMENTAL

Module Dimensions: 3.150" x 0.775" x 3.395"

Temperature Range, Rated Performance: −13 to 185°F

Storage Temperature Range: −67 to 185°F RFI

Susceptibility: ±0.5% span error, 5W @ 400 MHz @ 3 ft

Approval: FM approved, Class 1, Division 2, Groups A, B, C and D locations

OUTPUT MODULES

Input: 0 to +10 Vdc or −10 to +10 Vdc

Output: 4 to 20 mA or 0 to 20 mA

Accuracy: ±0.1% of span

Nonlinearity: ±0.01% of span

Isolated Modules—

Common Mode Voltage, Input to Output: ±1500 V peak continuous

Current Output Protection, Transient: Meets IEEE−Std 472 (SWC)

Current Output Protection, Continuous: 220 Vrms

Nonisolated Modules—

Current Output Protection: 130 Vrms, continuous

OMEGA
ENGINEERING, INC.

OMX-1301
POWER
SUPPLY

INPUT: 115 V ac
OUTPUT: ±15 V dc, 350 mA

Modules

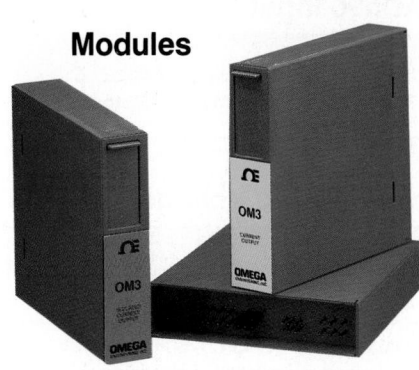

Power Supply

Cables and Accessories

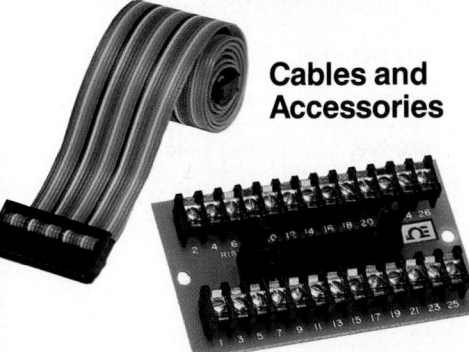

How To Order

To Assemble a Complete OM3 System, Order:

1. Desired input and output modules
2. Backplane; 4, 8 or 16 module models
3. Power supply; see table below
4. Voltage I/O Cables and Connectors
5. Power Cord
6. Rack or surface mount kit

Power supply selection

The OM3 can operate from a common ac power supply or a dc/dc (24 Vdc input) power supply mounted on the backplane, or by external +15, −15 and +24 Vdc supplies. The power is supplied to all modules on the backplane. System requirements are determined by the modules that are actual utilized. The user must select a power supply that meets the total requirements of each module used.

If the user wishes to use a +15 V supply or the current outputs, the +15 V output of either the OMX-1300 or OMX-1301 can be used, with a max. 400 ohm resistance on the current outputs.

Power Requirement Table

Model	+15V Current	−15V Current	+24V Current
OM3-MV	10 mA	10 mA	27 mA
OM3-IMV	10 mA	10 mA	27 mA
OM3-V	10 mA	10 mA	27 mA
OM3-IV	10 mA	10 mA	27 mA
OM3-WBV	10 mA	10 mA	27 mA
OM3-I	10 mA	10 mA	27 mA
OM3-II	10 mA	10 mA	27 mA
OM3-ACV	10 mA	10 mA	27 mA
OM3-ITC	10 mA	10 mA	27 mA
OM3-LTC	16 mA	14 mA	N/A
OM3-P	20 mA	20 mA	27 mA
OM3-IP	10 mA	10 mA	27 mA
OM3-A-590	10 mA	10 mA	27 mA
OM3-S-3	45 mA	10 mA	27 mA
OM3-WBS	50 mA	15 mA	27 mA
OM3-IFI	19 mA	19 mA	27 mA
OM3-VI	4 mA	4 mA	27 mA
OM3-IVI	5 mA	5 mA	35 mA

The OMX-1307 triple power supply has been designed to meet the power requirements of most OM3 applications.

If +24 Vdc is supplied from an external source, the OMX-1302 can be used to supply +15 V and −15 V to the modules. The current loop power is provided from the +24 V source, which must be capable of handling the desired number of current loop outputs.

If the +15 V, −15 V and +24 V are supplied from an external source, the power supply requirements must be satisfied for the desired number of modules.

Voltage I/O Cables

Voltage output signals from the OM3 input modules are accessed at the 26-pin system connector on the backplane. To utilize these outputs, a mating cable, the OMX-1315, is required. This 2′ cable mates directly to the OMX-1324 universal adaptor to provide screw terminals for the voltage signal.

Ordering Example

OM3 system with 4 OM3-LTC modules, 4 OM3-WBS modules, 4 OM3-V modules and 4 OM3-VI output modules in a OM3-BP-16 16 position backplane. The total current requirements are:

+15V: 4(16) + 4(50) + 4(10) + 4(4) = 320 mA
−15V: 4(14) + 4(15) + 4(10) + 4(4) = 172 mA
+24V: 4(27) + 4(27) + 4(27) = 324 mA

If the user supplies the +24V from an external source, the ac power supply is used only for the +15V and -15V. Since the OMX-1300 can only supply 200mA at +15V, and 320 mA are required, only the OMX-1301 can be used.

If the +15V output is used to supply the current outputs (instead of the +24V), 644mA @ +15V is required. Neither the OMX-1300 or OMX-1301 can be used. Only the OMX-1307 meets the requirements of each voltage level.

MODULAR SIGNAL CONDITIONERS

Input Modules

Thermocouple Input Nonlinearized

Model No.	Price	Input and Range	
OM3-ITC-J	$210	J	−100 to 760°C
OM3-ITC-K	210	K	−100 to 1350°C
OM3-ITC-T	210	T	−100 to 400°C
OM3-ITC-E	210	E	0 to 900°C
OM3-ITC-R	210	R	0 to 1750°C
OM3-ITC-S	210	S	0 to 1750°C
OM3-ITC-B	210	B	0 to 1800°C

Thermocouple Input Linearized, Isolated

Model No.	Price	Input and Range	
OM3-LTC-J1	$260	J	0 to 760°C
OM3-LTC-J2	260	J	−100 to 300°C
OM3-LTC-K1	260	K	0 to 1000°C
OM3-LTC-K2	260	K	0 to 500°C
OM3-LTC-T1	260	T	−100 to 400°C
OM3-LTC-T2	260	T	0 to 200°C
OM3-LTC-E	260	E	0 to 1000°C
OM3-LTC-R	260	R	500 to 1750°C
OM3-LTC-S	260	S	500 to 1750°C
OM3-LTC-B	260	B	500 to 1800°C
OM3-LTC-JC	260	J	0 to 500°C

RTD Input Isolated 2,3 or 4-Wire 100 Ohm Pt, =0.00385

Model No.	Price	Range
OM3-IP-N100	$210	−100 to 100°C
OM3-IP-00	210	0 to 100°C
OM3-IP-200	210	0 to 200°C
OM3-IP-600	210	0 to 600°C

RTD Input Nonisolated 2 or 3-Wire 100 Ohm Pt, =0.00385

Model No.	Price	Range
OM3-P4-N100	$170	−100 to 100°C
OM3-P4-100	170	0 to 100°C
OM3-P4-200	170	0 to 200°C
OM3-P4-600	170	0 to 600°C

RTD Input Nonisolated 4-Wire 100 Ohm Pt, =0.00385

Model No.	Price	Range
OM3-P3-N100	$170	−100 to 100°C
OM3-P3-100	170	0 to 100°C
OM3-P3-200	170	0 to 200°C
OM3-P3-600	170	0 to 600°C

Frequency Input

Model No.	Price	Range
OM3-IFI-25	$225	0 to 25 Hz
OM3-IFI-300	225	0 to 300 Hz
OM3-IFI-1.5K	235	0 to 1.5 kHz
OM3-IFI-3K	235	0 to 3 kHz
OM3-IFI-25K	235	0 to 25 kHz

Current Input

Model No.	Price	Range
OM3-II-4/20	$185	4 to 20 mA, isolated
OM3-II-0/20	185	0 to 20 mA, isolated
OM3-I-4/20	145	4 to 20 mA, nonisolated
OM3-I-0/20	145	0 to 20 mA, nonisolated

AC Voltage Input

Model No.	Price	Range
OM3-ACV-50MV	$210	0 to +50 mV rms
OM3-ACV-100MV	210	0 to +100 mV rms
OM3-ACV-10V	210	0 to +10 V rms
OM3-ACV-150V	210	0 to +150 V rms
OM3-ACV-250V	210	0 to +250 V rms

AD590 Input

Model No.	Price	Range
OM3-A-590	$170	-55 to 130°C

Nonisolated Voltage Input

Model No.	Price	Range
OM3-MV-10	$145	−10 to +10 mV
OM3-MV-50	145	−50 to +50 mV
OM3-MV-100	145	−100 to +100 mV
OM3-V-1	145	−1 to +1 V
OM3-V-5	145	−5 to +5 V
OM3-V-10	145	−10 to +10 V

Isolated Voltage Input

Model No.	Price	Range
OM3-IMV −10	$210	−10 to +10 mV
OM3-IMV-50	210	-50 to +50 mV
OM3-IMV −100	210	−100 to +100 mV
OM3-IV-1	185	−1 to +1 V
OM3-IV-5	185	−5to +5 V
OM3-IV −10	185	−10 to +10 V

Wide Band Voltage Input,

Model No.	Price	Range
OM3-WBV-10MV	$210	−10 to +10 mV
OM3-WBV-50MV	210	−50 to +50 mV
OM3-WBV-100MV	210	−100 to +100 mV
OM3-WBV-1V	210	−1 to +1 V
OM3-WBV-5V	210	−5 to +5 V
OM3-WBV-10V	210	−10 to +10 V

Position Input

Model No.	Price	Excitation
OM3-LV-25	$225	3 Vrms @ 2.5 kHz
OM3-LV-50	225	5 Vrms @ 5 kHz
OM3-LV-75	225	5 Vrms @ 7.5 kHz
OM3-LV-100	225	1 Vrms @ 10 kHz

Strain Gage Input

Model No.	Price	Description
OM3-S-3	$170	10 V excitation
OM3-WBS-30	185	wideband, 10 V excitation
OM3-WBS-10	185	wideband, 3.33 V excitation

Output Modules

Model No.	Price	Description
OM3-IVI	$160	Isolated output
OM3-VI	100	Nonisolated output

Cables, Connectors and Adaptors

Model No.	Price	Description
OMX-1312	$15	26-pin female connector
OMX-1315	19	2′ 26-pin cable with 2 connectors
OMX-1324	45	adaptor,26-pin connector in, 26 screw terminals out
OMX-1340	19	power cord
OMX-1342	4	100 ohm current sense resistor (current input)
OMX-1343	4	2k ohm current sense resistor (AD590 input)
OMX-1345	10	individual OM3 mounting kit
OMX-1554	25	26-pin connector with 3′cable
OMX-1330	60	19″ rack mount

Backplanes

Model No.	Price	No. of Positions
OM3-BP-16	$360	16
OM3-BP-8	250	8
OM3-BP-4	130	4

Power Supplies

OMX-1300 $110

Input Voltage: 115 Vac
Output Voltage: +15 Vdc, −15 Vdc
Output Current: +−200 mA
Dimensions: 3.5″ x 2.5″ x 1.25″

OMX-1301 $148

Input Voltage: 115 Vac
Output Voltage: +15 Vdc, −15 Vdc
Output Current: +−350 mA
Dimensions: 3.5″ x 2.5″ x 1.62″

OMX-1302 $120

Input Voltage: 24 Vdc
Output Voltage: +15 Vdc, −15 Vdc
Output Current: +−190 mA
Dimensions: 2.0″ x 2.0″ x 0.38″

OMX-1307 $220

Input Voltage: 115 Vac
Output Voltage: +15 Vdc, −15 Vdc, +24 Vdc (unregulated)
Output Current: +800 mA, −225 mA, +350 mA
Dimensions: 4.0″ x 2.8″ x 3.4″

MODULAR SIGNAL CONDITIONERS
OM5 SERIES

MADE IN USA | 1 YEAR WARRANTY

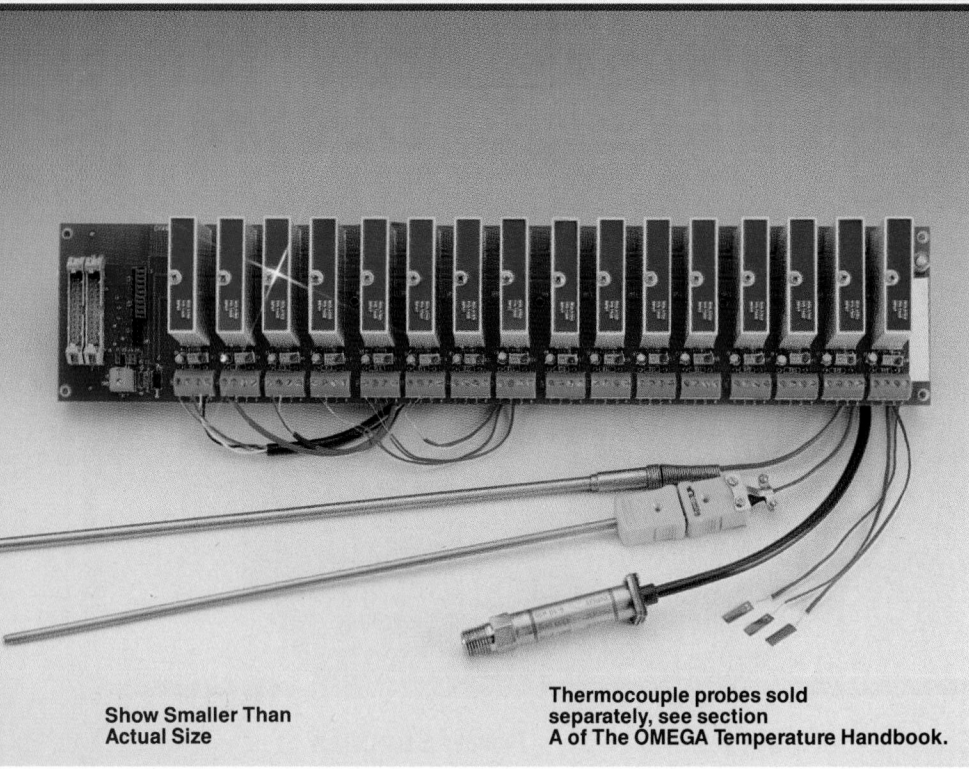

Show Smaller Than Actual Size

Thermocouple probes sold separately, see section A of The OMEGA Temperature Handbook.

✔ **Rugged, Compact, Economical Signal Conditioning**

✔ **Modular Design for Mix and Match Capability**

✔ **Analog Input Modules for Direct Interface to Sensors and Analog Voltage and Current**

✔ **±0.05% Accuracy**

✔ **Convenient Connection to User Equipment**

From
$150

Accessories

Model No.	Price	Description
OM5-BP-16	$250	16-channel backplane
OM5-BP-SKT	30	single channel socket
OMX-955	131	5 V, 1 A power supply
OMX-976	197	5 V, 3 A power supply
OMX-1363	32	19" rack mount adaptor
OMX-1315	19	2' 26-pin cable with 2 connectors
OMX-1324	45	adaptor, 26-pin connector in, 26 screw terminals out

Isolated Current Input $150 each

Model No.	Input	Output
OM5-II-4/20-C	4 to 20 mA	0 to 5 V
OM5-II-0/20-C	0 to 20 mA	0 to 5 V

Isolated Current Output $150 each

Model No.	Input	Output
OM5-IVI-B0-C	0 to 5 V	0 to 20 mA
OM5-IVI-A0-C	±5 V	0 to 20 mA
OM5-IVI-B4-C	0 to 5 V	4 to 20 mA
OM5-IVI-A4-C	±5 V	4 to 20 mA

Isolated Strain Gage Input, ±5 Vdc Output $180 each

Model No.	Input	Description
OM5-WBS-1-C	±30 mV @10V exc.	Full bridge 300-10 kΩ, 10 kHz bandwidth
OM5-WBS-2-C	±20 mV @100 V exc.	Full bridge 300-10 kΩ, 10 kHz bandwidth
OM5-WBS-3-C	±30 mV @10 V exc.	Half bridge 300-10 kΩ, 10 kHz bandwidth

Isolated Millivolt Input $150 each

Model No.	Input	Output
OM5-IMV-10A-C	±10 mV	±5 V
OM5-IMV-50A-C	±50 mV	±5 V
OM5-IMV-100A-C	±100 mV	±5 V
OM5-IMV-10B-C	±10 mV	0 to 5 V
OM5-IMV-50B-C	±50 mV	0 to 5 V
OM5-IMV-100B-C	±100 mV	0 to 5 V

Wideband Voltage Input $150 each

Model No.	Input	Output
OM5-WV-1A-C	±1 V	±5 V
OM5-WV-5A-C	±5 V	±5 V
OM5-WV-10A-C	±10 V	±5 V
OM5-WV-1B-C	±1 V	0 to 5 V
OM5-WV-5B-C	±5 V	0 to 5 V
OM5-WV-10B-C	±10 V	0 to 5 V

To Order
To Assemble a Complete OM5 System, Order:
1. Desired input and output modules
2. Backplane: OM5-BP-16
3. Power Supply: OMX-955 for up to 16 input modules, OMX976 for systems with out modules
4. Voltage I/O cables and connectors
5. Rack or Surface Mount Kit

Isolated Voltage Input $150 each

Model No.	Input	Output
OM5-IV-1A-C	±1 V	±5 V
OM5-IV-5A-C	±5 V	±5 V
OM5-IV-10A-C	±10 V	±5 V
OM5-IV-1B-C	±1 V	0 to 5 V
OM5-IV-5B-C	±5 V	0 to 5 V
OM5-IV-10B-C	±10 V	0 to 5 V

Wideband mV Input $150 each

Model No.	Input	Output
OM5-WMV-10A-C	±10 mV	±5 V
OM5-WMV-50A-C	±50 mV	±5 V
OM5-WMV-100A-C	±100 mV	±5 V
OM5-WMV-10B-C	±10 mV	0 to 5 V
OM5-WMV-50B-C	±50 mV	0 to 5 V
OM5-WMV-100B-C	±100 mV	0 to 5 V

SOLENOID VALVES
FOR PROCESS APPLICATIONS

For Use With Liquids, Steam, Gases and Hot Water

The OMEGA SV-100 and SV-200 series solenoid valves for liquids and gases cover most industrial and laboratory applications. The valves are available in sizes ranging from ¼″ to 2″ NPT, with CV's as high as 38. OMEGA also offers general-purpose 2, 3, and 4- way valves made of brass or stainless steel, and specialty valves for hot water and steam applications.

The SV-100/200 valves are modularly constructed from three basic parts: the valve body, the electrical coil, and the coil enclosure. The valve bodies are normally stainless steel or brass for greatest media compatibility, while the wetted parts consist of just the shading ring, valve material, and O-ring. The standard electric coils are all rated as "continuous duty" to eliminate overheating. Each coil is encased in a protective encapsulated material that resists moisture, fungus, and extreme environmental conditions. The standard electrical enclosures meet NEMA 4 ratings and have a ½″ conduit port.

OMEGA's SV-100/200 Series valves are of poppet, piston or diaphragm design.

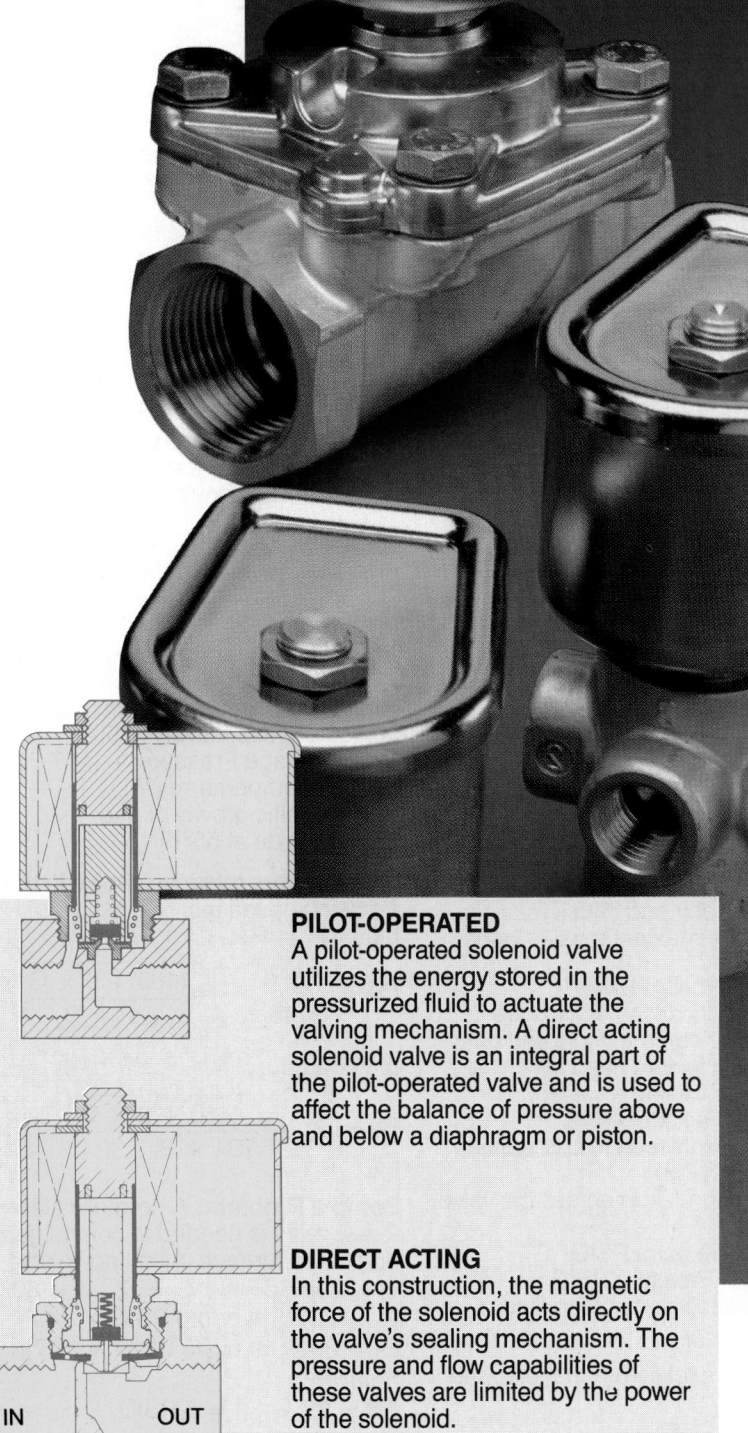

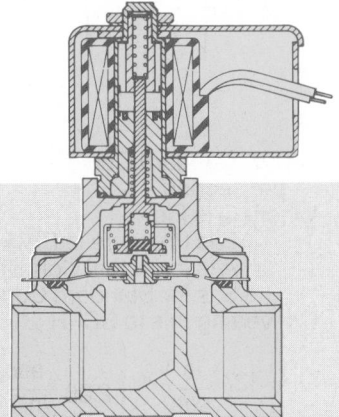

DIRECT LIFT
Direct lift valves combine the features of a direct acting valve with those of a pilot-operated valve. Due to a flexible link between the solenoid plunger and the diaphragm, the valve functions as a direct acting valve at low pressures and as a pilot-operated valve at higher pressures. It is sometimes referred to as a Zero Delta P (Pressure) valve or a hung diaphragm valve.

PILOT-OPERATED
A pilot-operated solenoid valve utilizes the energy stored in the pressurized fluid to actuate the valving mechanism. A direct acting solenoid valve is an integral part of the pilot-operated valve and is used to affect the balance of pressure above and below a diaphragm or piston.

DIRECT ACTING
In this construction, the magnetic force of the solenoid acts directly on the valve's sealing mechanism. The pressure and flow capabilities of these valves are limited by the power of the solenoid.

IN   OUT

ACCESSORIES C

SELECTING A SOLENOID VALVE
TO YOUR SYSTEM SPECIFICATIONS

SELECTION GUIDELINES

General purpose solenoid valves are used with a wide variety of liquids and gases in a broad spectrum of applications. Rating of the valve capacity in terms which relate to all operating conditions is accomplished by determining the "flow factor" (Cv) of the valve. The Cv value is the number of U.S. gallons of 60°F water per minute that, when flowing through the valve, causes a pressure drop of 1 PSI. This measure of capacity is stated for each model in this catalog.

There are five main parameters to consider when selecting a valve: Cv, media compatibility, pressure, temperature, and process fitting. For each of these parameters, maximum values are listed for each valve. To choose the correct valve, compare each parameter and check that it is less than the maximum value listed.

LIQUID APPLICATIONS

For most applications, liquids are considered incompressible and only the following factors need be considered in sizing a valve:
Cv = Flow Factor of valve.
Q = Flow expressed in U.S. gallons per minute (GPM)
ΔP = Pressure Drop across the valve
$= P_1 - P_2$
P_1 = Inlet Pressure PSIG
P_2 = Outlet Pressure PSIG
G = Specific Gravity of the fluid

(G = 1.0 for water at 60°F)

These factors relate per the following equation:

$$Cv = Q\sqrt{\frac{G}{\Delta P}}$$

Sample Problem: A 2-way normally closed valve is needed to control the transfer of a liquid (G = 1.1) at a rate of 2 GPM. The pressure available is 10 PSI; downstream pressure is 0 PSI.

Solution:
$\Delta P = P_1 - P_2 = 10 - 0 = 10$ PSI

$$Cv = Q\sqrt{\frac{G}{\Delta P}} = 2\sqrt{\frac{1.1}{10}} = 0.67$$

Therefore a valve is needed with a Cv of at least 0.67, and a max operating pressure differential of at least 10 PSID. Referring to the general purpose valves on C-28, the SV105 with a Cv = .75 is O.K. Check temperature, media compatibility and end fittings, to insure a correct valve choice.

Note: The Cv values given in this catalog are applicable to liquids with viscosities to 100 SSU (22 Centistokes)

GAS APPLICATIONS

When compressible media such as air or gases are used the sizing of the valve must include additional factors which affect performance.

Cv = Flow factor
Q = Flow expressed in Standard Cubic Feet per Hour (SCFH).

ΔP = Pressure drop across the valve (inlet to outlet) in PSID.
P_1 and P_2 = Inlet and outlet absolute pressures respectively (PSIA)
PSIA = Gage Pressure + (14.7 PSIA)
t = Gas temperature (°F)
G = Specific gravity of gas
(G = 1 for air at 55°F)

These factors relate as shown in the following equations:
If $(.53) P_1 < P_2$

$$Cv = \frac{Q}{1349}\sqrt{\frac{(460 + t) \times G}{\Delta P \times P_2}}$$

If $(.53) P_1 \geq P_2$

$$Cv = \frac{Q}{704 \times P_1}\sqrt{(460 + t) \times G}$$

Sample Problem: A normally closed 2-way valve is needed to control gas entering a furnace. Also known are:
Q = 500 SCFH   G = .7   t = 60°F.
P_1 = 35 PSIA or (20 PSIG + 14.7)
P_2 = 30 PSIA or (15 PSIG + 14.7)
Solution:
$\Delta P = 35 - 30 = 5$ PSID
$P_1(.53) = 35 (.53) = 18.55 < P_2$

---

therefore, use the formula:

$$Cv = \frac{Q}{1349}\sqrt{\frac{(460 + t) \times G}{\Delta P \times P_2}} =$$

$$CV = 0.58$$

Therefore, a valve is needed with a $C_V \geq .58$ and a max. operating pressure differential ≥ 5 PSID.

Again, the general purpose stainless steel SV105 with a C_V = .75 is sufficient, and temperature and media compatiblity are good.

Sample Problem: A 3-way normally closed valve is needed to control a single acting spring return cylinder. Also known are:
Q_A = 28.3 cubic inches/sec at 56 PSIG to obtain 2″ stroke of a 6″ diameter cylinder in 2 sec.
P_1 = 115 PSIA or (100 PSIG + 14.7)
P_2 = 71 PSIA or (56 PSIG + 14.7) (for a 1600 lb. force)
G = 1 for Air, t = 90°F
ΔP = 115 − 71 = 44 PSID

Since the flow was determined at a pressure of 56 PSIG; it must be converted to its equivalent volume at standard pressure. Boyles law for converting to standard conditions.

$$Qs = Q_A \left(\frac{P_A}{P_S}\right) \left(\frac{515}{t+460}\right)$$

= 127 Standard Cubic Inches per second
Where Q is Flow
P is Pressure in PSIA
A is for Actual Conditions
S is for Standard Conditions
Converting this to SCFH

$$Q = 127 \frac{in.^3}{sec.} \times \left[2.08 \frac{sec. - ft^3}{in.^3 - hr.}\right]$$

$$= 265 \text{ SCFH}$$

Select the Cv formula using:
$P_1 (.53) = 115 (.53) = 60.95 < P_2$

$$Cv = \frac{265}{1349}\sqrt{\frac{550 \times 1}{44 \times (56 + 14.7)}} = 0.083$$

Therefore, valve SV241, which has a C_V = .18, max. MODP = 150 PSID, and max. temp. = 165°F will work.

GENERAL PURPOSE NEMA 4 STAINLESS STEEL AND BRASS SOLENOID VALVES

✔ **NEMA 4 Standard**
✔ **Mounts in Any Position**
✔ **Continuous Duty**

Two-way solenoid valves cover most industrial laboratory applications. A two-way valve controls the flow of fluid through a single passage. It has two ports, an inlet (1) and an outlet (2). A normally closed valve does not pass fluid unless it is energized. A normally open valve operates just the opposite.

SPECIFICATIONS:

Wetted Parts: SV-100 Series: stainless steel, silver, and seal (SV-106 polysulfone additional); SV-200 Series: brass, stainless steel, copper and seal (SV-201, 202 Viton additional, SV-211, 212 Ruby additional)

Medium: Liquid or gases (SV-101-105, 107-113, Filter 40 microns)

Max. Static Pressure: 5 times max. PSID, vacuum (> 5 microns ABS)

Ambient Temp.: 15-122°F (−9 to 50°C)

Mounting: Pipe mounting, any direction

Power: 10 Watts, 120 Vac coils, Class F (SV-101-105 and SV-107, 22 Watts, 120 Vac coils, Class H)

Normally Closed

Normally Open

From $90

To Order (Specify Model number) GENERAL-PURPOSE VALVES

MODEL	PRICE	FITTING NPT	ORIFICE	CV	SEAL	DIFF. PRESS (PSID) MIN	MAX	TEMP (°F)	RESPONSE TIME OPEN	CLOSE
Direct Acting (*Pilot Operated), 2-Way Normally Closed Stainless Steel										
SV101	$90	1/4	3/32	0.18	Kel-F†	0	650	165	4-8 ms	4-8 ms
SV102	90	1/4	1/8	0.28	Kel-F†	0	520	165	4-8 ms	4-8 ms
SV103	90	1/4	5/32	0.4	Viton	0	115	210	4-8 ms	4-8 ms
SV104	90	1/4	3/16	0.5	Viton	0	100	210	4-8 ms	4-8 ms
SV105	90	1/4	1/4	0.75	Viton	0	50	210	4-8 ms	4-8 ms
SV106	145	1/4	1/4	0.76	Teflon†	5	1500	210	35-40 ms	35-40 ms*
SV107	90	1/4	5/16	0.95	Viton	0	35	210	4-8 ms	4-8 ms
Direct Acting (*Pilot Operated), 2-Way Normally Open Stainless Steel										
SV111	155	1/4	3/64	0.054	Kel-F†	0	750	165	4-8 ms	4-8 ms
SV112	155	1/4	1/16	0.107	Kel-F†	0	400	165	4-8 ms	4-8 ms
SV113	155	1/4	3/32	0.15	Kel-F†	0	170	165	4-8 ms	4-8 ms
SV114	165	1/4	1/4	0.76	Buna N	5	200	185	70-90 ms	70-90 ms*
Pilot Operated (*Direct Lift), 2-Way Normally Closed Brass										
SV201	115	3/8	5/8	4.4	Buna N	0	230	180	30-100 ms	350-900 ms*
SV202	115	1/2	9/16	4.6	Buna N	0	230	180	30-100 ms	350-900 ms*
SV203	140	3/4	3/4	9.5	Buna N	5	230	185	50-80 ms	1.8-3 s
SV204	170	1	1	13.0	Buna N	5	230	185	50-80 ms	1.8-3 s
SV205	250	1 1/4	1 1/8"	19.0	Buna N	5	230	185	50-80 ms	1.8-3 s
SV206	335	1 1/2	1 9/16	30.0	Buna N	5	170	185	50-80 ms	1.8-3 s
SV207	410	2	1 9/16	38.0	Buna N	5	170	185	50-80 ms	1.8-3 s
Pilot Operated, 2-Way Normally Open Brass Valves										
SV211	195	3/8	7/16	3.5	Buna N	5	600	185	120 ms	200 ms
SV212	285	1/2	9/16	4.2	Buna N	5	600	185	120 ms	200 ms
SV213	210	3/4	3/4	9.5	Buna N	5	230	185	50-80 ms	1.8-3 s
SV214	235	1	1	13.0	Buna N	5	230	185	50-80 ms	1.8-3 s
SV215	275	1 1/4	1 1/8	19.0	Buna N	5	230	185	50-80 ms	1.8-3 s
SV216	355	1 1/2	1 9/16	30.0	Buna N	5	170	185	50-80 ms	1.8-3 s
SV217	525	2	1 9/16	38.0	Buna N	5	170	185	50-80 ms	1.8-3 s

Replacement coils $30 each; SVCOIL-10AC (110 watts), SVCOIL-22AC (22 watts) and SVCOIL-22DC (22 watts).

*Non-Adjustable response time
†Not for gas use

SPECIAL PURPOSE SOLENOID VALVES

FOR STEAM, HOT WATER, ANTI-WATER HAMMER, 3-WAY, 4-WAY AND SELECTABLE SERVICE

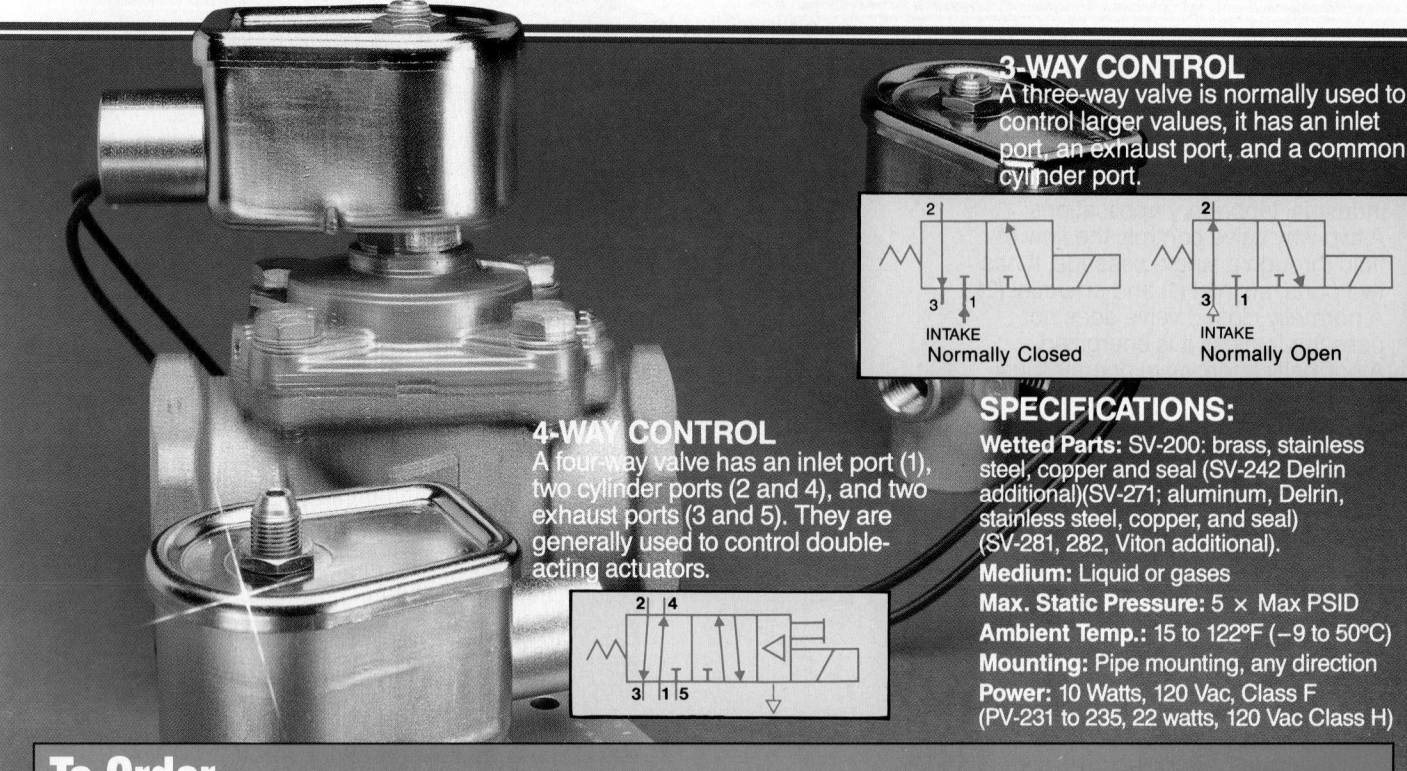

3-WAY CONTROL
A three-way valve is normally used to control larger values, it has an inlet port, an exhaust port, and a common cylinder port.

INTAKE Normally Closed   INTAKE Normally Open

4-WAY CONTROL
A four-way valve has an inlet port (1), two cylinder ports (2 and 4), and two exhaust ports (3 and 5). They are generally used to control double-acting actuators.

SPECIFICATIONS:
Wetted Parts: SV-200: brass, stainless steel, copper and seal (SV-242 Delrin additional)(SV-271; aluminum, Delrin, stainless steel, copper, and seal) (SV-281, 282, Viton additional).

Medium: Liquid or gases

Max. Static Pressure: 5 × Max PSID

Ambient Temp.: 15 to 122°F (−9 to 50°C)

Mounting: Pipe mounting, any direction

Power: 10 Watts, 120 Vac, Class F (PV-231 to 235, 22 watts, 120 Vac Class H)

To Order (Specify Model Number) SPECIAL PURPOSE VALVES

MODEL	PRICE	FITTING NPT	ORIFICE	CV	SEAL	DIFF. PRESS (PSID) MIN	MAX	TEMP (°F)	RESPONSE TIME OPEN	CLOSE
Hot Water (Direct Lift), 2-Way Normally Closed Brass										
SV221	$110	¼	¹³⁄₆₄	0.77	EPDM	0	60	210	4-8 ms	4-8 ms
SV222	110	⅜	⁹⁄₁₆	4.4	EPDM	0	150	210	30-100 ms	30-100 ms
SV223	110	½	⁹⁄₁₆	4.6	EPDM	0	150	210	30-100 ms	30-100 ms
SV224	135	¾	⁹⁄₁₆	5.6	EPDM	0	150	210	30-100 ms	30-100 ms
SV225	235	1	1	11.2	EPDM	0	150	210	30-100 ms	30-100 ms
Steam (Direct Lift), 2-Way Normally Closed Brass										
SV231	115	¼	¹³⁄₆₄	0.77	EPDM	0	40	285	4-8 ms	4-8 ms
SV232	115	⅜	⁹⁄₁₆	4.6	EPDM	0	45	293	30-100 ms	350-900 ms
SV233	115	½	⁹⁄₁₆	4.6	EPDM	0	45	293	30-100 ms	350-900 ms
SV234	145	¾	⁹⁄₁₆	5.6	EPDM	0	45	293	30-100 ms	350-900 ms
SV235	240	1	1	11.2	EPDM	0	45	293	30-100 ms	350-900 ms
General Purpose (Direct Acting), 3-Way Normally Closed, Exhaust Brass										
SV241	85	¼	1 to 2/2 to 3 ⁵⁄₆₄, ⅛	.18 .32	Viton	0	150	165	10 ms	10 ms
SV242	90	¼	³⁄₃₂, ⁹⁄₆₄	.25 .38	Viton	0	150	165	10 ms	10 ms
Selectable Service (Direct Acting), 3-Way Customer Switchable Normally Closed or Normally Open Brass										
SV251	90	¼	⁵⁄₆₄ ⁵⁄₆₄	.18 .18	Viton	0	100	165	10 ms	10 ms
Quick Exhaust (Pilot-Operated), 3-Way Normally Closed Brass										
SV261	195	¼	³⁄₃₂ ¼	.20 1.12	Buna N	2	100	165	15 ms	45 ms
General Purpose (Pilot-Operated), 4-Way Normally Closed Aluminum, Air only (filtered 40 microns)										
SV271	130	⅛	⁵⁄₃₂	.35	Buna N	15	150	165	10-30 ms	10-30 ms
Anti-Water Hammer (Pilot-Operated), 2-Way Normally Closed Brass										
SV281	145	⅜	⁷⁄₁₆	2.5	Buna N	3	150	185	0.015 s	0.85 s*
SV282	145	½	⁷⁄₁₆	2.5	Buna N	3	150	185	0.015 s	0.85 s*
SV283	155	¾	¾	9.5	Buna N	3	230	185	0.1-0.25 s	0.6-4.5 s
SV284	295	1	1	13.0	Buna N	3	230	185	0.1-0.25 s	0.5-4.5 s
SV285	355	1¼	1⅛	19.0	Buna N	3	230	185	0.2-0.5 s	0.8-5.8 s
SV286	515	1½	1⁹⁄₁₆	30.0	Buna N	3	170	185	0.2-0.4 s	1.5-9.0 s
SV287	595	2	1⁹⁄₁₆	38.0	Buna N	3	170	185	0.25-0.45 s	1.5-9.5 s
Anti-Water Hammer (Pilot-Operated), 2-Way Normally Open Brass										
SV291	175	¾	¾	9.5	Buna N	5	230	185	0.1-0.25 s	0.6-4.5 s
SV292	330	1	1	13.0	Buna N	5	230	185	0.1-0.25 s	0.5-4.5 s
SV293	380	1⅛	1⅛	19.0	Buna N	5	230	185	0.2-0.5 s	0.8-5.8 s
SV294	545	1⁹⁄₁₆	1⁹⁄₁₆	30.0	Buna N	5	170	185	0.2-0.4 s	1.5-9.0 s
SV295	655	1⁹⁄₁₆	1⁹⁄₁₆	38.0	Buna N	5	170	185	0.25-0.45 s	1.5-9.5 s

*Non-Adjustable response time

BATTERIES
Energy to Spare!

✔ **Wide Range of Styles Available**
✔ **Alkaline**
✔ **Mercury**
✔ **Mercury Oxide**

From those tiny cells on up—OMEGA has the battery you need. Look in the tables below for the correct replacement battery for your OMEGA instrument. Many units require more than one battery, so be sure to check how many you need before placing an order.

Alkaline

To Order *(Specify Model Number)*

	Model No.	Standard Size	Voltage	Price	Compatible OMEGA Units	
	MN1500-6	AA (alkaline)	1.5 V	$3.00	CT-410 Series CT-420 Series MM-1 OS71	PHH-47 PHB-51 and 52 PHB-62 T150
	MN1400	C (alkaline)	1.5 V	4.00	OmniAmp IIA, IIB	
	MN1300	D (alkaline)	1.5 V	3.00	CT485 Series DP-171 DP-172	DP-173 DP-174
	MN1604	K9V (alkaline)	9 V	3.00	383 CL-303 CL-304	CL-305 CL-306 HH-30

Mercury/Mercury Oxide

To Order *(Specify Model Number)*

	Model No.	Voltage	Price	Compatible OMEGA Units	
	CJ-BATT	1.35 V (mercury)	$3.00	CJ Series. Must be ordered through OMEGA.	
	PX625	1.35 V (mercury oxide)	3.00	LXCJ MCJ Series OmniAmp I	
	PH-BATT-1	1.4 V (mercury oxide)	1.00	CDH-1 CDH-2 PHH-1	PHH-1X PH-TC PH-TF
	RM12R	1.35 V (mercury)	6.00	OmniAmp IIB LXCJ Series	

CURRENT TO PRESSURE (I/P) CONVERTER

CN4400

PX635

U24Y101

IP210

IP210

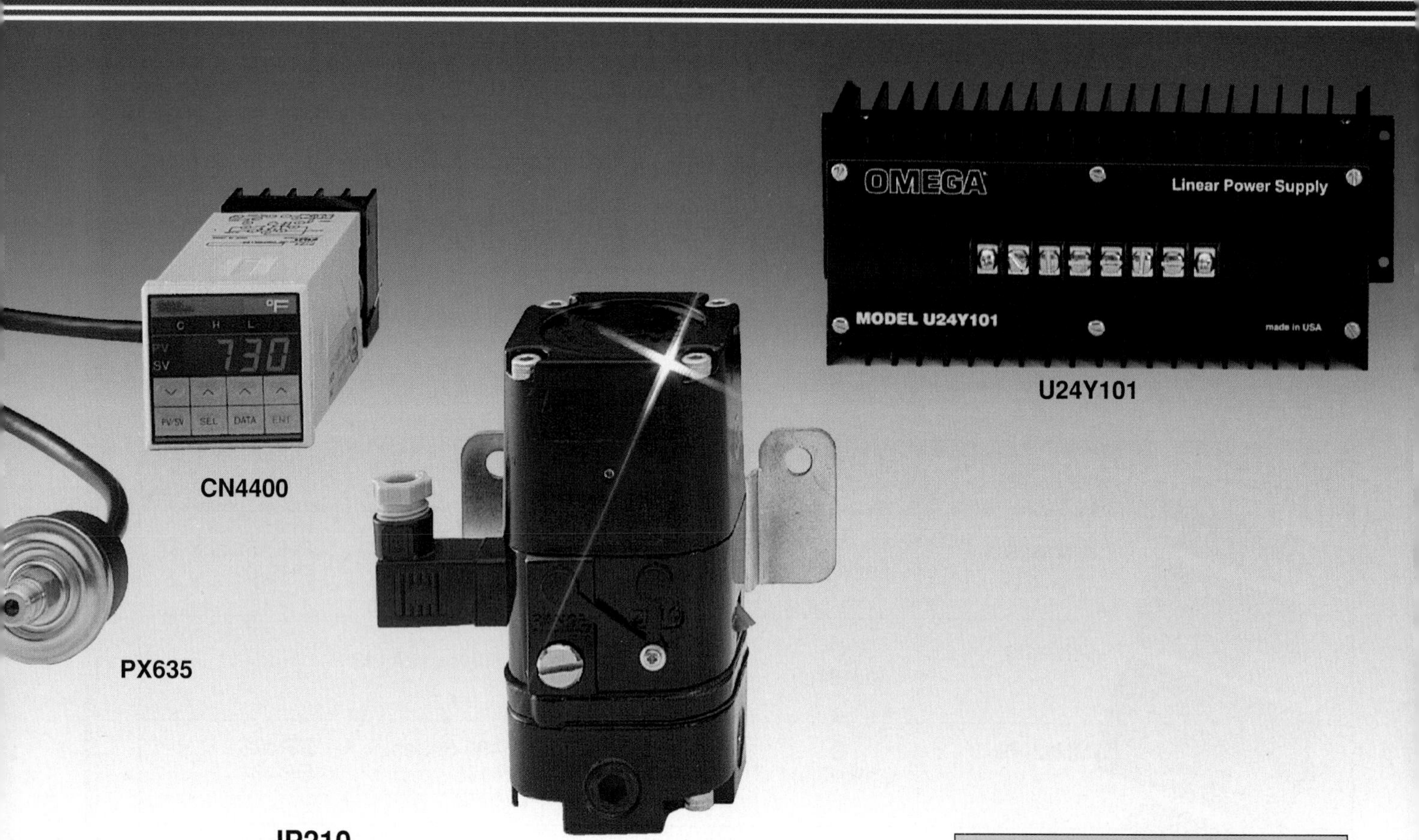

IP210

$350

The IP210 is Shown with the Model CN4400 Miniature Autotune Controller ($190), PX635 Sensor ($178) and U24Y101 Power Supply ($99). These Are Typical Devices in a Pneumatic Control System.

- ✔ **Loop Powered**
- ✔ **Ideal For Pneumatic Control Systems**
- ✔ **Certified to CENLEC and BASEEFA**
- ✔ **Field Selectable for Direct or Reverse Acting**
- ✔ **Zero and Span Adjustments for Field Calibration**
- ✔ **Rugged Zinc Cast Housing**

A "current to pressure" converter (I/P) converts an analog signal (4-20 mA) to a proportional linear pneumatic output (3-15 PSIG). Its purpose is to translate the analog output from a control system into a precise, repeatable pressure value to control pneumatic actuators/operators, pneumatic valves, dampers, vanes, etc… The IP210 is a loop powered instrument, which eliminates the need for an external power supply. The IP210 is field selectable for direct acting (increasing pressure with increasing current) or reverse acting (increasing pressure with decreasing current).

TM

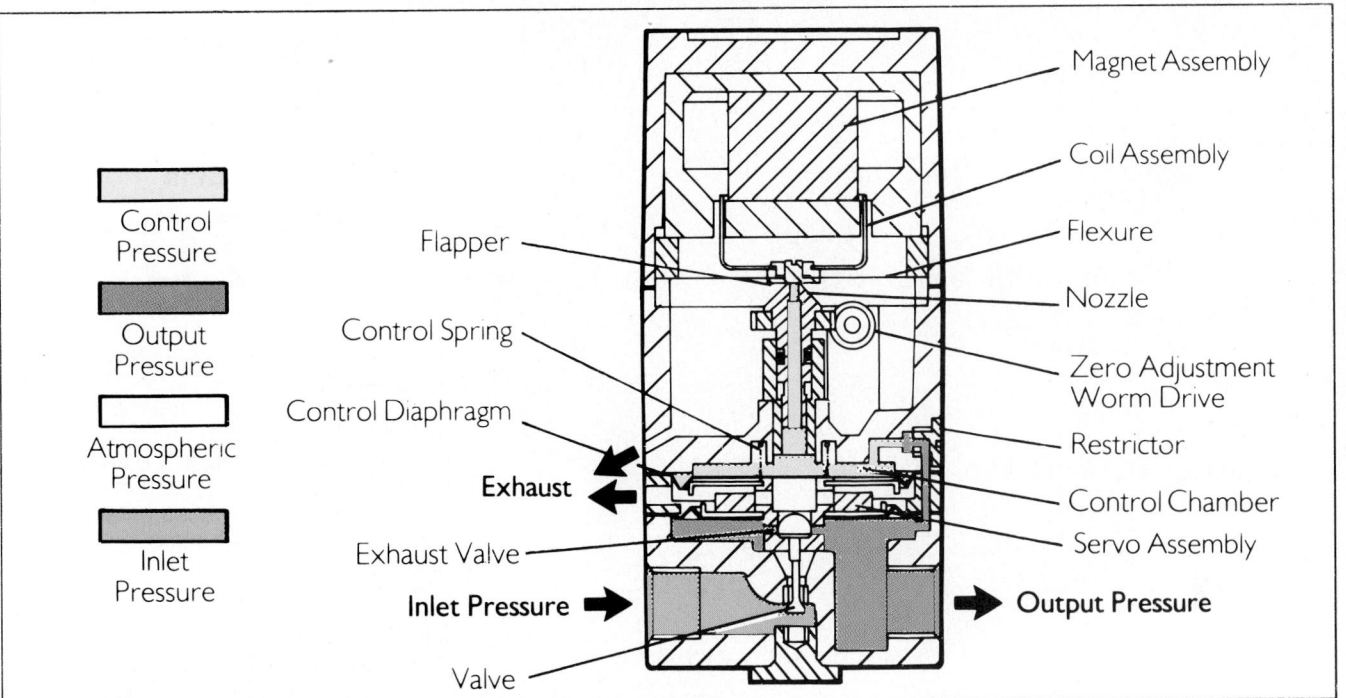

Control Pressure

Output Pressure

Atmospheric Pressure

Inlet Pressure

Magnet Assembly

Coil Assembly

Flexure

Nozzle

Zero Adjustment Worm Drive

Restrictor

Control Chamber

Servo Assembly

Output Pressure

Flapper

Control Spring

Control Diaphragm

Exhaust

Exhaust Valve

Inlet Pressure

Valve

Principle of Operation

The OMEGA IP210 converts an analog signal (4-20 mA) to a proportional linear pneumatic output (3-15 PSIG). Its uncomplicated design and proven electromagnetic force balance provides consistent high performance.

The IP210 provides a reliable, repeatable, and accurate means of converting an electrical signal into pneumatic pressure. Its force balance principle is a coil suspended in a magnetic field on a flexible mount. At the lower end of the coil is a flapper valve which operates against a precision ground nozzle to create a back pressure on the servo diaphragm of a booster relay. The input current flows in the coil and produces a force between the coil and the flapper valve, which controls the servo pressure and the output pressure.

Zero adjustment of the unit is made by adjusting a screw which varies the distance between the flapper valve and the air nozzle. Span adjustment is made by varying a potentiometer, which shunts input current past the coil. An integral volume flow booster provides adequate flow capacity, resulting in fast response time and accurate control.

SPECIFICATIONS

Accuracy: 0.5% F.S.
Zero Adjustment: 5% F.S.
Span Adjustment: 20% F.S.
Operating Temp.: -5 to 160°F (-20 to 70°C)
Compensated Temp.: 15 to 140°F (-10 to 60°C)
Thermal Effects:
Zero 0.06% F.S./°F
Span 0.06% F.S./°F
Input Resistance: <300 Ohms
Media: Oil free clean dry air filtered to 25 µm
Recommended Supply Pressure: 25-30 PSIG
Max. Supply Pressure: 80 PSIG

Min. Supply Pressure : 20 PSIG
Air Consumption (leakage): 0.03 sfcm
Flow Rate: 10 sfcm typical
Response Time: Less than 0.25 seconds
Pressure Port: ¼" NPTF
Minimum Control Pressure Electrical Conn.: DIN 43650 with screw terminals included
Housing Material: Epoxy painted zinc die castings
Construction: Nitrile diaphragms, SS. flapper, nozzle, and supply valve. Integral surface mounting bracket included.
Weight: 3 lbs (1.7 kg)

STOCKED FOR FAST DELIVERY!

To Order *(Specify Model Number)*

Model	Price	Input Range	Output Range
IP210-X15	$350	4-20 mA	3-15 PSIG

Accessories

Model	Price	Description
TX4-100	$28.50	100 ft. of 4 conductor shielded wire
*PX635-X15GI	197.00	P/I pressure transmitter
*DP205-E	195.00	Digital panel meter

* These accessories could be used when a feedback signal is required.
Comes with complete operator's manual.
Ordering Example: *IP210-X15 I/P converter, PX635-X15GI P/I pressure transmitter, DP205-E meter and TX4-100 wire, $350 + 345 + 197 + 28.50 =* ***$920.50.***

CURRENT TO PRESSURE (I/P) CONVERTER

NEW!

All Models

$170

A "current to pressure" converter (I/P) converts an analog signal (4-20 mA) to a proportional linear pneumatic output (3-15, 0-20, or 0-30 PSIG). Its purpose is to translate the analog output from a control system into a precise, repeatable pressure value to control pneumatic actuators/ operators, pneumatic valves, dampers, vanes, etc.

The I/P converter is commonly utilized in HVAC and industrial applications. Typical uses include controlling an inlet vane relative to duct air temperature, controlling a damper relative to the time of day, controlling a damper relative to humidity, controlling an actuator relative to air duct pressure, controlling an pneumatic valve proportional to air duct flow, among many more.

✔ **Ideal For Pneumatic Control Systems**
✔ **Solenoid Valve Design Eliminates Leaks**
✔ **Can Be Used With Unfiltered Main Air Supply**
✔ **Analog Output For Feedback Purposes**
✔ **Zero and Span Adjustments for Field Calibration**
✔ **Rugged 16 Gage Steel Construction**

In the pictorial example, the parameter being controlled is flow in an industrial piping system. The flow is increased or decreased utilizing the in-line pneumatic valve. The control system consists of a pitot tube and a differential pressure transmitter (pressure is proportional to flow) outputting to a controller. The controller then outputs a PID 4-20 mA signal to the I/P converter. The I/P converter can then send the correct pressure signal to open or close the pneumatic valve installed in the pipe, hence controlling the desired flow. A 4-20 mA feedback signal is sent to a meter indicating the actual control pressure. This can be used for troubleshooting and alarming purposes; an air leak or a failure of the main supply can be easily diagnosed by analyzing the feedback signal. This feature eliminates "blind" control problems.

TYPICAL APPLICATION

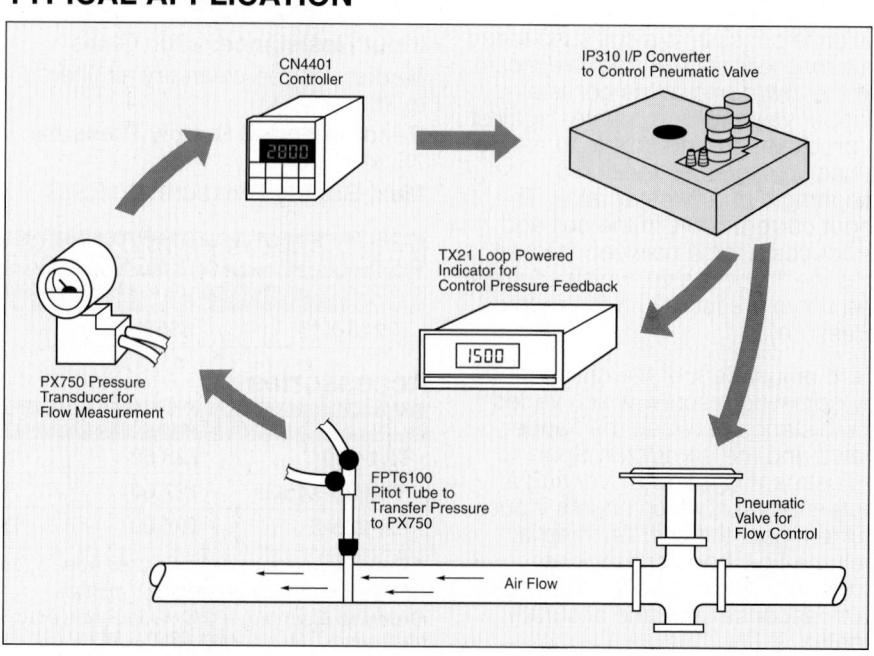

CN4401 Controller

IP310 I/P Converter to Control Pneumatic Valve

TX21 Loop Powered Indicator for Control Pressure Feedback

PX750 Pressure Transducer for Flow Measurement

FPT6100 Pitot Tube to Transfer Pressure to PX750

Pneumatic Valve for Flow Control

Air Flow

FOR ELECTROPNEUMATIC CONTROL

The OMEGA IP310/311 converts an analog signal (4-20 mA) to a proportional linear pneumatic output (3-15, 0-20, 0-30 psig). Unlike other units which bleed air to maintain pressure, the IP310/311 uses a silicon pressure sensor and an electropneumatic converter to provide the desired pneumatic pressure without constant air consumption. The converter's unique design eliminates common problems such as hose chattering, needless air consumption due to air leaks caused by heat, age, moisture, contamination, mounting orientation error, sticky valves, valve leakage and blockages. The IP310/311 provides a reliable, repeatable and accurate means of converting a current signal into a pneumatic pressure.

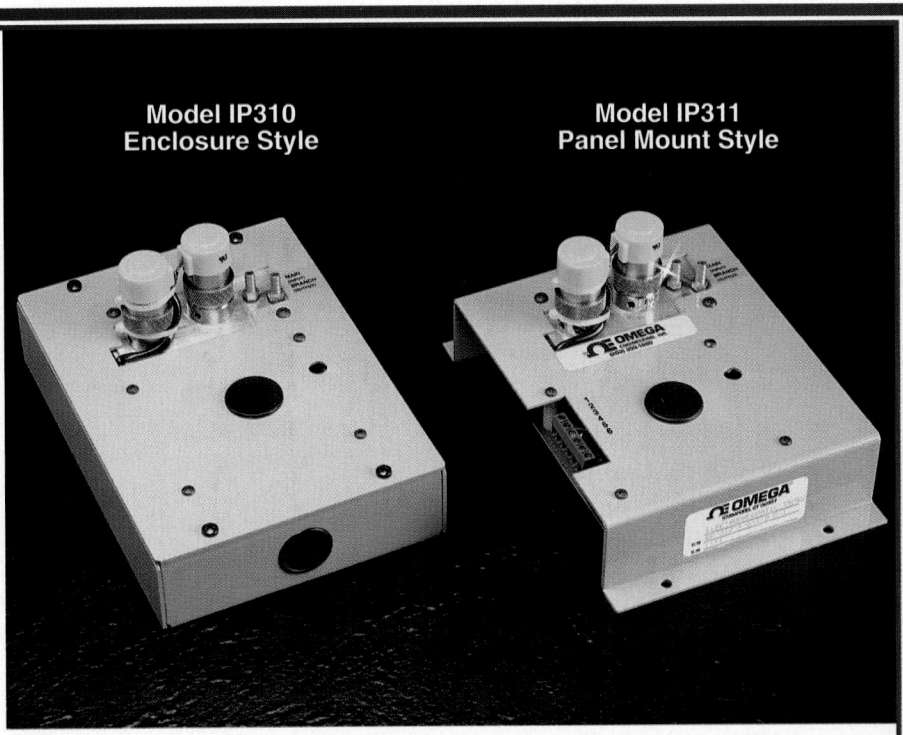

Model IP310
Enclosure Style

Model IP311
Panel Mount Style

HIGHLIGHTED MODELS IN STOCK FOR FAST DELIVERY!

To Order (Specify Model Number)

Model	Price	Acting	Input Range	Output Range
ENCLOSURE STYLE				
IP310D-X15	$170	Direct	4-20 mA	3-15 PSIG
IP310D-020	170	Direct	4-20 mA	0-20 PSIG
IP310D-030	170	Direct	4-20 mA	0-30 PSIG
IP310R-X15	170	Reverse	4-20 mA	15-3 PSIG
IP310R-020	170	Reverse	4-20 mA	20-0 PSIG
IP310R-030	170	Reverse	4-20 mA	30-0 PSIG
PANEL MOUNT STYLE				
IP311D-X15	$170	Direct	4-20 mA	3-15 psig
IP311D-020	170	Direct	4-20 mA	0-20PSIG
IP311D-030	170	Direct	4-20 mA	0-30 PSIG
IP311R-X15	170	Reverse	4-20 mA	15-3PSIG
IP311R-020	170	Reverse	4-20 mA	20-0 PSIG
IP311R-030	170	Reverse	4-20 mA	30-0 PSIG

Accessories	Price	Description
TX4-100	$28.50	100 ft of 4 conductor shielded wire
TY-18-100	25.00	100 ft of Tygon tubing

Comes with complete operator's manual.
Ordering Example: IP310D-030 enclosure style I/P connector is direct-acting 4-20 mA input, and 0-30 PSIG output, **$170.**

SPECIFICATIONS
Supply Voltage: 24 Vdc (14-28)
Supply Current: 150 mA/3.0 VA
Accuracy: 0.25 % FS
Zero Adjustment: ± 50 %
Span Adjustment: ± 25 %
Operating Temp.: 32 to 160°F (0 to 70°C)
Compensated Temp.: 32 to 160°F (0 to 70°C)
Thermal Effects:
Zero: ±0.025% FS/°F
Span: ±0.01% FS/°F
Max Supply Pressure: 40 PSIG
Min Supply Pressure: 0.1 PSIG above maximum control pressure
Solenoid Type: Floating poppet
Solenoid Coil: 3 watts
Flow Rate: 0.5 SCFM
Pressure Port: ¼ hose barb
Minimum Control Pressure Tubing Length: 5 ft.
Electrical Conn.: Screw terminals
Weight: 1.5 lbs (0.68 kg)
Manifold Material: Aluminum
Case: 16 gage steel
Dimensions: 7" H x 5" W x 1.5" D (178 x 127 x 38 mm)

LOW COST ADJUSTABLE SOLID STATE TIMER
DELAY-ON-MAKE, DELAY-ON-BREAK

TD-69 and TD-73

$25

- ✔ **Time Delay Ranges from 6 Seconds to 8 Minutes**
- ✔ **Easily Adjusted with Front Face Dial**
- ✔ **Ideal for Staging Two or More High Amperage Starting Loads**
- ✔ **Prevents Rapid Restarting Due to Sudden Power Loss**
- ✔ **For Use With AC or DC Voltage**

Shown Larger Than Actual Size.

The OMEGA TD-69 and TD-73 timers are ideal for use when a time delay in energizing a circuit is required. The TD-69 is a delay-on-make timer, and the TD-73 is a delay-on-break timer. When power is applied to the TD-69, the adjustable delay period starts. The load is energized at the end of the delay period. When power is removed from the TD-73 (due to a thermostat, etc.), the adjustable delay period starts. The load will remain de-energized until the delay period has ended. Typical applications for the TD-69 and TD-73 include: staging two or more high amperage starting loads (TD-69), preventing transient signals from activating high alarms (TD-69), preventing rapid re-starting after sudden power loss (TD-73) and use with thermostat controlled equipment (TD-73).

SPECIFICATIONS
Input Voltage: 19 to 288 volts ac or dc, 50/60 hz

Maximum Current: 1 amp (10 amp in rush)

Minimum Current: 40 mA (leakage)

Time Delay Range: TD-69: 6 seconds to 8 minutes/TD-73: 6 seconds to 5 minutes

Time Delay Range Adjustment: Front face dial

Repeatability: ±0.5 seconds

Response Time To Initiate Timer: 8 msec

Operating Temp Range: 0°F to 160°F (-18°C to 71°C)

Construction: Plastic housing

Electrical Connections: ¼" blade quick connect terminals

Dimensions: 2" W X 2"L X ¾"D (5.08 X 5.08 X 1.90 cm)

Mounting: Single ¼" dia. center hole

To Order *(Specify Model Number)*			
MODEL	**PRICE**	**ADJUSTABLE TIME DELAY**	**TYPE**
TD-69	$25	6 seconds to 8 minutes	Delay-on-make
TD-73	25	6 seconds to 5 minutes	Delay-on-break

Comes with complete operator's manual.
Ordering Example: *TD-69 is a solid state, delay-on-make timer, **$25**.*

SOLID STATE RELAYS
HIGH RELIABILITY

From

$27

- ✓ **Current Ratings to 90 Amps**
- ✓ **Multi-Million Cycle Life**
- ✓ **Compatible with Temperature Controllers**
- ✓ **Solid-State, SCR Design**
- ✓ **Zero Voltage Switching**
- ✓ **UL Recognized and CSA Certified**
- ✓ **Control ac Lines to 440 Vac**
- ✓ **ac and dc Control Signal Models**
- ✓ **200% Testing at Rated Current**

Control resistance heaters up to 10 kW using solid state relays in conjunction with lower-rated temperature controllers. Solid state relays are SPST, normally open, switching devices with no moving parts, capable of millions of cycles of operation. By applying a control signal, an SSR switches "ON" the ac load current, just as the moving contacts do on a mechanical contactor. Three phase loads can be controlled using 2 or 3 SSRs. Use 3 SSRs for "Y" or "star" 3-phase loads using a neutral line. Two SSRs will control "delta" loads with no neutral line. Three solid state relays are also used when there is no neutral load to provide redundancy and extra assurance of control.

"Switching" takes place at the zero voltage crossover point of the alternating current cycle. Because of this, no appreciable electrical noise is generated, making SSRs ideal for environments where there are apparatus susceptible to RFI.

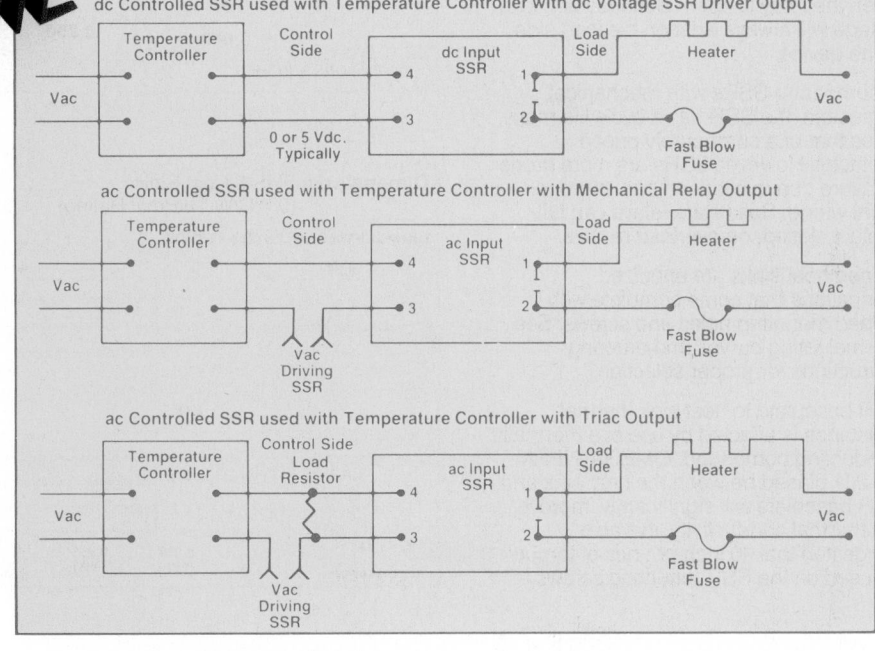

COMMON SPECIFICATIONS
Operating Temperature: −4 to 176°F (−20 to 80°C)

Storage Temperature: −40 to 176°F (−40 to 80°C)

Isolation: 4000 Vrms, input to output; 2500 Vrms input/output to ground

Capacitance: 8 pF, input to output (max)
Line Frequency Range: 47 to 63 Hz
Turn-On Time: 20 ms, ac; 0.5 cycle, dc
Turn-Off Time: 30 ms, ac; 0.5 cycle, dc

Output Specifications

Max On State Current, A	10	25	45	50	75	90
Min On State Current, mA			100			
Max 1-Cycle Surge, A	100	250	450	500	700	1000
Max 1 sec Surge, A	30	75	135	145	200	280
I^2T, (60 Hz), A²sec	200	260	840	1040	2345	3375

ACCESSORIES C

SOLID STATE RELAYS

These SSRs are of the twin SCR type, inherently more reliable and capable of higher overloads before failure than triacs. Heat is developed in a solid state relay due to the nominal voltage drop across the switching device. To dissipate the heat an SSR must be mounted on a finned heat sink or aluminum plate. An SSR should be located where the ambient temperature is relatively low, since the current switching rating is lowered as the temperature increases. Another SSR characteristic is a small leakage current across the output when the relay is open. Because of this, a voltage will always exist on the load side of the device.

In comparing SSRs with mechanical contactors, the SSR has a cycle life many times that of a comparably priced contactor. However, SSRs are more prone to failure due to overload and improper initial wiring. Solid state relays can fail, contact closed, on overload circuits.

Finned heat sinks are anodized fabrications that come complete with tapped mounting holes and screws. See thermal rating curves and ordering instructions for proper selection.

SSR baseplate to heat sink thermal resistance is affected by use of a thermally conducting compound. OMEGATHERM OT-201 placed between the heat sink and SSR baseplate will significantly improve the thermal conductivity. It is also suggested that 10 inch-pounds of torque be used on the SSR mounting screws.

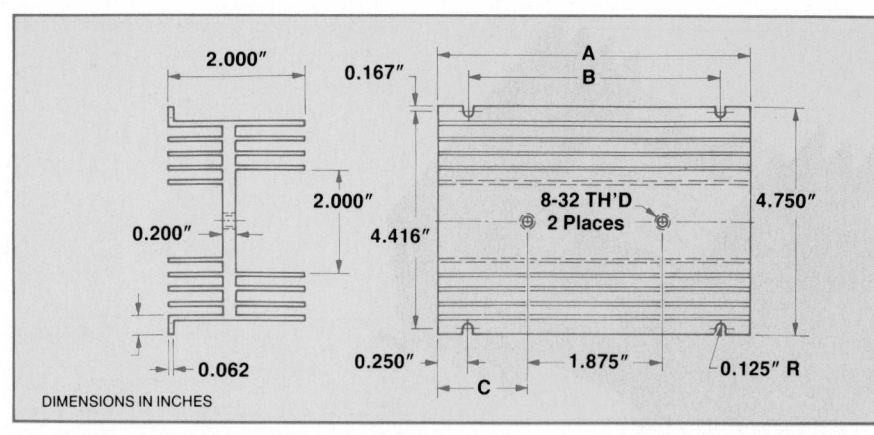

DIMENSIONS IN INCHES

Dimensions: FHS-6 Heat Sink (0.7°C/W Thermal Rating)

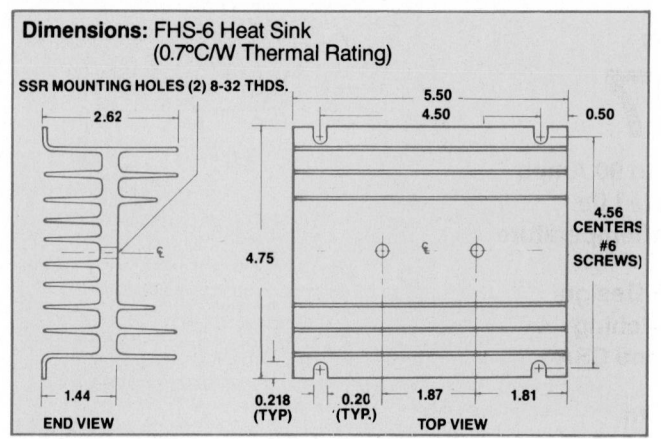

FHS Heat Sink Dimensions

Model No.	A	B	C	Thermal Rating
FHS-1	3.00"	2.50"	0.56"	2 °C/W
FHS-2	5.50"	5.00"	1.81"	1.2 °C/W

Electrical Specifications

Model No.	Type	Input-Control Signal				Input & Output
		Control Signal Voltage	Control Signal Turn-on	Control Signal Turn-off	Signal Input Impedance	Peak Repetitive Voltage Min.*
SSR240AC10 SSR240AC25 SSR240AC45 SSR240AC75 SSR240AC90	ac Control Signal	90 to 280 Vac	90 Vac	10 Vac	40 k	500 V
SSR240DC10 SSR240DC25 SSR240DC45 SSR240DC75 SSR240DC90	dc Control Signal	3 to 32 Vdc	3 Vdc	1 Vdc	1 k	500 V
SSR440AC50 SSR440AC75 SSR440AC90	ac Control Signal	90 to 280 Vac	90 Vac	10 Vac	40 k	1200 V
SSR440DC50 SSR240DC75 SSR440DC90	dc Control Signal	3 to 32 Vdc	3 Vdc	1 Vdc	1 k	1200 V

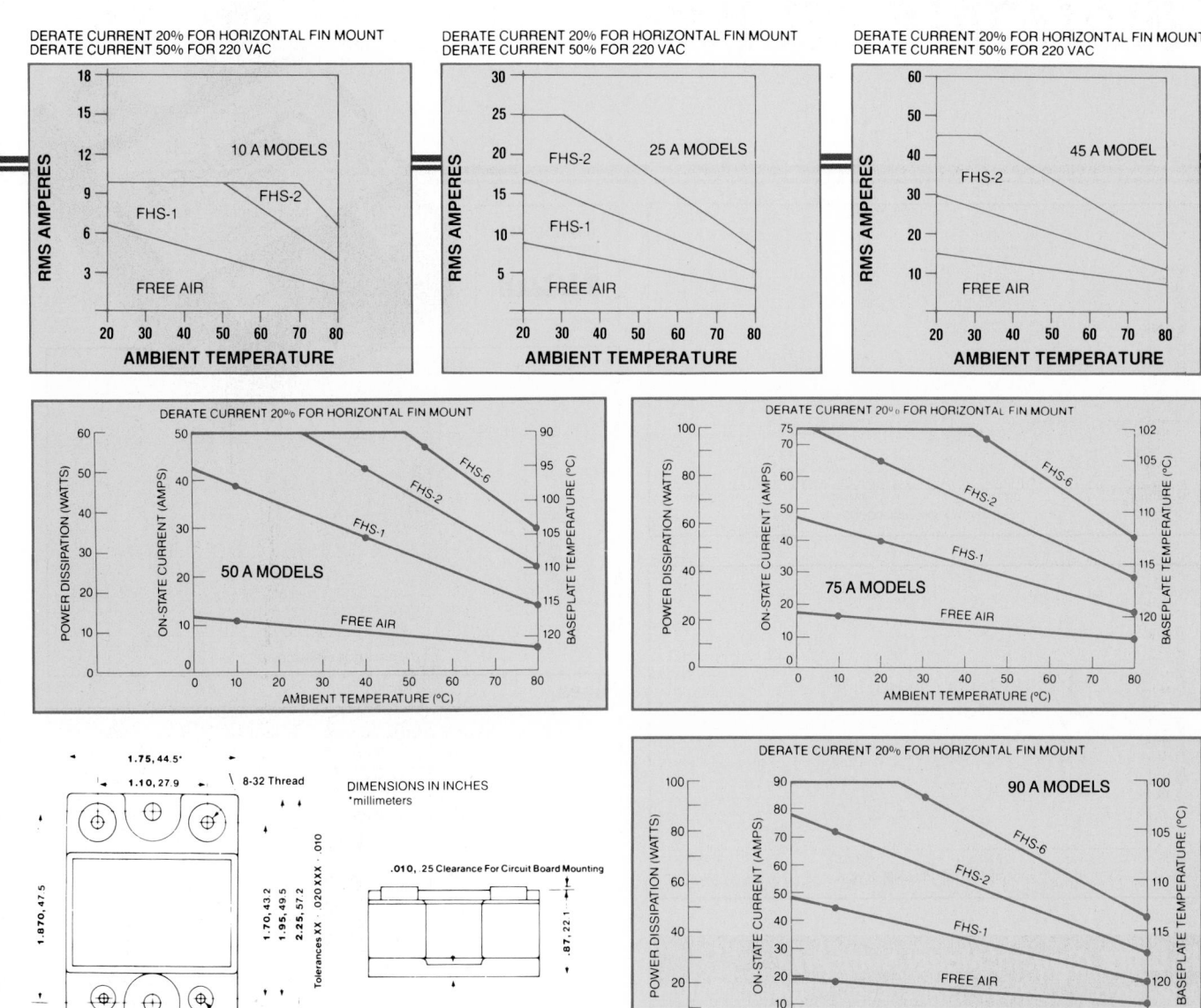

Output-ac Load

Model No.	Nominal ac Line Voltage	Nominal Load Current	Max. Contact Voltage Drop	Max. Off-State Leakage (25°C max. ambient)			Dissipation Watts/Amps
				120 Vac	240 Vac	440 Vac	
SSR240AC10		10A		7.5 mA	15 mA		1.6
SSR240AC25		25A		7.5 mA	15 mA		1.3
SSR240AC45	12 to 280 Vac	45A	1.6 V	7.5 mA	15 mA	N/A	0.9
SSR240AC75		75A		7.5 mA	15 mA		**
SSR240AC90		90A		7.5 mA	15 mA		**
SSR240DC10		10 A		7.5 mA	15 mA		1.6
SSR240DC25		25 A		7.5 mA	15 mA		1.3
SSR240DC45	12 to 280 Vac	45 A	1.6 V	7.5 mA	15 mA	N/A	0.9
SSR240DC75		75 A		7.5 mA	15 mA		**
SSR240DC90		90 A		7.5 mA	15 mA		**
SSR440AC50		50 A		4 mA	8 mA	15 mA	**
SSR440AC75	36 to 480 Vac	75 A	1.6 V	4 mA	8 mA	15 mA	**
SSR440AC90		90 A		4 mA	8 mA	15 mA	**
SSR440DC50		50 A		4 mA	8 mA	15 mA	**
SSR440DC75	36 to 480 Vac	75 A	1.6 V	4 mA	8 mA	15 mA	**
SSR440DC90		90 A		4 mA	8 mA	15 mA	**

* Transients of 1 min. max. duration above table value should be suppressed

** For base plate temperature and max. power dissipation, see figures above.

C-34

SOLID STATE RELAYS

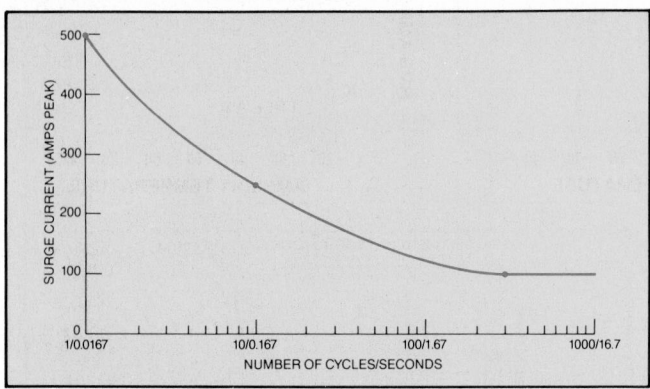

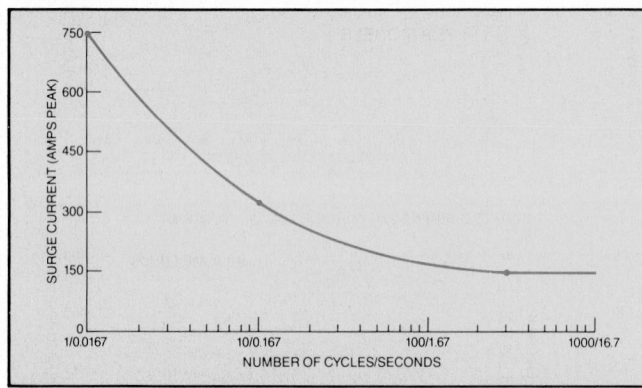

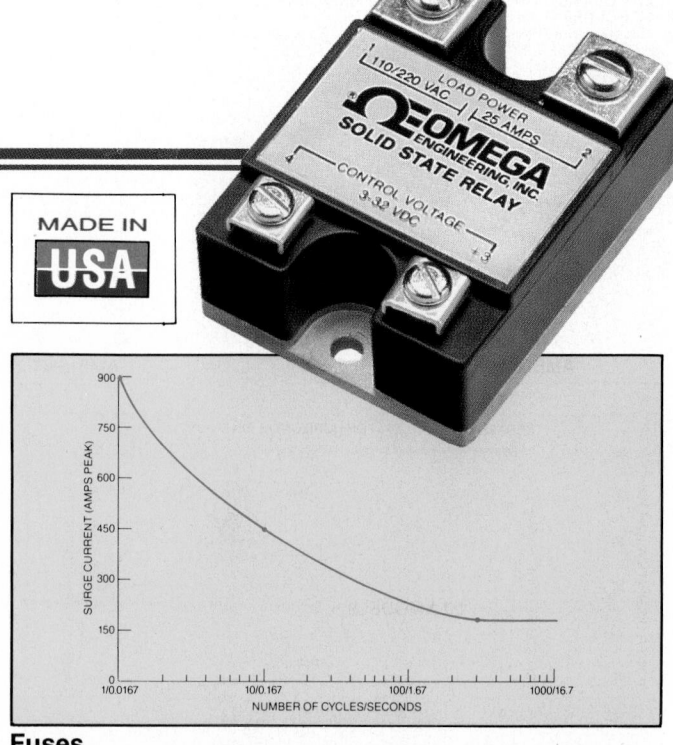

To Order (Specify Model Number)

Model No.	Price	Description	Nominal Rating
SSR240AC10	$27		10A
SSR240AC25	37	ac	25A
SSR240AC45	50	Control Signal	45A
SSR240AC75	96	(280 Vac line)	75A
SSR240AC90	114		90A
SSR240DC10	$21		10A
SSR240DC25	26	dc	25A
SSR240DC45	47	Control Signal	45A
SSR240DC75	91	(280 Vac line)	75A
SSR240DC90	118		90A
SSR440AC50	$108	ac	50A
SSR440AC75	118	Control Signal	75A
SSR440AC90	137	(440 Vac line)	90A
SSR440DC50	$91	dc	45A
SSR440DC75	109	Control Signal	75A
SSR440DC90	137	(440 Vac line)	90A
FHS-1	$13	Finned	2°C/W
FHS-2	17	Heat Sink	1.2°C/W
FHS-6	21		0.7°C/W

Shunt Resistors

To Order (Specify Model Number)

Model No.	Price	Value
SSRR20-12	$6	2000 ohms, 12 watts
SSRR20-50	9	2000 ohms, 50 watts
SSRR15-12	6	1500 ohms, 12 watts
SSRR15-50	9	1500 ohms, 50 watts

Fuses

Model No.	Price	Capacity
KAX-10	$10	10 A ac
KAX-25	10	25 A ac
KAX-45	43	45 A ac
KAX-75	41	75 A ac
KAX-90	46	90 A ac
KBH-50	35	50 A ac
KBH-75	41	75 A ac
KBH-90	46	90 A ac

Fuse Blocks

Model No.	Price	Compatible Fuse
FB-1	$ 5	KAX-10, KAX-25
FB-2	10	KAX-10, KAX-25
FB-3	16	KAX-10, KAX-25
BS101	46	KAX-45, KAX-75, KAX-90, KBH (all models)

Shunt Resistor Guide for Controllers with Triac or SSR Outputs

Controller Model No.	Page No.	Model No. Resistor, 120 Vac	Model No. Resistor, 240 Vac
4000/4000A with option T	P-79	SSRR20-12	SSRR20-50
4200/4200A with option T	P-79	SSRR20-12	SSRR20-50
CN6070/6070A with option T	P-39	SSRR20-12	SSRR20-50
CN2000, CN2010, CN2040	P-27	SSRR20-12	SSRR20-50
CN5000 Series (with 1.5 or 15 amp SSR)	P-74	SSRR15-12	SSRR15-50
CN5050 with 1 amp SSR	P-44	SSRR15-12	SSRR15-50
CN9131A, 9231, or 9231A	P-23	SSRR12-12	SSRR15-50

SSRL SERIES PUMP-UP/PUMP-DOWN RELAYS WITH LATCHING CAPABILITY

1 YEAR WARRANTY

MADE IN USA

Shown Larger Than Actual Size

The SSRL series are latching 5 amp SPST NO relays with a small output current to sense the closing of up to 2 dry mechanical relay contacts. They are ideal for differential level control for pump-up or pump-down applications when combined with any two level switches with dry relay contact closures, (such as 2 LV-10 switches or 2 LV-230 switches). The SSRL relays also convert non-latching mechanical relay outputs into latching alarm outputs, or allow low power reed relay switches to control high amperage or high voltage devices, such as pumps or motors. Latching operation is reset by making a momentary contact between the COM and OFF terminals. The SSRL holds its operational state for up to ½ second during momentary power loss to avoid nuisance shutdowns. A short between the COM and OFF terminals shuts the relay off, regardless of the switch status at the ON terminal.

To Order (Specify Model Number)

Model Number	Price	Description
SSRL2	$65	Switches 120 Vac @ 5 amps
SSRL3	84	Switches 220 Vac @ 5 amps

SPECIFICATIONS

Load Side Voltage Loss : 2 Vac
Maximum Relay Closure Sense Current/Voltage: 20 mA @ 11 Vdc nominal
Minimum Load: 10 times the leakage current

HIGHLIGHTED MODELS STOCKED

Leakage Current through Load Terminals: 2 mA at 120 Vac; 4 mA at 240 Vac
Housing Material: Polysulfone

U.S. AND CANADA
for placing orders, call: **1-800-82-66342™**
1-800-TC-OMEGA

The SSRL Series Relays are not failsafe; we recommend a third level switch independent of the SSRL for alarm of overfill or overdrain conditions.

Thermocouple Slip-Ring Assembly

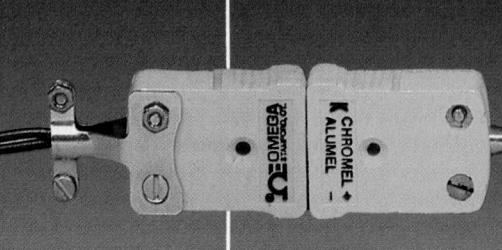

Low Noise
Model SR-2
Low Resistance

Mercury-Wetted Contacts

Rotate

Two times actual size

Slip-ring Assembly Shown Actual Size

This low noise thermocouple slip-ring assembly is ideal for transmission of low level emf's where it is necessary to attach thermocouples to rotating parts.

It can be used with any thermocouple calibration. Its low noise design introduces a total signal error of less than five microvolts at rotational speeds up to 2000 rpm.

The output leads consist of plain copper wires; no compensation is included. The slip-ring assembly will transfer the true microvolt signal coming from a rotating assembly.

SIDE VIEW

ROTOR RECEPTACLE
INSULATED STATOR
INSULATED LEAD WIRE
1 THREADED HOLE
3/4" Dia.
9/32" Dia.
3/4"
1 13/16"
2 5/16" = 1 1/8"

FRONT VIEW

7/32" Dia. SHAFT
3/4" Dia.
BALL BEARING WITH FEMALE ROTATING PLUG
MALE CONNECTING PIN
9/32" Dia.

TO THERMOCOUPLE

Rotor Receptacle Also Available Separately. $16 Each

Specifications:

Mechanical Specifications
- Sealed Ball Bearings
- Speed: 0-2000 rpm (either direction)
- Operates in Any Position. When used vertically, the small shaft should be kept above the horizontal.

Electrical Specifications
- Voltage: 120 V Maximum
- Current: 1.0 Amp Maximum
- Frequency: dc to 10 MHz
- Temperature: − 15° to 158 °F (− 26° to 70 °C)

Model SR-2
$125

OFF-THE-SHELF DELIVERY

SENSOR AND TRANSDUCER

WIRE AND CABLE

FINE GAGE .005″ DIA. SINGLE WIRE

- **3 Mil Teflon Wall**
- **Single Strand**
- **Extruded PFA (Teflon)**
- **Excellent in Vacuum**
- **Non-flammable**

OMEGA'S thin-wall covering process guarantees continuous lengths up to 1,000 feet. This wire is ideal for connecting the strain gages to solder terminal strips and pads.

Price Table	
Spool Size	**Price**
50 Ft.	**$16**
100 Ft.	**29**
500 Ft.	**119**

To Order (Specify catalog number)

Dia.	Length Ft.	Cat. No.	Price
.005	50	TFCP-005- 50	**$16**
.005	100	TFCP-005-100	**29**
.005	500	TFCP-005-500	**119**
.010	50	TFCP-010- 50	**16**
.010	100	TFCP-010-100	**29**
.010	500	TFCP-010-500	**119**
.015	50	TFCP-015- 50	**16**
.015	100	TFCP-015-100	**29**
.015	500	TFCP-015-500	**119**

MULTI-CONDUCTOR RIBBON CABLE

- **28 AWG 10-50 Conductor**
- **PVC Rating to 105°C**
- **26 AWG 4 Conductor**
- **100 Foot Rolls**

OMEGA'S ribbon cables are PVC preinsulated conductors laminated to a clear PVC film to allow easy termination. The color coding allows for quick identification and circuit tracing.
Can be easily trimmed to any desired conductor width for different uses.

To Order (Specify catalog number)

No. of Cond.	Cat No.	Price 100 ft
4	RC- 4-100	**$ 95**
10	RC-10-100	**65**
14	RC-14-100	**85**
16	RC-16-100	**95**
26	RC-26-100	**175**
50	RC-50-100	**325**

IN STOCK FOR FAST DELIVERY

MULTI-CONDUCTOR SHIELDED CABLE

- **24 AWG Tinned Copper Wires**
- **PVC Insulation**
- **Aluminum-Polyester Shield with #24 Drain Wire**
- **PVC Jacket Overall**
- **100 Foot Rolls**

Shielded cable provides the high conductivity and noise immunity required for instrumentation hook-ups to transducers. It is suitable for low and high level voltage signals and mA pick-up in high EMI/RFI environments.

To Order (Specify catalog number)

No. of Cond.	Nom. O.D.	Cat. No.	Price 100 ft.
4	.190″	TX- 4-100	**$28.50**
8	.220″	TX- 8-100	**45.50**
15	.280″	TX-15-100	**88.00**

CONVENIENT PRE-SPOOLED LENGTHS

OMEGAFLEX® TUBING AND ACCESSORIES

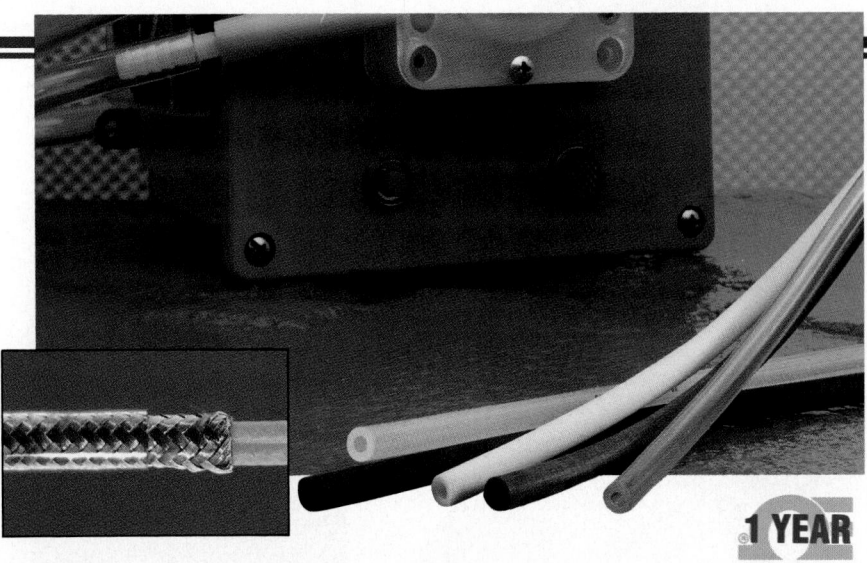

OMEGAFLEX® tubing is offered in a wide variety of materials to meet all your tubing requirements. From low cost Tygon, Vinyl and Polyethylene, to chemically inert Teflon,® spool sizes include 5, 50 or 100 foot spools for your ordering convenience. A wide variety of diameters are also available to suit your most demanding applications.

To improve durability, tubing up to ¾ inch diameter can be overbraided with 304 Stainless Steel on special order. As an additional option, OMEGA can supply overbraided tubing with an additional PVC coating to protect the 304SS overbraiding from chemical attach or to permit sealing the tubing with standard compression fittings. For details on overbraiding, consult sales department.

1 YEAR WARRANTY

To Order (Specify Model Number)

I.D. in.	I.D. mm	O.D. in.	O.D. mm	Wall in.	Wall mm	Silicone 50' PKG Model Number	$ Per 50' pkg	Norprene® A-60-G 50' PKG Model Number	$ Per 50' pkg	Tygon® R-3603 50' PKF Model Number	$ Per 50' pkg	Vinyl 100' PKG Model Number	$ Per 100' pkg
¹⁄₅₀	0.5	¹⁄₁₂	2.1	¹⁄₃₂	0.8	TYSC-112150-50	32.00	—	—	—	—	—	—
¹⁄₃₂	0.8	¹⁄₁₆	1.6	¹⁄₆₄	0.4	—	—	—	—	—	—	—	—
¹⁄₃₂	0.8	³⁄₃₂	2.4	¹⁄₃₂	0.8	TYSC-332132-50	24.00	—	—	—	—	—	—
¹⁄₁₆	1.6	¹⁄₈	3.2	¹⁄₃₂	0.8	TYSC-18116-50	34.00	—	—	TYTY-18116-50	8.00	TYVY-18116-100	8.00
¹⁄₁₆	1.6	³⁄₁₆	4.8	¹⁄₁₆	1.6	—	—	TYNP-316116-50	15.00	—	—	—	—
³⁄₃₂	2.4	¹⁄₈	3.2	¹⁄₆₄	0.4	—	—	—	—	—	—	—	—
³⁄₃₂	2.4	⁵⁄₃₂	4.0	¹⁄₃₂	0.8	TYSC-532332-50	32.00	—	—	TYTY-532332-50	11.00	—	—
¹⁄₈	3.2	³⁄₁₆	4.8	¹⁄₁₆	1.6	TYSC-31618-50	36.00	—	—	TYTY-31618-50	13.00	—	—
¹⁄₈	3.2	¹⁄₄	6.4	¹⁄₁₆	1.6	TYSC-1418-50	41.00	TYNP-1418-50	20.00	TYTY-1418-50	41.00	TYVY-1418-100	10.00
¹⁄₈	3.2	³⁄₈	9.6	¹⁄₈	3.2	TYSC-3818-50	76.00	TYNP-3818-50	40.00	—	—	—	—
⁹⁄₆₄	3.6	³⁄₁₆	4.8	¹⁄₄₀	0.6	—	—	—	—	—	—	—	—
⁵⁄₃₂	4.0	⁷⁄₃₂	5.6	¹⁄₃₂	0.8	TYSC-732532-50	99.00	—	—	TYTY-732532-50	21.00	—	—
⁵⁄₃₂	4.0	¹⁄₄	6.4	³⁄₆₄	1.2	—	—	—	—	—	—	—	—
³⁄₁₆	4.8	¹⁄₄	6.4	¹⁄₃₂	0.8	TYSC-14316-50	41.00	—	—	TYTY-14316-50	24.00	—	—
³⁄₁₆	4.8	⁵⁄₁₆	8.0	¹⁄₁₆	1.6	TYSC-516316-50	43.00	TYNP-516316-50	19.00	TYTY-516316-50	47.00	TYVY-516316-100	10.00
³⁄₁₆	4.8	⁷⁄₁₆	11.2	¹⁄₈	3.2	TYSC-716316-50	88.00	—	—	TYTY-716316-50	116.00	TYVY-716316-100	24.00
⁷⁄₃₂	5.6	⁵⁄₁₆	8.0	³⁄₆₄	1.2	—	—	—	—	—	—	—	—
¹⁄₄	6.4	⁵⁄₁₆	8.0	¹⁄₃₂	0.8	TYSC-51614-50	50.00	—	—	—	—	—	—
¹⁄₄	6.4	³⁄₈	9.6	¹⁄₁₆	1.6	TYSC-3814-50	51.00	TYNP-3814-50	29.00	TYTY-3814-50	53.00	TYVY-3814-100	12.00
¹⁄₄	6.4	⁷⁄₁₆	11.2	³⁄₃₂	2.4	TYSC-71614-50	73.00	TYNP-71614-50	47.00	TYTY-71614-50	98.00	TYVY-71614-100	20.00
¹⁄₄	6.4	¹⁄₂	12.8	¹⁄₈	3.2	TYSC-1214-50	102.00	TYNP-1214-50	69.00	TYTY-1214-50	107.00	TYVY-1214-100	29.00
¹⁹⁄₆₄	7.6	³⁄₈	9.6	¹⁄₂₅	1.0	—	—	—	—	—	—	—	—
⁵⁄₁₆	8.0	³⁄₈	9.6	¹⁄₃₂	0.8	—	—	—	—	—	—	—	—
⁵⁄₁₆	8.0	⁷⁄₁₆	11.2	¹⁄₁₆	1.6	TYSC-716516-50	68.00	TYNP-716516-50	34.00	TYTY-716516-50	69.00	TYVY-716516-100	15.00
⁵⁄₁₆	8.0	¹⁄₂	12.8	³⁄₃₂	2.4	TYSC-12516-50	82.00	TYNP-12516-50	56.00	TYTY-12516-50	92.00	TYVY-12516-100	26.00
⁵⁄₁₆	8.0	⁹⁄₁₆	14.4	¹⁄₈	3.2	TYSC-916516-50	114.00	—	—	TYTY-916516-50	92.00	TYVY-916516-100	54.00
³⁄₈	9.6	⁷⁄₁₆	11.2	¹⁄₃₂	0.8	—	—	—	—	—	—	—	—
³⁄₈	9.6	¹⁄₂	12.8	¹⁄₁₆	1.6	TYSC-1238-50	60.00	TYNP-1238-50	40.00	TYTY-1238-50	69.00	TYVY-1238-100	17.00
³⁄₈	9.6	⁹⁄₁₆	14.4	³⁄₃₂	2.4	TYSC-91638-50	98.00	TYNP-91638-50	64.00	TYTY-91638-50	117.00	TYVY-91638-100	27.00
³⁄₈	9.6	⁵⁄₈	16.0	¹⁄₈	3.2	TYSC-5838-50	112.00	TYNP-5838-50	92.00	TYTY-5838-50	102.00	TYVY-5838-100	39.00
²⁄₅	10.2	¹⁄₂	12.8	¹⁄₂₀	1.4	—	—	—	—	—	—	—	—
⁷⁄₁₆	11.2	¹⁄₂	12.8	¹⁄₃₂	0.8	—	—	—	—	—	—	—	—
⁷⁄₁₆	11.2	⁹⁄₁₆	14.4	¹⁄₁₆	1.6	—	—	TYNP-916716-50	55.00	TYTY-916716-50	72.00	TYVY-916716-100	23.00
¹⁄₂	12.8	⁹⁄₁₆	14.4	¹⁄₃₂	0.8	—	—	—	—	—	—	—	—
¹⁄₂	12.8	⁵⁄₈	16.0	¹⁄₁₆	1.6	TYSC-5812-50	104.00	TYNP-5812-50	51.00	TYTY-5812-50	111.00	TYVY-5812-100	24.00
¹⁄₂	12.8	³⁄₄	19.2	¹⁄₈	3.2	TYSC-3412-50	140.00	—	—	TYTY-3412-50	170.00	TYVY-3412-100	50.00
⁹⁄₁₆	14.4	⁵⁄₈	16.0	¹⁄₃₂	0.8	—	—	—	—	—	—	—	—
⁵⁄₈	16.0	³⁄₄	19.2	¹⁄₁₆	1.6	—	—	—	—	—	—	—	—
⁵⁄₈	16.0	¹³⁄₁₆	20.8	³⁄₃₂	2.4	TYSC-131658-50	158.00	TYNP-131658-50	98.00	TYTY-131658-50	122.00	TYVY-131658-100	54.00
⁵⁄₈	16.0	⁷⁄₈	22.4	¹⁄₈	3.2	TYSC-7858-50	210.00	TYNP-7858-50	136.00	TYTY-7858-50	215.00	TYVY-7858-100	59.00
⁵⁄₈	16.0	²⁹⁄₃₂	23.2	⁹⁄₆₄	3.6	—	—	—	—	—	—	—	—
³⁄₄	19.2	1	25.4	¹⁄₈	0.8	TYSC-134-50	230.00	TYNP-134-50	159.00	TYTY-134-50	242.00	TYVY-134-100	65.00
³⁄₄	19.2	1¹⁄₄₂	26.0	²³⁄₁₆₈	3.4	—	—	—	—	—	—	—	—
³⁄₄	19.2	1³⁄₁₆	21.2	¹⁄₂₅	1.0	—	—	—	—	—	—	—	—
³⁄₄	19.2	η1⁄₈	28.6	³⁄₁₆	4.8	—	—	—	—	—	—	—	—
³⁄₄	19.2	1⁵⁄₁₆	33.3	¹⁄₂₅	1.0	—	—	—	—	—	—	—	—

OMEGA tubing union connectors are offered in polyethylene, standard nylon, or rugged glass-filled nylon. They are one piece connectors, barbed at both ends. (Not suitable for use with Teflon® tubing.)

STRAIGHT TUBING UNION CONNECTORS

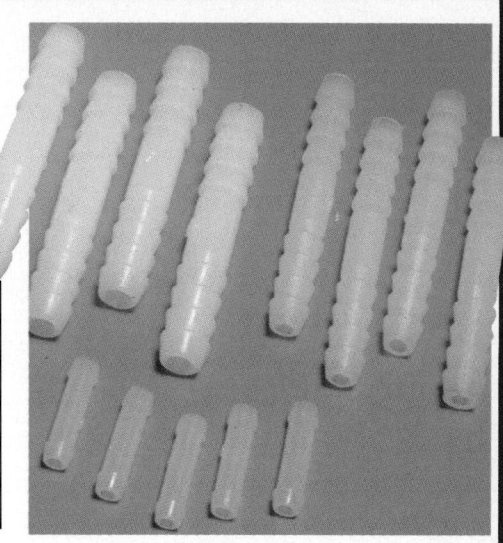

Model No. Polyethylene	Price PKG of 10	Model No. Nylon	Price PKG of 10	Tubing I.D.
TYPP-UN-116	$1.45	TYNY-UN-116	$1.90	1/16"
TYPP-UN-332	1.45	TYNY-UN-332	1.90	3/32"
TYPP-UN-18	1.45	TYNY-UN-18	1.90	1/8"
TYPP-UN-316	2.50	TYNY-UN-316	3.25	3/16"
TYPP-UN-14	1.55	TYNY-UN-14	2.10	1/4"
TYPP-UN-516	2.50	TYNY-UN-516	3.50	5/16"
TYPP-UN-38	1.65	TYNY-UN-38	2.15	3/8"
TYPP-UN-12	2.75	TYNY-UN-12	3.50	1/2"
TYPP-UN-58	3.00	TYNY-UN-58	4.00	5/8"
TYPP-UN-34	6.75	TYNY-UN-34	8.50	3/4"

Polypropylene 100' PKG		Viton 5' or 50' PKG		Teflon TFE 50' PKG		Teflon FEP 50' PKG		Teflon PFA 5' or 50' PKGS		Reinforced PVC 50' PKG	
Model Number	$ Per 100' pkg	Model Number	$ Per 5' or 50' pkg	Model Number	$ Per 50' pkg	Model Number	$ Per 50' pkg	Model Number	$ Per 5' or 50' pkg	Model Number	$ Per 50' Pkg
—	—	—	—	—	—	TYTF-116132-50	15.00	—	—	—	—
—	—	—	—	—	—	—	—	—	—	—	—
—	—	TYVT-18116-50	110.00	TYTT-18116-50	110.00	TYTF-18116-50	33.00	TYTP-18116-50	50.00	—	—
—	—	—	—	—	—	—	—	—	—	—	—
—	—	TYVT-31618-50	69.00	—	—	TYTF-532332-50	32.00	—	—	—	—
TYPP-1418-100	15.00	—	—	—	—	TYTF-31618-50	36.00	—	—	—	—
TYPP-14316-100	15.00	TYVT-14316-50	177.00	TYTT-14316-50	82.00	TYTF-14316-50	48.00	TYTP-14532-50	124.00	—	—
TYPP-516316-100	19.00	—	—	—	—	—	—	—	—	—	—
TYPP-51614-100	23.00	TYVT-51614-50	530.00	—	—	TYTF-51614-50	57.00	TYTP-516732-50	280.00	—	—
TYPP-3814-100	24.00	—	—	—	—	—	—	TYTP-3814-50	252.00	—	—
—	—	—	—	—	—	—	—	—	—	TYRP-1214-50	20.00
—	—	—	—	TYTT-381964-50	184.00	TYTF-38516-50	73.00	—	—	—	—
TYPP-716516-100	29.00	TYVT-716516-50	230.00	—	—	—	—	—	—	—	—
—	—	—	—	—	—	TYTF-71638-50	84.00	—	—	—	—
TYPP-1238-100	34.00	TYVT-1238-50	306.00	—	—	—	—	TYTP-1238-50	35.00/5'	—	—
—	—	—	—	—	—	—	—	—	—	TYRP-5838-50	26.00
—	—	—	—	TYTT-1225-50	227.00	TYTF-12716-50	111.00	—	—	—	—
—	—	—	—	—	—	TYTF-91612-50	124.00	—	—	—	—
TYPP-5812-100	44.00	TYVT-5812-50	340.00	—	—	—	—	—	—	TYRP-3412-50	32.00
—	—	—	—	—	—	TYTF-58916-50	142.00	TYTP-3458-5	50.00/5'	—	—
—	—	TYVT-7858-5	57.00/5'	—	—	—	—	—	—	TYRP-293258-50	83.00
—	—	TYVT-134-5	66.00/5'	—	—	—	—	—	—	—	—
—	—	—	—	—	—	—	—	TYTP-131634-5	35.00/5'	TYRP-114234-50	48.00
—	—	—	—	—	—	—	—	—	—	—	—

FLEXIBLE PLASTIC TUBING
MINIATURE STAINLESS STEEL CLAMPS

From
$18
100 FT. ROLL

Works with Tube Fitting Transducers in Section B.

Stainless Steel Clamps also available.

- **Temperature Range −49°F to 165°F**
- **Lightweight, Flexible**
- **Low Working Pressure**
- **Readily Curves Around Corners**
- **Flexibility Saves Footage**

Lightweight, flexible and easy to handle, PVC flexible plastic tubing goes into service fast. It is readily curved around corners and obstructions, requiring a minimum of couplings and fittings. Its flexibility can save up to one-third the footage and much of the labor required to install rigid tubing.

Only the simplest of tools and equipment are required to put the tubing into service. It is readily cut with any sharp knife.

Stainless Steel Hose Clamps

Where pressures are involved, it is considered "good practice" to use clamps on all connections between tubing and fittings. Although the tubing grips tightly to such fittings, clamps provide an added safety factor.

SPECIFICATIONS

Color: Clear
Durometer Hardness (Shore A) ASTM D2240: 63
Tensile Strength: 2300 psi (162 kg/cm^2)
Maximum Recommended Operating Temperature: 165°F (74°C)
Low Temperature Brittleness by Impact: −49°F (−45°C)
Steam Autoclaving Conditions: 30 min. @ 15 psi (1.1 kg/cm^2)
Elongation: 410%
Odor: None
Taste: None
Toxicity: Non-Toxic
Dielectric Strength (Rapid Rise Method): 385 v/mil (151 v/cm)

Chemical Resistance

Strong Acids: Good
Weak Acids: Excellent
Strong Alkalies: Good
Weak Alkalies: Excellent

Inside Diameter		Outside Diameter		Wall Thickness		Maximum Suggested Working Pressure at Room Temperature	
Inches	Milli-Meters	Inches	Milli-meters	Inches	Milli-meters	psi	kg/cm²
1/8	3.18	1/4	6.35	1/16	1.59	51	3.5
3/16	4.76	5/16	7.94	1/16	1.59	51	3.5
1/4	6.36	3/8	9.53	1/16	1.59	51	3.5
1	25.4	1 1/4	31.75	1/8	3.18	51	3.5

To Order *(Specify catalog number)*

Flexible Plastic Tubing			Stainless Steel Clamps		
			Pkg of 10		
Part No.*	Price	ID	Part No.	Price	Sizes
TY-18-100	$18	1/8″	CP-10	$15	1/8″ to 1/4″
TY-316-100	20	3/16″			
TY-14-100	25	1/4″	CP-14	$20	13/16″ to 1 1/2″
TY-100-100	160	1″			

* Price per 100 ft. for others lengths, consult sales.

PRESSURE & TEMPERATURE TEST PLUGS
OMEGA® SELF-SEALING

- **Up to 1,000 PSIG between −20°F and 140°F**
- **Up to 275°F**
- **Two Self-Closing Valves**
- **Heavy Duty Design**

OMEGA® Self-Sealing Plugs will allow you to take pressure and temperature readings quickly, and eliminate the need for leaving costly gages or temperature indicators on the line. The OMEGA plug is permanently installed in the line at recommended test points. The cap protects the valve and provides an additional positive seal. After the cap has been removed, either a test thermometer or a gage adaptor with the proper pressure gage attached can be inserted through the two self-closing valves in the plug. Readings are made, adjustments or tests can be accomplished, and when the probes are withdrawn, the two valves close. The protective cap is then reinstalled.

Neoprene is resistant to deterioration from waxes, oils, greases, fats, petroleum products, and most refrigerants. Can be operated at a maximum temperature of 200°F at 500 PSIG.

Nordel gives excellent service in hot or cold water and in some applications of low pressure steam. Nordel is resistant to detergents, phosphates, esters, ketones, alcohols, and glycols. It is not suitable for petroleum products. Can be operated at a maximum temperature of 275°F at 500 PSIG.

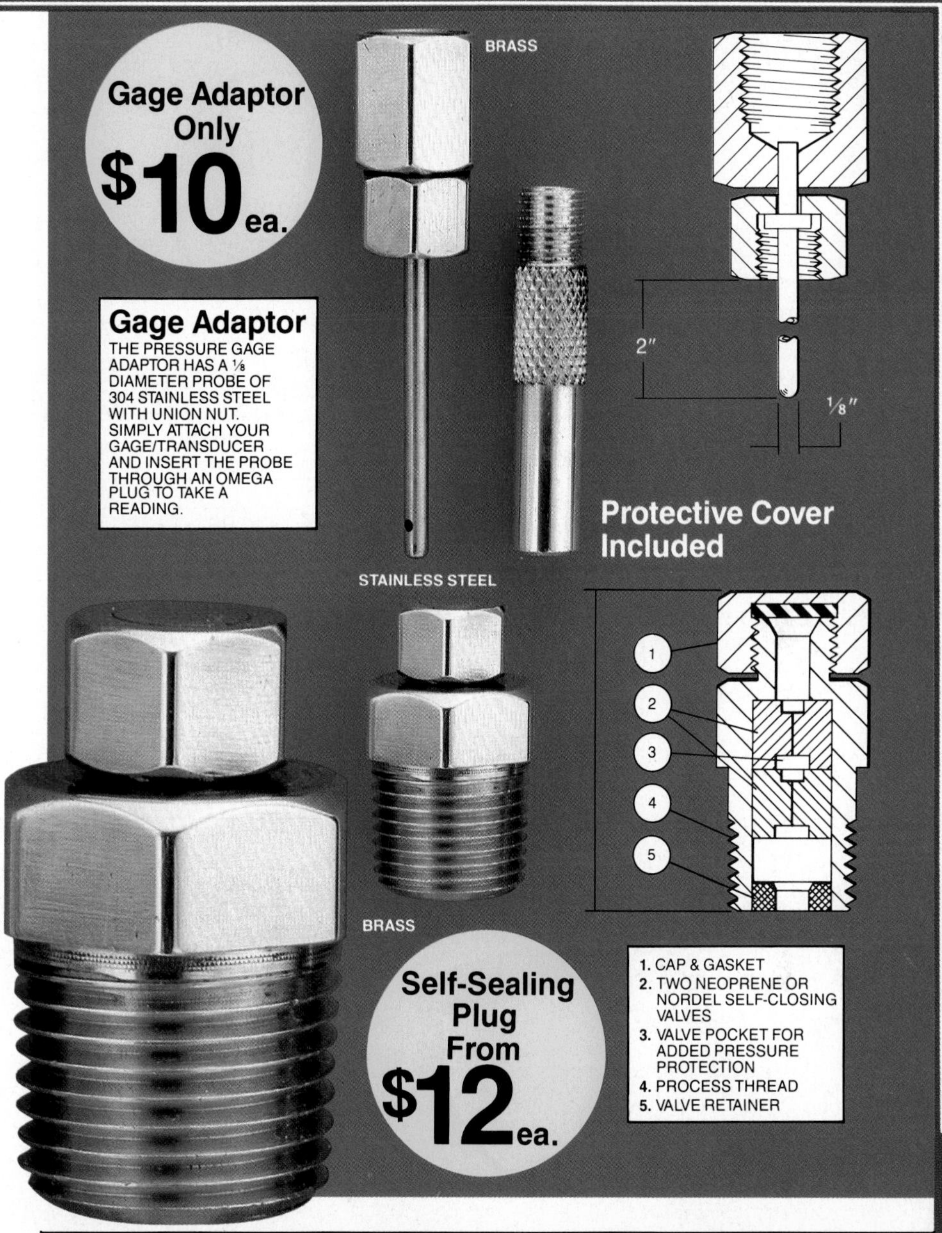

- **Any Size Plug Accepts up to a ⅛″ Dia. Probe**

BRASS

Gage Adaptor Only $10 ea.

Gage Adaptor
THE PRESSURE GAGE ADAPTOR HAS A ⅛ DIAMETER PROBE OF 304 STAINLESS STEEL WITH UNION NUT. SIMPLY ATTACH YOUR GAGE/TRANSDUCER AND INSERT THE PROBE THROUGH AN OMEGA PLUG TO TAKE A READING.

STAINLESS STEEL

2″   ⅛″

Protective Cover Included

BRASS

Self-Sealing Plug From $12 ea.

1. CAP & GASKET
2. TWO NEOPRENE OR NORDEL SELF-CLOSING VALVES
3. VALVE POCKET FOR ADDED PRESSURE PROTECTION
4. PROCESS THREAD
5. VALVE RETAINER

ACCESSORIES C

To Order (Specify part number)

OMEGA Plug

PART NO.	NPT MALE	VALVE CORE MATERIAL	PRICE
OPNE-14	¼″	NEOPRENE	**$12.00** ea.
OPNO-14	¼″	NORDEL	**13.50** ea.
OPNE-12	½″	NEOPRENE	**15.50** ea.
OPNO-12	½″	NORDEL	**17.00** ea.

Gage Adaptor

PART NO.	NPT FEMALE	PROBE DIA.	PRICE
GASS-18	¼″	⅛″	**$10.00** ea.

IN STOCK FOR IMMEDIATE DELIVERY!

ADAPTORS & BUSHINGS

BUSHINGS

ADAPTORS

- **Rugged Design**
- **Available in Stainless Steel, Brass, or Carbon Steel**
- **Reduce Down to ⅛″ NPT**
- **Adapt Up to 1″ NPT**

To Order *(Adaptors and Bushings, Specify Catalog Numbers)*

NPT THREAD		"B"	"A"	BRASS		STAINLESS STEEL	
MALE	FEMALE	HEX	IN	CATALOG #	PRICE	CATALOG #	PRICE
REDUCING ADAPTORS							
⅛	½	1⅛	1.50	RA-18-12-BR	**$5.00**	RA-18-12-SS	**$12.00**
¼	½	1⅛	1.69	RA-14-12-BR	4.00	RA-14-12-SS	10.75
½	¾	1⅜	1.94	RA-12-34-BR	6.00	RA-12-34-SS	15.00
½	1	1⅝	2.16	N/A		RA-12- 1-SS	27.00
REDUCING BUSHINGS							
½	⅛	⅞	1.09	RB-12-18-BR	**$3.25**	RB- 12-18-SS	**$11.50**
½	¼	⅞	1.09	RB-12-14-BR	2.50	RB- 12-14-SS	8.75
¾	½	1⅛	1.17	RB-34-12-BR	4.00	RB- 34-12-SS	14.00
1	½	1⅜	1.36	RB- 1-12-BR	6.00	RB- 1-12-SS	24.25
1	¾	1⅜	1.36	RB- 1-34-BR	5.00	RB- 1-34-SS	23.25
1¼	¾	1¾	1.48	—	N/A	RB-114-34-CS*	6.25
1¼	1	1¾	1.48	—	N/A	RB-114- 1-CS*	8.75
1½	1	2	1.56	—	N/A	RB-112- 1-CS*	14.75

* Those fittings are available only in carbon steel.

COMPRESSION FITTINGS
OMEGALOK™

- **Ferrule Design for Positive Pressure Seal**
- **Heavy Duty Construction in Stainless Steel or Brass**
- **For Protection Tube Diameters ¹⁄₁₆″ up to ½″**

To Order

Compression Fittings

Protection Tube O.D.	Male Th'd NPT	Length "A" In.	Brass		316 Stainless Steel	
			Cat. No.	Pr. Ea.	Cat. No.	Pr. Ea.
¹⁄₁₆	¹⁄₁₆	.97	N/A	—	SSLK-116-116	$14.50
¹⁄₁₆	⅛	1.03	BRLK-116-18	$4.75	SSLK-116-18	14.00
⅛	⅛	1.18	BRLK-18-18	3.00	SSLK-18-18	8.50
⅛	¼	1.74	BRLK-18-14	3.50	SSLK-18-14	10.00
³⁄₁₆	⅛	1.22	BRLK-316-18	3.00	SSLK-316-18	8.50
³⁄₁₆	¼	1.81	BRLK-316-14	3.50	SSLK-316-14	10.00
¼	⅛	1.29	BRLK-14-18	3.00	SSLK-14-18	8.00
¼	¼	1.48	BRLK-14-14	3.00	SSLK-14-14	8.50
⁵⁄₁₆	¼	1.54	N/A	—	SSLK-516-14	10.50
⅜	¼	1.59	BRLK-38-14	3.50	SSLK-38-14	11.00
⅜	⅜	1.59	BRLK-38-38	4.00	SSLK-38-38	12.50
⅜	½	1.81	BRLK-38-12	5.50	SSLK-38-12	15.50
½	½	1.94	BRLK-12-12	6.25	SSLK-12-12	18.00

Replacement Ferrules (package of 10)

Protection Tube O.D.	Brass ($10/pkg.)	Stainless Steel ($30/pkg.)	Teflon* ($40/pkg.)
¹⁄₁₆	B-FER-116	SS-FER-116	T-FER-116
⅛	B-FER-18	SS-FER-18	T-FER-18
³⁄₁₆	B-FER-316	SS-FER-316	T-FER-316
¼	B-FER-14	SS-FER-14	T-FER-14
⁵⁄₁₆	B-FER-516	SS-FER-516	T-FER-516
⅜	B-FER-38	SS-FER-38	T-FER-38
½	B-FER-12	SS-FER-12	T-FER-12

*NOTE: Teflon can only be used with stainless steel compression fittings.

MULTICONDUCTOR FEEDTHROUGHS
COMPRESSION-TYPE FOR VACUUM OR PRESSURE SEALING

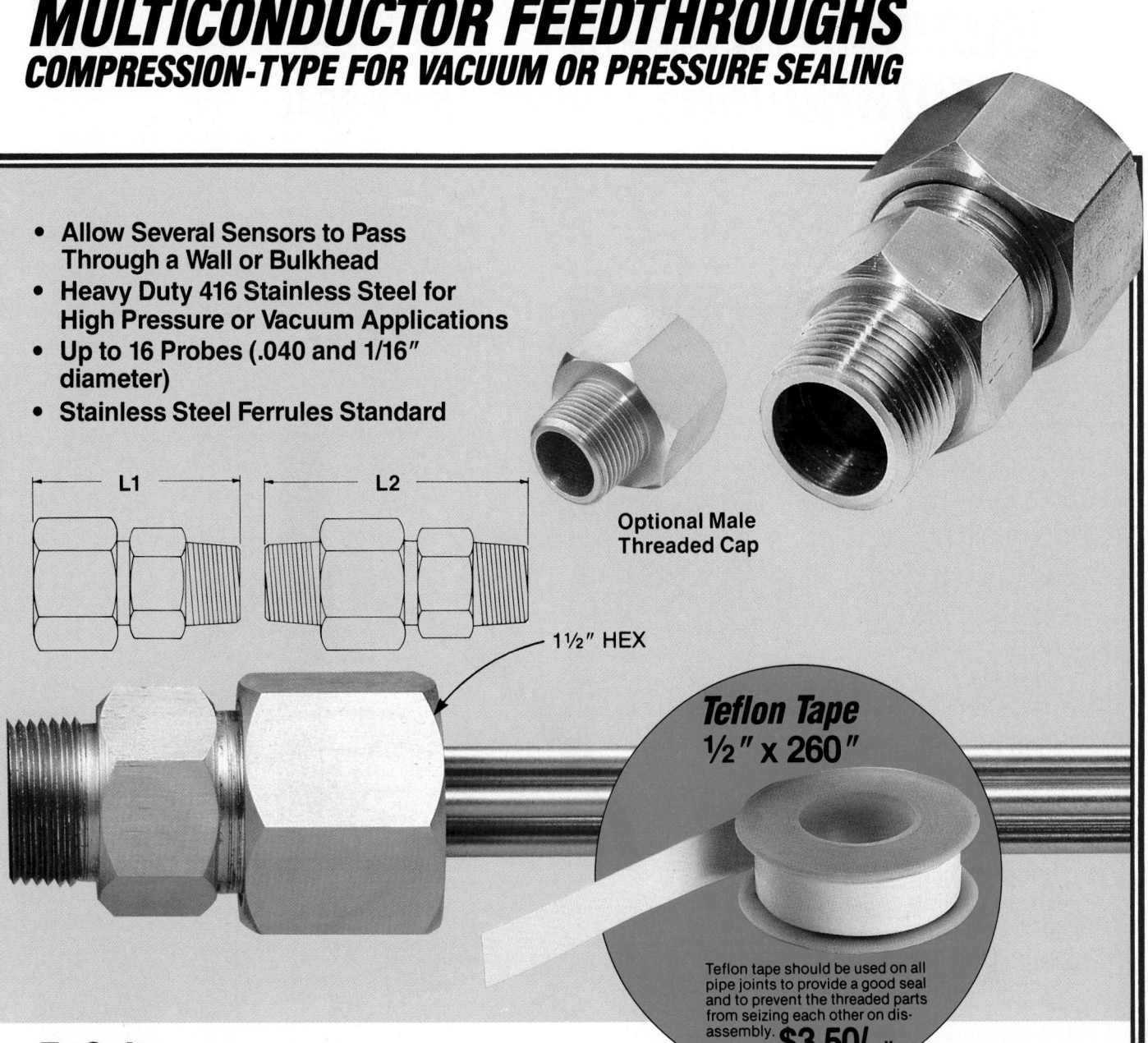

- **Allow Several Sensors to Pass Through a Wall or Bulkhead**
- **Heavy Duty 416 Stainless Steel for High Pressure or Vacuum Applications**
- **Up to 16 Probes (.040 and 1/16″ diameter)**
- **Stainless Steel Ferrules Standard**

L1   L2

Optional Male Threaded Cap

1½″ HEX

Teflon Tape
½″ x 260″

Teflon tape should be used on all pipe joints to provide a good seal and to prevent the threaded parts from seizing each other on disassembly. **$3.50/roll**

ACCESSORIES **C**

To Order

Sheath Diameter	Catalog Number	Diameter of Probe Inches	Number of Probes	Thread NPT	Length		Housing	Cap	Price
					L1	L2			
.040″	MFT-040-3	.040″	3	¼″	2″	2½″	¾″	⅞″	$ 89
	MFT-040-5	.040″	5	¼″	2″	2½″	¾″	⅞″	105
	MFT-040-6	.040″	6	½″	2⅝″	3⅜″	1⅛″	1⅜″	113
	MFT-040-8	.040″	8	½″	2⅝″	3⅜″	1⅛″	1⅜″	129
	MFT-040-10	.040″	10	¾″	2¹³⁄₁₆″	3½″	1¼″	1½″	145
	MFT-040-12	.040″	12	¾″	2¹³⁄₁₆″	3½″	1¼″	1½″	161
	MFT-040-16	.040″	16	¾″	2¹³⁄₁₆″	3½″	1¼″	1½″	177
1/16″	MFT-116-3	.062″	3	¼″	2″	2½″	¾″	⅞″	79
	MFT-116-5	.062″	5	¼″	2″	2½″	¾″	⅞″	95
	MFT-116-6	.062″	6	½″	2⅝″	3⅜″	1⅛″	1⅜″	103
	MFT-116-8	.062″	8	½″	2⅝″	3⅜″	1⅛″	1⅜″	119
	MFT-116-10	.062″	10	¾″	2¹³⁄₁₆″	3½″	1¼″	1½″	135
	MFT-116-12	.062″	12	¾″	2¹³⁄₁₆″	3½″	1¼″	1½″	151
	MFT-116-16	.062″	16	¾″	2¹³⁄₁₆″	3½″	1¼″	1½″	167
1/8″	MFT-18-3	.125″	3	½″	2⅝″	3⅜″	1⅛″	1⅜″	73
	MFT-18-4	.125″	4	½″	2⅝″	3⅜″	1⅛″	1⅜″	79
	MFT-18-6	.125″	6	¾″	2¹³⁄₁₆″	3½″	1¼″	1½″	91
	MFT-18-8	.125″	8	¾″	2¹³⁄₁₆″	3½″	1¼″	1½″	97
3/16″	MFT-316-3	.188″	3	½″	2⅝″	3⅜″	1⅛″	1⅜″	75
	MFT-316-5	.188″	5	¾″	2¹³⁄₁₆″	3½″	1¼″	1½″	87
1/4″	MFT-14-3	.250″	3	¾″	2¹³⁄₁₆″	3½″	1¼″	1½″	75

VACUUM/PRESSURE FEEDTHROUGHS HERMETIC FACE SEAL

From $**425**

- ✔ **2000 PSI Pressure Rating**
- ✔ **10⁻⁸ Torr Vacuum Rating**
- ✔ **Copper and Thermocouple Wire**
- ✔ **8 Wire Pairs for 8 Thermocouples**
- ✔ **Teflon insulated Wire**
- ✔ **Nitrile O-Ring and Jam Nut**
- ✔ **Each Unit Tested for Reliability**

CHEMICAL EXPOSURE
Compatible: oils, solvents, refrigerants, water, non-corrosive gases

Avoid: strong acids and bases

Specifications

Material: 300 series SS; nitrile o-ring

Maximum Pressure: 2000 PSI

Leak Rates, Pressure: 1×10^{-6} cc air/s at 2000 PSI; 1×10^{-7} cc air/s at 29″ Hg vacuum

Vacuum Limit: 1×10^{-8} Torr

Leak Rates, Vacuum: 1×10^{-8} cc He/s at 15 PSI; 1×10^{-8} cc He/s at 10^{-8} Torr

Temperature Limits: −40 to 250°F (−40 to 120°C)

Out Gassing: < 0.003% VCM; < 0.34% weight loss; sample at 125°C, surface at 25°C

Wire: 20 AWG solid with Teflon insulation; 48″L, −200 to 200°C rating

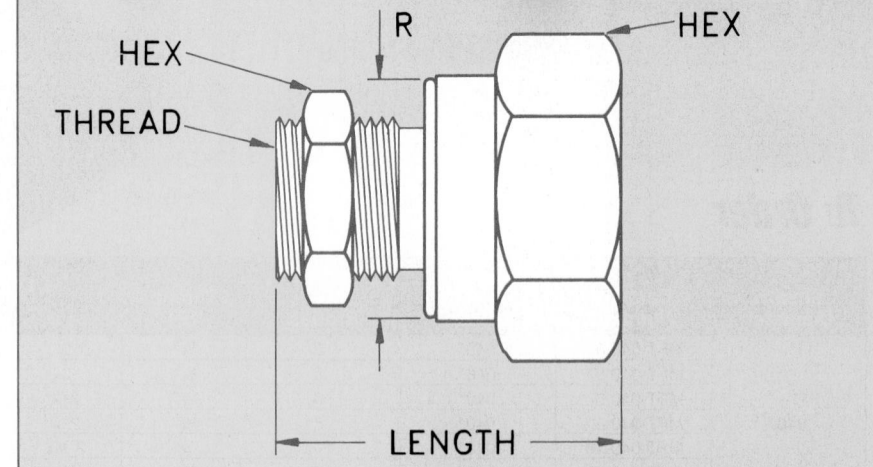

Area	Thread	Across Flats Hex	O-Ring Face R	Length	Max. Plate Thickness With Nut	Without Nut
0.357″	1 1/16 -12	1.50″	1.324″	1.19″	0.06	0.56″

To Order (Specify Model Number)

Model No.	Price	Wire	No. of Pairs
PFTFS-8CU	$425	Cu	8
PFTFS-8(*)	470	T/C	8

* Specify Thermocouple type: J, K, T or E
Ordering Example: PFTFS-8K, **$470.** Hermetic feedthrough, face seal design, for 8 type K thermocouples.

VACUUM/PRESSURE FEEDTHROUGHS HERMETIC FACE SEAL

MADE IN
USA

- ✔ **Copper and Thermocouple Wire**
- ✔ **1, 2 and 4 Wire Pairs**
- ✔ **Teflon insulated Wire**
- ✔ **10^{-8} Torr/120 PSI Rating**
- ✔ **Each Unit Tested for Reliability**

½" NPT Plug

From **$100**

½" NPT Couple

From **$115**

CHEMICAL EXPOSURE
Compatible: oils, solvents, refrigerants, water, non-corrosive gases

Avoid: strong acids and bases

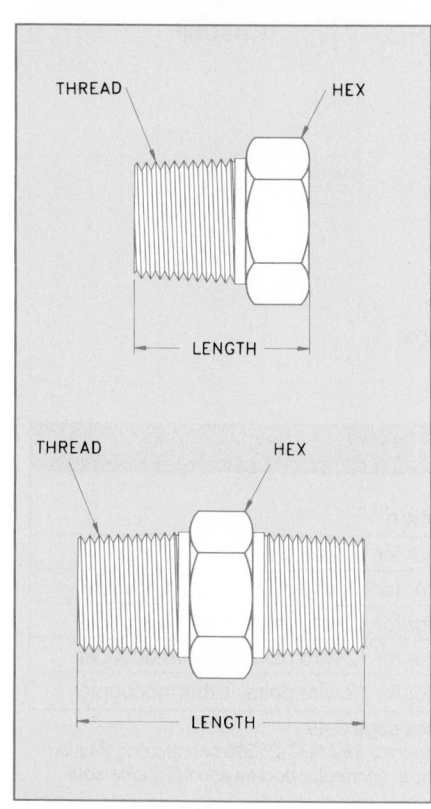

½" NPT Plug

½" NPT Couple

Specifications
Material: Brass
Maximum Pressure: 120 PSI
Leak Rates, Pressure: 1 x 10^{-6} cc air/s at 120 PSI; 1 x 10^{-7} cc air/s at 29" Hg vacuum
Vacuum Limit: 1 x 10^{-8} Torr
Leak Rates, Vacuum: 1 x 10^{-8} cc He/s at 15 PSI; 1 x 10^{-8} cc He/s at 10^{-8} Torr

Temperature Limits: −40 to 250°F (−40 to 120°C)

Out Gassing: < 0.003% VCM; < 0.34% weight loss; sample at 125°C, cold surface at 25°C

Wire: 20 AWG solid with Teflon insulation; 48" L, −200 to 200°C rating

Model Type	Area	Thread	Hex	Length
PFT2NPT	0.189"	½" NPT	0.88"	1.09"
PFT2CPL	0.189"	½" NPT	0.88"	1.89"

To Order *(Specify Model Number)*

Model No.	Price	Wire	No. of Pairs	Description
PFT2NPT-1CU	$60		1	
PFT2NPT-2CU	80	Cu	2	½" NPT Plug
PFT2NPT-4CU	120		4	
PFT2NPT-1(*)	75		1	
PFT2NPT-2(*)	95	T/C	2	½" NPT Plug
PFT2NPT-4(*)	140		4	
PFT2CPL-2CU	100	Cu	2	½" NPT Couple
PFT2CPL-4CU	155		4	
PFT2CPL-2(*)	115	T/C	2	½" NPT Couple
PFT2CPL-4(*)	175		4	

* Specify Thermocouple type: J, K, T or E
***Ordering Example:** PFT2CPL-4K, **$175.** Hermetic seal feedthrough, ½" NPT couple design, for 4 wire pairs for 4 type K thermocouples.*

ACCESSORIES C

VACUUM/PRESSURE FEEDTHROUGHS
HERMETIC SEAL MULTI-PIN CONNECTOR

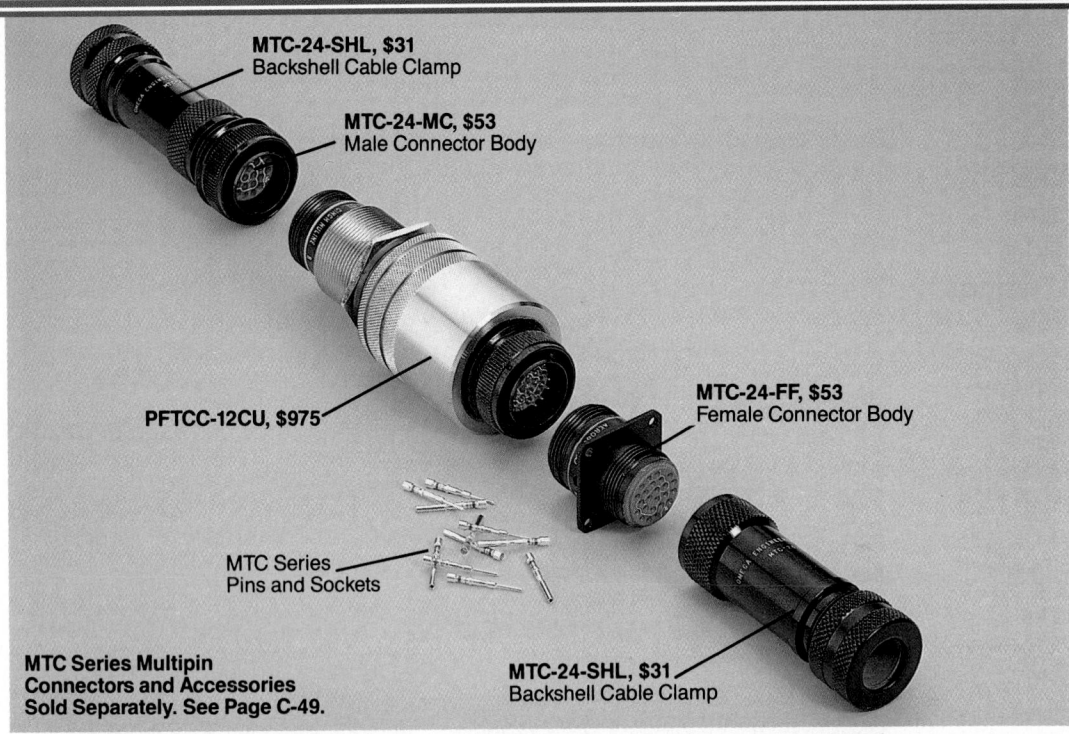

MTC-24-SHL, $31
Backshell Cable Clamp

MTC-24-MC, $53
Male Connector Body

PFTCC-12CU, $975

MTC Series
Pins and Sockets

MTC-24-FF, $53
Female Connector Body

MTC-24-SHL, $31
Backshell Cable Clamp

MTC Series Multipin
Connectors and Accessories
Sold Separately. See Page C-49.

**Fits Mil C-26500
Series Connectors**
From **$975**

✔ **Thermocouple Alloy or Copper Pins**
✔ **Fast Positive Connections**
✔ **Fully Compatible with OMEGA "MTC" Series Connectors**
✔ **100% Inspected and Tested**

Chemical Exposure
Compatible: Oils, Solvents, Refrigerants, Water, Non-Corrosive Gases
Avoid: Strong acids and bases

Specifications
Material: Housing and Nut, 300 Series stainless steel; connector shell, electroless nickel plated O-ring: Butyl Pins, fits 20-24 AWG wire
Pressure Rating: Maximum pressure: 120 PSI; Vacuum limit: 1×10^{-8} Torr
Leak Rates, Pressure: Leak rate at 120 PSI: 1×10^{-6} cc air/sec; Leak rate at 29 in. Hg vac: 1×10^{-7} cc air/sec
Leak Rates, Vacuum: Leak rate at 15 PSI: 1×10^{-8} cc He/sec; Leak rate at 10^{-8} Torr: 1×10^{-8} cc He/sec
Temperature Limits: $-40°$ to $225°$ F ($-40°$ to $120°$ C)
Out Gasing: $< 0.003\%$ VCM $< 0.4\%$ Weight loss; Sample at $125°$ C, cold surface at $25°$ C

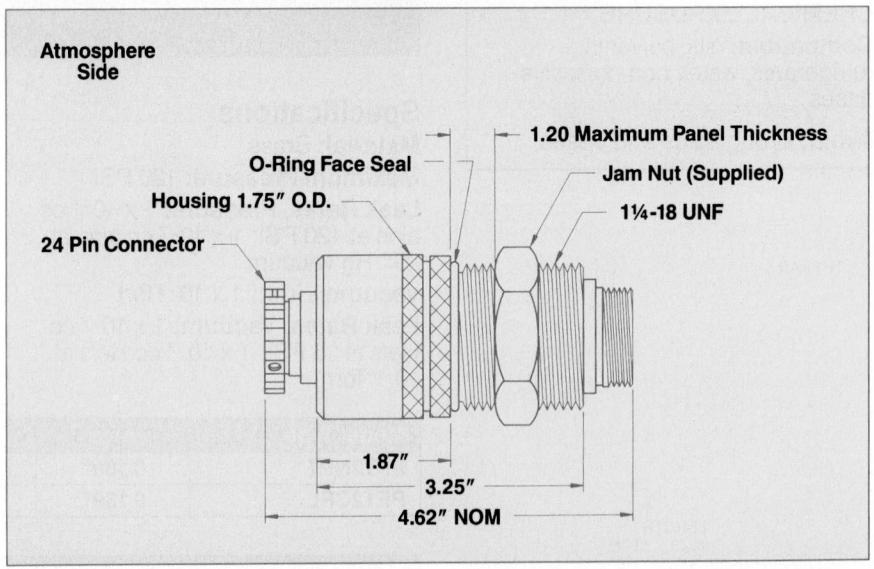

Atmosphere Side

1.20 Maximum Panel Thickness

O-Ring Face Seal

Jam Nut (Supplied)

Housing 1.75" O.D.

1¼-18 UNF

24 Pin Connector

1.87"

3.25"

4.62" NOM

	Price	
Model No.	**(pins included)**	**Description**
PFTCC-12CU	$ 975	Connector for 12 wire pairs, Cu
PFTCC-12J	2650	Connector for 12 wire pairs, J thermocouple
PFTCC-12K	2650	Connector for 12 wire pairs, K thermocouple
PFTCC-12E	2650	Connector for 12 wire pairs, E thermocouple
PFTCC-12T	2650	Connector for 12 wire pairs, T thermocouple

To Order (Specify Model Number)

PFTCC connectors are for use with MTC series pins, see page C-49.
Ordering Example: *PFTCC-12K,* **$2650***. Multipin connector for MIL C-26500 connectors, 24 pin. Compatible with 12 type-K thermocouples, cable clamps, connector bodies and MTC pins sold separately, page C-49.*

MADE IN USA

From $90 THERMOCOUPLE PASSTHRUS
STANDARD AND MINIATURE SIZES
PTS and PTM Series

✔ **Stainless Steel Housing**

✔ **Glass-Filled Nylon Connector**

✔ **100 PSI Pressure Limit**

✔ **Available in J, K, T, E Calibrations and Uncompensated**

✔ **6 Termination Styles Available**

The OMEGA thermocouple passthrus let you measure temperature through a sealed environment. They can be used in sealing moderate pressures (or vacuums) in many different applications, including sealed environments,

48″ Teflon Coated Lead Wires

Screw Terminals

Male Thermocouple Connector
Standard or Subminiature Size

hyperbaric chambers, etc. Rated from −40 to 300°F, these passthrus have either a ½″ NPT fitting with subminiature (SMP) connector, or ¾″ NPT fitting with standard size (OST) connector.

Thermocouple passthrus are available in 6 different Styles; the "front-end" termination can accept either male or female mating connectors, while the "back-end" can be either Teflon coated wire, a male thermocouple connector, or screw terminals. Teflon wire models have 48″ leads of 24 AWG wire.

ACCESSORIES C

To Order (Specify Model No.) *HIGHLIGHTED MODELS STOCKED FOR FAST DELIVERY*

Model No.	Price	Connector Size	Front-End Connection	Back-End Connection
PTM-1-(*)	$90		female	48″ lead wire
PTM-2-(*)	90		male	
PTM-3-(*)	90	Subminiature	female	submini male
PTM-4-(*)	90	Type SMP	male	connector-SMP
PTM-5-(*)	90		female	screw
PTM-6-(*)	90		male	terminals
PTS-1-(*)	105		female	48″ lead wire
PTS-2-(*)	105		male	
PTS-3-(*)	105	Standard	female	standard male
PTS-4-(*)	105	Type OST	male	connector-OST
PTS-5-(*)	105		female	screw
PTS-6-(*)	105		male	terminals

* Specify calibration, J, K, T, E, R/S, or U

Ordering Example: PTM-1-K, **$90.** Miniature passthru for type K thermocouples Accepts subminiature male connector (type SMP) and has 48″ Teflon coated lead wires.

THERMOCOUPLE CONNECTORS
MULTIPIN DESIGN

- ✓ **Rated to 392°F (200°C)**
- ✓ **Removable Crimp Contacts**
- ✓ **20-24 AWG Stranded Wire**
- ✓ **Aluminum Shells**
- ✓ **Black Anodized Finish**
- ✓ **Threaded Coupling**
- ✓ **Thermocouple Alloy Pins**
- ✓ **Air and Moisture Resistant Connection**

Shown with In-Line Cord Connector with Optional Backshell Cable Clamp

For Five Cavity Female Flanged Connector— Pins Sold Separately

From
$41

Rugged Flanged Body for Bulkhead and Chassis Mounting

ALTHOUGH MTC PINS DO NOT CARRY A MIL. SPEC. NUMBER, THEY DO MEET THE PERFORMANCE REQUIREMENTS OF MIL-C-26500E AND ARE INTERMATEABLE WITH MIL-C-26500 CONNECTORS. OMEGA sturdy multipin connectors provide an efficient means of joining multiwire thermocouple cables. They can be used with multiple OMEGA extension wire for rapid, convenient connections and dismantling of apparatus without handling individual sensors.

When used with the MTC Series pins, the connector design utilizes a combination of resilient and rigid dielectric insulators to eliminate internal air voids and prevent the passage of air and moisture into or through the connector. Connectors can withstand ambient temperatures to 392°F (200°C), contributing to an extended connector life.

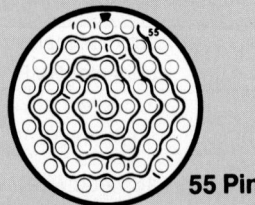

5 Pin   **12 Pin**

24 Pin   **41 Pin**

55 Pin

Contact cavities are identified with a spiral guide line indicating cavity sequence. The first and last cavities are numbered and every tenth cavity is bracketed.

Style FF

Flange mounted receptacle with threaded coupling. Uses sockets only.

Styles MC and FC

In-line cord connectors with threaded couplings. Style MC uses Pins, style FC uses sockets.

Multipin Connector Bodies*

Number of Cavities	MC Male Cord	Price	FC Female Cord	Price	FF Female Flanged	Price	Backshell Cable Clamp**	Price
5	MTC-5-MC	$43	MTC-5-FC	$50	MTC-5-FF	$41	MTC-5-SHL	$34
12	MTC-12-MC	46	MTC-12-FC	59	MTC-12-FF	46	MTC-12-SHL	30
24	MTC-24-MC	53	MTC-24-FC	61	MTC-24-FF	53	MTC-24-SHL	31
41	MTC-41-MC	63	MTC-41-FC	73	MTC-41-FF	63	MTC-41-SHL	36
55	MTC-55-MC	69	MTC-55-FC	81	MTC-55-FF	66	MTC-55-SHL	33

Contacts not included. Order from next page.
*** Backshell cable clamps provide effective support for the cable at the male or female connector and prevent twisting and pulling.*

THERMOCOUPLE CONTACTS
PRECISION SCREW MACHINED

- ✔ Crimp-Type Attachment
- ✔ Contacts are Color Coded
- ✔ Accessories Available
- ✔ High Performance Design

OMEGA push-in crimp style contacts are manufactured from thermocouple alloy materials and color-coded for easy identification. Contacts are crimp terminated outside the connector assembly and inserted into the appropriate cavity by means of an insertion tool. They can be readily removed from the connector assembly using a special removal tool. Sealing plugs are available to seal unused positions in lieu of pin or socket.

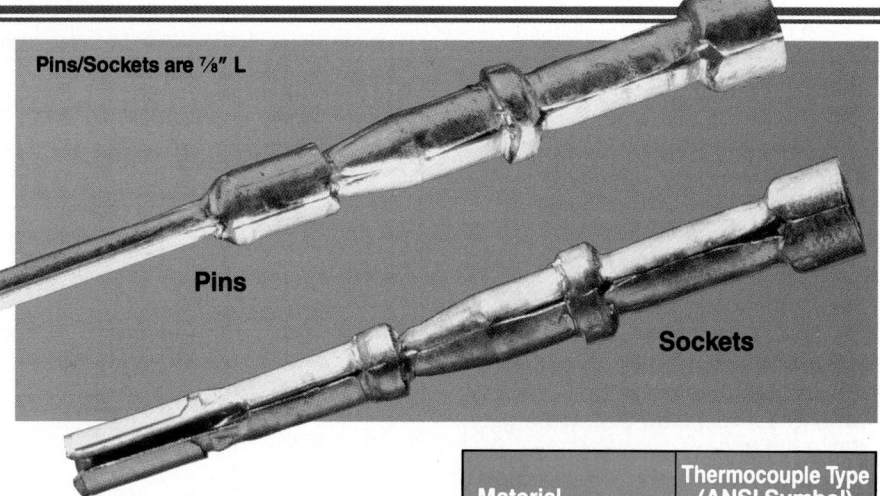

Pins/Sockets are ⅞" L

Pins

Sockets

Material	Thermocouple Type (ANSI Symbol)
Iron/Constantan	J
Chromega/Alomega	K
Copper/Constantan	T
Chromega/Constantan	E

Thermocouple Alloy and Gold Plated Copper Contacts for Multipin Connectors

Alloy Type	Pins (Male)	Coding Color Letter		Price Each	Sockets (Female)	Coding Color Letter		Price Each
Iron (+)	MTC-IR-P	BLK	M	$15	MTC-IR-S	BLK	M	$25
Constantan (−)	MTC-CO-P	YEL	N	25	MTC-CO-S	YEL	N	25
Copper (+)	MTC-CU-P	RED	C	20	MTC-CU-S	RED	C	20
Chromega™ (+)	MTC-CH-P	WHT	P	17	MTC-CH-S	WHT	P	25
Alomega™ (−)	MTC-AL-P	GRN	R	17	MTC-AL-S	GRN	R	25
*Gold Plated (Uncompensated)	MTC-AU-P	Color Bands RED, YEL, BRN		.75	MTC-AU-S	Color Bands RED, BLU, BLK		1.25

Sealing Plug, model MTC-HP, $.50 each
*For use with non-thermocouple wire in same body. Grommets available. Consult sales for price and delivery.

† Pins have red, yellow, brown color bars, sockets have red, blue, black color bars

Heavy Duty Crimping Tool

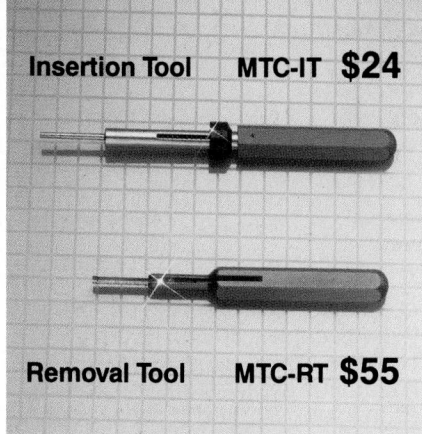

MTC-CT $192

Ratchet Action Easy-to-Use!
Specially designed MS standard crimping tool MUST be used to properly crimp wires to pins and sockets. Ratchet action ensures a complete crimp every time.

Assembly Tools

Insertion Tool MTC-IT $24

Removal Tool MTC-RT $55

To Order:

Specify Connector Body, Contacts and Backshell (See Note 1).
Example: Cord to Cord connectors for 6 type J (Iron-Constantan) thermocouple circuits (pairs).
Male Connector Assembly
1. Body: MTC-12-MC
2. Pins:
   (+) Pos. Alloy, MTC-IR-P, 6 ea.
   (−) Neg. Alloy, MTC-CO-P, 6 ea.
3. Backshell: MTC-12-SHL
Female Connector Assembly
1. Body: MTC-12-FC
2. Sockets:
   (+) Pos. Alloy, MTC-IR-S, 6 ea.
   (−) Neg. Alloy, MTC-CO-S, 6 ea.
3. Backshell: MTC-12-SHL

Important Notes

1. MS Standard Assembly Tools are required to properly crimp and assemble connectors. Order with first purchase.
2. Match Pins and Sockets to Thermocouple Alloys
Example: A 12 cavity connector carries 6 thermocouple circuits (pairs) requiring: 6 positive alloy pins or sockets and 6 negative alloy pins or sockets per body.
3. Order bodies in Mating Pairs. Style MC mates with both style FF and style FC.
4. Backshell Cable Clamps are recommended with each cord style connector.

INTRINSIC SAFETY

INTRODUCTION

Intrinsically safe equipment is defined as "equipment and wiring which is incapable of releasing sufficient electrical or thermal energy under normal or abnormal conditions to cause ignition of a specific hazardous atmospheric mixture in its most easily ignited concentration." (ISA-RP12.6) This is achieved by limiting the amount of power available to the electrical equipment in the hazardous area to a level below that which will ignite the gases.

In order to have a fire or explosion, fuel, oxygen and a source of ignition must be present. An intrinsically safe system assumes the fuel and oxygen is present in the atmosphere, but the system is designed so the electrical energy or thermal energy of a particular instrument loop can never be great enough to cause ignition.

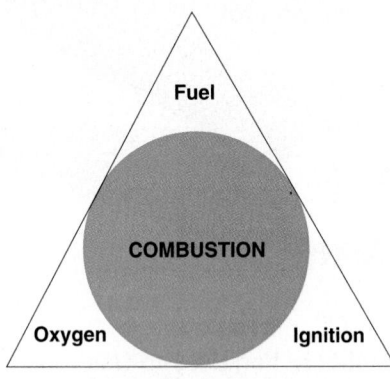

Traditionally, protection from explosion in hazardous environments has been accomplished by either using EXPLOSION PROOF apparatus which can contain an explosion inside an enclosure, or PRESSURIZATION or purging which isolates the explosive gas from the electrical equipment. Intrinsically safe apparatus cannot replace these methods in all applications, but where possible can provide significant cost savings in installation and maintenance of the equipment in a Hazardous area.

The basic design of an intrinsic safety barrier uses Zener Diodes to limit voltage, resistors to limit current and a fuse.

APPLICATIONS

A Hazardous Area may contain flammable gasses or vapors,

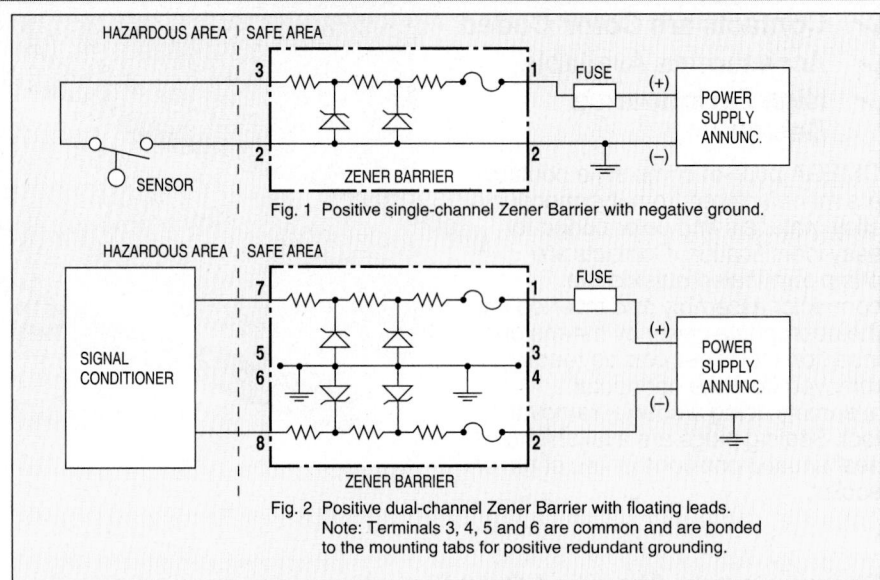

Fig. 1 Positive single-channel Zener Barrier with negative ground.

Fig. 2 Positive dual-channel Zener Barrier with floating leads.
Note: Terminals 3, 4, 5 and 6 are common and are bonded to the mounting tabs for positive redundant grounding.

combustible dusts, or ignitable fibers or flyings. There are different systems used in Europe or the United States to classify the type of hazard and whether the Hazard is always present or only present in an emergency condition such as a spill or failure of venting equipment. (refer to Pages Z-79, 80 in The Complete Temperature Measurement and Control Handbook and Encyclopedia® for U. S. Classifications). In most cases the equipment is designed for the worst case, which would be to assume the explosive atmosphere is always present and the electrical or thermal energy is the lowest required to cause a fire or explosion.

Most applications require a signal to be sent out of or into the hazardous area. The equipment mounted in the hazardous area must first be

hazard is not and will not be present.

Equipment which has been designed for and is available for use in hazardous areas with intrinsically safe barriers includes:

- 4-20 mAdc Two Wire Transmitters
- Thermocouples
- RTD's
- Strain Gages
- Pressure, Flow, & Level Switches
- I/P Converters
- Solenoid Valves
- Proximity Switches
- Infrared Temperature Sensors
- Potentiometers
- LED Indicating Lights
- Magnetic Pickup Flowmeters

Most of the apparatus that is mounted in the Hazardous area will have to be approved and certified for use in the Hazardous area with an approved barrier designed for use with that

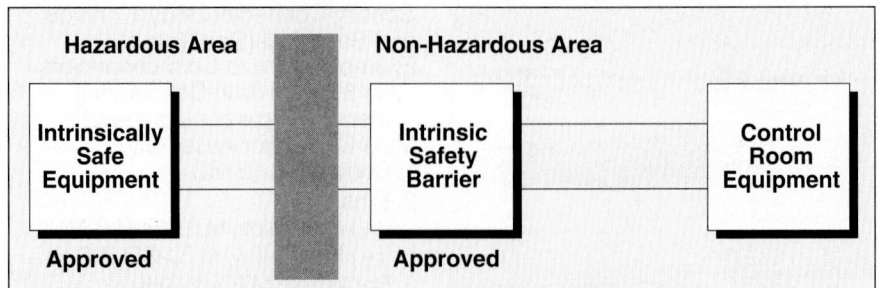

approved for use in an intrinsically safe system. The barriers designed to protect the system must be mounted outside of the hazardous area in an area designated as Non-hazardous or Safe in which the

apparatus. Some simple devices like thermocouples, RTD's, LED's and contacts can be used in the hazardous area without certification as long as it is wired in conjunction with an approved barrier.

APPROVALS

Intrinsic safety equipment must have been tested and approved by an independent agency to assure its safety. The customer should specify the type of approval required for their particular application. The most common Agencies involved are as follows:

COUNTRY	AGENCY
USA	FM, UL
CANADA	CSA
GREAT BRITIAN	BASEEFA
FRANCE	LCIE
GERMANY	PTB
ITALY	CESI
BELGIUM	INEX

NOTE: approval by any of the above European Agencies constitutes a CENELEC approval allowing the units to be considered approved in many of the European countries.

Products to be mounted in the hazardous area can be approved either under the LOOP or ENTITY approval concept.

The LOOP concept specifies the exact part number and products that can be used in the loop. No deviation from the specified units is allowed.

The ENTITY concept specifies parameters which any approved intrinsic safety barrier must meet. This allows the user to select barriers from different approved manufacturers.

Under entity approval two items may be interconnected if the following conditions are met (refer to chart at right):

For Additional Information on OMEGA's New Intrinsic Safety Barriers, Request Bulletin # Intrinsic.

TM

OMEGA offers the SBG Series Single & Dual Channel Zener Barriers and Solid State Relays For Intrinsic Safety, From $70

HAZARDOUS AREA		NON-HAZARDOUS (SAFE) AREA
Intrinsically Safe Approved Apparatus	must be	Intrinsically Safe Barrier
Vmax	less than	Voc
Imax	less than	Isc
La	greater than	Li + Lw
Ca	greater than	Ci + Cw

Where:
Vmax = Maximum Open Circuit Voltage
Imax = Maximum Short Circuit Current
L = Maximum Unprotected Inductance
Ci = Maximum Unprotected Capacitance
Voc = Maximum Open Circuit Voltage (barrier)
Isc = Maximum Short Circuit Current (barrier)
La = Maximum Allowed Inductance (barrier)
Ca = Maximum Allowed Capacitance (barrier)
Lw = Inductance of interconnecting wiring
Cw = Capacitance of interconnecting wiring

In all cases the intrinsically safe barriers and equipment MUST be wired per an approved drawing. Capacitance and inductance of the wiring and cables must be included in the loop evaluation.

ACCESSORIES C

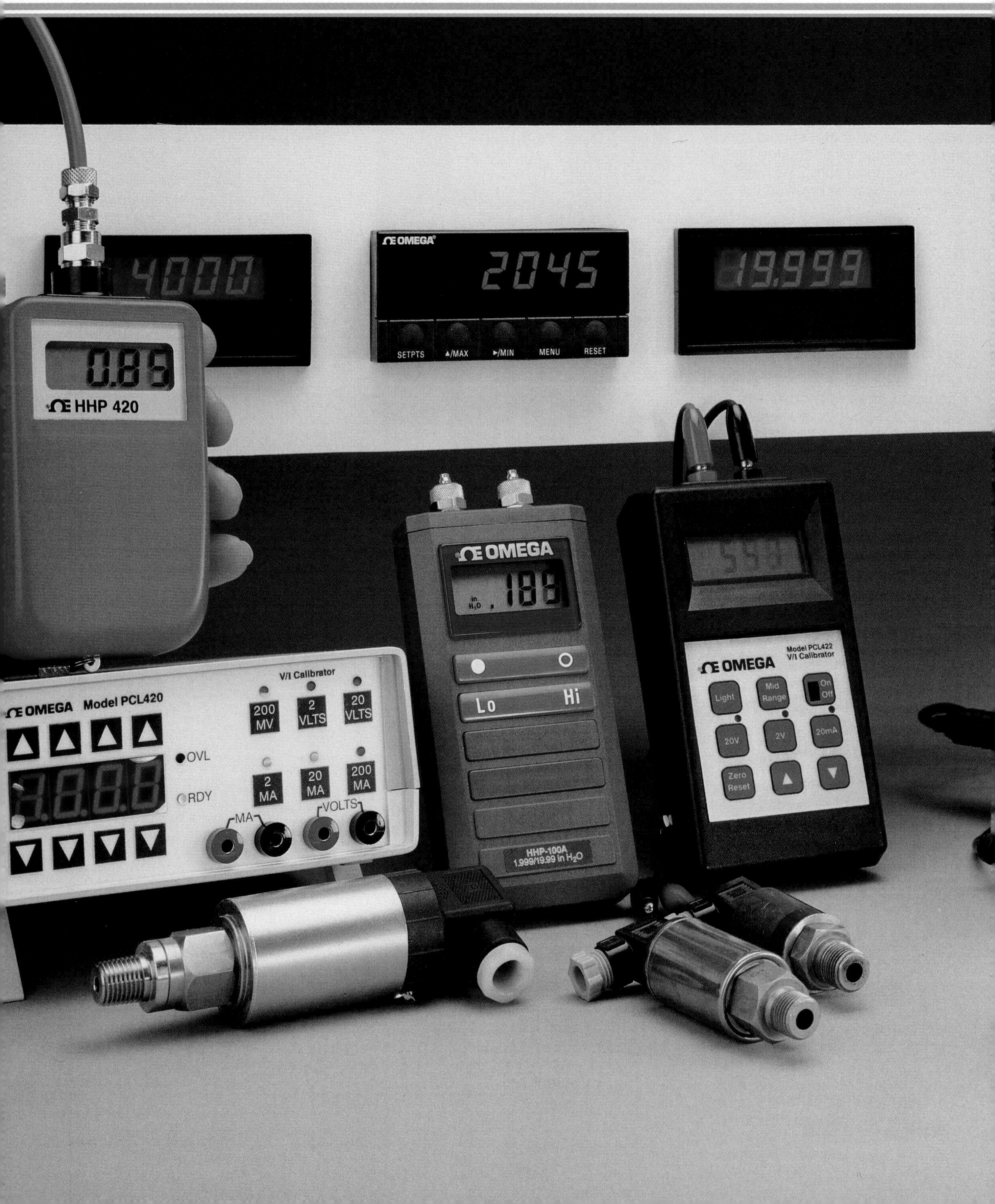

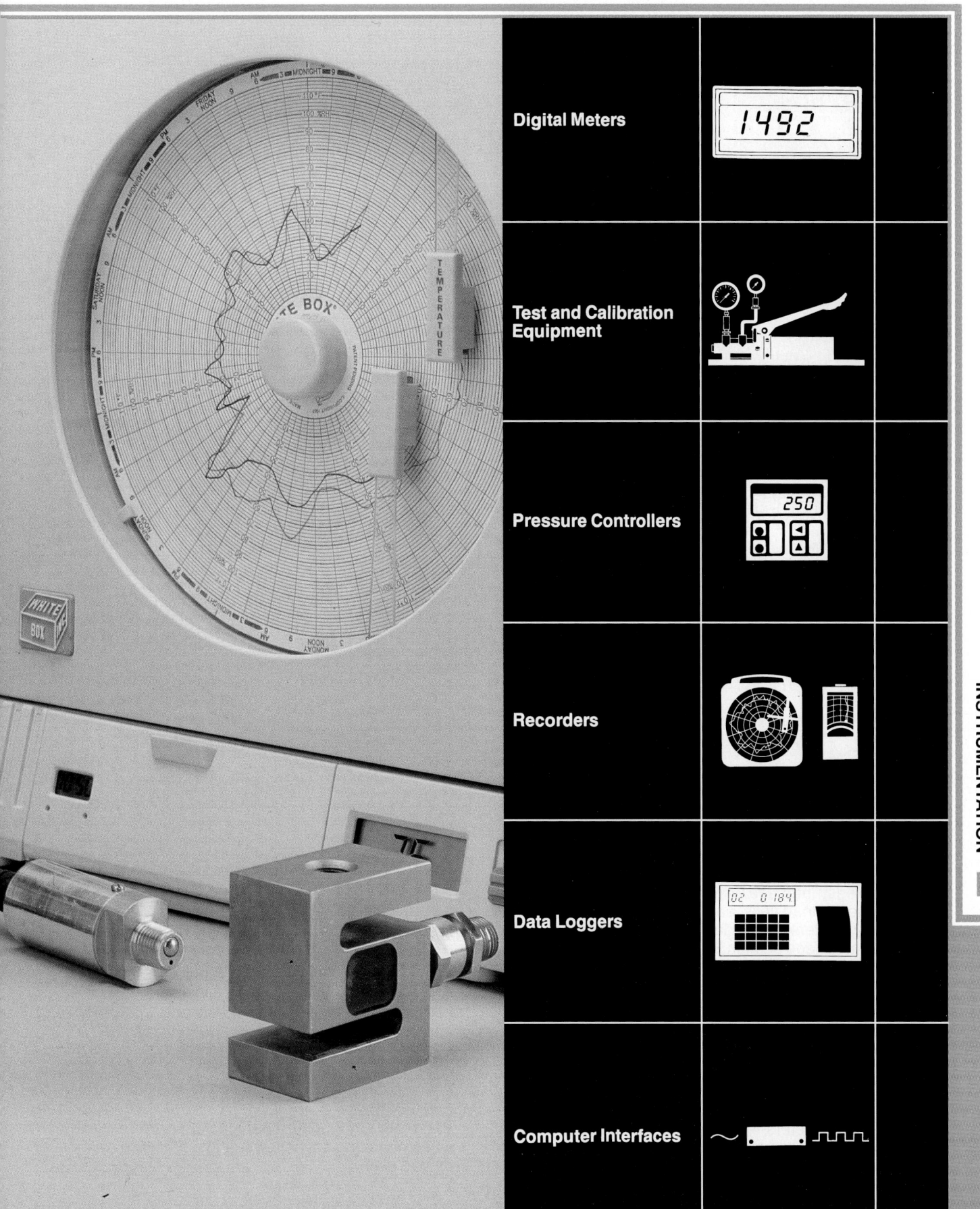

Digital Meters

Test and Calibration Equipment

Pressure Controllers

Recorders

Data Loggers

Computer Interfaces

INTRODUCTION TO PRESSURE MEASUREMENT INSTRUMENTATION

Is there a readout device for every type of transducer?

Yes, the instrumentation throughout this section will provide easy interface with the available pressure transducers, load cells, and strain gages. Additionally, specialty meters are available for strain gage applications (see section E).

What types of instrumentation are available for my application?

Selecting the appropriate instrument requires a complete understanding of the parameters of your application. A brief explaination follows, which describes the different types of available instrumentation.

digital panel meters—provide direct indication of pressure or force in engineering units; many include an excitation power supply.

test and calibration equipment—allows testing and adjustment of a pressure system against a known standard

controllers—monitors and maintains a process level

recorders—(circular, strip chart, XY) provide a permanent analog recording of the process variable

data loggers—store data in a digital format and provides a hard copy of the process variables

computer interface—for complete data acquisition and analysis in stand-alone or computer controlled configurations

How do I select an instrument to work with my pressure transducer?

There are three determinant factors to be considered when matching an instrument to a pressure transducer or load cell.

1) the output of the transducer
2) the engineering units to be displayed
3) the system electrical requirements

How does the transducer output effect my choice of instrumentation?

While selecting your instrumentation, keep in mind that the input range of the instrument must be compatible with the output signal of the transducer. There are three main transducer outputs; millivolts (mV), Volts (V), and milliamps (mA). This general rule can help narrow your selection.

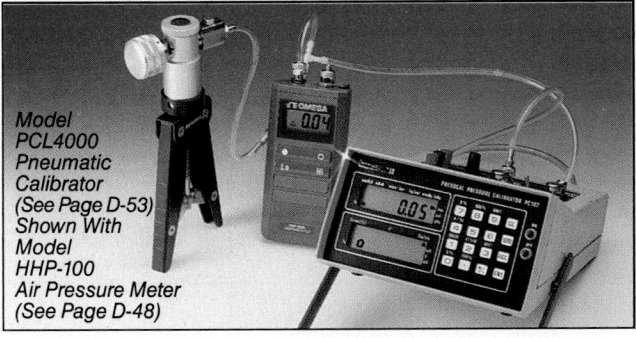

Model PCL4000 Pneumatic Calibrator (See Page D-53) Shown With Model HHP-100 Air Pressure Meter (See Page D-48)

Can I scale my instrument to read in custom engineering units?

The ability of an instrument to display in custom engineering units is dependant upon its sensitivity or gain. To determine the gain required, divide the full scale display (regardless of decimal points) by the output span of the transducer.

example: PX 176-100S 5V is a 100 PSI transducer that you wish to display in 1/10 PSI increments. The span of the display of the readout meter is 1000 counts. The output of the PX 176 is 1-6 volts over its 100 PSI range. Therefore the output span is 5 volts. The meter gain required is 1000 counts divided by 5 volts or 200 counts per volt.

According to this example, the instrument you select must accept an input of 6 volts and have a sensitivity or gain of 200 counts per volt.

Models DP302 and DP30002 See Secton B for Transducers (See Page D-19)

Model PCL-200-KIT-A (See Page D-51)

What additional features are available with the instrumentation?

Depending upon the specific model, the following features can be standard or optional to the instrumentation.

1) power supply—for transducer excitation.
2) alarms—to indicate exceeded limits or for on/off control.
3) analog output—signal conditioning for recorders or additional instrumentation.
4) min/max—display peaks and valleys over time
5) digital output—for computer interface

How can I calibrate my pressure system?

There are two different types of calibration equipment available, electronic digital gauges and precision dead weight testers.

electronic digital gauges—completely self contained transducer/readout device for comparison of the pressure within your system to the electronic pressure standard. These standards can be supplied with N.B.S traceability and some models can also monitor the electronic signal from the transducer.

precision dead weight tester—provides an accurately known pressure to the system for comparison. Also supplied with N.B.S traceablity.

How can I feed the output signal from my pressure transducer to a computer for storage and analysis?

The computer interface products should be selected in the same manner as other instrumentation, insuring the compatibility of the transducer with the instrument. The computer interface equipment can be divided into two distinct groups, those which utilize an RS-232 port for communications with any host computer, and plug-in cards which are dedicated for use with a specific computer.

DIGITAL METER SELECTION GUIDE

			FEATURES			
METER SERIES	PAGE NO.	PRICE STARTS AT	INPUT	NO. OF DIGITS	ACCURACY	VDC EXCITATION
DP41 Series	D-7	$345	mV, V, mA	6	0.005%	10 or 24
DP87/DP88	D-9	629	mV	5	0.01%	5, 10, 15
DP2000S/DP9000S	D-11	391	mV	3½ or 4	0.05%	1 to 10
DP2000P/DP9000P	D-12	301	mV, V, mA	3½ or 4	0.05%	N
DP2000H	D-13	356	hz	3½	0.05%	N
DP350	D-15	425	mV	3½	0.05%	5, 10
DP354	D-16	330	V	3½	0.05%	1.3 to 24
LDP2/LDP4	D-17	1050	All Types	4	0.05%	N
DP302 Series	D-19	187	mV, V, mA	3½	0.05%	Optional
DP3002 Series	D-19	259	mV, V, mA	4½	0.01%	Optional
DP760/770 Series	D-20	755	mV, V, mA	5½	0.05%	5, 10, 15
DP205 Series	D-21	199	mV, V, mA	4	0.02%	10 or 24
DP460 Series	D-22	229	mV, V, mA	4	0.02%	Optional
DP100 Series	D-23	295	mV, V, mA	3½	0.025%	Optional
DP110 Series	D-23	340	mV, V, mA	4½	0.025%	Optional
HHP-SG	D-25	575	mV	3½	0.1%	2.46
DPS3200 Series	D-26	695	mV, V, mA, T/C	4	0.5%	N
DP3400 Series	D-27	295	T/C	4	±2°C	N
DP3600/3700/3800	D-28	295	mV, V, mA	4	0.025%	N
DPF-64	D-29	220	V, mA	5½	0.15%	Y
DPF50 Series	D-30	139	mV, V, mA	3½	0.05%	Optional
TX81	D-33	229	mA	3½	0.1%	N
TX21	D-34	145	mA	3½	0.1%	N
TX82	D-35	165	mA	3½	0.1%	N
CN2000 Series	D-37	455	mV, V, mA	Counts to 3200	0.06%	Optional
CN4400 Series	D-39	190	V, mA, T/C, RTD	4	0.5%	N
DP434	B-96	430	mV	3½	0.1%	8.2
DP409	B-96	395	mV	Analog	2.0%	8.2

ALARMS	OTHER	COMMUNICATION OPTIONS			POWER OPTIONS	
		ANALOG OUTPUT	BCD OUTPUT	RS-232	230 VAC	VDC OPTIONS
Optional	Min/Max/Tare/Adjustable Filtering	Y	Y	Y	Y	N
Optional	Dual Engineering Units	Y	Y	Y	N	9-16, 18-32
Optional	Multiple Options See page D-13	STD	Y	N	Y	5, 9-32
Optional	Multiple Options See Page D-13	STD	Y	N	Y	5, 9-32
Optional	Used with Frequency Output & Flow Transducers	STD	Y	N	Y	5, 9-32
Optional	Optional Dummy Zero	STD	N	N	Y	N
N	Optional Dummy Zero	N	N	N	Y	N
N	Large Display (2¼" or 4" Digits)	Y	N	N	Y	N
N	Economical 3½ Digit Meter	N	N	N	Y	9-32
N	Economical 4½ Digit Meter	N	N	N	Y	9-32
Y	High Speed Sampling	Y	N	Y	Y	10-30
Y	Analog Output and Dual Alarms	STD	N	N	N	N
Optional	Multiple Inputs	N	N	N	Y	N
Optional	Minimum and Maximum	Y	N	Y	Y	N
Optional	Minimum and Maximum	Y	N	Y	Y	N
N	Handheld Meter	N	N	N	9 volt battery only	
Optional	7 Channel Display Scanner	N	N	N	Y	7.5 to 12
Optional	Min/Max/Rate	Y	N	N	Y	7 to 12
Optional	Min/Max/Rate/Tare	Y	N	N	Y	7.5 to 12
Y	Ratemeter, Totalizer	N	N	N	Y	N
N	Miniature Case	N	N	N	Y	7-32
N	Loop Powered, NEMA-13 Enclosure	N	N	N	N/A	N/A
N	Loop Powered	N	N	N	N/A	N/A
N	Loop Powered	N	N	N	N/A	N/A
Y	PID/Controller	N	N	Y	Y	N
Optional	PID/Controller	N	N	N	Y	N
Optional	Indicators for Melt Pressure Control	STD	N	N	Y	N
Optional	Indicators for Melt Pressure Control	STD	N	N	Y	N

HIGH PERFORMANCE PROCESS INDICATORS WITH BUILT-IN TRANSDUCER EXCITATION

DP41 Series From $345

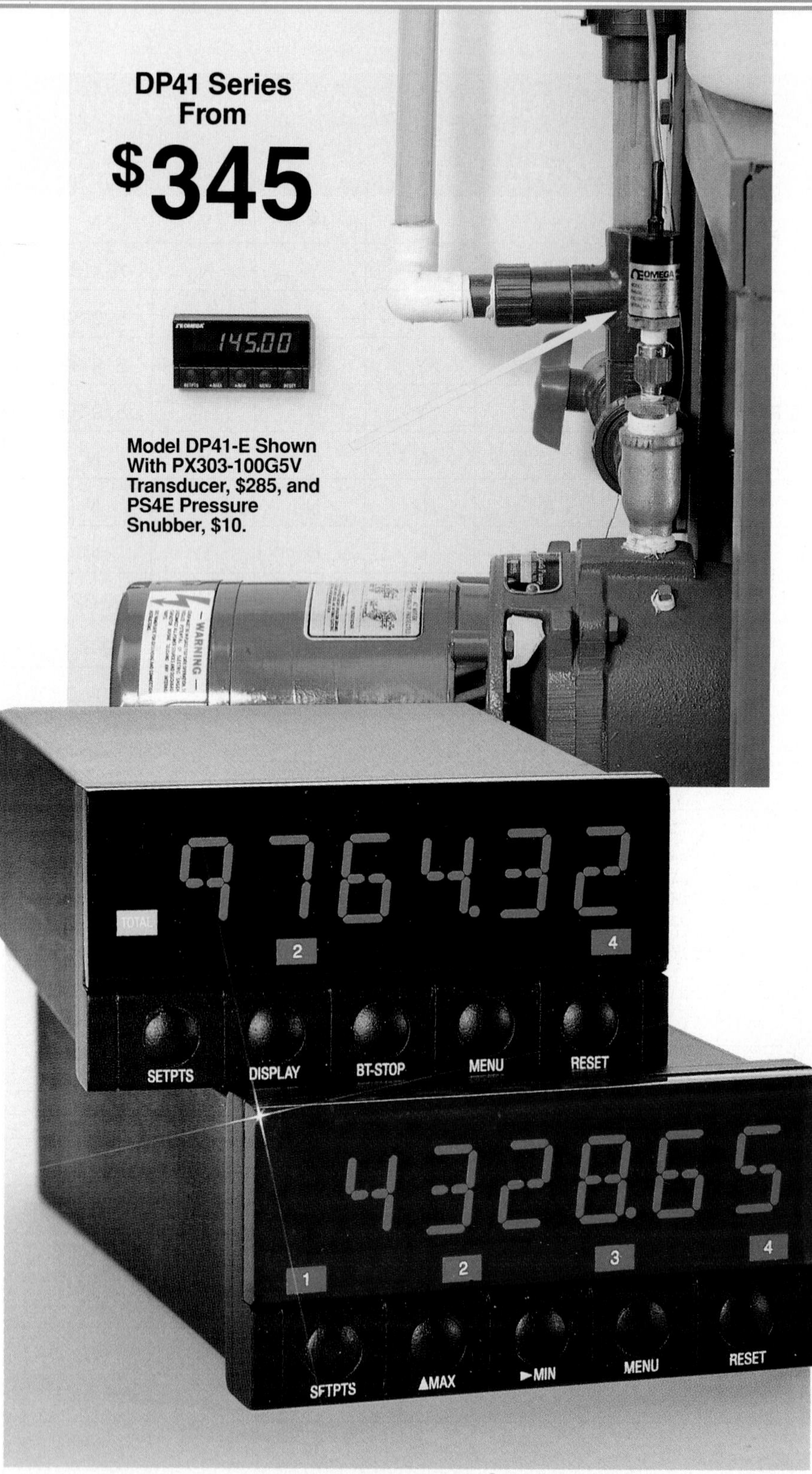

Model DP41-E Shown
With PX303-100G5V
Transducer, $285, and
PS4E Pressure
Snubber, $10.

✔ **DP41-E Works with Voltage or Current Output Transducers**

✔ **DP41-S Works with Strain Gage Bridge Sensors or Ratiometric Voltage Sensors**

✔ **Adjustable Filtering Up to 13 Hz**

✔ **Displays Up to 999,999 Counts**

✔ **Remote Tare, Min, Max, Reset and Hold Features**

✔ **Min/Max (Peak/Valley) Detection**

✔ **Standard 4 Alarms/Controller Outputs**

✔ **Optional BCD Output**

✔ **Optional Scalable Analog Output**

✔ **Optional Bi-Directional RS-232 or RS-485 Communciations**

✔ **NEMA 4 Front Panel**

The OMEGA DP41 Series indicators offer exceptional performance at an economical price. The DP41-E and DP41-S both have standard built in sensor excitation. The DP41 Series input range is selected via internal jumpers, and the scaling is performed utilizing the front key pad.

The DP41-E accepts voltage, current and potentiometer inputs. The DP41-S accepts strain gage bridge sensors, and ratiometric voltage measurements.

Programming the DP41 is accomplished through the 5 front panel keypads. If the optional RS-232 or RS-485 communications are installed, the operator may remotely set the display parameters.

Options to the DP41 include analog and BCD outputs, alarm/control outputs and RS-232 or RS-485 communications. Analog outputs are configurable for one of the following outputs: 0-20 mA, 4-20 mA, 0-5 Vdc, or 0-10 Vdc. The RS-232 or RS-485 communications options are bi-directional, allowing the user to configure the DP41 as well as read the current, max. and min. values. While each DP41 comes standard with 4 open collector outputs, the optional DP40-RELAY board provides dual 7A mechanical relays.

SPECIFICATIONS

Input Types: DP41-E, 0-20 mA, 4-20 mA, 0-1V, 0-10V, 0-100V, ±50 mV, ±500 mV, ±5 V, ±50 V; DP41-S, same voltage ranges as DP41-E but for ratiometric measurements.

DP41 MODELS ARE ALSO AVAILABLE WITH THERMOCOUPLE, RTD AND FREQUENCY INPUT, FOR MEASURING TEMPERATURE, FLOW, pH AND OTHER PROCESSES. CONSULT SALES FOR DETAILS.

NEW!

Excitation: DP41-E, 10 Vdc @ 30 mA or 24 Vdc @ 25 mA; DP41-S, -U, 1.25 to 10 Vdc (5 Vdc @ 60 mA, 10 Vdc @ 30 mA) or 24 Vdc @ 25 mA

Accuracy: 0.005% Rdg

Resolution: 100,000 parts

Span Adjustment: 1-999,999 counts

Offset Adj.: −99,999 to 999,999 counts

Filtering: Adj to 13 Hz

Remote Contacts: hold, min, max, reset, (tare DP41-S only)

Outputs: 4 open collectors, 150 mA sink @ 1 Vdc, 30 Vdc max; Optional 2 additional SPDT relays 7 amp @ 230 Vac; Deadband fully adjustable

Operating Ambient Range: 32 to 122°F (0 to 50°C), 95% RH, non-condensing

Storage Temperature: −40 to 185°F (−40 to 85°C)

Span Temp. Coefficient: 20 ppm/c

Step Response: 36 ms for 63%, 145 ms for 98%, 218 ms for 99.8%

Warmup to Rated Accuracy: 5 min.

A/D Conversion: dual slope technique

Display: 6-digit, 14-segment LED, red or green; 0.56″ H (14.2 mm); indicator lights for alarms and status modes

Connections: inputs screw terminal; Remote inputs terminal pins

RS-232 Communications (optional): 300/1200/2400/4800/9600/19.2k baud; RJ11 4-wire connection; complete program setup and message display capability; programmable to transmit current display, alarm status, min/max, actual measured input value (not scaled) and status

RS-485 Communications (optional): 300/1200/2400/4800/9600/19.2k baud; RJ11 6-wire connection; addressable from 0 to 199

Analog Output (optional): Selectable 0-5 Vdc, 1-5 Vdc, 0-10 Vdc, 0-20 mA, 4-20 mA; voltages @ 20 mA, current @ 12 Vdc

Power: 115 or 230 Vac, 49-440 Hz (DC power optional)

Power Consumption: 10 Watts max.

Isolation: 354 V

NMRR: 60 dB

CMRR: 120 dB

Common Mode Voltage: 1500 V peak per Hv test

Dimensions: 1.89″ H x 3.78″ W x 6.13″ D (48 x 96 x 156 mm)

Panel Cutout: 1.772″ H x 3.622″ W (45 x 92 mm); 1/8 DIN

Weight: 1.27 lb (574 g)

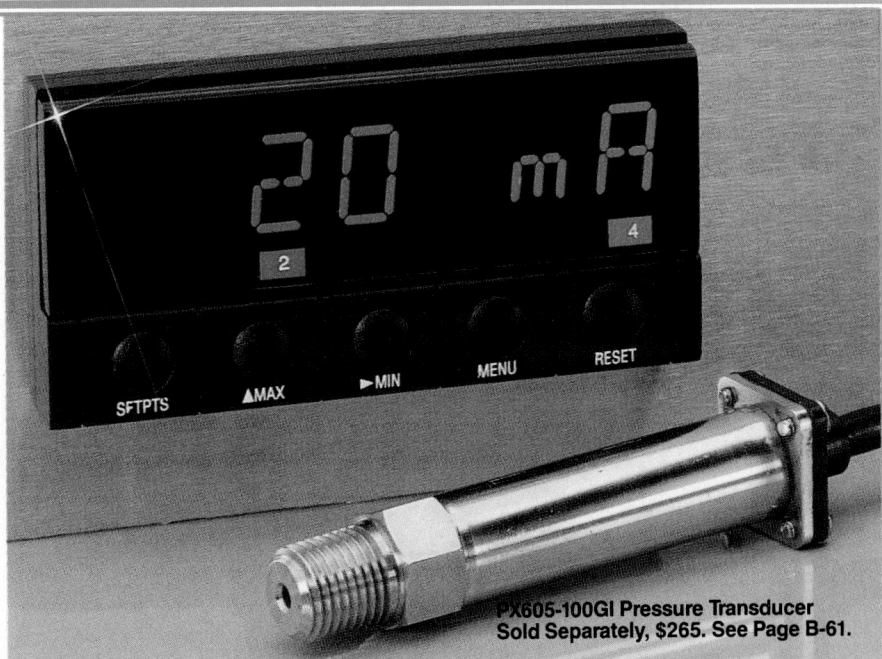

PX605-100GI Pressure Transducer Sold Separately, $265. See Page B-61.

To Order *(Specify Model Number)*

Model No.	Price	Description
DP41-E	$345	Process Meter (voltage/current inputs)
DP41-S	395	Strain Gage Meter (millivolt/voltage inputs)
DP41-TC	345	Temperature Meter (thermocouple inputs)
DP41-RTD	345	Temperature Meter (RTD inputs)
DP41-U	425	Universal Meter (accepts all inputs above)

To order with 230 Vac power, add suffix ''-230'' to Model No. No add'l cost. To order with green display, add suffix ''-GN'' to Model No. add $11 to price.

Control/BCD Outputs/Analog Output

Suffix	Model No.	Price	Description
-A	**DP40-A**	$ 60	Scalable Analog Output
-B	**DP40-B**	110	Isolated BCD Output Board
-R	**DP40-R**	60	Dual 7A Mechanical Relays

Note: Order either DP40-B or DP40-R. Both options are not available in one unit. Use Suffix for options installed in meter, use Model No. for field installable options.

Computer Communications

Suffix	Model No.	Price	Description
-S2	**DP40-S2**	$60	Isolated RS-232 Communications
-S4	**DP40-S4**	80	Isolated RS-485 Communications

Note: Order either DP40-S2 or DP40-S4. Both options are not available in one unit. DP40-S2 and DP40-S4 options come with both 3.5″ and 5.25″ setup/programming disks, and 6′ communications cable with phone plug termination. For proper termination to a computer a 9 pin and 25 pin connector are offered below.

Options

Model No.	Price	Description
DP40-9SC2	$30	9-pin Serial Connector for RS232
DP40-9SC4	30	9-pin Serial Connector for RS485
DP40-25SC2	30	25-Pin Serial Connector for RS232
DP40-25SC4	30	25-Pin Serial Connector for RS485

Ordering Example: *DP41-E-S2A and DP40-9SC: DP41 unit for voltage signal inputs, analog output, RS-232 communications and 9-pin serial connector.*
*$345 + 60 + 60 + 30 = **$495.***

5 DIGIT PRECISION STRAIN GAGE INDICATORS WITH EXCITATION

DP80 Series

99999 LBS

PGM ↑ ↓ ENT

Pressure Transducers and Load Cells Sold Separately See Sections B and F.

Model DP87 Shown

From

$629

MADE IN
USA

- **High Accuracy 0.01% Full Scale**
- **Precise Digital Scaling Through Front Panel Key Pad**

- **Dual Engineering Units Measuring with 3 Character Alphanumeric Labels**
- **Plug-in Options Include Alarms, Math, Analog Outputs, BCD Outputs, RS-232C/20mA, and DC Power**
- **Up to 1 μV/Count Sensitivity**
- **Lock-out Switch Prevents Unauthorized Program Tampering**
- **Power Cord Included**

The OMEGA DP80 Series digital strain gage indicators demonstrate impressive performance for wide compatibility with lower output, bonded foil type transducers, as well as higher output semiconductor type transducers (up to 1000mV). One of four input ranges are selectable within each instrument to optimize the sensitivity. The front panel membrane keypad facilitates accurate digital scaling, eliminating any dip switches, pot adjustments or reference standards. This also allows for drift free scaling to precise engineering units and decimal location. Three alphanumeric LEDs are included for engineering unit labels (e.g. PSI, KG, LBS) or can be

ACCURATELY MEASURES PRESSURE, STRAIN, FORCE, LOAD, THRUST, TORQUE

assigned as "0" for active display of dead zeros.

An additional feature of the DP80 is the inclusion of a primary and secondary engineering units display, both easily selected at the front panel. The secondary display can be any mathematical equivalent to the primary display. When activated this feature converts all programming to the secondary units regardless of the units displayed. For example if alarm points are set up in pounds (LBS) in the primary display, the instrument will convert the alarm point to an equivalent kilograms (KG) if the secondary display is active. System calibration can be accomplished using 3-point "live" load (actual weight on scale) or by entering the appropriate transducer sensitivity (mV/V). The meter can also convert to a voltmeter at the front keypad to facilitate set-up. Auto zero (tare) may be activated at any time via the auto zero menu prompt, or via the key pad. To reduce settling indications on display or outputs, the display may be rounded by 1, 2, 5, 10, or 100 counts via programming menu selection.

A variety of options are available to expand the capabilities of the instrument. These options include Alarms, Math, Analog outputs, BCD outputs, RS-232C/20mA, DC power, and Gross/Net.

SPECIFICATIONS

Excitation Supplies:
DP87: 5, 10, and 15 volts, switch selectable, isolated. Will drive two parallel 350 ohm strain gages @ 15 volts (90mA).
DP88: 5, 10, 15, and 20 volts, switch selectable, isolated. Will drive eight parallel 350 ohm strain gages at 15 volts (350mA).

Accuracy: 0.01% of full scale range, ±1 digit
Repeatability: ±1 digit
Zero Offset: Entire input range
Zero Stability: $0.5\mu V/°C$ no measurable drift with time
Span Stability: 0.005% of reading/°C; 0.1% of reading per year
Normal Mode Noise Rejection: > 60dB @ 50/60 Hz

Common Mode Noise Rejection: > 120dB @ 50/60 Hz
Input Impedance: > 10 Mohm to 500 Mohm depending on range
Display: 8 digits, 14 segment alphanumeric LED's, 0.54" high, and one negative (−) LED at left of LED array
Display Count Rate: ±100,000 active
Reading Rate: 2 readings per second
Overload Protection: 270 Vdc or ac RMS across inputs and input to ground. Power lead to ground 1500 Vdc or ac RMS
Ambient Operating Conditions: 0 to 50°C; 0 to 90% RH non-condensing

Storage Temperature: −40 to 65°C
Input Connections: AC power quick connect; DC power and sensors screw terminals; RS232C DB25 Connector
Case Construction: metal, black anodized, extruded aluminum
Power: 90 to 132 Vac; 48 to 400 Hz
Weight: DP87 4 lbs., DP-88 6 lbs. (without options)
Dimensions, DP87: 67mm H x 136mm W x 250mm D; 68mm H x 138mm W cutout.
Dimensions, DP88: 67mm H x 272mm W x 250mm D; 68mm H x 274mm W cutout.

▶ *HIGHLIGHTED MODEL STOCKED FOR FAST DELIVERY* ◀

To Order *(Specify Model Number)*

MODEL	PRICE	SELECTABLE INPUT RANGE	FULL SCALE DISPLAY MIN. GAIN	MAX. GAIN
DP87* Single Width	$629	−15 to 100mV −30 to 200mV −75 to 500mV −150 to 1000mV	0.10 cts/mV 0.05 cts/mV 0.02 cts/mV 0.01 cts/mV	1000 cts/mV 500 cts/mV 200 cts/mV 100 cts/mV
DP88* Double Width	$799	−15 to 100mV −30 to 200mV −75 to 500mV −150 to 1000mV	0.01 cts/mV 0.05 cts/mV 0.02 cts/mV 0.01 cts/mV	1000 cts/mV 500 cts/mV 200 cts/mV 100 cts/mV

Model DP87 can accommodate one additional option. Model DP88 can accommodate up to four additional options.

Options—Field Installable

MODEL	PRICE	DESCRIPTION
DP80-ALM	$169	Alarms, dual limits (up to 2 per unit) selectable hysteresis and alarm delay
DP80-MTH	99	Math, min., max., average, rate of change
DP80-AOV	169	Analog output, 0 to 10 Vdc isolated, linearized and scalable (n/a DP80-AOC)
DP80-AOC	169	Analog output, 4 to 20 mA isolated linearized and scalable (n/a DP80-AOV)
DP80-BCD	169	BCD output, tri-state, isolated, CMOS, DTL, TTL compatible. Includes mating connector
DP80-SER	249	RS-232C, 20mA serial output. Selectable baud rate from 300 to 9600. Includes DB-25 mating male connector
DP80-GNT	129	Gross/net switch for weighing applications (DP88 only)

DIGITAL TRANSDUCER INDICATORS
WITH EXCITATION FOR MILLIVOLT OUTPUT TRANSDUCERS

MODEL DP2000-S/9000-S INDICATORS FOR MILLIVOLT TRANSDUCERS

ALL RANGES $391 Standard Models

$440 DP9000-S Model

242PC100G
8331

Features

- ✓ ⅛ DIN Case
- ✓ Built-in Excitation
- ✓ 3½ or 4 Digit Display in Engineering Units
- ✓ Zero Offset Adjust Standard
- ✓ Works with Most Millivolt Output Transducers

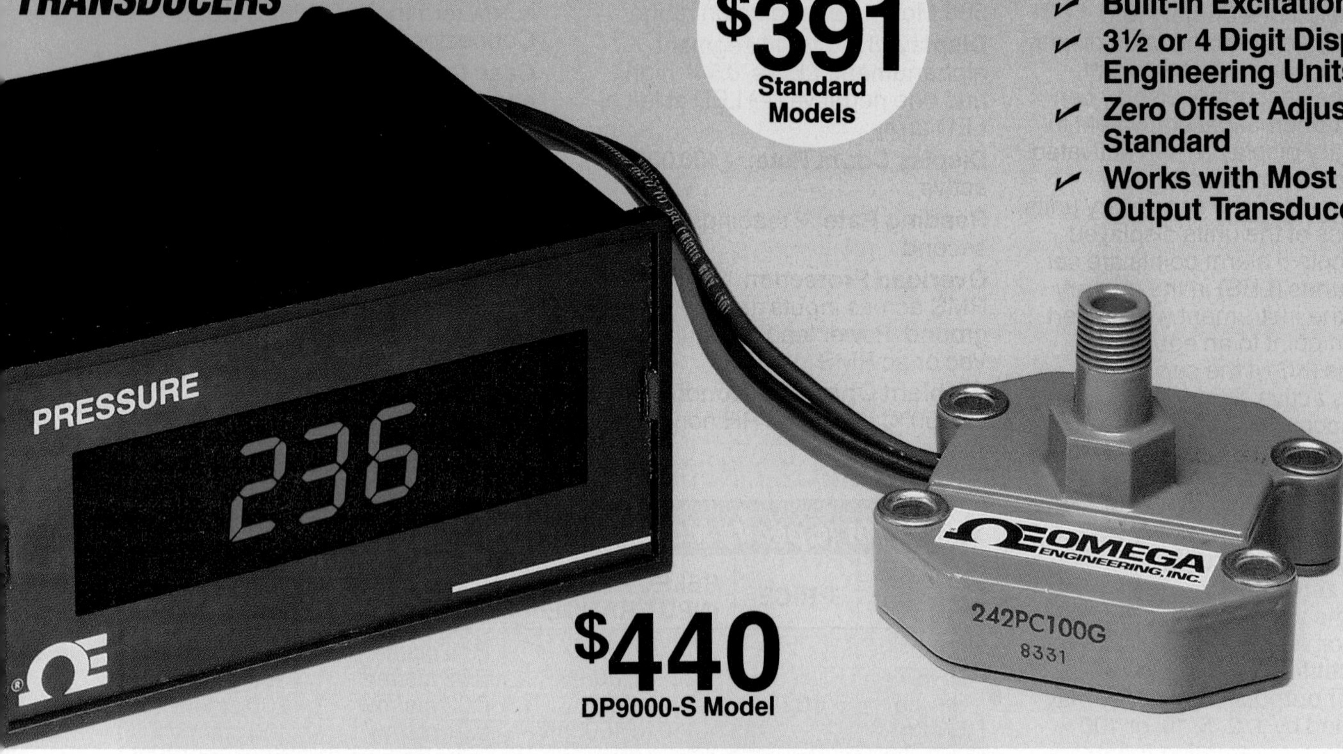

PRESSURE 236

Model Number	Maximum Input Signal	Full Span Display		Compatible Transducers*
		Minimum Gain*	Maximum Gain*	
▶ DP2000-S1	499 mV	4.01 counts/mV	9.9 counts/mV ◀	*Compatible with millivolt output transducers as shown on pages B-3 through B-30. Please refer to the exact transducer desired for the compatible indicator
▶ DP2000-S2	249 mV	8.02 counts/mV	19.8 counts/mV ◀	
▶ DP2000-S3	124 mV	16.10 counts/mV	39.7 counts/mV ◀	
▶ DP2000-S4	62.5 mV	32.00 counts/mV	79.0 counts/mV ◀	
DP2000-S5	31.2 mV	64.20 counts/mV	158.0 counts/mV	
DP2000-S6	15.6 mV	128.00 counts/mV	315.0 counts/mV	
DP2000-S7	7.8 mV	258.00 counts/mV	637.0 counts/mV	
DP9000-S	499 mV	20.1 cts/mV	5000 cts/mV	Field selectable

$$*Gain = \frac{Full\ Span\ Display\ (Counts)}{Input\ Span\ (mV)}$$

To Determine Model Number:
1. Determine display span (in counts) (maximum reading-minimum reading)
2. Determine input span (in mV) (max. input signal-min. input signal)
3. Determine gain; gain = display span/ input span (in counts per mV)
4. Find model number where desired gain is between minimum and maximum values listed.
5. Check compatibility of excitation voltage.

▶ **HIGHLIGHTED MODELS IN STOCK FOR FAST DELIVERY** ◀

Ordering Example:
PX100-050GV TRANSDUCER
Range: 0-50 PSIG
Output: 0-100 mV
Desired Display: 0.0-50.0 PSIG (0-500 counts)
Display Span = 500-0 = 500 counts
Input Span = 100-0 = 100 mV
Gain = 500/100 = 5 counts per mV
Select DP2000-S1, because
4.01 < 5 < 9.9

See Section B for a Full Selection of Transducers
See Section E for a Full Selection of Strain Gages
See Section F for a Full Selection of Load Cells.
For Additional Specifications, Please Refer to Pg. D-14

Millivolt Input

The DP2000-S and DP9000-S have been designed to be compatible with most millivolt output transducers, providing both built-in excitation and a scalable display for engineering units. The DP2000 has a 3½ digit display and can read 1999 counts. The DP9000 has a full 4 digit display, capable of reading ±9999 counts.

SPECIFICATIONS
Zero Offset: ±2.25 mV @ 10 V excitation, 1.1 mV @ 5 V
Excitation: 1 to 10 V @ 30 mA, customer selectable
Accuracy: ±.05 rdg, +1 count (DP2000) ±.05% rdg, + 2 counts (DP9000)
Range Temp. Coefficient: ±.01% rdg/°C
Operating Temperature: 32 to 140°F (0 to 60°C)
Common Mode Rejection Ratio: 120 dB
Normal Mode Rejection Ratio: 150 dB typical @ 50 or 60 Hz
Max Voltage Input: 500 mV
Maximum Sensitivity: 637 counts/mV
CMV: 1500 Vdc, ac to analog ground.
Reading Rate: 2.5 per second
Hook-up: 4 or 6 wire with capability for dead load compensation and calibration function.

DIGITAL TRANSDUCER INDICATORS
FOR VOLTAGE AND CURRENT OUTPUT TRANSDUCERS

Features:

✔ **Compatible with High Level Voltage and Current Output Transducers**

✔ **Wide Zero Offset Capability**

✔ **Scalable Display for Engineering Units**

$301 Standard Models

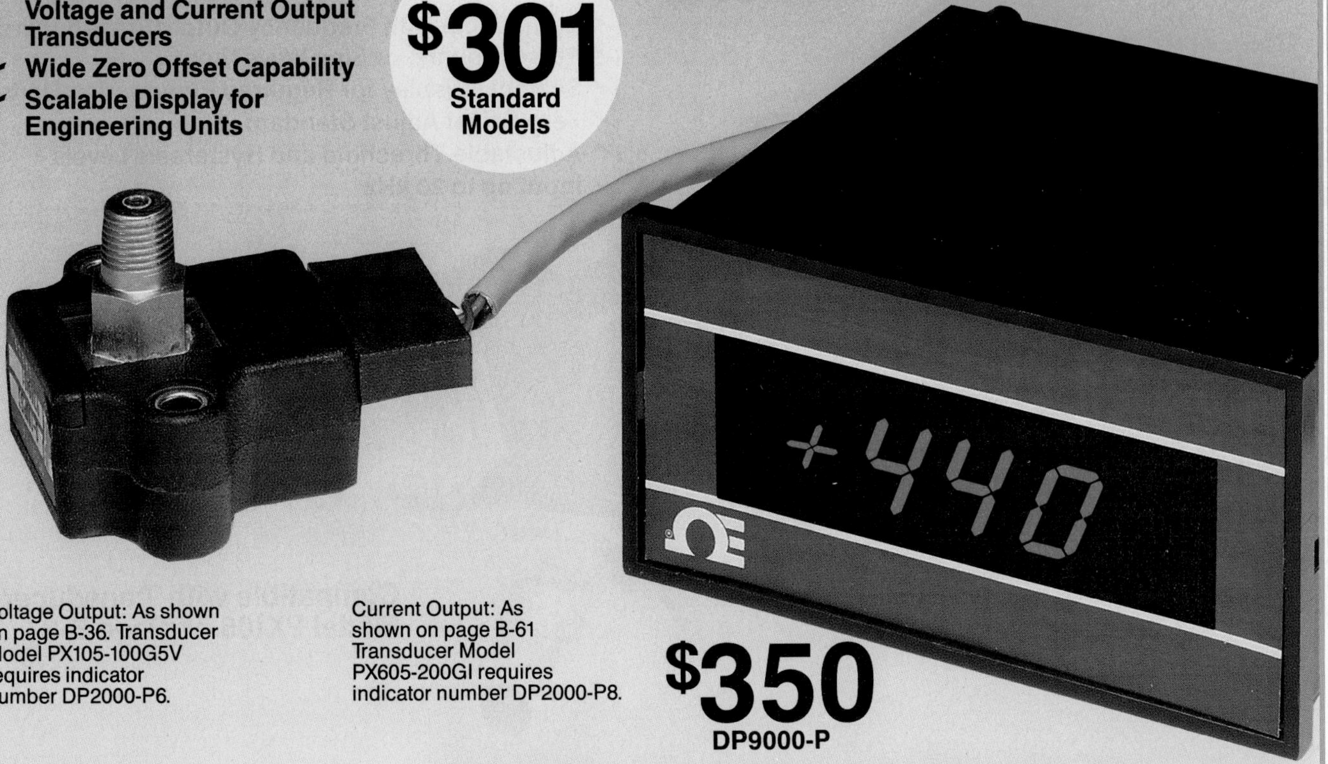

MODEL DP2000-P/9000-P PROCESS INDICATORS

$350 DP9000-P

Voltage Output: As shown on page B-36. Transducer Model PX105-100G5V requires indicator number DP2000-P6.

Current Output: As shown on page B-61 Transducer Model PX605-200GI requires indicator number DP2000-P8.

Specifications

Zero Offset: −3000 to +2100 counts
Excitation: User supplied, see power supplies on pages C-9 through C-11.
Accuracy: ±.05% rdg, +1 count (DP2000-P); ±.05% of rdg, +2 counts (DP9000-P)
Common Mode Voltage: ±1500 V dc, ac to analog ground
Normal Mode Rejection Ratio: 60 dB typical @ 50 or 60 Hz
Input Voltage Drop: 0.4 V full scale
Maximum Voltage Input: 250 V (on voltage input models)
Maximum Current Input: 124 mA (current input models)
Common Mode Rejection Ratio: 120 dB
Range Temp. Coefficient: ±.01% of range/°C
Reading Rate: 2.5 per second
Operating Temperature: 32 to 1140° (0 to 60°C)

To Determine Model Number:
1. Determine display span (in counts) (maximum reading-minimum reading)
2. Determine input span (in mV, V or mA) (max. input signal-min. input signal)
3. Determine gain; gain = display span/ input span (in counts per input signal unit)
4. Determine offset; offset = −(min. input signal x gain)
5. Find model number where desired gain is between minimum and maximum values listed.

Model Number	Max. Input Span	Full Span Display		Compatible Transducers*
		Minimum Gain*	Maximum Gain*	
DP2000-P1	0.5V	0.08 counts/mV	2.85 counts/mV	*Compatible with Voltage output transducers as shown on pages B-41 through B-56. Please refer to the exact transducer desired for the compatible indicator
DP2000-P2	0.5V	2.84 counts/mV	5.55 counts/mV	
DP2000-P3	0.5V	5.49 counts/mV	8.17 counts/mV	
DP2000-P4	5.0V	8.0 counts/Volt	231.0 counts/Volt	
DP2000-P5	5.0V	230.0 counts/Volt	449.0 counts/Volt	
DP2000-P6	10.0V	4.0 counts/Volt	114.5 counts/Volt	
DP2000-P7	10.0V	114.0 counts/Volt	223.0 counts/Volt	
DP2000-P8	4-20 mA	2.5 counts/mA	70.4 counts/mA	*Compatible with current output transducers as shown on pages B-58 through B-86.
DP2000-P9	4-20 mA	70.5 counts/mA	137.0 counts/mA	
DP2000-P10	10-50 mA	1.0 counts/mA	28.2 counts/mA	
DP2000-P11	10-50 mA	28.1 counts/mA	55.0 counts/mA	
DP9000-P	20 V or 50 mA	Selectable mV, V or mA		*Compatible with voltage or current output transducers

Ordering Example:
PX105-100G5V TRANSDUCER
Range: 0-100 PSIG: Output: 1-6 V dc
Desired Display: 0.0-100.0 PSIG (0-1000 counts)
Display Span = 1000-0 = 1000 counts
Input Span = 6-1 = 5 V dc
Gain = 1000/5 = 200 counts per V
Offset = −[200 (cts./V) x 1 (V)] = −200 cts.
Select DP2000-P4, because 8.0 < 200 < 231.0

Voltage and Current Input
The DP2000-P and DP9000-P accept voltage and current inputs from transducers and display readings in the engineering units required by your application. The DP2000 is a 3½ digit display and can read ±1999 counts. The DP9000 has a full 4-digit display capable of reading ±9999 counts.

INSTRUMENTATION

D

DIGITAL TRANSDUCER INDICATORS
FOR FREQUENCY OUTPUT PRESSURE AND FLOW TRANSDUCERS

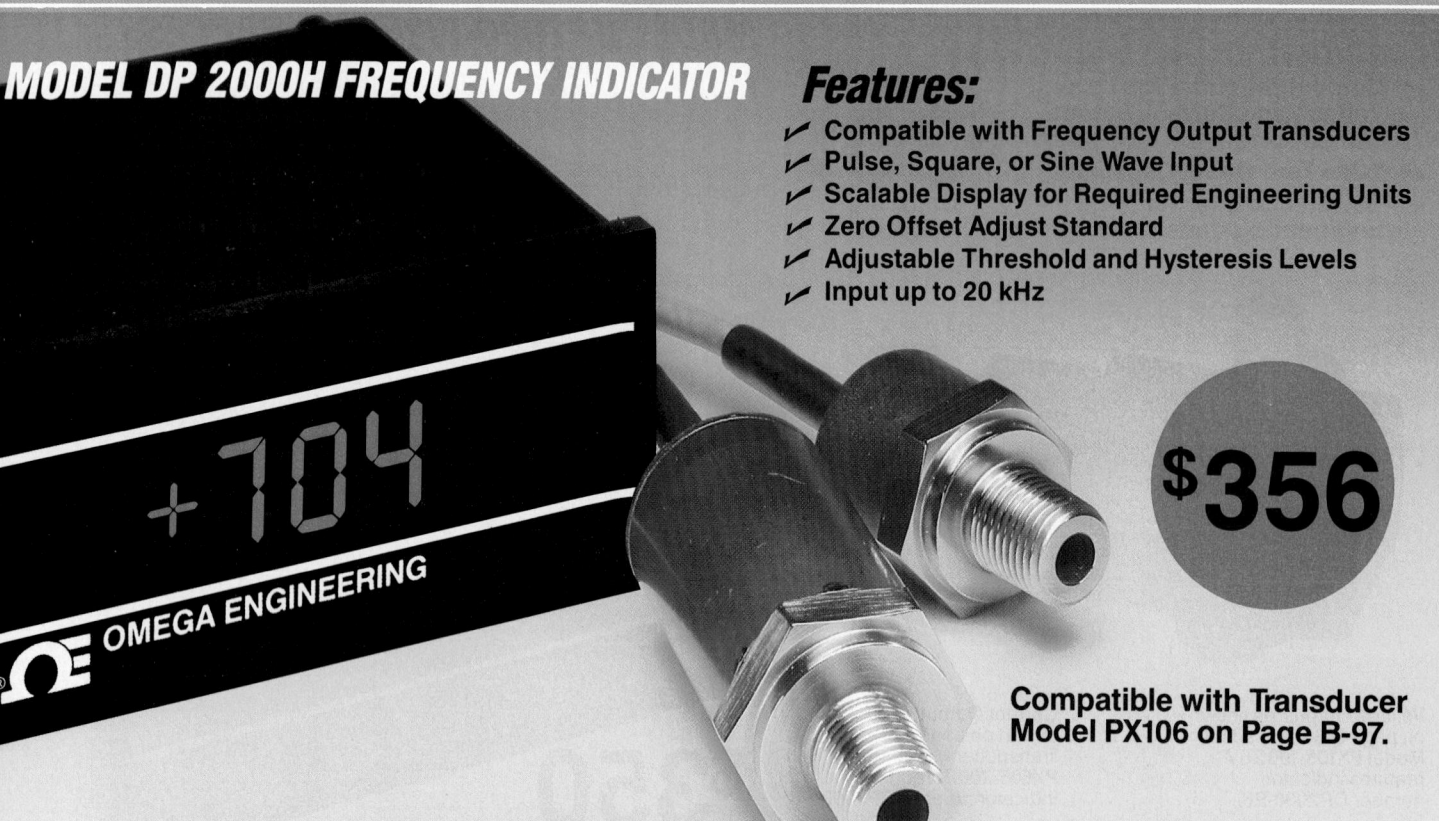

MODEL DP 2000H FREQUENCY INDICATOR

Features:
- ✓ Compatible with Frequency Output Transducers
- ✓ Pulse, Square, or Sine Wave Input
- ✓ Scalable Display for Required Engineering Units
- ✓ Zero Offset Adjust Standard
- ✓ Adjustable Threshold and Hysteresis Levels
- ✓ Input up to 20 kHz

$356

Compatible with Transducer Model PX106 on Page B-97.

Model Number**	Minimum Freq. for Full Scale Display	Minimum Input with:		Full Span Display	
		Low Level* Setting	High Level* Setting	Minimum Gain	Maximum Gain
DP2000-H1	100 to 200 Hz			10 counts/Hz	20 counts/Hz
DP2000-H2	200 to 400 Hz			5 counts/Hz	10 counts/Hz
DP2000-H3	400 to 800 Hz	15 mV P-P		2.5 counts/Hz	5 counts/Hz
DP2000-H4	500 to 1,000Hz		125 mV P-P	2 counts/Hz	4 counts/Hz
DP2000-H5	1,000 to 2,000 Hz			1 count/Hz	2 counts/Hz
DP2000-H6	2,000 to 4,000 Hz	30 mV P-P		.5 counts/Hz	1 count/Hz
DP2000-H7	2,500 to 5,000 Hz			.4 counts/Hz	.8 counts/Hz
DP2000-H8	5,000 to 10,000 Hz	90 mV P-P	175 mV P-P	.2 counts/Hz	.4 counts/Hz
DP2000-H9	10,000 to 20,000 Hz			.1 counts/Hz	.2 counts/Hz

* Low level setting has 10 mV hysteresis, i.e. turnoff signal is 10 mV less than table value. High level setting has 100 mV hysteresis, i.e. turnoff signal is 100 mV less than table value. Units are shipped with high level setting, low level setting may be selected by rear connector jumper.

** Compatible with frequency output transducers as shown on page B-97. Please refer to the exact transducer desired for the compatible indicator.

To Determine Ordering Code
1. Determine Maximum Input Frequency (Hz)
2. Determine Full Scale Span required (maximum reading-minimum reading).
3. Determine Gain = $\dfrac{\text{Display}}{\text{Maximum Freq.}}$

4. Find ordering code for which desired gain lies between minimum and maximum listed.
5. Use ordering code to complete part number (see page D-14).

EXAMPLE: As shown on Page B-97, transducer Model PX106-1KGSF requires indicator number DP2000-H9.

Ordering
Example: Input frequency: 400 Hz; Signal level: 200 mV; Full scale display: 500 PSI; Gain = $\dfrac{500}{400}$ = 1.25

Choose H5 because: 1 < 1.25 < 2

To Order, Specify
DP2000-H5 $356

Frequency Input
The DP2000H can display preselected engineering units of rate, strain, pressure, frequency, or percentage. Front panel adjustments provide scaling and zero offset necessary for use with many pressure and flow transducers.

SPECIFICATIONS
Zero Offset: +100 to −1000 counts
Excitation: User supplied, see power supplies on pages C-9 and C-10
Accuracy: ±0.1% of reading ±1 count
Maximum Input: 130 V RMS
CMV: ±1500 Vac to analog ground
Input Resistance: 150 kΩ
Minimum Display: 100 counts
Configuration: Single ended ac and dc coupled

DP2000/9000 SERIES
SPECIFICATIONS AND OPTIONS

Features
- ✓ ⅛ DIN Case
- ✓ LED or LCD Display
- ✓ 120 Vac Power Standard
- ✓ Standard Analog Output
- ✓ Wide Variety of Control Outputs Available

OMEGA's DP2000/DP9000 digital indicator/controller brings the end user a new world of versatility. A universal 1/8 DIN case houses your choice of thousands of configurations. Choose any combination of display resolution, display type (LED or LCD), operating power, input type, analog output and digital or control outputs. OMEGA will supply a fully burned-in and tested OMEGA DP2000 or DP9000 to suit your needs.

POWER REQUIREMENTS
AC Models: 24/120/240 Vac +10 −15%; 47-63 hz
DC Models: 5 Vdc ±5% or 9-32 Vdc

COMMON MODE
Voltage: 1500 Vp test (354 Vp per IEC spacing)
Rejection (DC to 60 Hz): 120 dB
Operating Temperature (Ambient): 32 to 140°F (0 to 60°C)
Case Material: 94 V-0 UL-rated, polycarbonate.

CONVERSION
Technique: Auto-Zero, Dual Slope, Average Value.
Signal Integration Period: 100 ms, nominal.
Reading Rate: 2.5/second, nominal.

DISPLAY
LED: 14.2 mm (0.56″), 7-segment Light Emitting Diode.
LCD: 12.7 mm (0.50″), 7-segment Liquid Crystal.
Lens Color: LED: Red. LCD: Clear.

SELECTION GUIDE

DP X X X X X

DISPLAY RESOLUTION

2	±1999 counts (3½ digits)
9	±9999 counts (4 digits)

DISPLAY TYPE & METER POWER
(LCD is Only Available on DP2000 Models)

Code	Description	PRICE DP2XXX	DP9XXX
0	LED; 120 Vac (50/60 Hz) (Standard)	$229	$278
1	LCD; 120 Vac (50/60 Hz) (Standard)	253	N/A
2	LED; 240 Vac (50/60 Hz)	229	278
3	LCD; 240 Vac (50/60 Hz)	253	N/A
4	LED; 9-32 Vdc Isolated	283	332
5	LCD; 9-32 Vdc Isolated	307	N/A
6	LED; 5 Vdc	271	320
7	LCD; 5 Vdc	295	N/A
8	LED; 24 Vac	259	308
9	LCD; 24 Vac	283	N/A

ANALOG OUTPUTS

Code	Description	Price
0	±1 or (±2 V standard on all models)	Std.
1	0-5 Vdc	$70
2	0-10 Vdc	70
3	0-1 mA (source or sink)	70
4	4-20 mA (source or sink)	70
5	4-20 mA sink (high compliance)	90

CONTROL OUTPUTS

Code	Description	Price
0	None	Std.
1	Dual-Setpoint 10A relays	$162
2	Proportional 4-20 mA	174
3	Proportional time-proportioning	222
4	Parallel BCD, Isolated	120

SIGNAL CONDITIONER
(DP9000 Available in "P" and "S" only)

Code	Description	Price
A	DC Voltage	N/C
B	DC Current	N/C
C	AC AVG Voltage	$ 36
D	AC AVG Current	36
F	TRUE RMS Voltage	120
G	TRUE RMS Current	120
H	Frequency/Rate	102
J	Type J Thermocouple (°C/°F)	96
K	Type K Thermocouple (°C/°F)	96
T	Type T Thermocouple (°C/°F)	96
P	Process Signal (e.g. 4-20 mA, 1-5V)	72
M	RTD, Normal Resolution	90
R	RTD, High Resolution	108
S	Strain-Gage/Low Level Input	162

INSTRUMENTATION

D

DIGITAL TRANSDUCER INDICATORS
WITH EXCITATION FOR MILLIVOLT OUTPUT TRANSDUCERS

Model DP-350 PRESSURE INDICATOR

Model DP-350
$425

PRESSURE MONITOR

660 psi

OMEGA ENGINEERING MODEL DP350

®2 YEAR WARRANTY

For Pressure Transducers, Load Cells and Strain Bridges
- High Impact Plastic Case
- Jumper Selectable Decimal Points
- Scalable Input 20 to 100 mV FS
- Scalable Gain 4.95 to 137 Counts/mV
- Zero Offset ±20% of Full Scale Display
- 5 or 10 V Excitation
- Optional Dual Set Point
- Scalable Display to Maximum of 1999 Counts

Mounting Dimensions

3.74
DUAL 15 PIN CONN
4.23
.44

3.924 ± .010
CUT OUT
1.682 ± .010

4.05
+1.9999
1.80
THRU PANEL MOUNTING

Note: Cutout is not to DIN dimensions.

Transducers sold separately.
See Section B.

▶HIGHLIGHTED MODELS ARE STOCKED ◀

To Order (Specify model number)

MODEL NO.	PRICE	DESCRIPTION
DP-350 115 Vac	$425	Transducer gain between 4.95 and 137 counts/mV. $$\text{Gain} = \frac{\text{Full Scale Display (counts)}}{\text{Full Scale Output (mV)}}$$
DP-350Z	475	3½ Digits with Dummy Zero
DP-352 115 Vac	475	Same as above, plus two setpoints with two 0.5 A relays. Requires external resistors (DP-352-KIT).
DP-352Z	525	3½ Digits with Dummy Zero
DP-352-KIT	69	Potenitometers and momentary switch for setpoint utilization.

See page D-31 for Bench Top Model.

The DP350 is a self-contained, panel mount meter providing bridge excitation and digital readout scaled to any engineering unit, i.e., weight, pressure, volume, etc. It provides optional analog set points, external rate, autozero, and analog output.

Excellent performance and reliability are obtained by conservative design

utilizing the dual slope conversion technique, selection of quality components, and extensive burn-in and quality control of all meters.

Compatible Transducers: The DP350 is compatible with millivolt output transducers on pages B-3 thru B-30, and all OMEGA Strain gages and load cells.

SPECIFICATIONS

Accuracy: ±0.05% of rdg ± 1 count
Linearity: ±0.05% of reading typical (±1 count max.)
Temp. Coefficient (−10 to 60°C):
 Full Scale: 0.005% of rdg./°C
 Zero: ±0.12 counts/°C
Common Mode Rejection: −80 dB @ dc
Normal Mode Rejection: −45 dB @ 60 Hz
Common Mode Voltage: ±4 volts max.
Bias Current: 1.5 nA
Read Rate: 3/sec.
SetPoints (optional)
Setability: ±1 count
Hysteresis: ±10 counts
 Temp. Co.: 0.14 counts/°C
Analog Output (1 mV/count)
 Accuracy: 0.5% rdg ±1 mV
 Load: 2 K ohm min. (1 mA max.)
Bridge Excitation: 10 Vdc (+ and −5 Vdc) @ 50 mA
Power: 3.5 watts typ., 115/230 Vac ±10%, 47-400 Hz

VOLTAGE INPUT PRESSURE MONITOR
ACCEPTS INPUTS FROM ALL VOLTAGE OUTPUT TRANSDUCERS

DP354 High Performance Indicator

MADE IN
USA

✓ **Fully Scalable Display — Can Read From 0 to 1999 With Inputs Between 4.9 to 10.1 V**

✓ **Works With All OMEGA Voltage Output Transducers**

✓ **Adjustable 1.3 to 24 Vdc Excitation for Transducers**

The DP354 voltage receiver is compatible with most voltage output pressure transducers, and displays scaling to readout in engineering units. It features expanded input and scaling capabilities, with an adjustable transducer excitation power supply. The DP354 also has an easy to read 3½ digit LED display, and accuracy of 0.05% of reading accuracy.

PERFORMANCE: DP354

Accuracy: 0.05% ±.5 digit

Linearity: ±.5 digit

Temperature Coefficient: 0.005% reading/°C: Zero: 1πV/°C max.

Common Mode Rejection: 80 dB at 60 Hz

Input Bias: 100 pA max.

Maximum Overload: 100V

Panel Cutout Size: 1.682 x 3.924 (not to DIN specifications)

Excitation: 1.3 to 24 V dc, adjustable at 30 mA

Operating Temperature: −10 to 60°C

To Order *(Specify Model Number)*

MODEL	INPUT	PRICE
DP354	Fully scaleable for any full scale input between 4.9 and 10.1 Vdc	$330
DP354Z	Same as above, with dummy zero	380

Comes with complete operator's manual.

DP302 Panel Meter, With .56" Digit Display, $187; LDP2 Panel Meter With 2¼" Display, $1050; LDP4 Panel Meter With 4" Display, $1550.

From
$1050

✔ **Large 2¼" or 4" Digit Displays for Easy Visibility**

✔ **Wide Variety of Inputs to Work with Most Common Sensors**

✔ **Displays Readings in Engineering Units**

The LDP2 and LDP4 are multipurpose large display digital meters, housed in extruded aluminum, suitable for panel mounting or free standing installations. The LDP2 has 2¼" digits, which are visible from 50 feet away. The LDP4 has 4" digits and can be seen from 200 feet.

OMEGACARE™ Extended Warranty Plan Available: consult sales for details.

To Order *(Specify Model Number & Signal Conditioner)*

MODEL NO.	PRICE	DESCRIPTION
LDP2-(*)	$930	Large Display Panel Meter with 2¼" High Digits
LDP4-(*)	1430	Large Display Panel Meter with 4" High Digits

* Insert Signal Conditioner Order Code from table below. Add appropriate price adder.

SIGNAL CONDITIONERS — *ALL MODELS STOCKED FOR FAST DELIVERY*

INPUT TYPE	ORDER CODE	PRICE ADDER	RANGE
Process Current/Voltage	P	$120	Scalable
Strain Gage/Millivolt	S	210	Scalable
Frequency/Rate Inputs	H	144	Scalable
J Thermocouple (°C)	J1	144	0 to 760°C
J Thermocouple (°F)	J2	144	32 to 1400°F
K Thermocouple (°C)	K1	144	0 to 1260°C
K Thermocouple (°F)	K2	144	0 to 1999°F
T Thermocouple (°C)	T1	144	-184 to 371°C
T Thermocouple (°F)	T2	144	-300 to 700°F
RTD 0.1° Res. (°C)	M1	132	-200 to 830°C
RTD 0.1° Res. (°F)	M2	132	-328 to 1526°F
RTD 0.1° Res. (°C)	R1	156	-199.9 to 199.9°C
RTD 0.1° Res. (°F)	R2	156	-199.9 to 199.9°F

Comes complete with power cord, mating input connectors and operator's manual.

Ordering Example: *LDP2-J1 is a digital meter with a 2¼" digits display, and a type J thermocouple input with 0 to 760°C range, $930 + 144 = **$1074**.*

IDEAL FOR DEMONSTRATION APPLICATIONS

The LDP2 and LDP4 use the DP2000 series signal conditioner modules which makes them compatible with most common sensor types. The P signal conditioner module accepts voltage inputs up to 10 Vdc, or current inputs up to 50 mA. For use with millivolt sensors, such as load cells or strain gages, the S signal conditioner accepts inputs up to 500 mV. Both the P and S models are fully scalable to read out in engineering units from ±9999 counts. The S models also have a 10 Vdc power supply for transducer excitation. Additional models for J, K, and T thermocouples and 100 Ohm Platinum RTD's are also available.

All large displays utilize a switching power supply which enables them to operate on any AC voltage between 95 and 265 Vac and 45 to 440 Hertz.

SPECIFICATIONS
Accuracy: See signal conditioner specs
Power: 95 to 265 Vac, 45 to 440 Hz
Power Consumption: 10 watts
Display Type: High efficiency red LED
Digit Height: LDP2; 2¼" (57mm)
LDP4; 4" (102mm)
Operating Temperature: 32 to 122°F (0 to 50°C) (reduced to 40°C if maximum display brightness is selected)
Storage Temperature: -4 to 185°F (-20 to 85°C)
Humidity: 85% RH non-condensing
Dimensions: LDP2; 10.4" W x 4.7" H x 4.6" D (264 x 120 x 117mm)
LDP4; 18.9" W x 7.1" H x 4.6" D (480 x 180 x 117mm)
Panel Cutout: LDP2; 10.16" W x 4.49" H (258 x 114mm) LDP4; 18.66" W x 6.85" H (474 x 174mm)
Depth Behind Panel: 4.21" (107mm)
Weight: LDP2; 5.5 lbs (2.5 kg)
LDP4; 9.9 lbs (4.5 kg)
Case Material: Aluminum extrusion, black anodized finish
Power Connector: IEC fused Connector, 6 ft. power cord included
Signal Connector: Mating 9 Pin sub-miniature D-Type or thermocouple input socket (SMP) for signal conditioner types J, K and T is included

The LDP4 Large Display (Shown With Displacement Transducer, Model LD600-300, $785) is Ideal for Demonstration Applications. LVDT Sensor Sold Separately, See Section J.

PROCESS & STRAIN GAGE INPUTS

ORDER CODE	DISPLAY INPUT RANGES	RANGE	ACCURACY (+ 2 COUNTS)
P	0-5Vdc/0-10Vdc/4-20mA User Selectable	±9999 Scalable	±0.05% of reading
S	10-500 mVdc input	±9999	±0.05% of reading
H	Frequency to 20KHz max.	±9999	±0.1% of reading

THERMOCOUPLE INPUTS

CODE	INPUT TYPE	RANGE	ACCURACY (+½ COUNT)
J1	Type J Thermocouple	0 to 760°C	0 to 277°C: ±1.2°C 277 to 760°C: ±0.5% rdg
J2	Type J Thermocouple	32 to 1400°F	32 to 530°F: ± 2.4°F 530 to 1400°F: ±0.5% rdg
K1	Type K Thermocouple	0 to 1260°C	0 to 277°C: ±1.8°C 277 to 1260°C: ±0.6% rdg
K2	Type K Thermocouple	32 to 1999°F	32 to 530°F: ±3.0°F 530 to 1999°F: ±0.6% rdg
T1	Type J Thermocouple	-184 to 371°C	-184 to -59°C: ±1.5% rdg -59 to 93°C: ±1.0°C 93 to 371°C: ±0.6% rdg
T2	Type T Thermocouple	-300 to 700°F	-300 to -75°F: ±1.5% rdg -75 to 200°F: ±1.5°F 200 to 700°F: ±0.6% rdg

RTD INPUTS

CODE	RTD TYPE	RANGE	ACCURACY (+½ COUNT)
M1	100 ohm Plat.	-200 to 830°C	±0.2% rdg, + 0.3°C
M2	100 ohm Plat.	-328 to 1526°F	±0.2% rdg, + 0.5°F
R1	100 ohm Plat.	-199.9 to 199.9°C	±0.05% rdg, + 0.1°C
R2	100 ohm Plat.	-199.9 to 199.9°F	±0.05% rdg, + 0.2°F

ECONOMICAL DIGITAL TRANSDUCER INDICATORS
FOR STRAIN GAGE OR PROCESS INPUTS

From $185

The DP302 and DP3002 Digital Indicators are Shown With the PX212 ($184) and PX215 ($268) Transducers. Transducers Sold Separately, See Pages B-19 and B-59 for Details .

✔ **Optional DC Powered**
✔ **Models Available for Millivolt, Voltage or Current Output Type Transducers**
✔ **Easily Scaled to Display Readings in Engineering Units**
✔ **3½ or 4½ Digit Models Available**

The DP302 and DP3002 Series are low cost digital panel meters designed for applications where indication only is required. The DP302 is a 3½ digit display capable of displaying ±1999 counts. The DP3002 is a 4½ digit display and can read ±19999 counts. Both models are fully scalable to display engineering units.

SPECIFICATIONS
Accuracy: (DP302) ±.05% of span + 1 count (DP3002) ±.01% of span +2 counts
Operating Temp: 32 to 140°F (0 to 60°C)
Span Temp Coefficient: ±.01% of span/°C
Zero Temp Coefficient: (DP302) ±.1 count/°C (DP3002) ±.5 count/°C
Storage Temperature: -40 to 185°F (-40 to 85°C)

Humidity: 95% RH to 40°C (non-condensing)
CMRR: 120 dB from DC to 60 Hz
Common Mode Voltage: 1500 Vpk per HV test 354 Vpk per IEC spacing
NMRR: 56 dB at 50/60 Hz
Display Type: 7 segment, Red LED
Display Digits: DP302 3½ (±1999 counts) DP3002 4½ (±19999 counts)
Digit Height: 0.56 in. (14.2 mm)
Conversion Rate: 2.5/sec
POWER REQUIREMENTS
AC Models: 115 Vac ±15% 230 Vac ±15% (optional)

Frequency Range: 47-400 Hz
DC Models: 9-32 Vdc (300V isolation) (optional)
Power Consumption: 2.4 W (3.7 W with excitation)
Excitation: Adjustable 10-24 Vdc @ 30 mA("-E" and "-S" models only)
MECHANICAL SPECIFICATIONS
Bezel: 3.78 x 1.89 x 0.20" (96 x 48 x 5.1 mm)
Depth Behind Bezel: 4.09" (104 mm)
Panel Cutout: 3.62 x 1.77" (92 x 45 mm)
Weight: 15 oz. (425 grams)

HIGHLIGHTED MODELS IN STOCK FOR FAST DELIVERY!

To Order (Specify Model Number)

MODEL NUMBER	DIGITS	PRICE	INPUT RANGES *	EXCITATION
DP302-P	3½	$185	4-20mA, 1-5Vdc, 0-10Vdc	None
DP302-E	3½	253	4-20mA, 1-5Vdc, 0-10Vdc	10-24 Vdc
DP302-S	3½	271	±20mVdc, 200mVdc, 2Vdc	10-24 Vdc
DP3002-P	4½	259	4-20mA, 1-5Vdc, 0-10Vdc	None
DP3002-E	4½	271	4-20mA, 1-5Vdc, 0-10Vdc	10-24 Vdc
DP3002-S	4½	325	±20mVdc, 200mVdc, 2Vdc	10-24 Vdc

Input ranges selected by internal jumpers.
For 230 Vac power add suffix "-230", no extra charge.
For 9-32 Vdc power add suffix "-DC", and add $72 to the price.
Ordering Example: DP3002-P is a 4½ digit display process panel meter, **$259.**

HIGH SPEED LOAD AND STRAIN GAGE METER 5½ DIGIT DISPLAY

- ✔ 62.5 to 500 Hz Adjustable Sampling Rate
- ✔ Min and Max Detect and Hold Functions
- ✔ Auto Tare up to 50% From Front Panel
- ✔ Four Programmable Limit Alarms
- ✔ Excitation For up to Four 350 Ohm Bridges

From

$740

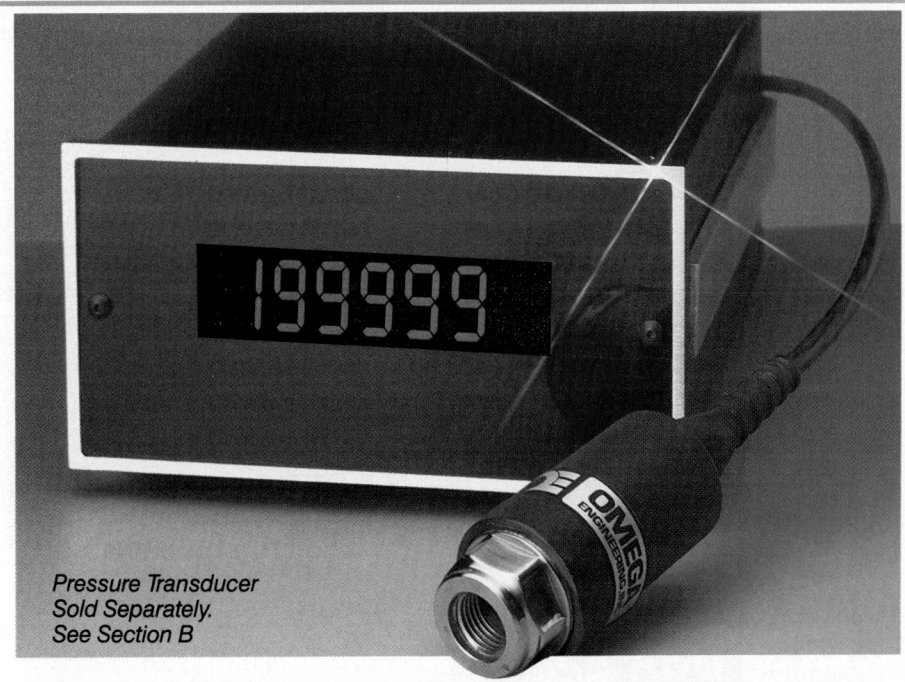

Pressure Transducer
Sold Separately.
See Section B

SPECIFICATIONS

Accuracy: ±0.05% of reading ±2 counts of A/D @ 25°C.

Temperature Coefficient: 25ppm/°C

Resolution of A/D: 12 bits

Input Impedance: 1000 Mohm

Input Bias Current: ±50 NA

Normal Mode Rejection: 70 dB

Common Mode Rejection: 70 dB

Rollover Error: ±3 counts of A/D

Sample Rate: Adjustable from 62.5 to 500 samples per second for min., max., and limits

Display Averaging: adjustable from 1 to 100 samples

I/O Method: Two subminiature "D" connectors supplied for strain gage hookup, RS232/RS422 output, alarms, remote min./max. display and reset, remote tare and reset

Output: 4 high alarms (5 Vdc @ 24mA) No deadband

Display: 5½ digits .56″ LED red with polarity

Power: 115 Vac 50-400 Hz. 8 watts maximum. Input power via screw terminals

Input Filter: 2.5 KHz single pole passive filter.

Operating Temperature: 0° to 50°C

Construction: All aluminum case

Dimensions: 2.7″H x 5.18″W x 6.75″D; Cutout: 2.45″H x 5.06″W

To Order (Specify Model Number)

MODEL	PRICE	INPUT	SCALABILITY	EXCITATION
▶DP-760	$745	0 to 35 mVdc	0.03 to 13,333 cts/mV	10 Vdc @ 120 mA ◀
DP-771	740	0 to 2 Vdc	fully scalable	±15 Vdc 50 mA/ 5 Vdc 30 mA
DP-772	740	0 to 5 Vdc (1-6Vdc)	fully scalable	±15 Vdc 50 mA/ 5 Vdc 30 mA
▶DP-773	740	0 to 10 Vdc (1-11Vdc)	fully scalable	±15 Vdc 50 mA/ 5 Vdc 30 mA ◀
▶DP-775	740	4 to 20 mA	fully scalable	±15 Vdc 50 mA/ 5 Vdc 30 mA ◀
▶DP-776	740	0 to ±200 mVdc	0.01 to 1000 cts/mV	10 Vdc @ 120 mA ◀
DP-777	740	0 to ±200 Vdc	0.01 to 1000 cts/V	±15 Vdc 50 mA/ 5 Vdc 30 mA

◆ *HIGHLIGHTED MODELS IN STOCK FOR FAST DELIVERY* ◆

Options

ORDERING SUFFIX	PRICE	DESCRIPTION
-1	$65	ASCII RS-232 (includes mating connector)
-2	65	ASCII RS-422 (includes mating connector)
-3	50	6 wire hook-up for remote sensing (DP-760 only)
-4	25	analog output 0 to ±10 Vdc @ 1 mA
-5	25	230 Vac @ 50 to 400 Hz, Ac input power
-6	95	10 to 30 Vdc @ 500 mA, Dc input power

ECONOMICAL DIGITAL INDICATORS WITH EXCITATION AND DUAL ALARM RELAYS

NEW!

The DP205 Comes with a Complete Operator's Manual. It is Shown with Model LCCA Load Cell. Load Cells are Sold Separately, See Section F.

DP205 SERIES
$199

- ✔ 4 Digit Display, -1999 to 9999 Counts
- ✔ Excitation, Dual Alarm Relays, and Scalable Analog Output Standard
- ✔ Models Available for Process Voltage and Current or Bridge Type Inputs
- ✔ Easily Scaled to Display Readings in Engineering Units

The OMEGA DP205 Series are low cost digital panel meters for use with voltage, current or bridge type transducers. A four digit LED display indicates from -1999 to 9999 counts. For amplified voltage and current output transducers, the DP205-E has a user selectable 12 or 24 Vdc excitation supply. For strain gage bridge transducers the DP205-S has a 5 or 10 Vdc supply.

Both models include analog output and dual alarm relays as standard equipment. The analog output is field scalable and configurable for 0-10V, 0-20mA, or 4-20mA. The dual alarm relays are fully configurable for high or low, latching or non-latching operation and include adjustable deadband.

SPECIFICATIONS
Accuracy (@ 25°C): ±0.02% of reading
Operating Temp: 0 to 50°C (32 to 122°F)
Span Temp Coefficient: ± 50 PPM/°C
Storage Temperature: -40 to 185°F (-40 to 85°C)
Relative Humidity: 95% at 104°F (40°C) (non-condensing)
CMRR: 120 dB
Common Mode Voltage: 1500 V peak per HV test 354 V peak per IEC spacing

NMRR: 60 dB
Display: 4 digit, red LED, 0.56" high
Display Range: -1999 to 9999 counts
Conversion Rate: 3/second
Step Response: 1-2 seconds
Relays: Dual 250 Vac, 6 amp, SPDT
Analog Output: Scalable 0-10 V or 4-20 mA

POWER REQUIREMENTS
Voltage: 115 (std) or 230 Vac (optional) ±15%
Frequency: 48 to 60 hz
Power Consumption: 6 watts maximum

MECHANICAL SPECIFICATIONS
Bezel: 3.78" W x 1.89" H x .30" D (96 x 48 x 7mm)
Panel Cutout: 3.622" W x 1.772" H (92 x 45mm)
Depth Behind Panel: 5.6"
Weight: 18 oz (509 g)

IN STOCK FOR FAST DELIVERY!

MODEL NO.	INPUT RANGES *	EXCITATION	PRICE
DP205-E	0-100 mV, ±50 mV, 0-10V ±5V, 0-20 mA, 4-20 mA	24V @ 50 mA or 12V @ 100 mA	**$199**
DP205-S	0-100 mV or ±50 mV	5 V @ 60 mA or 10V @ 120 mA	199

To Order *(Specify Model Number)*

* Input ranges are selected by internal DIP switches.
For 230 VAC power add suffix "-230," no extra charge.
Ordering Example: *DP205-E is a digital process indicator with 24V @50 mA or 12V@100 mA excitation, $199.*

ECONOMICAL PROCESS INDICATOR
ACCEPTS VOLTAGE AND CURRENT INPUTS

1 YEAR WARRANTY

MADE IN USA

CARE

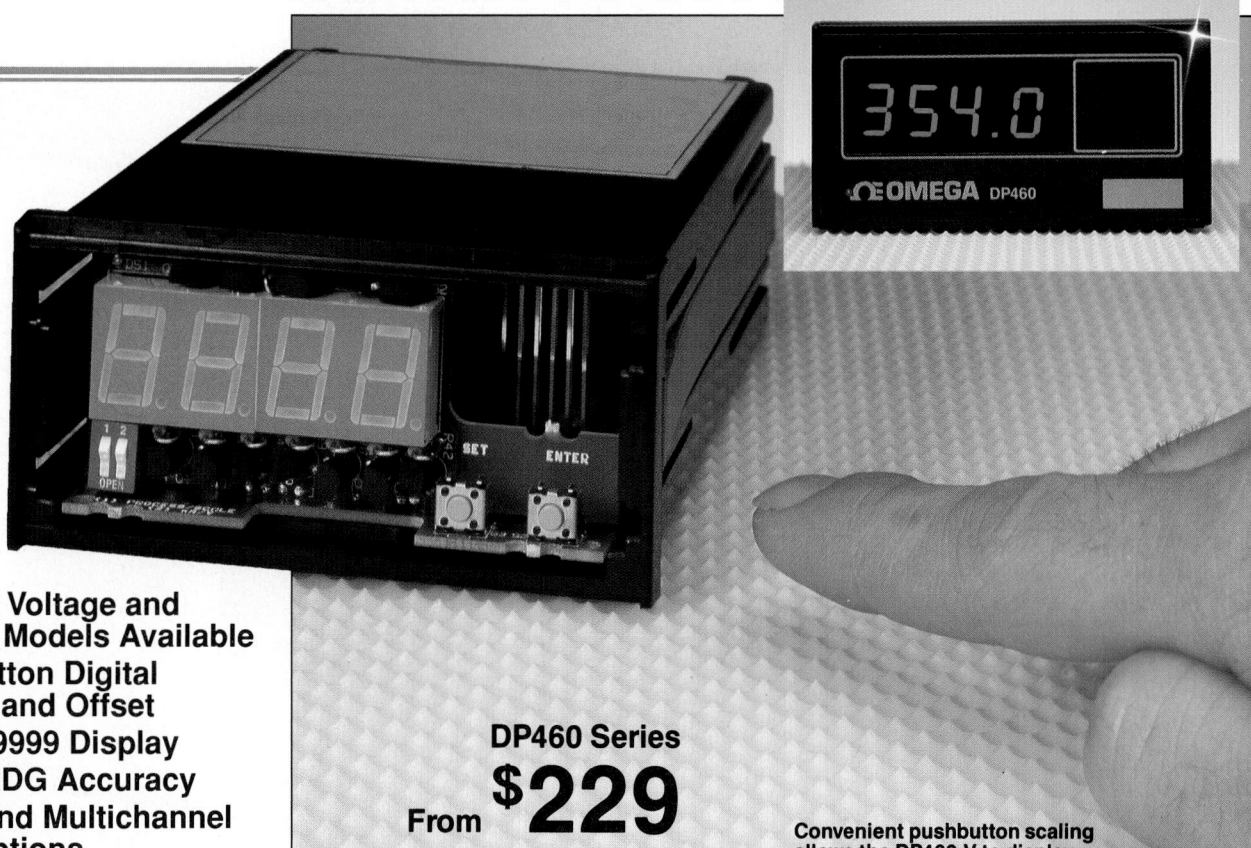

✔ **Millivolt Voltage and Current Models Available**
✔ **Pushbutton Digital Scaling and Offset**
✔ **-999 to 9999 Display**
✔ **0.02% RDG Accuracy**
✔ **Alarm and Multichannel Input Options**

The DP460 is an economical dc indicator, capable of measuring millivolts, voltage or current. The DP460-V accepts voltage inputs to 10 Vdc or current to 20mA. The DP460-E accepts the same ranges as the DP460-V, but includes a 24 Vdc transducer power supply. For transducers with millivolt outputs, the DP460-S accepts up to 500 mVdc and provides 10Vdc excitation. A front panel tare button is also available as an option for the DP460-S.

SPECIFICATIONS
Accuracy: .02% rdg, +1 count
Input Impedance: 1 Mohm, voltage;
Span Temp. Coeff: ±.01% rdg/C 5 ohm current
Zero Temp. Coeff: ±1 V/C
Display Range: -999 to 9999 counts
Operating Temperature: 5 to 45°C
Display Type: 4 digit red LED
Storage Temperature: -40 to 65°C
Digit Height: 0.56"
Relative Humidity: 80% RH max
Alarm Relay Contact: 0.5A @ 120Vac,
Repeatability: ±1 count non-inductive; form C (SPDT)
CMRR: 120 dB @ 50/60 Hz
Dimensions: 1.57"H x 3.54"W x 5.35"D

NMRR: 60 dB @ 50/60 Hz, with 250 ohm unbalanced
Overload Protection: 1500 Vdc or Vac RMS, power lead to ground
Max Input: 250 Vac/dc, across selectable 50-60 Hz inputs (V+ to V-); 150 mA

Excitation: 24 Vdc @ 30 mA (DP460-E) across inputs (1+ to 1-) 10 Vdc @ 30 mA (DP460-S)
Panel Cutout: 1.77"H x 3.62"W 250 ohm unbalance (45 x92 mm); ⅛ DIN
Weight: 1 lb
Power: 115/230 Vac ±10% switch

DP460 Series

From $229

Convenient pushbutton scaling allows the DP460-V to display from −999 to 9999.

To Order *(Specify Model Number)*

MODEL NO.	PRICE	INPUT RANGE	EXCITATION	OPTIONS
DP460-V	$229	0-20mA/0-10Vdc	NONE	NONE
DP461-V	328	0-20mA/0-10Vdc	NONE	ALARM RELAY
DP462-V*	328	0-20mA/0-10Vdc	NONE	MULTI INPUT*
DP460-E	259	0-20mA/0-10Vdc	24Vdc @ 30mA	NONE
DP461-E	358	0-20mA/0-10Vdc	24Vdc @ 30mA	ALARM RELAY
DP460-S	279	0-50/0-500mVdc	10Vdc @ 30mA	NONE
DP461-S	378	0-50/0-500mVdc	10Vdc @ 30mA	ALARM RELAY

OPTIONS

MODEL NO.	DESCRIPTION	PRICE
DP460-T	Front panel tare button for DP460-S	$12
DP461-T	Front panel tare button for DP461-S	12

* Multi-channel units require mating sensors of the exact same range and output, with zero and span adjustments.
Each unit is supplied with self-adhesive front panel labels for various engineering units, and complete operator's manual.
Ordering Example: *DP461-V is a voltage/current indicator with an input range of 0-20mA/0-10 Vdc, $328.*

INSTRUMENTATION

D

DIGITAL PROCESS INDICATORS WITH MICROPROCESSOR CONTROL

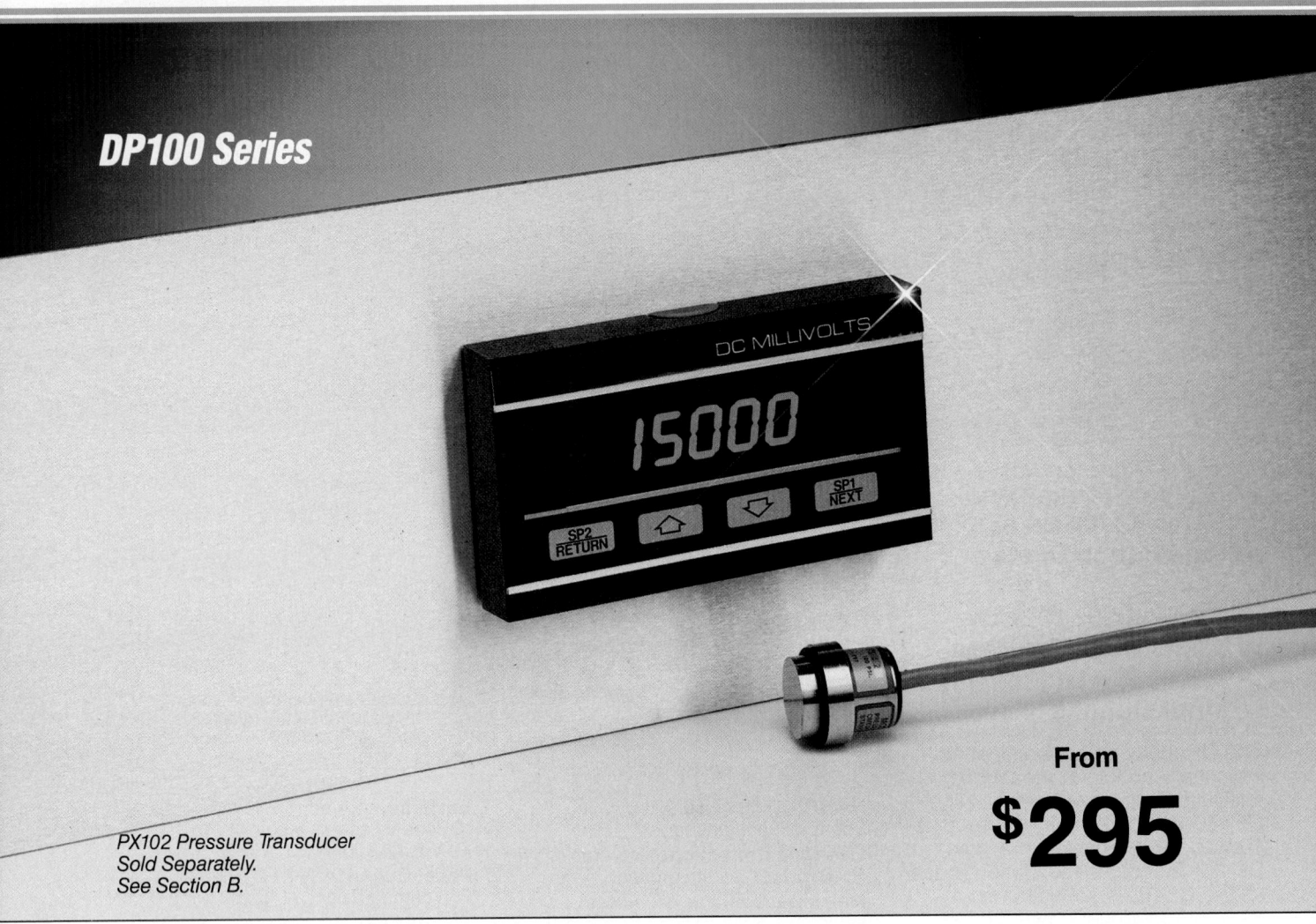

DP100 Series

From
$295

PX102 Pressure Transducer
Sold Separately.
See Section B.

- ✓ **Easily Displays Minimum and Maximum Process Value Input With Keypad Reset**
- ✓ **Models Available With 3½ or 4½ Digit Display**
- ✓ **3 Keypad Selectable Programming Loops Allow the User to Modify the Unit's Operating Parameters or Output Configuration**
- ✓ **Models Available With Dual Alarms and 10 or 20 Volt Excitation Power Supply**
- ✓ **RS232C and RS422 Communications Options Available**

Offering complete front keypad programmability and advanced microprocessor design, the OMEGA DP100 Series digital indicators easily display the minimum and maximum process values in the engineering units of your choice. The DP100 incorporates three programming loops; Operators Loop, Tune Loop, and Configuration loop. Each loop is presented by a series of numeric prompts allowing the user to adjust or change the unit's operating parameters or output configuration.

The Tune Loop and Configuration Loop each have a special coded entry procedure to prevent unauthorized tampering. An additional entry code is required for access to the calibration area. Once the indicator has been programmed, it will display only those tunable parameters that have been set.

Transducer Excitation

The DP100 Series includes models with transducer excitation capabilities. The 30 mV and 200 mV ranges are available with an optional 10 Vdc @ 30 mA power supply, a 20 Vdc @ 30 mA supply is available with all other ranges.

Alarms

Models are available that include two solid state relays rated to 500 mA @ 125 Vac. These relays are fully programmable. The primary output can serve as an on/off alarm or as a PID control output. The selectable primary and secondary alarms are high or low, on/off, process and deviation band alarms. Analog output can be used for primary control or retransmission of the signal via the front keypad.

OPTIONAL EXCITATION AND ALARM CAPABILITIES

SPECIFICATIONS

Display: 7 segment blue green vacuum fluorescent with negative sign and annunciator arrow. 0.6″ high for 3½ digit models; 0.4″ high for 4½ digit models

Connections: I/O connections are screw terminal; communication outputs are via 20 pin card edge

Power: 6 Watts typical at 117 Vac

Operable Temperature: 5 to 50°C

Storage Temperature: −20 to 85°C

Input Impedance: > 100 Megohms

Conversion Rate: 2.5/s

Response Time: Selectable 3.2 seconds or 4-7.2 seconds both with digital filtering

Common Mode Rejection: 130 db typical

Normal Mode Rejection: 90 db typical

Zero Offset: ±50% max. input range

Temperature Stability: 50ppm/°C max for 3½ digit/2 Vdc; 15ppm/°C for 4½ digit/2 Vdc range

Accuracy: 0.025% full scale.

Resolution: 3½ digit and 4½ digit models, each unit fully scalable for zero and span

Analog Output: 0 to 10 Vdc proportional to 0 to 100% output power, or scaled range 2k ohm maximum load; resolution 0.4%

Solid State Relays: Form C 500 mA @ 125 Vac maximum resistive load. 5 mA Ac maximum leakage current

On/Off Alarm Deadband Selection: 0.1%, 0.25%, 0.5%, or 1% of span

Deviation Alarm Deadband: 0.4% of span

Proportion Band Setting Selection: 1, 2, 4, 8, 16, 32, or 64% of span

Reset Setting Selection: Off, 0.5, 0.25, 0.08 repeats per Min.

Rate: ¼ the reset setting in minutes

Anti-Reset Windup: Standard

Cycletime Setting Selection: 2, 6, 15, 30 seconds

Cutout: 3.622″ × 1.732″

Bezel: 4.45″ × 2.43″

Behind Panel: 6.2″

OPTIONS

RS232C: Isolated or Non-isolated

RS422: Isolated

To Order *(Specify Model Number)*

MODEL	DISPLAY	PRICE	ALARMS	EXC.	OPTIONS
▶DP100-[*]◀	3½ digit	$338	—	—	"A" and/or (232 or 422)
DP101-[*]		432	Y	—	Only One -A, 232, 422
DP102-[*]		472	—	Y	None
▶DP103-[*]◀		560	Y	Y	None
▶DP110-[*]◀	4½ digit	392	—	—	"A" and/or (232 or 422)
DP111-[*]		486	Y	—	Only One -A, 232, 422
DP112-[*]		532	—	Y	None
▶DP113-[*]◀		618	Y	Y	None

[*] insert range code

RANGE CODE	MAX RANGE	POWER SUPPLY (optional)
R0	0 to 30 mVdc (only available with excitation models)	10 V
R1	0 to 200 mVdc	10 V
R2	0 to 2 Vdc	20 V
R3	0 to 20 Vdc	20 V
R4	0 to 200 Vdc	20 V
R5	0 to 20 μAdc	20 V
R6	0 to 200 μAdc	20 V
R7	0 to 2 mAdc*	20 V
R8	4 to 20 mAdc* (0 to 20 mA)	20 V
R9	0 to 200 mAdc	20 V

* 10Ω internal shunt

OPTIONS		
ORDERING SUFFIX	**PRICE**	**DESCRIPTION**
−232	$95	Isolated serial communications (requires external + 12 Vdc @ 100 mA and − 12 Vdc @ 25 mA)
−422	95	Isolated long distance serial communications (requires external 5 Vdc @ 130 mA)
−A	65	0 to 10 Volt analog output programmable for retransmission or control

−232 and −422 options are supplied with meter connector, 1 ft. of ribbon cable and a standard DB25 female connector

▶ **HIGHLIGHTED MODELS STOCKED FOR FAST DELIVERY** ◀

INSTRUMENTATION

D

NEW! HANDHELD TRANSDUCER INDICATOR
WITH EXCITATION FOR MILLIVOLT TRANSDUCERS

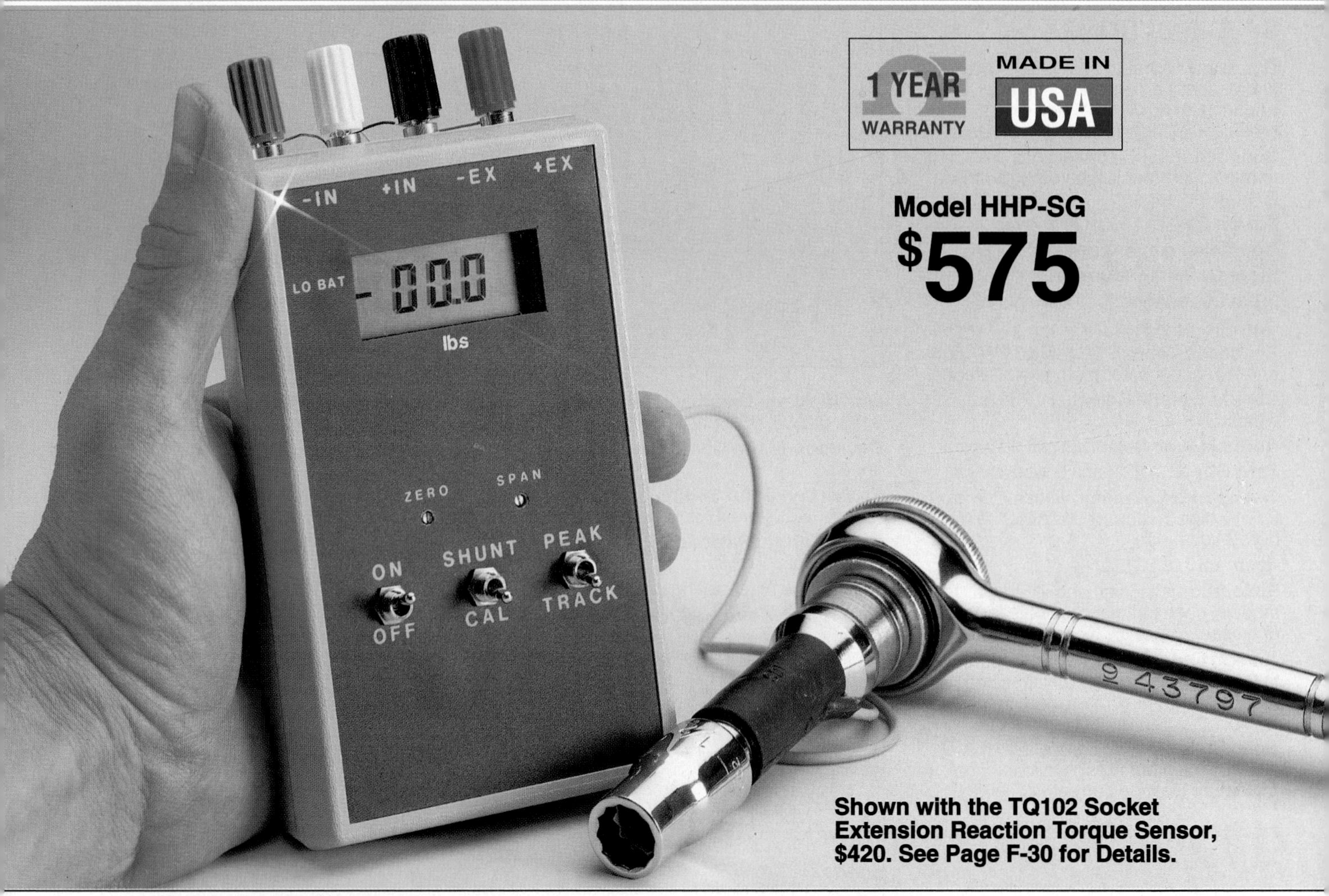

1 YEAR WARRANTY

MADE IN USA

Model HHP-SG
$575

Shown with the TQ102 Socket Extension Reaction Torque Sensor, $420. See Page F-30 for Details.

- ✔ **Handheld Indicator for Bridge Type Transducers**
- ✔ **9 Volt Battery Powered**
- ✔ **Scalable Display with Dummy Zero**
- ✔ **Built in Transducer Excitation**

The OMEGA Model HHP-SG is a handheld digital indicator for strain gage type transducers such as load cells, torque sensors or millivolt pressure sensors. It provides excitation voltage for the transducer and displays the readings on a liquid crystal indicator.

Front panel zero and span adjustments allow scaling the meter to provide readings in the desired engineering units. The LCD has 3½ active digits (0-1999 counts) and an additional dummy zero if needed. The HHP-SG can display either the actual value of the signal (tracking mode) or the peak value (peak mode). It operates on a standard 9 volt battery, and indicates if the battery is low.

SPECIFICATIONS
Transducer Excitation Voltage: 2.46 Vdc
Minimum Transducer Resistance: 120 Ohms

Input Signal Sensitivity: 0.5 to 4.0 mV/V for full scale indication
Peak Detector Bleed-Off: Less than 0.01% per second
Display Type: 3½ digit LCD (plus dummy zero if needed)
Digit Height: 0.4"
Conversion Rate: 3 readings per second
Power: 9 volt battery included
(low battery indication provided)
Battery Life: 15 hours minimum with 350 ohm bridge transducer
Size: 3.6" W X 6.75" L X 1.75" H (91 x 171 x 44 mm)
Weight: 9 oz. (229 g)
Case Material: Molded ABS impact resistant plastic
Connection Method: Four color coded binding posts to accept spade lugs, banana plugs, bare wire or alligator clips

IN STOCK FOR FAST DELIVERY

To Order (Specify Model Number)		
MODEL NUMBER	**PRICE**	**DESCRIPTION**
HHP-SG	**$575**	Handheld Strain Gage Indicator

Comes with 9V battery and complete operator's manual.

Ordering Example: *HHP-SG, handheld strain gage indicator and TQ-102, socket extension reaction torque sensor (pictured above and sold on page F-30), $575 + 420 = **$995.***

PROGRAMMABLE PROCESS SCANNERS
7-CHANNEL INPUT

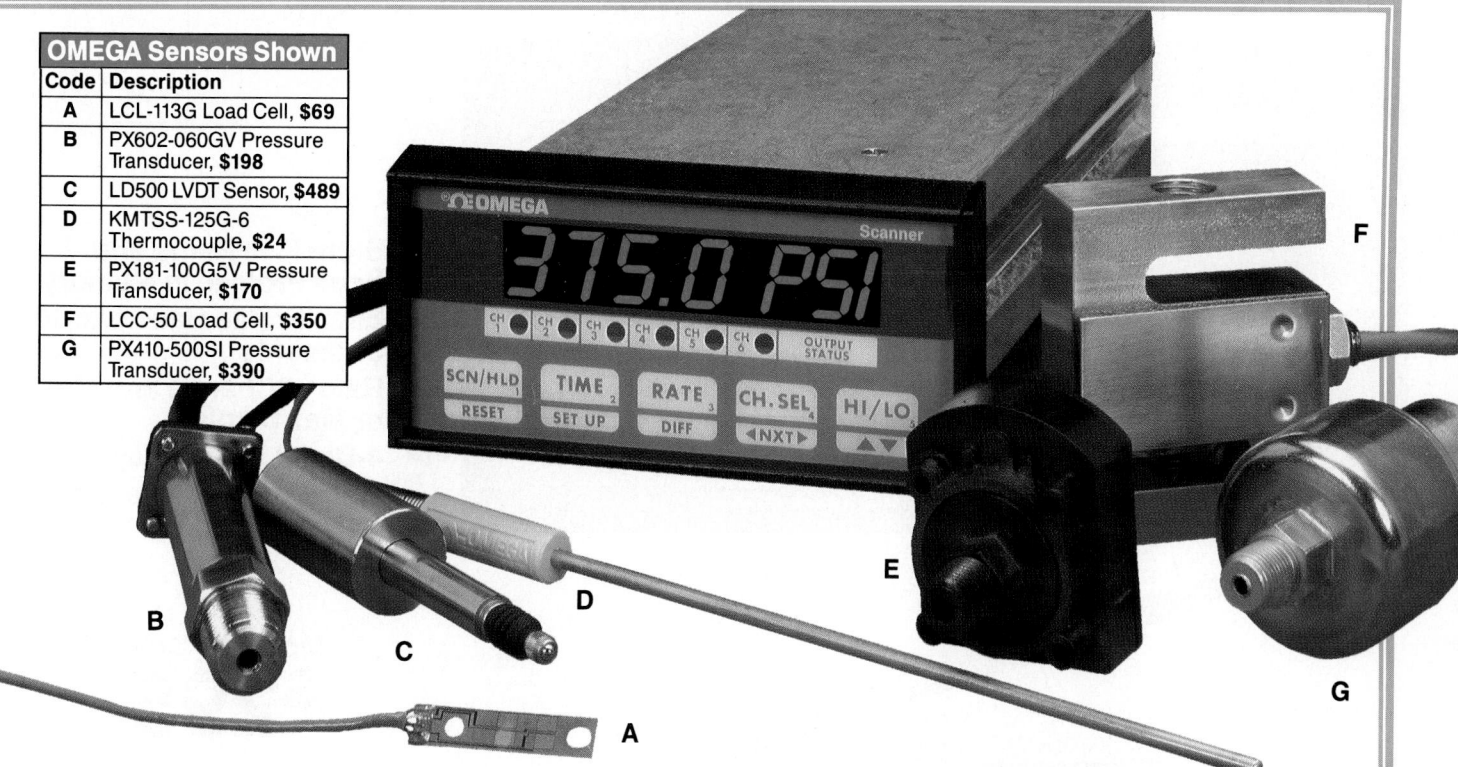

OMEGA Sensors Shown	
Code	**Description**
A	LCL-113G Load Cell, **$69**
B	PX602-060GV Pressure Transducer, **$198**
C	LD500 LVDT Sensor, **$489**
D	KMTSS-125G-6 Thermocouple, **$24**
E	PX181-100G5V Pressure Transducer, **$170**
F	LCC-50 Load Cell, **$350**
G	PX410-500SI Pressure Transducer, **$390**

DPS3000 Series **$595**

✔ **Independent Scaling**
✔ **Thermocouple, Voltage, Current Input**
✔ **Rate of Change and Min or Max Display**
✔ **4-Digit Display Plus 3 Alphanumeric**

The DPS3000 series scanners accept seven individual inputs. The DPS3200 can accept different input types on each channel, while the DPS3100 is limited to one input type on all seven channels.

Both the DPS3100 and DPS3200 meters can be setup to display in any of six operating modes. The unit can scan each channel; display elapsed time; display the channel with highest or lowest reading; scan each channels' deviation from a predetermined setpoint; scan the difference between a 'master' channel and the other 6 inputs.

Specifications
Accuracy: 0.5% Rdg (J, K, T, E: 1°C; S 2°C; R,B 3°C)
CJC Error: 1°C (10°C to 40°C)
Resolution: 1°C/1°F; .025% FS
Power: 120 Vac, 60 Hz
Scan Rate: fixed, 2 channels/s
Channel Display Time: 1 to 999 s per channel
Alarms (optional):
0.5 A @ 120 Vac, SSR; dc driver: 5 Vdc @ 50 mA. One alarm per channel
Deadband: 2 to full scale, adjustable
Cutout: 45 x 92 mm (1.772″ x 3.662″); ⅛ DIN; 9.0″ depth

To Order (Specify Model Number)

Model No.	Price	Input Type(s)
DPS3100-(*)	$595	see * below
DPS3200-TC	695	J, K, T, E, 4-20 mA, 0-10 V
DPS3200-R	695	R, 4-20 mA, 0-10 V
DPS3200-S	695	S, 4-20 mA, 0-10 V
DPS3200-B	695	B, 4-20 mA, 0-10 V
DPS3200-P	695	0-100 mV, 4-20 mA, 0-10 V

Specify input type: J, K, T, E, R, S, B
Ordering Example: *DPS3100-J, **$595.** DPS3100 7-channel scanner, dedicated to type J thermocouple input.*

Options-DPS3100 and DPS3200

Ordering Suffix	Add'l Price	Description
-1	**$ 5**	240 Vac power
-2	25	7 to 12 Vdc power
-3	125	7 alarms (SSR)
-4	125	7 alarms, all dc drivers

DIGITAL TEMPERATURE INDICATOR
OPTIONAL AS A RAMP AND SOAK CONTROLLER

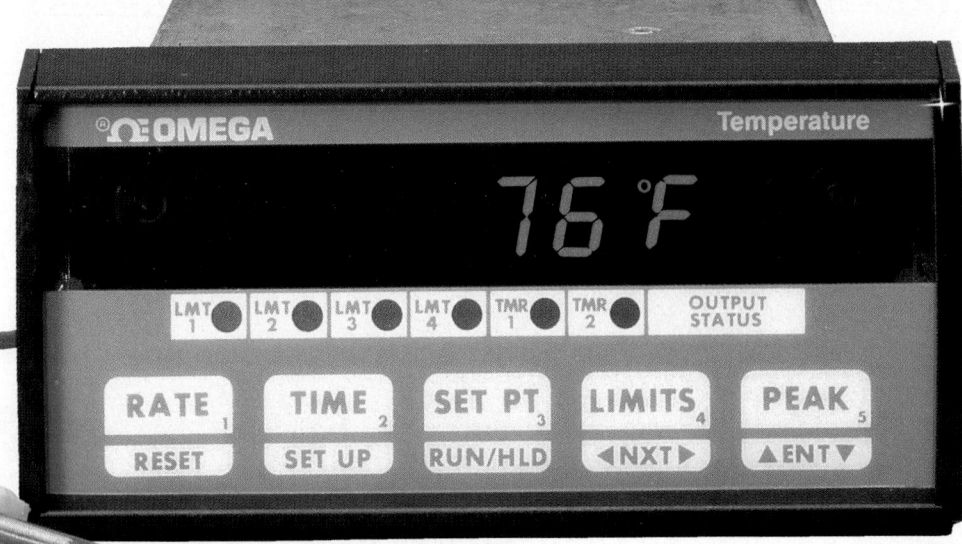

**KMTSS-125G-6 probe
sold separately, $24.**

✔ **Store Five Ramp and Soak Profiles In Memory**
✔ **Each Profile Has up to 10 Segments**
✔ **Rate of Change and Min or Max Display**
✔ **4-Digit LED Display**
✔ **Optional Alarm Relays**

Model DP3400
$295

The DP3400 controller offers sophisticated microprocessor-based temperature control with ramp and soak, in a convenient 1/8 DIN case. The DP3400 can store up to five ramp and soak profiles in memory; each profile can have up to 10 ramp/soak segments. The DP3400 uses on-off control to profile the correct temperature.

The DP3400 can display the average rate of temperature change per minute, as well as the instantaneous temperature. Low and high peaks are constantly monitored, and can be displayed at the touch of a key.

Specifications
Cold Junction Compensation Error: 0.5°C
Resolution: 1°C/1°F
A/D Conversion: 12-bit, dual-slope integrating
Display: 4-digit LED, 0.39"H; 3-digit alphanumeric for engineering units
Power: 120 Vac, 60 Hz; optional 240 Vac, 50 Hz; optional 7.5 to 12 Vdc, 900 mA
External Hold: external low level signal to "hold" pin on rear connector initiated display hold

Dimensions: 2.25"H x 4.4"W, bezel; 8.5"D behind panel
Cutout: 45 x 92 mm (1.772" x 3.662"); 1/8 DIN
Alarms (optional): mechanical relay rated 1 A @ 28 Vdc or 0.5 A @ 120 Vac, SPDT; dc driver rated 5 Vdc @ 50 mA
Deadband: 2 to full scale, adjustable
Termination: ac power, screw terminals; all others, 15-pin card edge connector (included) Analog Output (optional) linearized 1 mV/°C

Options

Ordering Suffix	Add'l. Price	Description
-1	$5	240 Vac power
-2	25	7.5 to 12 Vdc power
-3	110	4 SPDT process alarms, 2 open collector timer alarms
-4	110	6 open collectors: 4 process, 2 timer alarms
-6	125	Analog output

To Order (Specify Model Number)

Model No.	Price	Input	Range*	Accuracy
DP3400-J	$295	J	−200 to 1200°C	1°C + 1 digit
DP3400-K	295	K	−250 to 1370°C	1°C + 1 digit
DP3400-T	295	T	−250 to 400°C	1°C + 1 digit
DP3400-E	295	K	−160 to 990°C	1°C + 1 digit
DP3400-R	295	R	0 to 1750°C	3°C + 1 digit
DP3400-S	295	S	0 to 1750°C	2°C + 1 digit
DP3400-B	295	B	0 to 1800°C	3°C + 1 digit

Note: unit is °C/°F switchable from front panel.
Ordering Example: *DP3400-J-3 controller with type-J thermocouple input, **$295**.*

PROCESS MONITORS FOR FORCE, FLOW AND PRESSURE

✔ **Keypad Scaling to Display Engineering Units and Alphanumeric Label**
✔ **Six Optional Programmable Alarms**
✔ **Min/Max/Rate Std.**
✔ **External Hold and Tare**

All Models

$295

Exclusive! Heavy Duty Mounting Bracket-Standard On All Models

Ordering Example: DP3600-3 is a 4 to 20 mA input indicator with 4 SPDT process alarms and 2 open collector timer alarms, $295 + 110 = $405.

The easy-to-use DP3600 process meter can be user-programmed to work with a wide variety of pressure, flow, and force transducers. Totally programmable from the front panel, the DP3600 has a scaling range from 1 to 9999 units and optional user-defined limits that can be latching or non-latching.

Two time-based limits can range from 1 to 9999 minutes. A password is required to prevent unauthorized tampering with the unit.

SPECIFICATIONS
(typical at 25°C)

Accuracy: 0.025% ±½ digit
Inputs: 4-20 mA, 0-10 Vdc, 0-100 mV
A/D Conversion: 12-Bit, Dual slope integrating converter
Power Requirements: 120 Vac Std., 240 Vac/50 Hz, 7.5-12 Vdc at 900 mA
Display: Red 7-segment LED, 4 digit active display plus 3 "alphas" for units, 0.39" digit height
Excitation voltage output: 5 Vdc at 50 mA
External Features: Hold and tare can be done remotely
Dimensions: Case, 3.60" x 1.75" x 9.20"; Bezel, 4.40" x 2.25" x 0.45"; cutout, ⅛ DIN
Relays (optional): Set points must be positive numbers, SPDT, 1 A at 28 Vdc or 0.5 A at 120 Vac, open collectors 50 mA max

Deadband: 2 to 999 counts programmable
Serial output (optional): RS-232C serial communication
Analog output (optional): 4-20 mA @ 650Ω max load
Connections: ac, input, analog, are screw; terminals all others are 15-pin card edge connectors (included)

To Order Process Indicator

Model	Price	Input type
DP3600	$295	4-20 mA
DP3700	295	0-10 Vdc
DP3800	295	0-100 mV

Card edge connector included.

Options

Ordering Suffix	Price	Description
-1	$5	240 Vac power
-2	25	7.5 to 12 Vdc power
-3	110	4 SPDT process alarms, 2 open collectors timer alarms
-4	110	6 open collectors: 4 process, 2 timer alarms
-6	125	Analog output

DIGITAL PANEL INDICATOR
FOR VOLTAGE AND CURRENT INPUTS

✔ **Rate Alarm Acts as Window Alarm with Hysteresis Around Setpoint**
✔ **Front Panel Programming and Scaling**
✔ **Relays Latch or Auto-Reset**
✔ **Fully Adjustable Zero and Span**

Model DPF64
$255

Temperature Transmitters!

Pressure Transducers!

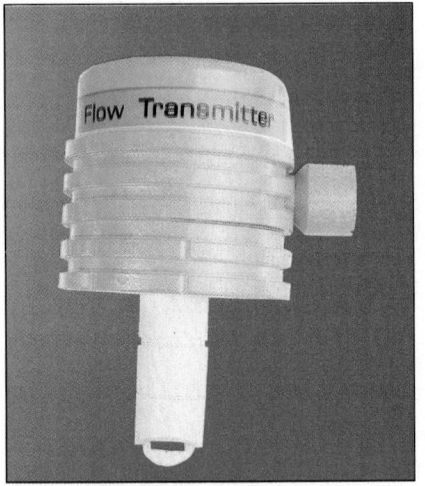

Flowmeters!

The DPF64 is a microprocessor based panel indicator which accepts inputs of 4-20 mA, 0-20 mA, 0-5 V or 1-5V and can be scaled for engineering units directly from the NEMA 4X rated front panel without tweaking internal potentiometers. The two standard 10A (@ 250 Vac) relays can be used for HI and LO setpoint alarm. The DPF64 has a 5-digit display with a floating decimal point that moves left or right depending on

how many "significant figures" have been selected from the front panel. The DPF64 is fully scalable for full scale display up to 59,999. A peak and valley feature allows the user to call up the high and low recent readings.

An optional square root extracting input is available for use with differential pressure flowmeters, such as orifice plates and pitot tubes.

SPECIFICATIONS

Accuracy: ±0.15% of reading

Temp. Range: 32°F to 130°F (Operating); −40°F to 200°F (Storage)

Relay Output: Two SPDT relays, 10A @ 250 Vac; relays latch on auto recycle after 0.1 to 99.9 seconds.

Power: 94-126 Vac, 50/60 Hz or 11-13 Vdc std.; 187-253 Vac or 11-13 Vdc optional-see ordering information for details

Display: 0.6"H 5 digits LED Standby - Non-volatile ram retains scale factor up to 1 year without power

Unregulated Power Output: 24 Vdc @ 50 mA

Panel Cutout: 1.772" H x 3.622" W (45 x 92 mm), 1/8 DIN standard; 4.4" depth

To Order *(Specify Model Number)*		
Model No.	**Price**	**Description**
DPF64	$255	Analog Input Ratemeter with Dual Alarms
DPF64-SQRT	330	DPF64 with square root extraction for use with differential pressure flowmeters

ECONOMICAL DIGITAL PROCESS METERS
SERIES DPF50

From
$139

- ✔ Miniature DIN case with 24 × 72 Bezel
- ✔ Full-Size, 0.56″ LED Display
- ✔ Isolated Transmitter Excitation Supply Optional
- ✔ Zero and Span Adjustments of 2,000 Counts each
- ✔ 99.9% accuracy
- ✔ Display Hold

The Model DPF50 is a low-cost 3½ digit process meter with a full-size 0.56 inch, red or green LED display, yet housed in a small ³⁄₆₄ DIN case (0.87″ × 2.68″ cutout) with a 0.94 × 2.83 in. bezel. The meter requires less than 4.72″ behind the panel, including plug-in screw-clamp connectors (standard).

The DPF52 includes a built-in, galvanically-isolated excitation supply to power two or four-wire transmitters, bridges or active transducers. Output levels of 24 Vdc @ 20 mA or 10 Vdc @ 30 mA are jumper-selectable. On board components allow the five analog input signal ranges to be selected via push-on jumpers in the field.

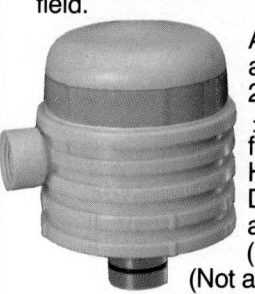

AC power options are 24, 100, 115 or 230 Vac (all ±15%. ac frequency is 49-63 Hz). Non-isolated DC power options are 5 or 7-32 Vdc (±5%) (Not available on Model DPF52).

Optional Flow Transmitter Shown Below. See Pages F-25 to F-27 of the OMEGA Flow and Level Handbook for Details.

199.3

Shown Larger Than Actual Size

SPECIFICATIONS

Range	4-20 mA	0-0.2V	1-5V	0-10V	0-100V
Input resist	13Ω	1 MΩ	1 MΩ	1 MΩ	1MΩ
Max gain	125 cts/mV	10 cts/mV	500 cts/mV	200 cts/mA	20 cts/V
Max input	55 mA	250 Vp	250 Vp	250 Vp	250 Vp

Accuracy at 25°C: ±0.05% of reading +1 count
Full-Scale Step Response: 1s
Read Rate: 2.5/s
Power Consumption, AC or DC: 1.5W, 2W for DPF52
DPF52 Excitation Supply:
Line Regulation . . . . +0.01% V of AC power
Load Regulation . . . . +0.5%
Environmental
Temperature: 32 to 140°F operating, −40 to +185°F storage
Relative Humidity . . . . .95% at 104°F (non condensing)
Mechanical
Bezel . . . . .0.94 × 2.83 in std., 0.98 × 2.96 in with optional DPF50-A adaptor
Weight . . . . .200 g (7 oz)

To Order (Specify Model Number)

Model No.	Price	Description
DPF51	$139	Field selectable for 4-20 mA, 0-199.9 mV, 1-5 Vdc, 0-10 Vdc, 0-100 Vdc input, 115 Vac power, no excitation, red LED display
DPF52	170	DPF51 with sensor excitation output

For 230 Vac power input, add suffix ''−230 Vac'' to part number. No charge. For 100 Vac or 24 Vac power input, add suffix ''−100 Vac'' or ''24 Vac'' to part number, and add $12 to price. For 5 Vdc or 7 to 32 Vdc power input for DPF51, add suffix ''5 Vdc'' or ''−7/32 Vdc'' to part number, and subtract $18 from price. To replace standard red LED display with green LED, add suffix ''−GR'' to part number, and add to $12 to price. For 25 × 75 mm bezel adaptor, order part number DPF50-A. Price= $6.

NEW! PORTABLE BENCHTOP METERS

MDS350 (Above Left) Contains a DP350 Meter and is Shown with an LCCA250 Load Cell ($395). See Page F-13 for Meter Details and Section F for OMEGA's Complete Selection of Load Cells.

MDS41-E-MA (Above Right) is Shown with Model PX305 Current Output Pressure Transmitter ($255). See Page D-7 for Additional Information on DP41 Meter and Page B-60 for Sensor Details.

OMEGA's models DP41, DP205 and DP-350 meters are all available in this attractive, sturdy benchtop case design. All meters can be programmed to display in engineering units of your choice, and come standard with power cord and operator's manual. This attractive case is 4.3" high, 10.2" wide and 10" deep; it weighs 5 pounds. Its light weight is ideally suited for portable benchtop operation. All units operate on 120 Vac for user convenience.

The MDS41 Series contains a powerful microprocessor with adjustable filtering, min/max detection, 6 digit display and 4 open collectors. Strain gage units have a tare button for quick rezeroing.

The MDS205 is an economical microprocessor with 4-20 mA scalable analog output, 2 mechanical relays, front panel tare and a 4 digit display.

The MDS350 utilizes potentiometer adjustments for scaling with a 3½ digit display and a 1mV/count analog output.

Consult Engineering for the Full Selection of Portable Benchtop Displays, Options and Accessories.

MOST POPULAR MODELS!

To Order *(Specify Model Number)*			
Strain Gage Models			
Model	**Price**	**Input**	**Excitation**
MDS41-S- 50MV	$570	± 50mV	10Vdc
MDS41-S-100MV	570	100mV	10Vdc
MDS205-S- 50MV	374	± 50mV	10Vdc
MDS205-S-100MV	374	100mV	10Vdc
MDS350	600	±100mV	5,10Vdc
Voltage/Process Models			
MDS41-E-10V	520	10Vdc	24Vdc
MDS205-E-10V	374	10Vdc	24Vdc
Current Process Models			
MDS41-E-MA	520	4-20mA	24Vdc
MDS205-E-MA	374	4-20mA	24Vdc

Comes with complete operator's manual.

Ordering Example: *MDS41-E-10V is a benchtop meter, with 10 Vdc range and 24 Vdc sensor excitation, **$520**.*

PRESSURE DISPLAY AND CONTROL SYSTEM

Model PC-3500

- Built-In 5 or 10 V Excitation
- Scalable Gain 4.95 to 137 Counts/mV
- Zero Offset ±20% of Full Scale Display
- Scalable Display to Maximum of 1999 Count
- Scalable Inputs from 20 to 100 mV FS
- Jumper Selectable Decimal Point
- Limits, Alarms or Control Functions

The Model PC-3500 Digital Pressure Display and Control System is the latest in readout, control, limits and/or alarms that is designed specifically for use with pressure transducers. Just connect the pressure transducer for display, or set in limits for simple control functions. Operates in minutes!

For complete specifications, see page D-15

19" Rack Panel For 1, 2 or 3 PC-3500's

$995
Base Unit PC 3500 Shown

Order on Right
One, Two or Three Channel Panel Models for Pressure
(Temperature Version Shown— Model RI-5000. See the OMEGA® Temperature Measurement Handbook Section S for details.)

THE MODEL PC-3500 IS DIRECTLY COMPATIBLE WITH PX100, 136, 200, 236, 300, 301, 302, 303, 304, 600, 610, 906, 931 TRANSDUCERS* AND ALL OMEGA LOAD CELLS.**

To Order (Specify model number)

Model	Price	Description
PC-3500	**$995**	Base unit in rack mountable 6" panel
PC-3500-P1	1039	One PC-3500 in a 19" panel
PC-3500-P2	1739	Two PC-3500's in a 19" panel
PC-3500-P3	2439	Three PC-3500's in a 19" panel

* PX 102 Requires External Power Supply, not to Exceed 5 V dc Max.
** May Require Dummy Zero Option for LCC and LCE Load Cells.

PROCESS LOOP INDICATOR
INSTALLS ANYWHERE IN A LOOP!

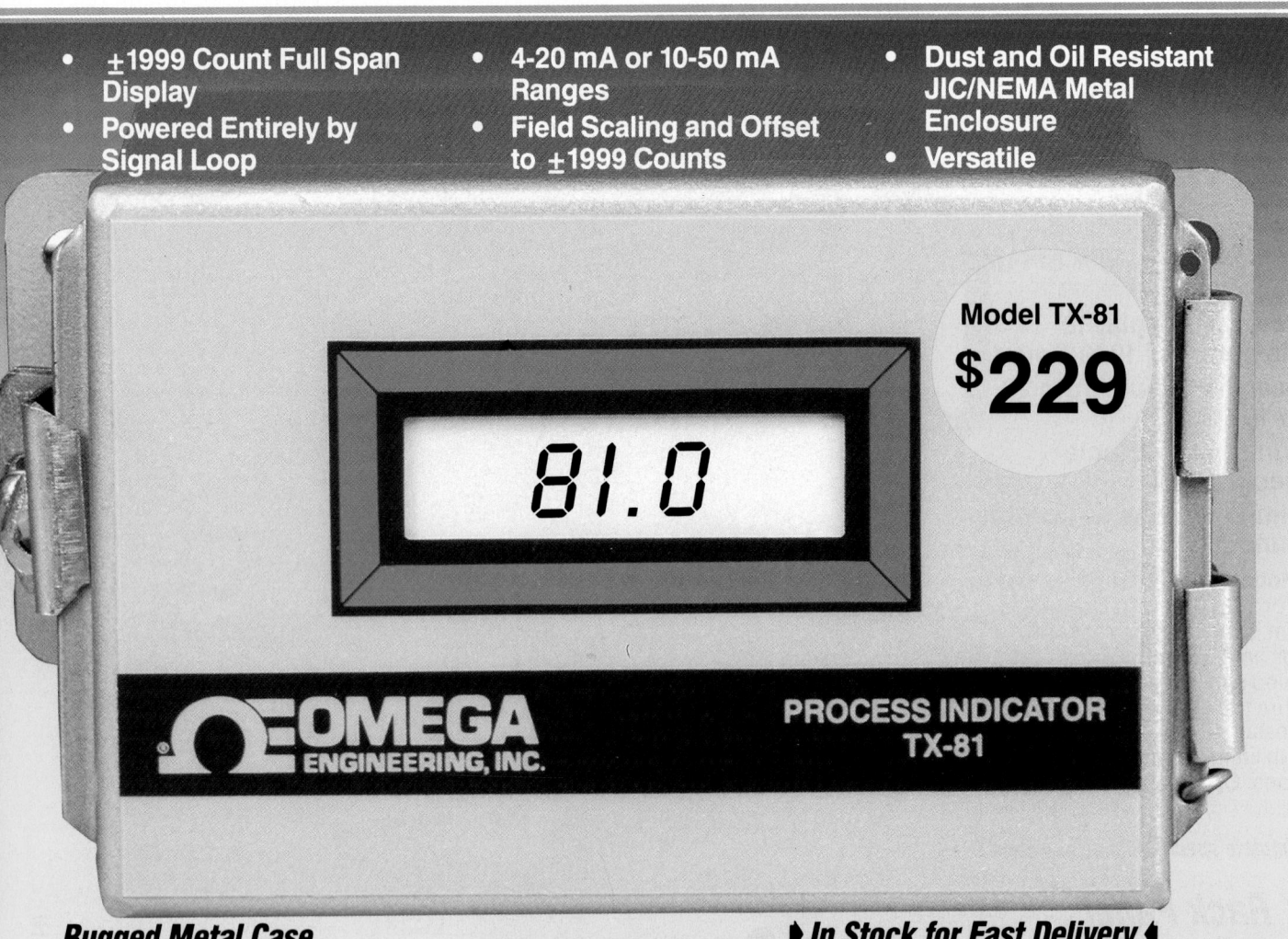

- ±1999 Count Full Span Display
- Powered Entirely by Signal Loop
- 4-20 mA or 10-50 mA Ranges
- Field Scaling and Offset to ±1999 Counts
- Dust and Oil Resistant JIC/NEMA Metal Enclosure
- Versatile

Model TX-81
$229

81.0

ΩEOMEGA ENGINEERING, INC.

PROCESS INDICATOR TX-81

Rugged Metal Case　　　　♦ *In Stock for Fast Delivery* ♦

Compatible Transducers: compatible with current output transducers up to 2000 PSI, on pages B-49 through B-91.

The Model TX-81 Process Loop Indicator is a versatile meter that can be used in any transmitter loop. It provides an easy-to-read liquid crystal display (LCD) from your 4 to 20 mA or 10 to 50 mA transmitter. The JIC/NEMA enclosure provides environmental protection for use in most industrial applications. It can be used in pressure, temperature, humidity or any process variable measurement application where a two wire transmitter is required. No external power is needed. The TX-81 works off your existing current loop power supply and has a voltage drop of only 3.27 volts. The independent adjustments for zero and span over the entire 4000 count range allow one model to be used for most process lab applications. Simply scale the display to match the input range from your transmitter.

SPECIFICATIONS
ELECTRICAL

Linearity: ±2 counts
Resolution: 500 ppm of full scale
Temperature Range: 0° to 50°C
Span Range: 200 counts (high reading minus low reading)
Offset Range Low: −200 min. +200 max.
Offset Range Positive: −72 min. +2000 counts max.
Offset Range Negative: −2000 min. +72 counts
Update Rate: 2.2 min., 2.5 typ., 2.7 updates/sec. max.
Voltage Drop 20 mA (4 mA to 20 mA): 2.20 min., 2.25 typ., 2.37 V max.
Equivalent Resistance @ 20 mA (4 mA to 20 mA): 110 min., 113 typ., 115 ohms max.

Voltage Drop 50 mA (10 mA to 50 mA): 2.30 min., 2.35 typ., 2.40 volts max.
Equivalent Resistance @ 50 mA (10 mA to 50 mA): 46 min., 47 typ., 48 ohms max.

PHYSICAL

JIC Enclosure: 16-gage steel construction EGP-1-1967; NEMA Type 13 Neoprene-gasketed cover, Mylar lens overlay
Dimensions: H: 4″ W: 6″ D: 3″
Weight: 3 lbs.
Display: 0.5″ LCD, 4½ digits 3½ digits of data, + LSD switch programmed zero, °F, °C Sign reversal switch Decimal point switches Overrange indication: MSD, decimal point, and LSD displayed, all others blanked

LOOP POWERED PROCESS INDICATORS

TX21

✔ **Easy Scaling**
✔ **Panel Mounting**

$145

Order TX21
$145

The TX21 panel mounted, loop powered indicator can be conveniently mounted anywhere in the loop. It draws its power from the loop, eliminating the need for hard wiring. Scaling is done via potentiometers and decimal point rocker switches. Independent scaling makes the TX21 perfect for display of temperature, pressure, and force.

SPECIFICATIONS

Input: 4-20 mA/10-50 mA
Accuracy: ±0.1% Rdg ±1 count
Operating Temp.: 10 to 50°C
Storage Temp.: -40 to 60°C
Relative Humidity: 0-90%
Temp. Effects: Zero, ±0.25 Cts/°C; Span, ±0.015% FS/°C
Voltage Drop: 4.2 Vdc @ 4-20 mA; 4.5 Vdc @ 10-50 mA
Read Rate: 3 Rdg/s
Scalability: Zero, ±20% FS; Span, 200-1999 counts
Terminals: Screw
Display: 3½ digit, 0.5" high, 7-segment LCD (black on silver)
Dimensions: Case, 4.05" W x 1.8" H x 4.67 D (102.9 x 45.7 x 118.7 mm)
Cutout Dimensions: 3.924" x 1.682" (99.7 x 142.4 mm)
Weight: 7 oz (198 g)

A Complete System

TX21

Pressure Transmitter
Section B

Power Supply
Section C

INSTRUMENTATION

D

PROCESS LOOP POWERED INDICATORS

Model TX-80 Series
From
$165

Model TX-82A

- ✓ **3½ Digit Display with Dummy Zero**
- ✓ **Powered Entirely by Signal Loop**
- ✓ **4 to 20 or 10 to 50 mA Ranges**
- ✓ **Scaleable Zero and Offset for Engineering Units**
- ✓ **Panel Mount or NEMA Enclosure**

The TX-80 Series two-wire current-loop indicators accept 4-20 or 10-50 mA signals and digitally display the process variable in percent or in engineering units such as pressure, flow, temperature, and level. No separate power supply is required, as these units take power directly from the current loop with a voltage drop of less than 2.5 mV. The units have full zero and span scaling capability for any desired engineering unit display, six coarse zero ranges, three coarse span ranges, three with jumper-select decimal location, and a dummy zero.

The TX-82A has a panel mount design while the TX-83 and TX-84 are more ruggedly designed, with the electronics securely connected to the top of the case. They are designed to withstand high vibration and shock with cases of die-cast metal that are waterproof to 35kPa (5 psi). The TX-83 has barrier strip terminals, and the TX-84 has a ½″ NPT conduit fitting with 12″ lead wires.

Specifications

Current: 4-20 mA and 10-50 mA; 1-5 mA (TX-83, TX-84 only)
Protection: 200 mA (250 mA, TX-83, TX-84) max., forward and 100 mA max. reverse
Voltage Drop: 2.5 mV
Zero Adjust: −2000 to +2000 counts
Span Adjust: 0 to 2000 counts
Normal Mode Rejection (NMR): 46 dB, 50-60 Hz

Accuracy at 25°C: Max. error: ±0.1% of span ±1 count; Zero Tempco: 0.1 count/°C typ., 0.2 count/°C max. Span Tempco: 0.005% of span/°C typ., 0.15% of span/°C max.
Integration Period: 100 ms
Read Rate: 2.5 s
Display Type: 7 segment LCD, 8.9 mm (0.35 in) high; jumper select decimal point
Overrange: Three least-significant active digits blank
Environmental Operating Temperature: (for TX-83, TX-84): −40 to +85°C (−40 to +185°F); for TX-82: 0 to 55°C) (32 to 131°F)
Mechanical (TX-82A)
  Weight: 128 g
  Case Material: ABS polycarbonate
  Case Size: Bezel: (W×H×T): 96×48×8 mm
  Depth behind bezel with cover: 100 mm
  Panel Cutout (W×H): 92×45 mm
Electrical Connections: plug-in socket with screw clamps for wire sizes 16 to 26 AWG
Mechanical (TX-83, TX-84):
  Weight: 400 g (14 oz.)
  Diameter: 74 mm (2.9 in)
  Height (incl. barrier): 48 mm (1.9 in)
Electrical Connections: TX-83: 3-terminal barrier; TX-84: ½″ NPT male conduit fitting with two 0.3 meter long #18 stranded wires

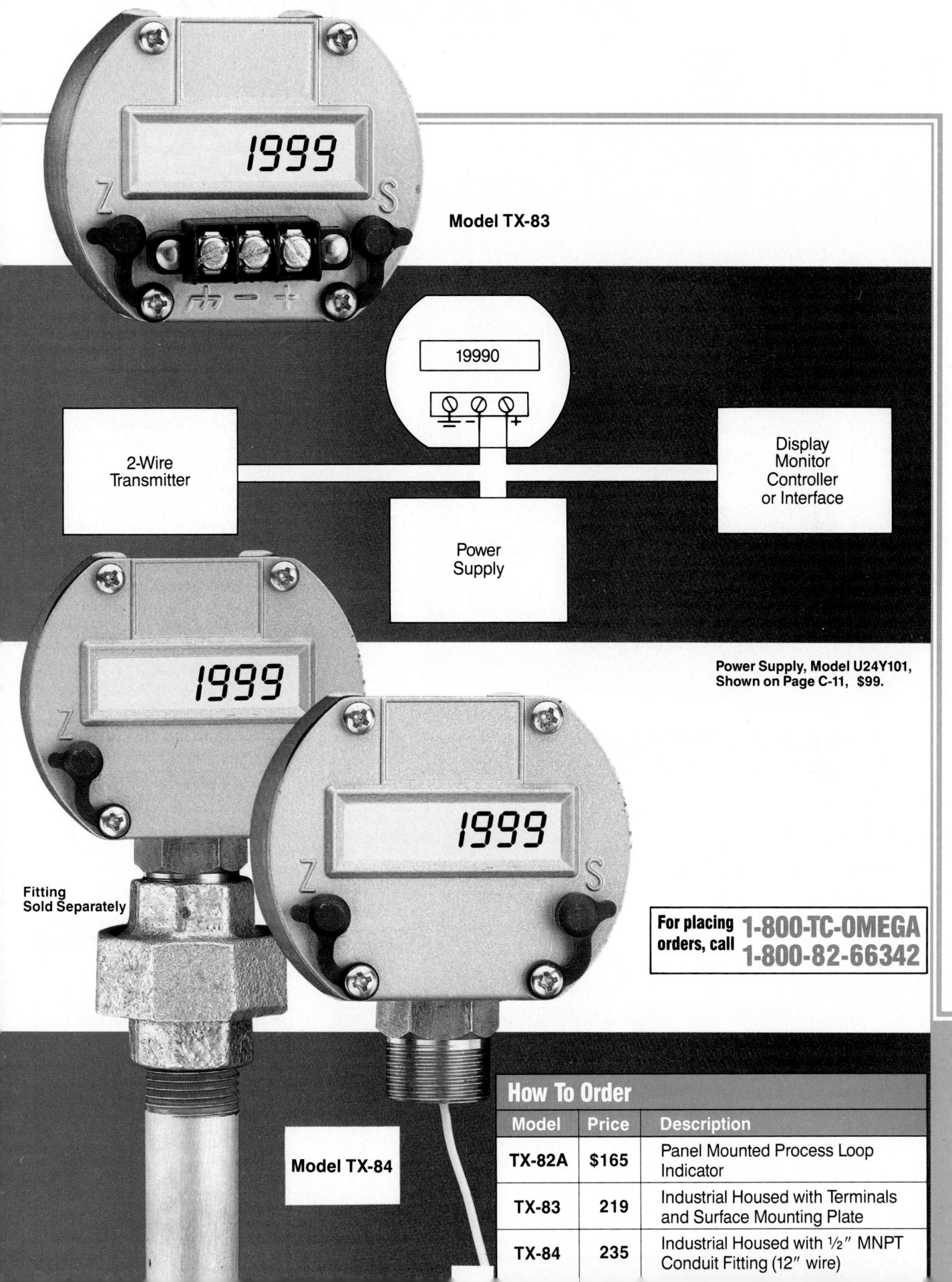

Model TX-83

19990

2-Wire
Transmitter

Power
Supply

Display
Monitor
Controller
or Interface

Power Supply, Model U24Y101,
Shown on Page C-11, $99.

Fitting
Sold Separately

Model TX-84

How To Order

Model	Price	Description
TX-82A	$165	Panel Mounted Process Loop Indicator
TX-83	219	Industrial Housed with Terminals and Surface Mounting Plate
TX-84	235	Industrial Housed with ½″ MNPT Conduit Fitting (12″ wire)

PROCESS CONTROLLER
CN2000 SERIES

MADE IN
USA

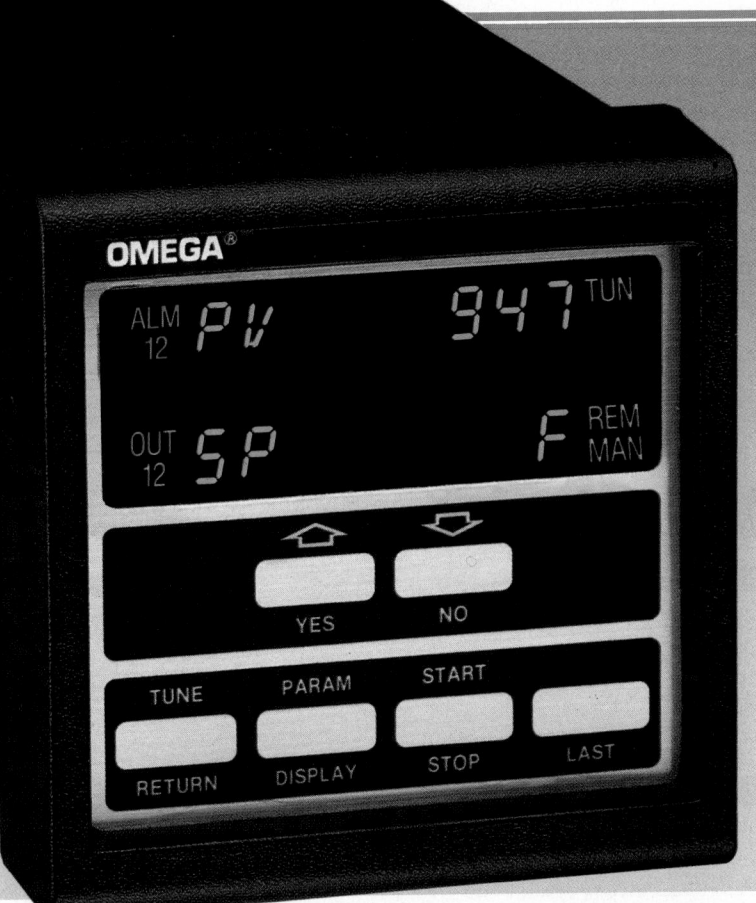

- ✔ For Millivolt, Volt and Milliamp Transducers
- ✔ RS-232 and RS-422 Communication for Remote Control through a Computer System
- ✔ Wide Variety of Output and Alarm Options Available

Features

- ✔ PID Control
- ✔ User Friendly Tuning Via Front Keypad
- ✔ Continuous Indication of Output, Alarm, and Operating Status
- ✔ Comprehensive Manual Included

From
$455

To Order (Specify model number)

Model No.	Price	1st Output and Mode	2nd Output and Mode	Alarms
CN2001(*)	$455	1A SSR PID	—	None
CN2002(*)	485		1 A SSR, ON/OFF	None
CN2001(*)-A	505		—	Dual
CN2002(*)-A	535		1A SSR, ON/OFF	Dual

Insert input code. Price includes range premiums.

INPUT TYPES

Code	Range	Type
MA	4-20 mA	Current
MV	0-100 mV dc	Voltage
V5	0-5 Vdc	Voltage
V10	0-10 Vdc	Voltage

Units factory scaled for 0-100% display.
Zero and span field selectable. Max. display
is 3200 counts.

OUTPUT OPTIONS

Ordering Suffix	Price	Description
-F1	N/C	4-20mA, output 1, reverse
-F2	N/C	4-20mA, output 2, direct
-DC1	N/C	0-5 Vdc, output 1, reverse
-DC2	N/C	0-5 Vdc, output 2, direct

EXCITATION OPTIONS*

Excitation	Code	Price	Description
*Not Available with Options D2-D6 or Model CN2000A.			
5 V dc	X5 V	$50	5 V dc @ 40 mA
10 V dc	X10 V	50	10 V dc @ 100 mA

COMMUNICATION OPTIONS

Code	Price	Description
D1	$ 50	remote analog setpoint (n/a with 2000A)
D2	205	non-isolated RS-232C
D3	205	isolated RS-232C
D4	205	non-isolated RS-422
D5	205	isolated RS-422
D6	205	isolated 20 mA loop
D7	50	remote start/stop (n/a with 2000A)

Also Available Auto/Manual Output Control. To Order, Add Suffix AM to Model No., and Add $50 to Price.

MICROPROCESSOR BASED CONTROLLER
CN2000 SERIES

Dimensions

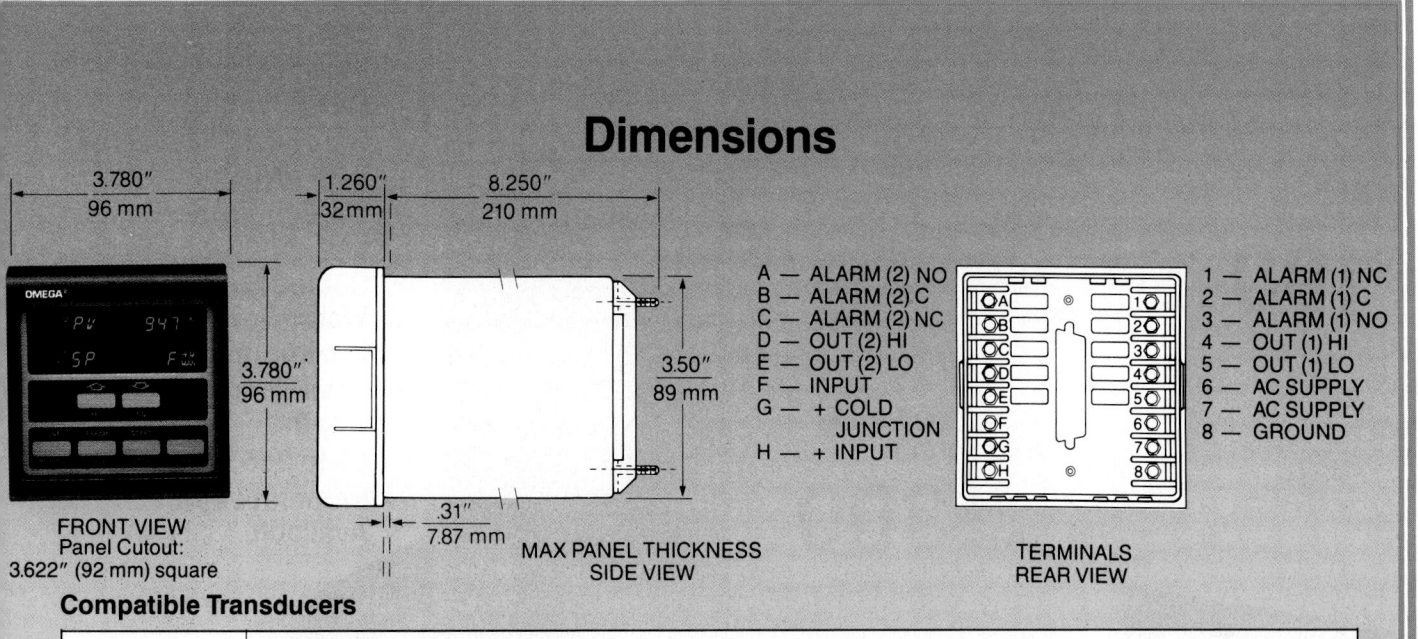

FRONT VIEW
Panel Cutout:
3.622" (92 mm) square

MAX PANEL THICKNESS
SIDE VIEW

TERMINALS
REAR VIEW

A — ALARM (2) NO
B — ALARM (2) C
C — ALARM (2) NC
D — OUT (2) HI
E — OUT (2) LO
F — INPUT
G — + COLD
       JUNCTION
H — + INPUT

1 — ALARM (1) NC
2 — ALARM (1) C
3 — ALARM (1) NO
4 — OUT (1) HI
5 — OUT (1) LO
6 — AC SUPPLY
7 — AC SUPPLY
8 — GROUND

Compatible Transducers

Input Type	Compatible transducer types
mV	Millivolt output transducers on pages B-10 thru B-40 with < 32 counts per mV (max display 3200)
V5	Amplified voltage transducers with 5V dc full scale output, on pages B-55 thru B-57
V10	Amplified voltage transducers with up to 10 V dc full scale output, on pages B-41 thru B-57
mA	Current loop transducers on pages B-58 thru B-87

Key Functions: Front Keypad is the operator interface. There are no internal pots, switches, or jumpers to set or adjust. Security key codes are required to access certain programs.

TUNE-RETURN
Calls up TUNE routine. Also RETURN program to normal operation.

UP-YES
Drive setpoint to increase in value. Positive response to displayed question.

DISPLAY
PARAM
Advances display in programmed sequence.

DOWN-NO
Drives setpoint to decrease in value. Negative response to displayed question.

START-STOP
Shuts off or turns on outputs. Not a power switch.

LAST
Recalls previous step to display. A backup key.

SPECIFICATIONS

INPUTS

Line Voltage: 117 Vac
Current Input: 4-20 mA
Voltage Input: 0-5 V dc, 0-10 V dc
Power Consumption: 8 watts typical
Accuracy: ±2 counts
Temperature Stability: 3μV/°C
Temperature Rating: 40-130°F
Common Mode Noise Rejection: 140 dB typical
Normal Mode Noise Rejection: 65 dB typical
RFI: Less than 0.5% of setpoint at 3 m from 5 watt source
Calibration: Permanent in memory
Break Protection: Upscale, alarms triggered

ADJUSTMENTS

Cycle Time: Adjustable from 1 to 60 seconds
Rate (derivative): Adjustable from 0.02 to 5 minutes; independent primary and secondary rates

Reset (integral): Adjustable from 0.01 to 20 repeats per minute; independent for primary and secondary outputs
Proportional Band (gain): Adjustable from 1 to 200% of span; independent primary and secondary bands
On/Off Output Type Deadband: Selectable at 0.25, 0.50, or 1.0% of span

OUTPUTS

Display: Vacuum Fluorescent type; two rows of 8 each alphanumeric characters; Indicators for output 1 and 2, alarm/timer 1 and 2
Primary and Secondary: Independent
Current: 4-20 mA proportional, into 1 kΩ max. load
Voltage: 0-5 V dc proportional, into 1 kΩ min. load
Solid State Relay: Optically isolated, SPST, normally open, 1 amp at 120/240 V ac
Alarms (CN2000A Models): Two independent; user select for high/low, process/deviation/deviation bond/timer type, SPDT relay, normally open, 1 amp at 120/240 V ac

INSTRUMENTATION

D

MICROPROCESSOR-BASED PROCESS CONTROLLERS

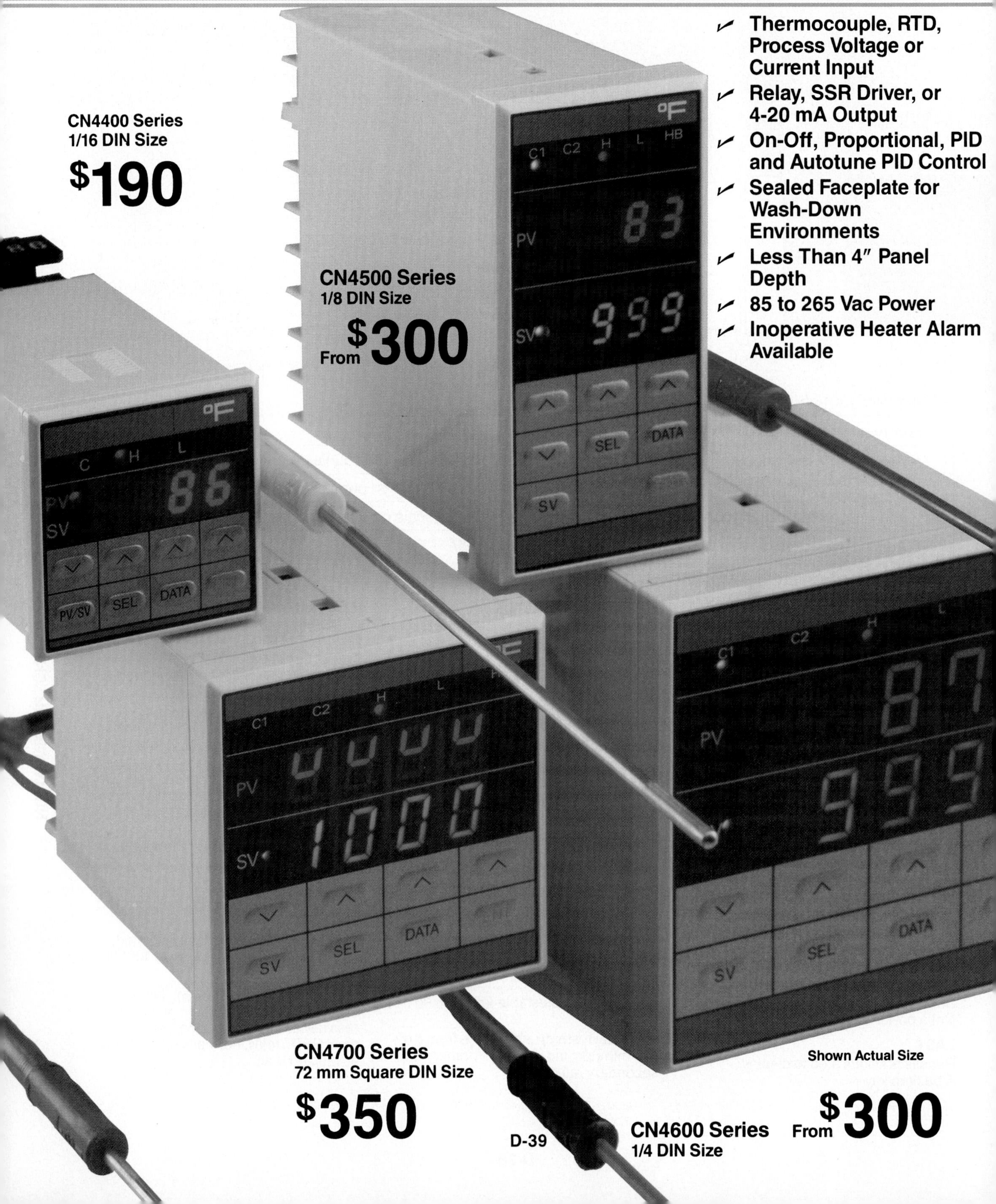

CN4400 Series
1/16 DIN Size

$190

CN4500 Series
1/8 DIN Size

From # $300

- ✔ Thermocouple, RTD, Process Voltage or Current Input
- ✔ Relay, SSR Driver, or 4-20 mA Output
- ✔ On-Off, Proportional, PID and Autotune PID Control
- ✔ Sealed Faceplate for Wash-Down Environments
- ✔ Less Than 4″ Panel Depth
- ✔ 85 to 265 Vac Power
- ✔ Inoperative Heater Alarm Available

CN4700 Series
72 mm Square DIN Size

$350

D-39

Shown Actual Size

CN4600 Series From # $300
1/4 DIN Size

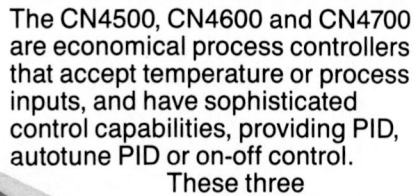

The CN4500, CN4600 and CN4700 are economical process controllers that accept temperature or process inputs, and have sophisticated control capabilities, providing PID, autotune PID or on-off control. These three controllers have common features,

but differ in panel size requirements. The CN4500, CN4600 and CN4700 are available with mechanical relay, 24 Vdc SSR driver or 4-20 mA output. All three units have dual digital displays, for continuous indication of process temperature and setpoint. These units are available with either single or dual outputs; dual output models can be used for heat/cool, heat/heat or cool/cool control. Options available include dual alarms (user-selectable between high/low and process/deviation action), as well as an inoperative heater alarm. The heater alarm is a 1 A mechanical relay that is triggered when the heater current transformer senses when the heater is not getting power.

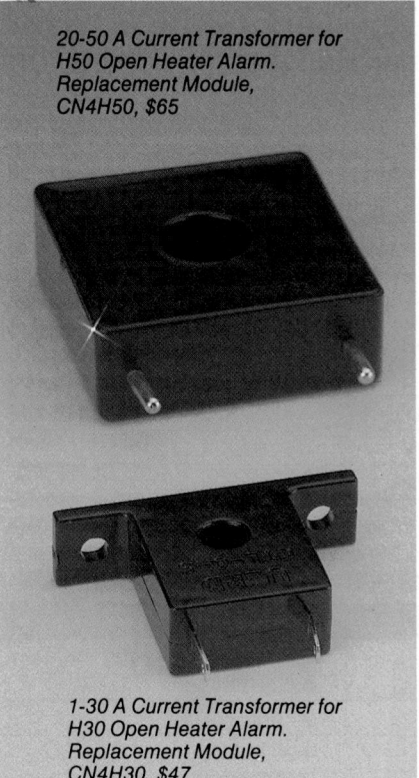

20-50 A Current Transformer for H50 Open Heater Alarm. Replacement Module, CN4H50, $65

1-30 A Current Transformer for H30 Open Heater Alarm. Replacement Module, CN4H30, $47

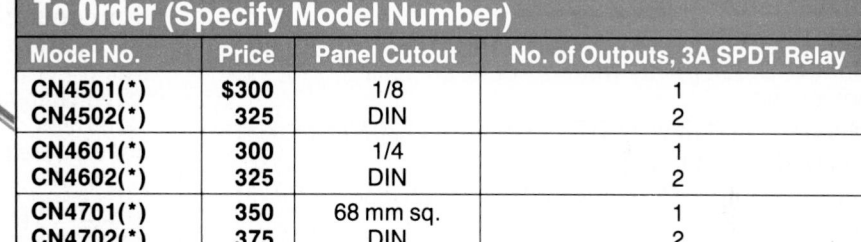

To Order (Specify Model Number)

Model No.	Price	Panel Cutout	No. of Outputs, 3A SPDT Relay
CN4501(*)	$300	1/8	1
CN4502(*)	325	DIN	2
CN4601(*)	300	1/4	1
CN4602(*)	325	DIN	2
CN4701(*)	350	68 mm sq.	1
CN4702(*)	375	DIN	2

* Specify TR for Thermocouple/RTD input or CV for current/voltage input

Output Options – No Additional Cost

Ordering Suffix	Output Type
-D1	SSR Driver, output 1
-F1	4-20 mA, output 1
-D2	SSR Driver, output 2*
-F2	4-20 mA, output 2*

* Available with CN4502, CN4602 and CN4702 only.

Alarm Options

Ordering Suffix	Price	Description
-A	$25	Dual Alarms
-H30*	73	Non-operative Heater Alarm, includes C4H30 1 to 30 A transformer
-H50*	90	Non-operative Heater Alarm, includes C4H50 20 to 50 A transformer

* Note: Not available with options F1 or F2

Ordering Example: CN4502TR-D1-H30, $398; CN4500 series controller, 1/8 DIN size, thermocouple/RTD input (user selectable for calibration), optional 24 Vdc SSR driver for output 1, standard 3 A mechanical relay for output 2, 'no heater current' alarm with a 1-30 A current transformer.

INSTRUMENTATION

D

CN4000 SERIES
PANEL CUTOUTS

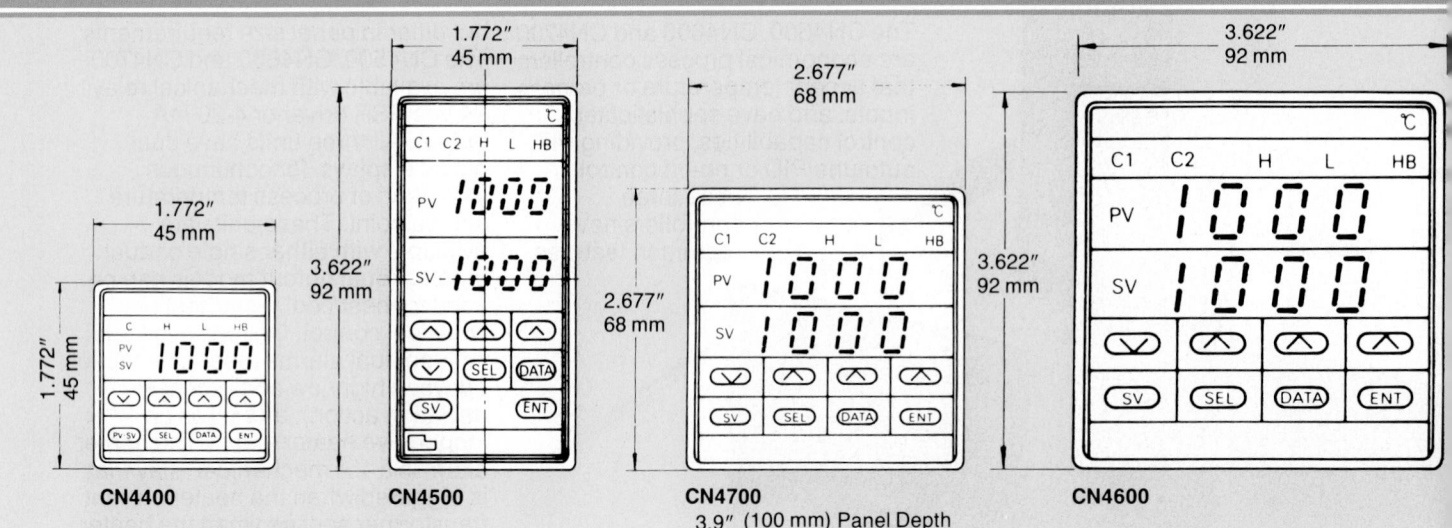

CN4400

CN4500

CN4700
3.9″ (100 mm) Panel Depth

CN4600

Common Specifications

Proportional Band: 0 to 999.9%

Integral Time: 0 to 9999 s

Derivative Time: 0 to 3600 s

Tuning: P, PI, PID, autotune PID, on-off

Cycle Time: 1 to 150 s

On-Off Deadband: 0 to 20%

Anti-Reset Windup: standard

Sensor Break Protection: up- or down-scale, selectable

Mechanical Relay: SPDT, 3 A max and 220 Vac max

SSR Driver: 24 Vdc @ 60 mA

Current Output: 4-20 mA, 600 ohm max. load resistance

Accuracy: 0.5% FS + 1 digit

Display: dual 4-digit LED displays

Memory: setpoint and PID parameters retained in non-volatile memory

Self-Diagnostics: standard

Operating Ambient Range: 14 to 122°F (−10 to 50°C); 0 to 90% RH

Storage Ambient Range: −4 to 130°F (−20 to 60°C)

Power: 85 to 265 Vac

Power Consumption: 10 VA

Isolation: 1500 Vac

Lock-Out: unauthorized changes of settings prohibited for all changes, or all changes except setpoint

Ramp to Setpoint: 0.1 to 999° (C/F) min, if activated

Dimensions, CN4500: 3.78″ H x 1.89″ W x 3.94″ D (96 mm x 48 mm x 100 mm); 10.7 oz (300 g) weight; 1.772″ H X 3.622″ W (45 x 92 mm) cutout (1/8 DIN)

Dimensions, CN4600: 3.78″ sq face, 3.94″ D (96 mm sq x 100 mm D); 14.3 oz (400 g) weight; 3.622″ sq (92 mm) cutout (1/4 DIN)

Dimensions, CN4700: 2.83″ sq face, 3.94″ D (72 mm sq x 100 mm D); 10.7 oz (300 g) weight; 2.68″ sq (68 mm) cutout (DIN)

OPTIONS

Alarms: user-select for high or low, process level or deviation from setpoint action; rated 1 A at 220 Vac

Non-operative Heater Alarm: current transformer senses loss of power to heater, to trigger alarm; alarm rated 1 A @ 220 Vac; integral self-compensation circuit minimizes effects of heater voltage variation; controller must be powered from same power supply for the heater

Input Types and Ranges – All CN4000 Units

Input		Range	
Code	Type	°F	°C
TR	J	32 to 1832	0 to 1000
	K	32 to 2192	0 to 1200
	T	−328 to 752	−200 to 400
	E	32 to 1472	0 to 800
	R	32 to 2912	0 to 1600
	S	32 to 2912	0 to 1600
	B	32 to 3212	0 to 1800
	RTD	−238 to 752	−150 to 400
CV	V	1 to 5 Vdc	
	mA	4 to 20 mA dc	

Output Types – All CN4000 Units

Type	Description
Mechanical Relay	SPDT, Rated 3 A @ 220 Vac
SSR Driver	24 Vdc Pulse
Current	4-20 mA dc <600Ω load resistance

AUTOTUNE PROCESS CONTROLLERS
1/16 DIN MICRO CONTROLLER CN4400 SERIES

2 YEAR WARRANTY / *CARE*

$190

- ✔ Thermocouple, RTD, Voltage or Current Input
- ✔ Ramp to Setpoint Control
- ✔ Relay, SSR Driver, or 4-20 mA Output
- ✔ On-Off, Proportional, PID and Autotune PID Control
- ✔ Sealed Faceplate for Wash-Down Environments
- ✔ Less Than 4″ Panel Depth
- ✔ 85 to 265 Vac Power
- ✔ Optional Alarm Available

The CN4400 is an economical 1/16 DIN process controller that accepts temperature or process inputs. It has sophisticated control capabilities, providing PID, autotune PID and on-off control. The CN4400 is available with mechanical relay, SSR driver or 4-20 mA output. For fast hook-up, the CN4400 features a removeable socket mount design with screw terminals. The ramp to setpoint function allows control of the rate of ascent/descent each time the setpoint is changed.

SPECIFICATIONS
Proportional Band: 0 to 999.9%
Integral Time: 0 to 9999 s
Derivative Time: 0 to 3600 s
Tuning: P, PI, PID, autotune PID, on-off
Cycle Time: 1 to 150 s
On-Off Deadband: 0 to 20%
Anti-Reset Windup: standard
Sensor Break Protection: up- or down-scale, selectable
Mechanical Relay: SPDT, 3 A @ 220 Vac max
SSR Driver: 24 Vdc @ 60 mA
Current Output: 4-20 mA, 600 ohm max. load resistance
Ramp to Setpoint: 0.1 to 999°C (0°C/°F) per minute, if activated
Accuracy: 0.5% FS + 1 digit
Display: single 4-digit LED, selectable for PV/SP indication
Memory: setpoint and PID parameters retained in non-volatile memory
Self-Diagnostics: standard
Operating Ambient Range: 14 to 122°F (– 10 to 50°C); 0 to 90% RH
Storage Ambient Range: – 4 to 130°F (– 20 to 60°C)
Power: 85 to 265 Vac; 10 VA consumption
Isolation: 1500 Vac
Dimensions: 1.89″ sq face, 3.7″ D including socket (48 mm sq. x 93 mm D); 5.4 oz (150 g weight); 1.772″ sq (45 mm) cutout (1/16 DIN)
Alarms: user-select for high or low, process level or deviation from setpoint action; rated 1 A at 220 Vac

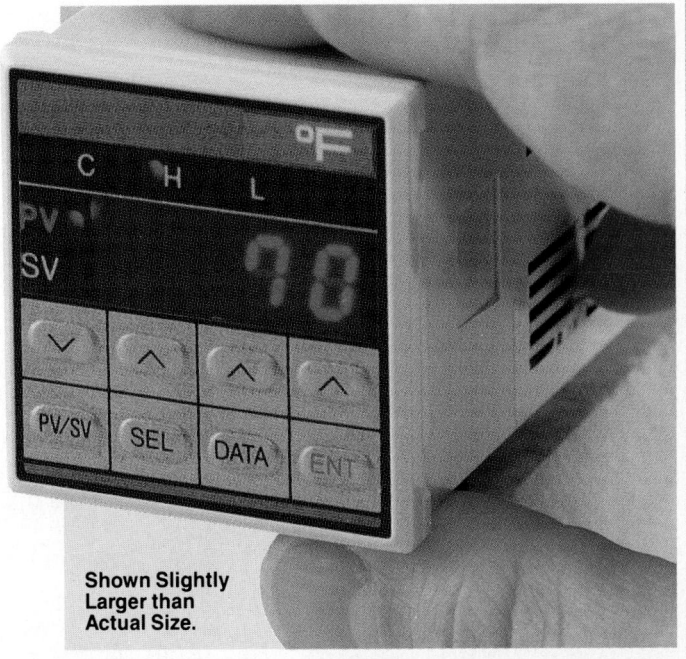

Shown Slightly Larger than Actual Size.

To Order *(Specify Model Number)*

Model No.	Price	Description
CN4401TR	$190	Thermocouple or RTD input
CN4401CV	190	1-5 Vdc/4-20 mA input

Each unit includes mounting socket and complete operator's manual.

Output Types and Options

Ordering Suffix	Add'l Price	Description
-D	N/C	SSR Driver, 24 Vdc Pulse
-F	N/C	4-20 mA Output
-A	25	Single 1 A (SPST) Alarm Relay

Input Types and Ranges

Input		Range	
Code	Type	°F	°C
TR	J	32 to 1832	0 to 1000
	K	32 to 2192	0 to 1200
	T	– 328 to 752	– 200 to 400
	E	32 to 1472	0 to 800
	R	32 to 2912	0 to 1600
	S	32 to 2912	0 to 1600
	B	32 to 3212	0 to 1800
	100Ω Pt RTD	– 238 to 752	– 150 to 400
CV	1-5 Vdc	Scalable – 1999 to 2999	
	4-20 mAdc		

Ordering Example: *CN4401TR-F is a controller with thermocouple or RTD input and 4-20 mA output (no charge), **$190**.*

HIGH ACCURACY BENCHTOP VOLTAGE AND CURRENT CALIBRATOR
FOR THE PROCESS INDUSTRY

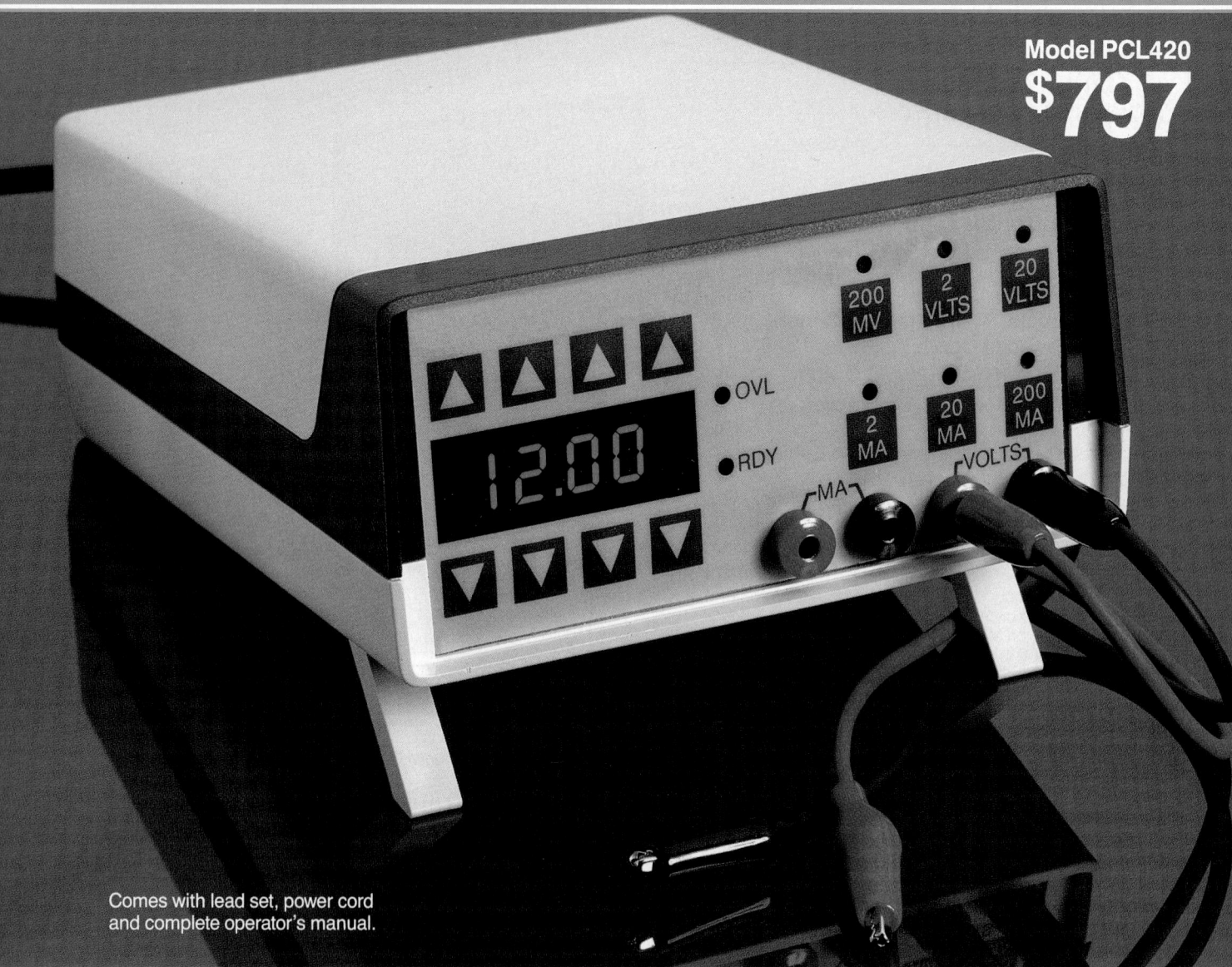

Comes with lead set, power cord and complete operator's manual.

- **High Accuracy - 0.025% FS on All Ranges**
- **Rugged - High Impact Case With Foldaway Tilt Legs Provides Knock-Around Ruggedness and Easy Viewing of Display**
- **Easy-To-Use - Range Selection Keys Selects Any of 6 Ranges Just By Pushing Key. Output Changes Also for Stepping Output Between Ranges.**
- **Quick Output Selection - Up/Dn Scroll Keys Provide Quick Step Changes of Each Decade of Output. They Also Allow Precise Adjustment of Each Setting.**
- **Six Ranges**

Voltage	Current
0-199.9 mV	0-1.999 mA
0-1.999 V	0-19.99 mA
0-19.99 V	0-199.9 mA

The PCL420 is a high accuracy benchtop calibrator, rugged enough for industry, precise enough for electronic testing. Its unique combination of voltage and current sourcing and high accuracy and stability make it a versatile instrument used in many industries.

PCL420 calibrators can be found in quality control, field service, calibration laboratories, aerospace, and process measurement and control applications.

SPECIFICATIONS

Accuracy: 0.025% FS on all ranges
Load Driving Capability: $\pm$5mA on all voltage ranges
Voltage Source: 15 Vdc available on current ranges to drive loop
Temperature Stability: 50 ppm/°C
Temperature Range: 32 to 104°F
Output Impedance: less than 0.5 ohms (voltage ranges only)
Power: 115 Vac $\pm$10% (230 Vac optional)
Weight: 4 lbs. (1.8 kg)

RUGGED, HANDHELD CALIBRATORS

PORTABLE VOLTAGE AND CURRENT CALIBRATOR

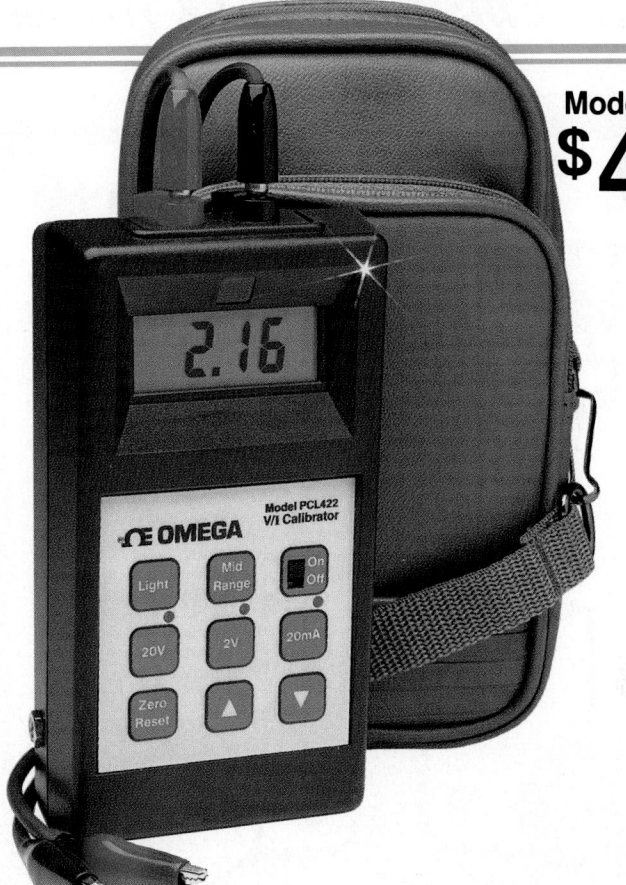

Model PCL422
$430

- ✓ **Back Lighted Display for Visibility in Low Light Areas or at Night**
- ✓ **Mid-Range Key Sets Output to 1V, 10V, or 10mA Depending Upon Pre-selected Range**
- ✓ **Built-In 20V Supply for Driving Current Loop**
- ✓ **Two Modes of Operations (Sources and Simulates)**

SPECIFICATIONS:
Accuracy: 0.05% FS
Ranges: 0-19.99 mA; 0-1.999 V; 0-19.99 V
Operating Temperature: 0 to 104°F
Temperature Stability: 50 ppm/°C
Power: 9V battery
Weight: 12 oz (340 g)

Model PCL401
$179

Supplied with Lead Set, Soft Carrying Case and 9V Battery

Supplied with 8″ Leads with Alligator Clips and Long Life 9V Battery

MINIATURE LOOP CALIBRATOR

- ✓ **Five Precalibrated 20 mA Settings: 4, 8, 12, 16**
- ✓ **Easy One-Hand Operation**

Two Operating Modes
1. **Source: Unit Controls Loop Current and Provides Loop Excitation Up to 30 Vdc.**
2. **Simulate: Unit Controls Loop Current Using External Loop Power Supply.**

SPECIFICATIONS
Accuracy: ± 0.075% FS
Temperature Stability: 100 ppm/°C
Internal Power: 9V battery
External Power: up to 30 Vdc max.
Max. Loop Resistance: 300 ohms
Operating Temp.: 0 to 120°F
Battery Life: > 25 hr
Dimensions: 1.0″ H x 2.4″ W x 3.8″ D (25.4 x 61 x 96.5 mm)
Weight: 8 oz.

COMPACT PROCESS CALIBRATORS
FOR CURRENT AND VOLTAGE
CALIBRATE DISPLAYS/CHECK TRANSDUCERS

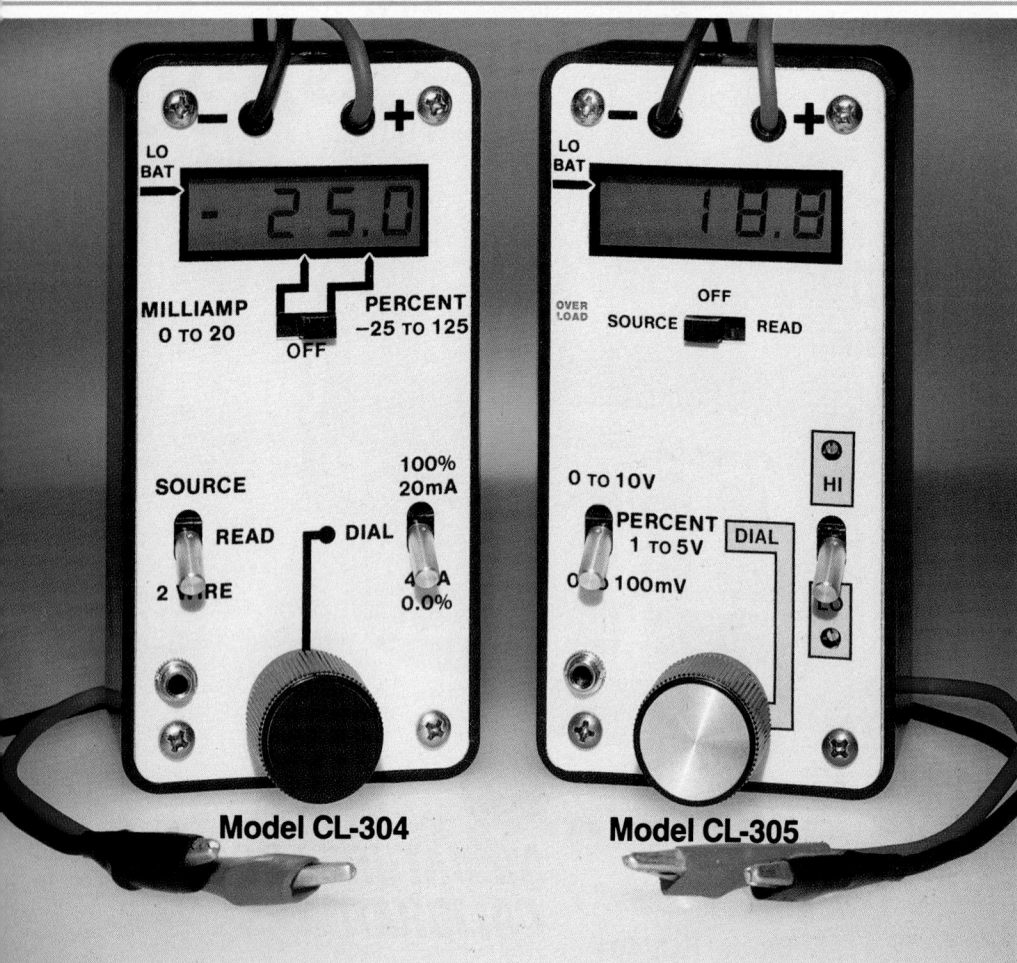

Model CL-304 **Model CL-305**

damaging the calibrator or the loop to be calibrated. Special protective circuitry withstands accidental misconnection in any mode without fuses.

Model CL-305

✔ **Calibrate, Indicate and Test Voltage Signals**

✔ **Volts—3 Way**
Voltage Source
Voltage Sink
Voltage Read

✔ **3 Ranges**
0 to 100 mV
0 to 10 mV
0 to 100% (1 to 5 V)

✔ **"Quick Check" Switch**
User Adjustable HI and LO Plus Continuous Dial

The Model CL-305 Process Voltage Analyzer combines a self-contained voltage source, a voltage sink and a large LCD digital readout in a pocket sized instrument.

Three ranges provide 0.1% resolution from 0 to 100 mV, 0 to 10 V and 0 to 100% (of 1 to 5). 100% overrange capability allows signals up to 200 mV or 20 V to be sourced or read.

Source mode uses built-in batteries to calibrate high or low impedance voltage or millivolt instruments.

User adjustable quick check switch provides instant HI and LO settings in source mode. Dial position selects a continuously adjustable potentiometer.

Sink mode operates automatically in source position to allow calibration of live circuits without disconnecting wires.

Read mode provides precise indication of both positive and negative voltages in the 100 mV and 10 V ranges. 0 to 100% is displayed in the 1 to 5 volt range for checkout of process control instruments.

$405
Process Loop Analyzer

Model CL-304
✔ **Calibrate, Indicate and Test 4-20 mA Systems**
✔ **Triple Function: Source, Read & 2-Wire Simulate**
✔ **Precise 3½ Digit LCD Display**
✔ **"Quick-Check" Zero and Full Scale Functions**

The Model CL-304 Signal Analyzer combines a self-contained 0-24 mA source, a two-wire simulator and a large LCD digital readout in a single pocket sized instrument.

Dual range allows display of each function in percent of 4-20 mA signal, as well as directly in milliamps.

$405
Voltage Analyzer

110 V AC Adaptor CL-303-AC $22

Percent range displays minus 25.0% to plus 125.0% with 0.1% resolution. Milliamp range displays from 0.00 to 19.99 mA with 10 microamp resolution.

Source mode uses built-in batteries to provide 0-24 mA into any load from 0-1000 ohms. An optional AC adaptor plugs in for continuous bench use. Two-wire transmitters can be powered and measured in this mode.

Two-wire simulator mode modulates external power to pass 4-20 mA. The Model CL-304 uses any loop power from 2 to 100 Vdc.

Read mode displays either milliamps or percent of 4-20 mA signal. Maximum read current is limited to 25 mA to minimize the possibility of

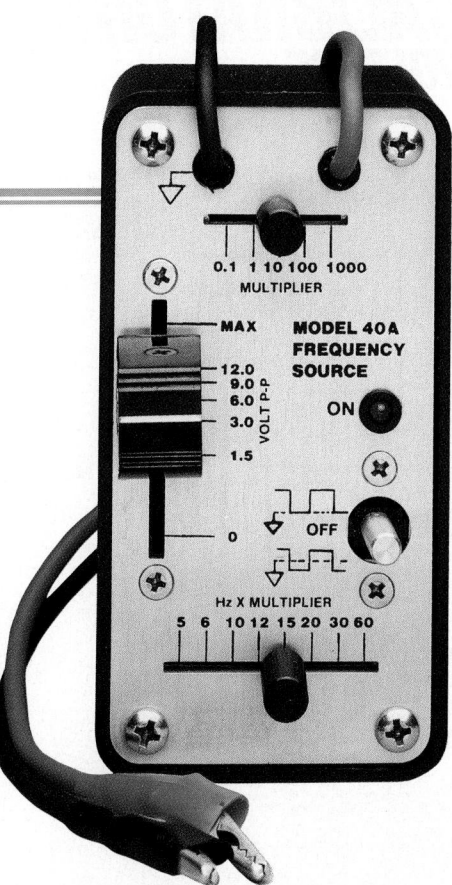

Model CL-306 Frequency Simulator

$195

For Calibrating Frequency Readouts

- **Direct 0.5 Hz to 60 kHz Output in 40 Steps**
- **Tuning Fork Crystal for 0.0008% Accuracy**
- **±0.001% per Degree C Stability·**
- **Zero Based and Zero Center Outputs**

Model CL-306

The CL-306 frequency source provides 40 precise frequencies from 0.5 to 60,000 Hertz, with a square wave of 15 V p-p amplitude which can be set to any lower value with the built-in attenuator. Switch selects zero based or center based outputs standard or zero crossing input.

The CL-306 can be used to check and calibrate flowmeter displays, counters, tachometers, oscilloscopes and other frequency input devices.

Model CL-304 Specifications

(Unless otherwise indicated, specifications are in % of 16 mA span)

Accuracy: ±0.1% (±½ digit)
Display: Liquid Crystal; 3½ digit
Display Ranges: 0.00 to 19.99 mA (−25.0 to +125.0%)
Resolution: 0.1% 0.01 mA
Read Protection: Limited to nominal 25 mA against accidental misconnection
Output/2-Wire Ranges: 0 to 24 mA dc (−25 to +125%) continuous
Quick Check Settings: 4.00 and 20.00 mA (00.0 and 100.0%)
Built-In Batteries: 3 × 9 volt alkaline; included
Power to External 2-Wire Transmitter: 24 volts
Battery Life: Source, 20 hours at 20 mA continuous; Read and 2-wire mode, 150 hours; alkaline
Loop Voltage Limits: 2-wire simulator mode; minimum, 2 V dc; maximum, 100 V dc
Operating Ambient Temperature: −5 to +140°F (−20 to +60°C)
Storage Temperature: −22 to +175°F (−30 to +80°C)
Relative Humidity: 10 to 90%, non-condensing
Overall Size: 2½ × 2⅝ × 5⅛ inches (63.5 × 66.7 × 130 mm)
Weight: 12.5 oz. (0.35 kg)

Model CL-305 Specifications

(Unless otherwise indicated, specifications are in % of span at 25°C)

Accuracy: ±(0.1% 1 digit)
Display: Liquid Crystal; 3½ digit
"Quick-Check" Factory preset at 0% and 100% (1 and 5 V)

Adjustment Range	LO	HI
10 V	−0.1 V to +1.5 V	0.75 V to 11 V
0-100%	−25% to +12%	−10% to 199%
100 mV	−4 mV to +25 mV	10 mV to 199 mV

Built-In Batteries: 3 × 9 Volt alkaline; included
Battery Life: 100 hours, sourcing into high impedance loads; 20 hours at 20 mA drain; alkaline
Source Current: 30 mA maximum
Sink Current: 20 mA maximum
Output Impedance: < 0.3 ohm
Input Resistance (Read Mode): > 2 megohms
Source Resistance Effect (Read Mode): 0.1% of span error per 2000 ohms
Overload Protection: Protected to 120 V ac or dc
Overload Indicator: Lamp indicates high current or misconnection
Short Circuit Duration: Continuous
Temperature Coefficient: ±0.01% of span/°C (Based on 25°C ±25°C recommended range)
Operating Ambient Temperature: −5 to +140° F (−20 to +60° C)
Relative Humidity: 10 to 90%, non-condensing
Overall Size: 2½ × 2⅝ × 5⅛ inches (63.5 × 66.7 × 130 mm)
Weight: 12.5 oz. (0.35 kg)

Model CL-306 Specifications

Accuracy: ±0.0008% (8 parts per million)
Frequencies: 5, 6, 10, 12, 15, 20, 30 and 60 Hz times the multiplier value
Multiplier: 0.1, 1,10, 100 and 1000 times the frequency scale
Output: Nominal 15 V p-p square wave; 1:3 ratio 20 kHz, 2:5 ratio 12 kHz
Output Modes: Switch selected; zero based or zero crossing
Attenuator: Sliding potentiometer, logarithmic taper
Output Impedance: 2500 ohms maximum
Output Current Drive: 6 mA at max. output voltage
Rise Time: 1 μs nominal into resistive load
Battery: two 9V, alkaline included; 200 h life, alkaline
Dimensions: 2.125" (54 mm) × 4" (102 mm) × 2.25" (55 mm)
Weight: 7 oz (0.2 kg)

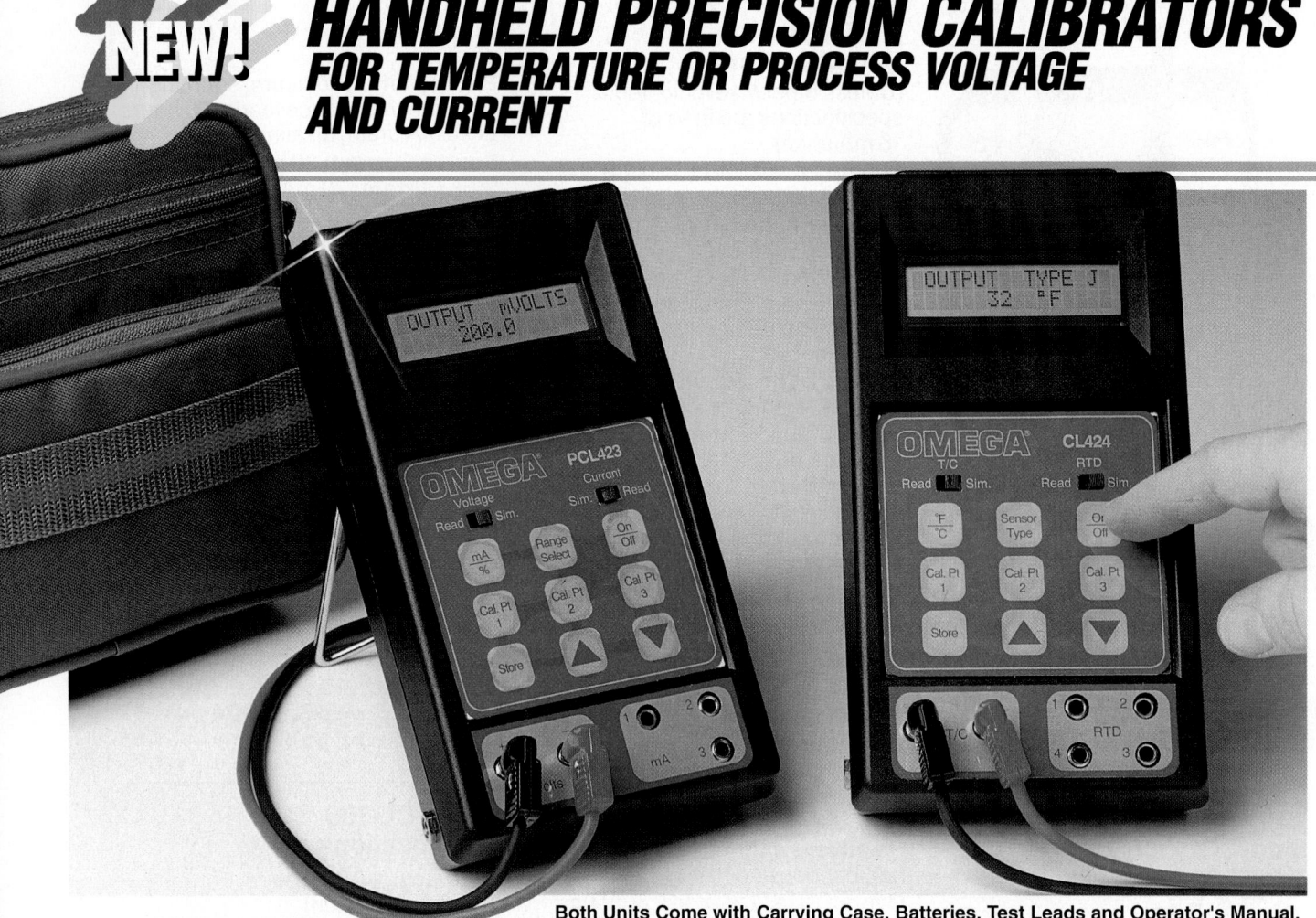

Both Units Come with Carrying Case, Batteries, Test Leads and Operator's Manual.

1 YEAR WARRANTY

MADE IN USA

From

$729

- ✔ High Accuracy
- ✔ Large 32 Character Dot Matrix Display
- ✔ Memory for 3 Calibration Points in Each Range
- ✔ Capable of Reading or Simulating Sensor Signals

The OMEGA PCL423 and CL424 are portable, handheld, microprocessor based calibrators for process voltage and current signals or temperature sensors. The PCL423 process signal calibrator has multiple input and output ranges for dc millivolts, volts and milliamps. In the milliamp range it can supply 24 Vdc to power a two wire transmitter while simultaneously displaying its output in milliamps or

% of full scale. The CL424 temperature calibrator can read or simulate J, K, T or E thermocouples as well as most common RTD types. Both models utilize a large 32 character dot matrix display to simultaneously display the reading, operating mode (input or output) and range selected. For convenience three calibration points can be stored for each range for quick recall.

SPECIFICATIONS

Ranges (PCL423):
Current: 0 to 24.00 mA; -25.0 to 125%
Voltage: 0 to 200.0 mV; 0 to 20.00 V
Ranges (CL424):
J T/C: -238 to 2192°F/(-150 to 1200°C)
K T/C: -328 to 2372°F/(-200 to 1300°C)
T T/C: -328 to 752°F/(-200 to 400°C)

E T/C: -400 to 1742°F (-240 to 950°C)
RTD Pt 392: -328 to 1562°F (-200 to 850°C)
Pt 385: -328 to 1562°F (-200 to 850°C)
10 Ohm Cu: -112 to 608°F (-80 to 320°C)
120 Ohm Ni: -148 to 482°F (-100 to 250°C)
Accuracy: ± 0.025% FS + 1 LSD
Temp. Stability: ± 0.01% FS /°C
Operating Temp. Range: 32 to 122°F (0 to 50°C)
Storage Temp. Range: -4 to 140°F (-20 to 60°C)
Input Impedance: (T/C or Volt) 1 MOhm typ. (current) 20 Ohms
Display: 32 character dot matrix 2 x 16 format
Power Requirements: 4AA batteries
Battery Life: Approximately 50 hours
Size: 7" x 1.6" x 3.8 (178 x 41 x 97mm)
Weight: 1.5 lbs (680 g)

IN STOCK FOR FAST DELIVERY

To Order (Specify Model Number)		
MODEL NUMBER	**PRICE**	**DESCRIPTION**
PCL423	**$729**	**Process Signal Calibrator ***
CL424	**$799**	**Temperature Calibrator ***

* Both the PCL423 and CL424 come with carrying case, 4AA batteries test leads and operator's manual.
Ordering Example: *PCL423 is a handheld process signal calibrator, **$729**.*

HANDHELD AIR PRESSURE METER
FOR DIFFERENTIAL AND ABSOLUTE AIR PRESSURES

NEW!

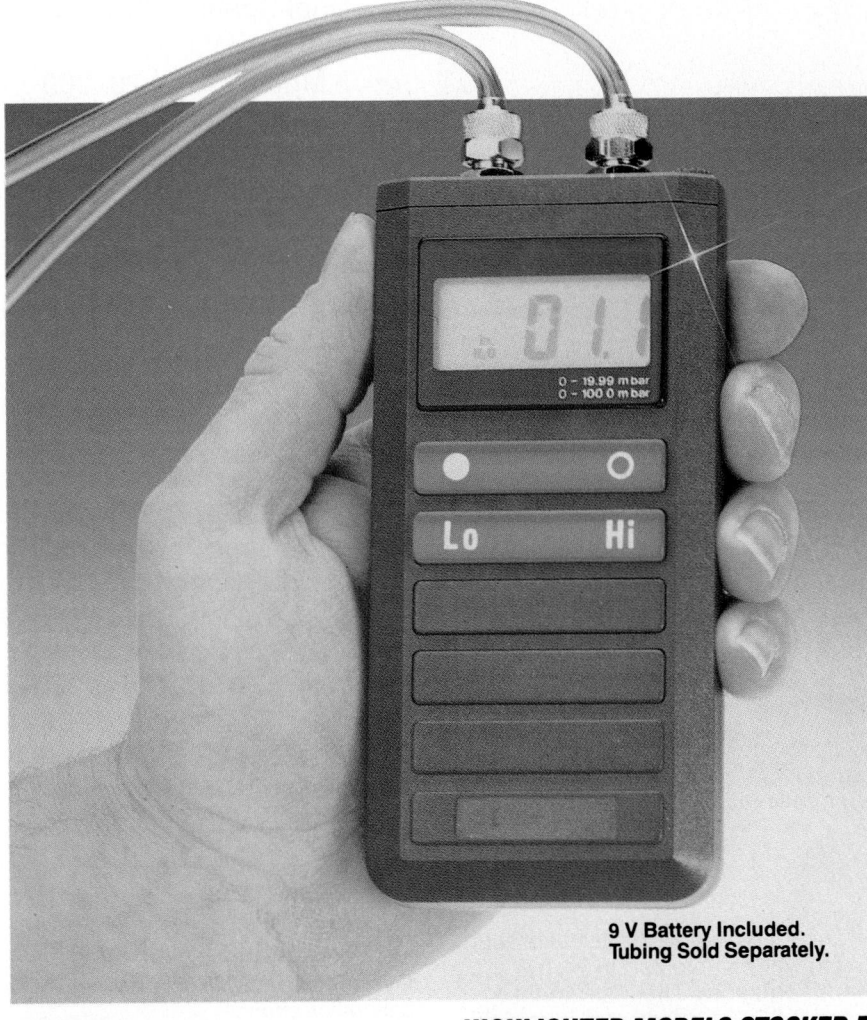

9 V Battery Included.
Tubing Sold Separately.

From
$375

✓ **Simple One-Handed Operation**
✓ **Rugged Water-Resistant Case**
✓ **Wide Ranges for Differential, Gauge, and Absolute Pressures**
✓ **Resolution Range Switch and Zero Adjustment Standard**

The HHP-100 Series handheld air pressure meter is designed for one-handed industrial or laboratory use. The custom molded case allows this manometer to withstand continual heavy use and operation in industrial or humid conditions. Each unit has a high contrast liquid crystal display coupled with a backlight feature, allowing readings to be seen in all applications.

All of the differential models can measure gauge or vacuum pressures, as well as differential, by venting the low and high ports to atmosphere, respectively. Each unit has a low and high range, offering greater resolution and accuracy.

INSTRUMENTATION D

SPECIFICATIONS

Accuracy: 0.2% FS of high range
Operating Temp: 59 to 77°F (15 to 25°C), (0.3% accuracy, 32 to 122°F)
Compatible Media: dry non-corrosive gases
Power: 9 V battery included (approx. 250 hrs operation)
Proof Pressure: "A" 15 psi; "B and D" 30 psi; "E" 150 psi; "C, F, and G" 60 psi
Zero Adjustment: on top of unit
Display: 3½ digit, 0.5" high, backlit
Pressure Port: Tube (not included) (0.155" <ID>0.195"; OD < .24"), Tygon® or silicone
Dimensions: 5.51" H x 2.75" W x 1.02" D (140 x 70 x 26 mm)
Weight: 8.8 oz (250 g)

HIGHLIGHTED MODELS STOCKED FOR FAST DELIVERY

To Order *(Specify Model Number)*

Differential Models		Range	
Model	Price	Low	High
HHP-100A	$399	1.999" H$_2$O D	19.99" H$_2$O D
HHP-100B	375	19.99" H$_2$O D	199.9" H$_2$O D
HHP-100C	375	199.9" H$_2$O D	800" H$_2$O D
HHP-100D	375	1.999 PSID	15.00 PSID
HHP-100E	545	19.99 PSID	100.0 PSID
Absolute Models			
HHP-100F	445	1.999 PSIA	19.99 PSIA
HHP-100G	445	150.0 mm HgA	1500 mm HgA

Comes with 9 V battery and complete operator's manual. Purchase tubing separately below.

Accessory Tubing

Model	Price	Description
TYTY-732532-50	$12	50' Tygon tubing
TYSC-732532-50	36	50' Silicone tubing

Ordering Example: *HHP-100C is a differential model pressure meter, with 199.9" H$_2$O low range and 800" H$_2$O high range. TYTY-732532-50 is 50' of Tygon tubing, $375 + 12 = **$387.***

PORTABLE PRESSURE GAUGE
LIGHTWEIGHT BATTERY-POWERED FIELD INDICATOR
COMPATIBLE WITH MOST COMMON FLUIDS

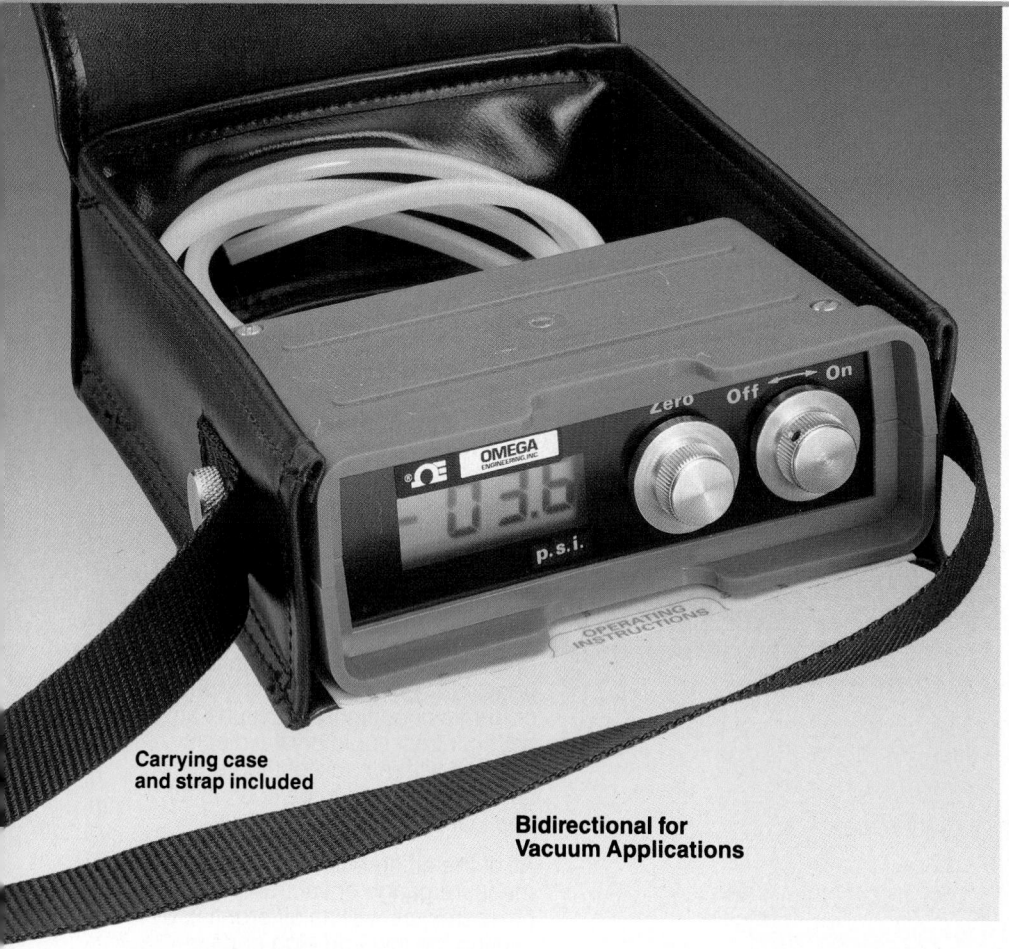

Carrying case
and strap included

Bidirectional for
Vacuum Applications

- ✔ Dual Scale — PSI and Inches H_2O
- ✔ 3 Models — 2, 20, 200 PSIG
- ✔ 200% Overpressure Protection
- ✔ 3 Ft. x ¼" PVC Tubing Supplied
- ✔ Lightweight — Less than 25 Oz., Including Carrying Case
- ✔ N.I.S.T. Traceability*
- ✔ 9 Volt Battery Included

From
$515

Measuring pressure in either PSIG or Inches H_2O under diverse operating conditions, the compact HHP701 portable pressure gages assure quality performance, particularly for on-site applications. Housed in a specially designed case of polycarbonate, the instrument and its front panel controls and displays can withstand rough usage in the shop or in the field. The pressure transducer maintains its calibration, even when subjected to 2 x full scale input pressure. The instrument's clear LCD ±1999 display provides 0.05% FS resolution and an accuracy rating of ±0.15% of full scale. The unit's light weight (less than 25 oz., including carrying case), compact size and easy portability make it ideal for remote or on-site usage.

SPECIFICATIONS

Overpressure: 200% FS with negligible calibration change

Pressure Media: Compatible with most common fluids

Position Effect: Negligible

Display and Readout: 0.5 inch high LCD ±1999 digits

Resolution: 0.05% FS

Accuracy: ±0.15% FS (including combined non-linearity, hysteresis, and repeatability). Accuracy setting at 78°F also included. Instruments can be used in bi-directional mode, but calibration is in positive direction only.

Temperature Effects: 0.01% reading/°F for 32 to 122°F operating range.

Zero Control: Front Panel Adjustment

Dimensions: Instrument only: 6.10" W x 2.36" H x 3.54" D. Case depth: 6.69" overall.

Weight: Instrument only: 16 oz. Including case: 25 oz.

Power Supply: 9V Battery. Battery low display reads LO BAT.

Battery Life: 100 +hours

▶ *HIGHLIGHTED MODELS STOCKED FOR FAST DELIVERY* ◀

To Order *(Specify Model Number)*

MODEL	PRICE	RANGE	
		PSI	INCHES H_2O
HHP701-2	$515	±1.999	55.3"-H_2O
HHP701-20	515	±19.99	555"-H_2O
HHP701-200	515	±199.9	461'(ft)-H_2O

Each instrument comes complete with a carrying case that has ample room for stowing pressure hose and fitting.
* National Institute of Standards and Technology (formerly National Bureau of Standards)

HANDHELD PRESSURE METERS
FOR GAUGE AND DIFFERENTIAL PRESSURES

- ✓ **Versatile, Easy to Use**
- ✓ **Gage or Differential Models**
- ✓ **Interchangeable Couplings for Any Installation or Hose**
- ✓ **Bidirectional Indications**

OMEGA's handheld models are extremely versatile and cover most portable pressure measurement needs. The HHP-4 series is an economical model to measure gauge pressure in conventional american units. The HHP-5 series covers all international gauge pressure measurements by offering the user a choice of 3 different display scales.

The differential pressure line can be used to measure differential, gauge and vacuum pressures. The HHP-6 series offers differential pressure measurement in standard american units. The HHP-7 series units combines the differential capabilities with 3 display choices for international pressure conversions.

From
$330

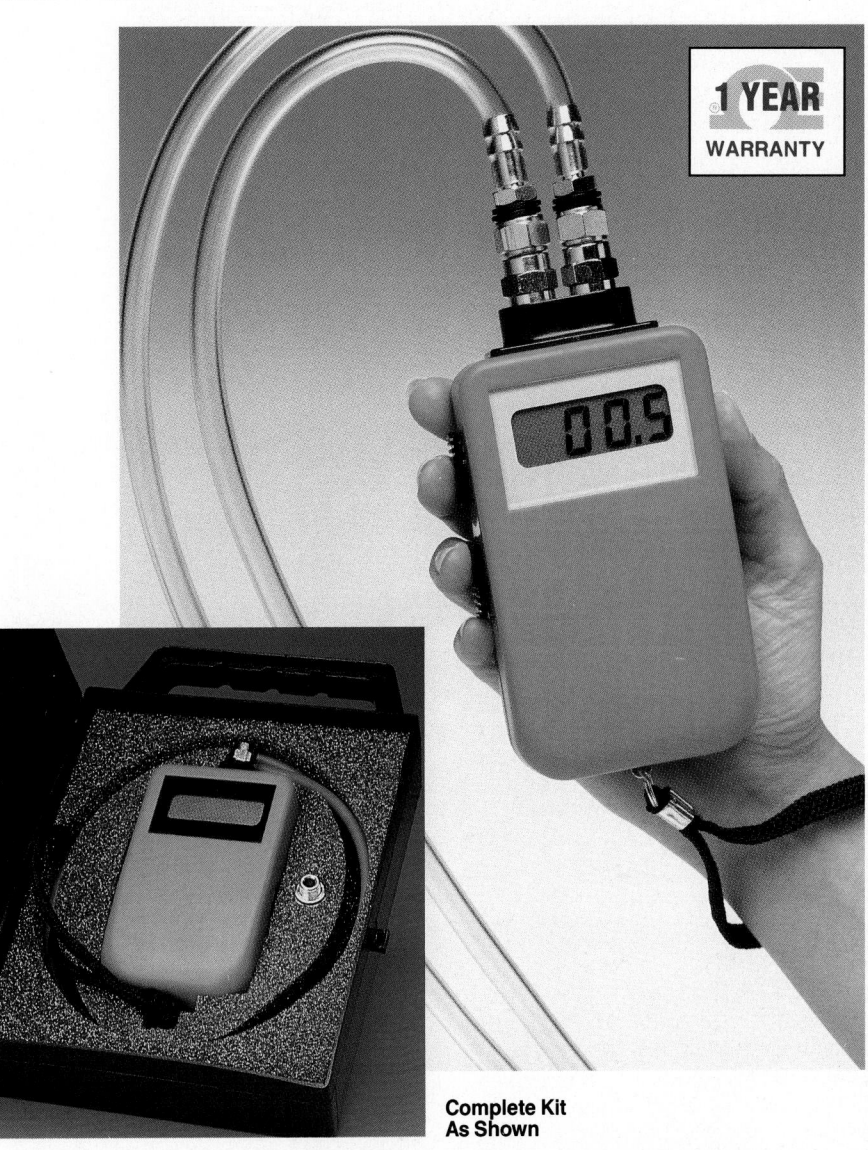

1 YEAR WARRANTY

Complete Kit As Shown

SPECIFICATIONS
Accuracy: 0.1% Full Scale

Operating Temp: 0 to 40°C

Power: 9 Vdc Battery

Proof Pressure: 1 bar, 150″ H_2O models; 4 bar, 19.99 PSI models; 8 bar, 100.0 PSI models

Max Static Pressure: 30 PSI, 150″ H_2O D models; 100 PSI, 19.99 PSID models

Kit Contents: ¼″ PVC tube with ⅛″ BSP coupling and ⅛″ NPT adaptor (HHP-4100,HHP-5100; 6.4 mm polyurethane tube with quick release ⅛″ BSP coupling and a ⅛″ NPT adaptor)

Dimensions: 130 x 70 x 35 mm

Weight: 9 ounces (250g)

Pressure Port: ⅛″ BSP ½″ NPT Adaptor Supplied

HIGHLIGHTED MODELS STOCKED FOR FAST DELIVERY!

To Order *(Specify Model Number)*

GAGE MODELS	PRICE	RANGES		
HHP-4150	$370	0-150.0″ H_2OG	—	—
HHP-420	330	0-19.99 PSIG	—	—
HHP-4100	370	0-100.0 PSIG	—	—
HHP-5150	389	0-150.0″ H_2OG	0-1999 mmH_2O	0-199.9 mbar
HHP-520	342	0-19.99 PSIG	0-199.9 kPa	0-1.999 bar
HHP-5100	394	0-100.0 PSIG	0-700 kPa	0-7.00 bar
DIFFERENTIAL MODELS				
HHP-6150	370	0-150.0″ H_2OD	—	—
HHP-620	370	0-19.99 PSID	—	—
HHP-7150	436	0-150.0″ H_2OD	0-1999 mmH_2OD	0-199.9 mbar
HHP-720	436	0-19.99 PSID	0-199.9 kPaD	0-1.999 bar

Each instrument comes complete with a rugged plastic carring case, hook-up tubing, NPT adaptor fittings, and a 9 Vdc battery.

PORTABLE TEST & CALIBRATION KITS
IDEAL FOR FIELD TESTING APPLICATIONS

- **Gage or Differential Pressure Models**
- **Portable: Long-life Rechargeable Batteries**
- **Auto Zero/Auto Ranging**
- **Highly Accurate Within ±0.1% of Reading**
- **Push-Button Conversion to 8 Programmed Units**
- **Includes User Programmable Factor**

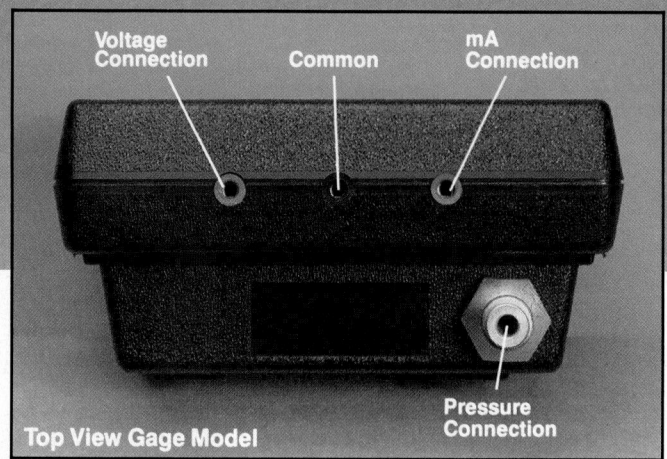

Top View Gage Model

$650
Meter and Soft Carrying Case Only

For high accuracy, rugged design, and precise measurement, the PCL-200 Series of portable manometer/calibrators provides quality performance, reliability and simple push-button operation. Ideally suited to on-site applications, the PCL-200 models effectively bring laboratory/test calibration capabilities directly into the field. Depending on the specific model ordered, the simultaneous dual display indicates pressure (or differential pressure) and electronic transducer/transmitter output on any of 8 key selectable engineering units.

The PCL-200 auto zero/auto ranging feature eliminates the need to compensate for local gravity, temperature, barometric pressure or head difference due to the location of testor vs. unit being tested. The push of a button automatically establishes zero for both pressure and electrical inputs, while the auto-ranging feature selects either full range span or 1/10th of span for optimum display accuracy.

HAND HELD MANOMETER
GAGE AND DIFFERENTIAL PRESSURE

$995
Complete
Kit as
Shown

Kit Includes
- ✔ PCL 200 Meter
- ✔ FREE Test Lead Kit
- ✔ Calibration Fitting Kit
- ✔ Precision Hand Pump
- ✔ 110/220 AC Battery Charger
- ✔ Rugged Attache Case

SPECIFICATIONS

Accuracy: ±0.1% of reading (including combined effects of linearity, hysteresis, repeatability and temperature over calibrated range)

Elec. Accuracy: 0.1% of reading ±2 counts

Pressure: See "To Order" Matrix

Display: 8 Digit (4 pressure or D/P and 4 voltage or current) LCD type with .3" high (7.6mm) digits.

Operating Temperature: −20 to +122°F (−29 to +50°C)

Power Supply: Rechargeable Ni-Cad Battery
Minimum 40 hours @ 70°F (21°C)
Minimum 20 hours @ −20°F (−29°C)

Proof Pressure: 2 x FS

Media Compatability: Clean dry gases only.

To Order Digital Meter with Padded Carrying Case Only.

MODEL	PRICE
PCL-200 A	$650
PCL-200 B	650
PCL-200 C	740
PCL-200 D	740

Battery Charger not Included.

To Order Complete Kit *(Specify Model Number)*

MODEL	PRICE	TYPE	RANGE
PCL-200-KIT A	$995	Gage*	0-200"-H$_2$O (0-7.2 PSI)
PCL-200-KIT B	995	Gage*	0-2000"-H$_2$O (0-72 PSI)
PCL-200-KIT C	1085	Differential	0-200"-H$_2$O (0-7.2 PSI)
PCL-200-KIT D	1085	Differential	0-2000"-H$_2$O (0-72 PSI)

* Units are not Bi-Directional

▶ *HIGHLIGHTED MODELS STOCKED FOR FAST DELIVERY* ◀

To Order Individual Components

*PCL-2 CFK	Calibration Fitting Kit	$ 60
PCL-2 TLK	Test Lead Kit	24
PCL-2 HP	Precision Test Pump	270
PCL-2-CBC	Cigarette Lighter Style Battery Charger	15
*PCL-2-SBC	120/220 Vac Switchable Battery Charger	36
PCL-2-APK	World-Wide AC Outlet Adaptor Kit	15

* Recommended accessories when ordering Digital Meter separately.

INSTRUMENTATION

D

PORTABLE, HIGHLY ACCURATE PNEUMATIC CALIBRATOR

1 YEAR WARRANTY

From

$2870

- ✔ **Top Display Indicates Pressure in 10 Engineering Units and in % of Span**
- ✔ **Lower Display Indicates Output of Unit Under Test in Electrical Units, % of Span, or in % of Full-Scale Error**
- ✔ **Works with Linear and Square Root Transducers**
- ✔ **Simple User Friendly Programming**
- ✔ **Rugged Construction for Industrial Calibrations**

SPECIFICATIONS
Pressure Ports: ⅛ NPT
Proof Pressure: 10X full scale
Media Compatibility: non-corrosive gases compatible with nickel-plated brass, quartz, titanium, and urethane
Storage Temperature: −4 to 140°F (−20 to 60°C)
Operating Temperature: 32 to 104°F (0 to 40°C)
Humidity: <80% RH, non-condensing
Power: NiCad battery, 50 hours life
Dimensions (with Carrying Case): 5.2″H × 8.2″W × 12.4″D (130 × 205 × 310 mm)
Weight: 4.4 lb (2 kg)

The PCL4000 Series pressure calibrators come in single or dual range models for increased accuracy and versatility. Each unit is equipped with two displays. The top display shows the pressure in percentage of full scale or 10 other engineering units of your choice. The bottom display shows the sensor being tested in electrical units or in percentage of full scale. Twenty calibration points may be stored in memory for easy recall when writing calibration certificates.

A unique feature of this calibrator is its ability to accept the test unit's unique output and pressure range

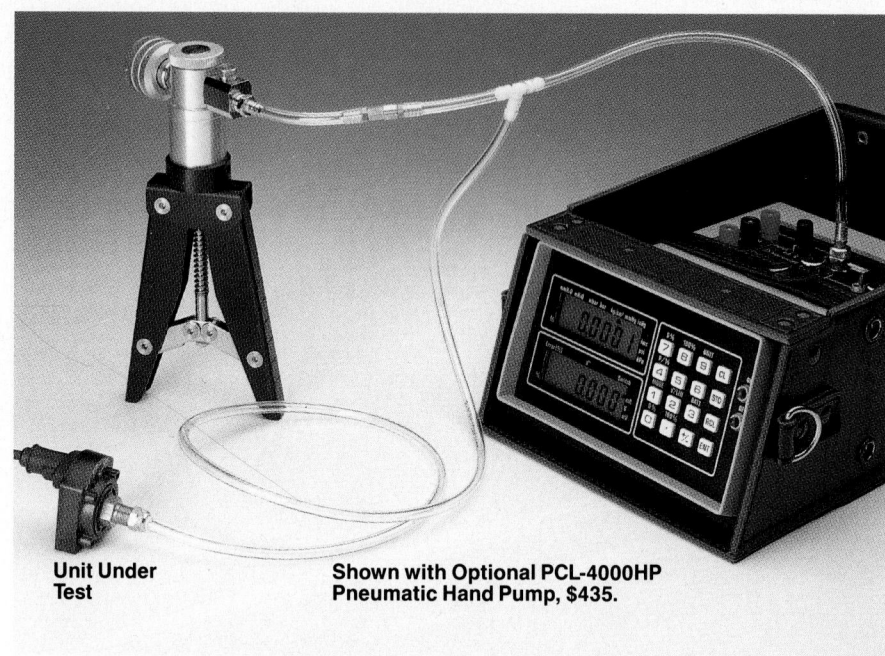

Unit Under Test

Shown with Optional PCL-4000HP Pneumatic Hand Pump, $435.

and display a percentage of full-scale error. Calibrating pressure switches can be easily performed using the pressure switch option. The top display indicates the actual pressure and the lower display will indicate the pressure when the switch changes state. The switch option indicates a "C" (closed) or "O" (open) to show the state of the switch. Built into the calibrator is a 24 Vdc power supply capable of

driving voltage and current transducers. An optional handheld pressure pump (Model PCL-4000HP) completes the calibrating system by providing stable pressures.

Each calibrator includes carrying case, strap, charger, tubing and connectors, test leads and complete operator's manual.

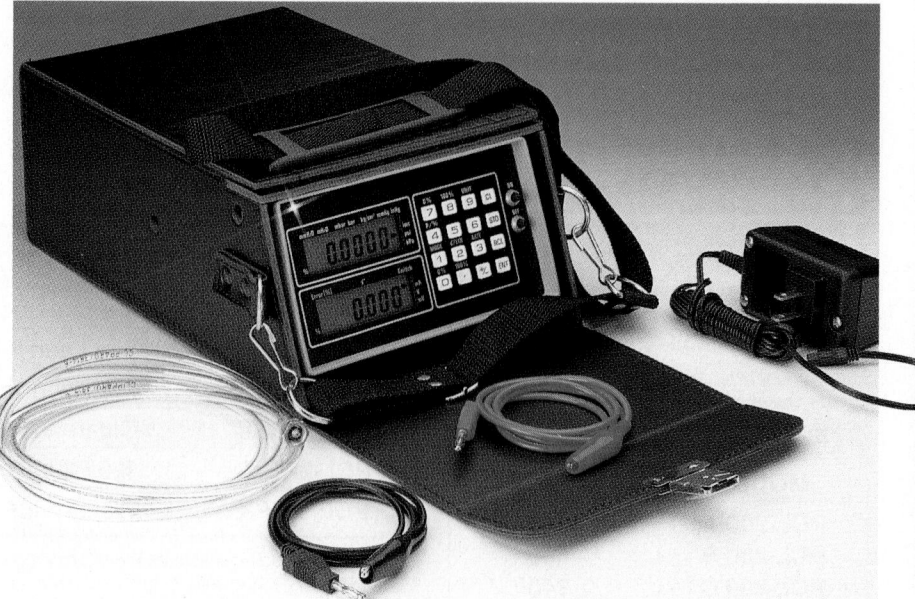

Numeric keyboard for convenient entry of span

Key for selecting pressure scalings (10 different pressure units)

Key for selecting display I mode:
- pressure engineering units
- % of given pressure span

6 digit LCD display indicating:
- pressure readings in 10 eng. units
- pressure readings in % of given span

STORE and RECALL keys for 10 memories

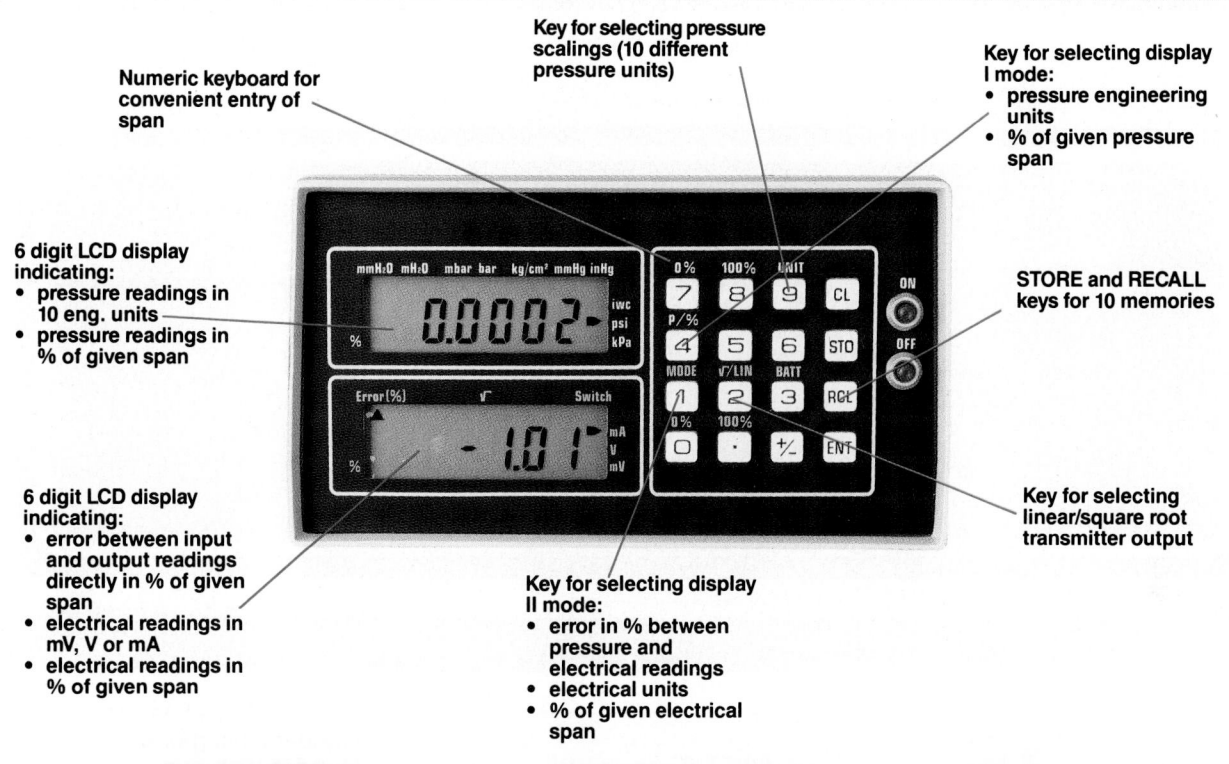

6 digit LCD display indicating:
- error between input and output readings directly in % of given span
- electrical readings in mV, V or mA
- electrical readings in % of given span

Key for selecting display II mode:
- error in % between pressure and electrical readings
- electrical units
- % of given electrical span

Key for selecting linear/square root transmitter output

Pressure Chart

Units	Low Range 30 PSI			High Range 300 PSI		
	Range	Resol.	Accuracy†	Range	Resol.	Accuracy†
PSI	0 - 30	0.001	0.006 ±0.05% Rdg	0 - 300	0.01	0.06 ±0.05% Rdg
in. H₂O	0 - 800	0.05	0.2 ±0.05% Rdg	0 - 8000	0.5	2 ±0.05% Rdg
in. Hg	0 - 60	0.005	0.015 ±0.05% Rdg	0 - 600	0.05	0.15 ±0.05% Rdg
mm Hg	0 - 1500	0.1	0.3 ±0.05% Rdg	0 - 15000	1	3 ±0.05% Rdg
mH₂O	0 - 20	0.001	0.006 ±0.05% Rdg	0 - 200	0.01	0.04 ±0.05% Rdg
kPa	0 - 200	0.01	0.04 ±0.05% Rdg	0 - 2000	0.1	0.4 ±0.05% Rdg
bar*	0 - 2000	0.1	0.4 ±0.05% Rdg	0 - 20	0.001	0.004 ±0.05% Rdg

in. H₂O → in. H$_2$O, mH₂O → mH$_2$O

* Low range units are millibar.
† Accuracy is the sum of the two numbers. **Example:** Low range, 1.000 PSI on display, accuracy is ±.0065 PSI

Electrical Chart

Units	Range	Resol.	Accuracy
mV	±150	0.005	0.01 ±0.03% Rdg
V	±15	0.001	0.002 ±0.03% Rdg
mA	±24	0.001	0.002 ±0.03% Rdg
mA	±60	0.002	0.004 ±0.03% Rdg

The PCL4000 Series pressure calibrators come in a rugged leather case and strap. A storage compartment inside the leather case includes tubing, tube-to-tube connectors, tube-to-⅛″ NPT adaptors, electrical test leads, and an ac adaptor for recharging the batteries.

U.S. AND CANADA

for placing orders, call: **1-800-82-66342**™
1-800-TC-OMEGA

To Order *(Specify Model Number)*

Model No.	Price	Description
Pressure Calibrators		
PCL-4000E	$2870	Calibrator, low range (30 PSI)
PCL-4000F	2870	Calibrator, high range (300 PSI)
PCL-4000G	4615	Calibrator, low and high ranges (30/300 PSI)
Field Installable Options		
PCL-4000PS	$595	Pressure switch testing and checking
PCL-4000RS3	260	RS-232 with 3½″ disk
PCL-4000RS5	260	RS-232 with 5¼″ disk
Accessories		
PCL-4000HP	$435	Pneumatic hand pump (max. 300 PSI)
PCL-4000MA	550	Current simulator module

Each calibrator includes carrying case, strap, charger, tubing and connectors, test leads, and complete operator's manual.

Ordering Example: *PCL-4000G calibrator (30/300 PSI) plus PCL-4000HP pneumatic hand pump, $4615 + 435 = **$5050.***

ACCURATE BENCHTOP PRESSURE STANDARD

NEW!

PCL41
$725

- ✔ **NIST Traceable**
- ✔ **Display Hold, for Testing Pressure Switches**
- ✔ **Adjustable High Resolution**
- ✔ **Min/Max Standard**
- ✔ **Adjustable Filtering**
- ✔ **Front Panel Tare**

The PCL41 Series pressure standard incorporates features found in high-end standards into an affordable, portable benchtop unit. The microprocessor controller allows the user to adjust display filtering for the particular application. The front panel tare allows zeroing of the display with a single push button.

Testing pressure switches is done by utilizing the display hold capabilities of the microprocessor. An external connection is completed when the pressure switch under test changes state. The switch freezes the display which shows the true actuating pressure.

The microprocessor allows adjusting of the unit for increased or decreased resolution. All the options associated with the DP41 panel meter are available on this benchtop unit.

The PCL41 combined with its unique options can turn the unit into a sophisticated data collection system. Scalable analog outputs, RS-232 or RS-485 communications and mechanical relays are all available options with the PCL41.

FROM 15 TO 6,000 PSI

Comes with Power Cord and Complete Operator's Manual.

IN STOCK FOR FAST DELIVERY!

SPECIFICATIONS

Accuracy: 0.25% FS (linearity, hysteresis and repeatability)

Operating Temp.: 32 to 122°F (0 to 50°C)

Media Temp.: -4 to 176°F (-20 to 80°C)

Temp. Effects: .008% FS/F

Proof Press.: 150% FS

Output: 4 Open collectors 150 mA sink @ 1 Vdc max; optional 2 SPDT relays 7 amp @ 230 Vac; deadband fully adjustable

Warmup to Rated Accuracy: 5 min.

A/D Conversion: Dual slope technique

Display: 6-digit, 14-segment LED, red or green; 0.56" H (14.2 mm); indicator lights for alarms and status modes

RS-232 Communications (Option -S2): 300/1200/2400/4800/9600/19.2k baud; RJ11 4-wire connection; complete program setup and message display capability; programmable to transmit current display, alarm status, min/max, actual measured input value (not scaled) and status

RS-485 Communications (Option -S4): 300/1200/2400/4800/9600/19.2k baud; RJ11 6-wire connection; addressable from 0 to 199

Analog Output (Option -A): Selectable 0-5 Vdc, 1-5 Vdc, 0-10 Vdc, 0-20 mA 4-20 mA; voltages @ 20 mA, current @ 12 Vdc

Read Rate: 3/second (adjustable to 13/second)

Power: 120 Vac @ 10 watts

Size: 4.3"H x 10.2"W x 10"D (109 x 259 x 254 mm)

Weight: 5 lbs (3.6 kg)

To Order *(Specify Model Number)*

RANGE	MODEL NO.	PRICE	RESOLUTION
0-15 PSIG	**PCL41-015**	$725	0.001
0-30 PSIG	**PCL41-030**	725	0.001
0-60 PSIG	**PCL41-060**	725	0.01
0-100 PSIG	**PCL41-100**	725	0.01
0-300 PSIG	**PCL41-300**	725	0.01
0-600 PSIG	**PCL41-600**	725	0.1
0-1000 PSIG	**PCL41-1.5K**	725	0.1
0-3000 PSIG	**PCL41-3K**	725	0.1
0-6000 PSIG	**PCL41-6K**	725	1.0

Comes with power cord and complete operator's manual.

Ordering Example: *PCL41-030-R and PS-4G is a benchtop pressure standard, with 0 to 30 PSIG range and optional dual 7 amp SPDT relay, and a pressure snubber for gas applications,* $725 + 120 + 10 = **$855.**

OPTIONS (NOT FIELD INSTALLABLE)

SUFFIX	PRICE	DESCRIPTION
-R	$120	Dual 7 amp SPDT mechanical relay
-A	120	Scalable analog output
-S2	120	RS232 serial output (requires connector below)
-S4	160	RS485 serial output (requires connector below)

ACCESSORIES

MODEL NO.	PRICE	DESCRIPTION
PS-4D	$10	Pressure snubber for motor oil
PS-4E	10	Pressure snubber for water
PS-4G	10	Pressure snubber for gas
DP40-9SC2	30	9 pin serial connector for RS-232
DP40-9SC4	30	9 pin serial connector for RS-485
DP40-25SC2	30	25 pin serial connector for RS-232
DP40-25SC4	30	25 pin serial connector for RS-485

INSTRUMENTATION

D

PORTABLE PRESSURE TRANSDUCER/ DIGITAL GAUGE
AVAILABLE WITH LCD OR LED DISPLAY

✔ **Photo-Optic Pressure Transducer**

✔ **Repeatability of 0.05%**

✔ **Inconel and 316SS Wetted Parts Compatible With Most Media**

✔ **Portable — All Batteries Included**

From
$730

Shown wtih Optional Hand

To Order *(Specify Model Number)*

RANGE	3½ Digit			4½ Digit		
PSI	MODEL	PRICE	RESOL.	MODEL	PRICE	RESOL.
10	PCL2535-10	$730	.01	PCL2545-10	$870	.001
15	PCL2535-15	730	.01	PCL2545-15	870	.001
20	PCL2535-20	730	.01	PCL2545-20	870	.001
30	—	—	—	PCL2545-30	870	.01
60	PCL2535-60	730	.1	PCL2545-60	870	.01
100	PCL2535-100	730	.1	PCL2545-100	870	.01
150	PCL2535-150	730	.1	PCL2545-150	870	.01
200	PCL2535-200	730	.1	PCL2545-200	870	.01
300	—	—	—	PCL2545-300	890	.1
500	PCL2535-500	760	1	PCL2545-500	890	.1
600	PCL2535-600	760	1	PCL2545-600	890	.1
1000	PCL2535-1K	760	1	PCL2545-1K	890	.1
1500	PCL2535-1.5K	760	1	PCL2545-1.5K	890	.1
2000	PCL2535-2K	760	1	PCL2545-2K	890	.1
3000	—	—	—	PCL2545-3K	890	1
				PCL2545-5K	955	1
				PCL2545-10K	955	1

INCHES OF WATER	3½ Digit			4½ Digit		
	MODEL	PRICE	RESOL.	MODEL	PRICE	RESOL.
50	PCL2535-WC50	$730	.1	PCL2545-WC50	$870	.01
100	PCL2535-WC100	730	.1	PCL2545-WC100	870	.01
200	PCL2535-WC200	730	.1	PCL2545-WC200	870	.01
300	—	—	—	PCL2545-WC300	870	.1
500	PCL2535-WC500	730	1	PCL2545-WC500	870	.1
600	PCL2535-WC600	730	1	PCL2545-WC600	870	.1
800	PCL2535-WC800	730	1	PCL2545-WC800	870	.1
1000	PCL2535-WC1K	730	1	PCL2545-WC1K	870	.1

LED display with 120 Vac power, add suffix LED to model number, no additional charge.
***OPTIONS** PCL2500-HK Handle Kit $40. PCL2500-CC Carrying Case, $95.*

Precise pressure readouts every time are provided by the PCL2535 and PCL2545 Series of rugged, compact, portable pressure gauges. With an accuracy rating of 0.25% FS, including linearity, hysteresis and repeatability, these precision instruments use a unique photo-optic sensor to measure pressure without the usual friction-induced errors associated with conventional analog pressure gauges. The battery-powered units have 3½ or 4½ digit liquid crystal displays (LCD) and are available in pressure ranges from 0-50 in H_2O to 10,000 PSI.

SPECIFICATIONS

Accuracy: ±0.25% FS (including repeatability, hysteresis, and linearity)

Pressure Connection: 1/8" NPTF

Wetted Parts: Pressure element inconel 718, AISI 316 Stainless Steel

Operating Temperature: 32 to 110°F, 10 to 100% humidity

Temperature Effect: Not to exceed ±0.01%/°F between 32 and 110°F

Overpressure Limit: 175% over state range without shift of range or calibration

Repeatability: Better than 0.05%

Power Supply: 9V battery

Size: 2.83" x 5.66" x 8.13"

Reading Rate: 3/sec

HIGH ACCURACY PRESSURE STANDARD
MICROPROCESSOR BASED DUAL DISPLAY — DIGITAL AND ANALOG

PCL-3000 Series

- ✔ **Switch Selectable Ranges — Absolute or Gauge**
- ✔ **Accuracy ±.05% FS, All Ranges**
- ✔ **Range — From 10 to 10,000 PSI**
- ✔ **Automatic Zeroing (No Potentiometers Needed)**
- ✔ **Self-Calibrating**
- ✔ **Digital Output — RS-232 Optional**
- ✔ **Integral Stainless Steel Transducer**

The PCL-3000 Series digital pressure standards are specifically designed for use in the manufacture, test, or calibration of pressure sensitive devices. Using a patented, bonded foil strain gage sensor and advanced microcircuitry, these rugged, compact instruments provide simultaneous digital and analog readouts of the pressures applied.

Standard front panel switches permit desired pressure range selection, automatic zeroing of the display and actuation of a unique internal self-calibration feature.

Each instrument has two displays — digital and analog. The digital display provides precise pressure information and the analog display gives a quick reference to direction and level of pressure.

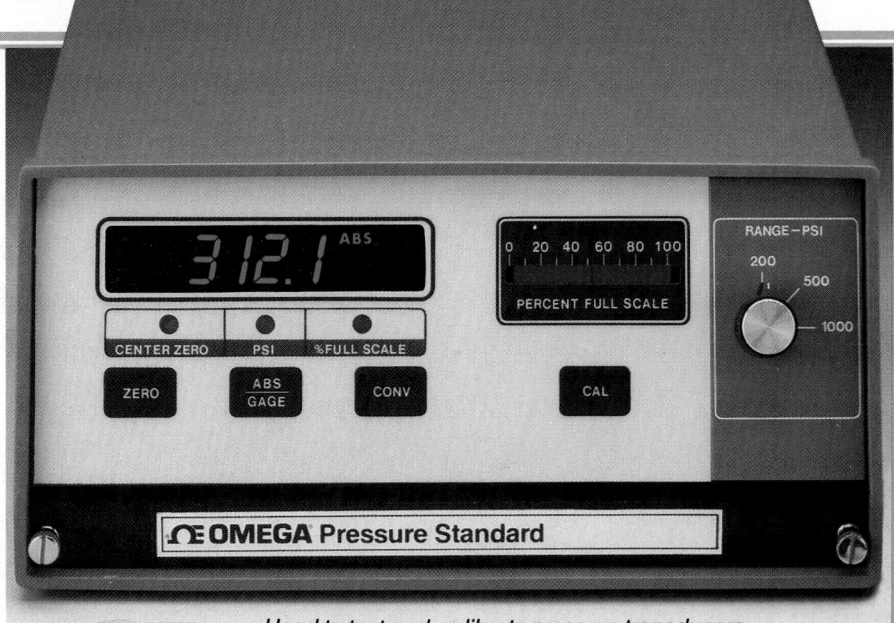

Used to test and calibrate pressure transducers.

2 YEAR WARRANTY

Dual Display — Digital and Analog

Each instrument comes complete with two-year warranty, a free pocket thermometer, N.I.S.T. certificate (National Institute of Standards and Technology, formerly National Bureau of Standards) and complete operator's manual.

SPECIFICATIONS

Accuracy: ±0.05% FS max., each range. Accuracy statement includes linearity, hysteresis and repeatability.

Operating Temperature: +50 to +110°F

Pressure Media: Any media compatible with 17-4PH Stainless Steel

Overpressure Capability: 750% FS on lowest range; 300% FS on mid. range; 150% FS on highest range

Display Resolution: Nominally 0.02% FS for each pressure range

Reading Rate: 10/sec

Input Voltage: 117 or 220 Vac ±10%, 50/60 Hz Voltage selected via transformer taps.

Power Consumption: 8 watts, typical

Nominal Size: 10¾" W x 4 7/8" H x 9 7/8" D

Panel Cutout: 10.62" x 4.75"

Pressure Connection: 7/16-20 UNFM

OPTIONS *(add suffix to Model No.)*		PRICE
-1	Analog Output Selectable 0-10 Vdc or 4-20 mA Isolated	$250
-4	RS-232 Simplex Output	250
-5	Peak Hold*	175
-7	Battery Operation**	375
-9	Panel Mounting Kit	50
-10	Freeze Mode for Testing Pressure Switches*	125

* *The Peak Hold and Freeze Mode Options require a $200 set-up when ordered in one unit. Please list as separate line item.*

** *Excludes Bar Graph Display.*

To Order *(Add required option suffixes to model number)*

MODEL NO.	PRICE	RANGE	TYPE
PCL-3000A	$2095	5000/2500/1000	PSIG and PSIA
PCL-3000B	2095	1000/500/200	PSIG and PSIA
PCL-3000C	2095	500/250/100	PSIG and PSIA
PCL-3000D	2095	100/50/20	PSIG with conversion to "inch H₂O"
PCL-3000E	2095	50/25/10	PSIG with conversion to "inch H₂O"
PCL-3000G	2695	10000/5000/2000	PSIG and PSIA

PORTABLE DIGITAL PRESSURE CALIBRATOR AND DISPLAY
DPI 601 RANGES FROM 5 PSI TO 300 PSI

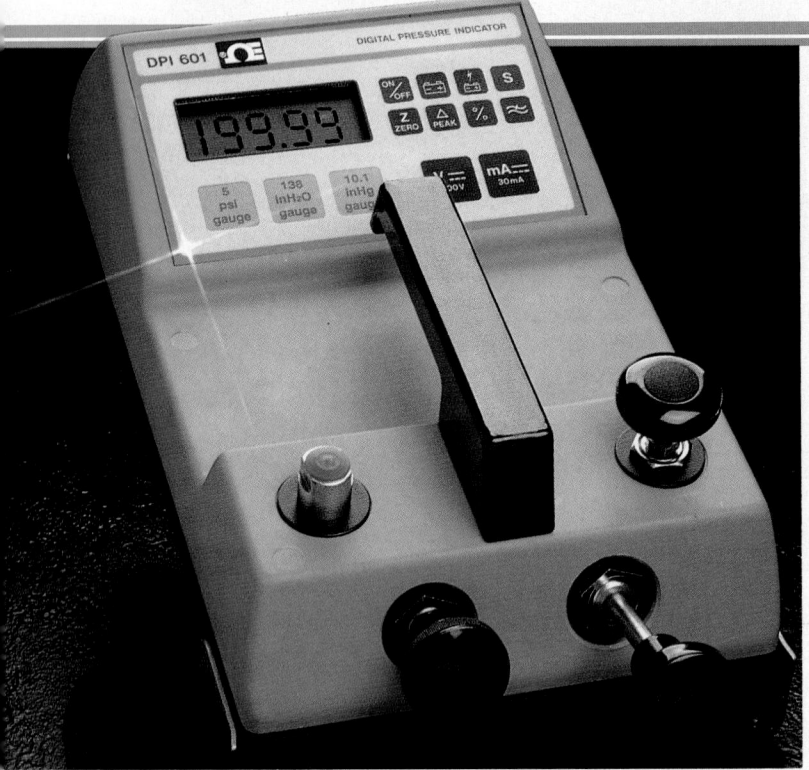

Supplied with carrying case, and probe set, 300 PSI Hand Pump

From

$2215

Model DPI 601 Shown

MADE IN **USA**

✔ **New—All Models Now with 2-Stage Easy to Use Pump**

✔ **Measures Pressure in Three Scales — PSI, Inches H₂O, Inches Hg**

✔ **Voltage — Three Ranges 0-2 V, 0-20 V, 0-200 V**

✔ **Current — 0 to 30.000 mA**

✔ **Self Contained Hand Pressure Pump**

✔ **0.05% Accuracy**

✔ **Truly Portable — Weighs Only 9 lbs**

Rugged and portable, the DPI 601 is a battery powered instrument for field calibration and servicing of pressure instrumentation. For easy calibration without using other test equipment, four pressure scales are provided together with voltage and current measurement capability. Excellent reliability is provided by a precision sensor which is unaffected by overpressures up to four times the rated pressure. Three standard pressure ranges are available and these instruments incorporate a pressure pump, internal volume adjustment and vent valve. Also included are rechargeable batteries, AC charger, leatherette carrying case and test leads for voltage and current testing.

Pneumatic Operations
The DPI 601 is designed to incorporate a variety of different pneumatic components to suit various user requirements. Where equipment to be calibrated is effectively airtight and of small volume, then the use of a hand pump and small volume adjuster to give fine control of the desired values is the preferred method.

SPECIFICATIONS

Overpressure: The rated pressure can be exceeded by 4X causing negligible calibration change

Compatible Media: Fluids compatible with brass, nylon, quartz and titanium.

Display: LCD, 15mm high

Resolution: 0.005% F.S. maximum. For ranges below 1.999 PSI, 0.05%

Accuracy: Combined non-linearity, hysteresis and repeatability. ±0.05% F.S. for 5 PSI to 300 PSI ranges. Instruments are calibrated in the positive direction only unless specified.

Operating Temperature Range: 14° to 122°F (−10 to +50°C) standard (this temperature range can be extended)

Calibrated Temperature Range: 32° to 104°F (0° to 40°C)

Thermal Sensitivity Shift: <0.003% of reading/°F

Response: 333 ms to full scale on digital display

Position Effect: Negligible

Weight: 9 lb

Pressure Connections: 1/8″ NPTF

Dimensions: 12.6″L x 7.7″W x 5″D

Power Supplies: Battery powered, 4 x 1.5 V cells provide up to 50 h continuous operation. Unit will operate with 110Vac supply and recharge batteries.

Electrical Inputs

RANGE	RESOL.	ACCURACY
0-2 Vdc	2.0000	±0.07% Rdg
0-20 Vdc	20.000	±0.07% Rdg
0-200 Vdc	200.00	±0.07% Rdg
0-30 mA	30.000	±0.1% Rdg

To Order (Specify Model Number)

MODEL	PRICE	RANGE		
		PSI	INCHES H₂O	″Hg
DPI601-5	$2215	5.000	140.00	10.000
DPI601-30	2215	30.00	800.0	60.00
DPI601-100	2215	100.00	2800	199.99
DPI601-300	2215	300.0	8300	600.0

PORTABLE PRESSURE CALIBRATOR
FOR PRESSURE OR 4-20 mA CURRENT

NEW!

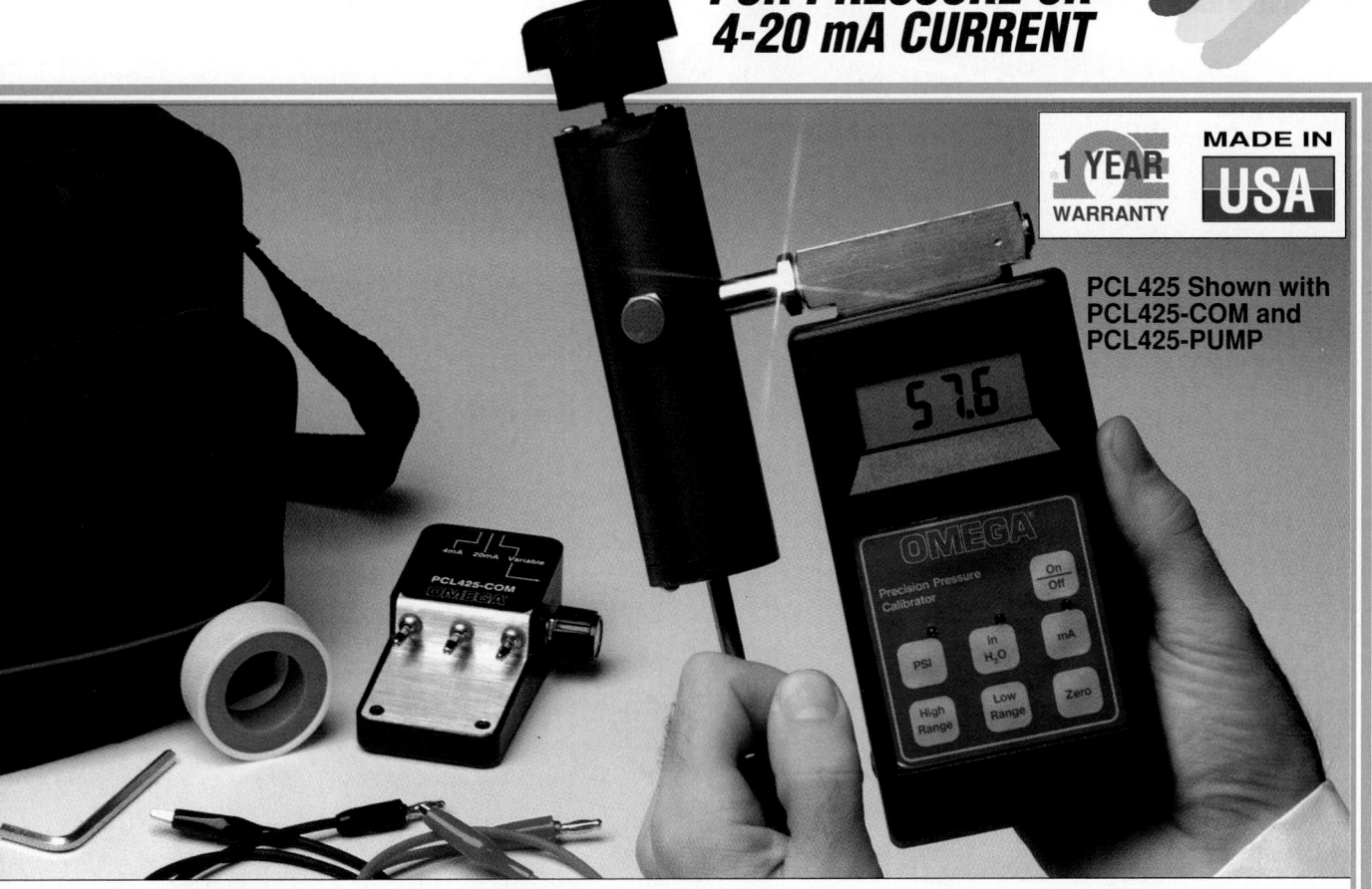

1 YEAR WARRANTY

MADE IN USA

PCL425 Shown with PCL425-COM and PCL425-PUMP

PCL425
From
$599

- ✓ **Measures Both Pressure and Current**
- ✓ **Accuracy of 0.1%**
- ✓ **Wide Range of Media Compatibility**
- ✓ **Built-in 24 Vdc Supply for Powering 2 Wire Transmitters**

The OMEGA PCL425 is a handheld calibrator capable of reading pressure or dc current. A front panel keyboard allows easy selection of PSI, inches of water, milliamp scales, high or low measuring range and adjustment of zero offset on pressure ranges. All readings are displayed on an LCD with ½" digits. In addition to reading pressure and current, the PCL425 can also generate pressure and current when used together with the optional hand pump and current output module.

SPECIFICATIONS
Ranges:

LOW	HIGH
0-19.99 PSI	0-30.0 PSI
0-199.9 in H_2O	0-830 in H_2O
0-19.99 mA	0-50.0 mA

Accuracy: 0.1% FS.
Temp. Stability: ±0.01% FS. per °C
Operating Temp. Range: 0 to 50°C
Storage Temp. Range: -20 to 60°C
Media Compatibility: Non-corrosive gases and liquids
Overpressure Protection: 3 times maximum range without recalibration
Pressure Connections: ⅛" FNPT inlet with two ⅛" FNPT fittings for use with optional hand pump or pressure gauge

Current Overload Protection: 1A/250V fuse
Current Connections: Banana jacks, 0.75" centers
Loop Power Supply: 24Vdc ±10%
Power: 9 Volt battery or optional AC adapter
Size: 6.5" x 3.2" x 1.5" (165 x 81 x 38 mm)
Weight: 15 ounces with battery (420 g)

ACCESSORIES

MODEL NO.	PRICE	DESCRIPTION
PCL425-COM	$199	4-20 mA current output module
PCL425-PUMP	229	Handheld pressure pump
PCL425-9VA	20	9 Volt ac adapter

To Order *(Specify Model Number)*		
MODEL NUMBER	**PRICE**	**DESCRIPTION**
PCL425	**$599**	Handheld pressure calibrator*
PCL425-KIT	999	Calibrator, pump, rugged carrying case, 9 Vac adapter and assorted fittings

Both models come with complete operator's manual.
* The PCL425 comes with a soft carrying case, 9 volt battery, Teflon tape, test leads and fitting wrench.
Ordering Example: *PCL425-KIT is a complete portable pressure calibrator kit, **$999.***

PORTABLE PNEUMATIC PRESSURE CALIBRATOR

Features

- ✔ Displays Pressure and Calibrates Transducers
- ✔ Optional Current Display for Transmitter Calibration
- ✔ Easy-to-Read LCD Display
- ✔ Portable with Heavy Duty Carrying Case & Battery
- ✔ Requires External Air Supply
- ✔ Supplied with 10-Point N.I.S.T. Tracable Calibration*

The OMEGA® Pressure Calibrator Model PCL730 provides accurate display and regulation of user supplied pneumatic pressure for calibration of process transmitters and pressure instruments along with digital display of measured pressure.

An optical sensor provides pressure signals through a microprocessor controlled circuit. The system is comprised of a reference diode, a motion measuring diode and an LED light source. Electrical current created by light interruptions to the dual photodiode system is sent through the microprocessor circuitry for a controlled output display.

To Order (Specify Model Number)

Model No.	Price	Current Display	Accuracy % Span	Primary Pressure Range	Selectable Pressure Units
PCL730A-01	$2650	NO	0.1	−2 to 0 to 15 psi	−50 to 0 to 415 inches of water and 3—15 PSI control loop = 0 to 100%
PCL730B-01	3750	NO	0.05	−2 to 0 to 15 psi	−50 to 0 to 415 inches of water and 3—15 PSI control loop = 0 to 100%
PCL730A-02	3190	YES	0.1	−2 to 0 to 15 psi	−50 to 0 to 415 inches of water and 3—15 PSI control loop = 0 to 100%
PCL730B-02	4360	YES	0.05	−2 to 0 to 15 psi	−50 to 0 to 415 inches of water and 3—15 PSI control loop = 0 to 100%
PCL730A-03	2650	NO	0.1	−4 to 0 to 31 psi	−100 to 0 to 860 inches of water and 3—15 PSI control loop = 0 to 100%
PCL730B-03	3750	NO	0.05	−4 to 0 to 31 psi	−100 to 0 to 860 inches of water and 3—15 PSI control loop = 0 to 100%
PCL730A-04	3190	YES	0.1	−4 to 0 to 31 psi	−100 to 0 to 860 inches of water and 3—15 PSI control loop = 0 to 100%
PCL730B-04	4360	YES	0.05	−4 to 0 to 31 psi	−100 to 0 to 860 inches of water and 3—15 PSI control loop = 0 to 100%
PCL730A-05	2650	NO	0.1	−5 to 0 to 50 psi	−10 to 0 to 100 inches of mercury and −35 to 0 to 430 kiloPascals
PCL730B-05	3750	NO	0.05	−5 to 0 to 50 psi	−10 to 0 to 100 inches of mercury and −35 to 0 to 430 kiloPascals
PCL730A-06	3190	YES	0.1	−5 to 0 to 50 psi	−10 to 0 to 100 inches of mercury and −35 to 0 to 430 kiloPascals
PCL730B-06	4360	YES	0.05	−5 to 0 to 50 psi	−10 to 0 to 100 inches of mercury and −35 to 0 to 430 kiloPascals
PCL730A-07	2650	NO	0.1	−15 to 0 to 100 psi	−30 to 0 to 200 inches of mercury and −100 to 0 to 650 kiloPascals
PCL730B-07	3750	NO	0.05	−15 to 0 to 100 psi	−30 to 0 to 200 inches of mercury and −100 to 0 to 650 kiloPascals
PCL730A-08	3190	YES	0.1	−15 to 0 to 100 psi	−30 to 0 to 200 inches of mercury and −100 to 0 to 650 kiloPascals
PCL730B-08	4360	YES	0.05	−15 to 0 to 100 psi	−30 to 0 to 200 inches of mercury and −100 to 0 to 650 kiloPascals

* National Institute of Standards and Technology (Formerly National Bureau of Standards)

PORTABLE PNEUMATIC PRESSURE CALIBRATOR

Model PCL 730 Series

SPECIFICATIONS

Accuracy: "A" models: +0.1% of span, including sensitivity, linearity, repeatability and hysteresis at 73°F; "B" models: +0.05% of span.
Repeatability: +0.005% of span
Pressure Ranges: See "How To Order" Box.
Operating Temperature Range: 25°F to 125°F

Temperature Compensated Range: 45°F to 95°F
Maximum Temperature Effect: +0.004% of span per °F over temperature compensated span, from 73°F
Storage Temperature: −22°F to 160°F
Pressure Sensor: Optical non-contacting type. Diaphragm of Inconel 718. Housing of 316SS.
Wetted Materials: Inconel 718, 316SS, aluminum, brass, Teflon and polyethylene tubing.

Overpressure Capability: Sensor will withstand 100% overpressure. Minor span or zero adjustment may be required after overpressure.
Pressure Display: LCD with 0.5" high numerals
Current Display (optional): 4½ digit LCD display
Power Supply: 115 Vac, ±10%, 50/60 Hz
Battery: One 12 volt gel type lead-acid battery

From
$2650

Selector Valve
Quick selection or switching of pressure to sensor and indicator. Schematic shows flow.

Pressure Regulators
Precise control of pressures to instruments.

External Air Supply

Connection Block
Convenient instrument connections.

Digital Current Display
Optional current display with voltage supply to set-up current loop.

Digital Pressure Display
Easy-to-read LCD display of pressure in one of three selectable units.

Pressure Unit Selector
Pushbutton selection to read pressure in psi, inches of water, or percent of 12 psi span. Selected unit indicated on display.

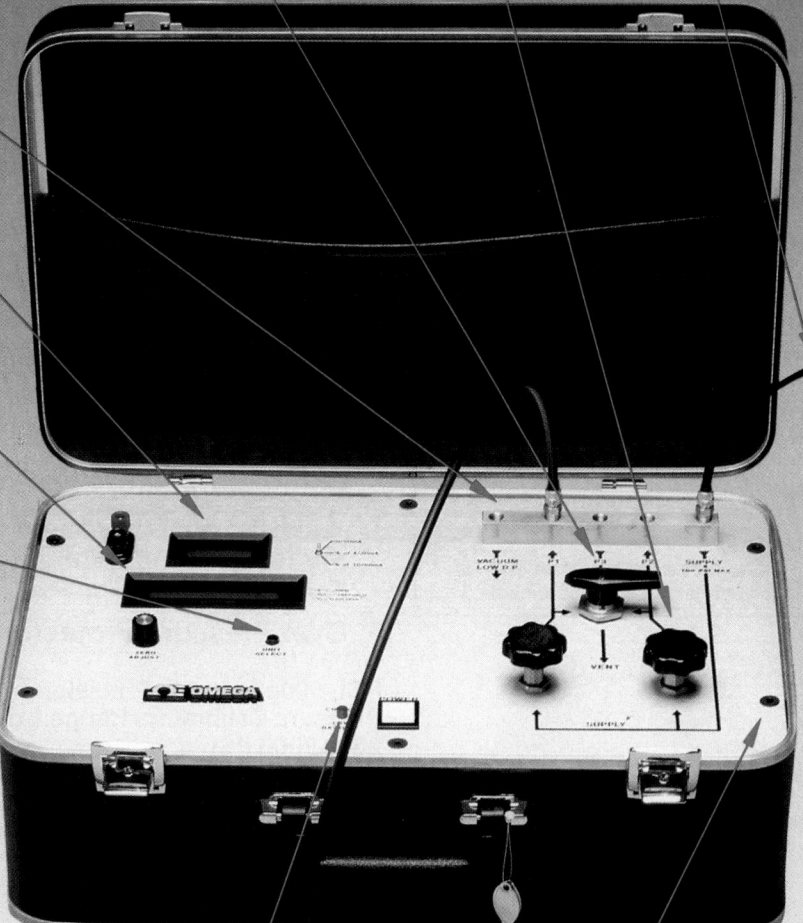

Fittings, ¼" tubing and power cord included

Battery Charge Indicator
Shows when battery is charging or indicates low voltage.

Transducers sold separately, see section B.

Panel
Easy removal for inspection or servicing. Quick access to all components.

PORTABLE PRESSURE CALIBRATORS
WITH INTERNAL PRESSURE SOURCE

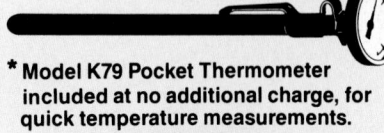

Supply pressure gauge display showing 0.74, with ABS GAGE OVRNG indicators and Pressure Limit Monitor gauge

OPERATE / OFF / BATT TEST — POWER

SUPPLY PRESSURE

MAX REGULATED 500 PSI

250 / 100 / 500 — RANGE SELECT PSI

ZERO

ABS/GAGE

VOLTAGE / PRESSURE / CURRENT — DISPLAY SELECT

TRANSDUCER TEST

PRESSURE LIMIT MONITOR

VENT/VACUUM

PRESSURE

VERNIER

VENT

TEST

FILL PORT MAX 2015 PSI NITROGEN ONLY

CAUTION HIGH PRESSURE CYLINDER INSIDE

ΩE OMEGA Pressure Calibrator

* Model K79 Pocket Thermometer included at no additional charge, for quick temperature measurements.

All Models

$6420

- **.05% FS Accuracy**
- **Dual Scale Gauge and Absolute Pressure Ranges**
- **Portable, Lightweight, Less than 25 lbs**

- **N.B.S. Certificate Provided**
- **All Hoses, Fittings, Connectors Supplied**
- **Voltage/Current Display Mode for Transducer Testing**
- **Over Pressure Protection**

PCL-5000 Portable Precision Pressure Calibrators Range from 20 to 2000 PSI

For rapid on-site calibration of transducers, transmitters, gauges, and many other pressure-sensitive devices, the Omega 5000 Series Calibrators provide high accuracy, reliability, and automatic push-button operation. The OMEGA PCL-5000 portable, precision pressure calibrator is designed for the higher pressure range calibrations (20 to 2000 psi) and has its own self-contained 2000 PSI nitrogen cyclinder. It also provides push-button operation and switch selectable calibration modes —

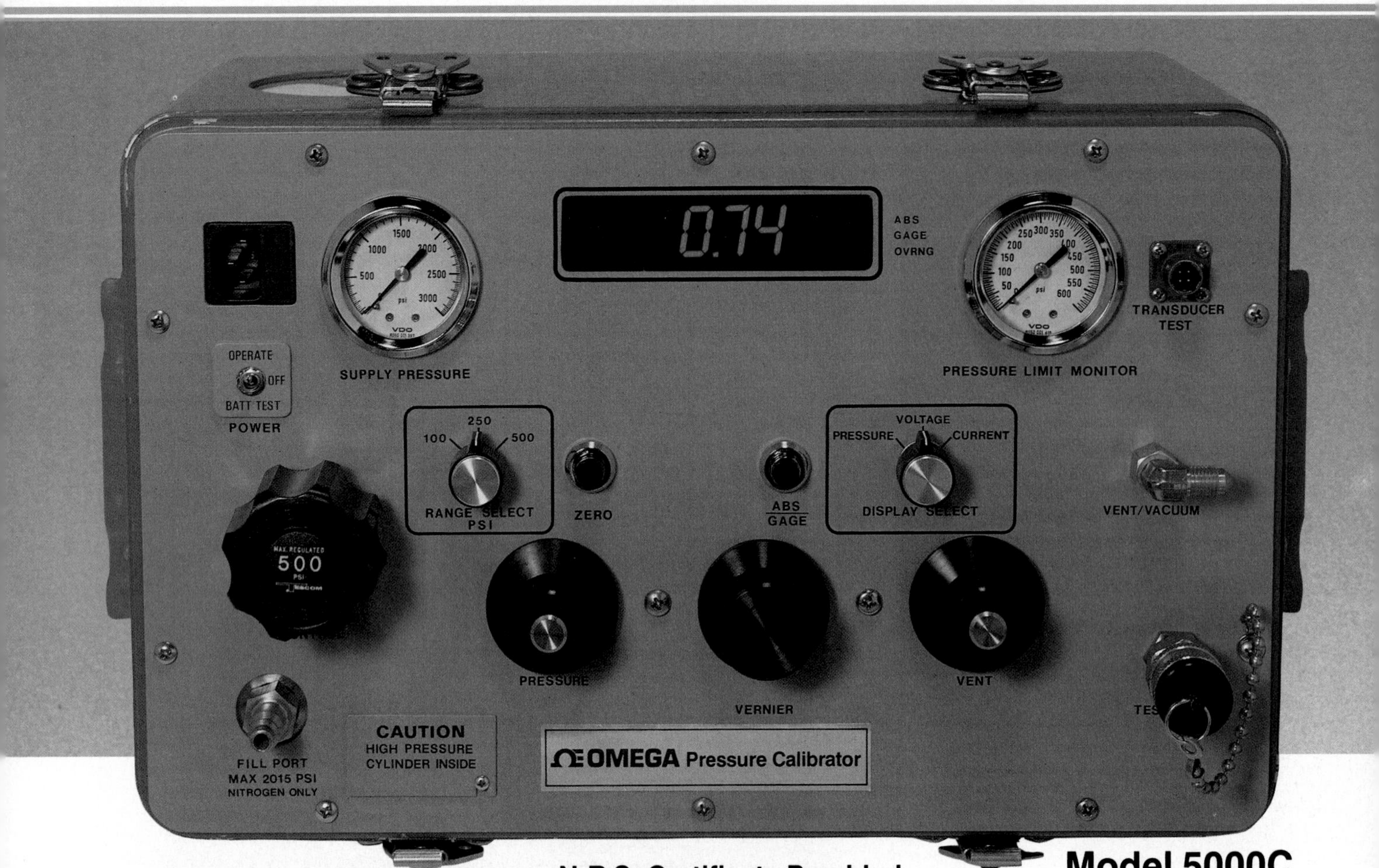

Model 5000C

2 YEAR WARRANTY

absolute or gauge. An extremely accurate instrument (±0.05% FS), the PCL-5000 comes complete with quick disconnect fittings and hoses for input and output pressure.

The PCL-5100, a low-pressure unit with ranges from 27″ HG to 100 PSI, offers five independent selectable ranges. Specifically designed for rugged field usage, it weighs less than 25 pounds and has its own built-in pressure and vacuum source, complete with hose and couplings for immediate on-site use. Its internal microcircuitry provides automatic maintenance of both zero and span calibration data to ensure long-term stability and accuracy. A "pressure limit" control provides over-pressure protection for any type or range of devices being tested by these units.

PCL-5000 SERIES
0.05% ACCURACY 30" H₂O TO 2000 PSI

Hoses and Couplings Supplied

Pressure Hoses: Quantity Supplied: Two (1 input, 1 output); Length: Five ft, nominal, each hose
External Carrying Case: Rugged aluminum case with cover and carrying handle

Model 5100

Weight: 24 lb, (including all hoses and cables)
Size: 10" W x 16" L x 11.5" H

SPECIFICATIONS

Overall Accuracy: ±0.05% FS Max. Accuracy statement includes all effects of linearity, hysteresis, repeatability and ambient temperature.
Operating Temperature: +40 to +110°F
Internal Pressure Cylinder: Capacity: 9.0 Standard Cubic Feet; Volume: 80 Cubic inches; Rating: 2015 PSI
Overpressure Rupture Disc: Rating: 3000 PSIG, Nominal
Pressure Media Filter: Rating: 7 microns, nominal; Type: Field Replaceable Filter Cartridge
Control Valves: Type: Micrometering with positive shutoff. Adjustable stop and replaceable seat, non-destructible
Fill and Test Ports: Style Quick Disconnect type; Pressure Rating: 3000 PSIG, min. connected or disconnected

◆ HIGHLIGHTED MODELS STOCKED FOR FAST DELIVERY ◆

To Order *(Specify Model Number)* 110 Vac Power Models

MODEL	PRICE	TYPE	RANGES	RESOLUTION
PCL-5000A	$6420	PSIG & PSIA	2000/1000/400	.5/.2/.05
PCL-5000B	6420	PSIG & PSIA	1000/500/200	.2/.1/.05
PCL-5000C	6420	PSIG & PSIA	500/250/100	.1/.05/.002
PCL-5000D	6420	PSIG	100/50/20	.02/.01/.005
PCL-5000DB	6420	PSIA	100/50/20	.02/.01/.005
Low Pressure/Vacuum Model				
PCL-5100	$6420	(5 ranges: ±30" Hg to 100 PSI)		.5/.1/.01

OPTIONS *(Add Suffix to Model Number)*

Rechargeable Battery System (all models) [-1]	**$375**	Second Scale on PCL-5000D and DB inches of H20 [-2]	**$200**

All models are shipped with hoses, couplings and complete operator's manual.

PRECISION DEADWEIGHT TESTER
0.1% ACCURACY
RANGE 15 TO 10,000 PSI

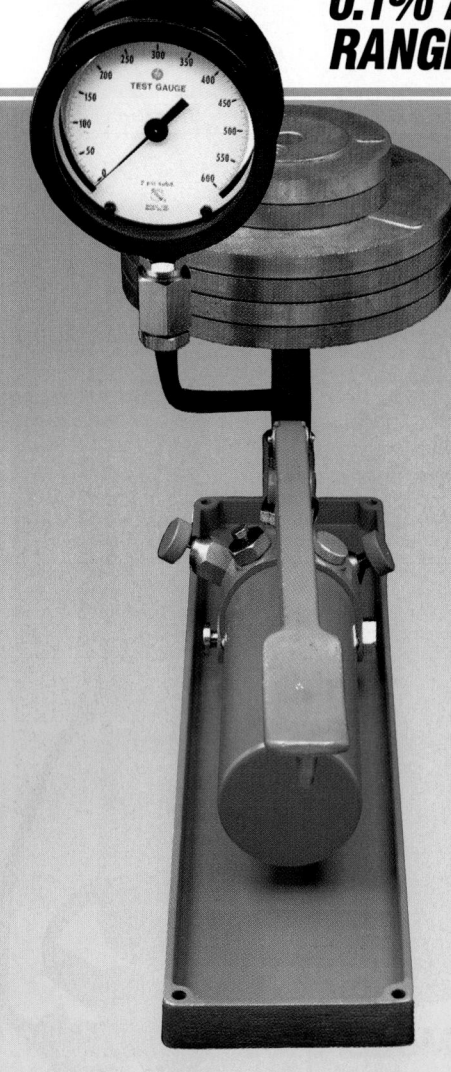

Each Unit Includes:
Hydraulic Pump,
Weight Set,
Two Piston/Cylinder, Assemblies,
Three Wrenches,
Spare O-Rings,
Piping and Fittings,
Rugged Carrying Case,
N.I.S.T. (NBS) Traceable
Certificate of Calibration and
Complete Operator's Manual

DWT 1305 Series

✔ **Easy-to-use Two Stage Hydraulic Pump**
✔ **Two Interchangeable Piston/Cylinder Assemblies**
✔ **Vernier Screw Adjustment for Pressure Settings**
✔ **Portable — Rugged Carrying Case Provided**

From
$2405

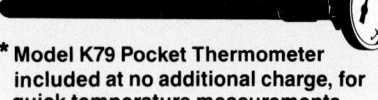

* **Model K79 Pocket Thermometer included at no additional charge, for quick temperature measurements.**

SPECIFICATIONS

Accuracy: 0.1% of produced pressure
Operating Pressure: 15 PSI to 10,000 PSI max. (100 kPa to 70,000 kPa)
Body Material: Aluminum Alloy
Piston and Cylinder Material: Stainless Steel
Weights: Non-magnetic die-cast zinc alloy, NBS traceable
Operating Fluid: SAE 20 Automotive or Machine Oil
"O" Rings: Standard — Buna N
Reservoir Volume: Approximately 1.5 pints (0.7 liter)

The model DWT1305 Deadweight Testers are dual range, precision built hydraulic instruments for testing, setting, calibrating or repairing pressure measuring devices. Each instrument is self-contained and comes complete with tools and metal carrying case.

As a primary standard with 1/10th of 1% accuracy of the pressure produced, each unit is adjusted for standard gravity conditions and is certified N.I.S.T. (NBS) traceable.

To maintain optimum accuracy, deviation from standard gravity conditions must be applied to the readings.

These deadweight testers are dual range: each unit is supplied with two interchangeable piston and cylinder assemblies. One is for low pressure (below 2000 PSI/14,000 kPa); the other is for high pressure (through 10,000 PSI/70,000 kPa). The same weights are used with both pistons.

To Order (Specify Model Number)

| MODEL | PRICE | PISTON ASSEMBLY PRESSURE RANGE | | PISTON VALUE | | NUMBER OF WEIGHTS BY VALUE | | | | | NET WEIGHT | |
PSI TYPE		Low	High	Low	High	L-5 H-25	L-10 H-50	L-20 H-100	L-40 H-200	L-100 H-500	lb	kg
▶ DWT1305D-10	$2405	15/200	75/1000	5	25	1	3	2	3	—	60	27
▶ DWT1305D-20	2520	15/400	75/2000	5	25	1	3	2	3	2	70	32
▶ DWT1305D-30	2635	15/600	75/3000	5	25	1	3	2	3	4	85	39
▶ DWT1305D-50	2865	15/1000	75/5000	5	25	1	3	2	3	8	105	48
▶ DWT1305D-100	3560	15/2000	75/10000	5	25	1	3	2	3	18	175	80

◆ *HIGHLIGHTED MODELS IN STOCK FOR FAST DELIVERY* ◆

PORTABLE PRESSURE TEST SET
FOR USE WITH ¼% ACCURACY TEST GAUGES

- ✔ **Portable—(Weighs Less than 40 lbs)**
- ✔ **¼% Accuracy—When Used with OMEGA Gauges**
- ✔ **Two Stage Hydraulic Pump**
- ✔ **Vernier Screw Adjustment**
- ✔ **Rugged Metal Case (Holds Up to 4 Gauges)**

A compact, lightweight portable pressure standard with ¼% accuracy gauges, the DWT1327D Test Set is ideally suited to field testing or remote in-plant applications. Similar to model DWT1305D, the test set consists of a two-stage hydraulic pump and a manifold which is pressurized during operation. An integral part of the pump is a new shuttle valve feature that can increase the speed of pressure build-up or reduce the effort necessary to operate the pump handle. One connection to the manifold is for a 4½" type PGT solid front test gauge (¼ of 1% of gauge span accuracy), the other accommodates most standard size dial gauges.

$1425
Complete Kit

SPECIFICATIONS Test Set

Accuracy: ¼ of 1% of Gauge Span
Operating Pressure: 0 to 10,000 Max. (0 to 70,000 kPa)
Body Material: Aluminum Alloy
Operating Fluid: SAE 20 Automotive or Machine Oil
"O" Ring: Standard-Buna N
Reservoir Volume: Approximately 1.5 Pints (0.7 liter)

SPECIFICATIONS Gauges

Type and Size: OMEGA 4½" Test Gauges
Accuracy: ¼% of Gauge Span
Bourdon Tube Materials: 316 Stainless Steel (150 to 1000 PSI) Monel (5000 to 10,000 PSI)

To Order *(Specify model number)*

MODEL	PRICE	DESCRIPTION
DWT1327D	$1425	Portable Pressure Test Set

¼% Test Gauges-4½" Dial Size *(Order Test Gauges Separately)*

MODEL	PRICE	RANGE (PSI)	GRADUATIONS	
			MAJOR	MINOR
PGT-45L-100	$227	0 to 150	10	0.5
PGT-45L-600	227	0 to 600	50	2
PGT-45L-1000	227	0 to 1000	50	5
PGT-45L-5000	263	0 to 5000	500	10
PGT-45L-10,000	297	0 to 10,000	1000	50

For a complete selection of test gauges, including additional ranges and dial sizes, see Section G. Complete Test Set includes: two-stage hydraulic pump with base; three wrenches for gauge installation and removal; spare "O" rings; all piping, fittings and ¼ and ½ NPT adaptors; rugged metal carrying case that holds up to four test gauges, and complete operator's manual.

PORTABLE LEAK DETECTOR
PROVIDES AUDIBLE AND VISUAL SIGNAL

1 YEAR WARRANTY _CARE_

$863

✓ **Easily Locates Leaks in Many Locations and Applications**

✓ **Audible and Visual Signal Response**

✓ **Optional Ultrasonic Transmitter for Evaluating Container Integrity**

The model FLCK1 is an ideal portable instrument for locating leaks in many applications including pneumatic systems, leak tightness, and mechanical noise location. This highly accurate instrument provides an audible and visual signal in response to the ultrasound produced by such phenomena. Simply point the instrument in the general direction of analysis, and watch the LCD bargraph display for maximum reading. Then, use one of the supplied extension tubes to narrow down the band of signal. The source can be rapidly identified. The FCLK1 pays for itself quickly by helping you seal leaks in compressed air lines that keep your compressor running, robbing you of valuable energy dollars.

Model FLCK1 is supplied with an attractive carrying case, two extension tubes, headphones, and one 9V battery. Optional equipment includes an ultrasonic transmitter. The transmitter is designed to act as an ultrasonic source for evaluating the integrity of containers, seals and other applications where gas pressure is not available.

SPECIFICATIONS
Instrument Construction: ABS plastic
Dimensions: 12.0″ × 3.2″ × 1.8″ (305 x 81 x 46 mm)
Weight: 0.9 lb. (410 g)
Sensitivity: Requires a min. of 5 psig pressure. Will detect a 10 micron hole at a max. of 15′ (5 m) distance. Senses a 4′ (1.2 m) diameter circular area at 15′ (4.5 m) distance (15° cone)

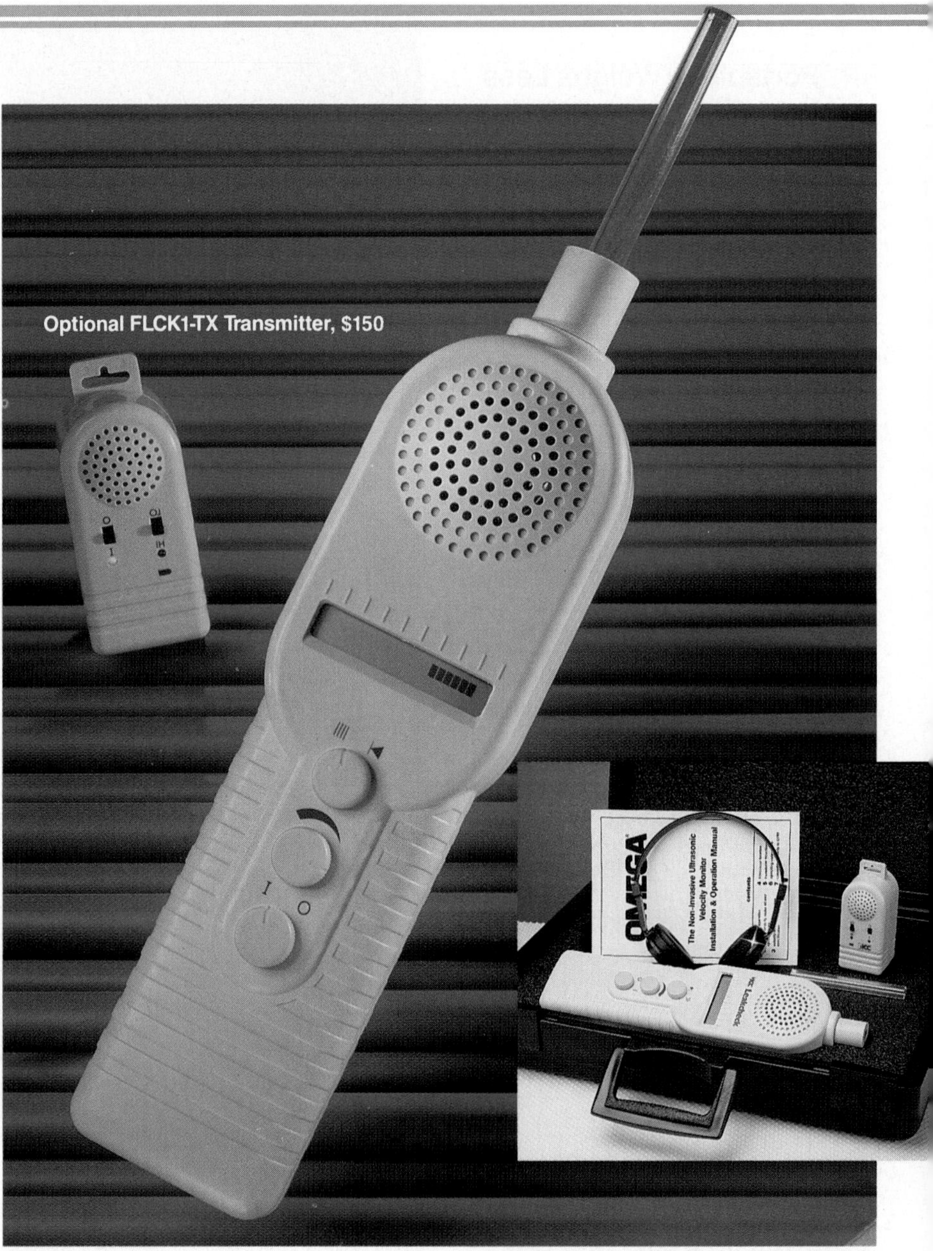

Optional FLCK1-TX Transmitter, $150

Complete with leak detector, extension tubes, headphones, rugged carrying case, 9V battery, and complete operator's manual.

To Order (Specify Model Number)

Model Number	Price	Description
FLCK1	**$863**	Leak Detector with Carrying Case, Extension Tubes, Headphones and one 9V Battery
FLCK1-TX	200	Ultrasonic Transmitter (38.5 kHz output). Includes 2 9V batteries
OCW-1	78	OMEGACARE™ 1-year warranty extension (2-year total warranty)
OCW-2	140	OMEGACARE™ 2-year warranty extension (3-year total warranty)
OCW-3	195	OMEGACARE™ 3-year warranty extension (4-year total warranty)

Ordering Example: *FLCK1 leak detector with carrying case, extension tubes, headphones and 9V battery, plus OCW-3 three-year warranty extension, $863 + 195 = **$1058.***

MICROPROCESSOR BASED PRESSURE, TEMPERATURE RECORDER
WITH LARGE 8" (200 MM) DIAMETER CHART

NEW!

1 YEAR WARRANTY

Model CT585
$700

✔ **Temperature to 120°F (49°C); Pressure to 100 PSI**

✔ **Double-Sided Circular Charts: 1, 7, 32 Day Records**

✔ **Easy Front Panel Setup**

✔ **Table Top or Wall Mount**

✔ **Battery or Wall Socket Powered**

✔ **Hi/Lo Alarms and Relay Standard**

✔ **Optional Calibration Lockout**

The CT585 sets a new standard in temperature and pressure measurement. This completely self-contained recorder is microprocessor-based for accurate indication of temperature and pressure, along with the current time and storage of peak values (max. and min.). Each function of the recorder is easily accessible from the front panel. The user may select 1, 7 or 32 day operation on the large, 8" (200mm) chart, and may program the digital display for PSIG, °F or °C indication.

SPECIFICATIONS
TEMPERATURE INPUT (AT PRESSURE SENSOR):
Temp. Range: 2 to 120°F (-17 to 49°C)
Accuracy: ±1°C
Sensor: Solid state
Response Time: 1 min. for 63% step
Resolution: 1°F/°C
Voltage Input: 0.02 to 1.2 Vdc displayed as 2 to 120°F; disables temperature and pressure input adapter

PRESSURE INPUT:
Range: 2 to 100 PSIG
Media: clean dry air
Accuracy: 2% FS
Response Time: 1 min., 63% of step
Hysteresis: 1%
Repeatability: 1%
Mounting: ¼" NPT, male
Cable Length: 3 ft (91 cm)
Oper. Temp Range: 2 to 120°F (-17 to 49°C)
Comp. Temp. Range: 32 to 120°F (0 to 49°C)
Operable Overpressure: 150 PSI
Burst Pressure: 250 PSI
Sensor Material: polyester, silicon, fluorosilicone, Buna-N

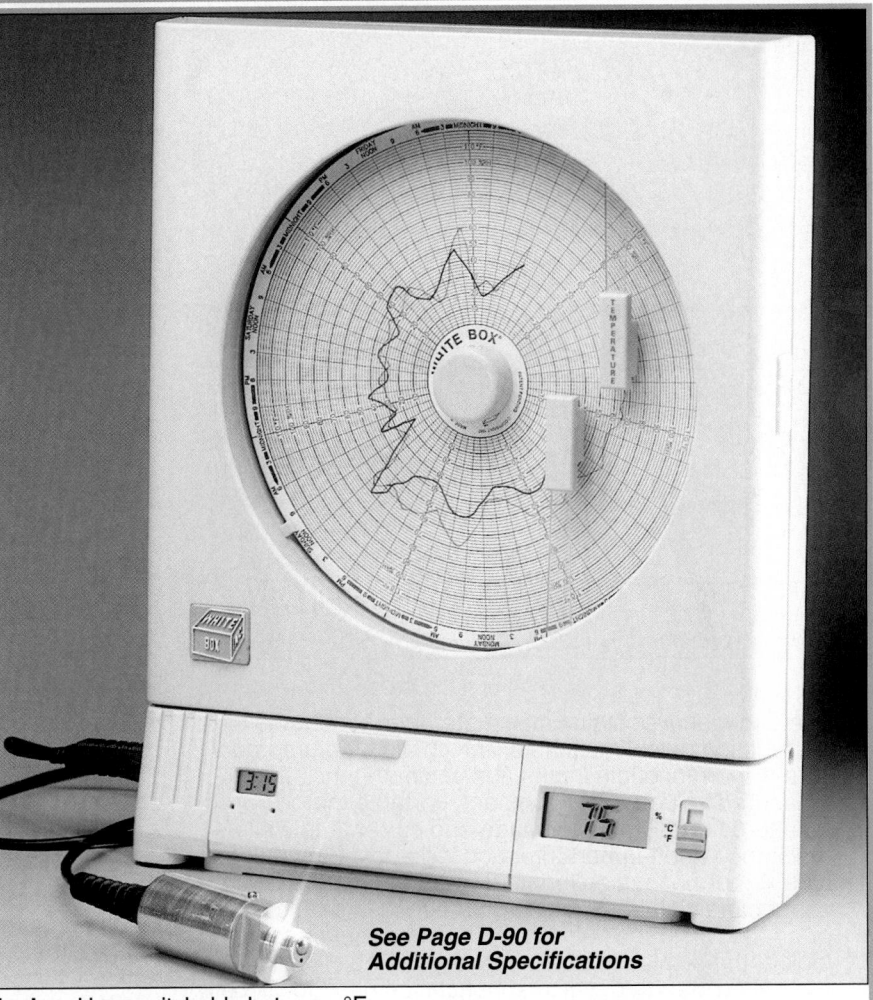

See Page D-90 for Additional Specifications

Display: User switchable between °F, °C and PSIG; 2½ digit LCD, 0.5" (13mm), low battery indicator

Chart: 8" (200mm) circular, linear radial div. 0,1,7,32 day, with PSIG, °F, °C scales

Patents: U.S., 311,695 (design); Canada, Rd. 1990; Germany, M8803842.4; Korea, 102897; Taiwan, 22507; U.K., 1055583

Comes with detachable solid state pressure/temp. transducer (with 6 ft cable,) additional 6 ft extension cable, voltage signal input adapter, 120 double-sided charts (CT585-CS), two pressure and two temperature pens, wall mount template and hardware, 110 Vac adapter, 4 "D" alkaline batteries and complete operator's manual.

To Order *(Specify Model Number)*

MODEL	PRICE	DESCRIPTION
CT585-W-AL-110	$700.00	White recorder with alarms, 110 Vac power
CT585-CAL-LOCK	25.00	Calibration lockout option
CT585-PS	9.00	Red (temp) and green (pressure) pen set
CT585-PS-6	52.00	Package of six (6) pen sets
CT585-C [*] [**]	19.00	200 charts (100 sheets printed both sides)
CT585-CSP	15.00	120 charts (printed both sides), 20 of each combination of temperature scale and days of recording

* *[a]- Insert 1,7 or 32 for days of recording period*
** *[b]- Insert F or C for temperature units*
Ordering Example: *CT585RS-W-AL recorder with CT585-C7F pack of 200 7-day, °F charts, $700 +12 = $712.*

HIGH PERFORMANCE DIGITAL MULTIMETER/THERMOMETER

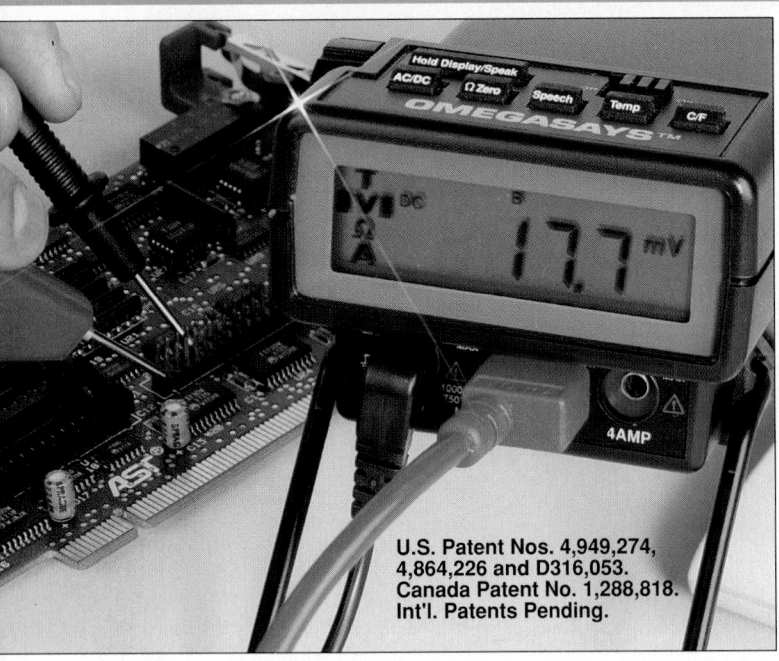

U.S. Patent Nos. 4,949,274, 4,864,226 and D316,053. Canada Patent No. 1,288,818. Int'l. Patents Pending.

Model HHM1
From

$595

- ✔ **True RMS ac Measurement**
- ✔ **Voice Annunciation of Measured Parameters in a Choice of 5 Languages**
- ✔ **0.25 % Basic dc Accuracy**
- ✔ **20 kHz ac Bandwidth**
- ✔ **Dual Type K Thermocouple Inputs With Differential Measurements**
- ✔ **4 Digit Temperature Display, 3¾ Digit DMM Display**
- ✔ **0.1° Resolution to 1000°**
- ✔ **Continuous or Manual Button Control of Voice Annunciation**

The Omegasays® digital multimeter/thermometer is a full function digital multimeter, which also features dual type K thermocouple inputs and voice annunciation of measured values. This compact, portable meter measures true RMS ac voltage and current, as well as resistance and temperature, and will accept any two type K thermocouples terminated with miniature SMP connectors. Whether sitting on a bench in a laboratory or on the run in the field, the HHM1 user never has to look at the display to obtain readings. The HHM1 features a standard voice annunciation used to verbally tell the user the current measurement in a choice of five different languages. This unique speech feature will continuously announce measurements, may be operated manually with the push of a button to speak on demand, or may be disabled. One of five field installable voice chips determines whether the meter will speak English, French, Spanish, German or Japanese.

The Omegasays displays measured values on an easy to read LCD for visual indication, which also includes an indication of the current measurement function, the other available measurement functions, speech function status (continuous, on demand or off), measurement units, thermocouple probe input (T1, T2 or T1-T2), display hold and low battery. All DMM connections plug into the front of the unit. Thermocouples, earphones and the ac adaptor plug into the rear panel of the unit. This rear panel also contains a three position volume selector switch.

On top of the HHM1 meter is an on/off switchj along with six pushbuttons used to select between a variety of unique additional functions. These include a "TEMP" function, which selects the thermocouple input T1, T2 or the differential. The "Ω ZERO" function compensates for the resistance of the test leads for resistance

measurements. "DISPLAY HOLD/SPEAK "selects continuous or on demand speech or freezes the display. The "SPEECH" button turns the speech function on and off. "°F/°C" switches the temperature units. "AC/DC" similarly switches between ac and dc measurements.

Included with each HHM1 is a set of test leads for measuring voltage, current and resistance. The red lead handle includes a convenient pushbutton to easily operate the speech function while holding the leads. An optional pistol grip type K thermocouple handle is also available with a similar pushbutton to activate the voice function remotely for temperature measurements. This handle accepts both standard OST and miniature SMP type thermocouple connectors.

To Order *(Specify Model Number)*

Model No.	Price	Description
HHM1	$595	High performance DMM/thermometer
HHM1A	695	Very high performance DMM/thermometer
HHM1-FR	75	Plug-in speech chip - French
HHM1-SP	75	Plug-in speech chip - Spanish
HHM1-GR	75	Plug-in speech chip - German
HHM1-JP	85	Plug-in speech chip - Japanese
HHM1-EG	65	Add'l. English speech chip
SDX-HHM1	35	Pistol grip thermocouple handle with speech actuator button and KMQSS-125G-6 thermocouple probe

Ordering Example: *HHM1A high performance DMM/thermometer with English speech chip, plus SDX-HHM1 thermocouple probe and handle with speech button, $595 + $35 = **$630.***

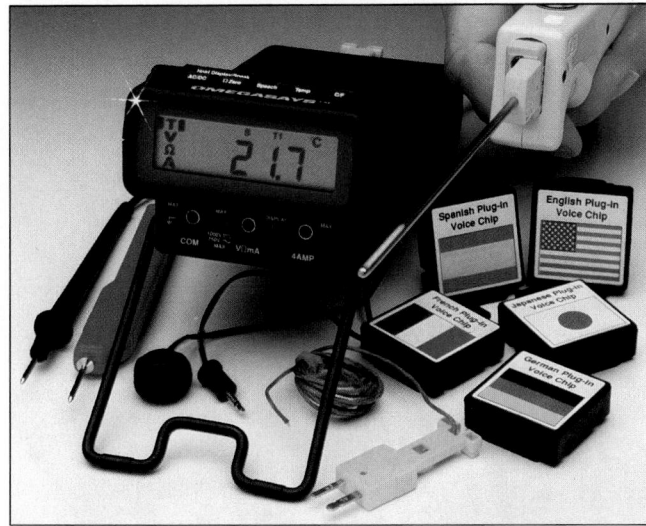

The Omegasays® meter comes complete with fuses, two glass braid insulated beaded wire type K thermocouples, TAS standard-to-mini thermocouple transition adaptor, custom test leads, English speech chip, earphone, soft carrying case, 9V battery, 110 Vac adaptor and operator's manual

SPECIFICATIONS

Power Supply: 9 V battery or 110 Vac adaptor (included)

Battery Life: Approx. 150 hrs no speech, approx. 30 hrs continuous speech; alkaline battery

Ambient Operating Conditions: 32 to 122°F (0 to 50 °C); 0 to 80 % RH

Storage Temperature: 14 to 140 °F (-10 to 60 °C)

Dimensions: 2.36" H x 3.15" W x 6.69" D (6 x 8 x 14 cm)

Weight: 18 oz (0.5 kg), including battery, fuses, speech module

CURRENT MEASUREMENT

Range	Resolution	Accuracy	
		dc	ac
400 mA	0.1 mA	±0.5% ±2 d	±2% ±2 d
4 A	1 mA	±1% ±2 d	±2% ±2 d

Note: ac bandwidth is 50 to 20 KHz; 50 Hz to 5 KHz for signals > 40 mA in 400 mA range, for signals < 0.4 A in 4 A range.

Ranges: The 400 mA and 4 A current ranges have separate individually fused inputs

TEMPERATURE MEASUREMENT

Range	Resolution	Accuracy	
		HHM1	HHM1A
-200 to -150°C	0.1°C	+/-12°C	+/-1.5°C
-328 to -238°F	0.2°F	+/-24°F	+/-3.0°F
-150 to -100°C	0.1°C	+/-6.0°C	
-238 to -148°F	0.2°F	+/-12°F	
-100 to -50°C	0.1°C	+/-3.0°C	
-148 to -58°C	0.2°F	+/-6.0°F	+/-1°C
-50 to 0°C	0.1°C	+/-1.5°C	
-58 to 32°F	0.2°F	+/-3.0°F	
0 to 999°C	0.1°C	+/-1.0°C	
32 to 999°F	0.2°F	+/-2.0°F	
1000 to 1372°C	1°C	+/-1°C	
1000 to 2502°F	1°F	+/-2°F	

Functions: Dual input, with differential measurement capability (T1, T2, T1-T2)

Input Type: Type K thermocouple

Units: User selectable °F or °C

Input Protection: 24 V rms or 60 Vdc max. input voltage on any combination on input pins

Common Mode Voltage: 0.5 V max., between T1 and T2 during measurement

VOLTAGE MEASUREMENT

Range	Resolution	Accuracy	
		dc	ac
400 mV	0.1 mV		
4 V	1 mV		
40 V	10 mV	±0.25%	±0.25%
400 V	100 mV	±2 digits	±2 digits
1000 Vdc/ 750 Vac	1 V		

RESISTANCE MEASUREMENT

Range	Resolution	Accuracy
400 Ω	0.1 Ω	
4 kΩ	1 Ω	
40 kΩ	10 Ω	±0.25% ±2 digits
400 kΩ	100 Ω	
4 MΩ	1 kΩ	
40 MΩ	10 kΩ	±0.5% ±2 digits

Input Protection: 400 mA/250 V fast acting fuse, 400 mA range; 4 A/250 V fast acting fuse, 4 A range

Input Protection: 250 V rms ac or dc

Autoranging: Unit autoranges over all six ranges

Digital Ohms Zero: Nulls out test lead impedance for low resistance readings in the 4000 Ω range

   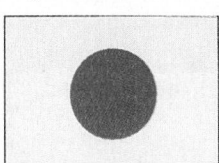 

DIGITAL HYGRO-THERMOMETER
DUAL ANALOG OUTPUTS STANDARD

NEW!

1 YEAR WARRANTY *CARE*

Model RH411
$349

- ✔ **Unique Dual Display for Simultaneous Indication of BOTH Temperature and Relative Humidity**
- ✔ **Dual Simultaneous Analog Outputs for Temperature and Relative Humidity**
- ✔ **°C/°F Switchable**
- ✔ **Display Hold**
- ✔ **Min/Max Storage**
- ✔ **Sleep Mode to Prolong Battery Life**
- ✔ **Digital Calibration for Accuracy and Repeatability**

The RH411 handheld digital thermo-hygrometer has a custom LCD display that lets you read temperature and relative humidity simultaneously. Perfect for any application where spot checks of temperature and relative humidity are needed, the RH411 offers fast and accurate measurements. The combination temperature/humidity sensor connects to the unit through a 5' (1.5m) cable. The sensor is housed in an easy-grip handle, in a protective metal mesh.

Other unique features make the RH411 an even better value: digital calibration, display hold, min and max storage, and individual analog outputs for both temperature and %RH.

SPECIFICATIONS
(Humidity)
Range: 2 to 98% RH
Accuracy: 3% at 25°C, between 20 and 90% of range; 5% at 25°C, below 20% or above 90%
Response Time: 30 sec for a 30 to 80% step change

(Temperature)
Range: 2 to 120°F (-17 to 48°C)
Accuracy: 1°F
Response Time: 3 min in still air, 20 sec in moving air for 63% step change
Analog Output: 10 mV/°F and 10 mV/% RH; continuous output; connected to 47 kohm min. impedance

MECHANICAL
Power: 9V battery and 110 Vac adaptor (included)
Battery Life: 100 h, alkaline battery
Sleep Mode: Unit shuts off after 15 min if no buttons are pushed. User can disable on power-up

U.S. Patent #D316,053

The RH411 Comes Complete with Handheld Temperature/ Humidity Probe with 5' Cable, 110 Vac Adaptor, 9V Battery, Operator's Manual and Dewpoint Reference Chart

To Order *(Specify Model No.)*

MODEL NO.	PRICE	DESCRIPTION
RH411	**$349**	Digital temperature/ relative humidity indicator

RH411 supplied complete with handheld temperature/humidity sensor with 5' cable, 9V battery, 110 Vac adaptor, operator's manual and dewpoint reference chart.

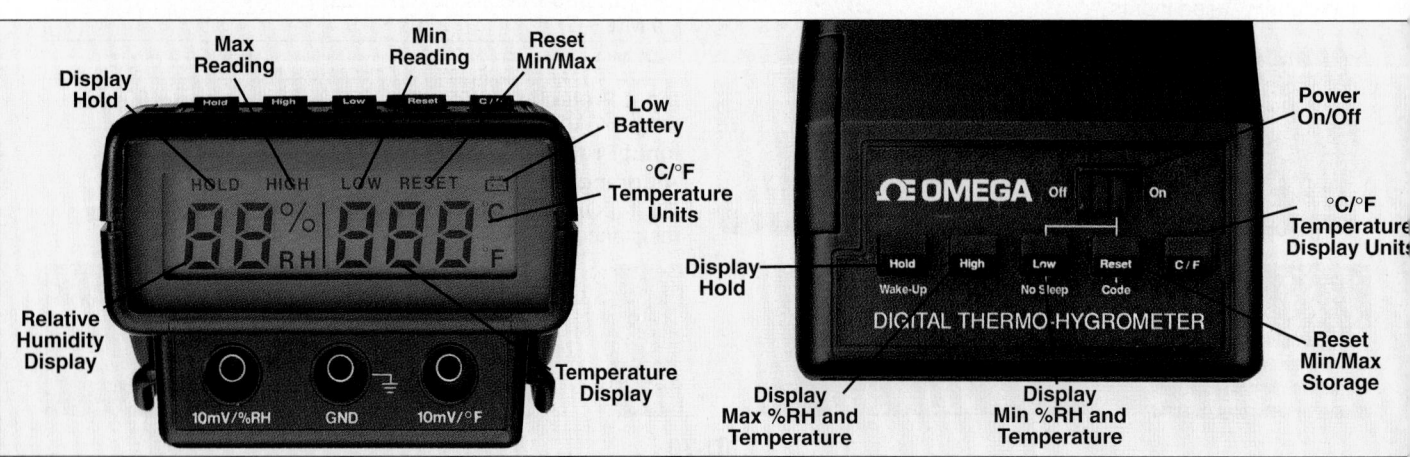

D-71

COMPACT RECORDERS
EVENT, dc INPUT, AND THERMOCOUPLE INPUT MODELS

1 YEAR WARRANTY

MADE IN USA

From
$324

- ✔ **Event, dc Input, and Thermocouple Input**
- ✔ **2⁵⁄₁₆″ Recording Width**
- ✔ **1 in/hr Standard Chart Speed**

OMEGA offers three compact units for recording events, dc signals, and temperature (from thermocouples). The RD292 event recorder monitors from one to eight channels of on-off operations. The RD288 galvanometric recorder permits full-scale measurement of signal by striking a stylus against pressure-sensitive paper. The economical RD255 thermocouple recorder measures temperature from remote thermocouple probes.

Specifications
Ambient Temp.: 0-50°C, 32-122°F
Primary Power: 100-130 Vac 50/60 Hz
Dimensions: RD255 and RD288: 3⅝″ W × 5⅝″ H × 4⁵⁄₁₆″ D (93 × 143 × 110 mm); RD292: 3⅝″ W × 5⅝″ H × 6″ D (93 × 143 × 152 mm)
Weight: RD255 and RD288: 3.75 llb (1.7 kg); RD292: 4.4 lb (2 kg) (4 input); 4.8 lb (2.18 kg) (8 input)

RD292 EVENT RECORDER
TTL Type: Input: 3-50 Vac or dc; current: −0.5-10 mA; input resistance: 6 k ohms
HIV Type: Input: 50-500 Vac or dc; current: 0.5-5 mA; input resistance: 100 k ohms
Repetition Rate: Up to 10 events/s
Connections: Input, barrier strip; power, fixed line cord

RD288 DC INPUT RECORDER
Inputs (resistance in ohms): 0-1 mA (100), 4-20 mA (6.25), 0-100 mV (100)
Striking Rate: Once every 2 s
Accuracy: ±2%
Maximum Continuous Input: 150%
Connections: Input, 6 pin connector; detachable line cord

KMTSS-125G-6 thermocouple, $24

RD255 THERMOCOUPLE RECORDER
Input Types: E, J, K, R, S, T thermocouples
Ranges: 0-250°F, 0-500°F, 0-1000°F, 0-100°C, 0-300°C
Accuracy: ±2% span
T/C Break Protection: Upscale
Maximum Loop Resistance: 1000 ohms
Connections: Inputs, SMP connector; power, line cord

To Order *(Specify Model Number)*

Model No.	Price	Description
RD288-1MA	$324	Recorder, 1 input, 1 mA
RD288-100MV	324	Recorder, 1 input, 100mV
RD288-4-20MA	378	Recorder, 1 input, 4-20 mA
RD292-TTL4	500	Recorder, 4 input, TTL, event
RD292-TTL8	705	Recorder, 8 input, TTL, event
RD292-HIV4	500	Recorder, 4 input, HIV, event
RD292-HIV8	705	Recorder, 8 input, HIV, event
RD255J-500F	483	Recorder, 1 input, J T/C
RD255K-1000F	483	Recorder, 1 input, K T/C
RD255E-1000F	483	Recorder, 1 input, E T/C
RD255R-1000F	483	Recorder, 1 input, R T/C
RD255S-1000F	483	Recorder, 1 input, S T/C
RD255T-250F	483	Recorder, 1 input, T/TC
SL-650	8	Paper, 1 roll, 63′, event
SL-651	8	Paper, 1 roll, 63′, 50 divisions
SL-652	9	Paper, 1 roll, 63′, 40 divisions
SL-653	9	Paper, 1 roll, 63′, 60 divisions

INSTRUMENTATION

D

COMPACT FLATBED RECORDER
FOR LABORATORY AND INDUSTRY APPLICATIONS

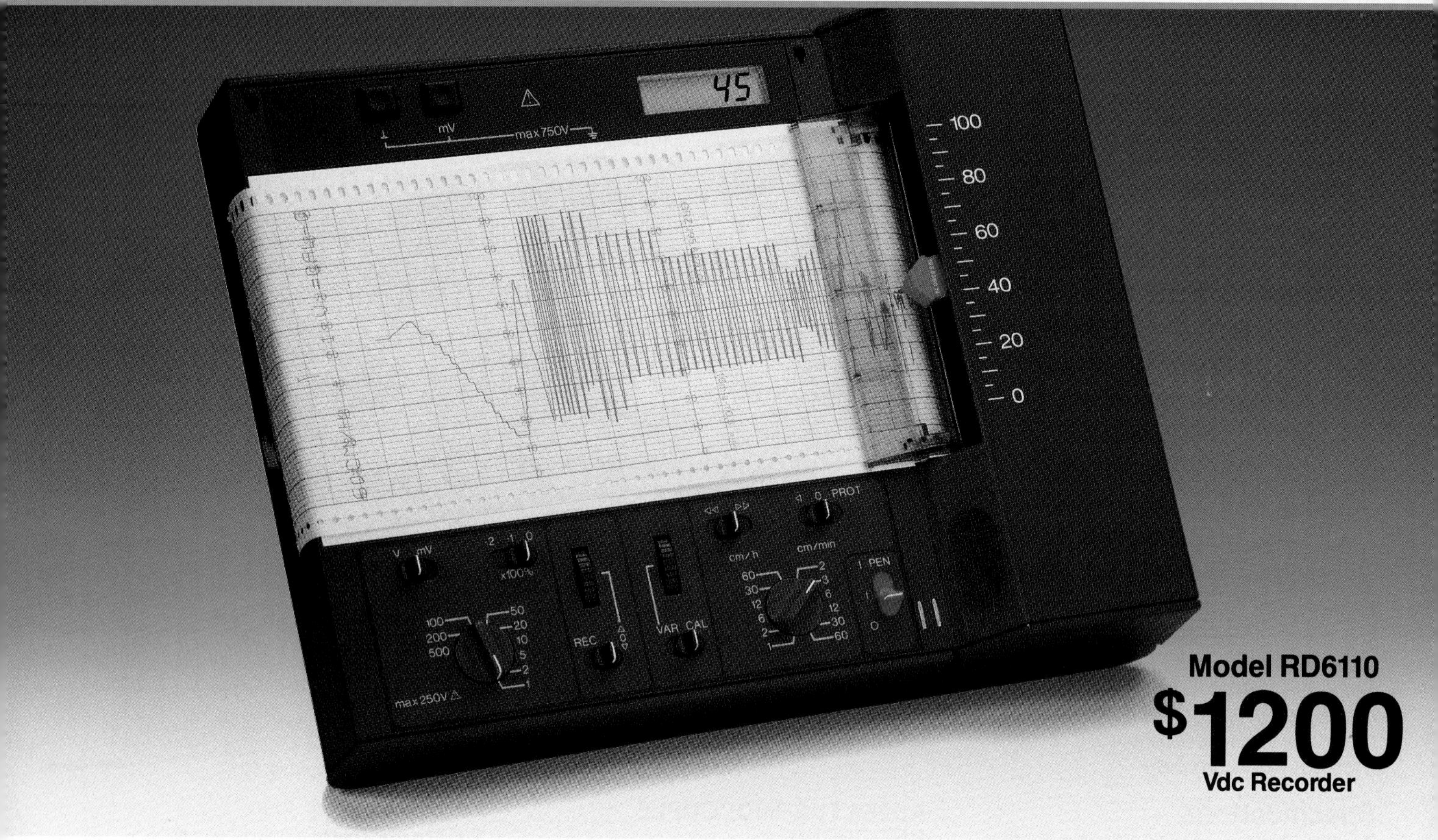

Model RD6110
$1200
Vdc Recorder

- ✔ **Built-In Digital Display**
- ✔ **Models for dc Voltage or ac/dc Voltage/Current**
- ✔ **Protocol Print Documents Chart Speed and Measurement Range**
- ✔ **Remote Control Paper Advance, Pen Lift and Event Marker Standard**

The RD6110 and RD6111 compact flatbed recorders are designed to meet the demands of engineering and electronic applications, with the ability to measure dc voltages or ac/dc voltage/current, respectively. For use in almost any application, the RD6110/6111 can operate on ac power using the 120 Vac to 12 Vdc transformer included with each unit, external 12 Vdc or internal batteries. A built-in digital display lets the user read the input at a glance, no matter what the zero adjustment and zero suppression are set to. Both units also have protocol printing, to permanently record charging status, measurement range and chart speed on the chart paper.

The RD6110 and RDG6111 have a compact 100 mm chart, and use a large 16 meter paper roll. Pens are disposable fiber. Other features include built-in remote control of paper advance, pen lift and event marker, chart speeds from 1 cm/hr to 60 cm/min, and a transparent, removable dust cover.

RD6110
For recording dc voltage levels, the RD6110 has 18 calibrated ranges from 1 mV to 500 Vdc (250 Vdc max). It also has a continuously adjustable variable range, allowing the user to set the full scale from 40 to 100% of each calibrated range. Built-in zero suppression of 100 and 200 percent is also standard.

RD6111
The RD6111 is the perfect recorder where flexibility is needed. Capable of measuring voltages and currents in both ac and dc, the RD6111 can measure from 150 mV to 750 V and from 0.6 mA to 6 A.

SPECIFICATIONS

Operating Ambient Temperature: 0 to 50°C

Power Supply: 120 Vac (through external transformer), 50/60 Hz; 12 Vdc; internal C-size (9 ea.) NiCad batteries

Dimensions: 3"H x 12"W x 9.1"D

Weight: 4.9 lb

Recording Width: 100 mm

Scale: 0 to 100 or 0 to 30

Linearity: 0.25%

Cutoff Frequency: 1 Hz

Protocol Print: charge status, measurement range, chart speed

Digital Display: 3½ digit LCD; indicated measured value, polarity and overload

Chart Speeds: 1,3,6,12,30,60 cm/hr and cm/min

Remote Control: TTL/CMOS signal control for STOP/ENABLE, REVERSE, PULSE paper feed control & pen lift

Zero Offset: -100 to +105%, adjustable

Event Marker: 3mm positive needle pulse; activated by TTL or CMOS signal, or contact closure

Input Type: floating, asymmetrical

Max Overload: RD6110 - 250 V; RD6111 - 300 V for ranges to 300 V, 750 V for 750 V range, 1.5 x I(rated) for current input

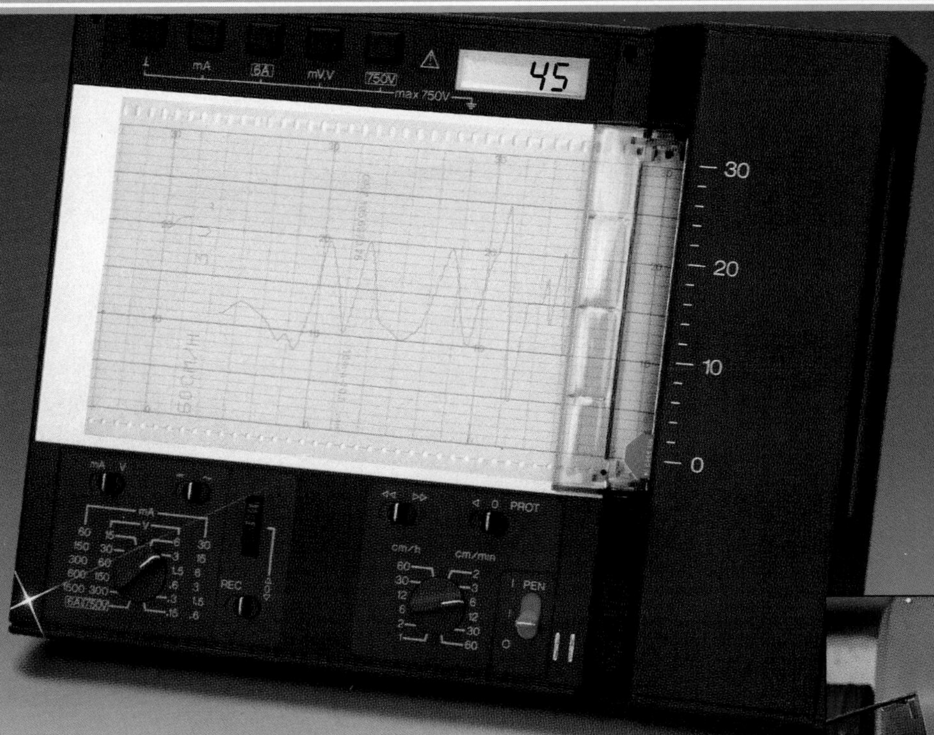

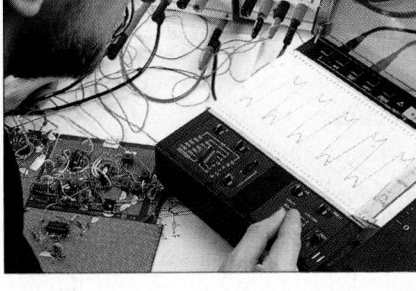

Model RD6111
$1300
Vac/dc/and Aac/dc Recorder

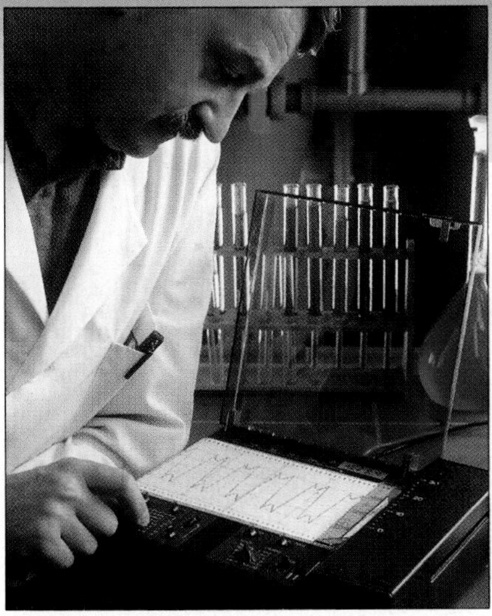

Input Impedance: RD6110 - 1 ohm; RD6111 - 1 Mohm for V ranges
Voltage Drop, RD6111: 150 mV for A ranges

Source Resistance: 100 ohm, rated; 1 kohm max. for V ranges

AC SMR: greater than or equal to 40 dB

AC CMR: greater than or equal to 70 dB

DC CMR: greater than or equal to 90 dB

RD6110
Input Ranges: 1,2,5,10,20,50,100,200,500 mV and Vdc (250 Vdc max.)

Variable Sensitivity: up to 2.5x
Zero Suppression: 0, 100%, 200%
Accuracy: 0.5% full scale

RD6111
Input Ranges:
0.15,0.3,0.6,1.5,3,6,15,30,60,150, 300,750 Vac/dc; 0.6,1.5,3,6,15,30,60,150,300,600, 1500,6000 mAac/dc

Accuracy, Vdc Input: 1% FS

Accuracy, Vac Sinusoidal Input: 1.5% FS at 50-60 Hz; 3% FS at 60 to 10 kHz; for ranges 0.15 to 300 V; 6% FS at 10 kHz to 20 kHz for ranges 0.15 to 300 V

Accuracy, Adc Input: 1% FS

Accuracy, Aac Sinusoidal Input: 2% FS at 50-60 Hz; 4% FS at 60 Hz to 10 kHz; 8% FS at 10 kHz to 20 kHz

To Order *(Specify Model No.)*

Model No.	Price	Description
RD6110	$1200	Vdc recorder
RD6111	1300	Vac/dc and Aac/dc recorder

Each recorder is supplied complete with dust cover, ac power adaptor, roll of paper, disposable felt-tip pen, manual

ACCESSORIES

Model No.	Price	Description
RDX6110-CASE	$140	carrying case
RDX6110-RP	83	10 rolls paper, 100 mm x 16 m, 0-100 scale
RDX6111-RP	83	10 rolls paper, 100 mm x 16 m, 0-30 scale
SL-301	13	disposable felt-tip pen, pkg of 3

X-Y RECORDERS
OMEGALINE ® 790

- ✔ **11″ x 7″ Recording Area**
- ✔ **X-Y and X-Y/Y-t Models**
- ✔ **0.5% Accuracy**
- ✔ **Input Ranges from 1 mV to 10 V per cm**
- ✔ **Continuous Zero Adjustment**
- ✔ **Electrostatic Paper Hold and Electric Pen Lift**
- ✔ **Sweep Speeds from 0.1 to 20 sec/cm**
- ✔ **Single and Repeating Sweep Capability**

**Model 790
X-Y Recorder
From**

$1890

Shown smaller than actual size.

SPECIFICATIONS:

Design: Flatbed

Recording Area: 11″ x 7″ (280 x 180 mm)

Deadband: 0.3%

Scale: 0-28, X-axis; 0-18, Y-axis

Response Time: 0.6 sec (X), 0.4 sec (Y)

Slew Speed: 0.6 m/sec (X), 0.8 m/sec (Y)

Limiting Frequency: 1 Hz

Operating Temperature Range: 32 to 122°F

Paper Format: Single sheet, 11.7″ x 8.2″

Pen Lift: Electromagnetic, external control from TTL, CMOS or switch

Operating Position: Horizontal up to max. 85° angle

Power: 110, 220, 240 Vac, 50/60 Hz

Power Consumption: 20 VA

Dimensions: 5.2″ H x 15.2″ W x 14.2″ D

Weight: 14.3 lbs.

Sensitivity: 0.1, 0.2, 0.5, 1, 2, 5, 10, 20, 50, mV/cm, V/cm

Accuracy: 0.5%

Linearity: 0.3%

Variable Sensitivity: Increases up to 10 times per range

Zero Adjust: Continuous adjustment between −5 and 105%

Input Type: Floating, asymmetrical, 4 mm safety sockets

Potential Between Input and Ground: 250 V max.

Overload: 250 V max.

Input Resistance: 1000 M ohm, up to 100 mV/cm; 1M ohm, over 1 V/cm

Input Current: 10 nA max.

Source Resistance: 1 K ohm; 10 k ohm max.

CMR: >80 dB, ac; 90 dB, dc

Time Base (Model 791 only): Quartz controlled, single or repeating sweeps on X-axis

Sweep Speeds: 0.1, 0.2, 0.5, 1, 2, 5, 10, 20 sec/cm

To Order *(Specify model no.)*

Model No.	Price	Description
790	$1890	X-Y recorder
791	2060	X-y/Y-t recorder
790E	2160	X-Y recorder with enhanced input*
791E	2330	X-y/Y-t recorder with enhanced input*

*18 dc voltage ranges from 0.1 to 50 V/cm

Options and Accessories

Ordering Code	Price	Description
E-00	$115	19″ rack mount assembly
E-02	180	Multifunction accessory
E-06	30	DIN input connector
SL-623	149	50 Sheet chart paper, 5 pkgs.
SL-301	13	Disposable red pens, 3

MICROPROCESSOR-BASED CIRCULAR CHART RECORDER
CT1700 Series

- ✔ **14 Programmable Chart Speeds**
- ✔ **2¾″ (70 mm) Writing Width**
- ✔ **NEMA 4 Enclosure**
- ✔ **1 and 2 Channel Versions**
- ✔ **Accepts Thermocouple, RTD, V, mV, or mA Signal**

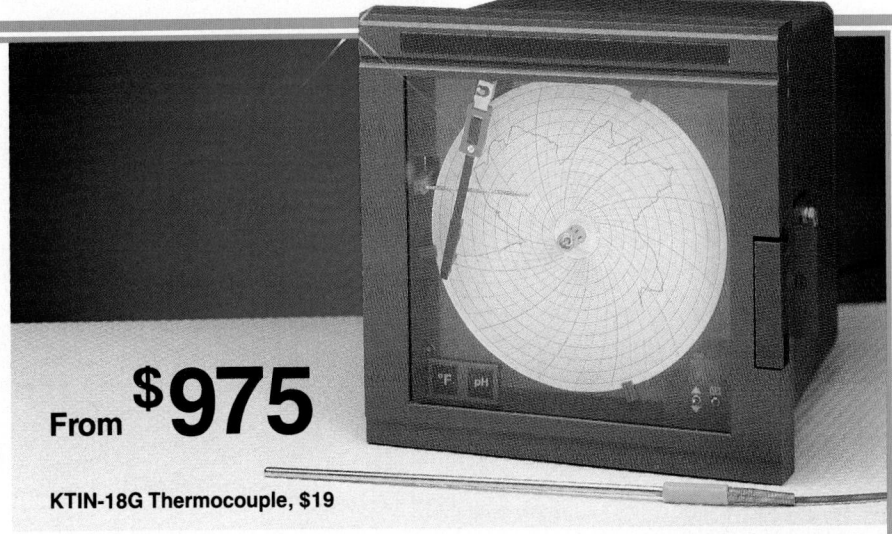

From **$975**

KTIN-18G Thermocouple, $19

The OMEGA CT1700 Series microprocessor-based circular chart recorders give readings on small 6″ charts. These recorders offer from 1 hr up to 32 days of chart recording time, versatile control of the input ranging and linearization, control of the pen drive, pen referencing, visual alarms, and control outputs. Units accept thermocouple (K, R, S, T, J, E, or B), RTD, volt, millivolt or milliamp signal output; two-pen units accept any input signal combination desired. Ranging is achieved without the use of range cards and ranging components; the pens and chart rotation are driven by reliable stepper motors, eliminating the need for mechanical feedback components.

Specifications
Input Impedance: mV, >10 MΩ; V, 500 kΩ; current, 10Ω
Relay Action: Switch selectable, energized above or below setpoint, 3-state or latching
Chart Speed: Programmable for 1, 2, 3, 4, 6, 8, 12, 24, 48, 72 hr/rev and 7, 8, 30, and 32 days/rev
Resolution:
  Measurement (mV, V, mA, T/C): ≤0.1% span
  RTD: 0.06Ω
  Pen: ≤0.1% full scale travel
Voltage Requirements: 110 V or 230 V, 50 or 60 Hz or 10 to 30 Vdc
Transmitter Power Supply:
  Output Voltage: 25 V ±0.5 V at 0 or 20 mA
  Output Ripple: 100 mV peak to peak max
  Regulation: ±0.1 V for output change 4-20 mA
Dimensions: 8⅞″W × 8⅞″H × 9″D
Panel Cutout: 8¼″ square
Weight: 13 lb approx.

mV, V, mA Inputs

Input Type	Min. Start Value	Min. Span	Max Span & Range Value
mV	−999	5.00	1000
V	−20.0	0.50	20.0
mA	−99.9	0.50	100.0

Temperature Inputs

| Input Type | °C/°F | | |
	Min. Start Temp	Min. Span	Max Temp
RTD(100Ω Pt) DIN 43760	−200/−300	50/100	500/1000
K	0/0	150/300	1300/2400
R & S	0/0	600/1100	1700/3100
T	−250/−400	200/400	300/600
J	−100/−150	100/200	900/1600
E	−100/−150	100/200	900/1600
B	0/0	1000/1800	1800/3300

Accessories

Model No.	Price	Description
CT1700C-0-100	$110	Additional 500 charts, 0-100 scale
CT1700C-GEN	110	Additional 500 charts, general purpose
CT-1000-Red	17	Additional 5 pens, channel 1
CT-1000-Green	17	Additional 5 pens, channel 2

To Order *(Specify Model Number)*

Model No.	Price	No. Alarms Relays	Ext. Trans. Power Supply	No. Inputs
CT1701	$975			1
CT1701-M1	1085	1		1
CT1701-M2	1195	2		1
CT1701-M1-MA	1255	1	X	1
CT1701-M2-MA	1365	2	X	1
CT1702	1100			2
CT1702-M1	1210	1 (Ch. 1 only)		2
CT1702-M2	1320	2 (Ch. 1 only)		2
CT1702-M1-M1	1320	1 (Ch. 1 and 2)		2
CT1702-M2-M2	1540	2 (Ch. 1 and 2)		2

Note: For DC option add -DC suffix and $50 to price.
Comes complete with chart, pen, and complete operator's manual.

INSTRUMENTATION

D

FUNCTION RECORDERS
SERIES RD-2000

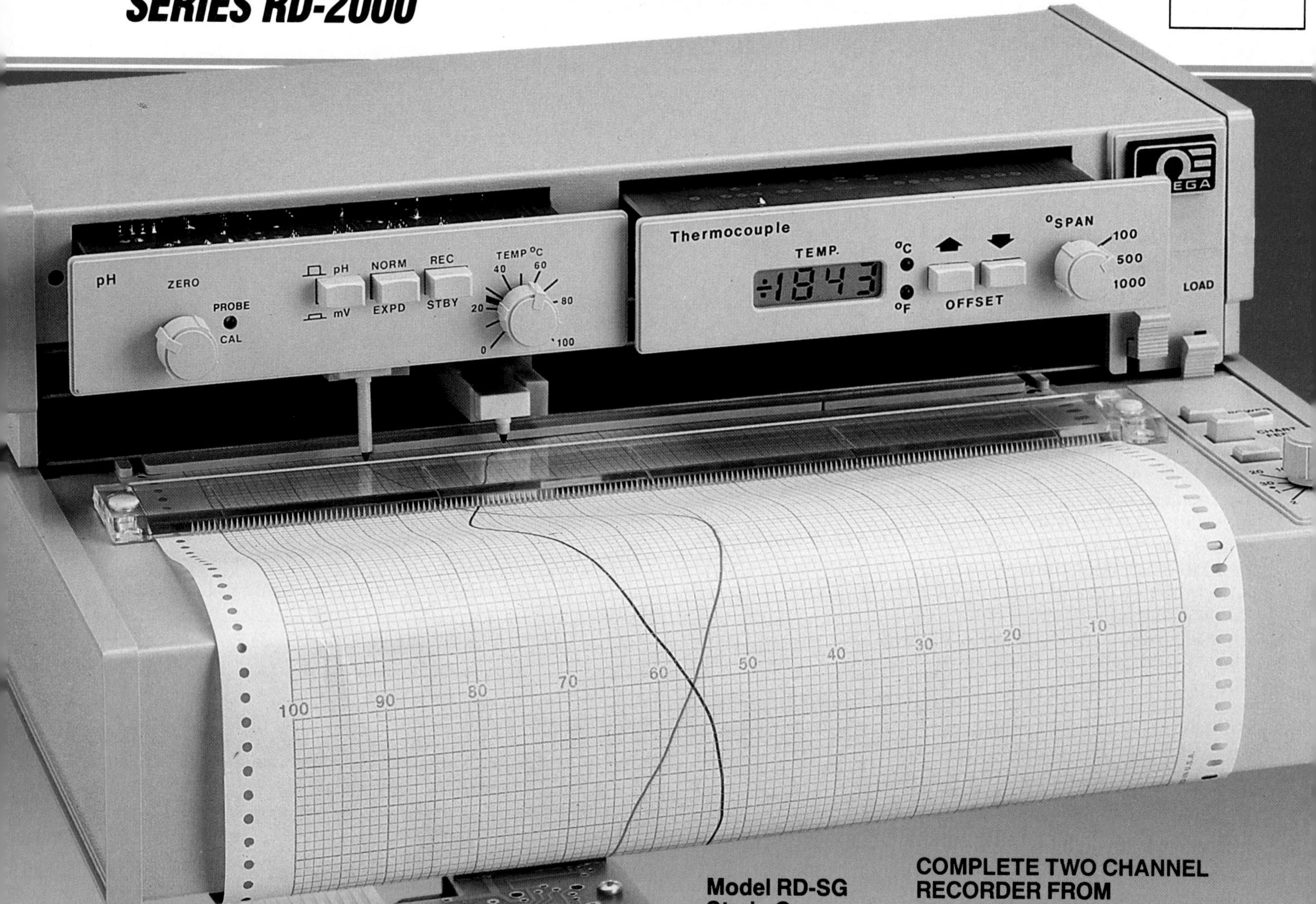

Model RD-SG
Strain Gage
Module
$435

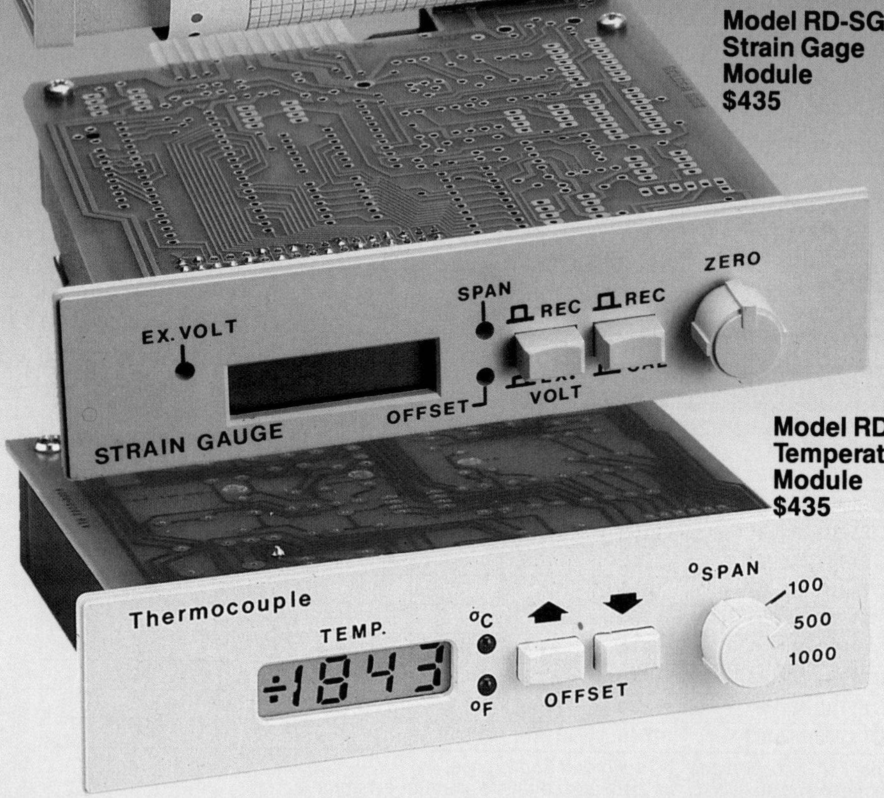

Model RD-TC
Temperature
Module
$435

**COMPLETE TWO CHANNEL
RECORDER FROM**

$1345

- ✔ **100 and 200 mm Chart Recording System with Plug-in Input Modules**
- ✔ **Modules for Temperature, Strain, pH, Voltage and Current**
- ✔ **Convenient Front Panel Paper Loading**
- ✔ **ac or 12 Vdc Power**
- ✔ **12 Chart Speeds**
- ✔ **Digital Display with Thermocouple and Strain Module**
- ✔ **Thermocouple Types J, K, T and E**

FUNCTION RECORDERS
SERIES RD-2000

Shown Smaller Than Actual Size

COMPLETE ONE CHANNEL RECORDER FROM

$860

RD-MV INPUT MODULE

The RD-2000 Function Recorder System introduces low cost to modular recorders. With a choice of input modules, the RD-2000 can measure temperature from thermocouples, pH, millivolts/volts, or milliamps. To select any input type, simply plug in the appropriate module. The mainframe recorder is available in three varieties; a one pen model with a 100 mm chart, and a 200 mm chart model with either one or two pens. With the two pen model, you can record two completely different input signals, such as temperature and pH, or have two channels record the same type of input signal. Designed for ease of use, the RD-2000 system has all user controls on the main control panel. Select one of 12 chart speeds (from 1 cm/hr to 30 cm/min), chart feed, chart start/stop, power and pen lift. For easy paper loading, the control deck unlatches and swings away to reveal the paper feed spindle. A roll of chart paper is dropped into place, and the deck is then lowered and latched.

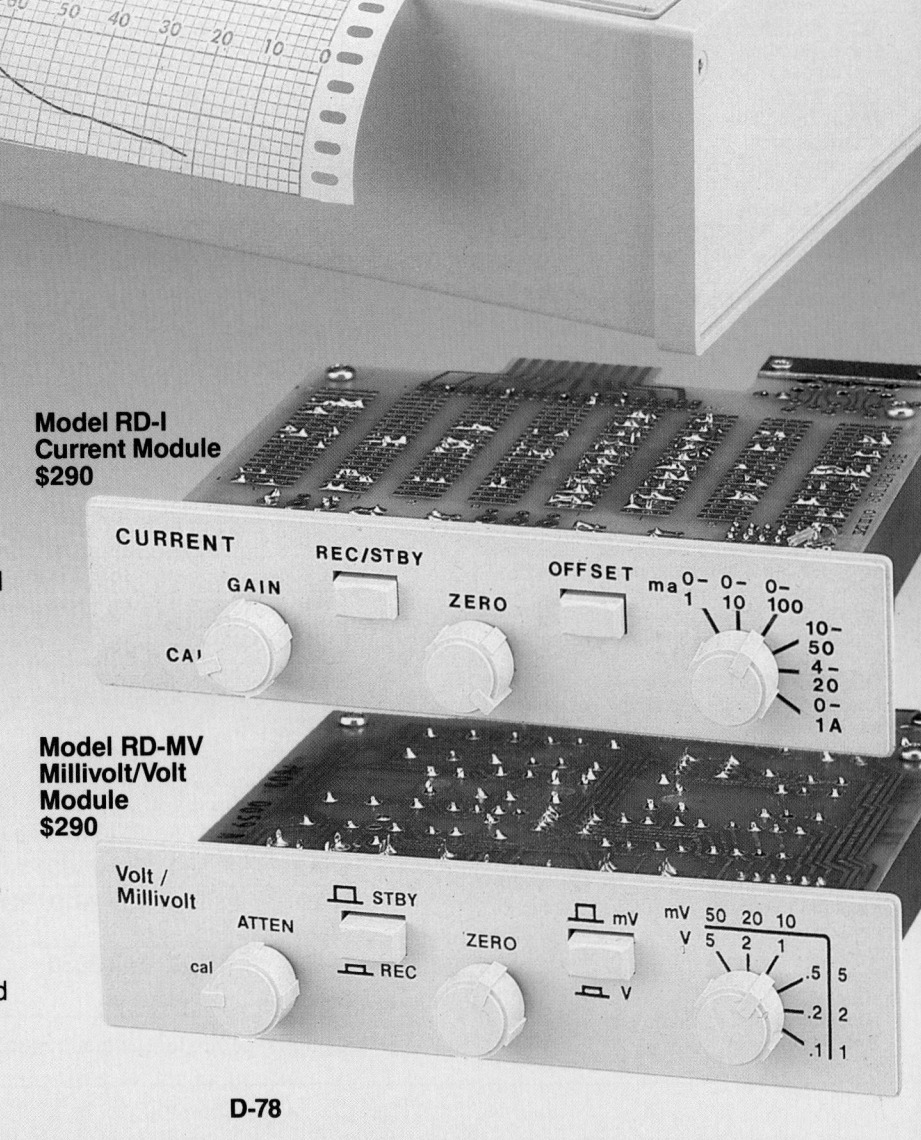

Model RD-I Current Module $290

Model RD-MV Millivolt/Volt Module $290

FUNCTION RECORDERS
SERIES RD-2000

Specifications

Recorders
Power: 120 Vac, or 12-15 Vdc
Chart Speeds: 1,2,5,10,20,30 cm/min and cm/hr
Chart Speed Accuracy: ±0.1%
Full Scale Response Time: 0.5 sec
Overshoot: None, system critically damped
Override Event Marker: Standard, approx. 2% spike
Pen Lift: Manual external lever
Alarms: 3A @ 120 Vac relay

RD-MV Module   **$290**
Ranges: 1,2,5,10,20,50,100 mV and 0.2, 0.5, 1,2,5 V
Zero Adjust: ±100%
Attenuation: 2.5:1
Connection: 5-way binding post
Input Type: Single ended floating to ±50V
Input Impedance: 2.5M ohm fixed
Accuracy: ±0.1% full scale
Output Buffer: 0-5 Vdc (customer adjustable), 0-100 mV (factory set)

RD-I Modules   **$290**
Ranges: 0-1 mA, 0-10 mA, 0-100 mA, 10-50 mA, 4-20 mA, 0-1 A
Zero: 0-100%
Offset Zero: 25%, switch selectable
Attenuation: 4:1
Accuracy: ±1% FS

RD-TC Module   **$435**
Ranges: 0-100, 0-500, 0-1000°C or °F span within −250 to 1900°F range
Display: 3½ digit LCD
Thermocouple Types: J,K,T,E; jumper selectable
Analog Output: 1 mV per degree
Input Connector: SMP Connector
Indications: Open circuit, over-and underrange
Accuracy: ±1.5°C or °F

RD-PH Module   **$255**
Range: 0-14, 0-1.4 (expanded scale) pH
Zero: −150 to 50%, −1500 to 500% (expanded scale)
Temperature Compensation: 32 to 212°F
Accuracy: ±0.1% full scale
mV Mode: ±700 mV range
Probe Calibration: ±20% from normal

RD-SG Module   **$435**
Excitation Voltage: 0 to 11 Vdc, 350 ohm transducers
Display: 3½ digit, LCD
Input Range: 10 mV to 10 Vdc full scale, selectable
Maximum Sensor Offset: ±20%
Zero Adjustment: ±100%

RD-LV Module   **$255**
Excitation Voltage: 0 to 11 Vdc, 350 ohm transducers
Display: 3½ digit, LCD
Input Range: 10 mV to 10 Vdc full scale, selectable
Maximum Sensor Offset: ±20%
Zero Adjustment: ±100%

To Order *(Specify model number)*

Model Number	Price	Chart Width	No. of Channels
RD-2010*	$605	100 mm	one
RD-2020*	655	200 mm	one
RD-2030	835	200 mm	two

*Short pen models

Modules

Model Number	Price	Input Type
RD-MV	$290	Millivolt/Volt
RD-I	290	Current
RD-TC	435	Thermocouple
RD-PH	255	pH
RD-SG	435	Strain Gage
RD-LV	255	LVDT/RVDT
RD-EXT	150	Extension card for module calibration
RD-CAL	175	Calibration module

Accessories

Part Number	Price	Description
0100-0011	$51	100 mm chart paper, 0-10 scale*
0100-0026	51	200 mm chart paper, 0-10 scale*
0100-0042	51	200 mm chart paper, 0-14 scale*
0100-0105	15	blue pens, short, 6 pack
0100-0109	15	blue pens, long, 6 pack
0100-0106	15	red pens, short, 6 pack
0100-0110	15	red pens, long, 6 pack
0100-0107	15	black pens, short, 6 pack
0100-0111	15	black pens, long, 6 pack
0100-0108	15	green pens, short, 6 pack
0100-0112	15	green pens, long, 6 pack

* Paper sold in package of 6 rolls.

Options

Suffix Number	Price	Model Availability	Description
-A1	$175	RD-2010, RD-2020	Alarm for 1 pen units
-A2	350	RD-2030	Alarms for 2 pen units
-B1	150	RD-2010, RD-2020	Battery Pack for 1 pen units
-B2	300	RD-2030	Battery Pack for 2 pen units

Options require longer lead times for installation.

INDUSTRIAL FUNCTION RECORDERS
RD-2080

From
$1245

- ✔ **NEMA 13 Sealed Case**
- ✔ **Compact, Vertical Package with 100 mm Chart Width**
- ✔ **Wall, Pipe, or Panel/Rack Mount Design with Options**
- ✔ **Single and Dual Channel Models**
- ✔ **Inputs Selected from Plug-In Function Modules for Voltage, Current, Thermocouple, pH, Strain Gage and Position Sensors**

The RD-2080 series industrial function recorders are rugged, universal measurement systems designed to operate effectively under the harshest industrial environments. These units are housed in a NEMA 13 enclosure for oil-tight and dust-tight operation. These recorders accept RD-2000 series plug-in signal conditioning modules, for a variety of input types. To change the input, simply remove the old module, and insert the desired module into the recorder. Modules are available for thermocouples, voltage, current, pH, strain gage and position sensors.

The RD-2080 recorders standard features include individual scales for each channel with easy-to-see pointers, an analog output for each channel, and an override event marker. Available options for these units include a pipe mounting kit, wall/surface mounting kit, and alarms for each channel.

Specifications
Power: 120/240 Vac, 50/60 Hz; (12 Vdc or 12 Vac special order)
Chart Speeds: 1, 2, 4, 8, 16 cm/hr and 0.5, 1, 2, 4, cm/min
Enclosure: Steel housing; removable door with Lexan window
Event Marker Override: Standard, approx. 2% spike
Dimensions: 8″ W × 10″ H × 7″ D
Ambient Temperature Range: 32 to 104°F
Accuracy: ±0.75% F.S.

To Order *(Specify Model Number)*

Model No.	Price	No. of Channel
RD-2081	$990	one
RD-2082	1190	two
RD-2081-A	1165	one, with alarm; 3A @ 120 Vac
RD-2082-A2	1540	two, with alarms; 3A @ 120 Vac

Ordering Example:** RD-2082-A2 with RD-mV and RD-TC, 2-channel recorder with alarms, and one mV input module, one thermocouple input module, $1540 + 290 + 435 = **$2265.

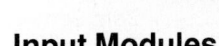

Input Modules

Model No.	Price	Input Type
RD-MV	$290	Volt/Millivolt
RD-I	290	Current
RD-TC	435	Thermocouple
RD-PH	255	pH, BNC Connector
RD-SG	435	Strain gage
RD-LV	255	LVDT/RVDT
RD-EXT	150	Extension card for module calibration

Options and Accessories

Model No.	Price	Description
RD-2080-PM	$40	Pipe mounting kit
RD-2080-WM	40	Wall/surface mount kit
RD-2080-BM	40	Bench mount
0100-0011	51	Chart paper, 0-100 scale

Note: Chart paper is 30 m per roll, supplied in packages of 6 rolls. To order pens, see page D-79. Short pens for channel 1, long pens for channel 2.

STRIP CHART RECORDERS
SINGLE OR DUAL PEN FLATBED RECORDERS

**Compact
200 mm Chart
Model RD-1201**

$945

One Channel

Event Marker
Now Standard

**Model
RD-1202**

$1375

Dual Channel

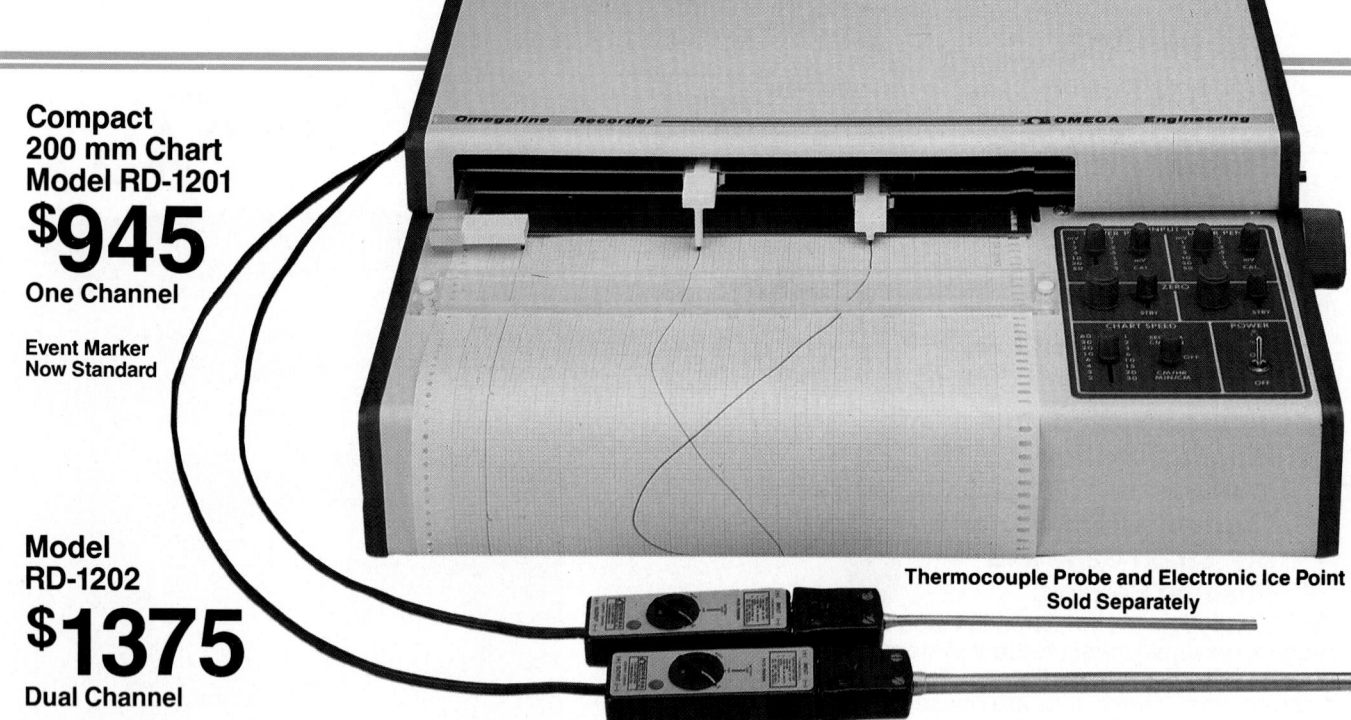

**Thermocouple Probe and Electronic Ice Point
Sold Separately**

MODEL RD-1201 and RD-1202

Precision Design
- ✓ 16 Chart Speeds
- ✓ 12 Input Spans
- ✓ ±100% Zero Suppression
- ✓ 1 Millivolt to 5 Volts—Variable Attenuator
- ✓ 0.4 Second Pen Response
- ✓ Two Phase Stepper Motor Chart Drive
- ✓ Pulse-Modulated Servo System

The **Model 1201** (1 pen) and **Model 1202** (2 pen) recorders are the newest and most dramatic in the line of intelligntly priced recorders. This versatile recorder provides user with optimum flexibility, accuracy, and reliability.

In addition to the features listed above, Model Rd-1201 and RD-1202 offer:

- ✓ **Override event marker**
- ✓ **Paper reversal control**
- ✓ **No overshoot—critically damped**
- ✓ **Remote chart programming (TTL)**
- ✓ **Zero switch**
- ✓ **Linearity accuracy less than 0.5%**
- ✓ **Electronic pen lift**

All of the performance and quality you could ask for in a single pen or dual pen recorder.

General Specifications

Number of Channels: One or two

Full Scale Spans: 1, 2, 5, 10, 20, 50, 100, 200, 500 mV; 1, 2, 5, Volts

Impedance: 2.5 megohms

Accuracy:
  Dead band: Less than ±0.1%
  Linearity: ±0.5%
  Repeatability: Less than ±0.1%

Zero Setting: Continuously adjustable from −100% to +100%

Chart Drive: 16 speeds: 1, 2, 3, 6, 10, 15, 20, 30 cm/min and per hour

Control/Accuracy: Less than ±0.03%. External—can be remotely programmed by pulse train (TTL).

Writing System Type: Disposable cartridge, fiber tip.

Response: 0.4 seconds F.S.

Drive: Potentiometric, null balance with sealed long-life servo pot

Chart Width: 8″ (203 mm)

Dimensions: H: 4.38″ (111 mm) x W: 15″ (381 mm) x D: 10.5″ (267 mm)

Weight: RD-1201: 9 lbs (4.1 kg); RD-1202: 11lbs (5 kg)

Power: 115/230 V ac 50/60 Hz, 17.5 W (RD-1201); 22.5 W (RD1202)

How To Order
Specify **Model RD-1201**
One Pen—**$945**

Specify **Model RD-1202**
Two Pen—**$1375**

Accessories: *Keep extra pens and paper on hand*
Each instrument is shipped with one roll of chart paper, one pen per input channel, and one instruction manual.

Chart Paper:	0-100 grid, 25 meters long		No. 0100-0026	6 rolls/$51
Disposable Pens:	Short Nib		Long Nib	
Blue	No. 0100-0105		No. 0100-0109	6 pack/$15
Red	No. 0100-0106		No. 0100-0110	6 pack/$15
Black	No. 0100-0107		No. 0100-0132	6 pack/$15
Green	No. 0100-0108		No. 0100-0132	6 pack/$15
Dust Cover:	Clear		No. 0100-209	each/$25

Works with Thermocouples! Use 1, 2, 5, 10, 20 or 50 mV range and a cold junction compensator or a digital instrument with analog output.

STRIP CHART RECORDERS
1, 2 AND 3 PEN

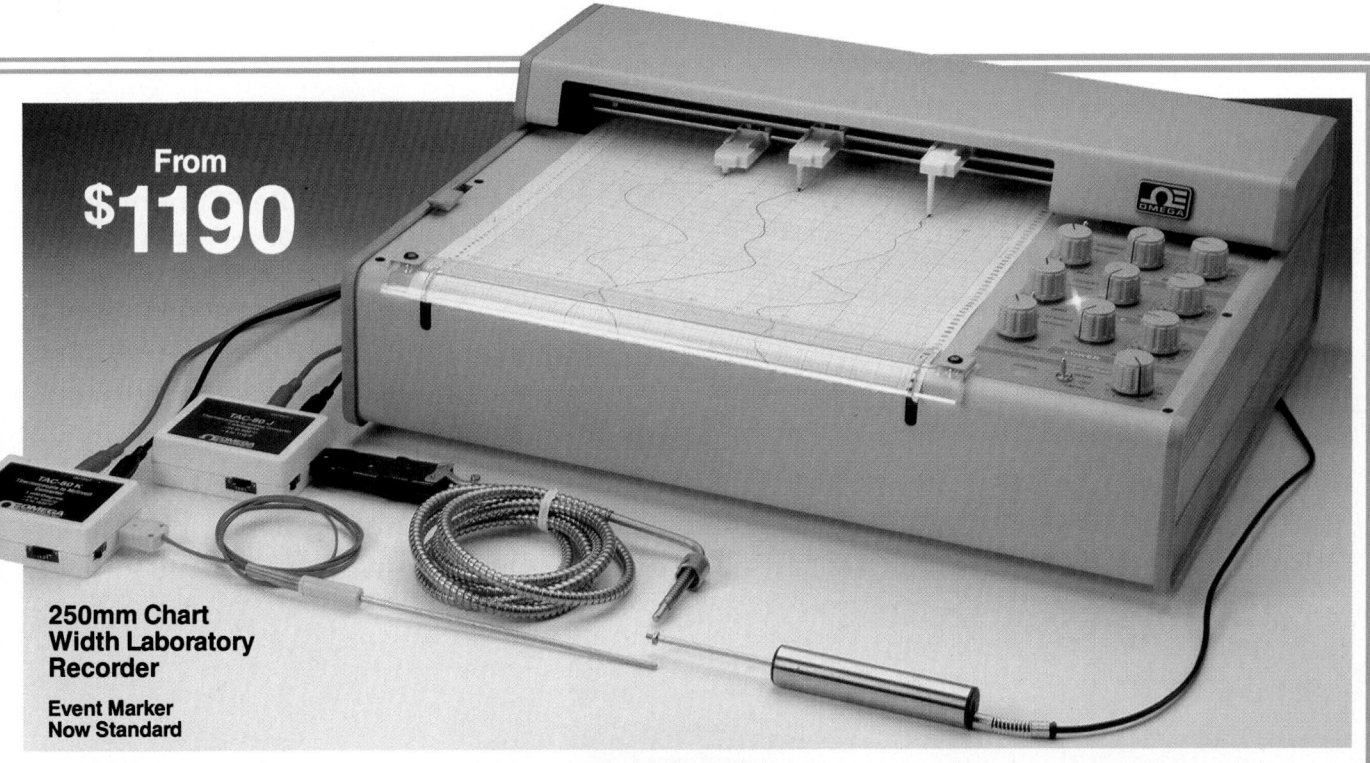

From
$1190

250mm Chart Width Laboratory Recorder

Event Marker Now Standard

Precision Design
- ✔ 1, 2 and 3 Pen
- ✔ 22 Chart Speeds
- ✔ 12 Input Spans
- ✔ 1 mV to 50 Volts—Variable Attenuator
- ✔ 0.5 Second Pen Response
- ✔ Crystal Controlled Stepper Chart Drive
- ✔ Pulse-Modulated Servo System

These three laboratory recorders are the newest and most dramatic in the line of intelligently priced recorders. Every possible feature has been included in these versatile recorders to provide the user with optimum flexibility, accuracy, and long-term reliability.

In addition to the features listed above, these units offer:
- Electronic "servo kill"
- Remote chart programming (TTL)
- Zero switch
- 100% suppression (overranging)
- Maximum limit of error less than 0.5%

All of the performance and quality you could ask for!

General Specifications
Number of Channels: 1, 2, or 3
Full Scale Spans: 1, 2, 5, 10, 20, 50, 100, 200, 500 mV; 1, 2, 5, Volts plus 10:1 attenuator to 50 Volts each channel
Impedance: 200 M Ω through 100 mV, 2.5 M Ω through 5 Volts
Accuracy: Overall limit of error from all sources is less than 0.5%
Zero Setting: Continuously adjustable from −100% to +100%
Chart Drive 22 Speeds: 1, 2, 3, 4, 5, 6, 10, 12, 15, 20, 30 cm/min and per hour (direct reading in absolute time)
Control/Accuracy: Internal—crystal controlled. External—can be remotely programmed by pulse train (TTL).
Writing System Type: Disposable cartridge, nylon tip.

Response: ½ sec. F.S.
Drive: Potentiometric, null balance with sealed long-life servo pot
General Chart Width: 25 cm (10″)
Dimensions: H: 5.5″ (139.7 mm) x W: 17.75″ (451 mm) x D: 14″ (355.6 mm)
Weight: 555, 12.5 lbs (5.7 kg); 585, 14.5 lbs (6.85 kg); 595, 17 lbs (7.7 kg)
Power: 115/230 Vac 50/60 Hz, 38 Watts

To Order (Specify Model Number)
Model No.	Price	Description
555	**$1190**	One-pen recorder
585	**1690**	Two-pen recorder
595	**2090**	Three-pen recorder

Accessories: *Keep extra pens and paper on hand*
Each instrument is shipped with one roll of chart paper, one pen per input channel, and one instruction manual. Electronic event marker is standard on channel 1.

Proper matching of ink and paper is essential to provide records which have minimum bleeding or starvation and provide writing clarity over a wide range of temperature, relative humidity, and writing speeds. Our standard pens and paper provide these characteristics. We can provide both pens and paper to give excellent recording under the most demanding circumstances.

Paper:	100 grid, 30 m long		No. 0100-0025	6 rolls/$51

Pens:	555 or 585 Short Nib	585 Only Long Nib	595 Only	
Blue	0100-0105	0100-0109	0100-0105 Short	6 pack/$15
Red	0100-0106	0100-0110	0100-0106 Short	6 pack/$15
Black	0100-0107	0100-0111	0100-0131 Medium	6 pack/$15
Green	0100-0108	0100-0112	0100-0132 Long	6 pack/$15

Works with Thermocouples! Use 1, 2, 5, 10, 20 or 50 mV range and a cold junction compensator or a digital instrument with analog output.

U.S. AND CANADA
for placing orders, call: 1-800-82-66342
1-800-TC-OMEGA

100mm *PROGRAMMABLE FUNCTION RECORDERS*

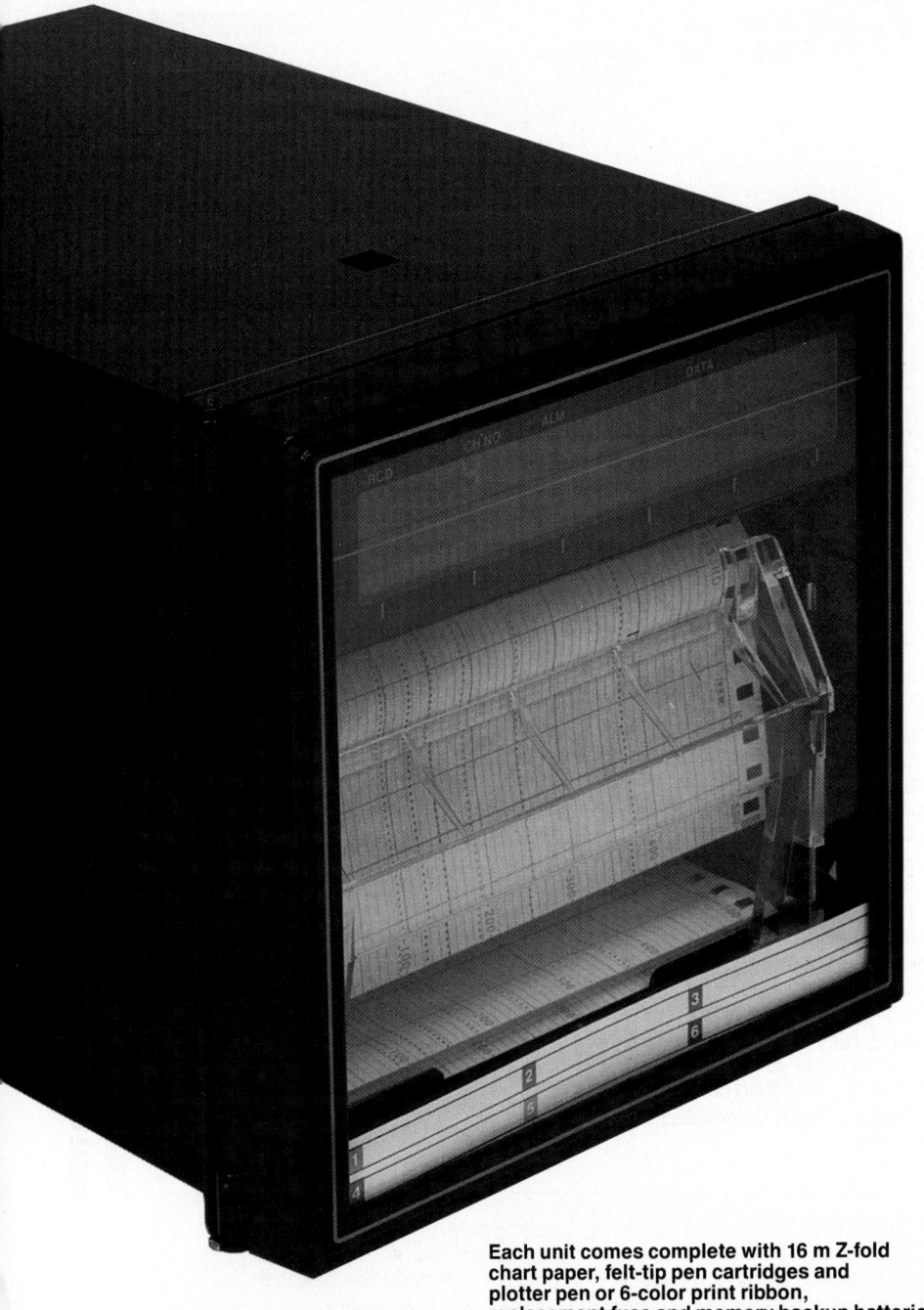

Each unit comes complete with 16 m Z-fold chart paper, felt-tip pen cartridges and plotter pen or 6-color print ribbon, replacement fuse and memory backup batteries

- ✓ **Analog/Digital Recording and Display**
- ✓ **1, 2 or 3 Pen Continuous Writing or 6-Point Dot Printing Models**
- ✓ **Voltage/Thermocouple or RTD Input Models**
- ✓ **Programmable Input Types, Full Scale Ranges, Alarms and Chart Speeds**
- ✓ **Convenient, Color-Coded Analog Bar Graph and Digital Monitoring Display**

RD-100 Series From

$1195

The RD100 Series programmable 100 mm chart recorders are available in 1, 2 or 3 pen continuous models, or 6-point dot printing model, with thermocouple/voltage, or RTD input. In addition to analog chart recording, the recorders also have digital printing capabilities. The front panel of each unit also features an analog bar graph and digital display for easy monitoring.

The RD100 recorders are designed for ease of use. In addition to the clear, easy-to-read analog chart, each recorder prints out on the chart paper the date and time, channel numbers, scale markings, tag

To Order *(Specify Model Number)*

Model No.	Price	Description
RD101-(*)	$ 1195	1-pen recorder
RD102-(*)	1595	2-pen recorder
RD103-(*)	2095	3-pen recorder
RD106-(*)	1895	6-point dot printing recorder

* Insert T for thermocouple/mV input, or R for RTD input; upscale break protection standard

Analog/Digital Front Panel Display
Model RD106

Model RD103

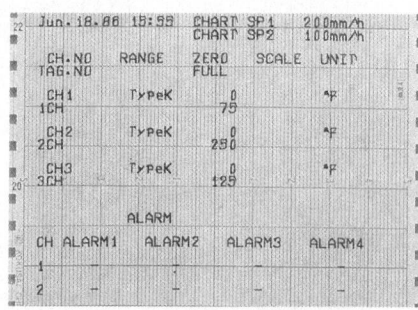

Analog/Digital Data Printout

Digital Program Listing Printout

Specifications

No. of Inputs: 1, 2 or 3 pen continuous; 6-point dot printing
Max. Allowable Input Voltage: 10 Vdc for 2 Vdc range, 100 Vdc for ranges up to 50 Vdc
Effective Recording Span: 100 mm
Scan Cycle Time: 125 ms/pen, or 5 s/6 points
Print Cycle Time: 30 s/6 points (model RD106)
Chart Paper: 16 m long
Chart Speeds: 5 to 12,000 mm/hr (RD106 to 1,500 mm/hr)
Data Printout: Measured data, tag no., scale markings, chart speed, data, time
Alarm Printout: Channel no., hi or lo indication, time of alarm on/off
Digital Data Display: Measured data, alarm (high or low), chart speed, (or data and time)
Analog Bar Graph: 2% of span resolution
Accuracy: ±0.5% of span
Dead Band; 0.2% of span
Input Impedance: >10 Mohm; 1 Mohm on 6 to 50 V ranges
External Resistance: <2 kohm; <10 ohm/wire for RTD
Weight: 11 lb, max.
Power: 115 Vac, 50/60 Hz; 100, 200, 230 Vac also available
Power Consumption: 26 VA max.
Ambient Conditions: 41 to 104°F, 45 to 85% RH
Alarms: Up to 4 set points per pen (high, low) via keyboard; relays rated 0.1 A @ 100 Vac
Hysteresis: 0.5% of span
Break Protection: Upscale, standard

Dimensions: 5¹¹⁄₁₆″ H × 5¹¹⁄₁₆″ W × 12⁷⁄₁₆″ D (10⅛″ for 1-pen and 6-point models)
Front Bezel: 5¹¹⁄₁₆″ square
Depth Behind Panel: 11⁷⁄₁₆″ for 2- and 3- pen models; 9⅛″ for 1-pen and 6-point models
Panel Cutout: 5⅜″ square
Memory Backup: 3 "AA" batteries with 3 mo. life

Input Type	Maximum Ranges	
dc Voltage	−50 to 50 Vdc	
J thermocouple	−200 to 1100°C	−328 to 2012°F
K thermocouple	−200 to 1370°C	−328 to 2498°F
T thermocouple	−200 to 400°C	−328 to 752°F
E thermocouple	−200 to 800°C	−328 to 1472°F
R, S thermocouple	0 to 1760°C	32 to 3200°F
B thermocouple	400 to 1820°C	752 to 3308°F
N thermocouple	0 to 1300°C	32 to 2372°F
C thermocouple	0 to 2315°C	32 to 4200°F
RTD	−200 to 550°C	−328 to 1022°F

Note: Current inputs may be used when a current shunt is applied.

Options and Accessories		
Part No.	**Price**	**Description**
-AR	$200.00	Four internal alarm outputs, common to all start/stop and chart speed; 0.1A @ 100 Vac start/stop and chart speed
-PS	100.00	Pen offset compensation for 2 and 3 pen model recording with common time axis
RD100-ZFP	40.50	Z-fold paper, 16 m, pkg of 6
RD100-RC	17.00	6-color print ribbon for RD106
RD100-01	10.75	3 red pens, channel 1
RD100-02	10.75	3 green pens, channel 2
RD100-03	10.75	3 blue pens, channel 3
RD100-11	9.00	Plotter pen for RD101, 102, 103
Power Cord	7.00	115 Vac power cord

 **NEW!**

MICROPROCESSOR-BASED CIRCULAR RECORDER
UP TO 12 OUTPUT RELAYS

From
$1200

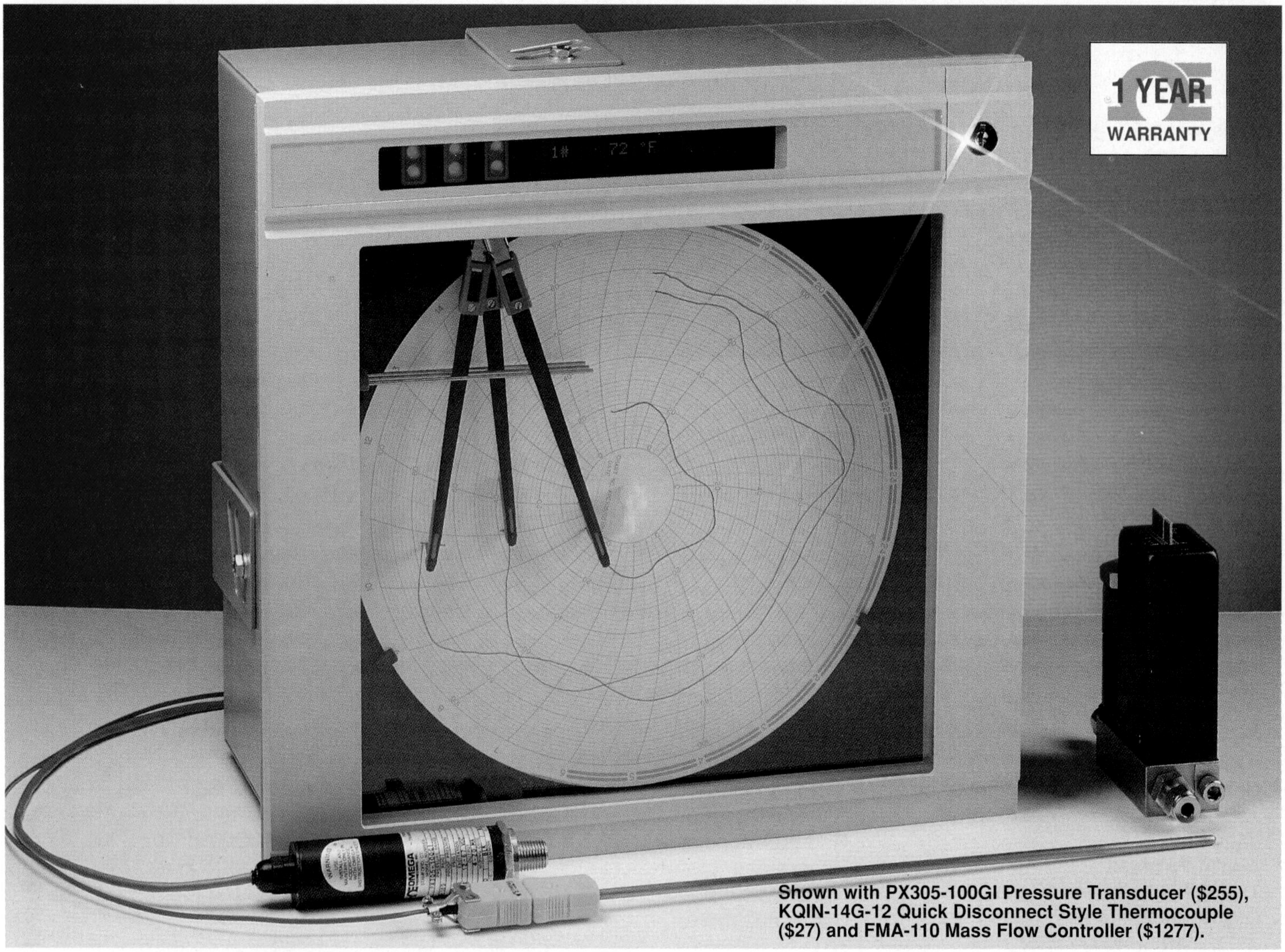

Shown with PX305-100GI Pressure Transducer ($255), KQIN-14G-12 Quick Disconnect Style Thermocouple ($27) and FMA-110 Mass Flow Controller ($1277).

- ✔ **Accepts Thermocouple, RTD, V, mV or mA Signals**
- ✔ **Overall Accuracy of ±0.25% of Span**
- ✔ **Up to Six I/O Modules Available, Including Input Isolation**
- ✔ **Up to Three Pens**
- ✔ **Retransmission Options Available On Up to Three Channels**
- ✔ **Flow Totalization On All Three Channels**
- ✔ **One or Two PID Control Outputs Available**

The new OMEGA CT1000A microprocessor-based circular recorder offers a wide range of measurement and control capabilities. The recorder is available as a one-, two-, or three-channel recorder offering up to 12 output relays allocated to six setpoints which in turn may be allocated to any channel or channels.

The unit can be supplied for flow indication and recording with totalization on up to three channels. Flow indication and recording with totalization on all channels is also available. Each channel has two totalizers, one of which can be used for a batch total resettable from the front panel, and displayed in

sequence with flow rate. The other is used for display of a secure total accessible only by operating the appropriate channel select buttons.

SPECIFICATIONS
INPUTS
No. of Inputs: 1, 2, or 3

Input Impedance: Millivolt inputs >10 Mohms
Voltage inputs 500 kohms
Current inputs 10 ohms

Temperature: Thermocouple 3090°F (1700°C) max.
Minimum span 180°F (100°C)
Resistance thermometer 1000°F (600°C) max. Minimum span 90°F (50°C)

Cold Junction: Automatic cold junction compensation (ACJC) fitted

Linearization: Programmable for all inputs. State whether linear, square root, power 3/2, 5/2 law, or type of thermocouple or RTD

Broken Sensor Protection: Programmable, upscale or downscale drive or none (not available on mA and V inputs)

Filter Time: Programmable from 0 to 60 sec in 1-sec steps

Event Marker: Voltage free contacts or 0-5 V logic level

Change of Input Mode: By repositioning plug-in link

Change of Input Range/Scan: Programmable

Program Modification: By user-operated membrane switches above chart

Floating Inputs-Isolation: 2.5 Vdc max between channels upon removal of terminal block links

Insulation, Inputs to Ground: 500 Vdc

Interference Suppression (based on 0-1000 mV range input):
Radiated (r.f.): F.S. <±2% over range 20 MHz to 1000 MHz at field strength of 5 V

Line Interruption: <100 ms loss, no effect, >110 ms loss instrument returns to operation after automatic reset

Line Interference: <500 V input, pulse width up to 125 µS, no effect

Common Mode: <1% span error max for 250 V rms 50 Hz

Series Mode: <1% span error for 200% span, 50 Hz

OUTPUTS AND SETPOINTS
No. of Setpoints: Up to two setpoints per channel

Setpoint Adjustment: Programmable

No. of Relays: Up to two per channel

Relay Contacts: Single pole changeover

Voltage: 250 Vac, 250 Vdc max

Current: 5A ac, 5A dc max

Loading (non-inductive): 1250 VA, 50W max

Insulation, Contacts to Ground: 2 kV rms

Relay Action (programmable): Energized above (EA) setpoint or energized below (EB) setpoint, 3 state or latching; external counter drive option (module 5) 50 ms pulse 24V max current 150 mA

ANALOG OUTPUTS
Output module (module 8) is isolated and includes a relay. The maximum isolation voltage is 1000 V between input and output.

Retransmission: Programmable min (zero) and max (full scale) values from 0-20 mA in 0.1 mA steps, up to 20 mA into 1 kohm max

Control: P, PI or PID.

Analog Output: Up to 20 mA at 15 V; channel 1 reverse or direct

Analog Controller Output: Up to 20 mA 1 kohm max (reverse or direct)

Time Proportioning Controller Action: Time proportioning, reverse or direct programmable

Time Proportioning Cycle Time: 5 to 60 sec, programmable in 1 sec steps

Proportional Band: 2 to 500%, programmable in 1% steps

Integral Action Time: 1 to 1800 sec, programmable in 1 sec steps and OFF

Derivative Action Time: 0 to 600 sec, programmable in 1 sec steps and OFF

Approach Band: 0.1 to 3.0 proportional bands, programmable in 0.1 steps

Setpoint Change: No erroneous generation of derivative response

ACCURACY
±0.25% span max for all zero-based ranges within permitted limits. Ref. conditions 68°F (20°C) and 115 V or 230 V apply

Linearizer Accuracy: ±0.1°C typical

Resolution
   Measurement: mV, V, mA, TC

≥ 0.1% span, for all zero-based ranges within permitted limits

R/T: 0.06 ohm

Pen: ≤0.13% full scale travel

Display: ±1 digit

Pens Response Time: 6 sec for 10% to 90% typical. Input signals can be averaged over a 0 to 60 sec (filter) time, programmable in 1 sec steps

Ramp/Soak Option: Allows four "menus"; each menu can contain up to 30 segments that can be split into 1 to 9 profiles

Solid State Relay Option (Module J): Provides two solid state switching 24 Vdc at 30 mA drive outputs used to drive externally mounted solid state relays

Isolated Input Option (Module K): Provides up to 2 kV isolation channel-to-channel and channel-to-ground. Up to two allowed, position 2 for channel 2 and/or position 3 for channel 3

DISPLAYS AND RECORDS
Display: 20 character, dot matrix vacuum fluorescent with blue filter

Programming: Up, down scroll switches above chart

Chart: Circular with linear graduations

Chart Speed: 1 rev per hour up to 1 rev per week (168 hr), programmable in 1-hour steps

Pens: Red: channel 1; Green: channel 2; Blue: channel 3, disposable

Event Pen: Pen 3, 3 positions: center, off, at chart rim. Time line coincident with pen 1; contact closure or 0-5V logic

FLOW INPUT VERSION GENERAL
Flow Total: Programmable ON or OFF

Count Rate Zero: Programmable from 0 to 0.999 in 0.001 pps steps then 1.0 to 9.99 in 0.01 steps

Please See Page D-88 to Order.

INSTRUMENTATION

D

MICROPROCESSOR-BASED CIRCULAR RECORDERS

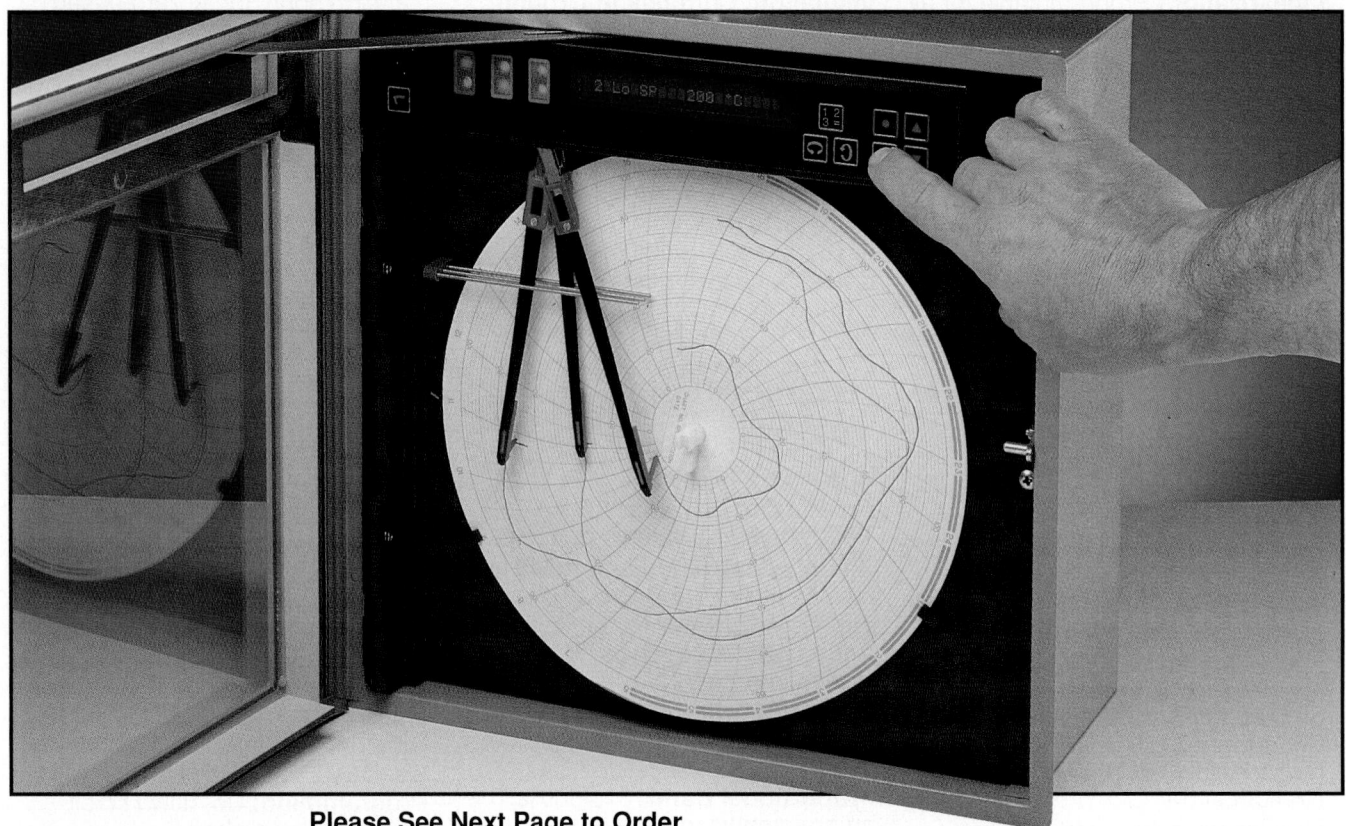

Please See Next Page to Order

Count Rate Cut Off: Totalization can be stopped if flow rate falls below preset value. Preset value adjustable over full span

Count Rate Full Scale: Programmable from 0.001 to 0.999 then 1.00 to 10.00 pps

ANALOG INPUTS
Mathematical Function Accuracy

x1/2-   0 to 100%   0.1% of reading
x3/2-   7 to 100%   0.2% of reading
x5/2-   18 to 100%   0.3% of reading

Below these values the error increases asymptotically as input approaches zero

Frequency Inputs: Module C accuracy ±0.1% or 1 digit, whichever is greater for zero based ranges

High Level Input:

Frequency Range: Between 0-0.1 Hz and 0-4 kHz

a. TTL level square wave

b. Open collector to accept current level 2 mA at 5 V

c. Volt free contacts to accept current level 2 mA at 5 V

d. Voltage square wave. When the peak value lies between +2 V and +50 and the trough value lies between −50 V and +1 V

Low Level Inputs:

a. Vortex and Electromagnetic Flowmeters:
Amplitude: 4 mA or greater square wave, with an offset up to 20 mA, e.g., 0-4 mA, 16-20 mA or 4-20 mA

Volt drop: Maximum 2 V at 20 mA

Frequency Range: 0.1 Hz to 4 kHz

b. Turbine and Rotary Shunt Meters
Amplitude: 1 mV/Hz
Frequency Range: 3 Hz to 4 kHz

c. General Purpose ac Coupled
Amplitude: Fixed or variable between the limits of 5 mV peak to peak to 50 V peak to peak

Frequency Range: 3 Hz to 4 kHz on inputs where the amplitude is proportional to frequency, automatic variable gain (maximum sensitivity 1 mV/Hz) can be achieved by link positioning.

d. General Purpose dc Coupled
Frequency Range: 0.1 Hz to 4 kHz

PHYSICAL SPECIFICATIONS
POWER
Voltage Requirements: 110 V (min 93 V, max 127 V), or 230 V(min 195 V, max 265 V), 50 or 60 Hz Alternatively 10 to 30 Vdc

Power Requirements: <28 VA

Warm-up Time: approx. 10 s

Error Due to Power Supply Voltage Fluctuation: ±0.1% span for ±15% fluctuation

Insulation: Mains to ground 2 kV rms

Transmitter Power Supply
Output Voltage: 25 V ±0.5 V at 0 or 60 mA (loaded with 3 transmitters)

Output Ripple: 100 mV peak to peak max.

Load Regulation: ±0.1 V for output change 4-20 mA
Output Voltage Variation with Supply Voltage: ≤1 V for ±15% supply voltage

ENVIRONMENTAL DATA
Operating Temperature Limits: 32 to 130°F (0 to 55°C)
Operating Humidity Limits: 0 to 80% RH (paper and ink system, 0 to 95% RH electronics)
Error Due to Ambient Temperature Variation (unsuppressed ranges): ±0.02% span/°C typical

MECHANICAL DATA
Mounting: Wall or panel by 3 brackets (supplied)
Dimensions: 14.18" H x 14.58" W x 6.7"D (360 x 370 x 170 mm)
Panel Cutout: 13.5"H x 13.7" W (342 + 1-0 mm x 348 + 1-0 mm)
Panel Space Requirement: 16.15" (410 mm) wide x 15.76" (400 mm) high x 5.9" (150 mm) deep from face panel
Case and Door: Sheet steel case with hinged chart plate. Foam-molded door with glass window. (Polycarbonate available as special order)
Weight: 23.15 lb (10.5 kg) approx

To Order (Specify Model Number)

Model No.	Price	Description
CT1100A	$1200	1 Pen recorder, base unit**
CT1200A	1650	2 Pen recorder, base unit**
CT1300A	2100	3 Pen recorder, base unit**
CT1205A-MB	1920	2 Pen recorder, 1 analog, 1 event
CT1305A-MB	2370	3 Pen recorder, 2 analog, 1 event

Each unit comes complete with one package of chart paper, pen(s), and complete operator's manual.
**For options, see table at right.

Modules

Ordering Suffix	Add'l Price	Description
-M1	$135	Single relay output
-M2	270	Dual relay output
-M5	205	24 V counter drive
-M8	140	Isolated analog output with relay
-MA	205	Transmitter power supply
-MB	120	Event pen input
-MC	205	Frequency input
-ME	145	Ramp/soak digital input
-MJ	110	Solid state relay output
-MK	180	Isolated analog input
-MS	290	RS-485 serial interface

Note: *Up to six I/O modules may be installed. The -M1, -M2 and -MA modules may be field installed and ordered as CT1000A-M1 etc. Other modules may require options added to base recorder.*

Ordering Example: *CT1146A-MS-M8 is a one-pen recorder with control and RS-485 ability with the analog output and RS-485 modules included (1200 + 350 + 300 + 290 + 140 = $2280), plus CT-1000-RED extra pens for channel 1 ($17) and CT-1000C-100/7 package of 500 charts. Total price = $2280 + 17 + 110 = **$2407.***

Accessories
Remember to Purchase Extra Pens and Paper!

Model No.	Price	Description
CT-1000-RED	17	5 Red pens, channel 1
CT-1000-GREEN	17	5 Green pens, channel 2
CT-1000-BLUE	17	5 Blue pens, channel 3
CT-1000C-100/7	110	500 Charts, 0-100 range, 7 day

Custom charts available on special order. Consult Sales.

Range Limits

Electrical Input Type	Min. Start Value	Min. Span	Max. Span & Range Value
mV	-999	5.00	1000
V	-20.0	0.50	20.0
mA	-99.9	0.50	100.0
J T/C*	-100°C	100°C	900°C
K T/C*	-100°C	150°C	1300°C
R, S T/C*	-15°C	600°C	1700°C
T T/C	-250°C	170°C	300°C
E T/C*	-100°C	100°C	900°C
B T/C*	-18°C	1100°C	1800°C
N T/C*	-200°C	180°C	1300°C
RTD*	-200°C	50°C	600°C

*Temperature inputs are °C/°F switchable

Options for Base Units

Options may be added to the base units by changing the third and/or fourth (i.e. last two) digits in the part number and adding the appropriate modules and prices.

1) Flow option: change the third digit in the model number to a "5" and add $200 to base price. No modules required.
Example: CT1150A is a 1-pen unit with flow option, $1200 + 200 = **$1400.**

2) Control option (supports control on channel 1 and/or 2): change the third digit in the model number to a "4" and add $350 to base price. This option also requires you to purchase additional module(s) for the required output(s). **Example:** CT1240A-M8-M8 is a two-pen recorder with control option on both channels and two isolated analog outputs, $1650 + 350 + 140 + 140 = **$2280.**

3) Ramp/soak control option (supports control on channel 1 and/or 2): change the third and fourth digits to "44" and add $700 to base price. This option also requires you to purchase additional module(s) for the required output(s). **Example:** CT1344A-M8 is a three-pen recorder with ramp/soak control option and one isolated analog output (control on 1 channel), $2100 + 700 + 140 = **$2940.**

4) RS-485 Communications option: change the fourth digit in the model number to "6" and add $300 to price. This option also requires the -MS module ($290). **Example:** CT1106A-MS is a one-pen recorder with RS-485 communications, $1200 + 300 + 290 = **$1790.** (Note: the RS-485 option may be used with options 1 or 2).

MICROPROCESSOR-BASED TEMPERATURE/ RELATIVE HUMIDITY RECORDER

✔ **Combination Temperature/RH Probe Mounts Remotely or Attaches Directly to Unit**

✔ **Large 8" (200mm) Diameter Chart for Easy Viewing**

✔ **Available With or Without High/Low Alarms**

✔ **Designed for Benchtop or Wall Mounting**

✔ **Prescaled Charts for 1, 7 or 32 Days in °F or°C**

✔ **Available in Charcoal Gray or Computer Room White**

CT485RS Series From

$592

Includes 120 Double-Sided Charts

The new White Box® Model CT485RS sets a new standard in hygrothermography. This completely self-contained temperature/relative humidity recorder is microprocessor-based to accurately measure, indicate and record temperature and relative humidity. A second, smaller LCD displays the current time or date, or can continuously alternate between the two.

Unrivaled in the industry, this rugged unit is available with or without alarms. Alarm models contain a single, integral relay contact which closes in response to an alarm condition. Simultaneous high and low alarm points for temperature and relative humidity are user selectable. When the current conditions exceed any of the preset values, the 2 Amp relay contact closes and an audible alarm sounds. Non-alarm models store the high and low measured values (max and min) for both temperature and relative humidity.

Flipping open a hinged front panel door permits access to the power switch and controlling functions of

WITH VERSATILE REMOTE MOUNTING SENSOR

Save on Standard Chart Paper! $87.50 for 6 Boxes of 100 Double-Sided Charts! Add Suffix "-6" to Model No. for Chart Type Selected. Example: CT485-CDC-6.

Patents:
U.S. #5,019,838 and D311,695
Canada #8042 Rd.
OMEGA Engineering
Germany #M88 03 842.4
Italy #0055451
Korea #102879
Taiwan #22507
U.K. #1 055 583

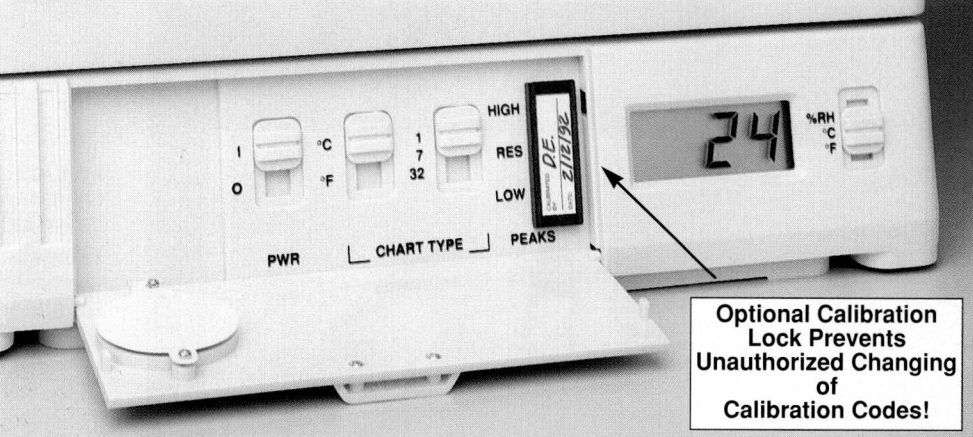

Optional Calibration Lock Prevents Unauthorized Changing of Calibration Codes!

the recorder. The user may select 1, 7 or 32 day operation, program the instrument to record in °F or °C, and access alarm and calibration controls or max/min functions.

A separate 3-position switch next to the digital display selects a °F, °C or %RH readout. The chart drive is quartz controlled for precision, and a unique magnetic retaining knob eliminates the possibility of paper tear.

Calibration of alarm models is digital, and a user may make calibration adjustments in the field using the convenient panel pushbuttons. An optional calibration lockout cover is available to prevent unauthorized changing of calibration codes.

The CT485RS demonstrates its impressive versatility and rugged performance by allowing both laboratory and portable operation. A desk stand provides added stability for benchtop use, which conveniently rotates under the unit for wall mounting. Recessed rear mounting slots and a wall template enable easy wall mounting. A standard 110 Vac power adaptor is supplied for continuous long-term operation, along with four D-cell batteries for backup power or field use.

To handle a variety of measurement applications, each unit includes 6 feet of cable for remotely mounting the sensor.

SPECIFICATIONS

MEASUREMENT INPUTS: temperature and humidity, with plug-in external sensor, removable for remote location, 6' extension cable included; 0.02 to 1.20 Vdc signal with voltage input adaptor

TEMPERATURE
Range: 2 to 120°F (-17 to 49°C)
Accuracy: ±1°C
Sensor: solid state
Response Time: 5 minutes for 63% step change
Display Resolution: 1°F/1°C

HUMIDITY
Range: 2 to 98% RH
Accuracy: ±3% @25°C, between 20 and 90% of range (±5% below 20% and above 90% @25°C)
Sensor: resistive polymer
Response Time: 5 minutes for a 30 to 80% step change
Display Resolution: 1% RH

DISPLAY
Right Display: 2 1/2 digit LCD, 0.5" high; low battery and parameter indication
Left Display: Digital time-of-day and date clock
Display Modes: Front panel switchable between °F, °C and %RH for continuous digital display; max/min storage for both temperature and humidity or flashing to indicate alarm condition

ELECTRONICS

Type: microprocessor-controlled and linearized high and low peak hold for both temperature and humidity, re-initializes position at every chart change

MICROPROCESSOR-BASED TEMPERATURE/ RELATIVE HUMIDITY RECORDER
WITH VERSATILE REMOTE MOUNTING SENSOR

Pen Arms: clear plastic to allow full chart viewing

OPERATING CONDITIONS (Recorder)

Temperature: 32 to 122°F (0 to 50°C)

Humidity: 0 to 90% RH, non-condensing

OPERATING CONDITIONS (Sensor Remote)

Temperature: 2 to 122°F (-17 to 50°C)

Humidity: 0 to 98% RH

ALARMS (OPTIONAL)

Alarms: User-selectable for high or low temperature and humidity

Audible Alarm: Integral piezoelectric beeper

Alarm Relay Contacts: 2 Amps, 24 V ac or dc, NO, SPST

POWER (Recorder): four D cells or 9V/110 Vac, 50/60 Hz power adapter (supplied); 220 Vac power adapter supplied where applicable

Battery Life: more than 1 month continuous operation in 32-day mode (average conditions)

Power Requirements: 400 mA "normal" during pen movement; 1.25 A max. surge

DC Power Jack Voltage: 7.2 to 14 Vdc, 1.25 A

POWER (Clock):

Battery: one watch-type battery, Eveready 392 or equivalent

Battery Voltage: 1.5 V

Battery Life: approx. 2 years typically

MECHANICAL

Dimensions: 12" H x 10" W x 2.5" D (304 x 254 x 63.5 mm)

Weight: approx. 7 lbs including alkaline batteries

Mounting: T-slots for wall mount and rotating desk stand for benchtop

Case: rugged ABS plastic, charcoal gray or computer room white

ANALOG VOLTAGE INPUT ADAPTOR

Input: 0.02-1.20 Vdc records as 2 to 120°F, input protection up to 20 Vdc or 10 Vac RMS

Input Impedance: 330 Kohms min.

Input Connections: Banana jacks, 0.75" spacing

Cable Length: 12" (305 mm)

Miscellaneous: recessed handgrip, swing-out desk stand for benchtop use, 6' sensor extension cord for remote sensing

CHART

Type: 8" circular, with linear radial divisions; 1, 7 and 32 days with both °F and °C scales

CHART DRIVE

Type: quartz clock stepper drive

Ranges: 1, 7 and 32 day, selectable

Accuracy: 1% of rotation

Chart Paper Hold Down: magnetic hub lock

RECORDING PENS

Type: disposable fiber tip, red for temperature, blue for humidity

PEN DRIVES

Type: motorized linear screw drive

Deadband: 1.5°F, 1.5% RH

Zero: automatic zero during chart change or power interruption

Penlift: automatic on door opening; pens are door mounted and swing clear of the chart when door opens

The CT485RS Includes:

QTY	Description
1	Package of 120 double-sided charts (20 each of six styles)
1	Remote mounting sensor and 6' extension cord
1	Voltage input adaptor cable
1	AC adaptor/power cord, 110 or 220 V
4	D cell batteries
1	Wall mounting template with mounting hardware
2 ea.	Red pens (temp.) and blue pens (humidity
1	Operator's manual

To Order (Specify Model Number)

Model No.	Price	Description
CT485RS-110V	$592	Charcoal gray recorder, 110 Vac
CT485RS-110V-W	620	Computer room white recorder, 110 Vac
CT485RS-110V-AL	642	Charcoal gray recorder, 110 Vac, with alarms and relay contact
CT485RS-110V-W-AL	650	Computer room white recorder, 110 Vac, with alarms and relay contact
CT485-PR	5	Red pen (temperature)
CT485-PB	5	Blue pen (humidity)
CT485-PS	10	Pen set, red and blue
CT485-CDF	19	200 Charts, 1 day, °F (100 double-sided sheets)
CT485-CDC	19	200 Charts, 1 day, °C (100 double-sided sheets)
CT485-CWF	19	200 Charts, 7 day, °F (100 double-sided sheets)
CT485-CWC	19	200 Charts, 7 day, °C (100 double-sided sheets)
CT485-CMF	19	200 Charts, 32 day, °F (100 double-sided sheets)
CT485-CMC	19	200 Charts, 32 day, °C (100 double-sided sheets)
CT485CSP	15	240 Charts, 20 each of six styles listed above (120 double-sided sheets)
CAL-LOCK	25	Calibration lockout cover
CT485-RP	89	Replacement temperature/RH probe

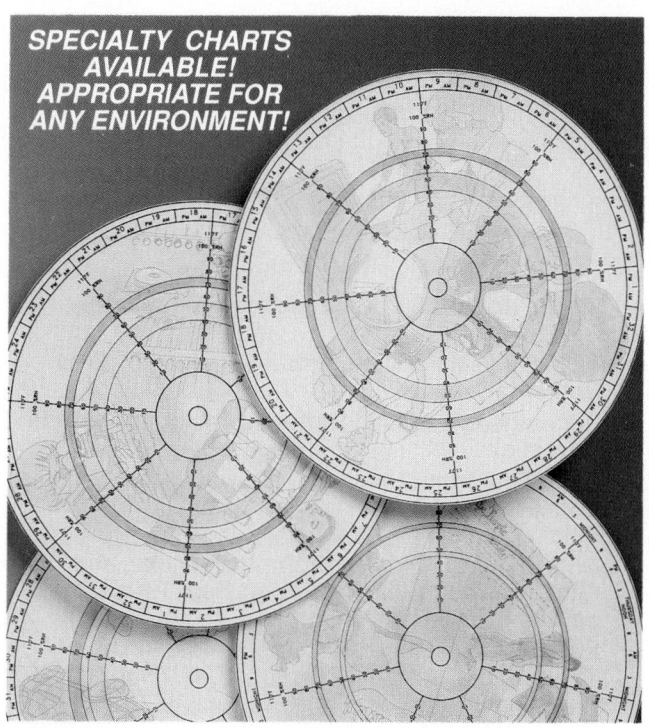

SPECIALTY CHARTS AVAILABLE! APPROPRIATE FOR ANY ENVIRONMENT!

Ordering Example: *CT485RS-110V-W-AL white recorder, 110 Vac, with alarms and relay contact ($650), plus CT485-MW specialty charts (museum/art gallery, $20) and CT485-PS pen set ($5),* *$650 + 20 + 5 = **$675**.*

Specialty Charts (20 Double-Sided Charts Per Package)

Model No.	Price	Application	Days
CT485-MW	$20	Museum/Art Gallery	7
CT485-MM	20	Museum/Art Gallery	32
CT485-HW	20	Hospitals	7
CT485-HM	20	Hospitals	32
CT485-LW	20	Labs/Clean Rooms	7
CT485-LM	20	Labs/Clean Rooms	32
CT485-PW	20	Computer Room/Office	7
CT485-PM	20	Computer Room/Office	32

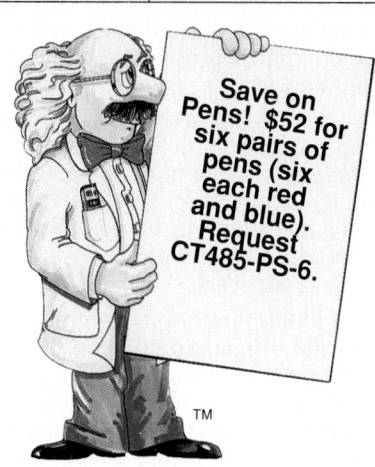

Save on Pens! $52 for six pairs of pens (six each red and blue). Request CT485-PS-6.

PORTABLE INTELLIGENT DATALOGGER
FOR REMOTE DATA COLLECTION IN ANY ENVIRONMENT FOR IBM PC OR COMPATIBLES

MADE IN **USA**

From
$687

- ✔ **Stores Up to 100 Days of Trend Data for Later Review**
- ✔ **Includes IBM PC Compatible Software for Easy Data Analysis**
- ✔ **Rechargeable Ni-Cad Batteries Facilitate Remote Operation**
- ✔ **Up to Four Input Channels Accept Analog Signals from Standard Sensors when Used with OMEGA Data Modules**
- ✔ **An 8 digit LCD Display Prompts the User, and Also Functions as a Meter to Report Real Time Display on Any of The Four Channels**
- ✔ **Input Types Include Thermocouples, RTDs, Thermistors, Voltage, Current, MPH, Event, and Pulse Counting**

Take sophisticated datalogging capabilities directly into the field, with the OMEGA OM-160. This pocket-sized device features 1-4 channels with an adaptive memory that adjusts to the stored data to provide optimum resolution and accuracy for up to 100 days. Its encapsulated design and battery operation permits data recording in locations that were formerly inaccessible. An optional weatherproof housing enables usage outdoors, for applications such as water analysis, sewage treatment, geological surveying, and remote weather stations. System setup is accomplished by a simple two key sequence in conjunction with an eight digit LCD display which prompts the operator. Analog inputs from standard sensors are accepted in conjunction with OMEGA data modules that provide signal conditioning where needed. These data modules function as signal conditioners which provide excitation as well as signal amplification which may be required to match the sensors to the datalogger.

Once logging is complete, data may be sent to an IBM PC or compatible via the built-in RS-232C port. The transmission rate is selectable from 300 to 9600 baud using the keys at the front panel. The total transfer is completed in just a few seconds, for even the longest recordings. A powerful software package is included for easy data review and analysis.

The OM-160 allows for operator programming of sensor type, calibration, real time and date, recording start, playback, channel display and recording time from a few minutes up to 100 days. Other features include display of battery voltage, and available memory. If required the unit can act as a meter for real time data display.

Applications

The OM-160 is designed to operate in any environment, the optional weatherproof housing permits use both in and out of doors. Its rugged, compact design is ideal for data accumulation of air, ship, train, or truck freight where information collection of variables such as temperature, pressure, relative humidity or run time is required but difficult to obtain by conventional strip chart recorders because of excessive shock and vibration.

Its portability and simple operation make it well suited for many field service applications such as HVAC, process control trouble shooting, electrical power monitoring, event recording and many other plant maintenance functions. An optional tamper-proof enclosure protects the data collection process and prevents unauthorized access to the controls. Wall mounting and real time display aids remote datalogging in blood banks, laboratories and computer rooms, providing long term review and analysis of data.

SPECIFICATIONS

Number of channels: 4 (Channels 1, 2, and 3 are analog and digital inputs; channel 4 is analog input only) 1 manual event marker activated via enter key during recording session

Sampling rate: Every 650 ms. recording rate is automatically adapted to suit record period and the dynamics of the signal

Input Impedance: 1×10^{12} ohms

Minimum Discernible Change: 0.5 mV

Resolution: 0.1%

Real Time Clock: Programmable display in day, hour, minute, second

Recording Time: Programmable from 1 m to 100 days
Display: 8 character alphanumeric LCD
Programming: Menu driven via 2 keys on front panel
Output: RS-232C with programmable baud rates of 300, 1200, 4800, and 9600
Power: 4.5 Vdc AA size rechargeable Ni-Cad batteries
Operating Temperature: −10 to 60°C
Relative Humidity: 10 to 90% non-condensing
Dimensions: 5.71″ H x 3.15″ W x 1.44″ D
Weight: 10 oz.
Sensor Types: 100Ω Pt RTD, α = 0.00385; Series 400 thermistor. MOD-02 uses OMEGA ON-900 44006 probes; MOD-03 uses OMEGA ON-400 probes or ON-900 44004 probes.
Module Connections: Thermistor–phone plug; RTD-TA4F; thermocouple–SMP; all else–banana plug

OMEGACARE™ Extended Warranties of one, two and three years are available for the OM-160. Pricing varies depending on the configuration ordered. Please consult Sales for details.

To Order (Specify Model Number)

Model	Price	Description
OM-160	$540	4 channel datalogger with software, purchase modules separately. See Ordering Example below.

Comes with batteries, operator's manual, and software package for IBM compatible PC.
Ordering Example: *Purchase datalogger plus from one to four modules. We also suggest purchasing a battery charger plus an interface cable for the PC. Example:*

OM-160	Datalogger	$540
MOD-12	dc voltage module	115
MOD-05/16	Type J thermocouple module	125
RR-120A	120V, 60 Hz battery charger	35
RR-101F	6 ft interface cable (female connector)	37
	Total	**$852**

Accessories

Model	Price	Description
RR-120A	$ 35	120 V, 60 Hz, battery charger
RR-120B	90	220 V, 50 Hz battery charger
RR-130	180	30 day rechargeable battery pack
RR-101M	37	4 ft. computer interface cable (male connector)
RR-101F	37	4 ft. computer interface cable (female connector)
RR-200	65	Wall Mounting Plate
RR-210	198	Weatherproof Enclosure
RR-100	85	Input Connector Kit (Pkg. of 10)
RR-105	160	Clamp-on transformer 2-150A
RR-106	160	Clamp-on transformer 4-400A

Applications Software

The OMEGA OM-160 portable datalogger system includes a software package that provides the operator with a great deal of flexibility to review, analyze, store report and prepare data for use in other software products such as Lotus 123. Plotting, min/max, annotating, and expanded viewing of data is also provided.

The software is designed to operate on IBM compatible computers with CGA, Hercules or EGA graphics.

Signal Conditioner Modules

Model No.	Input Type	Accuracy % FS	Resol.	Price
MOD-02	Thermistor, 10kΩ −50 to 150°C	±0.4	0.1°C	$75
MOD-03	Thermistor, 2252Ω −40 to 110°C	±0.3	0.1°C	75
MOD-04/15	T/C Type K −250 to 1370°C	±0.5	1°C 1°F	125
MOD-05/16	T/C Type J −250 to 750°C	±0.4	1°C 1°F	125
MOD-18/19	T/C Type T −200 to 400°C	±0.4	1°C 1°F	125
MOD-08/09	RTD, 100Ω Pt −200 to 250°C	±0.3	0.1°C 0.1°F	125
MOD-10	dc Current 4 to 20 mA	±0.3	0.1%	75
MOD-11	dc Current 0 to 100 mA	±0.3	0.1 mA	75
MOD-12	dc Voltage 0 to 100 mV	±0.3	0.1 mV	115
MOD-13/14	dc Voltage 0 to 2 V	±0.3	1 mV	75
MOD-20	ac Voltage 0 to 600 V	±0.5	1.0 V	165
MOD-21	ac Current 0 to 1000 A (1 amp input) 48 to 500 Hz	N/A	1.0A	155
MOD-21A	ac Current 0-1000 A 5 amp input	N/A	1.0A	155
MOD-29/03	Humidity/Temp. 0 to 100% RH 0 to 50°C	±0.3	0.1% RH 0.1°C	400
MOD-PC	Pulse Counting 0 to 100 Hz 0 to 1000 Hz 0 to 10 KHz 0 to 50 KHz	±0.04	0.1 1 10 1 K	75

DIGITAL TRANSMITTERS AND DATA ACQUISITION SOFTWARE

D1000 AND D2000 OMEGABUS® SYSTEM

From

$250

✔ **Complete Sensor To RS-232C or RS-485 Interface**
✔ **Input Modules for Thermocouples, RTDs, Voltages, Currents, Pulse and Frequency, and Bridge Inputs**
✔ **RS-485 Format Permits Remote Communications Up To Ten Thousand Feet**
✔ **D2000 Series Provide Linearization of Non-Standard Sensors**
✔ **Connect Up To 32 Modules On One Cable Set; Up To 124 Using a Repeater**
✔ **Alarm Outputs Standard**
✔ **Continuous Self Calibration, No Adjustment Requirements**

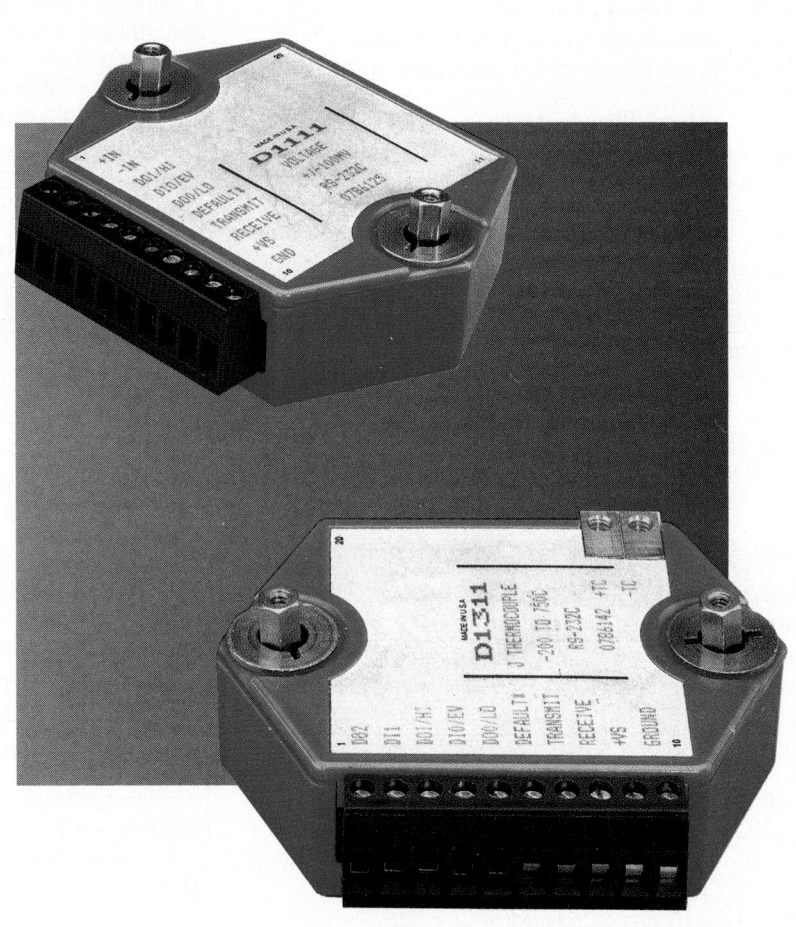

The D1000 and D2000 Series digital transmitters are a complete family of easy to use interface modules based on personal computers and other processor based equipment with standard serial I/O ports. The modules convert analog input signals to engineering units and transmit, in ASCII format, to any host computer with a standard RS-232C or RS-485 port. This modular design enables anyone familiar with a personal computer to construct a flexible and cost effective data acquisition system. These modules can measure temperature, pressure, flow, voltages, currents and various types of digital signals. The 1000 Series provide direct interface to a wide variety of sensors and perform all signal conditioning, scaling, linearization and conversion to engineering units. Each module also provides digital I/O lines for controlling devices through solid state relays or TTL signals. These digital I/O lines along with integral limit setting capability provide alarm and control outputs. With the exception of the D1400 RTD and D1500 bridge modules, every D1000 module contains an on-board event counter. The event counter will count up to ten million transitions on the digital input line. All user selectable options (address, baud rate, alarms, etc.) are done through the communications port and stored in nonvolatile memory thereby eliminating switches or external adjustments of any kind.

The flexibility of this system allows users to mix and match the modules to fit their exact requirements. As many as 124 modules can be connected on one 4 wire cable. They can be placed remote from the host computer and from each other.

The D2000 Series of user programmable data acquisition and control modules allow direct interface of non-standard analog sensors to computers with serial I/O ports. Use of these modules enables

Use the RS-485 Communications Format for Remote Operation Up to 10,000 ft. from the Host Computer.

Connect up to 32 Modules on One Cable Set.

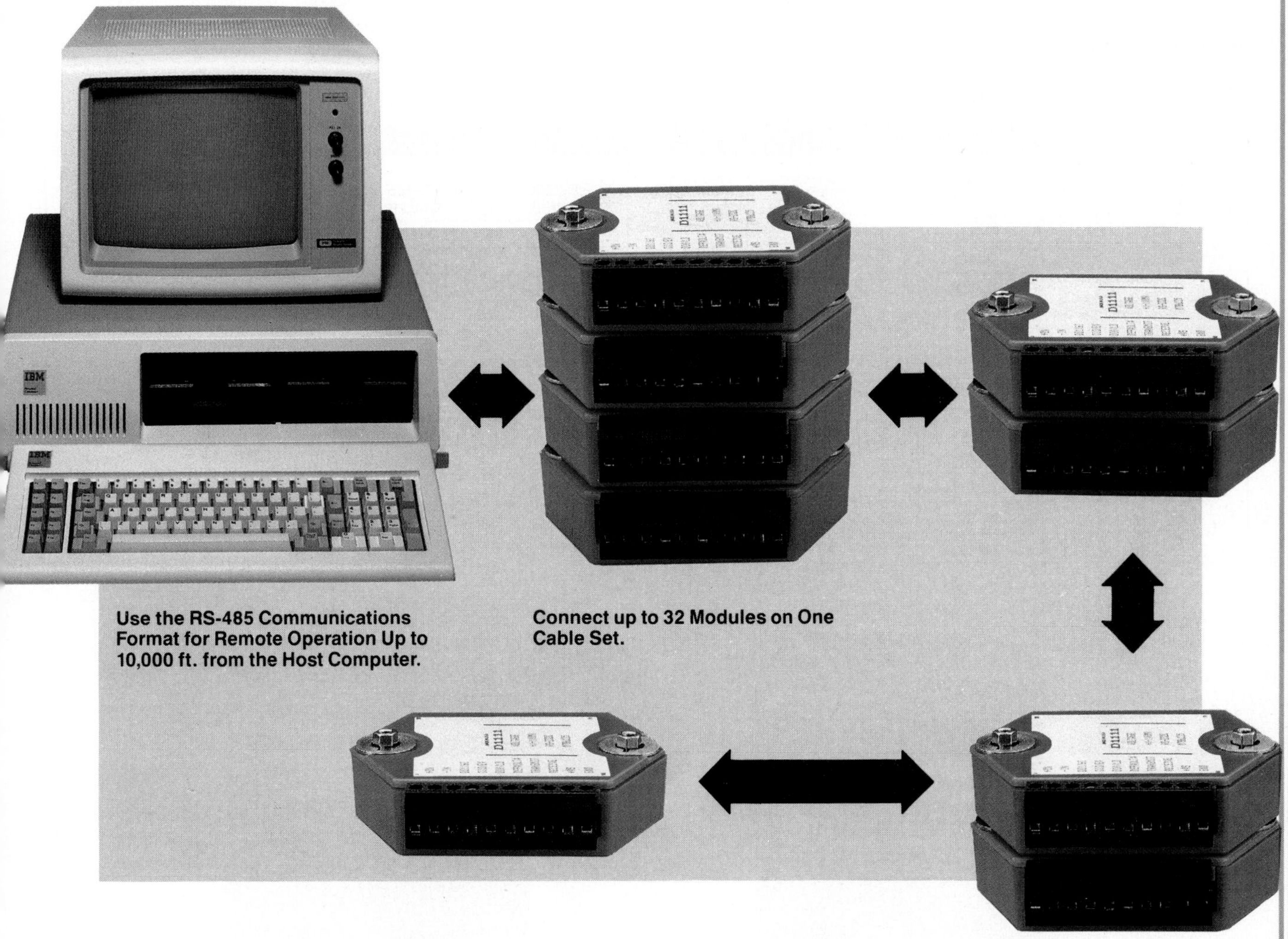

downloading up to 23 breakpoints through the communications port. With these breakpoints the user can program a module to virtually any transfer function.

The ability to provide an arbitrary user programmable nonlinear transfer function is the most powerful feature of the D2000 series. Use this feature to linearize non-standard sensors or to provide outputs in engineering units, which are nonlinear to functions of the input. The 2000 Series can be programmed to approximate square law, root, log, high-order polynomial or any other nonlinear function. The 2000 may also be empirically field-programmed when the exact transfer function is unknown.

If transmitting long distances is required, selection of the RS-485 communications format is encouraged. This permits remote operation of up to ten thousand feet from the host computer. For computers which do not include a RS-485 port, OMEGA offers the A1000 Series of RS-232 signal converters (page H-10). The modules are also capable of operating in a multidrop fashion supporting up to 32 units one one cable set. With use of the OMEGA 1300 repeater (page H-10) as many as 124 modules may be joined together. A utility software

package (for IBM PC or compatibles) is also available, this software eliminates the need for programming skills to easily communicate with the modules. This software package is available upon request at no charge. Request model D1000-SW1, for D1000, D3000 and D4000 modules; model D2000-SW1 for D2000 modules. (One per order.)

All modules are supplied with screw terminal plug connectors and captive mounting hardware. Their encapsulated design allows for mounting in virtually any location including explosion proof housings and DIN rails.

OMEGABUS® DIGITAL TRANSMITTERS
D1000 AND D2000 MODELS

How To Order

D2000 Series Transmitter Modules

Voltage Inputs			
Model			
RS-232C Output	RS-485 Output	Price	Inputs
D2111	D2112	$275	10 mV
D2121	D2122	275	1 V
D2131	D2132	275	5 V
D2141	D2142	275	10 V

Bridge Inputs				
Model				
RS-232C Output	RS-485 Output	Price	Input	Excitation
D2511	D2512	$350	30 mV	5 V
D2521	D2522	350	30 mV	10 V
D2531	D2532	350	100 mV	5 V
D2541	D2542	350	100 mV	10 V

Current Inputs			
Model			
RS-232C Output	RS-485 Output	Price	Inputs
D2221	D2222	275	10 mA
D2231	D2232	275	100 mA
D2241	D2242	275	1 A
D2251	D2252	275	4 to 20 mA

Pulse and Frequency Inputs			
Model			
RS-232C Output	RS-485 Output	Price	Inputs
D2601	D2602	$275	Frequency
D2611	D2612	275	Pulse

Shown in Multidrop Fashion

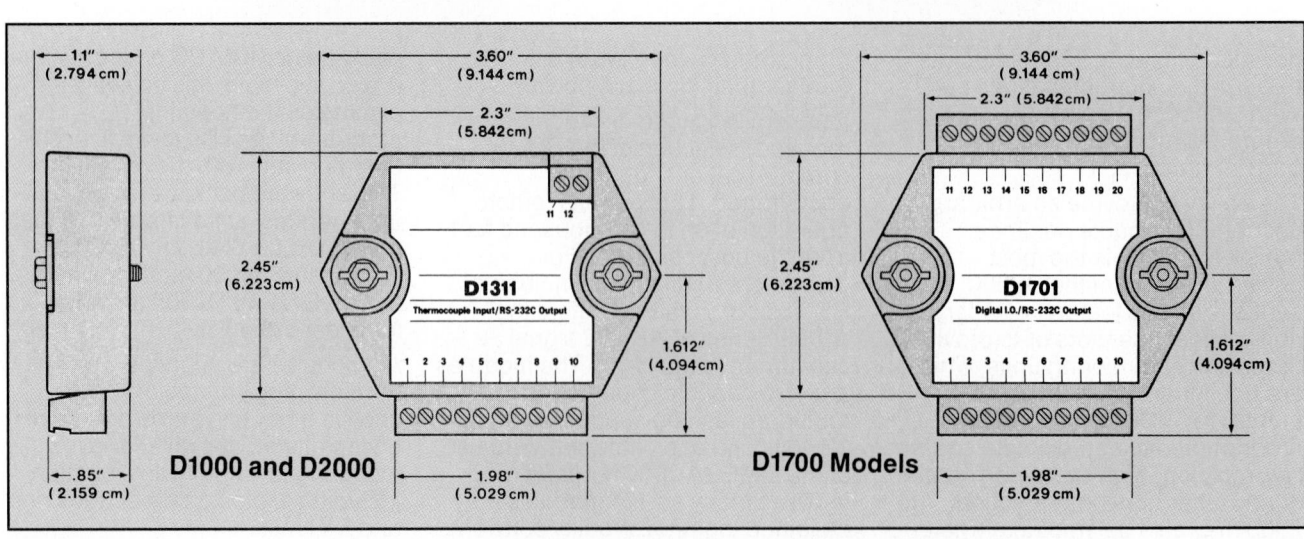

OMEGABUS® COMPUTER-TO-ANALOG OUTPUT MODULES

D3000 AND D4000 SERIES

MADE IN USA

1 YEAR WARRANTY

D3000 Series $275

D4000 Series $350

From $275

output functions. These modules offer an extremely flexible, easy-to-use, and cost-effective approach to data acquisition. The D3000 and D4000 are compatible with the Omegabus D1000 and D2000 and may be used in any combination. Up to 124 modules may be strung on one set of wires. All modules are supplied with screw terminal plug connectors and captive mounting hardware. The connectors allow system expansion, reconfiguration, or repair without disturbing field wiring. Their small size allows them to be mounted in virtually any location or position including explosion-proof housings and DIN rails. Although software is not required, utility software (S3000) is available upon request at no charge on an IBM-compatible disk.

The D4000 modules offer several additional features. A slew rate may be programmed, which causes the output to ramp at an adjustable rate in either an increasing or decreasing direction. The ramp can be initiated and maintained by commands from the computer or with external switch closures to the module. The D4000 module provides a readback feature which allows the computer to verify the integrity of the output. The D4000 modules also include a watchdog timer circuit that can be set such that if the computer fails to communicate with the module after a preset time period, the module will reset itself to an adjustable default value. This feature minimizes the risks of communication failure.

- ✔ **Analog Output Ranges: 0-1 V, ±1 V, 0-5 V, ±5 V, 0-10 V, ±10V, 0-20 mA, 4-20 mA**
- ✔ **Programmable High/Low Output Limits**
- ✔ **500 V rms Output Isolation**
- ✔ **Scaling in Engineering Units**
- ✔ **12-Bit Resolution**
- ✔ **Baud Rates: 300 to 38,400**
- ✔ **Output Protection: 240 Vac (Current Output), ±30 V (Voltage Outputs)**

The D3000 and D4000 computer-to-analog output interfaces are designed to be mounted remotely from a host computer and communicate with standard RS-232 and RS-485 serial ports. Simple ASCII commands are used to control a 12-bit digital-to-analog converter that is scaled to provide commonly used current and voltage ranges. An on-board microprocessor provides the communications interface and many intelligent analog

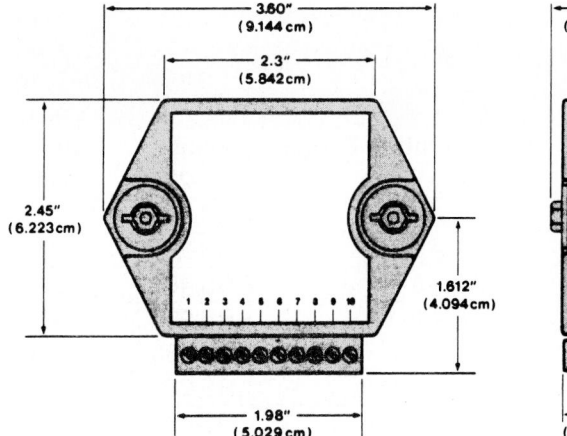
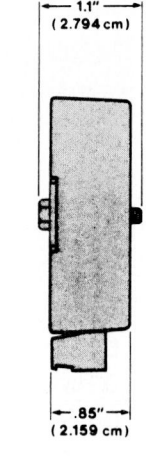

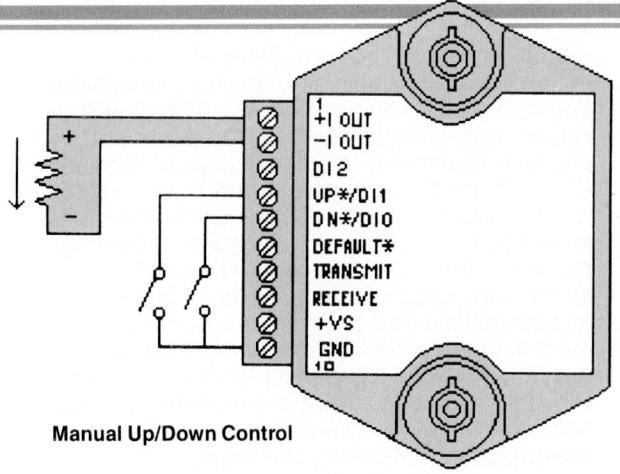

Manual Up/Down Control

Common Specifications, D3000 and D4000
ANALOG OUTPUT
- Single channel analog output
  Voltage: 0-1 V, ±1 V, 0-5 V, ±5 V, 0-10 V, ±10 V
  Current: 0-20 mA
- Input isolation to 500 V rms
- 12-bit measurement resolution
- Accuracy (integral and differential nonlinearity): 0.1% FSR (max)
- Zero drift: ±30 μV/°C (voltage output)
  ±1.0μA/°C (current output)
- 1000 conversions per second
- Settling time to 0.1% FS 300 μs typical (1 ms max)
- Programmable output slew rate: 0.01 V/s (mA/s) to 10,000 V/s (mA/s) (D4000 only)
- Autozero and autocalibration—no adjustment pots
- Voltage compliance: ±12 V
- Output current, short circuit current: 5 mA min, 10 mA max.

ANALOG OUTPUT READBACK (D4000)
- 8-bit analog-to-digital converter
- Accuracy over temperature (−25 to +70°C); 2.0 FS max
DIGITAL INPUTS
- Voltage levels: ±30 V without damage
- Switching levels: High, 3.5 V min, low, 1.0 V max
- Internal pull-up resistors for direct switch input
COMMUNICATIONS
- RS-232, RS-485
- Up to 124 with A1300 repeater, 32 without repeater multidrop modules/host communications port
- User selectable channel address
- Selectable baud rates: 300, 600, 1200, 2400, 4800, 9600, 19,200, 38,400
- ASCII format command/response protocol
- Parity: odd, even, none
- All communications setups (address, baud rate, parity) stored in nonvolatile memory using EEPROM
- Checksum can be added to any command or response
- Communications distance up to 10,000 feet with RS-485 modules

Power Requirements: Unregulated +10 V to +30 Vdc, 0.75 W max (voltage output), 1.0 W max (current output)
Case: ABS with captive mounting hardware
Connectors: screw terminal barrier plug (supplied)
Temperature Range: Operating: −25°C to +70°C; Storage −25°C to +85°C
Relative Humidity: 0 to 95% noncondensing

D3000 Series Output Module Current Output			
D3251	0 to 20 mA	RS-232C	$275
D3252	0 to 20 mA	RS-485	275

D4000 Series Output Module			
Model No.	Output Range	Input	Price
D4121	±1 V	RS-232C	$350
D4122	±1 V	RS-485	350
D4131	±5 V	RS-232C	350
D4132	±5 V	RS-485	350
D4141	±10 V	RS-232C	350
D4142	±10 V	RS-485	350
D4161	0 to 1 V	RS-232C	350
D4162	0 to 1 V	RS-485	350
D4171	0 to 5 V	RS-232C	350
D4172	0 to 5 V	RS-485	350
D4181	0 to 10 V	RS-232C	350
D4182	0 to 10 V	RS-485	350

D4000 Series Output Module Current Ouptut			
D4251	0 to 20 mA	RS-232C	$350
D4252	0 to 20 mA	RS-485	350

To Order *(Specify Model Number)*

D3000 Series Output Modules Voltage Output			
Model No.	Output Range	Input	Price
D3121	±1 V	RS-232C	$275
D3122	±1 V	RS-485	275
D3131	±5 V	RS-232C	275
D3132	±5 V	RS-485	275
D3141	±10 V	RS-232C	275
D3142	±10V	RS-485	275
D3161	0 to 1 V	RS-232C	275
D3162	0 to 1 V	RS-485	275
D3171	0 to 5 V	RS-232C	275
D3172	0 to 5 V	RS-485	275
D3181	0 to 10 V	RS-232C	275
D3182	0 to 10 V	RS-485	275

SIGNAL CONVERTERS/REPEATERS
USED WITH D1000 AND D2000 DIGITAL TRANSMITTERS

- ✔ **Fully Adjustable Baud Rates**
- ✔ **Integral 24 Volt 1 Amp Power Supply Can Power Up To 32 Transmitter Modules**
- ✔ **A1300 Repeater Amplifies RS-485 Signal To Drive 32 Additional Modules**
- ✔ **Use Three A1300 Repeaters To Interface Up To 124 Modules To a Single Computer Port**
- ✔ **A1300 Provides RS-485 Bus Control In Both Directions To The Host Computer**

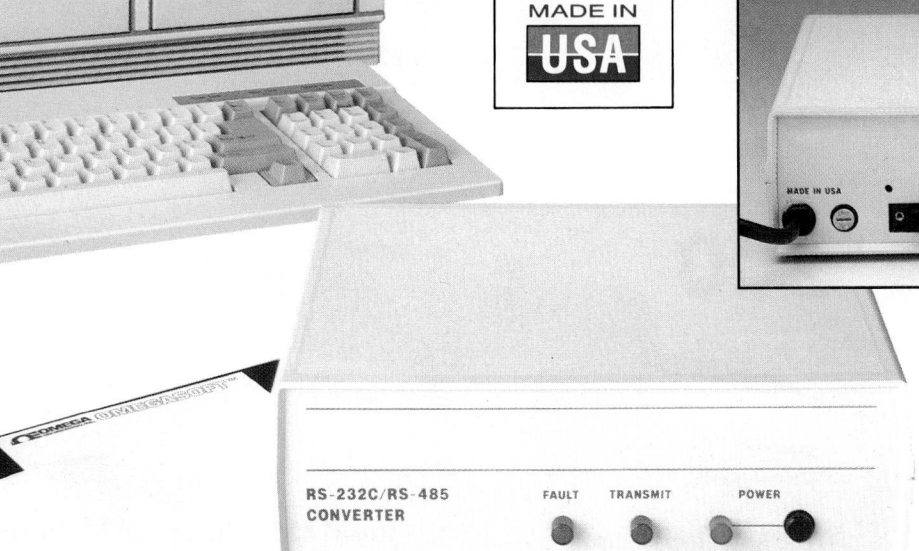

MADE IN USA

From

$250

The OMEGA® A1000 Signal Converter allows users to establish an effective data acquisition system over long distances. The converter changes the RS-232C and RS-422 communications signal to the correct electrical signals required by RS-485. The RS-485 signal accommodates remote field communications by allowing bus lengths up to 10 miles and baud rates up to 38.4 KHz.

RS-485 is a true transmit/recieve bus, which requires some means of controlling the bus direction, the A1000 automatically performs this task eliminating any hand-shaking signals from the host. Thus, existing software written for RS-232 or RS-422 may be used without modification. The RS-485 bus control is completely transparent to the user.

The A1000 also contains a 24 volt 1 amp power supply capable of powering up to 32 transmitter modules. The supply is fully protected against overloads and short circuits. The power supply may also be used to power accessory circuits such as relays or 4 to 20mA transmitters.

For interfacing to radio modems, the A1400 converter should be used. The A1400 provides two basic functions: performs the electrical conversion from RS-232 to RS-485, and provides the programmable delay times between the transmitter key signal (RTS) and the transmitted data.

Specifications
Power Input: 120 Vac @ 50-60 Hz

Baud Rate: Switch selectable 300, 600, 1200, 2400, 4800, 9600, 19.2K, 38.4K

Excitation: 24 Volt 1 Amp

Connections: RS-232C-Female D-25
RS-422-Female D-9
RS-485-4 position screw terminal

Dimensions: 2.5" H x 8.0" W x 6.25" D

To Order (Specify Model Number)

Model	Price	Description
A1100	$250	RS-232 to RS-485 Converter
A1200	250	RS-422 to RS-485 Converter
A1300	250	RS-485/RS-485 Repeater
A1400	250	Radio Modem Interface

CONFIGURABLE, DIGITIZING SIGNAL CONDITIONERS

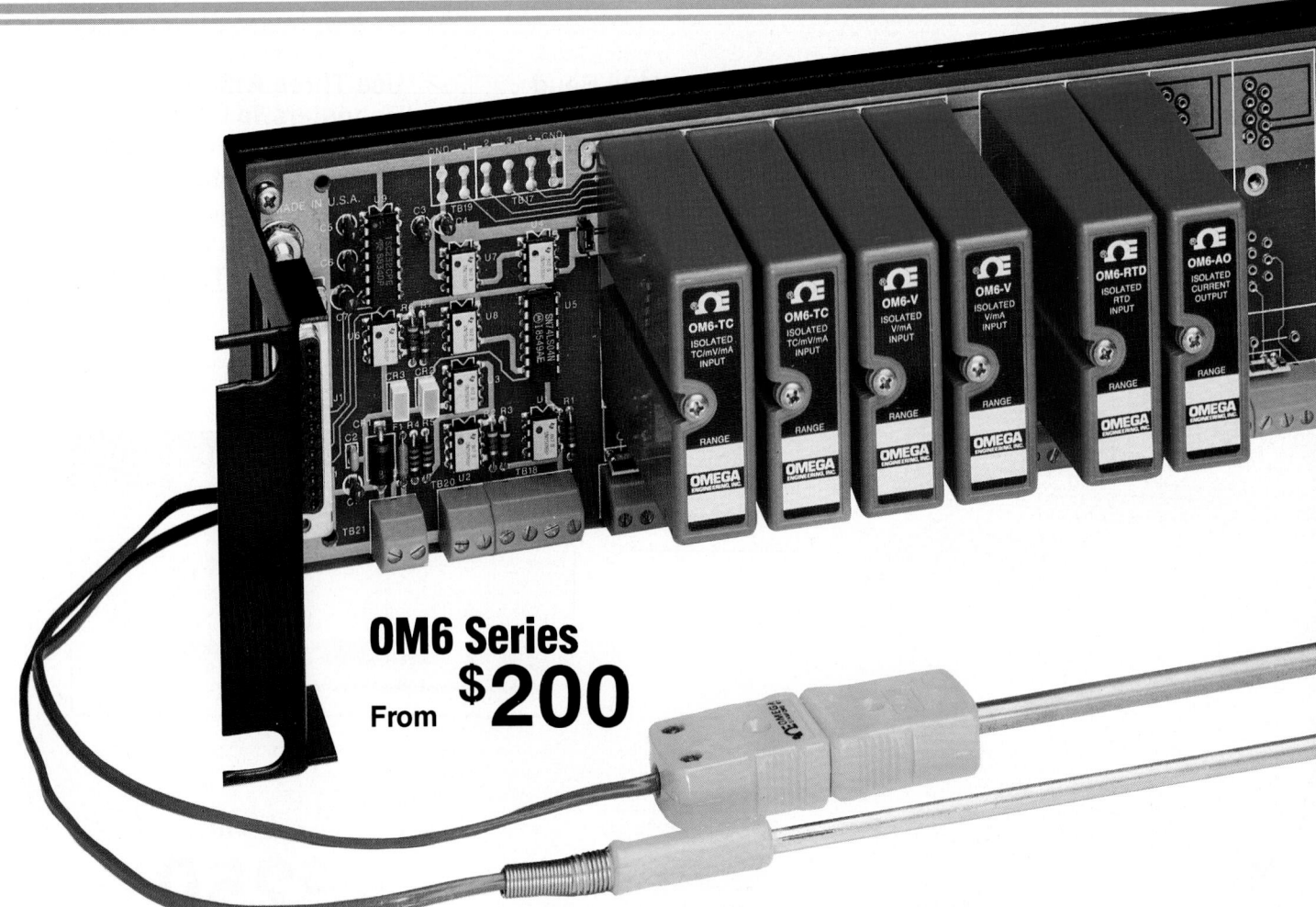

OM6 Series
From $**200**

- ✓ **Sensor-to-Computer Conditioning and Digitizing**
- ✓ **Thermocouple, RTD, mV, V, Process Current Inputs/Outputs**
- ✓ **Transmission Distances up to 4000 ft**

The OM6 Series modular signal conditioner makes interfacing a sensor to a computer serial port as easy as turning a screwdriver. These self-contained digitizing signal conditioners provide isolation, ranging, and serial digital communications for thermocouples, RTDs, millivolts, volts, and current. Up to 16 modules can be plugged into a backplane, which connects to a computer serial port via an RS-232 or RS-485 interface.

The three input modules cover everything from voltage (±15 mV to ±50 V) and current inputs (0-20 and 4-20 mA) to thermocouples and RTDs. Each module is field configurable by software for range, sensor type, calibration, and communications format. The analog I/O modules work in conjunction with a single, four or 16 channel backplane, available with either an RS-232 or RS-485 communication link to the host computer. For discrete I/O requirements the OM6-DIO backplanes provide 24 channels of digital I/O. For isolation and signal conditioning, these backplanes connect directly to solid state I/O module backplanes. Multiple backplanes may be daisy-chained together for implementing high-channel capacity systems with up to 256 modules on the network. The OM6 system is ideally suited for distributed process measurement applications. Since the backplanes interconnect via an RS-485 link, the OM6 network may extend up to 4000 feet.

Utility software included with the OM6 system provides easy communication with the modules.

Input Module Specifications (typical at 25°C and +5 V power)

Output: RS-485

Accuracy: ±0.05% or better

Zero Drift: ±0.3 μV/°C

Span Drift: ±25 ppm/°C max

Common Mode Voltage, Input to Output: 1500 V rms continuous

Common Mode Rejection at 50 Hz or 60 Hz: 1 kΩ, Source Imbalance: 160 dB

Normal Mode Rejection at 50 or 60 Hz: 50 dB

Differential Input Protection: 240 V rms continuous

Bandwidth: 4 Hz

Conversion Rate: 9 samples/s

Power Supply: +5 V ±5%

Power Consumption: 1.12 W (225 mA)

Dimensions: 2.3″ H x 3.1″ W x 0.75″ D (58.4 x 78.7 x 19.1 mm)

Temperature Range: −25°C to +85°C; 0 to 95% RH at 60°C

Storage Temp.: −40°C to +85°C

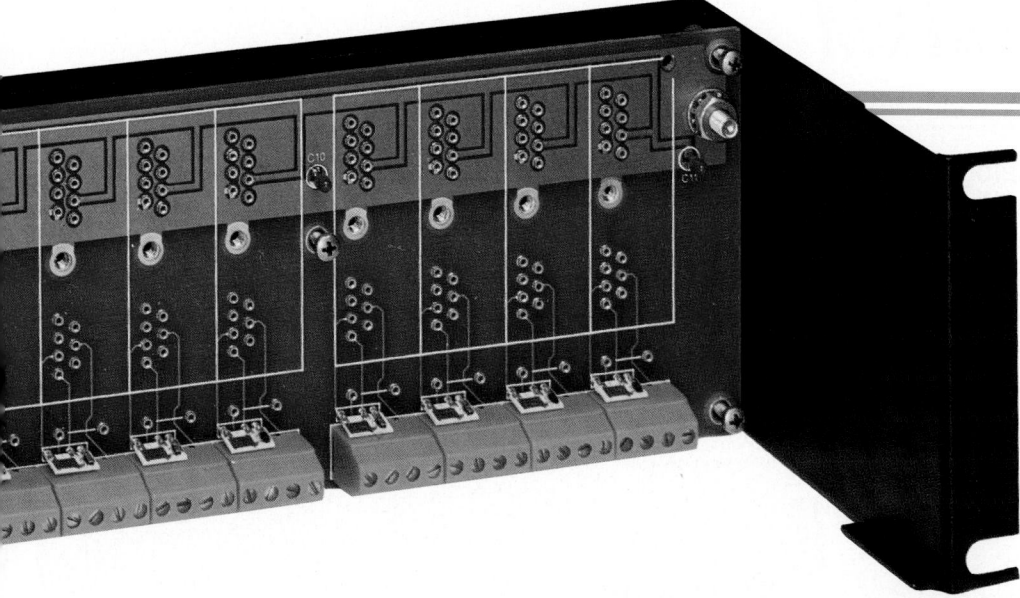

Thermocouple Probes Sold Separately. See Section A.

Power Supplies

Model No.	Price	Description
OMX-955	$131	5 V, 1 Amp
OMX-976	197	5 V, 3 Amp
OMX-977	235	5 V, 5 Amp

Accessories

Model No.	Price	Description
OMX-1380	$ 39	Rack mount kit
OMX-1381	3	Current conversion resistor
OMX-1382	45	RS-232 cable

To Order *(Specify Model Number)*
Analog I/O Modules

Model No.	Price	Description
OM6-TC	$200	Thermocouple, mV, V, mA input module
OM6-V	200	Voltage input module
OM6-RTD	200	RTD input module
OM6-AO	250	0-20/4-20 mA output module

Analog I/O Backplanes

Model No.	Price	Description
OM6-BP1-485	$ 45	1 channel RS-485 output
OM6-BP1-232	65	1 channel RS-232 and RS-485
OM6-BP4-485	110	4 channel RS-485 output
OM6-BP4-232	140	4 channel RS-232 and RS-485 output
OM6-BP16-485	260	16 channel RS-485 output
OM6-BP16-232	290	16 channel RS-232 and RS-485 output

Digital I/O Backplanes

Model No.	Price	Description
OM6-DIO-1*	$220	24 channel RS-485 digital I/O backplane
OM6-DIO-2*	250	24 channel RS-232 digital I/O backplane

Both digital I/O backplanes require OMX-CAB-03 cable, 6000-DEXB solid state switch backplane and solid state switches. (See Section H.)

How to Order

To Assemble a Complete OM6 System, Order:
1. Desired input modules
2. Desired backplane
3. Power supply
4. Cable: OMX-1382
5. Rack mount kit

Ordering Example
1. Two OM6-TC input modules @ $200 . . . $400
2. OM6-BP4-232 backplane 140
3. OMX-955 power supply 131
4. OMX-1382 RS-232 cable 45
5. OMX-1380 rack mount kit 39

Total $755

Ranges, OM6-V

±50V
±5V
±500mV
±10V
±1V
±150mV

Ranges, OM6-TC

15mV	J	Thermocouple, 0 to +760°C
50mV	K	Thermocouple, 0 to +1000°C
100mV	T	Thermocouple, −100 to +400 °C
500mV	E	Thermocouple, 50 to +1400°C
1V	R	Thermocouple, 50 to +1750°C
5V	S	Thermocouple, 50 to +1750°C
0-20mA	B	Thermocouple, 50 to +1800°C

Ranges, OM6-RTD

Pt	−100°C to +100°C	$\propto$ = 0.00385
Pt	0°C to +100°C	$\propto$ = 0.00385
Pt	0°C to +200°C	$\propto$ = 0.00385
Pt	0°C to +600°C	$\propto$ = 0.00385
Pt	−100°C to +100°C	$\propto$ = 0.003916
Pt	0°C to +100°C	$\propto$ = 0.003916
Pt	0°C to +200°C	$\propto$ = 0.003916
Pt	0°C to +600°C	$\propto$ = 0.003916
Ni	0°C to +100°C	
Cu	0°C to +120°C	10Ω @ 25°C
Cu	0°C to +120°C	10Ω @ 0°C

REMOTE, INTELLIGENT MEASUREMENT AND CONTROL SYSTEM

- ✔ **Expandable to 48 Analog Inputs, 10 Analog Outputs and 64 Digital I/O**
- ✔ **A Wide Variety of Signal Inputs Available, Both Isolated and Non-Isolated**
- ✔ **Event Counting, Pulse Duration Measurement, Period Measurement, and Time Proportional Outputs Provided**
- ✔ **Up to 64 Units May be Multidropped on a Single Link**
- ✔ **Connection to PC via RS-232 or RS-422**

μMEGA-1050 $995

OM-1050 Interface with Optional Cover

The μMEGA-1050 provides a simple means of interfacing to real-world signals with a host computer. In its simplest configuration, a host computer running applications software, a μMEGA-1050 and one 5 V power supply are all that is required to monitor eight differential or 16 single-ended analog input signals directly through screw terminals. Two non-isolated analog outputs are also provided. Sixteen digital I/O, plus two channels of low and high speed event counting, period measurement, or time proportional outputs can be accessed directly as TTL level signals on the base unit.

By using expander panels, the μMEGA-1050 is readily expandable up to 48 channels of analog input, 10 channels of analog output, and 64 channels of digital I/O. The analog input expansion panels may be intermixed up to a maximum channel count of 32, which when added to the base 16 channels yields a system total of 48 channels.

For applications requiring high isolation up to 1500 Vrms the OM5 modules and 6000-AMUX backplane provide access to a wide variety of signal types. For lower isolation requirements the OMX-STB-HLI and the OMX-STB-TCI provide 750 Vrms isolation. The OMX-STB-HLI has eight channels of analog input in the range ± 5 V and ±10 V, while the OMX-STB-TCI provides eight channels of low level voltage and thermocouple input. Each channel is configurable for an input range of ±5 mV, ±25 mV, ±50 mV or ±100 mV. Cold junction compensation is provided for thermocouple measurements.

If isolation is not required, the OMX-STB-HL02 and OMX-STB-TC allow extremely economical process measurement. The OMX-STB-HL02 provides 16 channels of ±5 V or ±10 V input and four channels of ± 5V analog output. The OMX-STB-TC can accept 16 low level voltage or thermocouple inputs. All channels must be set to the same input range, which may be ±5 mV, ±10 mV, ±25 mV, ±50 mV, ±100 mV or ±5 V. Cold junction compensation is also provided for thermocouple measurement.

The digital I/O capacity of the μMega-1050 can be expanded to 32 channels by employing two 6000-DMUX panels. Each panel accepts 32 channels of solid state switches.

Communication to the μMEGA-1050 from the host computer is possible with an RS-232 or isolated RS-422 communications link. The RS-422 provides the multidrop capability to put up to 64 μMEGA-1050's on a single serial link. The μMEGA-1050 uses a binary communication protocol, which provides a substantial increase in speed over ASCII protocols since the data is more tightly packed. Shipped with each μMEGA-1050 is exerciser software which, although not specific to an application, allows the user to configure the units and exercise the I/O commands. This package is mainly used to test the μMEGA-1050 and to become familiar with the command set.

OMX-STB-TCI
Expander Board, $795

1 YEAR WARRANTY

MADE IN USA

Specifications
ON-BOARD ANALOG INPUTS
Optional Cover, from $50

Number of channels: 16 Single ended/ 8 differential

Input range: $\pm$ 10 V

Overvoltage protection: $\pm$ 35 V

A/D converter: 14 bit plus sign integrating

Accuracy: $\pm$ 0.005% of span ($\pm$ 0.001 V)

Resolution: $\pm$ 0.003% of span

Input impedance: 100 Megohm

Common Mode Rejection: 90 dB @ 50 Hz and 60 Hz minimum

Normal Mode Rejection: 30 dB @ 50 Hz and 60 Hz minimum

ON-BOARD ANALOG OUTPUTS

Number of channels: 2

Output range: $\pm$ 10V

D/A converter
  Resolution: 12 bits (0.024% of span)
  Accuracy: $\pm$ 0.024% of span
  Drive capability: 2 mA @ $\pm$ 10 V

To Order (Specify Model Number)

Model No.	Price	Description
OM-1050	$995	µMEGA 1050 remote intelligent measurement and control system
OMX-STB-TCI	795	8 channel isolated thermocouple/low level voltage expander board
OMX-STB-HLI	695	8 channel isolated high level voltage expander board
OMX-STB-TC	495	16 channel thermocouple/low level voltage expander board
OMX-STB-HL02	395	16 input channel/4 output channel high level voltage expander board
OMX-STB-AOT	600	8 channel analog output expander panel with ±5 V, 0-5 V, ±10 V, 0-20 mA and 4-20mA ranges
6000-AMUX	260	16 channel OM5 backplane. (Requires OM5 modules, see Section H)
OMX-STB-50A	140	16 channel digital I/O screw terminal panel and 3 ft cable
6000-DMUX	370	32 channel digital I/O expander board (Requires 4 channel solid state switch modules, see Section H)
6000-DEXB	144	16 channel solid state switch backplane. (Requires 4 channel solid state switch modules, see Section H)
OMX-CAB-01	40	3 ft cable required to connect analog expander panel to µMEGA-1050.
OMX-CAB-02	40	5 ft cable required to connect a 6000-DMUX to a µMEGA-1050 or to another 6000-DMUX
OMX-CAB-03	40	5 ft cable connects 6000-DEXB to µMEGA-1050
OMX-PWR-01	250	Power supply; 90-264 Vac input, 5 Vdc 5 A output
OMX-RM-03	100	19" Rack mount kit. Mounts µMEGA-1050 with one OMX-STB expander panel or 6000-DEXB
OMX-RM-02	100	19" Rack mount kit. Mounts any two of OMX-STB panel, 6000-DEXB, 6000-DMUX or OMX-PWR-01
OMX-1363	32	19" Rack mount for 6000-AMUX
OMX-CV-01	50	Cover for OMX-STB panels
OMX-CV-02	85	Cover for µMEGA-1050
OMX-SWC-1050D	195	DOS software drivers for Microsoft C
OMX-SWB-1050D	195	DOS software drivers for Interpreted, BASIC Microsoft, compiled BASIC and QUICKBASIC
OMX-SWP-1050D	195	DOS software drivers for Turbo Pascal
SWD-LTN-2	995	Labtech Notebook Software
SWD-LCT-2	3995	Labtech Control Software

ON-BOARD DIGITAL I/O
Number of channels: 16 indvidually programmable as input or output

Signal levels: TTL solid state switch compatible

ON-BOARD HIGH SPEED PULSE I/O

Number of channels: 2

Event counting
  Count rate: 1.0 MHz max
  Max count: 4,294,967,296

Pulse Output: 1.0 MHz max

Power: 5V, 1.0A typical 1.5A Max

Ordering Example
The following is an example configuration of a 1050 system with 16 non-isolated high level voltage inputs, eight isolated high level inputs and 16 low level/thermocouple inputs. The system also includes 16 optically isolated solid state relay ouputs and menu driven software.

1	µMEGA-1050	$995
1	OMX-STB-TC	495
1	OMX-STB-HLI	695
1	OMX-STB-DEXB	144
4	SSS-QOA240 (solid state switches, $50 each)	200
1	OMX-CAB-01	40
1	OMX-CAB-03	40
1	OMX-CV-02	85
2	OMX-CV-01 ($50 each)	100
1	OMX-PWR-01	250
1	SWD-LTN-2	995
	Total	4039

PLUG-IN INTERFACE SYSTEMS
With Applications Software for Apple and IBM PCs

From
$**745**

✔ **RTD Measurement with Optional Screw Terminal Panel**
✔ **Easy to Use Menu Driven Software for Operation Without Programming**
✔ **Standard 12-Bit Resolution with 16-Bit Models for High Precision Measurements**
✔ **All Cards Contain Independently Selectable Digital Input and Output Channels**

✔ **Complete System with Plug-In Card, Terminal Box and Software**
✔ **Software Selectable Input Types Include Thermocouples, mV and V**

The White Box interface system provides both the hardware and software for a computerized data acquisition and control system. Included is a card which plugs into one of the internal slots of an IBM PC XT, AT or compatible, a terminal box which resides externally to the computer for easy hook-up to sensors and a user-friendly menu driven software package. All you need is a computer and sensors to complete the system.

The Hardware
The hardware provides the ability to interface with a wide variety of analog signals including thermocouples, millivolts, volts, currents and even RTD's. The standard model, the WB-FAI, features 12-bit A/D resolution, and

includes a battery backed clock and on-board current shunts for easy measurement of milliamp signals. The WB-FAI is available in two models, with either 8 or 16 analog input channels. The WB-AAI includes all features of the WB-FAI with improved accuracy and resolution (16-bit) for high precision applications. As an economical alternative, the WB-ASC is a half card version of the WB-FAI lacking only the battery backed clock and on-board current shunts. In addition to the analog input channels, all models include a number of digital I/O channels. Each of these channels may be independently selected through software as digital inputs for switch sensing type applications or digital outputs for alarm or control purposes.

The Software
Included with the White Box System is a menu-driven data acquisition and control software package for easy operation without programming. The software includes many featues such as graphical and tabular display of real-time data, control of alarm conditions, datalogging to printer or disk (in a format that can be easily imported to most spreadsheet programs for further data analysis) as well as many other features. The software is written in BASIC for those who may want to customize it for a special application. OMEGA also offers many other software packages that also work with the hardware. See the software section of the OMEGA Data Acquisition Systems Handbook and Encyclopedia®.

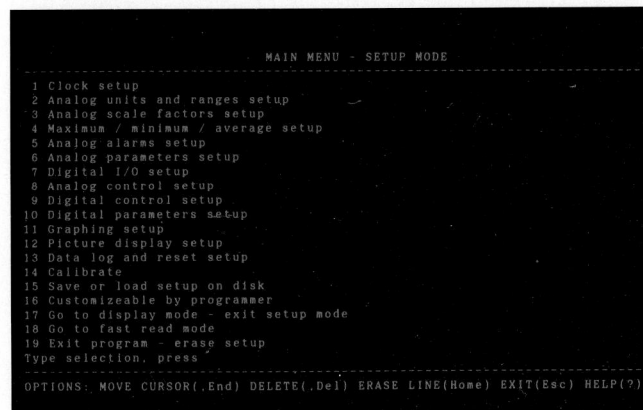

Each menu in the control software is a step-by-step procedure for fast, easy system installation and operation

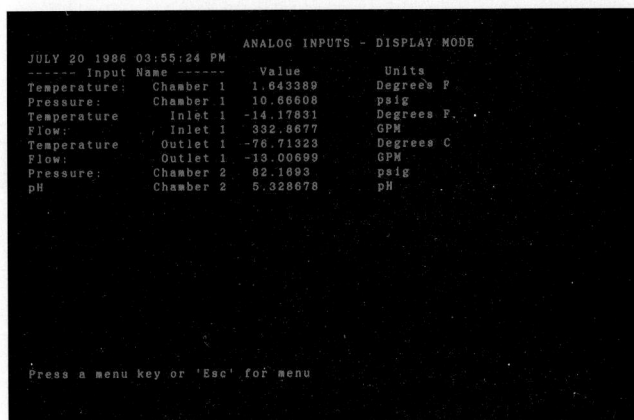

The software provides a tabular display of inputs with continuous updating. The user can select names, engineering units, and data logging to both disk and printer

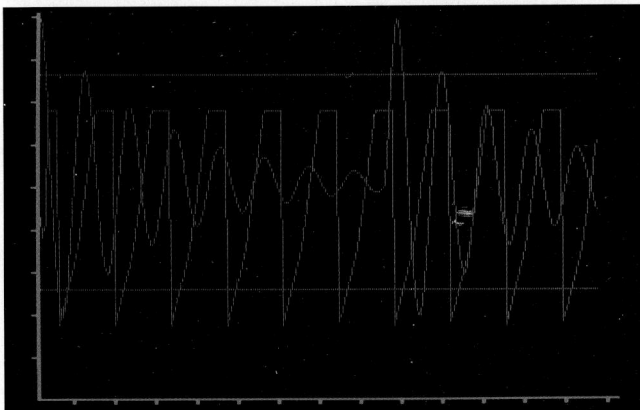

Graphics capabilities of the WB-AAI, FAI and ASC allow inputs to be plotted in real time against the control setpoint and alarm limits

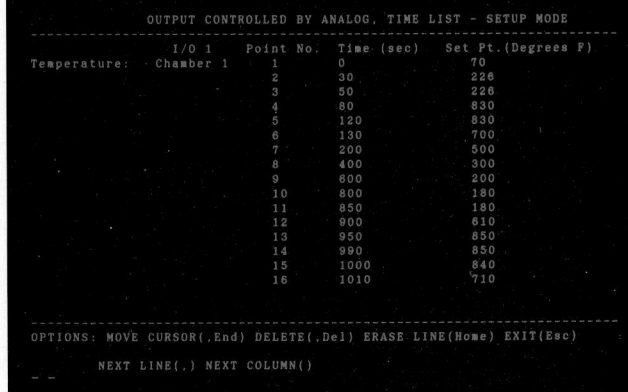

For accurate control, digital outputs can be configured quickly and easily in menus

INSTRUMENTATION

D

WHITE BOX® COMPUTER INTERFACES FOR APPLE II

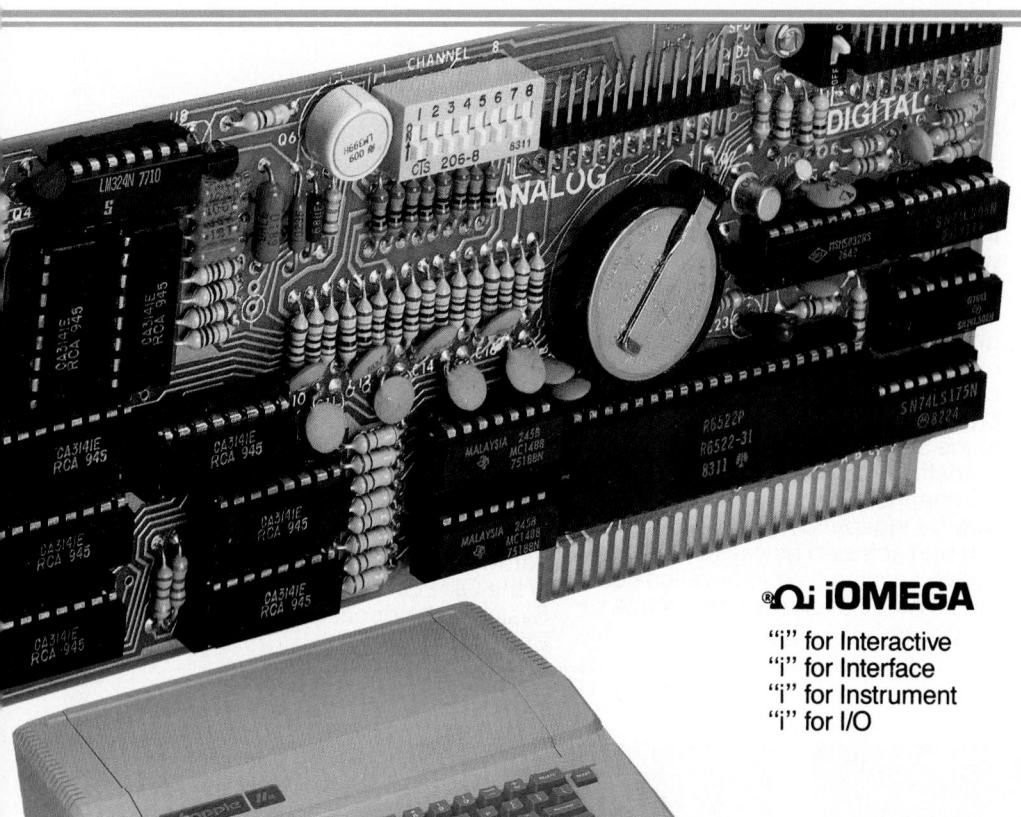

Each unit includes:
- Plug-in A/D Board
- Terminal Board(s) With Isothermal Plate
- Connection Cables
- Data Acquisition Software
- Comprehensive User's Manual
- 100' Type K Thermocouple Wire

WB-AIO-A   **$ 890**   8 channel

Ωi iOMEGA
"i" for Interactive
"i" for Interface
"i" for Instrument
"i" for I/O

$890

WB-AIO-A requires
Apple II+, IIe; 48K RAM

Input Type	Range	Resol.	Accuracy
J	−80 to 100°C 100 to 760°C	0.2°C 0.1°C	±0.9°C ±0.6°C
K	−110 to 0°C 0 to 1260°C	0.2°C 0.1°C	±1.0°C ±0.8°C
T	−120 to 0°C 0 to 400°C	0.2°C 0.1°C	±1.2°C ±0.8°C
E	−60 to 150°C 150 to 980°C	0.1°C 0.1°C	±0.7°C ±0.5°C
R	0 to 200°C 200 to 1770°C	0.5°C 0.3°C	±4.0°C ±2.5°C
S	0 to 200°C 200 to 1770°C	0.5°C 0.3°C	±4.0°C ±2.5°C
B	200 to 300°C 300 to 500°C 500 to 1000°C 1000 to 1820°C	0.8°C 0.5°C 0.3°C 0.3°C	±10.0°C ±6.0°C ±4.0°C ±2.2°C
G	25 to 200°C 200 to 2315°C	0.5°C 0.2°C	±6.0°C ±2.5°C
C	−20 to 2315°C 100 to 1500°C	0.3°C 0.2°C	±3.0°C ±2.0°C
D	−20 to 2315°C 150 to 1500°C	0.5°C 0.2°C	±3.0°C ±2.0°C

Resolution	Cycle Time, 8 Channels	
	Read & Control	**Read, Control & Datalog**
14 bit, 0.006%	8 sec	18 sec
13 bit, 0.012%	6 sec	16 sec
12 bit, 0.024%	5 sec	15 sec
11 bit, 0.05%	4 sec	14 sec
10 bit, 0.1%	4 sec	14 sec
9 bit, 0.2%	4 sec	14 sec
8 bit, 0.4%	4 sec	14 sec

Analog Ranges	Resolution	Accuracy—larger of	
		% of range	**% of rdg**
−5 to 50 mV	3 μV	0.04	—
−25 to 25 mV	3 μV	0.08	—
−50 to 500 mV	30 μV	0.05	0.1
−250 to 250 mV	30 μV	0.05	0.1
−1 to 10 V	600 μV	0.05	0.1
−5 to 5 V	600 μV	0.05	0.3
−0.5 to 5 mA	0.3 μA	0.2	1
−2.5 to 2.5 mA	0.3 μA	0.2	1
−5 to 50 mA	3 μA	0.2	1
−25 to 25 mA	3 μA	0.2	1

Standard screw terminal input with isothermal block for thermocouple input. Included with WB-AIO, WB-AAI, WB-FAI and WB-ASC.

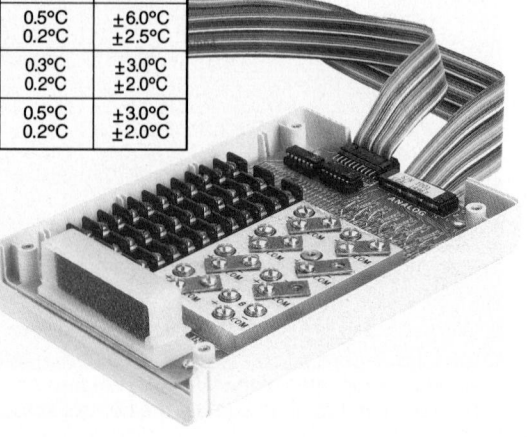

HIGH SPEED, HIGH RESOLUTION AND HALF SIZED CARDS FOR THE IBM PC

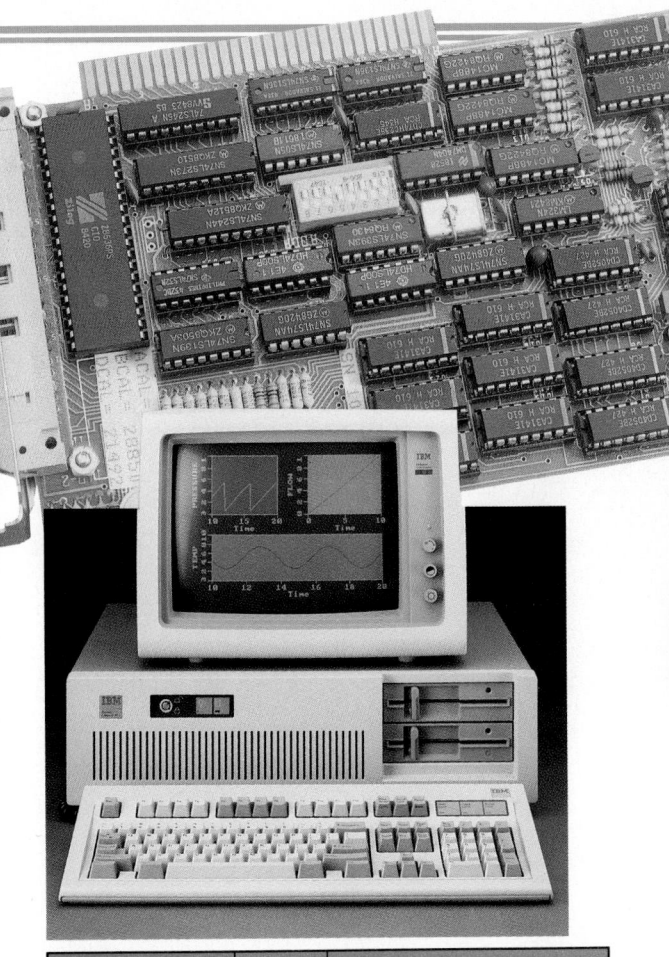

From **$745**

Model	WB-AAI High Resolution		WB-FAI High Speed	WB-ASC Short Card
Digital I/O	16 Channels		16 Channels	12 Channels
Scan Frequency	1 channel / 8 channels		1 channel / 8 channels	
Low Noise	60 Hz	7 Hz	60 Hz	7 Hz
16 bit, 0.0015%	225 Hz	25 Hz	—	—
15 bit, 0.003%	440 Hz	45 Hz	—	—
14 bit, 0.006%	830 Hz	80 Hz	—	—
13 bit, 0.012%	1500 Hz	120 Hz	—	—
12 bit, 0.024%	2500 Hz	160 Hz	2500 Hz	160 Hz
11 bit, 0.05%	—	—	5000 Hz	200 Hz
10 bit, 0.1%	—	—	7500 Hz	220 Hz
9 bit, 0.2%	—	—	10 KHz	240 Hz

*1Hz = 1 sample per second

Analog Ranges	WB-AAI			WB-FAI, WB-ASC		
	Resol.	Accuracy-larger of:		Resol.	Accuracy-larger of:	
		% range	% of rdg		% range	% of rdg
−5 to 50 mV	0.8 μV	0.04	—	12 μV	0.08	—
±25 mV	0.8 μV	0.08	—	12 μV	0.16	—
−50 to 500 mV	8 μV	0.01	0.05	120 μV	0.05	0.2
±250 mV	8 μV	0.01	0.05	120 μV	0.05	0.2
−1 to 10 V	150 μV	0.01	0.05	2.4 mV	0.05	0.2
−5 to 5 V	150 μV	0.01	0.10	2.4 mV	0.05	0.3
−0.2 to 2 mA*	0.03 μA	0.1	0.3	0.5 μA	0.2	0.5
−1 to 1 mA*	0.03 μA	0.1	0.3	0.5 μA	0.2	0.5
−2 to 20 mA*	0.3 μA	0.02	0.3	5 μA	0.1	0.5
±10 mA*	0.3 μA	0.02	0.3	5 μA	0.1	0.5
±50 mA*	6 μA	0.02	0.3	100 μA	0.1	0.5

*Requires user-supplied shunt resistor with WB-ASC

Thermocouple Type	Range	WB-AAI		WB-FAI, WB-ASC	
		Resol.	Accuracy	Resol.	Accuracy
J	− 80 to 100°C	0.02°C	± 0.9°C	0.3°C	± 1.6°C
	100 to 760°C	0.01°C	± 0.6°C	0.2°C	± 1.2°C
K	− 110 to 0°C	0.03°C	± 1.0°C	0.4°C	± 1.9°C
	0 to 1260°C	0.02°C	± 0.8°C	0.3°C	± 1.5°C
E	− 60 to 150°C	0.01°C	± 0.7°C	0.3°C	± 1.3°C
	150 to 680°C	0.01°C	± 0.5°C	0.2°C	± 1°C
T	− 120 to 0°C	0.03°C	± 1.2°C	0.4°C	± 2°C
	0 to 400°C	0.02°C	± 0.8°C	0.3°C	± 1.5°C
R	0 to 200°C	0.1°C	± 4.0°C	2°C	± 8°C
	200 to 1770°C	0.08°C	± 2.5°C	1°C	± 5°C
S	0 to 200°C	0.1°C	± 4.0°C	2°C	± 8°C
	200 to 1770°C	0.08°C	± 2.5°C	1°C	± 5°C
B	200 to 300°C	0.3°C	± 10°C	5°C	± 20°C
	300 to 500°C	0.2°C	± 6°C	3°C	± 12°C
	500 to 1000°C	0.1°C	± 4°C	2°C	± 8°C
	1000 to 1820°C	0.1°C	± 2.2°C	1°C	± 5°C
G	25 to 200°C	0.2°C	± 6°C	3°C	± 15°C
	200 to 2315°C	0.06°C	± 2.5°C	1°C	± 5°C
C	− 20 to 2315°C	0.06°C	± 3°C	1.5°C	± 5°C
	100 to 1500°C	0.05°C	± 2.0°C	1°C	± 3.5°C
D	− 20 to 2315°C	0.1°C	± 3°C	1.5°C	± 5°C
	150 to 1500°C	0.04°C	± 2.0°C	1°C	± 3.5°C

Model No.	Price	Description
WB-FAI-B8	$1190	12-bit resolution 8 input: T/C, mV, V, mA 8 digital I/O
WB-FAI-B16	1690	12-bit resolution 16 input: T/C, mV, V, mA 16 digital I/O
WB-AAI-B8	1690	16-bit resolution 8 input: T/C, mV, V, mA 8 digital I/O
WB-AAI-B16	2290	16-bit resolution 16 input: T/C, mV, V, mA 16 digital I/O
WB-ASC-GP	745	12-bit short card 8 input: mV, V 8 digital I/O
WB-ASC-TC	895	12-bit short card 8 input: T/C, mV, V 8 digital I/O
WB-ASC-RTD	780	12-bit short card 8 input: Pt RTD 8 digital I/O
SWD-LTN-2	995	Labtech Notebook Data Acquisition Software

Requires: IBM PC, XT, AT; 192K RAM; Color Graphics adaptor required for graphic displays.

WHITEBOX® ANALOG OUTPUT CARD
WITH APPLICATION AND DRIVER SOFTWARE FOR IBM PC/XT/AT

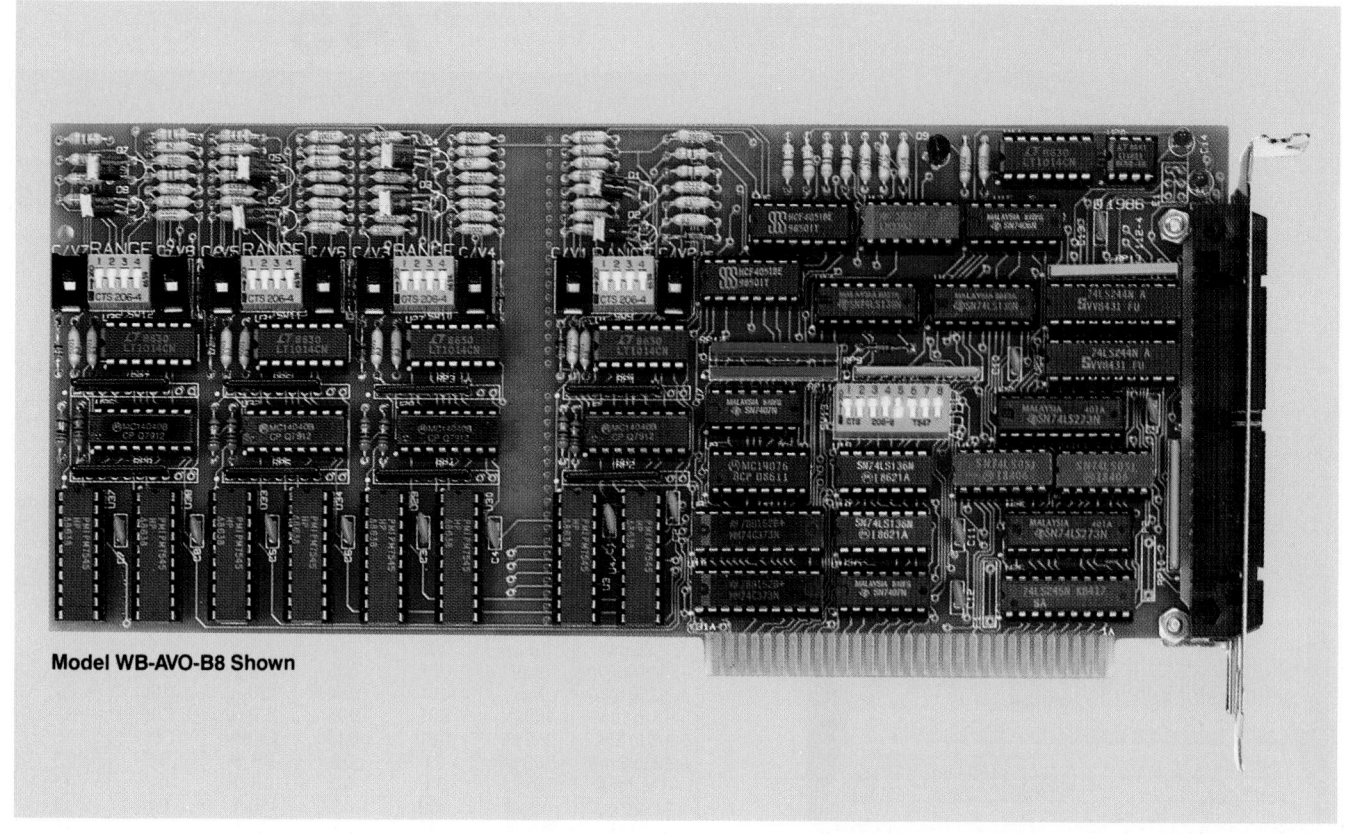

Model WB-AVO-B8 Shown

Model WB-AVO
From
$545
**Includes Terminal
Board and Cable**

- ✓ **Available with 2, 4, 6 or 8 Output Channels**
- ✓ **0 to 5 V, 0 to 10 V, −5 to 5 V and 4 to 20 mA Ranges**
- ✓ **Self Calibrating Design for High Accuracy and Stability with Low Noise and Drift**
- ✓ **8 Digital I/O Channels Individually Selected for Input or Output**
- ✓ **Includes Menu-Driven Data Acquisition and Control Software Along with Drivers for Advanced Programming**

The WB-AVO analog output card for the IBM PC turns your PC into an industrial controller, with the ability to control based upon time, digital I/O, or analog inputs from the WB-AAI/FAI/ASC interface cards. The WB-AVO is an integral portion of a complete data acquisition and control package, working together with other White Box interface cards under the same software; a complete system that's easy to install and operate. Menu-driven software is included which will allow open-loop control with ramp, step or soak capability. Closed-loop control is supported through additional software packages. (Consult Engineering.)

Model WB-AVO-B8

Model WB-AVO-B2

Specifications

GENERAL

Output Ranges: 0 to 5 V, 0 to 10 V, −5 to 5 V, 4 to 20 mA

Range Selection: by switches

No. of Outputs: 2, 4, 6 or 8 (depending on model)

Resolution: 12 bit; i.e. 1 part in 4096; 5000/4096 equals 1.22 mV resolution in the 0 to 5 V range

Speed: 130,000 outputs per s max. with standard IBM PC

Power Consumption: 2.6 watts max.

VOLTAGE OUTPUT

Mode Output Current: ±15 mA max.

Accuracy, including calibration: 0.02% (0 - 10 V range); 0.03% (0-5 V range); 0.07% (−5 to 5 V range)

Response Time: 2.5 µs

CURRENT OUTPUT MODE

Max. Output Voltage: 50 V

Min. Output Voltage: 2.6 V Accuracy, including calibration: 0.05%

Response Time: 2.5 µs

DIGITAL I/O

No./ of Channels: 8

Type: input or output, individually selected

Input Type: 0 to 5 V TTL level; direct interface to SSS series solid state switches

Output Level: 0 to 5 V TTL; direct interface to SSS series solid state switches

Included terminal board with screw terminal connections for analog outputs and digital I/O lines with mounting position for OMEGA solid state switches (optional).

INSTRUMENTATION

D

To Order *(Specify Model Number)*			
Model No.	Price	Analog Output Channels	Digital I/O Channels
WB-AVO-B2	$545	2	8
WB-AVO-B4	745	4	8
WB-AVO-B6	945	6	8
WB-AVO-B8	1145	8	8

8 CHANNEL ECONOMICAL HIGH SPEED
FOR IBM PC/XT/AT AND COMPATIBLES

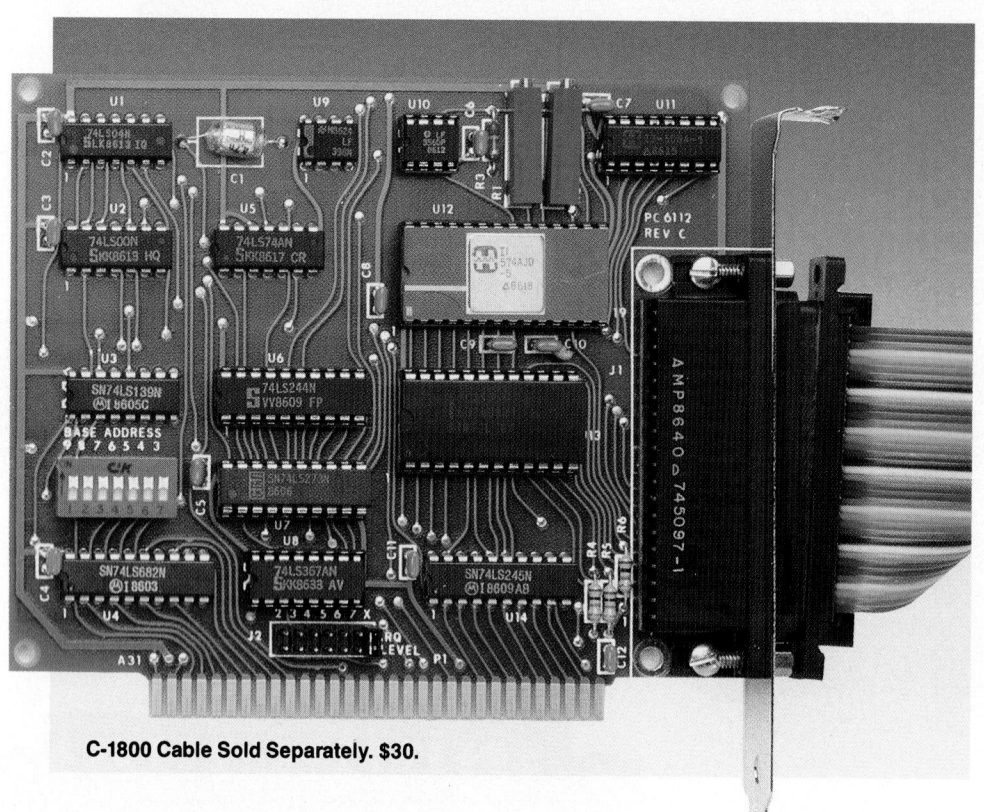

C-1800 Cable Sold Separately. $30.

Model DAS-8
$425
Includes Utility Software

- ✔ **8 Input Channels With 12 Bit Resolution**
- ✔ **4 Digital Outputs, 3 Digital Inputs**
- ✔ **Hardware Supports 30,000 Samples/s in Assembly Language**
- ✔ **Event, Period, Pulse Width and Frequency Counting**
- ✔ **Software Included: Graphics, Calibration, Linearization, Installation, I/O Driver**
- ✔ **Programmable Scan Rate**
- ✔ **Foreground/Background Operation**
- ✔ **Accessories Connect Via Screw Terminals and Expand to 128 Channels**

The DAS-8 is an 8 channel 12 bit high speed A/D converter and timer/counter board for the IBM PC and compatibles. For easy installation, all connections are made through a standard 37 pin D connector that projects through the rear of the computer.

To ensure versatility, the DAS-8 provides the following functions:

An 8 channel 12 bit successive approximation A/D converter with sample hold with full scale input of each channel of ±5 volts and a resolution of 2.4 mV. It features fail safe single ended inputs with a common ground that can withstand a continuous overload of ±30 V. A/D conversion time is typically 25 μS, and using the supplied software driver, through puts of up to 4000 samples/s are attainable. The hardware will support 30,000 samples/s in assembly language.

To Order *(Specify Model No.)*		
Model No.	**Price**	**Description**
DAS-8	$425	8-channel high speed acquisition board
STA-08	120	Screw terminal board; C-1800 needed
C-1800	30	18″ mating cable
EXP-16	399	Expansion multiplexer

A/D CONVERTER AND TIMER INTERFACE

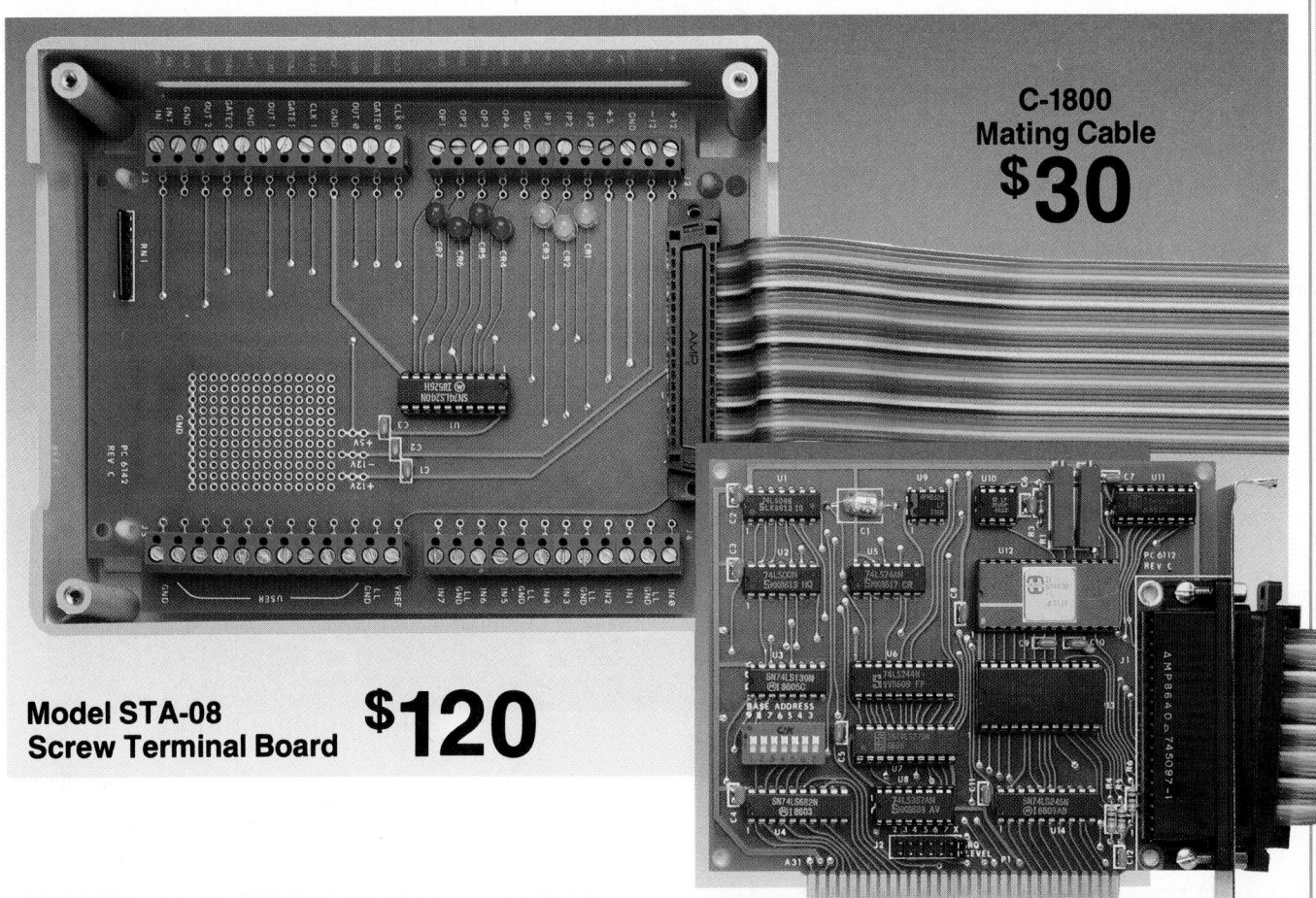

C-1800
Mating Cable
$30

**Model STA-08
Screw Terminal Board** **$120**

A programmable counter timer provides periodic interrupts for the A/D converter and can be additionally used for event counting, pulse and waveform generation, frequency, period and pulse width measurements. There are three separated down counters available; one is connected to a submultiple of the systems clock, and all I/O functions of the remaining two are accessible to the user. 7 bits of TTL digital I/O provided are composed of one output port of 4 bits and one input port of 3 bits. Each output will handle 5 standard TTL loads. One precision + 10.00V reference voltage is available on the board.

An external interrupt input is provided that is jumper selectable for any of the IBM P.C. interrupt levels 2-7 and allows interrupt routines to provide background data acquisition or interrupt driven control. IBM P.C,. buss power (+5, +12, −12) is provided along with all other I/O connections on the rear connector. This makes for simple addition of user designed interfaces, input conditioning circuits, expansion multiplexers etc.

Software

The following utility software is included at no additional expense with the DAS-8. It is contained on a a single sided PC-DOS 1.10 format 5¼″ floppy disc.

- ✔ A machine language I/O driver for control of A/D, timer and digital I/O channel functions via Basic Call.
- ✔ Transducer Linearization (including thermocouples)

- ✔ Initial setup and installation aids.
- ✔ Examples and demonstration programs.
- ✔ Graphics package for display of processed data.

Specifications
POWER CONSUMPTION
+5V Supply: 107 mA typ/80 mA max.
+12V Supply: 6 mA typ/10 mA max.
−12V Supply: 10 mA typ/16 mA max.

8 Analog Input Channels
Resolution: 12 bits (2.4 mV/bit)
Accuracy: 0.01% of reading ±1 bit
Full Scale: ±5 V
Overvoltage: to ±30V
Configuration: Single ended
Input current: 100 nA max at 25° C
Temp Coeff: Gain or F.S.; ±25 ppm/°C max. zero, ±10μV/°C max.

ENVIRONMENTAL
Operating temperature range: 0 to 50°C
Storage Temperature range: −20 to 70°C
Humidity: 0 to 90% non-condensing
Connector: 37 pin ''D'' type

16 CHANNEL HIGH SPEED A/D INTERFACES
FOR IBM PC/XT/AT AND COMPATIBLES

Model DAS-16
50,000 Samples Per Second

$999

Includes Utility Software

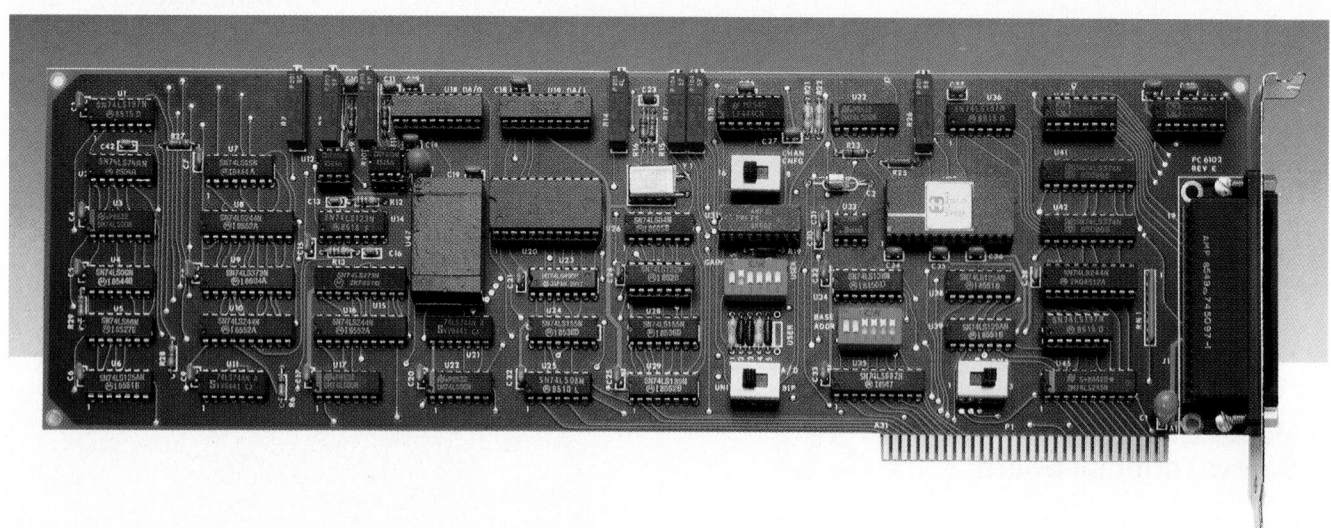

- ✔ **16 Single Ended/8 Differential Analog Input Channels**
- ✔ **DAS-16: 50,000 Samples Per Second A/D Throughput with DMA**
- ✔ **DAS-16F: 100,000 Samples Per Second A/D Throughput with DMA**
- ✔ **2 Channels of Multiplying 12 Bit D/A Output**
- ✔ **8 Digital I/O Output Lines (4 input, 4 output)**
- ✔ **Foreground/Background Operation**
- ✔ **Programmable Scan Rate**
- ✔ **Software Included: CALL Statement, Graphics, Linearization, Calibration, Set-Up and Example Programs**

The DAS-16 and DAS-16F are multifunction high speed analog/digital I/O expansion boards for the IBM Personal Computer that turns a PC into a a fast high precision data acquisition and signal analysis instrument. For complete versatility, the they can also be used in other bus compatible computers. Using state of the art data conversion components, the DAS-16 and DAS-16F have been designed to provide a powerful and inexpensive analog/digital interface on a full size slot board. Ideally suited to any application requiring high speed 12 bit data acquisition at the lowest possible cost both boards have the freedom from complexity and the mapped I/O mapped control make programming straightforward. The DAS-16 and DAS-16F implement the following functions: A 12 bit successive approximation converter with 12 μs conversion time for DAS-16, 8.5 μs for DAS-16F.

The channel input configuration is switch selectable on the board, providing a choice between 16 single ended channels or 8 differential channels with $\pm$10V common mode range. Throughput depends on the operating configuration.

WITH DIRECT MEMORY ACCESS (DMA)

Model DAS-16F
100,000 Samples Per Second

$1165

Includes Utility Software

C-1800 Cable Sold Separately. $30.

High input impedance ranges of +1V, +2V, +5V and +10V unipolar and ±0.5V, ±1V, ±2.5V, ±5V, and ±10V are switch selectable. 2 channels of multiplying 12 bit D/A output with 0 to 5 V available using −5V reference on board. Other outputs are available with an external dc source. A 3 channel programmable interval timer provides trigger pulses for the A/D at any rate from 250 KHz to 1 pulse/h. Digital I/O consists of 4 bits of TTL/DTL compatible digital output and 4 bits of digital input.

Software

The following utility software for DAS-16 is provided on a single sided PC-DOS 1.10 format 5¼″ floppy disc:

- ✔ A machine language driver for control of A/D, D/A, and digital I/O channel functions and data transfer modes via BASIC CALL.
- ✔ Programmable interval timer-setting pulse rate.
- ✔ Initial setup and installation aids.
- ✔ Graphical display of data versus time and x/y mode.
- ✔ Calibration and test programs.
- ✔ Examples and demonstration programs.
- ✔ Transducer linearization.

How To Order

Model No.	Price	Description
DAS-16	$ 999	High speed acquisition board
DAS-16F	1165	Very high speed acquisition board
STA-16	120	Screw terminal board; C-1800 needed
FOR-16	150	Fortran library
PCF-16G	149	Drivers for Microsoft Pascal, C and Fortran
STREAMER	275	High speed disk streaming software
EXP-16	399	Expansion sub-multiplexer; up to 16 channels for each DAS-16 channel; page D-29
C-1800	30	18″ 37-pin mating cable

INSTRUMENTATION

D

16 CHANNEL HIGH SPEED A/D INTERFACES
WITH DIRECT MEMORY ACCESS (DMA)

Model DAS-16
$999

Model DAS-16F
$1165

Model STA-16
Screw Terminal Board
$120

Specifications

POWER CONSUMPTION

+5V power: −800mA typ, 1A max.
+12V power: 2mA typ, 5 mA max.
−12V power: 20mA typ, 30mA max.

INSTRUMENTATION AMPLIFIER SWITCH

Selectable Gains: 0.5, 1, 2, 5, 10
Resolution Range: 0.244 mV to 4.88 mV/bit
Analog Inputs Switch Selectable: 16 single ended or 8 differential
Converter Type: 12-bit successive approximation
Conversion Time: 12 μs
Accuracy: 0.01% of reading, ±1 bit
Full Scale: ±10 volts
Input Current: 100 μA max at 25 °C
Temp Coeff.: Gain or F.S., ±25 ppm/°C max. zero, ± 10μV/°C max.

ANALOG OUTPUTS
2 ea 12 bit multiplying D/A (unipolar)

Voltage Ranges: 0 to +5V with reference supply (+10 V with external reference)
Maximum Load Current: 5 mA
Digital Inputs: 4 bits (one port, TTL compatible)
Digital Outputs: 4 bits (one port, TTL compatible)

ENVIRONMENTAL

Operating Temperature Range: 0 to 50°C
Storage Temperature Range: −20 to 70°C
Humidity: 0 to 90% non-condensing
Connection: Requires full size slot. Standard 37-pin ''D'' type male connector

Operating Mode	Throughput (Conversions/s)
Program transfer to simple variable	Up to 200
Program transfer to array variable	Up to 4000
Interrupt driven driven transfer	Up to 4000
DMA transfer on scan of channels	Up to 50,000 (100,000 for DAS-16F)
DMA transfer on single channel	Up to 50,000 (100,000 for DAS-16F)

RESISTANCE MEASUREMENT ACCESSORY BOARD

NEW!

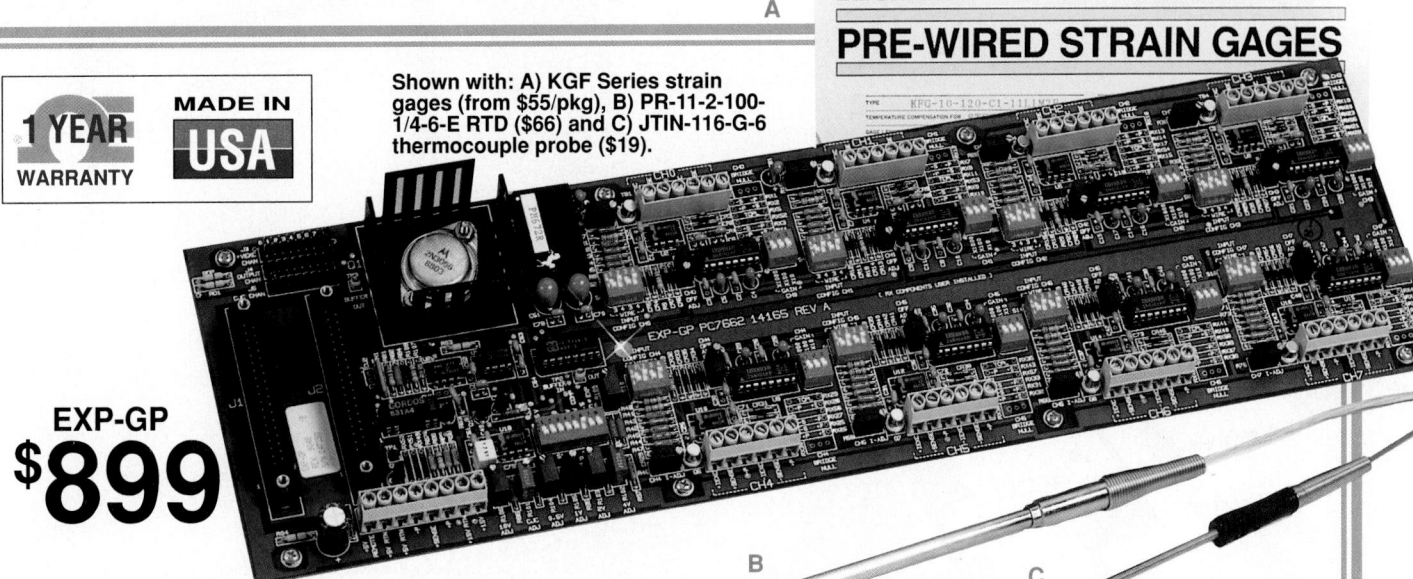

1 YEAR WARRANTY

MADE IN USA

Shown with: A) KGF Series strain gages (from $55/pkg), B) PR-11-2-100-1/4-6-E RTD ($66) and C) JTIN-116-G-6 thermocouple probe ($19).

ΩOMEGA
PRE-WIRED STRAIN GAGES

EXP-GP
$899

- ✔ **Allows Up to 64 Input Channels to Be Monitored By a Single A/D Board (With the Use of 8 EXP-GP Boards)**
- ✔ **Interface to RTD's, Thermistors, Strain Gages and a Wide Variety of Other Variable Resistance Sensors**
- ✔ **Provides Thermocouple Cold-Junction Compensation Circuitry**

The EXP-GP is ideally suited for measurement of devices which are typically operated in current excitation mode or in standard bridge configurations. Sensors in these categories include 2, 3, or 4 wire RTDs, thermistors, strain gages, variable potentiometer devices, and many, many other sensors. In addition, the EXP-GP has been designed with all cold-junction compensation circuitry required for accurate thermocouple measurements.

The EXP-GP accepts up to 8 input sensors, and multiplexes the inputs into a single A/D board channel. Each EXP-GP input channel includes a fully differential input amplifier with jumper selectable input gains of 1, 2.5, 10, 25, 100, 250, 1,000 and 2,500. Also included for each input channel is a 1 mA precision current source and a 0.50, 1.00, 2.00, 4.00, or 10.00 V (switch selectable) precision reference voltage (for voltage excited sensor types). A +15 Vdc external source is required for voltage excitation.

When used for bridge measurements, the EXP-GP allows the bridge completion resistors to be mounted either on or off the board. The EXP-GP provides thermocouple cold-junction compensation circuitry that measures the actual input terminal temperature and allows linearization software to subtract out the CJ error.

SPECIFICATIONS
Gains: Switch selectable gains of 1, 10, 100 and 1000 or 2.5, 25, 250 and 2500
Accepts Thermocouple Types: J, K, T, E, S, R, B
Cold-Junction Compensation: +24.4 mV/°C (0.1°C/bit)
Max. Settling Time: 4μ sec
OVERVOLTAGE PROTECTION
Common Model Voltage: ±50V continuous
MEASUREMENT EXCITATION CURRENT SOURCES
Number: 8
Excitation Current: 1 mA
Compliance: 0 to 2 V

MEASUREMENT VOLTAGE EXCITATION (requires external +15 Vdc source)
Values of 0.5, 1.0, 2.0, 4.0 and 10.0 V (Trimmable)
Current: 350 mA (current limited)
Power: +5 Vdc @ 380 mA max
Dimensions: 16" x 4.75" (406 x 121 mm)
Screw Terminals: accept wire sizes 12-22 AWG
Operating Temperature Range: 32 to 140°F (0 to 60°C)
Storage Temperature Range: -40 to 212°F (-40 to +100°C)
Relative Humidity: 0 to 90%, non-condensing

To Order *(Specify Model No.)*

Model No.	Price	Description
EXP-GP	$899	Resistance measurement accessory board
C-1800	30	DAS-8 Interconnect cable
S-1600	30	DAS-16 Interconnect cable
CEXP-2000	30	DAS-20 Interconnect cable

Comes with complete operator's manual.
Ordering Example: *EXP-GP resistance measurement accessory board ($899) plus C-1800 cable to connect to DAS-8 ($30), $899 + 30 = **$929**.*

INSTRUMENTATION

D

See Secion B of the OMEGA Complete Data Acquisition and Computer Interface Handbook and Encyclopedia®.

- ✔ **Cards with Either 12 or 16-Bit A/D Resolution**
- ✔ **Software Selected Input Types and Ranges for Each Channel**
- ✔ **Built-In Thermocouple Compensation and RTD Linearization**
- ✔ **Individual Selection of Digital Lines as Input/Output**

The White Box® plug in cards for the Macintosh SE and Macintosh II computers are high performance data acquisition boards, with either 12 or 16 bit A/D resolution. For the Mac II, three models are available; the model 8 features 8 analog inputs and 8 digital I/O lines; the model 8A adds two analog outputs; the model 16 features 16 analog inputs and 16 digital I/O lines. Two models for the Mac SE are available, featuring 8 analog inputs and 8 digital I/O lines, with either 12 or 16 bit A/D resolution.

The 12 bit cards feature dynamic resolution, where resolution actually increases as the input level decreases, resulting in 12-bit resolution all the way down to 1/10 of full scale. These cards are also capable of data storage at up to 10,000 samples per second. Both the 12 and 16 bit cards feature low-noise integrating A/D converters, this allows sampling at 1/60 second with 60 Hz noise rejection.

The White Box Macintosh® cards are designed to measure voltage, thermocouples and RTD sensors, depending on the terminal board installed with the card. Three different terminal boards are available, designed for different input types. The WB-T21 terminal board is designed for precision thermocouple and general purpose

use. It features terminals for 8 differential analog inputs and 8 digital I/O lines; an isothermal plate with an integral cold junction sensor, provides the highest accuracy possible with a plug-in acquisition system. The WB-T51 terminal board is a general purpose panel for use with all input types. It has terminals for 8 differential analog inputs, 8 digital I/O lines, and 2 analog output lines (on cards so equipped). Cold junction sensing for thermocouples is provided, without the high accuracy isothermal plate. This panel also has room for up to 8 optically isolated I/O modules (see the SSS series solid state switches, section H). For use with current inputs, a section of the board has room for a current shunt resistor. The third panel, model WB-T55, is designed specifically for RTD inputs. The WB-T55 is similar to the WB-T51, with current sources available for RTD excitation. Two models are available, with the appropriate resistors installed to give ranges of

PLUG-IN INTERFACES
FOR MACINTOSH® SE AND MACINTOSH® II

System Requirements

Macintosh® SE or Macintosh® II computer, any configuration; plug-in acquisition board; two terminal boxes for WB-FAI-M2-16 and WB-AAI-M2-16 cards, one terminal box for all other models

MADE IN USA

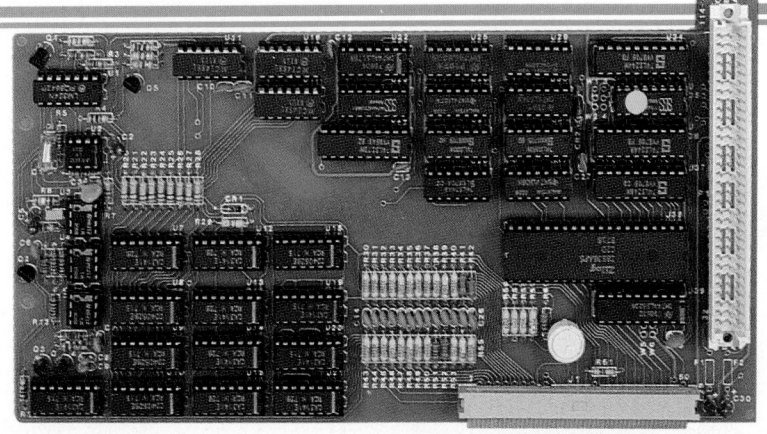
For Macintosh SE

For Macintosh II

−200 to 750°C and −200 to 850°C, respectively.

Data acquisition, logging and display software is included with each model. Omegalog™ software is built around the Macintosh®interface to provide fast, easy data acquisition. Omegalog™ uses icons and pull down menus for truly intuitive operation, with a design for both novices and hackers.

For more sophisticated requirements, Omegabench™ software, with its sophisticated data acquisition and control capabilities, can be used by both first time and advanced users with capabilities never before possible.

To maintain specified accuracies, the boards and the T21 terminal boxes must be calibrated together and ordered as a system. To do this add "-TC" to the board part number and the price of the terminal box to the board.
Example: *WB-FAI-SE-TC, 695 + 300 = $995, gives a WB-FAI-SE card and T21 terminal box.*
Example: *WB-AAI-M2-16-TC, 1845 + 300 + 300 = $2445, gives a WB-AAI-M2-16 card and two T21 Terminal boxes.*

To Order *(Specify Model Number)*

Model No.	Price	Computer	A/D Resolution (bits)	Analog Input Channels	Analog Output Channel
WB-FAI-SE-8A	$ 695	Mac SE	12	8	—
WB-AAI-SE	1145	Mac SE	16	8	—
WB-FAI-M2-8	795	Mac II	12	8	—
WB-FAI-M2-8A	1190	Mac II	12	8	2
WB-FAI-M2-16	1145	Mac II	12	16	—
WB-AAI-M2-8	1490	Mac II	16	8	—
WB-AAI-M2-8A	1790	Mac II	16	8	2
WB-AAI-M2-16	1845	Mac II	16	16	—
SWD-WBM-A	995	WorkBench software for the Macintosh			

Terminal Board Model No.	Price	Description
WB-T21	$300	thermocouple panel
WB-T51	179	8-channel general purpose panel
WB-T55-050	214	RTD panel, − 200 to 750°C range
WB-T55-100	214	RTD panel, − 200 to 850°C range

INSTRUMENTATION D

WHITE BOX® MACINTOSH®
DATA ACQUISTION BOARDS

Model WB-T21

Model WB-T51

Macintosh SE

MADE IN
USA

Terminal Box Enclosure Model No.	Price	Compatible Interface	Input Types
WB-T11	$300	WB-AAI-B WB-FAI-B WB-AIO	thermocouple/general purpose (included with card) for IBM PC version
WB-T21	300	WB-ASC-TC All Macintosh Cards	thermocouple/general purpose (included with WB-ASC-TC)
WB-T31	179	WB-ASC-GP WB-AVO-B	general purpose (included with card)
WB-T35-050	214	WB-ASC	RTD, −200 to 750°C range
WB-T35-100	214	WB-ASC	RTD, −200 to 850°C range
WB-T41	179	WB-AAI-B	general purpose
		WB-FAI-B WB-AIO	(included with card)
WB-T51	179	All Macintosh cards	general purpose
WB-T45-050	214	WB-AAI-B WB-FAI-B	RTD, −200 to 750°F range RTD, −200 to 850°F range
WB-T55-050	214	All Macintosh Cards	RTD, −200 to 750°C range
WB-T55-100	214	All Macintosh Cards	RTD, −200 to 850°C range

Specifications

Analog Inputs: 8 or 16 differential, depending on model

Resolution: 12 bit dynamic, or 16 bit, depending on model

Analog Input Ranges: ±25 mV, 50 mV, 500 mV, 5 V, 10 V, autorange; software selectable

Input Types: types and ranges are software selectable for each channel

Thermocouple Types: J, K, T, E, R, S, B, G, D

RTD Types: Platinum, 50 to 1000 ohms, 0.00385 or 0.00392

Speed: 10,000 samples per secord

Noise: low-noise integrating A/D converter with 2 μV noise; can sample at 1/60 s to reject 60 Hz noise

Input Protection: 50 V continuous, 150 V momentary

Input Impedance: > 1000 Mohm for 25 and 50 mV ranges; 200 Kohm for all other ranges

Digital I/O: 8 lines, individually configured as input or output; 5 V TTL compatible

Type	12 BIT RESOLUTION BOARDS			16 BIT RESOLUTION BOARDS		
	Range	Resolution	Accuray	Range	Resolution	Accuracy
J	−210 to −100°C −100 to 0°C 0 to 880°C	0.1-0.3°C 0.05°C 0.05-0.2°C	2.3°C 1.2°C 1.0°C	−210 to −100°C −100 to 100°C 100 to 880°C	0.02-0.04°C 0.02°C 0.01°C	1.2°C 0.7°C 0.5°C
K	−250 to −75°C −75 to 1260°C 0 to 900°C	0.15-1°C 0.07-0.3°C 0.06-0.2°C	8°C 1.4°C 1.2°C	−250 to 150°C −150 to −50°C −50 to 1260°C	0.03-0.15°C 0.03°C 0.02°C	4°C 1.0°C 0.7°C
E	−250 to −70°C −70 to 100°C 100 to 680°C	0.1-0.5°C 0.04°C 0.04-0.15°C	4°C 1.0°C 0.8°C	−250 to −100°C −100 to 200°C 200 to 680°C	0.08-0.01°C 0.01°C 0.01°C	2°C 0.6°C 0.4°C
T	−250 to −50°C −50 to 10°C 10 to 150°C 150 to 400°C	0.15-0.8°C 0.06°C 0.06°C 0.06-0.1°C	6°C 1.4°C 1.2°C 1.0°C	−250 to −120°C −120 to −25°C −25 to 200°C 200 to 400°C	0.03-0.1°C 0.02-0.03°C 0.01-0.02°C 0.01°C	3°C 0.9°C 0.7°C 0.5°C
S	−50 to 120°C 120 to 380°C 380 to 1770°C	0.4°C 0.3°C 0.2-0.6°C	10°C 5°C 4°C	−50 to 50°C 50 to 300°C 300 to 1770°C	0.1-0.2°C 0.1°C 0.08°C	5°C 3°C 2°C
R	−50 to 250°C 250 to 800°C 800 to 1770°C	0.2-0.4°C 0.2°C 0.2-0.4°C	10°C 4°C 3°C	−50 to 25°C 25 to 200°C 200 to 1770°C	0.1-0.2°C 0.1°C 0.08°C	5°C 3°C 2°C
B	200 to 300°C 300 to 500°C 500 to 1000°C 1000 to 1820°C	0.7-1°C 0.4-0.7°C 0.2-0.4°C 0.2-0.4°C	20°C 13°C 8°C 4°C	200 to 300°C 300 to 500°C 500 to 1000°C 1000 to 1820°C	0.25-0.4°C 0.15-0.25°C 0.08-0.15 0.08°C	10°C 6°C 4°C 2°C
G	25 to 200°C 200 to 2315°C	0.2-1°C 0.15-0.8°C	15°C 4°C	25 to 200°C 200 to 2315°C	0.08-0.3°C 0.08°C	8°C 2°C
D	−20 to 2315°C 150 to 2000°C	0.2-1°C 0.15-0.6°C	4°C 3°C	−20 to 2315°C 300 to 1500°C	0.4-0.08°C 0.04°C	2°C 1.3°C
C	−20 to 2315°C 100 to 1500°C	0.15-1°C 0.15-0.4°C	4°C 3°C	−20 to 2315°C 100 to 1500°C	0.04-0.08°C 0.05°C	2°C 1.5°C

Resolution & Accuracy	12-Bit Resolution Boards					16-Bit Resolution Boards				
		Accuracy–Larger of			Internal		Accuracy–Larger of			Internal
Range	Resolution	% Range	% Rdg.	CMRR	Noise	Resolution	% Range	% Rdg.	CMMR	Noise
− 5 to 50 mV	12μV	0.08	—	110 dB	2 μV	0.8 μV	0.04	—	110 dB	1μV
− 25 to 25 mV	12 μV	0.16	—	>100 dB	2 μV	0.8 μV	0.08	—	>100 dB	1 μV
− 50 to 500 mV	120 μV	0.05	0.2	>85 dB	10 μV	8 μV	0.01	0.05	>85 dB	5 μV
− 250 to 250 mV	120 μV	0.05	0.2	>75 dB	10 μV	8 μV	0.01	0.05	>75 dB	5 μV
− 1 to 10 V	2.4 mV	0.05	0.2	>60 dB	200 μV	150 μV	0.01	0.05	>60 dB	100 μV
− 5 to 5 V	2.4 mV	0.05	0.2	>50 dB	100 μV	150 μV	0.01	0.1	>50 dB	100 μV

Resolution and Scan Times	Resolution	Scan Rate One Channel	Scan Rate Multi-Channels	Resolution	Scan Rate One Channel	Scan Rate Multi-Channels
	low noise mode	60 Hz	60 Hz	low noise mode	60 Hz	60 Hz
	12 bit, 0.024%	2500 Hz	2000 Hz	16 bit, 0.0015%	225 Hz	200 Hz
	11 bit, 0.05%	5000 Hz	2000 Hz	15 bit, 0.003%	440 Hz	360 Hz
	10 bit, 0.1%	7500 Hz	2300 Hz	14 bit, 0.006%	830 Hz	640 Hz
	9 bit, 0.2%	10,000 Hz	2400 Hz	13 bit, 0.012%	1500 Hz	960 Hz
				12 bit, 0.024%	2500 Hz	1300 Hz

OMEGA®

OMEGA® STRAIN GAGES, ACCESSORIES AND INSTRUMENTATION

Selection Guide		E-3 to E-6
Strain Gages with 1 Measuring Grid		E-7 to E-10
Strain Gages with 2 Measuring Grids		E-11
Strain Gages with 3 Measuring Grids		E-13 to E-15
Crack and Diaphragm Strain Gages		E-16
Terminal Pads, Adhesives and Bridge Completion Resistors		E-17
Protective Coverings for Strain Gages		E-18
Application Kits for Strain Gages and Accessories		E-19
Strain Gage Wire		E-20
Portable Strain Gage Indicators		E-21
Amplifiers, Meters, Computer Cards		E-23 to E-30
Strain Gage Principles		E-31 to E-58

STRAIN GAGES **E**

STRAIN GAGE TECHNICAL DATA

Strain Gage Measurement

The most universal measuring device for the electrical measurement of mechanical quantities is the strain gage. Several types of strain gages depend on the proportional variance of electrical resistance to strain: the piezoresistive or semi-conductor gage, the carbon-resistive gage, the bonded metallic wire, and foil resistance gages.

The bonded resistance strain gage is by far the most widely used in experimental stress analysis. These gages consist of a grid of very fine wire or foil bonded to the backing or carrier matrix. The electrical resistance of the grid varies linearly with strain. In use, the carrier matrix is bonded to the surface, force is applied, and the strain is found by measuring the change in resistance. The bonded resistance strain gage is low in cost, can be made with a short gage length, is only moderately affected by temperature changes, has small physical size and low mass, and has fairly high sensitivity to strain.

In a strain gage application, the carrier matrix and the adhesive must work together to transmit the strains from the specimen to the grid. In addition, they serve as an electrical insulator and heat dissipator.

The three primary factors influencing gage selection are operating temperature, state of strain (gradient, magnitude, and time dependence) and stability required.

Because of its outstanding sensitivity, the Wheatstone bridge circuit is the most frequently used circuit for static strain measurements. Ideally, the strain gage is the only resistor in the circuit that varies and then only due to a change in strain on the surface.

There are two main methods used to indicate the change in resistance caused by strain on a gage in a Wheatstone bridge. Often, an indicator will rebalance the bridge, displaying the change in resistance required in micro-strain. The second method installs an indicator, calibrated in micro-strain, that responds to the voltage output of the

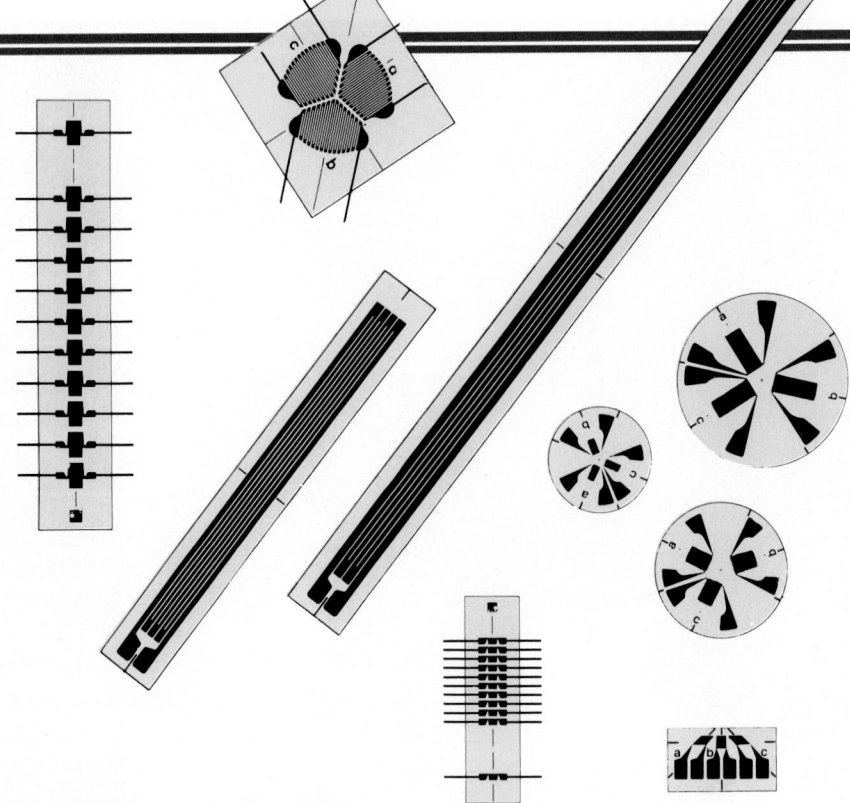

bridge. This method assumes a linear relationship between voltage out and strain, an initially balanced bridge, and a known V in. In reality, the V out–strain relationship is nonlinear, but for strains up to a few thousand micro-strain, the error is not significant.

Potential Error Sources

In a stress analysis application, the entire gage installation cannot be calibrated as can some pressure transducers. Therefore, it is important to examine potential error sources prior to taking data.

Some gages may be damaged during installation. It is important therefore to check the resistance of the strain gage prior to stress.

Electrical noise and interference may alter your readings. Shielded leads and adequately insulating coatings may prevent these problems. A value of less than 500 M ohms (using an ohmmeter) usually indicates surface contamination.

Thermally induced voltages are caused by thermocouple effects at the junction of dissimilar metals within the measurement circuit. Magnetically induced voltages may occur when the wiring is located in a time varying magnetic field.

Magnetic induction can be controlled by using twisted lead wires and forming minimum but equal loop areas in each side of the bridge.

Temperature effects on gage resistance and gage factor should be compensated for as well. This may require measurement of temperature at the gage itself, using thermocouples, thermistors, or RTD's. Most metallic gage alloys, however, exhibit a nearly linear gage factor variation with temperature over a broad range which is less than ±1% within ±100°C.

Prime Strain Gage Selection Considerations

- Gage Length
- Number of Gages in Gage Pattern
- Arrangement of Gages in Gage Pattern
- Grid Resistance
- Strain Sensitive Alloy
- Carrier Material
- Gage Width
- Solder Tab Type
- Configuration of Solder Tab
- Availability

THE STRAIN GAGE IS ONE OF THE MOST IMPORTANT TOOLS of the electrical measurement technique applied to the measurement of mechanical quantities. As their name indicates, they are used for the measurement of strain. As a technical term "strain" comprises of tensile and compressive strain, distinguished by a positive or negative sign. Thus, strain gages can be used to pick up expansion as well as contraction.

The strain of a body is always caused by an external influence or an internal effect. Strain might be caused by forces, pressures, moments, heat, structural changes of the material and the like. If certain conditions are fulfilled, the amount or the value of the influencing quantity can be derived from the measured strain value. In experimental stress analysis this feature is widely used. Experimental stress analysis uses the strain values measured on the surface of a specimen or structural part to state the stress in the material and also to predict its safety and endurance. Special transducers can be designed for the measurement of forces or other derived quantities, e.g., moments, pressures, accelerations, and displacements, vibrations and others. The transducer generally contains a pressure sensitive diaphragm with strain gages bonded to it.

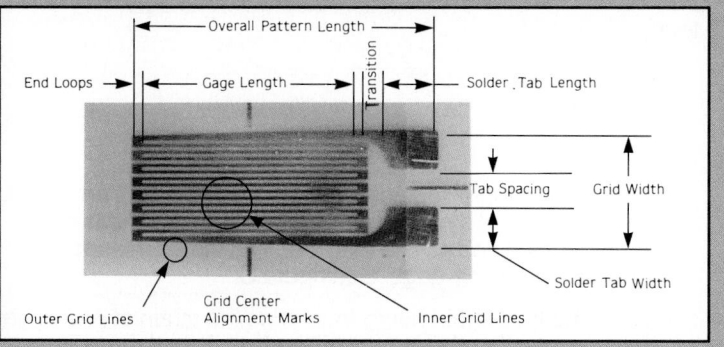

Strain gage dimensions

The active grid length, in the case of foil gages, is the net grid length without the tabs and comprises the return loops of the wire gages.

The carrier dimensions are designed by OMEGA for the optimum function of the strain gage.

Strain gage resistance

The resistance of a strain gage is defined as the electrical resistance measured between the two metal ribbons or contact areas intended for the connection of measurement cables. The range comprises strain gages with a nominal resistance of 120, 350, 600, and 700 Ohms.

Gage factor (strain sensitivity)

The strain sensitivity k of a strain gage is the proportionality factor between the relative change of the resistance.

The strain sensitivity is a figure without dimension and is generally called gage factor.

The gage factor of each production lot is determined by sample measurements and is given on each package as the nominal value with its tolerance.

Reference temperature

The reference temperature is the ambient temperature for which the technical data of the strain gages are valid, unless temperature ranges are given.

The technical data quoted for strain gages are based on a reference temperature of 23°C.

Temperature characteristic

Temperature dependent changes of the specific strain gage grid resistance occur in the applied gage owing to the linear thermal expansion coefficients of the grid and specimen materials. These resistance changes appear to be mechanical strain in the specimen. The representation of the apparent strain as a function of temperature is called the temperature characteristic of the strain gage application.

In order to keep apparent strain through temperature changes as small as possible, each strain gage is matched during the production to a certain linear thermal expansion coefficient. OMEGA offers strain gages with temperature characteristics matched to ferritic steel and aluminum.

Service temperature range

The service temperature range is the range of ambient temperature where the use of the strain gages is permitted without permanent changes of the measurement properties. Service temperature ranges are different whether static or dynamic values are to be sensed.

Maximum permitted rms bridge energizing voltage

The maximum values quoted are only permitted for appropriate application on materials with good heat conduction (e.g., steel of sufficient thickness) if room temperature is not exceeded. In other cases temperature rise in the measuring grid area may lead to measurement errors. Measurements on plastics and other materials with bad heat conduction require the reduction of the energizing voltage or the duty cycle (pulsed operation).

POSITIONING STRAIN GAGES TO MONITOR BENDING, AXIAL, SHEAR, AND TORSIONAL LOADS

In the glossary of the Pressure Reference Section strain is defined as; The ratio of the change in length to the initial unstressed reference length. A strain gage is the element that senses this change and converts it into an electrical signal. This can be accomplished due to the fact that a strain gage changes resistance as it is stretched or compressed, similar to wire. For example, when wire is stretched its cross sectional area decreases, therefore it increases resistance.

The important factors that must be considered before selecting a strain gage are the direction, type, and resolution of strain you wish to measure.

To measure minute strains the user must be capable of measuring minute resistance changes. The Wheatstone Bridge configuration as shown in figure B. is capable of measuring these small resistance changes Note the signs associated with each gage numbered 1 through 4. The total strain is always the sum of the four strains.

$$\epsilon_T = \epsilon_1 - \epsilon_2 + \epsilon_3 - \epsilon_4$$

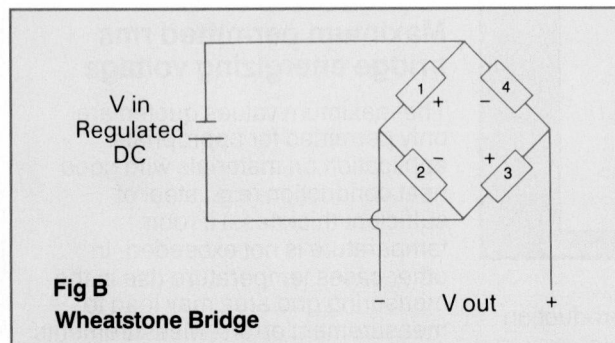

Fig B
Wheatstone Bridge

The total strain is represented by a change in V out. If each gage had the same positive strain, the total would be zero and V out would remain unchanged. Bending, Axial, and Shear strain make up the most common types of strain measurements. The actual arrangement of the strain gages will determine the type of strain measured and the output voltage change. See figures C through F.

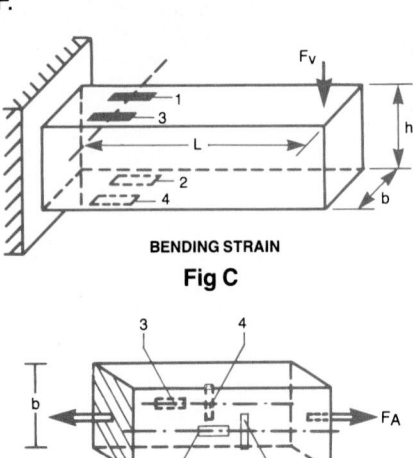

BENDING STRAIN
Fig C

AXIAL STRAIN
Fig D

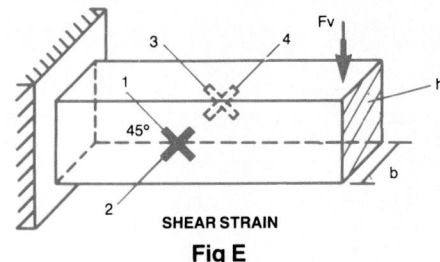

SHEAR STRAIN
Fig E

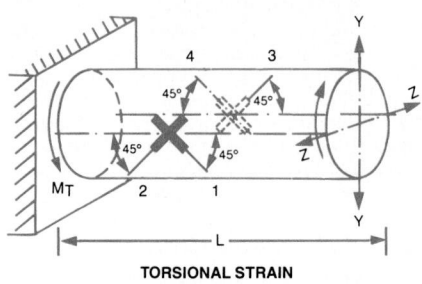

TORSIONAL STRAIN
Fig F

For example, if a positive (tensile) strain was on gages 1 and 3, and a negative (compressive) strain was on gages 2 and 4. The total strain would be 4 times the strain on one gage. See figure C.

The total strain being four times the strain of one gage, means that the output will be four times larger. Therefore greater sensitivity and resolution occures when more than one strain gage is used.

The following equations show the relationships between stress, strain, and force for bending, axing, shear, and torsional strain.

1) BENDING STRAIN or moment strain is equal to bending stress divided by Young's Modulus of Elasticity.

$$\epsilon_B = o_B/E \qquad o_B = M_B/Z = F\nu\,(\ell)/Z$$

Moment stress (o_B) equals bending moment ($F\nu \times \ell$) divided by sectional modulus. Sectional modulus (z) is a property of the cross sectional configuration of the specimen. For rectangles only, the sectional modulus is ($bh^2/6$). Strain gages used in the bending strain configuration can be used to determine vertical load ($F\nu$), more commonly referred to as a bending beam load cell.

$$F_\nu = E\,\epsilon_B\,(Z)/\ell = E\,\epsilon_B\,(bh^2/_6)/\ell$$

2) AXIAL STRAIN equals axial stress divided by Youngs Modulus.

$$\epsilon_A = o_A/E \qquad o_A = F_A/A$$

Where axial stress (o_A) equals the axial load divided by the cross sectional area. The cross sectional area for rectangles equals (b x d). Therefore strain gages used in axial configurations can be used to determine axial loads (F (axial)).

$$F\,(axial) = E\,\epsilon_A bh$$

3) SHEAR STRAIN equals shear stress divided by modulus of shear stress.

$$\gamma = \tau/G \qquad \tau = F\nu \times Q/bI$$

Where shear stress (τ) equals (Q), the moment of area about the neutral axis multiplied by the vertical load ($F\nu$) divided by the thickness (b) and the moment of inertia (I). Both the moment of area (Q) and the moment of inertia (I) are functions of the specimens cross sectional geometry.

For rectangles only $Q = bh^2/8$ and $I = bh^3/12$

The shear strain (γ) is determined by measuring the strain at 45° angle as shown in Figure E.

$$\gamma = 2 \times \epsilon_{@\ 45°}.$$

The modulus of shear strain (G) = $E/2 (1 + \mu)$. Therefore, strain gages used in a shear strain configuration can be used to determine vertical loads ($F\nu$), more commonly referred to as a shear beam load cell.

$$F\nu = G\ (\gamma)\ bI/Q = G\ (\gamma)\ b\ (bh^3/12)/(bh^2/8) = G\ (\gamma)bh(2/3)$$

4) TORSIONAL STRAIN equals torsional stress (τ) divided by torsional modulus of elasticity (G). See figure F.

$$\gamma = 2 \times \epsilon_{@}\ 45° = \tau/G \qquad \tau = M_t\ (d/2)/J$$

Where torsional stress (τ) equals the torque (M_t) multiplied by the distance from the center of section to outer fiber (d/2), divdied by (J), the polar moment of inertia. The polar moment of inertia is a function of the cross sectional area. For solid circular shafts only ($J = \pi\ (d)^4/64$). The modulus of shear strain (G) has been defined in the preceeding discussion on shear stress. Strain gages can be used to determine torsional moments as shown in the equation below. This represents the principle behind every torque sensor.

$$M_t = \tau\ (J)\ (2/d) = \gamma\ G\ (J)\ (2/d) = \gamma\ G\ (\pi\ d^3/16)$$
$$\varnothing = M_T\ L/G\ (J)$$

STRAIN		BRIDGE TYPE	POSITION OF GAGES Figs. C-F	SENSITIVITY mV/V @ 1000$\mu\epsilon$	OUTPUT PER $\mu\epsilon$ @ 10V EXCITATION	TEMP. COMP.	SUPERIMPOSED STRAIN COMPENSATED
BENDING		¼	1	0.5	5μV/$\mu\epsilon$	No	None
		½	1,2	1.0	10μV/$\mu\epsilon$	Yes	Axial
		Full	All	2.0	20μV/$\mu\epsilon$	Yes	Axial
AXIAL		¼	1	0.5	5μV/$\mu\epsilon$	No	None
		½	1,2	0.65	6.5μV/$\mu\epsilon$	Yes	None
		½	1,3	1.0	10μV/$\mu\epsilon$	No	Bending
		Full	All	1.3	13μV/$\mu\epsilon$	Yes	Bending
SHEAR & TORSIONAL		½	1,2	1.0	10μV/$\mu\epsilon$ @ 45°F	Yes	Axial and Bending
		Full	All	2.0	20μV/$\mu\epsilon$ @ 45°F	Yes	Axial and Bending

Note: Shear and Torsional strain = 2 x ϵ @ 45°

The following table shows how bridge configuration affects output, temperature compensation, and compensation of superimposed strains. This table was based on using a gage factor of 2.0, Poisson's Ratio of 0.3, and disregards the lead wire resistance. This chart is quite useful in determining a required meter sensitivity to read strain values.

Temperature compensation is achieved in many of the above configurations. Temperature compensation means that the gages thermal expansion coefficient does not have to match the specimens thermal expansion coefficient, therefore, any OMEGA strain gage regardless of temperature characteristic can be used with any specimen material. ¼ bridges can have temperature compensation if a dummy gage is used. A dummy gage is a strain gage used in place of a fixed resistor. When this dummy gage is mounted on a small piece of material (same as specimen's) which undergoes temperature changes (same as specimen's) but not strain. Strain temperature compensation is not load (stress) temperature compensation. Strain temperature compensation does not mean load or stress temperature compensation, because Young's Modulus of Elasticity varies with temperature.

STRAIN GAGES

E

OMEGA® STRAIN GAGES
SPECIFICATIONS

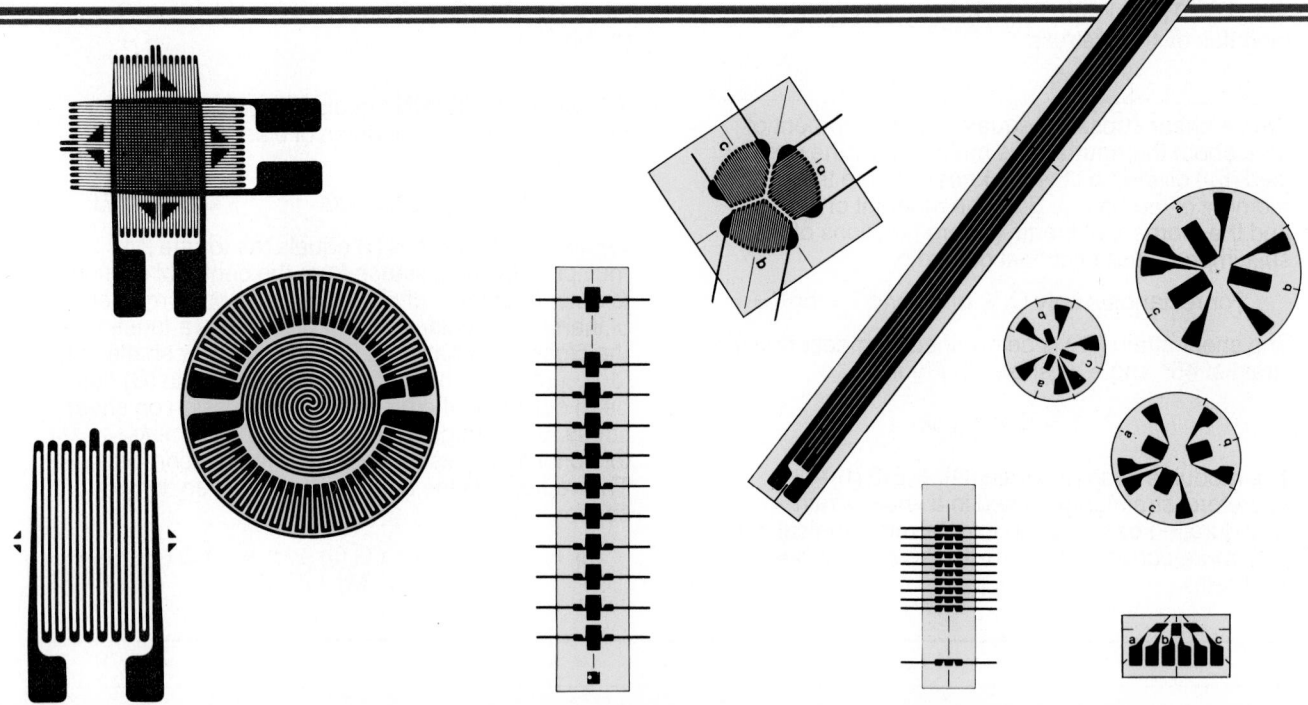

	SG Series	KFG Series

Foil strain gages are constructed by embedding a foil measuring element into a carrier.
Foil measuring grid
Carrier
  Substrate thickness
  Cover thickness
Connections dimensions in (mm) [in]
	Constantan foil 5μm thick
	Polyimide
	50μm
	25μm
	Solder Pads or Ribbon leads (30 mm long .05 mm thick x .3 mm wide) [1.2″ Long x .002″ thick x .012″ wide]
		Constantan Foil 6μm thick
		Kapton
		15 μm
		9 μm
		27 AWG strand polyvinyl insulation (1 mm x 2 mm) [.04″ x .08″]

Nominal resistance Resistance tolerance per package Gage factor (actual value printed on each package) Gage factor tolerance per package	Stated in 'to order box' 0.5% Approximatly 2.0 1.0%	120 ±0.4 ohms 0.3% 2.10 ±10% 1.0%

Thermal Properties
Reference temperature
Service temperature
  Static measurements
  Dynamic measurements
Temperature characteristics
  Steel
  Aluminum
  Uncompensated
Temperature compensated range
Tolerance of temp. compensation
	23°C
	
	−30 to 250°C (−22 to 482°F)
	−30 to 300°C (-22 to 572°F)
	
	11 ppm°C (6.1 ppm°F)
	23 ppm°C (12.8 ppm°F)
	±20ppm°C (±11.1ppm°F)
	−5 to 120°C (5 to 248°F)
	1 ppm°C (.5ppm°F)
		23°C
		
		−20 to 100°C (−4 to 212°F)
		−20 to 100°C (−4 to 212°F)
		
		10.8 ppm°C (6 ppm°F)
		—
		—
		10 to 80°C (50 to 176°F)
		1 ppm°C (.5ppm°F)

Mechanical Properties Maximum strain Hysteresis Fatigue (at ±1500$\mu\epsilon$) Smallest bending radius Transverse sensitivity	3% or 30,000 $\mu\epsilon$ Negligible >10,000,000 cycles 3mm (⅛ inch) —	5% or 50,000$\mu\epsilon$ Negligible >10,000,000 cycles 3mm (⅛ inch) Stated on each package

OMEGA STRAIN GAGES
GENERAL PURPOSE STRAIN GAGES FOR STATIC AND DYNAMIC APPLICATIONS

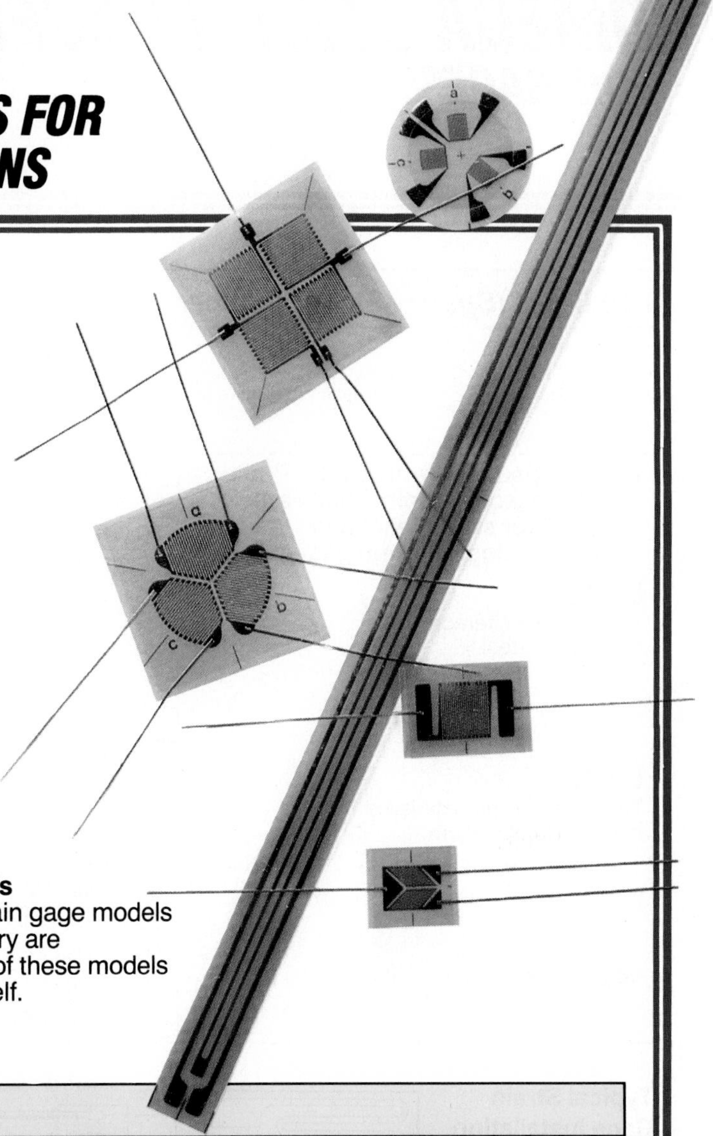

From
$44.**10**

From $44.¹⁰

✔ **Very Flexible, Mechanically Strong**
✔ **Small Bending Radius**
✔ **Broad Temperature Range**
✔ **Ribbon Leads, Solder Pads, or Wire Lead Connections**
✔ **Clear Alignment Marks**
✔ **Affix with Cold or Hot Curing Adhesives**

OMEGA strain gages are available in a variety of different models to cover most strain measurement applications. Their rugged construction and flexibility make them suitable for static and dynamic measurement with a high degree of accuracy.

The measuring grid is formed by etching Constantan foil which is then completely sealed in the carrier of polyimide film.

Most Popular Models
The most popular strain gage models in stock for fast delivery are highlighted. Delivery of these models is normally off-the-shelf.

HIGHLIGHTED MODELS STOCKED FOR FAST DELIVERY

To Order *(Specify Model Number)*

Type Series	Diagrams to actual size	Model No.	Price per pkg. of 10	Nominal resistance [Ohm]	grid a	grid b	carrier c	carrier d	Max. Permitted bridge energizing voltage [V rms]	Accessory Terminal Pads Part No.	Fig.
✔ **Encapsulated with Ribbon Leads** (Accessory terminal pads are used to attach heavier gage wire to the ribbon leads.)		SG-1.5/120-LY11	$47	120	1.5	1.1	4.8	3.5	2.5	TP-1	1
		SG-2/350-LY11	55	350	2.0	1.8	7.5	4.5	4	TP-1	2
		SG-3/120-LY11	47	120	3.0	1.5	8.0	4.0	4	TP-2	3
		SG-3/350-LY11	74	350	3.0	2.5	8.0	6.0	8	TP-2	3
LY 11 Temperature characteristic matched to steel		SG-6/120-LY11	47	120	6.0	3.0	12.5	6.0	9	TP-3	4
		SG-7/350-LY11	72	350	7.0	3.5	14.0	8.0	15	TP-3	4
		SG-7/1000-LY11	138	1000	7.0	3.8	12.0	6.0	20	TP-3	4
LY 13 Temperature characteristic matched to aluminum		SG-13/120-LY11	69	120	12.5	5.0	23.0	10.0	15	TP-3	5
		SG-13/1000-LY11	119	1000	13.5	5.5	24.0	12.0	30	TP-3	5
		SG-1.5/120-LY13	$47	120	1.5	1.1	4.8	3.5	3	TP-1	1
		SG-2/350-LY13	55	350	2.0	1.8	7.5	4.5	5	TP-1	2
		SG-3/120-LY13	47	120	3.0	1.5	8.0	4.0	6	TP-2	3
		SG-3/350-LY13	74	350	3.0	2.5	8.0	6.0	8	TP-2	3
		SG-6/120-LY13	47	120	6.0	3.0	12.5	6.0	10	TP-3	4
		SG-7/350-LY13	72	350	7.0	3.5	14.0	8.0	15	TP-3	4
		SG-7/1000-LY13	138	1000	7.0	3.8	12.0	6.0	20	TP-3	4
		SG-13/120-LY13	69	120	12.5	5.0	23.0	10.0	15	TP-3	5
		SG-13/1000-LY13	119	1000	13.5	5.5	24.0	12.0	30	TP-3	5

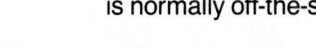

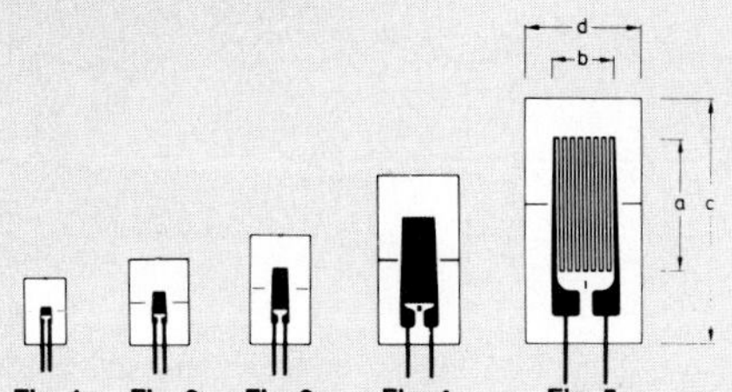

Fig. 1 Fig. 2 Fig. 3 Fig. 4 Fig. 5

Accessory terminal pads (TP-1, TP-2 and TP-3) **$10 each.**

E

OMEGA STRAIN GAGES
FOIL GAGES

To Order *(Specify Model Number)*

Type Series / Diagrams to actual size	Model No.	Price per pkg. of 10	Nominal resistance [Ohm]	Dimensions [mm] grid a	b	carrier c	d	Max. Permitted bridge energizing voltage [V rms]	Accessory Terminal Pads Part No.	Fig.
✔ **Encapsulated with Solder Pads** (Accessory terminal pads are used for strain relief and connecting different gage wires.)	SG-1.5/120-LY41	**$37**	120	1.5	1.1	4.8	3.5	2.5	TP-1	1
	SG-2/350-LY41	45	350	2.0	1.8	7.5	4.5	4	TP-1	2
	SG-3/120-LY41	38	120	3.0	1.5	8.0	4.0	4	TP-2	3
LY 41	SG-3/350-LY41	64	350	3.0	2.5	8.0	6.0	8	TP-2	3
Temperature characteristics matched to steel	SG-6/120-LY41	38	120	6.0	3.0	12.5	6.0	9	TP-3	4
	SG-7/350-LY41	62	350	7.0	3.5	14.0	8.0	15	TP-3	4
	SG-7/1000-LY41	**129**	1000	7.0	3.8	12.0	6.0	20	TP-3	4
	SG-13/120-LY41	60	120	12.5	5.0	23.0	10.0	15	TP-3	5
	SG-13/1000-LY41	109	1000	13.5	5.5	24.0	12.0	30	TP-3	5
LY 43	SG-1.5/120-LY43	**$37**	120	1.5	1.1	4.8	3.5	3	TP-1	1
Temperature characteristics matched to aluminum	SG-2/350-LY43	45	350	2.0	1.8	7.5	4.5	5	TP-1	2
	SG-3/120-LY43	38	120	3.0	1.5	8.0	4.0	6	TP-2	3
	SG-3/350-LY43	64	350	3.0	2.5	8.0	6.0	8	TP-2	3
	SG-6/120-LY43	38	120	6.0	3.0	12.5	6.0	10	TP-3	4
	SG-7/350-LY43	62	350	7.0	3.5	14.0	8.0	15	TP-3	4
	SG-7/1000-LY43	**129**	1000	7.0	3.8	12.0	6.0	20	TP-3	4
	SG-13/120-LY43	60	120	12.5	5.0	23.0	10.0	15	TP-3	5
	SG-13/1000-LY43	**109**	1000	13.5	5.5	24.0	12.0	30	TP-3	5

Typical Strain Gage Installation

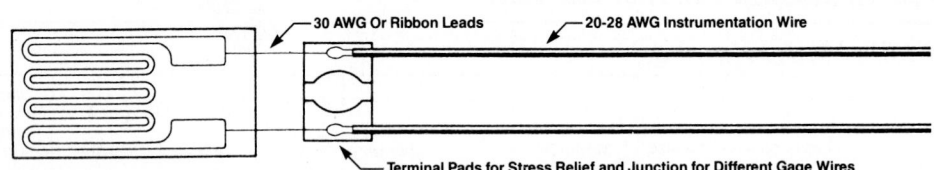

30 AWG Or Ribbon Leads — 20-28 AWG Instrumentation Wire — Terminal Pads for Stress Relief and Junction for Different Gage Wires

To Order *(Specify Model Number)*

Type Series / Diagrams to actual size	Model No.	Price per pkg. of 5	Nominal resistance [Ohm]	Dimensions [mm] grid a	b	carrier c	d	Max. Permitted bridge energizing voltage [V rms]	Accessory Terminal Pads Part No.	Fig.
✔ **Extra Long Gages for Inhomogeneous Material**	SG-30/120-LY40	**$41**	120	24.5	8.0	41.0	13.0	20	TP-3	1
✔ **Solder Pads, not Encapsulated** (Accessory terminal pads are used for strain relief and connecting different gage wires.)	SG-50/120-LY40	69	120	51.5	8.0	68.5	16.0	25	TP-3	2
	SG-100/240-LY40	126	240	101.5	6.6	115.0	16.5	30	TP-3	3
	SG-150/240-LY40	127	240	153.0	3.5	167.0	10.0	35	TP-3	4

LY40
Temperature characteristics uncompensated

*Accessory terminal pads (TP-1, TP-2 and TP-3) **$10 each**.*

OMEGA STRAIN GAGES
PRE-WIRED GAGES

HIGHLIGHTED MODELS STOCKED FOR FAST DELIVERY

To Order *(Specify Model Number)*

Type Series / Diagrams to actual size	Model No.	Price per pkg. of 10	Nominal resistance [Ohm]	grid a	grid b	carrier c	carrier d	Max. Permitted bridge energizing voltage [V rms]	Fig.
✔ **Encapsulated with 2 Lead Wires, 3 Feet Long, Attached**	KFG-02-120-C1-11L1M2R	$93.20	120	0.2	1.3	3.3	2.4	1	1
	KFG-1N-120-C1-11L1M2R	72.60	120	1.0	0.7	4.2	1.4	1.5	2
	KFG-2N-120-C1-11L1M2R	64.20	120	2.0	0.9	5.3	1.4	2	2
	KFG-3-120-C1-11L1M2R	60.60	120	3.0	1.3	7.4	2.8	4	3
	KFG-5-120-C1-11L1M2R	55.60	120	5.0	1.4	9.4	2.8	8	3
	KFG-10-120-C1-11L1M2R	67.90	120	10.0	3.0	16.0	5.2	15	4
	KFG-30-120-C1-11L1M2R	81.20	120	30.0	3.3	37.0	5.2	25	5

Dimensions [mm] columns: grid (a, b) and carrier (c, d)

Shown 4X Actual Size

1   2   3

Shown Actual Size

4   5

HIGHLIGHTED MODELS STOCKED FOR FAST DELIVERY

To Order *(Specify Model Number)*

Type Series / Diagrams to actual size	Model No.	Price per pkg. of 10	Nominal resistance [Ohm]	grid a	grid b	carrier c	carrier d	Max. Permitted bridge energizing voltage [V rms]	Fig.
✔ **Encapsulated with 3 Lead Wires, 9 Feet Long, Attached to Minimize Lead Wire Resistance Effects**	KFG-02-120-C1-11L3M3R	$124.00	120	0.2	1.3	3.3	2.4	1	1
	KFG-1N-120-C1-11L3M3R	103.00	120	1.0	0.7	4.2	1.4	1.5	2
	KFG-2N-120-C1-11L3M3R	95.00	120	2.0	0.9	5.3	1.4	2	2
	KFG-3-120-C1-11L3M3R	91.60	120	3.0	1.3	7.4	2.8	4	3
	KFG-5-120-C1-11L3M3R	86.40	120	5.0	1.4	9.4	2.8	8	3
	KFG-10-120-C1-11L3M3R	98.40	120	10.0	3.0	16.0	5.2	15	4
	KFG-30-120-C1-11L3M3R	111.00	120	30.0	3.3	37.0	5.2	25	5

Shown 4X Actual Size

1   2   3

Shown Actual Size

4   5

*Ordering Example: KFG-02-120-C1-11L1M2R are pre-wired strain gages encapsulated with two leads wires attached, **$93.20** (pkg. of 10).*

OMEGA STRAIN GAGES
PERPENDICULAR GRIDS FOR MEASURING AXIAL STRAIN

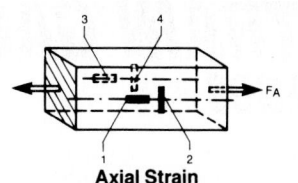

Axial Strain

2 Measuring Grids   *HIGHLIGHTED MODELS STOCKED FOR FAST DELIVERY*

To Order (Specify Model Number)

Type Series	Diagrams to Actual Size	Model No.	Price per pkg. of 5	Nominal resistance [Ohm]	grid a	b	carrier c	d	Max. Permitted bridge energizing voltage [V rms]	Accessory Terminal Pads Part No.	Fig.
✓ **Encapsulated with Ribbon Leads** **XY11** Temperature characteristics matched to steel **XY13** Temperature characteristiscs matched to aluminum		SG-3/350-XY11	$116	350	3.0	2.8	8.0	8.0	8	TP-2	1
		SG-7/350-XY11	147	350	7.0	3.5	13.0	13.0	15	TP-3	2
		SG-3/350-XY13	116	350	3.0	2.8	8.0	8.0	8	TP-2	1
		SG-7/350-XY13	147	350	7.0	3.5	13.0	13.0	15	TP-3	2

Fig. 1   Fig. 2

✓ **Encapsulated with Solder Pads** **XY41** Temperature characteristics matched to steel **XY43** Temperature characteristics matched to aluminum		SG-3/350-XY41	$92	350	3.0	2.8	8.0	8.0	8	TP-2	1
		SG-7/350-XY41	124	350	7.0	3.5	13.0	13.0	15	TP-3	2
		SG-3/350-XY43	92	350	3.0	2.8	8.0	8.0	8	TP-2	1
		SG-7/350-XY43	124	350	7.0	3.5	13.0	13.0	15	TP-3	2

Fig. 1   Fig. 2

✓ **Encapsulated with 2 Lead Wires**		KFG-1-120-D16-11L1M2S	$179.00	120	1.0	1.2	5.0		1.5		1
		KFG-2-120-D16-11L1M2S	129.00	120	2.0	1.3	8.0		2		2
		KFG-3-120-D16-11L1M2S	129.00	120	3.0	1.3	10.0		4		3
		KFG-5-120-D16-11L1M2S	129.00	120	5.0	1.4	11.0		8		4

Fig. 1   Fig. 2   Fig. 3   Fig. 4
Dia. "C"

✓ **Encapsulated with 3 Lead Wires**		KFG-1-120-D16-11L3M3S	$239.00	120	1.0	1.2	5.0		1.5		1
		KFG-2-120-D16-11L3M3S	191.00	120	2.0	1.3	8.0		2		2
		KFG-3-120-D16-11L3M3S	191.00	120	3.0	1.3	10.0		4		3
		KFG-5-120-D16-11L3M3S	191.00	120	5.0	1.4	11.0		8		4

Fig. 1   Fig. 2   Fig. 3   Fig. 4
Dia. "C"

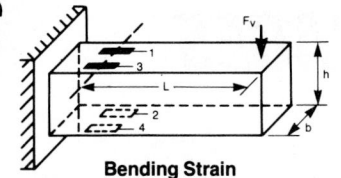

Bending Strain

NEW!

HIGHLIGHTED MODELS STOCKED FOR FAST DELIVERY

To Order *(Specify Model Number)*

Type Series	Diagrams to Actual Size	Model No.	Price per pkg. of 10	Nominal resistance [Ohm]	grid a	grid b	carrier c	carrier d	Max. Permitted bridge energizing voltage [V rms]	Accessory Terminal Pads Part No.	Fig.
✔ **Encapsulated with Ribbon Leads** **DY11** Temperature characteristics matched to steel		SG-2/1000-DY11	$61	1000	2.1	2.7	8.0	9.0	5	TP-2	1
		SG-3/1000-DY11	52	1000	3.0	3.0	9.0	9.0	10	TP-3	2
		SG-7/1000-DY11	66	1000	7.0	3.8	12.0	11.0	15	TP-3	3
DY13 Temperature characteristics matched to aluminum		SG-2/1000-DY13	$61	1000	2.1	2.7	8.0	9.0	5	TP-2	1
		SG-3/1000-DY13	52	1000	3.0	3.0	9.0	9.0	10	TP-3	2
		SG-7/1000-DY13	66	1000	7.0	3.8	12.0	11.0	15	TP-3	3

Fig. 1 Fig. 2 Fig. 3

Type Series	Model No.	Price per pkg. of 10	Nominal resistance [Ohm]	grid a	grid b	carrier c	carrier d	Max. Permitted bridge energizing voltage [V rms]	Accessory Terminal Pads Part No.	Fig.
✔ **Encapsulated with Solder Pads** **DY41** Temperature characteristics matched to steel	SG-2/1000-DY41	$52	1000	2.1	2.7	8.0	9.0	5	TP-2	1
	SG-3/1000-DY41	43	1000	3.0	3.0	9.0	9.0	10	TP-3	2
	SG-7/1000-DY41	57	1000	7.0	3.8	12.0	11.0	15	TP-3	3
DY43 Temperature characteristics matched to aluminum	SG-2/1000-DY43	$52	1000	2.1	2.7	8.0	9.0	5	TP-2	1
	SG-3/1000-DY43	43	1000	3.0	3.0	9.0	9.0	10	TP-3	2
	SG-7/1000-DY43	57	1000	7.0	3.8	12.0	11.0	15	TP-3	3

Shear Strain

Fig. 1 Fig. 2 Fig. 3

Type Series	Model No.	Price per pkg. of 10	Nominal resistance [Ohm]	grid a	grid b	carrier c	carrier d	Max. Permitted bridge energizing voltage [V rms]	Accessory Terminal Pads Part No.	Fig.
✔ **Encapsulated with Ribbon Leads** **XY21** Temperature characteristics matched to steel	SG-5/350-XY21	$63	350	4.7	2.4	11.5	8.1	10	TP-3	1
	SG-5/350-XY23	63	350	4.7	2.4	11.5	8.1	10	TP-3	1
XY23 Temperature characteristics matched to aluminum										

Fig. 1 Actual Size

STRAIN GAGES E

STRAIN GAGES
ROSETTES

To Order *(Specify Model Number)*

Type Series	Diagrams to Actual Size	Model No.	Price per pkg. of 10	Nominal resistance [Ohm]	grid a	grid b	carrier c	carrier d	Max. Permitted bridge energizing voltage [V rms]	Accessory Terminal Pads Part No.	Fig.
✔ 0°/45°/90° Encapsulated with Ribbon Leads **RY11** Temperature characteristics matched to steel **RY13** Temperature characteristics matched to aluminum		SG-3/120-RY11 SG-3/350-RY11	$109 135	120 350	3.0 3.0	2.2 2.2	16.0 16.0	16.0 16.0	4 8	TP-3 TP-3	1 1
		SG-3/120-RY13	$135	120	3.0	2.2	16.0	16.0	4	TP-3	1
✔ 0°/45°/90° Encapsulated with Solder Pads **RY31** Temperature characteristics matched to steel **RY33** Temperature characteristics matched to aluminum		SG-3/120-RY31 SG-3/350-RY31	$104 121	120 350	3.0 3.0	2.2 2.2	16.0 16.0	16.0 16.0	4 8	TP-3 TP-3	1 1
		SG-3/120-RY33	$121	120	3.0	2.2	16.0	16.0	4	TP-3	1
✔ 0°/60°/120° Encapsulated with Ribbon Leads **RY41** Temperature characteristics matched to steel **RY43** Temperature characteristics matched to aluminum		SG-3/120-RY41 SG-3/350-RY41	$109 135	120 350	3.0 3.0	2.2 2.2	16.0 16.0	16.0 16.0	4 8	TP-3 TP-3	1 1
		SG-3/120-RY43	$135	120	3.0	2.2	16.0	16.0	4	TP-3	1
✔ 0°/60°/120° Encapsulated with Solder Pads **RY71** Temperature characteristics matched to steel **RY73** Temperature characteristics matched to aluminum		SG-3/120-RY71 SG-3/350-RY71	$104 121	120 350	3.0 3.0	2.2 2.2	16.0 16.0	16.0 16.0	4 8	TP-3 TP-3	1 1
		SG-3/120-RY73	$121	120	3.0	2.2	16.0	16.0	4	TP-3	1

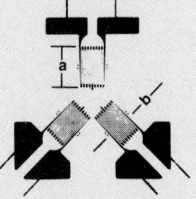
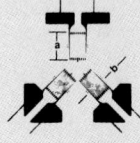

Enlarged 1.5 Times   **Actual Size**

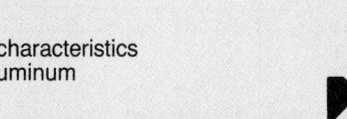
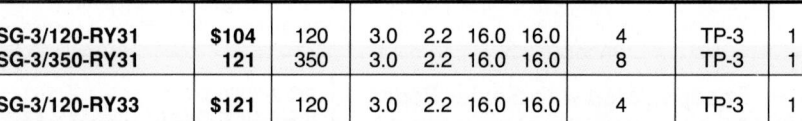
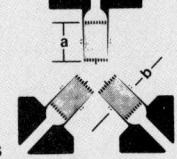
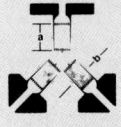

Enlarged 1.5 Times   **Actual Size**

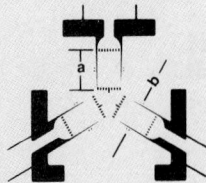
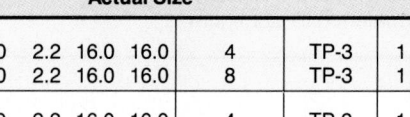
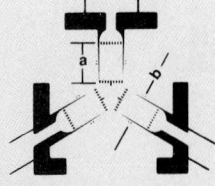
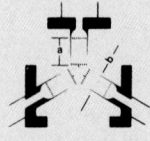

Enlarged 1.5 Times   **Actual Size**

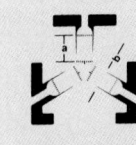

Enlarged 1.5 Times   **Actual Size**

OMEGA STRAIN GAGES
PRE-WIRED ROSETTES

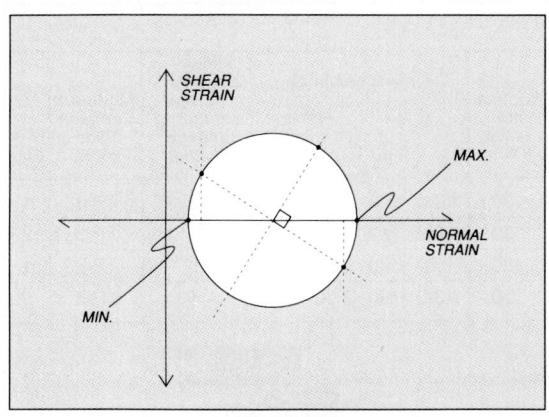

Mohrs Circle

Rosettes are used to compute the state of stress at a particular point. The results will plot out Mohr's circle, which gives value and orientation of principal strains.

HIGHLIGHTED MODELS STOCKED FOR FAST DELIVERY

To Order *(Specify Model Number)*

Type Series	Diagrams to actual size	Model No.	Price per pkg. of 10	Nominal resistance [Ohm]	Dimensions [mm] grid a	b	carrier c	Max. Permitted bridge energizing voltage [V rms]	Fig.
✔ 0°/45°/90° Encapsulated with 2 Lead Wires (3 feet long) Attached to Each Element		KFG-1-120-D17-11L1M2S	$256	120	1.0	1.2	5.0	1.5	1
		KFG-2-120-D17-11L1M2S	191	120	2.0	1.3	8.0	2	2
		KFG-3-120-D17-11L1M2S	191	120	3.0	1.3	10.0	4	3
Temperature characteristics matched to steel		KFG-5-120-D17-11L1M2S	191	120	5.0	1.4	11.0	8	4

Fig. 1   Fig. 2   Fig. 3   Fig. 4

To Order *(Specify Model Number)*

Type Series	Diagrams to actual size	Model No.	Price per pkg. of 10	Nominal resistance [Ohm]	Dimensions [mm] grid a	b	carrier c	Max. Permitted bridge energizing voltage [V rms]	Fig.
✔ 0°/45°/90° Encapsulated with 3 Lead Wires (9 feet long) Attached to Each Element		KFG-1-120-D17-11L3M3S	$347	120	1.0	1.2	5.0	1.5	1
		KFG-2-120-D17-11L3M3S	282	120	2.0	1.3	8.0	2	2
		KFG-3-120-D17-11L3M3S	282	120	3.0	1.3	10.0	4	3
Temperature characteristics matched to steel		KFG-5-120-D17-11L3M3S	282	120	5.0	1.4	11.0	8	4

Fig. 1   Fig. 2   Fig. 3   Fig. 4

E

Ordering Example: KFG-4-120-D17-11L3M3S are pre-wired rosette strain gages, encapsulated with three lead wires attached to each element and temperature characteristics matched to steel, *$282* (pkg. of 10).

OMEGA STRAIN GAGES
CORNER ROSETTES AND STRESS RELIEF GAGES

To Order *(Specify Model Number)*

Type Series	Diagrams to actual size	Model No.	Price per pkg. of 5	Nominal resistance [Ohm]	grid a	grid b	carrier c	carrier d	Max. Permitted bridge energizing voltage [V rms]	Accessory Terminal Pads Part No.	Fig.
✔ **Corner Rosette Encapsulated Gages**		SG-13/120-RY91	$128	120	13.0	5.0	27.0	27.0	15	TP-3	1
RY91 Ribbon Leads Temperature compensated to steel		SG-13/120-RY21	113	120	13.0	5.0	27.0	27.0	15	TP-3	2
RY21 Solder Pads Temperature compensated to steel		SG-13/120-RY93	128	120	13.0	5.0	27.0	27.0	15	TP-3	1
RY93 Ribbon Leads Temperature compensated to aluminum		SG-13/120-RY23	113	120	13.0	5.0	27.0	27.0	15	TP-3	2
RY23 Solder Pads Temperature compensated to aluminum											

Fig. 1   Fig. 2

Typical Installation

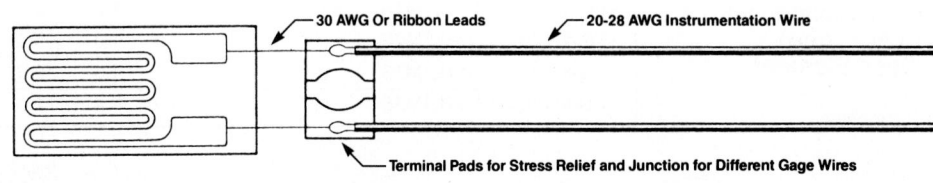

30 AWG Or Ribbon Leads

20-28 AWG Instrumentation Wire

Terminal Pads for Stress Relief and Junction for Different Gage Wires

To Order *(Specify Model Number)*

Type Series	Diagrams to actual size	Model No.	Price per pkg. of 5	Nominal resistance [Ohm]	grid a	grid b	carrier c	carrier d	Max. Permitted bridge energizing voltage [V rms]	Accessory Terminal Pads Part No.	Fig.
✔ **Stress Relief Encapsulated Gages**		SG-1.5/120-SR11	$128	120	1.6	1.6	10.7	10.7	2.5	TP-2	1
SR11 Ribbon Leads Temperature compensated to steel		SG-1.5/120-SR41	113	120	1.6	1.6	10.7	10.7	2.5	TP-2	2
SR41 Solder Pads Temperature compensated to steel		SG-1.5/120-SR13	128	120	1.6	1.6	10.7	10.7	2.5	TP-2	1
SR13 Ribbon Leads Temperature compensated to aluminum		SG-1.5/120-SR43	113	120	1.6	1.6	10.7	10.7	2.5	TP-2	2
SR43 Solder Pads Temperature compensated to aluminum											

Fig. 1   Fig. 2

Enlarged 2 Times

OMEGA STRAIN GAGES
CRACK AND DIAPHRAM GAGES

Crack Propagation gages are used to monitor crack growth. The gage is gluded in place, and as the crack grows under the gage, each of the limbs undergoes strain. The limbs are equalled space, and when the limb undergoes 2% strain, it breaks. By monitoring the continuity of each limb, and the time when the limbs break, studies of the crack growth can be completed. The gages also incorporate a boundary limb, so that measuring equipment may be switched on when the crack reaches the gage area.

To Order *(Specify Model Number)*

Type Series	Model No.	Price per pkg. of 5	Nominal resistance [Ohm]	limbs a	limbs b	carrier c	carrier d	Max. Permitted bridge energizing voltage [V rms]	Accessory Terminal Pads Part No.	Fig.
✔ **Crack Propagation Gage**	SG-CP1	$128	—	1.6	1.6	10.7	10.7	—	TP-2	2

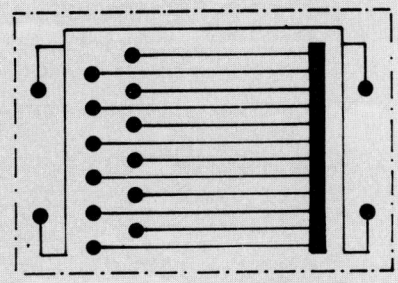

Fig. 2   Enlarged

Full Bridge Diaphragm Strain Gage	SG-13/200-DG11	$156	200	Carrier Dia.		13.2	10	TP-2	1
✔ **Encapsulated Diaphragm Gage with Ribbon Leads**	SG-20/240-DG11	194	240	Carrier Dia.		20	15	TP-2	2

Fig. 1

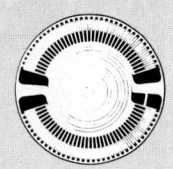

Fig. 2

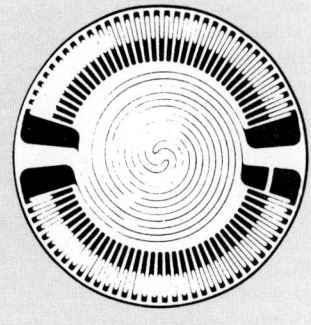

Enlarged

OMEGA STRAIN GAGE ACCESSORIES

TERMINAL PADS

Terminal pads serve two main purposes. First, they act as an intermediate point for attaching ribbon leads, thin gage wire, to the heavier instrumentation wires. Second, they provide stress relief to your strain gage system. When the heavier instrumentation wire moves, the terminal pad protects the strain gage.

HIGHLIGHTED MODELS STOCKED FOR FAST DELIVERY

Model No.	Price Per pkg 10 Pairs	Dimmensions (mm)				
		a	b	c	d	t
TP-1	$10	2.8	1.2	4.0	2.8	0.9
TP-2	10	3.6	1.6	5.3	3.7	1.1
TP-3	10	5.4	2.4	8.0	5.6	1.5

Terminal Pads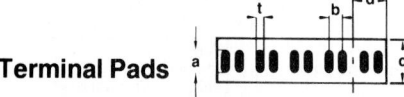

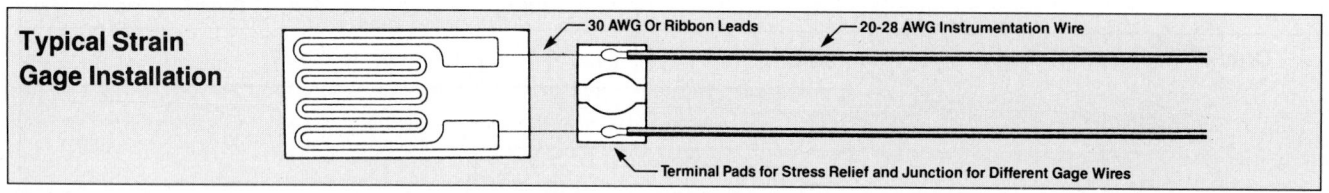

Typical Strain Gage Installation

— 30 AWG Or Ribbon Leads   — 20-28 AWG Instrumentation Wire

— Terminal Pads for Stress Relief and Junction for Different Gage Wires

FIXED BRIDGE COMPLETION RESISTORS

Accuracy: .1%
Temperature Compensation: 5 ppm (−20°C to 80°C)
Power: ¼ Watt

Model No.	Price	OHMS	Max Bridge Exc.
RES-120	$7.50	120	10 Vdc
RES-250	7.50	250	15 Vdc
RES-350	7.50	350	18 Vdc

*Ordering Example: RES-120 are fixed bridge completion resistors, **$7.50**.*

ADHESIVES

TT300 cement is a high quality two-part epoxy. It has a temperature range of up to 250°C. This adhesive insures the strongest possible bond for transducer quality gluing. Elevating curing temperatures of 100°C and 250°C are required to set the adhesive. TT300 is comprised of 1 oz bottle of resin, 1 oz bottle of hardener, 2 oz mixing bottle, bottle of acetone, and 1 dropper.
TT300 $29.50

SG496 and SG401 are a general purpose cold curing one-part glue. It is the easiest and most commonly used adhesive for strain gaging. The glue is a cyanoacrylate based adhesive. It cures in one minute, but completely sets in 24 hours. The SG401 is an ethyl-based cyanocsylate and the SG496 is a methyl-based cyanocsylate. There is a one-year shelf life at cool room temperature, but increased shelf life can be obtained by cold storage. The glue temperature range is −65 to 180°F (−54 to 82°C).
SG496 $22.00 1 oz. (28.4 gm) (Approx. 750 gages)
SG401 $9.50 0.1 oz. (3 gm) (Approx. 50 gages)

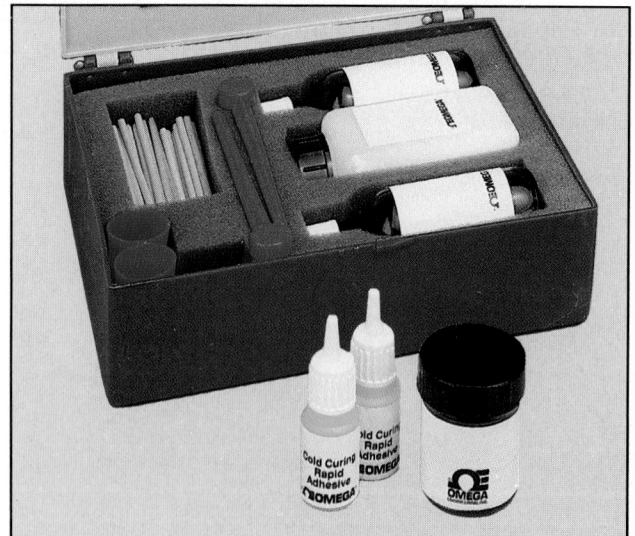

STRAIN GAGE ACCESSORIES
PROTECTIVE COVERINGS

Protective Coating SG 250
for strain gages
Keep tube tightly closed below 30°C (90°F). Contents: 85 grams (3 oz.).

PU 100
Polyurethane
Varnish

OMEGA
ENGINEERING, INC.

**Shown approximately
⅔ actual size**

**Model AK22
Tough Putty**

**Model
ABM 75**

Protective Coverings
for Strain Gages

Strain gages need protection against outer influences according to the ambient conditions: e.g. against humidity or mechanical damage.

In Stock for Immediate Delivery!

Survey: Possible Application and Technical Data

Strain gage cover	Price	Protects against	Temperature range of stability in air in °C [°F]	Contents package	Package sufficient for about	Application method	Hardening conditions	Shelf life at temperature	Composition
AK 22 Tough putty	$40	mechanical influences, weather, water (no vapor), pressurized water to 400 bar	−50… +170 [−58… +338]	1 kg	30 strain gages	knead on by hand	—	unlimited	tough kneadable putty, highly adhesive
ABM 75 Aluminum foil with putty	58	mechanical influences (Al foil must not be damaged), weather, water	−196… + 75 [−321… +167]	11 pieces 205 × 100 mm	200 strain gages	press on by hand	—	unlimited	aluminum laminate 0.05 mm thick with a 3 mm layer of putty
SG 250 Transparent silicon rubber	94	mechanical influences, weather, water at room temperature, oil	−70… +260 [−94… +500]	tube of approx. 85 g	20 strain gages	paste on from tube	air drying at room temperature	6 months	transparent single component silicon rubber, solvent-free
PU 100 Polyurethane varnish	64	mechanical influences, weather, oil, solvents	−32… +100 [−25… +212]	4 bottles 30 ml each	250 strain gages	brush on with small brush	room temperature up to… +100°C [+212°F]	1 year	single component polyurethane varnish containing solvents
Thermcoat SL Transparent silicon resin (2 oz.)	5	weather oil solvents	−155… +235 [−250… +450]	3 bottles 25 g each	90 strain gages	brush on with small brush	in temperature steps up to 200°C [up to 382°F]	9 months	transparent silicon resin, solvent-free

STRAIN GAGES   E

STRAIN GAGE ACCESSORIES
STRAIN GAGE APPLICATION KIT

The Complete Application Kit "SG1-Kit" Contains the Tools Necessary to Properly Apply Strain Gages Plus an Assortment of Popular Strain Gages.

✔ **Tools**
✔ **Adhesives**
✔ **Coatings**
✔ **Strain Gage Assortment**

Complete Application and Tool Kit

$549

All Contents Not Shown

KIT CONTENTS:
STRAIN GAGES (10 PER PKG)
SG-3/350-LY11 (Ribbon Leads)
SG-7/350-LY41 (Solder Pads)
KFG-10-120-C1-11L1M2R (Lead Wire)
TP-2 (Terminal Pads)
TP-3 (Terminal Pads)

COATINGS
ABM75 Aluminum Foil with Putty
(Two ¼" x 4' sheets)

ADHESIVES
SG401 (.1 ounce)
SG496 (1 ounce)

APPLICATION NOTE
10 Steps to Applying Strain Gages

TOOLS
Flat Brush
Fold-Out Magnifier, 6x Magn.
12" Ruler
10' Flexible Ruler
Glass Fiber Eraser
Scissors, Dented
Scissors, Pointed
Dental Probe with Bent Point
Dental Spatula for Cement
Stripper for Removing Insulation
Knife with Six Blades
10 ft. Roll Multicolored Ribbon Cable
Roll Mylar Tape

Sheet of 180, 240, 400 Grade of Emery Cloth
Straight Tweezers
Curved Tweezers
Rugged Carrying Case

STOCKED FOR FAST DELIVERY!

MODEL NO.	PRICE	DESCRIPTION
SG1-KIT	$549	Complete strain gage application kit

To Order (Specify Model No.)

SENSOR AND TRANSDUCER

WIRE AND CABLE

FINE GAGE .005″ DIA. SINGLE WIRE

- 3 Mil Teflon Wall
- Single Strand
- Extruded PFA (Teflon)
- Excellent in Vacuum
- Non-flammable

OMEGA'S thin-wall covering process guarantees continuous lengths up to 1,000 feet. This wire is ideal for connecting the strain gages to solder terminal strips and pads.

Price Table	
Spool Size	Price
50 Ft.	$16
100 Ft.	29
500 Ft.	119

To Order (Specify catalog number)			
Dia.	Length Ft.	Cat. No.	Price
.005	50	TFCP-005- 50	$16
.005	100	TFCP-005-100	29
.005	500	TFCP-005-500	119
.010	50	TFCP-010- 50	16
.010	100	TFCP-010-100	29
.010	500	TFCP-010-500	119
.015	50	TFCP-015- 50	16
.015	100	TFCP-015-100	29
.015	500	TFCP-015-500	119

MULTI-CONDUCTOR RIBBON CABLE

- 28 AWG 10-50 Conductors
- PVC Rating to 105°C
- Color Coded
- 100 Foot Rolls

OMEGA'S ribbon cables are PVC preinsulated conductors laminated to a clear PVC film to allow easy termination. The color coding allows for quick identification and circuit tracing. The multi-conductor ribbon cable can be easily trimmed to any desired conductor width for different uses.

To Order (Specify catalog number)		
No. of Cond.	Cat No.	Price 100 ft
4	RC- 4-100	$ 95
10	RC-10-100	65
14	RC-14-100	85
16	RC-16-100	95
26	RC-26-100	175
50	RC-50-100	325

All Wire Stocked For Immediate Delivery

MULTI-CONDUCTOR SHIELDED CABLE

- 24 AWG Tinned Copper Wires
- PVC Insulation
- Aluminum-Polyester Shield with #24 Drain Wire
- PVC Jacket Overall
- 100 Foot Rolls

Shielded cable provides the high conductivity and noise immunity required for instrumentation hook-ups to transducers. It is suitable for low and high level voltage signals and mA pick-up in high EMI/RFI environments.

To Order (Specify catalog number)			
No. of Cond.	Nom. O.D.	Cat. No.	Price 100 ft.
4	.190″	TX- 4-100	$28.50
8	.220″	TX- 8-100	45.50
15	.280″	TX-15-100	88.00

CONVENIENT PRE-SPOOLED LENGTHS

NEW!

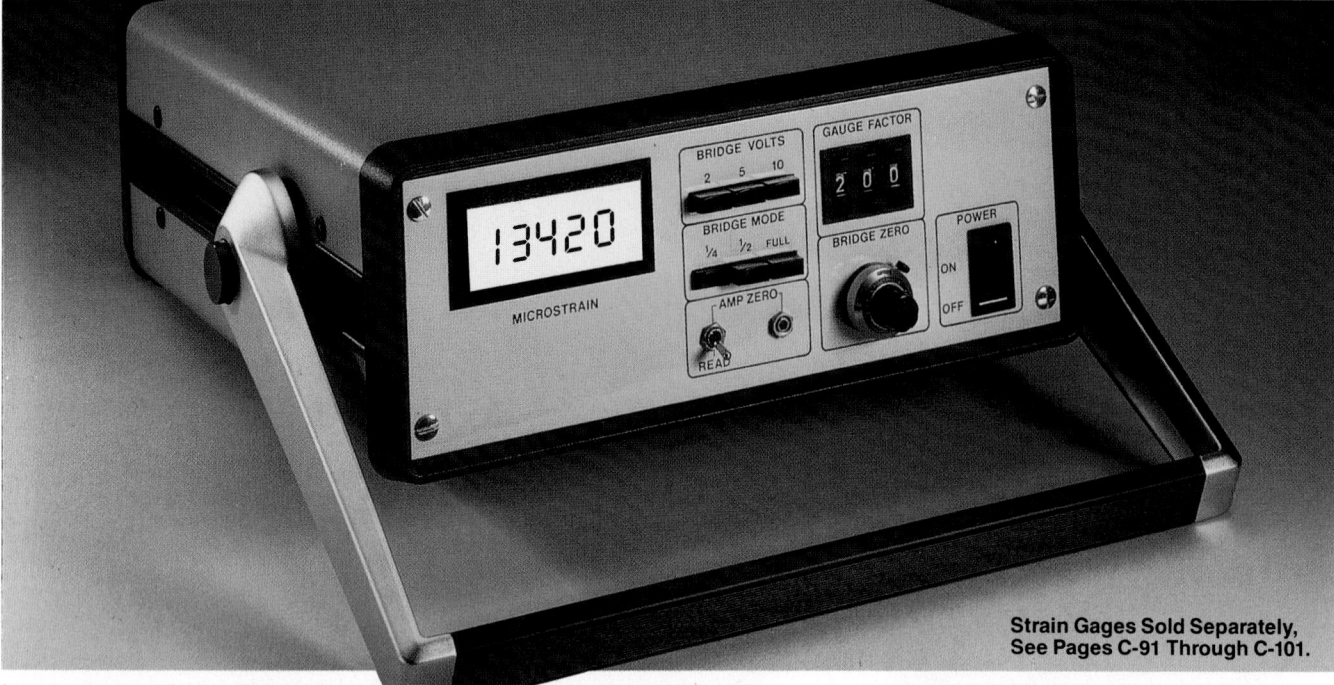

Strain Gages Sold Separately, See Pages C-91 Through C-101.

1 YEAR WARRANTY

DMD-21
$2585

- ✔ **Highly Stable Measurement**
- ✔ **Battery & AC Power**
- ✔ **Reads Directly In Micro Strain & Engineering Units**

The OMEGA DMD-21 makes reading strain gages easy, so that you can concentrate on your stress analysis. Quarter and half bridges can be directly wired to the DMD-21 because it contains bridge completion resistors. Since the DMD-21 accepts bridge inputs, load cells and pressure transducers can be monitored in engineering units of your choice. Static readings are displayed on the unit, while dynamic strains can be monitored via the analog output.

The optional switch box, DMD-21SB is a perfect companion to the DMD-21 in performing multiple strain gage measurements. The DMD-21SB offers independent zeroing of each channel, and bridge completion resistors.

SPECIFICATIONS
Linearity: .02% FS
Range: ±19,999 $\mu\epsilon$
Zero Balance: 50% FS
Resolution: 1 $\mu\epsilon$
Excitation: 2, 5, or 10 Vdc
Bridge Type: ¼, 120Ω and 350 Ω; ½ and full, >120Ω
(Internal bridge completion resistors)
Gage Factor: 1 to 2.99
Operating Temp: 41 to 95°F (5 to 35°C)
Thermal Effects: Zero, 0.3 $\mu\epsilon$/F (0.5 $\mu\epsilon$/C) Span, 0.003%Rdg/F (0.0005%Rdg/C)

Analog Output: ±2 Vdc
(over ±20,000 $\mu\epsilon$, DC to 20 KHz)
Input Impedence: 1000 Mega ohms
Power: 115 or 230 Vac @ 50/60 Hz Ni-cad batteries, 40 hours/charge
Dimensions: DMD-21: 4.4″ H × 12″ W × 18″ D (111.7 × 304 × 457 mm); DMD-21SB: 6.3″ H × 19″ W × 9.3″ D (160 × 482 × 236 mm)
Connection: Rear screw terminals
Weight: 11 lbs (5 Kg)
[DMD-21 SB 11 lbs (5 kg)]

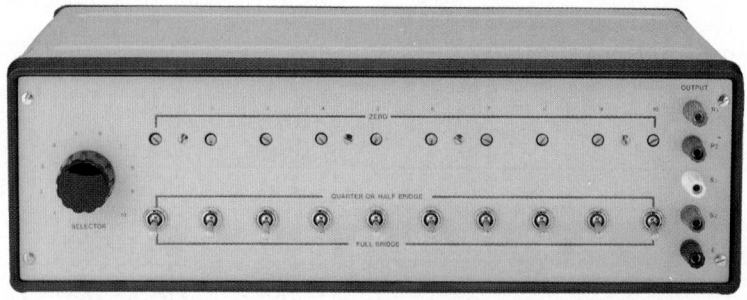

OMEGACARE™ Extended Warranty Plan: not available for this product.

To Order (Specify Model Number)		
Model No.	**Price**	**Description**
DMD-21	$2585	Portable, strain gage meter
DMD-21SB	1885	10 channel switch

Comes with operator's manual.
Ordering Example: *DMD-21 is a single channel portable strain gage meter, **$2585**.*

10 CHANNEL PORTABLE STRAIN GAGE MONITORING SYSTEM

 **NEW!**

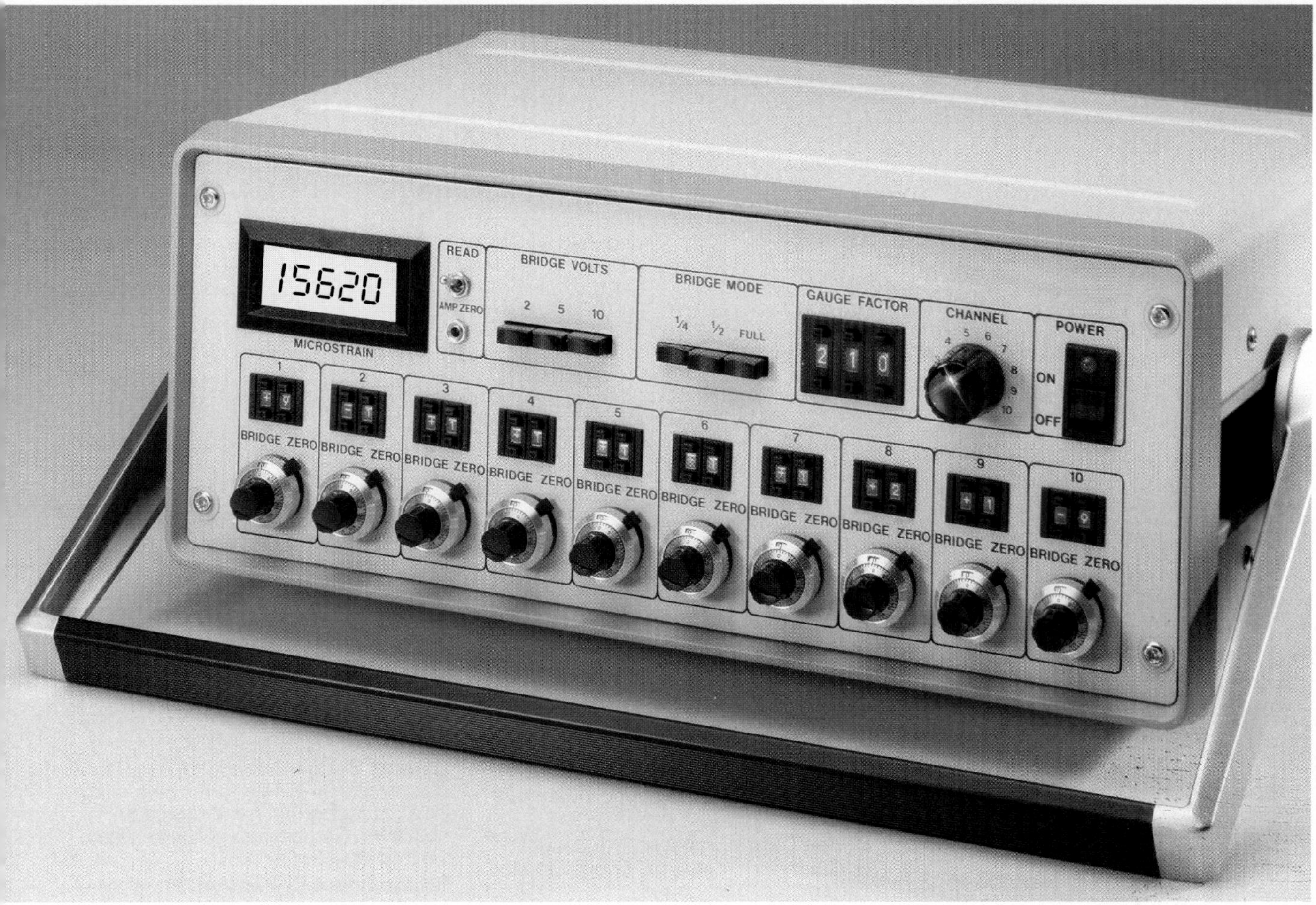

1 YEAR WARRANTY

DMD-22
$4495

- ✓ **Reads Directly in Micro Strain & Engineering Units**
- ✓ **Independent Zeroing On Each Channel**
- ✓ **High Accuracy and Resolution**

The DMD-22 is a portable ten channel strain gage system. It combines the features the DMD-21 and DMD-21SB into one powerful monitoring system. The DMD-22 monitoring system is completely portable. Independent zeroing on each channel eliminates subtracting unstrained readings to arrive at true strained results. Push button front keys and clearly labeled switches ensure strain gage measurements.

Selectable bridge configuration, via internal fixed resistors, eliminates complex and time consuming external bridge completion. Readings in microstrain take the mystery out of transposing millivolt to strain readings.

SPECIFICATIONS
Linearity: .02%FS
Range: ±19.999 $\mu\epsilon$
Zero Balance: 50%FS
Resolution: 1 $\mu\epsilon$
Excitation: 2, 5, or 10 Vdc
Bridge Type: ¼, 120Ω and 350Ω; ½ and full, >120Ω
(Internal bridge completion resistors)
Gage Factor: 1 to 2.99
Operating Temp: 41 to 95°F (5 to 35°C)
Thermal Effects: Zero, 0.3$\mu\epsilon$/F (0.5 $\mu\epsilon$/C) Span, 0.003%Rdg/F (0.0005%Rdg/C)
Analog Output: ±2 Vdc
(over ±20,000 $\mu\epsilon$, DC to 20 KHz)
Input Impedence: 1000 Mega ohms

Power: 115 or 230 Vac @ 50/60 Hz Lead Acid rechargeable batteries, 8-hours
Dimensions: 16.5"W × 6"H × 14"D (419 × 152 × 356 mm)
Connections: Rear screw terminals
Weight: 15.5 lbs (7 Kg)

To Order *(Specify Model No.)*

Model No.	Price	Description
DMD-22	$4495	Portable, ten-channel strain gage monitor

Comes with operator's manual.

Ordering Example: *DMD-22 is a portable, ten channel strain gage monitor, $4495.*

STRAIN GAGES E

HIGH PERFORMANCE STRAIN GAGE AMPLIFIER

NEW!

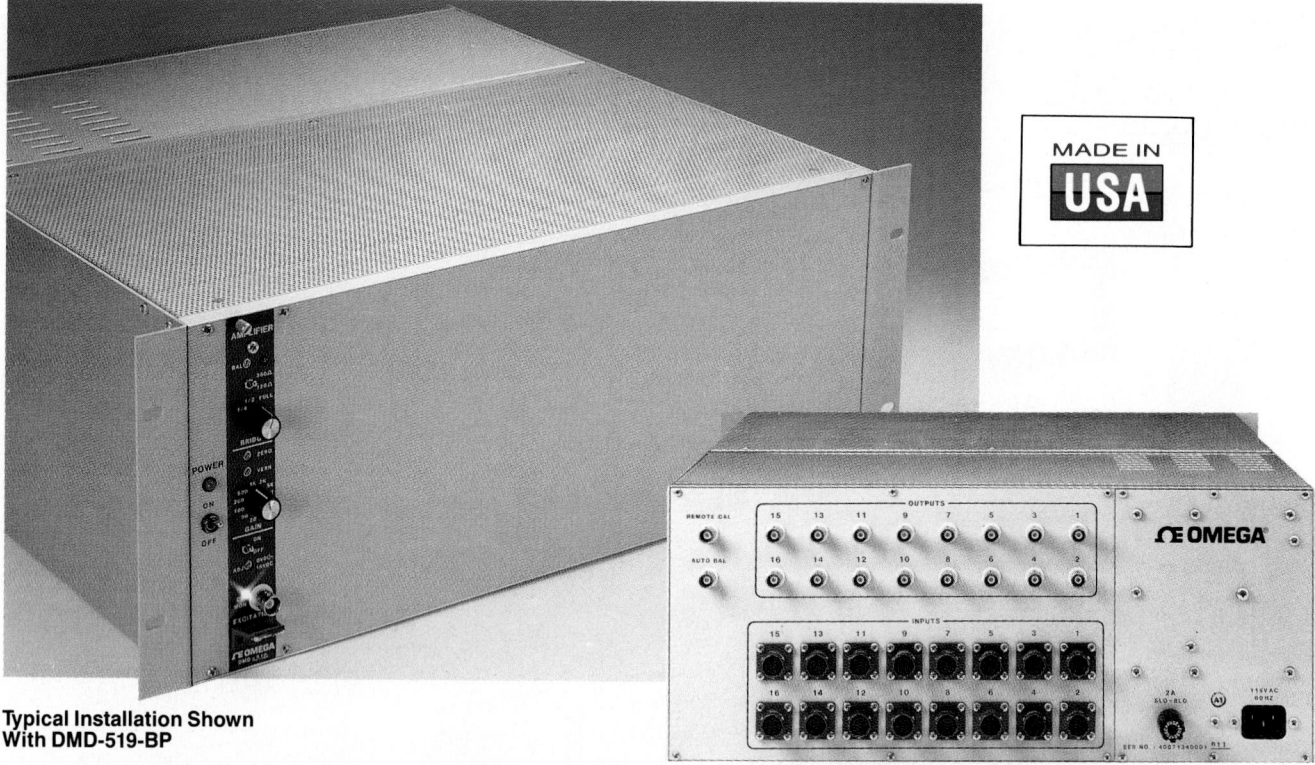

Typical Installation Shown With DMD-519-BP

MADE IN **USA**

Rear View of DMD-519-BP

- ✔ 16 Channels Per Rack
- ✔ Selectable Bridge Completion
- ✔ Auto-Balance
- ✔ Adjustable Bridge Excitation
- ✔ Wide Frequency Response
- ✔ High Grade Amplifier

Sixteen channels of the DMD-519 strain gage amplifier are mounted in a rack adaptor. An unregulated AC to DC supply is internally mounted at the rear of the rack to energize all 16 channels. Each channel has its own on-board regulators to provide the voltage for the logic circuits, op-amps and bridge excitation. In this manner, a load fault to any module will not affect the remaining units.

The DMD-519 provides all of the operating features normally provided in this type of instrument in addition to offering a switch selectable auto-balance circuit as a standard feature.

SPECIFICATIONS

Bridge Excitation: 0-15 Vdc front panel adjustable

Bridge Configurations: Front panel switch for ¼, ½, and full bridge, and for 120 and 350 ohm gages

Input/Output: 1 Input and 1 Output per module

Gain: Front panel switch 1, 2, 5, 10, 20, 50, 100, 200, 500, 1000, 2000, 5000, with verner and zero front panel screw adj.

Frequency Response: dc to 100 KHz (-3dB)

Output: ±10 Vdc @ 100 mA

Output Noise: 5 μV RMS referred to input (RTI), over DC to 100 KHz, at 1000 gain

Output Drift: 10 μVdc RTI for 24 hours, after 1 hour warm up, at 1000 gain

Bridge Balance: Front panel screw adj.

Remote Bridge Balance: ±2.5 μVdc/V one remote switch performs balancing on all modules that have auto tare activated. Remote balance is activated via PCB switch

Bridge Shunt Calibration: Front panel switch (shunt resistor is internal to module)

Remote Shunt Calibration: One remote switch closure on the rack performs shunt calibration on all channels

DMD-632-BP RACK SPECIFICATIONS

Size: 7"H × 19"W x 20"D (17.7 × 48 × 50.8 cm)

Power: 115 Vac @ 50/60 Hz 2 Amp slow blow fuse installed, with detachable 6 ft, 18 gage power cord

Connections: 16 Input signals use PT06F10-6S; 16 Output signals use BNC; 1 remote calibration uses BNC; 1 remote Balance uses BNC; 1 Excitation adj. monitor per module uses BNC connector

OMEGACARE™ Extended Warranty: not available for this product.

To Order *(Specify Model Number)*		
Model No.	**Price**	**Description**
DMD-519	**$1110**	Single channel strain gage amplifier (needs DMD-519-BP)
DMD-519-CC	870	Benchtop case for 2 DMD-519 modules
DMD-519-BP	1950	Rack mount holds up to 16 DMD-519 amplifiers

Comes with operator's manual.

Ordering Example: *4 DMD-519 and 1 DMD-519-BP is a 4-channel, rack-mounted strain gage system, $4440 + 1950 = **$6390**.*

ECONOMICAL, HIGH-PERFORMANCE STRAIN GAGE AMPLIFIER

✓ **2 Channels Per Module**
✓ **Available in Benchtop or Rack Mount Case**
✓ **High Grade Amplifier**

The DMD-520 high performance strain gage amplifier uses cost-cutting techniques such as packaging two-channels per module in an eight module rack. The result is a quality instrument at an attractive price.

SPECIFICATIONS

Bridge Excitation: 0-10 Vdc front panel adjustable

Bridge Configurations: ¼, ½, and full bridge, completion resistors 120 and 350 ohms are included, which user solders onto internal header

Input/Output: 2 Input and 2 Output per module

Gain: Front panel switch 1, 100, 200, 500, 1000, with verner and zero front panel screw adj.

Frequency Response: dc to 20 KHz (-3dB)

Output: ± 10 Vdc @ 10 mA

Output Noise: 5 μV RMS referred to input (RTI), over DC to 20KHz, at 1000 gain

Output Drift: 10 μVdc RTI for 24 hours, after 1 hour warm up, at 1000 gain

Bridge Balance: Front panel screw adj.

Bridge Shunt Calibration: Front panel switch (User solders shunt resistor onto internal header)

Remote Shunt Calibration: One remote switch closure on the rack or case performs shunt calibration on all the channels

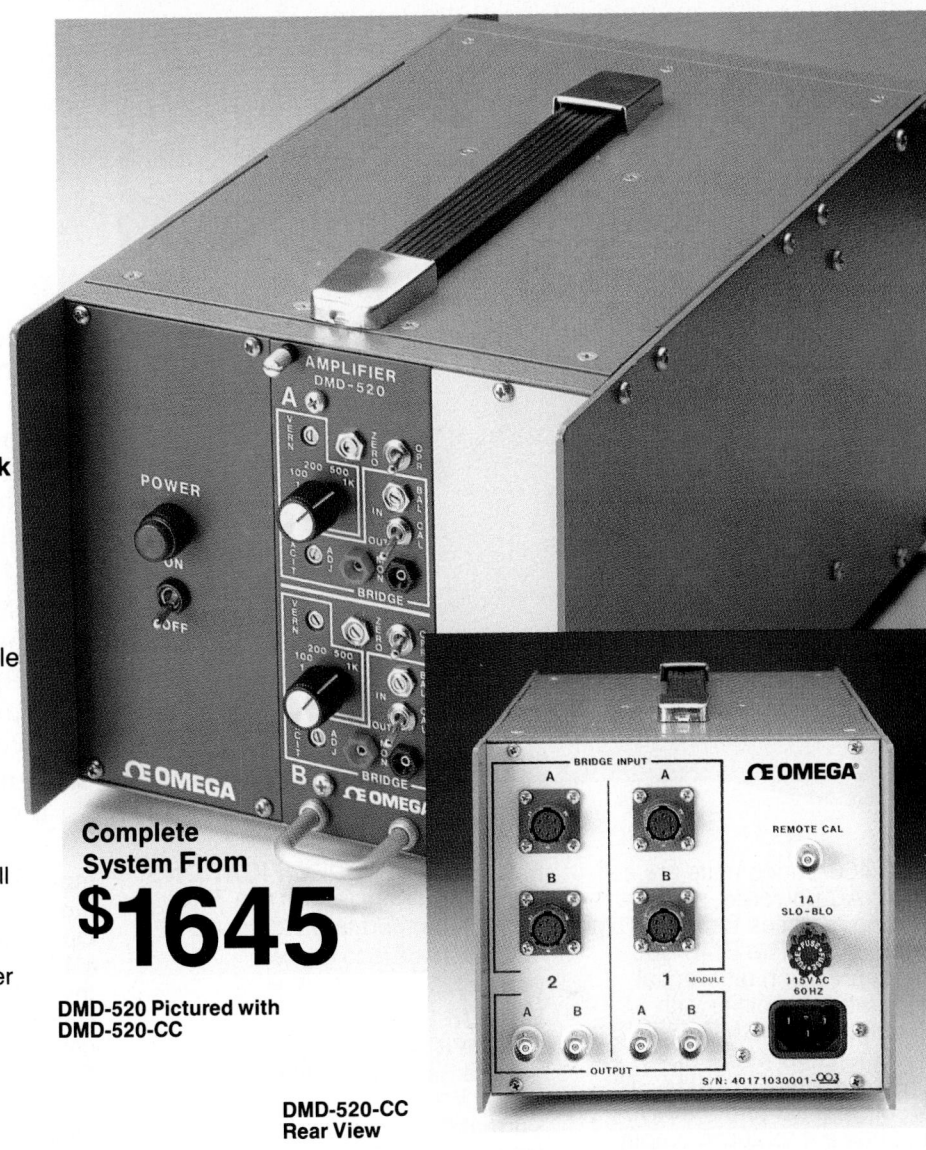

Complete System From

$1645

DMD-520 Pictured with DMD-520-CC

DMD-520-CC Rear View

DMD-520-BP and 'CC' SPECIFICATIONS

Size: BP: 5.25″H × 19″W × 12″D (13.3 × 48.2 × 30.4 cm) CC: 5.25″H × 6.4″W × 12″D (13.3 × 16.2 × 30.4 cm)

Weight: DMD-520-CC: 5.5 lbs (2.5 kg) DMD-520-BP: 20 lbs (9 kg)

Power: 115 Vac @ 50/60 Hz 2 Amp slow blow fuse installed, with detachable 6 ft, 18 gage power cord

Connections: 16 Input signals use PT06F10-6S;16 Output signals use BNC 1 Remote Shunt Calibration use BNC (CC: Has 4 input, 4 output and 1 remote shunt calibration)

OMEGACARE™ Extended Warranty: not available for this product.

To Order (Specify Model Number)

Model No.	Price	Description
DMD-520	$ 810	Two channel strain gage amplifier
DMD-520-CC	835	Benchtop case for 2 DMD-520 modules
DMD-520-BP	1555	Rack Mount For 8 DMD-520 modules

Comes with operator's manual.

Ordering Example *(DMD-520 and DMD-520-CC is a two-channel strain gage amplifier in a benchtop case, $810 + 835 = **$1645**.*

STRAIN GAGES E

STRAIN GAGE AMPLIFIER/SIGNAL CONDITIONER MODULES
FOR STRAIN GAGES, LOAD CELLS AND TRANSDUCERS

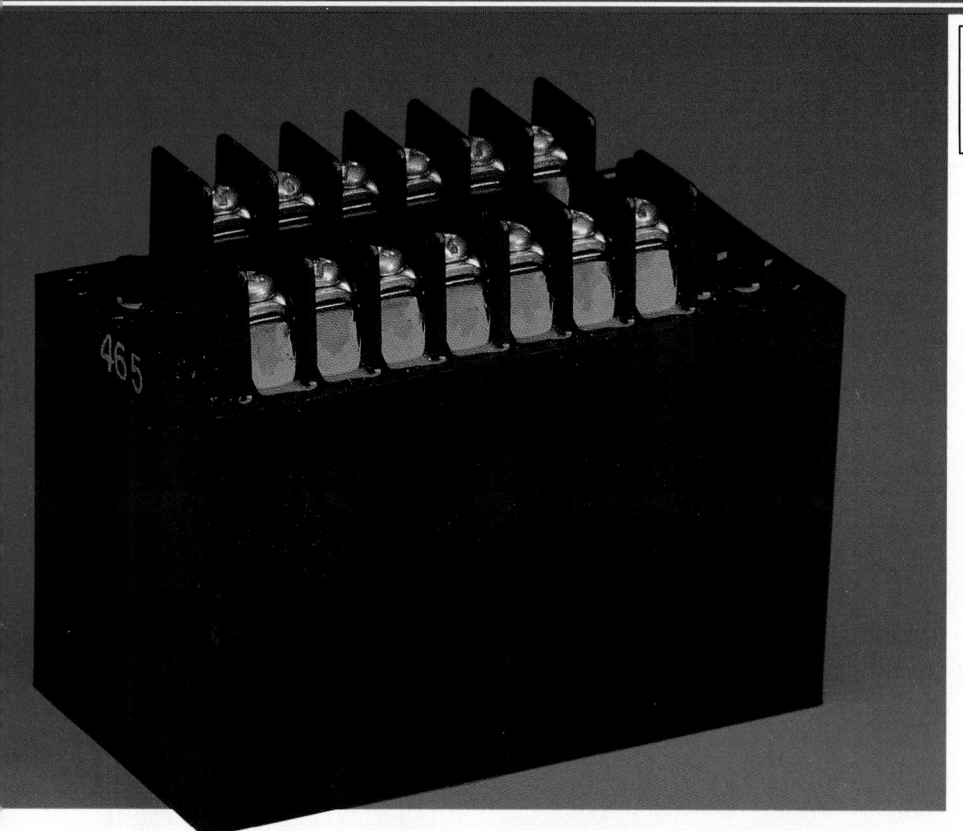

DMD 460 SERIES

$295

✔ **Bridge Excitation 4 to 16V dc; Up to 150 mA**
✔ **Works with 120, 350, 500 ohm and Greater Bridge Circuits**
✔ **Adjustable Gain and Offset**
✔ **6 Wire Bridge Connections**
✔ **Voltage and Current Output Versions Available**
✔ **Rugged Self Contained Module**

The DMD 460 Series units are self contained, AC powered, signal conditioning modules for bridge type instrumentation. The DMD 465 contains a precision differential instrumentation amplifier with filtered output. The DMD 465WB is similar to the DMD 465, but has a frequency response of 2KHZ. The DMD 466 is similar to the above units but has a 4 to 20mA output instead of voltage.

To Order (Specify Model No)

MODEL NO.	PRICE	DESCRIPTION
DMD-465	$295	Amplifier
DMD-465WB	295	High Frequency Amplifier
DMD-466	295	Transmitter (4-20mA)
DMD-465-220V	295	220 Vac powered DMD-465
DMD-465WB-220V	295	220 Vac powered DMD-455WB
DMD-466-220V	295	220 Vac powered DMD-466

Comes with complete operator's manual.

Ordering Example: *DMD-465WB is high frequency amplifier/signal conditioner module, $295.*

MECHANICAL SPECIFICATIONS:
Operating Temperature: 0 to 70°C
Storage Temperature: -25 to +85°C
Weight: 18 oz.(510 grams)
Size: 3.75" L x 2" W x 3" H

BRIDGE SUPPLY SPECIFICATIONS:
Voltage Range Adjustment: 4 to 15 Vdc

Current Output: 100 mA
Line and Load Regulation: (0 to 100 mA) 0.05% max.
Output Noise: 0.5 mV RMS
Power Input: 115 Vac ±10% 50 to 60 Hz

AMPLIFIER SPECIFICATIONS:
DMD 465 AND DMD 465WB
Gain Range: 40-250, (up to 1000 with external gain on DMD 465 only)
Dynamic Response: DMD 465, DC to -6 dB=5 Hz
DMD 465WB, DC to -3 dB=2 KHz
Max Output(2K Load): ±10V
Output Impedance: 0.01 ohms to 1 ohm
Output Offset: -5V to +2V (only for DMD 465WB only)
Gain Temp. Coef.: DMD 465 3ppm/C, DMD 465WB 200ppm/C

Input Bias Current: 30nA
Input Impedance: 3000 Megohms
Output Noise(RTO): 2 mV pp @ gain = 100, 1Hz to 2KHz
Input Noise Line Frequency: 15 µV pp
Common Mode Rejection: 90 dB @ gain 40, 100 dB @ gain 250
Common Mode Input Voltage: ±10V

TRANSMITTER SPECIFICATIONS:
DMD 466
Output: 4 to 20 mA,0 to 20 mA (25mA max, @ 10 Ac)
Zero Adjust: 0 to +12 mA
Accuracy: ±0.05% FS
Gain Range: 0.084 to 3.2 mA/mV
Input for 4-20 mA Output: 5 to 190 mV
Temperature Stability: 200 ppm/C @ GAIN 0.084 mA/mV 135 ppm/C @ gain 2.0 mA/mV
Input Impedance: 1000 megaohms
Common Mode Rejection: 90 dB @ gain 0.084 mA/mV 100 dB @ gain 2.0 mA/mV
Common Mode Input: ±10volts
Output Noise: 1µA RMS @ gain 0.2 mA/mV, 1 to 100 Hz
Dynamic Response: DC to -6dB=5 Hz, to 1% of final value 200 mS, typical, to 0.1% of final value 300 mS, typical

ECONOMICAL DIGITAL INDICATORS WITH EXCITATION AND DUAL ALARM RELAYS

NEW!

The DP205 Comes with a Complete Operator's Manual. It is Shown with Model LCCA Load Cell. Load Cells are Sold Separately, See Section F.

1 YEAR WARRANTY | **MADE IN USA** | **CARE**

DP205 SERIES
$199

- ✔ **4 Digit Display, -1999 to 9999 Counts**
- ✔ **Excitation, Dual Alarm Relays, and Scalable Analog Output Standard**
- ✔ **Models Available for Process Voltage and Current or Bridge Type Inputs**
- ✔ **Easily Scaled to Display Readings in Engineering Units**

The OMEGA DP205 Series are low cost digital panel meters for use with voltage, current or bridge type transducers. A four digit LED display indicates from -1999 to 9999 counts. For amplified voltage and current output transducers, the DP205-E has a user selectable 12 or 24 Vdc excitation supply. For strain gage bridge transducers the DP205-S has a 5 or 10 Vdc supply.

Both models include analog output and dual alarm relays as standard equipment. The analog output is field scalable and configurable for 0-10V, 0-20mA, or 4-20mA. The dual alarm relays are fully configurable for high or low, latching or non-latching operation and include adjustable deadband.

SPECIFICATIONS
Accuracy (@ 25°C): ±0.02% of reading
Operating Temp: 0 to 50°C (32 to 122°F)
Span Temp Coefficient: ± 50 PPM/°C
Storage Temperature: -40 to 185°F (-40 to 85°C)
Relative Humidity: 95% at 104°F (40°C) (non-condensing)
CMRR: 120 dB
Common Mode Voltage: 1500 V peak

IN STOCK FOR FAST DELIVERY!

per HV test 354 V peak per IEC spacing
NMRR: 60 dB
Display: 4 digit, red LED, 0.56" high
Display Range: -1999 to 9999 counts
Conversion Rate: 3/second
Step Response: 1-2 seconds
Relays: Dual 250 Vac, 6 amp, SPDT
Analog Output: Scalable 0-10 V or 4-20 mA

POWER REQUIREMENTS
Voltage: 115 (std) or 230 Vac (optional) ±15%
Frequency: 48 to 60 hz
Power Consumption: 6 watts maximum

MECHANICAL SPECIFICATIONS
Bezel: 3.78" W x 1.89" H x .30" D (96 x 48 x 7mm)
Panel Cutout: 3.622" W x 1.772" H (92 x 45mm)
Depth Behind Panel: 5.6"
Weight: 18 oz (509 g)

To Order (Specify Model Number)			
MODEL NO.	**INPUT RANGES ***	**EXCITATION**	**PRICE**
DP205-E	0-100 mV, ±50 mV, 0-10V ±5V, 0-20 mA, 4-20 mA	24V @ 50 mA or 12V @ 100 mA	$199
DP205-S	0-100 mV or ±50 mV	5 V @ 60 mA or 10V @ 120 mA	199

* Input ranges are selected by internal DIP switches.
For 230 VAC power add suffix "-230", no extra charge.
Ordering Example: *DP205-E is a digital process indicator with 24V @50 mA or 12V @100 mA excitation, $199.*

STRAIN GAGES **E**

PLUG-IN CARDS WITH DIRECT CONNECTION TO THERMOCOUPLES, RTDS AND STRAIN GAGES

For Temperature Sensors, See the OMEGA Temperature Measurement Handbook and Encyclopedia®.

OMD-5508TC Thermocouple Input, $650. Shown with KMTSS-125G-6 Thermocouple Probe, $24.

OMD-5508 RTD Input, $795. Shown with PR-11-2-100-1/4-6-E RTD Probe, $66.

OMD-5508 Series
From

$650

✔ **Connects Directly to Thermocouples, RTDs, Strain Gages**
✔ **8 Differential Analog Inputs**
✔ **12 Bit Resolution**
✔ **High Speed A/D Throughputs**
✔ **Simplifies Signal Connection and Eliminates Cabling**
✔ **Detachable Screw Terminal Mates with Board Connector at Rear of PC**
✔ **On-Board Signal Conditioning Lets Boards Accept Field Wiring Directly**
✔ **Menu-Driven Software Included**

OMEGA's new OMD-5508 Series offers a unique approach to plug-in data acquisition. Designed to simplify signal connection and eliminate cabling costs, each I/O module contains a detachable screw terminal panel that mates with the board connector at the rear of

the PC. On-board signal conditioning allows the boards to connect to sensors directly, eliminating the need for expensive external signal conditioning and ribbon cabling.

Three different models are available to provide direct connection to thermocouples, RTDs and strain gages. These boards are ideally suited for medium speed data acquisition with sample rates up to 8000 samples per second (7000 samples per second for OMD-5508BG). For high speed strain measurements, a faster version (200 kHz) of the OMD-5508BG with anti-aliasing filtering is available. Consult Engineering for details.

All OMD-5508 boards include utility software which not only supports data collection but also greatly facilitates configuring the boards. The software, supplied on a single floppy with no need for a user's manual, is a complete I/O board tutorial on a diskette. The friendly menu-driven interface guides the user through board jumper settings, with help screens to explain the function of each jumper. Once the board has been configured for your application, the software can be used to perform low speed (1 Hz) data acquisition on all channels, expressing the data as temperature or strain. The software performs real time display and storage of data to an ASCII file.

The boards are supplied with one mating screw terminal panel to accept field wiring. For portable applications, extra terminal panels may be purchased.

OMD-5508 SERIES
FOR IBM PC/XT/AT AND 386 COMPATIBLES

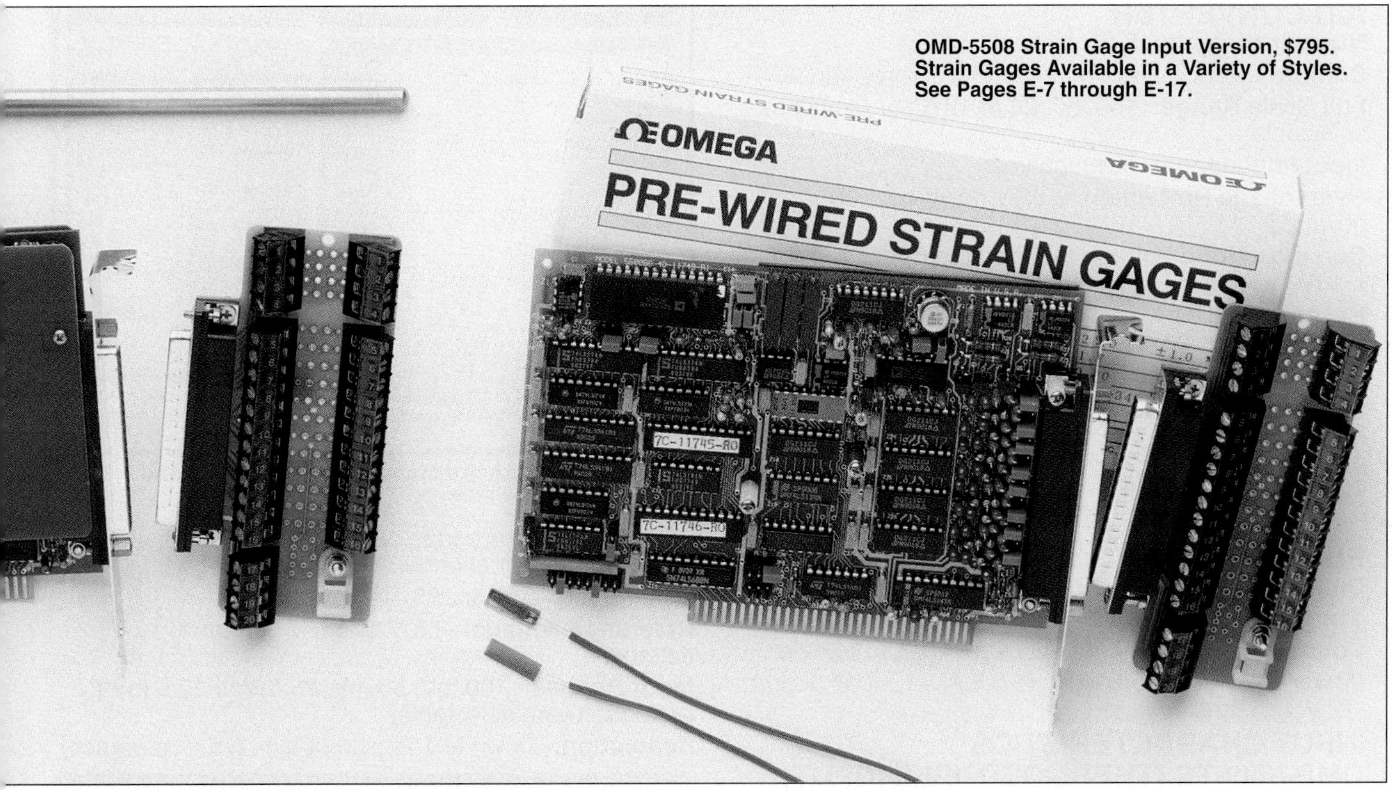

OMD-5508 Strain Gage Input Version, $795.
Strain Gages Available in a Variety of Styles.
See Pages E-7 through E-17.

PRE-WIRED STRAIN GAGES

OMD-5508TC Ranges/Accuracy

See Page E-29 for Specifications and Ordering Information

Input Type		HW Range	SW Range	Resolution	HW Accuracy, ±0.01% rdg	SW Accuracy+ hardware ±0.01% rdg
mV		-100 to 100 mV	-100 to 100 mV	48.8 μV	±150 μV	±150 μV
		-50 to 50 mV	-50 to 50 mV	24.4 μV	±76.3 μV	±76.3 μV
		-25 to 25 mV	-25 to 25 mV	12.2 μV	±45.8 μV	±45.8 μV
		-12.5 to 12.5 mV	-12.5 to 12.5 mV	6.1 μV	±27.5 μV	±27.5 μV
Iron Constantan	J	-210 to 760°C	0 to 760°C	0.49°C at 0°C	±1.52°C	±1.62°C
		-210 to 457°C	0 to 457°C	0.24°C at 0°C	±0.91°C	±1.01°C
		-210 to 231°C	0 to 231°C	0.12°C at 0°C	±0.55°C	±0.65°C
Chromega™ - Alomega™	K	-270 to 1372°C	0 to 1370°C	1.24°C at 0°C	±3.80°C	±4.50°C
		-270 to 1232°C	0 to 1232°C	0.62°C at 0°C	±1.94°C	±2.64°C
		-270 to 602°C	0 to 602°C	0.31°C at 0°C	±1.16°C	±1.86°C
		-270 to 307°C	0 to 307°C	0.15°C at 0°C	±0.70°C	±1.40°C
Copper Constantan	T	-270 to 400°C	-160 to 400°C	0.32°C at 0°C	±1.20°C	±1.70°C
		-270 to 259°C	-160 to 259°C	0.16°C at 0°C	±0.72°C	±1.22°C
Chromega™ Constantan	E	-270 to 1000°C	-100 to 1000°C	0.83°C at 0°C	±2.56°C	±3.06°C
		-270 to 661°C	-100 to 661°C	0.42°C at 0°C	±1.30°C	±1.80°C
		-270 to 350°C	-100 to 350°C	0.21°C at 0°C	±0.78°C	±1.28°C
		-270 to 188°C	1-00 to 188°C	0.10°C at 0°C	±0.47°C	±0.97°C
Pt 13% Rh Pt	R	-50 to 1768°C	0 to 1000°C	1.06°C at 600°C	±3.98°C	±4.48°C
		-50 to 1148°C	0 to 1000°C	0.53°C at 600°C	±2.39°C	±2.89°C
Pt 10% Rh Pt	S	-50 to 1768°C	0 to 1750°C	1.19°C at 600°C	±4.44°C	±5.44°C
		-50 to 1246°C	0 to 1246°C	0.59°C at 600°C	±2.67°C	±3.67°C
Pt 30% Rh Pt 6% Rh	B	0 to 1820°C	V to °C not available	2.03°C at 600°C	±7.63°C	V to °C not available
		0 to 1760°C		1.02°C at 600°C	±4.58°C	

STRAIN GAGES

E

Common Specifications
A/D CONVERTER
Number of Inputs: 8, multiplexed
Configuration: Fully differential with sample and hold
Full Scale Range: 100, 50, 25 or 12.5 mV (software selectable)
Input Impedance: 10 megohms
Overvoltage Protection: ± 32 V powered, ±20 V not powered
Common Mode Voltage (acceptable operating limit): ± 10V max
Resolution: 12 bit

A/D TRIGGER
Source: on-board clock, direct external trigger, or software trigger jumper selectable. On board clock preset to 8 kHz for OMD-5508TC and OMD-5508RTD, 7 kHz for OMD-5508BG-Q/H/F models

PHYSICAL
Dimensions: 3.9" x 6.0" (99 x 152.5 mm)
Temperature Range: 32 to 130°F (0 to 55°C)
Connector: 37-pin standard D subminiature female
Power Consumption: +5 V @ 0.6 A, +12 V @ 30 mA, -12 V @ 50 mA

INPUT CHARACTERISTICS
OMD-5508TC (THERMOCOUPLE INPUT)
Throughput: 8 kHz
Cold Junction Connection: DC-TC isothermal screw terminal panel with semiconductor sensing of terminal temperature
Cold Junction Compensation: Software selectable for J, K, T, E, R, S, B or none (for straight mV inputs) on a channel-to-channel basis
Open Thermocouple Detection: Broken wire TC produces + full scale
Channel-to-Channel Offset: ±3 µV
Noise Referred to Input: 10 µV peak-to-peak maximum
Resolution: 0.1°C for J, K thermocouples

OMD-5508RTD (RTD INPUT)
Throughput: 8 kHz
Type of Measurement: Full 4-wire, with 0°C voltage nulled to zero
Current Source: Precise 1.00 mA source per each channel
Type of Input: 100 ohm platinum (alpha = 0.00392 or 0.00385)
Input Ranges: 100 mV, 50 mV, 25 mV or 12.5 mV full scale (software selectable)
Resolution: 0.03°C (at gain = 800)

OMD-5508BG-Q/H/F (STRAIN GAGE INPUT)
Throughput: 7 kHz
Type of Measurement: Bridge completion circuit with

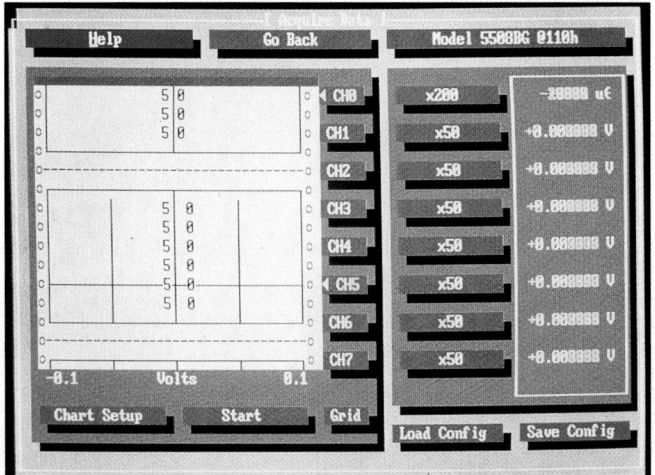

Utility Software (Included) Supports Data Collection and Facilitates Configuration

quarter, half or full bridge configuration, individual bridge supply per channel
Resistance: 350 or 120 ohm operation
Reference Voltage: 2.5 V or 5.0 V on-board, 10 V external
Input Ranges: 100 mV, 50 mV, 25 mV or 12.5 mV full scale (software selectable)
Resolution: Down to 1.2 microstrain (@5 V reference)

To Order *(Specify Model Number)*

Model No.	Price	Description
OMD-5508TC	$650	8-channel thermocouple input board, includes one OMD-DC-TC termination panel
OMD-DC-TC	85	Additional termination panel for thermocouple input board
OMD-5508RTD	795	8-channel RTD input board, includes one OMD-DC-36
OMD-5508BG-Q-350	795	Strain gage card for external 350 ohm quarter bridge
OMD-5508BG-H-350	795	Strain gage card for external 350 ohm half bridge
OMD-5508BG-F-350	795	Strain gage card for external 350 ohm full bridge
OMD-5508BG-Q-120	795	Strain gage card for external 120 ohm quarter bridge
OMD-5508BG-H-120	795	Strain gage card for external 120 ohm half bridge
OMD-5508BG-F-120	795	Strain gage card for external 120 ohm full bridge
OMD-DC-36	65	Additional bridge screw termination panel for OMD-5508RTD

Each board comes with mating screw termination panel, sample software, and complete operator's manual.

Ordering Example: *OMD-5508TC 8-channel thermocouple input board (includes termination panel),* ***$650.***

TEMPERATURE ACCESSORIES FOR STRAIN MEASUREMENT AREA

Self Adhesive Fast Response Thermocouple

- ✔ **Easy to Install**
- ✔ **Available in J, K, T, and E Calibrations**
- ✔ **Better Than 0.3 Second Response Time**
- ✔ **36″ Color-Coded Teflon® Insulated Leads**
- ✔ **Rated to 500°F Long Term**
- ✔ **Convenient 5 Pack**

Convenient 5-Pack

$60

Available in J, K, T, or E Thermocouple Calibrations

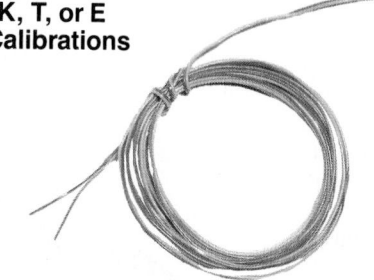

To Order: *(Specify Model Number)*

MODEL	THERMOCOUPLE TYPE	PRICE
SA1-J	**J** Iron-Constantan	$60/5-Pack
SA1-K	**K** Chromega™-Alomega™	$60/5-Pack
SA1-E	**E** Chromega-Constantan	$60/5-Pack
SA1-T	**T** Copper-Constantan	$60/5-Pack

IN STOCK FOR FAST DELIVERY!

SPECIFICATIONS

Thermocouple Calibrations: J (Iron-Constantan), K (Chromega™-Alomega™), T (Copper-Constantan), E (Chromega-Constantan)
Adhesive: Pressure sensitive silicone polymer
Maximum Temperature: 350°F, continuous
Minimum Temperature: −75°F, continuous
Laminates: High temperature polymer, and fiberglass reinforced polymer layers
Wire: 36″ leads, 30 AWG Teflon® coated (72″ leads available, add suffix -72 to model number and $20 to the price.)

Temperature Indicating Labels for a Permanent Record of Measurement Areas

To Order *(Specify Model Number)*

8 Dot Labels $30.00 pack of 10

Model	Temperature Range °F *							
TL-E-105	105	110	115	120	130	140	150	160
TL-E-170	170	180	190	200	210	220	230	240
TL-E-250	250	260	270	280	290	300	310	320
TL-E-330	330	340	350	360	370	380	390	400
TL-E-410	410	420	435	450	465	480	490	500

Model	Temperature Range °F `				
TL-F-105	105	110	115	120	130
TL-F-140	140	150	160	170	180
TL-F-190	190	200	210	220	230
TL-F-240	240	250	260	270	280
TL-F-290	290	300	310	320	330
TL-F-340	340	350	360	370	380
TL-F-390	390	400	410	420	435
TL-F-450	450	465	480	490	500

All labels show the °C equivalent to the °F rating.

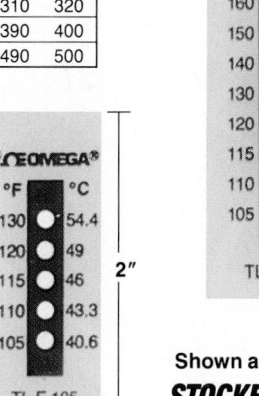

TL-F-105

¾″

Shown actual size

STOCKED FOR FAST DELIVERY

8-Dot Labels

TL-E labels have 8 different temperature ratings on a single label, which give the user the most information about the highest temperature reached. These indicators are supplied 10 to a package.

5-Dot Labels

TL-F labels have five temperature dots aligned in a straight line. This design gives the user the maximum temperature, with just a quick glance. The TL-F series labels are supplied 10 to a package.

For more information: See the OMEGA Complete Temperature Measurement Handbook and Encyclopedia®

PRACTICAL STRAIN GAGE MEASUREMENTS

Introduction

With today's emphasis on product liability and energy efficiency, designs must not only be lighter and stronger, but also more thoroughly tested than ever before. This places new importance on the subject of experimental stress analysis and the techniques for measuring strain. The main theme of this application note is aimed at strain measurements using bonded resistance strain gages. We will introduce considerations that affect the accuracy of this measurement and suggest procedures for improving it.

We will also emphasize the practical considerations of the strain gage measurement, with an emphasis on computer controlled instrumentation.

Appendix B contains schematics of many of the ways strain gages are used in bridge circuits and the equations which apply to them. Readers wishing a more thorough discussion of bridge circuit theory are invited to read Reference 7 noted in the bibliography.

Stress and Strain

The relationship between stress and strain is one of the most fundamental concepts from the study of mechanics of materials and is of paramount importance to the stress analyst. In experimental stress analysis we apply a given load and then measure the strain on individual members of a structure or machine. Then we use the stress-strain relationships to compute the stresses in those members to verify that these stresses remain within the allowable limits for the particular materials used.

Strain

When a force is applied to a body, the body deforms. In the general case this deformation is called strain. In this application note we will be more specific and define the term STRAIN to mean deformation per unit length or fractional change in length and give it the symbol, ϵ. See Figure 1. This is the strain that we typically measure with a bonded resistance strain gage. Strain may be either tensile (positive) or com-

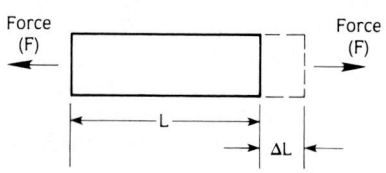

Figure 1: Uniaxial Force Applied

pressive (negative). See Figure 2. When written in equation form, $\epsilon = \Delta L/L$, we see that strain is a ratio and therefore dimensionless.

To maintain the physical significance of strain, it is often written with units of inch/inch. For most metals the strains measured in experimental work are typically less than 0.005000 inch/inch. Since practical strain values are so small, they are often expressed in micro-strain which is ϵ x 10^6 (note this is equivalent to parts per million or ppm) and has the symbol, $\mu\epsilon$. Still another way to express strain is as percent strain, which is ϵ x 100. For example: 0.005 inch/inch = 5000 $\mu\epsilon$ = 0.5%.

As described to this point, strain is fractional change in length and is directly measurable. Strain of this type is also often referred to as normal strain.

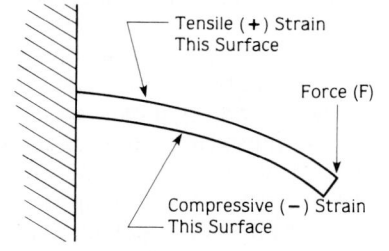

Figure 2: Cantilever in Bending

Shearing Strain

Another type of strain called SHEARING STRAIN is a measure of angular distortion. Shearing strain is also directly measurable but not as easily as normal strain. If we had a thick book sitting on a table top and we applied a force parallel to the covers, we could see the shear strain by observing the edges of the pages.

See Figure 3. Shearing strain, γ, is defined as the angular change in radians between two line segments that were orthogonal in the undeformed state. Since this angle is very small for most metals, shearing strain is approximated by the tangent of the angle.

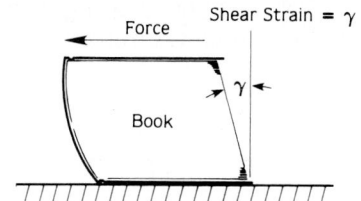

Figure 3: Visualizing Shearing Strain

Poisson Strain

In Figure 4 is a bar with a uniaxial tensile force applied, like the bar in Figure 1. The dashed lines show the shape of the bar after deformation, pointing out another phenomenon,

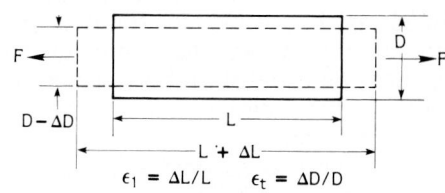

$$\epsilon_1 = \Delta L/L \qquad \epsilon_t = \Delta D/D$$

Figure 4: Poisson Strain

that of Poisson strain. The dashed lines indicate that the bar not only elongates but that its girth contracts. This contraction is a strain in the transverse direction due to a property of the material known as Poisson's Ratio. Poisson's ratio, ν, is defined as the negative ratio of the

Stress and Strain (continued)

strain in the transverse direction to the strain in the longitudinal direction. It is interesting to note that no stress is associated with the Poisson strain. Referring to Figure 4, the equation for Poisson's ratio is $\nu = -\epsilon_t/\epsilon_1$. Note that ν is dimensionless.

Normal Stress

While forces and strains are measurable quantities used by the designer and stress analyst, stress is the term used to compare the loading applied to a material with its ability to carry the load. Since it is usually desirable to keep machines and structures as small and light as possible, the parts should be stressed, in service, to the highest permissible level. STRESS refers to force per unit area on a given plane within a body.

The bar in Figure 5 has a uniaxial tensile force, F, applied along the x-axis. If we assume the force to be

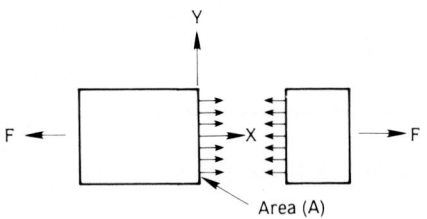

Figure 5: Normal Stress

uniformly distributed over the cross-sectional area, A, the "average" stress on the plane of the section is F/A. This stress is perpendicular to the plane and is called NORMAL STRESS, σ. Expressed in equation form, $\sigma = F/A$, and has units of force per unit area. Since the normal stress is in the x direction and there is no component of force in the y direction, there is no normal stress in that direction. The normal stress is in the positive x direction and is tensile.

Shear Stress

Just as there are two types of strains, there is also a second type of stress called SHEAR STRESS. Where normal stress is normal to the designated plane, shear stress is parallel to the plane and has the symbol, τ. In the example shown in Figure 5, there is no y component of force, therefore no force parallel to the plane of the section, so there is no shear stress on that plane. Since the orientation of the plane is arbitrary, what happens if the plane is

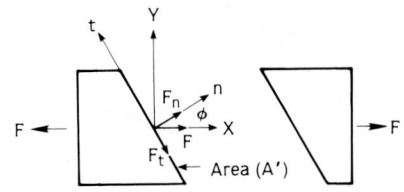

Figure 6: Shear Stress

oriented other than normal to the line of action of the applied force? Figure 6 demonstrates this concept with a section taken on the n-t coordinate system at some arbitrary angle, ϕ, to line of action of the force.

We see that the force vector, F, can be broken into two components, F_n and F_t, that are normal and parallel to the plane of the section. This plane has a cross-sectional area of A' and has both normal and shear stresses applied. The average normal stress, σ, is in the n direction and the average shear stress, τ, is in the t direction. Their equations are: $\sigma = F_n/A'$ and $\tau = F_t/A'$. Note that it was the force vector that was broken into components, not the stresses, and that the resulting stresses are a function of the orientation of the section. This means that stresses (and strains), while having both magnitude and direction, are not vectors and do not follow the laws of vector addition, except in certain special cases, and they should not be treated as such. We should also note that stresses are derived quantities, computed from other measurable quantities, and are not directly measurable. [3]

Principal Axes

In the preceding examples the x-y axes are also the PRINCIPAL AXES for the uniaxially loaded bar. By definition, the principal axes are the axes of maximum and minimum normal stress. They have the additional

characteristic of zero shear stress on the planes that lie along these axes. In Figure 5 the stress in the x direction is the maximum normal stress, and we noted that there was no force component in the y direction and therefore zero shear stress on the plane. Since there is no force in the y direction, there is zero normal stress in the y direction and in this case zero is the minimum normal stress. So the requirements for the principal axes are met by the x-y axes. In Figure 6 the x-y axes are the principal axes since that bar is also loaded uniaxially. The n-t axes in Figure 6 do not meet the zero shear stress requirement of the principal axes. The corresponding STRAINS on the principal axes are also maximum and minimum and the shear strain is zero.

The principal axes are very important in stress analysis because the magnitudes of the maximum and minimum normal stresses are usually the quantity of interest. Once the principal stresses are known then the normal and shear stresses in any orientation may be computed. If the orientation of the principal axes are known, through knowledge of the loading conditions or experimental techniques, the task of measuring the strains and computing the stresses is greatly simplified.

In some cases we are interested in the average value of stress or load on a member, but often we want to determine the magnitude of the stresses at a point. The material will fail at the point where the stress exceeds the load-carrying capacity of the material. This failure may occur because of excessive tensile or compressive normal stress or excessive shearing stress. In actual structures the area of this excessive stress level may be quite small. The usual method of diagramming the stress at a point is to use an infinitesimal element that surrounds the point of interest. The stresses are then a function of the orientation of this element, and in one particular orientation, the element will have its sides parallel to the principal axes. This is the orientation that gives the maximum and minimum normal stresses on the point of interest.

Stress-Strain Relationships

Now that we have defined stress and strain we need to explore the stress-strain relationship, for it is this relationship that allows us to calculate stresses from the measured strains. If we have a bar made of mild steel and incrementally load it in uniaxial tension and plot the strain versus the normal stress in the direction of the applied load, the plot will look like the stress-strain diagram in Figure 7.

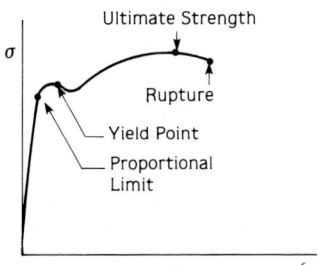

Figure 7:
Stress-Strain Diagram for Mild Steel

From Figure 7 we can see that up to a point, called the proportional limit, there is a linear relationship between stress and strain. Hooke's Law describes this relationship. The slope of this straight line portion of the stress-strain diagram is the MODULUS OF ELASTICITY or YOUNG'S MODULUS for the material. The modulus of elasticity, E, has the same units as stress (force per unit area) and is determined experimentally for materials. Written in equation form this stress-strain relationship is $\sigma = E \cdot \epsilon$. Some materials, for example cast iron and concrete, do not have a linear portion to their stress-strain diagrams. To do accurate stress analysis studies for these materials it is necessary to determine the stress-strain properties, including Poisson's ratio, for the particular material on a testing machine. Also, the modulus of elasticity may vary with temperature. This variation may need to be experimentally determined and considered when performing stress analysis at temperature extremes. There are two other points of interest on the stress-strain diagram in Figure 7, the yield point and the ultimate strength value of stress.

The yield point is the stress level at which strain will begin to increase rapidly with little or no increase in stress. If the material is stressed beyond the yield point, and then the stress is removed, the material will not return to its original size but will retain a residual offset or strain. The ultimate strength is the maximum stress developed in the material before rupture.

The examples we have examined to this point have been examples of uniaxial forces and stresses. In experimental stress analysis the biaxial stress state is the most common. Figure 8 shows an example of a

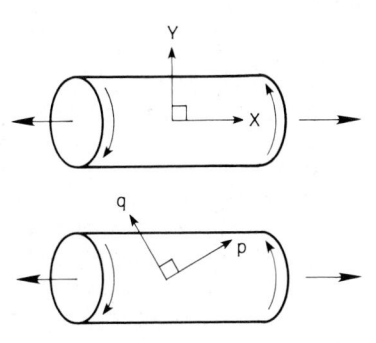

Figure 8: Shaft in Torsion and Tension

shaft with both tension and torsion applied. The point of interest is surrounded by an infinitesimal element with its sides oriented parallel to the x-y axes. The point has a biaxial stress state and a triaxial strain state (remember Poisson's ratio). The element, rotated to be aligned with the principal (p-q) axes, is also shown in Figure 8. Figure 9 shows the element removed with arrows added to depict the stresses at the

point for both orientations of the element.

We see that the element oriented along the x-y axes has a normal stress in the x direction, zero normal stress in the y direction and shear stresses on its surfaces. The element rotated to the p-q axes orientation has normal stress in both directions but zero shear stress as it should, by definition, if the p-q axes are the principal axes. The normal stresses, σ_p and σ_q, are the maximum and minimum normal stresses for the point. The strains in the p-q direction are also the maximum and minimum, and there is zero shear strain along these axes. Appendix C gives the equations relating stress to strain for the biaxial stress state.

If we know the orientation of the principal axes, we can then measure the strain in those directions and compute the maximum and minimum normal stresses and the maximum shear stress, for a given loading condition. We don't always know the orientation of the principal axes, but if we measure the strain in three separate directions, we can compute the strain in any direction including the principal axes directions. Three and four element rosette strain gages are used to measure the strain when the principal axes orientation is unknown. The equations for computing the orientation and magnitudes of the principal strains from 3-element rosette strain data are found in Appendix C.

For further study of mechanics of materials refer to References [1, 4, 6] noted in the bibliography. Properties of several common engineering materials are listed in Appendix A.

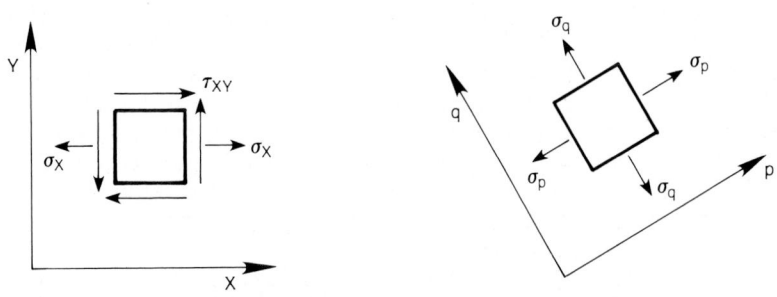

Figure 9: Element on X-Y Axes and Principal Axes

Measuring Strain

Stress in a material can't be measured directly. It must be computed from other measurable parameters. Therefore the stress analyst uses measured strains in conjunction with other properties of the material to calculate the stresses for a given loading condition. There are methods of measuring strain or deformation based on various mechanical, optical, acoustical, pneumatic, and electrical phenomena. This section briefly describes several of the more common methods and their relative merits.

Gage Length

The measurement of strain is the measurement of the displacement between two points some distance apart. This distance is the GAGE LENGTH and is an important comparison between various strain measurement techniques. Gage length could also be described as the distance over which the strain is averaged. For example, we could, on some simple structure such as the part in Figure 10, measure the part length with a micrometer both before and during loading. Then we would subtract the two readings to get the total deformation of the part. Dividing this total deformation by the original length would yield an average value of strain for the entire part. The gage length would be the original length of the part.

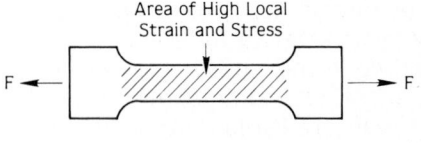

Figure 10

If we used this technique on the part in Figure 10, the strain in the reduced width region of the part would be locally higher than the measured value because of the reduced cross-sectional area carrying the load. The stresses will also be highest in the narrow region and the part will yield there before the measured average strain value indicates a magnitude of stress

greater than the yield point of the material.

Ideally, we want the strain measuring device to have an infinitesimal gage length so we can measure strain at a point. If we had this ideal strain gage we would place it in the narrow portion of the specimen in Figure 10 to measure the high local strain in that region. Other desirable characteristics for this ideal strain measuring device are small size and mass, easy attachment, high sensitivity to strain, low cost and low sensitivity to temperature and other ambient conditions. [2,6]

Mechanical Devices

The earliest strain measurement devices were mechanical in nature. We have already considered an example using a micrometer to measure strain and observed a problem with that approach. Extensometers are a class of mechanical devices used for measuring strain that employ a system of levers to amplify the minute strains to a level that can be read. A minimum gage length of 1/2 inch and a resolution of about 10 $\mu\epsilon$ is the best that can be achieved with purely mechanical devices. The addition of light beam and mirror arrangements to extensometers improves resolution and shortens gage length, allowing 2 $\mu\epsilon$ resolution and gage lengths down to 1/4 inch.

Still another type of device, the photoelectric gage, uses a combination of mechanical, optical, and electrical amplification to measure strain. This is done by using a light beam, two fine gratings and a photocell detector to generate an electrical current that is proportional to strain. This device comes in gage lengths as short as 1/16 inch but it is costly and delicate. All of these mechanical devices tend to be bulky and cumbersome to use, and most are only suitable for static strain measurements.

Optical Methods

Several optical methods are used for strain measurement. One of

these techniques uses the interference fringes produced by optical flats to measure strain. This device is sensitive and accurate but the technique is so delicate that laboratory conditions are required for its use. Reference 5 in the bibliography gives excellent introductions to the optical methods of photoelasticity, holography, and moire' methods of strain analysis. [2,5]

Electrical Devices

Another class of strain measuring devices depends on electrical characteristics which vary in proportion to the strain in the body to which the device is attached. Capacitance and inductance strain gages have been constructed but sensitivity to vibration, mounting difficulties, and complex circuit requirements keep them from being very practical for stress analysis work. These devices are, however, often employed in transducers. The piezoelectric effect of certain crystals has also been used to measure strain. When a crystal strain gage is deformed or strained a voltage difference is developed across the face of the crystal. This voltage difference is proportional to the strain and is of a relatively high magnitude. Crystal strain gages are fairly bulky, very fragile, and not suitable for measuring static strains.

Probably the most important electrical characteristic which varies in proportion to strain is that of electrical resistance. Devices whose output depend on this characteristic are the piezoresistive or semiconductor gage, the carbon-resistor gage, and the bonded metallic wire and foil resistance gages. The carbon-resistor gage is the forerunner of the bonded resistance wire strain gage. It is low in cost, can have a short gage length, and is very sensitive to strain. A high sensitivity to temperature and humidity are the disadvantages of the carbon-resistor strain gage.

The semiconductor strain gage is based on the piezoresistive effect in certain semiconductor materials such as silicon and germanium.

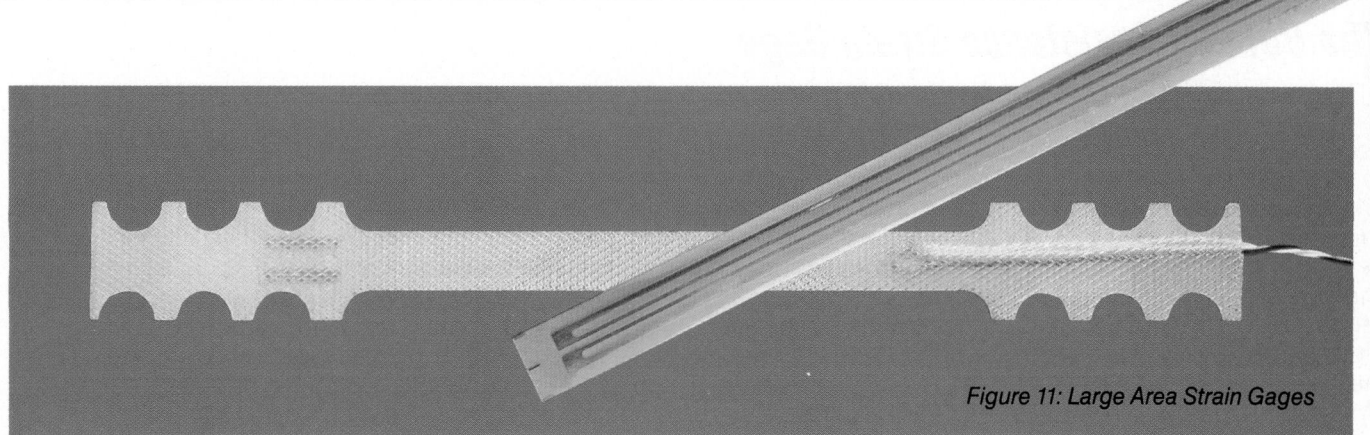

Figure 11: Large Area Strain Gages

Semiconductor gages have elastic behavior and can be produced to have either positive or negative resistance changes when strained. They can be made physically small while still maintaining a high nominal resistance. The strain limit for these gages is in the 1000 to 10000 $\mu\epsilon$ range with most tested to 3000 $\mu\epsilon$ in tension. Semiconductor gages exhibit a high sensitivity to strain but the change in resistance with strain is nonlinear. Their resistance and output are temperature sensitive and the high output, resulting from changes in resistance as large as 10-20%, can cause measurement problems when using the devices in a bridge circuit. However, mathematical corrections for the temperature sensitivity, the nonlinearity of output, and the nonlinear characteristics of the bridge circuit (if used), can be made automatically when using computer controlled instrumentation to measure strain with semiconductor gages. They can be used to measure both static and dynamic strains. When measuring dynamic strains temperature effects are usually less important than for static strain measurements and the high output of the semiconductor gage is an asset.

The bonded resistance strain gage is by far the most widely used strain measurement tool for today's experimental stress analyst. It consists of a grid of very fine wire, or more recently of thin metallic foil, bonded to a thin insulating backing called a carrier matrix. The electrical resistance of this grid material varies linearly with strain. In use the carrier matrix is attached to the test specimen with an adhesive. When the specimen is loaded, the strain on its surface is transmitted to the grid material by the adhesive and carrier system. The strain in the specimen is found by measuring the change in the electrical resistance of the grid material. Figure 12 is a picture of a bonded resistance strain gage with a constantan foil grid and polyimide carrier material. The bonded resistance strain gage is low in cost, can be made with a short gage length, is only moderately affected by temperature changes, has small physical size and low mass, and has fairly high sensitivity to strain. It is suitable for measuring both static and dynamic strains. The remainder of this application note deals with the instrumentation considerations for making accurate, practical strain measurements using the bonded resistance strain gage. [2,5,6]

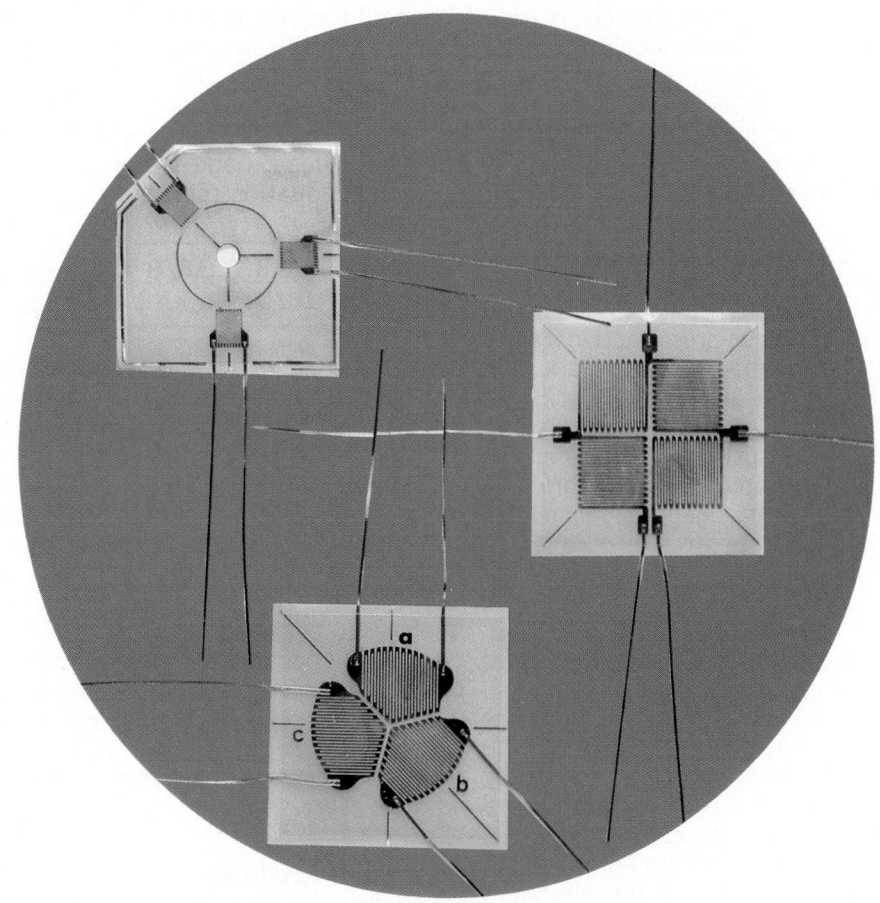

Figure 12: Foil Bonded Resistance Strain Gages

The Bonded Resistance Strain Gage

The term "bonded resistance strain gage" can apply to the nonmetallic (semiconductor) gage or to the metallic (wire or foil) gage. Wire and foil gages operate on the same basic principles and both can be treated in the same fashion from the measurement standpoint. The semiconductor gage, having a much higher sensitivity to strain than metallic gages, can have other considerations introduced into its measurement. We will use the term STRAIN GAGE or GAGE to refer to the BONDED METALLIC FOIL GRID RESISTANCE STRAIN GAGE throughout the rest of this application note. These foil gages are sometimes referred to as metal-film gages.

Strain gages are made with a printed circuit process using conductive alloys rolled to a thin foil. The alloys are processed, including controlled-atmosphere heat treating, to optimize their mechanical properties and temperature coefficient of resistance. A grid configuration for the strain sensitive element is used to allow higher values of gage resistance while maintaining short gage lengths. Gage resistance values range from 30 to 3000 ohms, with 120 ohm and 350 ohm being the most commonly used values for stress analysis. Gage lengths from 0.008 inch to 4 inches are commercially available. The conductor in a foil grid gage has a large surface area for a given cross-sectional area. This keeps the shear stress low in the adhesive and carrier matrix as the strain is transmitted by them. This larger surface area also allows good heat transfer between grid and specimen. Strain gages are small and light, will operate over a wide temperature range and can respond to both static and dynamic strains. They have wide application and acceptance in transducers as well as stress analysis.

In a strain gage application, the carrier matrix and the adhesive must work together to faithfully transmit the strains from the specimen to the grid. They also serve as an electrical insulator between the grid and the specimen and must transfer heat away from the grid. Three primary factors influencing gage selection are operating temperature, state of strain (including gradients, magnitude and time dependence) and stability requirements for the gage installation. The importance of selecting the proper combination of carrier material, grid alloy, adhesive, and protective coating for the given application cannot be over-emphasized. Strain gage manufacturers are the best source of information on this topic and have many excellent publications to assist the customer in selecting the proper strain gages, adhesives and protective coatings.

Gage Factor

When a metallic conductor is strained it undergoes a change in electrical resistance, and it is this change that makes the strain gage a useful device. The measure of this resistance change with strain is GAGE FACTOR, GF. Gage factor is defined as the ratio of the fractional change in resistance to the fractional change in length (strain) along the axis of the gage. Gage factor is a dimensionless quantity and the larger the value the more sensitive the strain gage. Gage factor is expressed in equation form as:

$$GF = \frac{\Delta R/R}{\Delta L/L} = \frac{\Delta R/R}{\epsilon}$$

Equation No. 10

It should be noted that the change in resistance with strain is not just due to the dimensional changes in the conductor, but that the resistivity of the conductor material also changes with strain. The term gage factor applies to the strain gage as a whole, complete with carrier matrix, not just to the strain sensitive conductor. The gage factor for constantan and nickel-chromium alloy strain gages is nominally 2 and various gage and instrumentation specifications are usually based on this nominal value.

Transverse Sensitivity

If the strain gage were a single straight length of conductor, of small diameter with respect to its length, it would respond to strain along its longitudinal axis and be essentially insensitive to strain perpendicular or transverse to this axis. For any reasonable value of gage resistance it would also have a very long gage length. When the conductor is in the form of a grid to reduce the effective gage length, there are small amounts of strain sensitive material in the end loops or turn-arounds that lie transverse to the gage axis. See Figure 13. This end loop material gives the gage a non-zero sensitivity to strain in the transverse direction. TRANSVERSE SENSITIVITY FACTOR, K_t, is defined by:

$$K_t = \frac{GF(transverse)}{GF(longitudinal)},$$

and is usually expressed in percent. Values of K range from 0 to 10%.

To minimize this effect, extra material is added to the conductor in the end loops and the grid lines are kept close together. This serves to minimize the resistance in the transverse direction. Correction for transverse sensitivity may be necessary for short, wide-grid gages, or where there is considerable misalignment between the gage axis and the principal axis, or in rosette analysis where high transverse strain fields may exist. Data supplied by the manufacturer with the gage can be entered into the computer controlling the instrumentation and corrections for transverse sensitivity made to the strain data as it is collected.

Temperature Effects

Ideally we would prefer the strain gage to change resistance only in response to the stress-induced strain in the test specimen, but the resistivity and the strain sensitivity of all known strain sensitive materials vary with temperature. Of course that means the gage resistance and the gage factor will change when the temperature changes. This change in resistance with temperature for a mounted strain

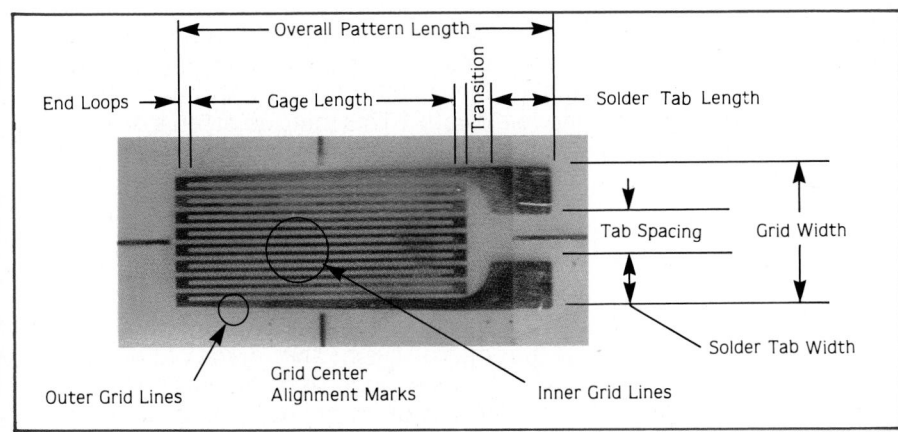

Figure 13: Strain Gage Nomenclature

gage is a function of the difference in the thermal expansion coefficients between the gage and the specimen and of the thermal coefficient of resistance of the gage alloy. Self-temperature compensating gages may be produced for specific

Approximate Thermal Expansion Coefficient	
Material	PPM/°C
Quartz	0.5
Titanium	9
Mild Steel	11
Stainless Steel	16
Aluminum	23
Magnesium	26

Table 2
Thermal Expansion Coefficients of Some Common Materials for which Temperature Compensated Strain Gages Are Available

materials by processing the strain sensitive alloy such that it has thermal resistance characteristics that compensate for the effects of the mismatch in thermal expansion coefficients between the gage and the specific material. A temperature compensated gage produced in this manner is accurately compensated only when mounted on a material that has a specific coefficient of thermal expansion. Table 2 is a list of common materials for which self-temperature compensated gages are available.

The compensation is only effective over a limited temperature range because of the nonlinear character of both the thermal coefficients of

expansion and the thermal coefficient of resistance.

The Measurement

From the gage factor equation we see that it is the FRACTIONAL CHANGE in resistance that is the important quantity rather than the absolute resistance value of the gage. Let's see just how large this resistance change will be for a strain of 1 $\mu\epsilon$. If we use a 120 ohm strain gage with a gage factor of +2, the gage factor equation tells us that 1 $\mu\epsilon$ applied to a 120 ohm gage produces a change in resistance of

$$\Delta R = 120 \times 0.000001 \times 2 = 0.000240 \text{ ohms,}$$

or 240 micro-ohms. That means we need to have micro-ohm sensitivity in the measuring instrumentation. Since it is the fractional change in resistance that is of interest and

since this change will likely be only tens of milliohms, some reference point is needed from which to begin the measurement. The nominal value of gage resistance has a tolerance equivalent to several hundred microstrain and will usually change when the gage is bonded to the specimen, so this nominal value can't be used as a reference.

An initial, unstrained, gage resistance is used as the reference from which strain is measured. Typically the gage is mounted on the test specimen and wired to the instrumentation while the specimen is maintained in an unstrained state. A reading taken under these conditions is the unstrained reference value and applying a strain to the specimen will result in a resistance change from this value. If we had an ohmmeter that was accurate and sensitive enough to make the measurement, we would measure the unstrained gage resistance and then substract this unstrained value from the subsequent strained values. Dividing the result by the unstrained value would give us the fractional resistance change caused by strain in the specimen. In some cases it is practical to use just this method, and these cases will be discussed in a later section of this application note. A more sensitive way of measuring small changes in resistance is with the use of the Wheatstone bridge circuit and in fact most instrumentation for measuring static strain uses this circuit. [2,5,6,7,8]

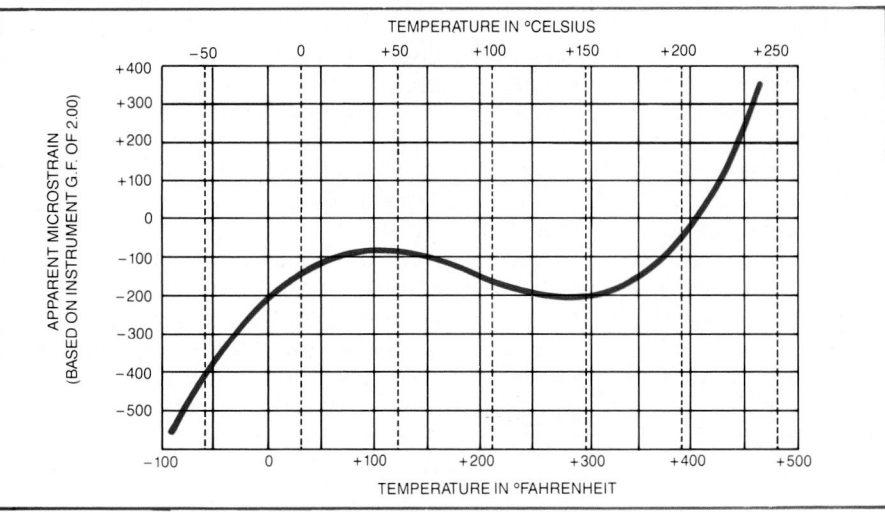

Figure 14: Typical Temperature Induced Apparent Strain

Measurement Methods

Wheatstone Bridge Circuit

Because of its outstanding sensitivity, the Wheatstone bridge circuit (depicted in Figure 15) is the most frequently used circuit for static strain measurements. This section examines this circuit and its application to strain gage measurements. By using a computer in

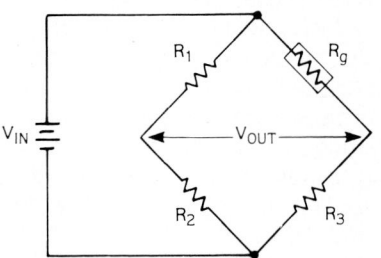

Figure 15: Wheatstone Bridge Circuit

conjunction with the measurement instrumentation, we can simplify using the bridge circuit, increase measurement accuracy, and compile large quantities of data from multichannel systems. The computer also removes the requirement for balancing the bridge, compensates for nonlinearities in output and handles the switching and data storage in multichannel applications.

Balanced Bridge Strain Gage Measurement

In Figure 15, V_{IN} is the input voltage to the bridge, R_g is the resistance of the strain gage, R_1, R_2, and R_3 are the resistances of the bridge completion resistors, and V_{OUT} is the bridge output voltage. A ¼ bridge configuration exists when one arm of the bridge is an active gage and the other arms are fixed value resistors or unstrained gages as is the case in this circuit. Ideally the strain gage, R_g, is the only resistor in the circuit that varies, and then only due to a change in strain on the surface of the specimen to which it is attached. V_{OUT} is a function of V_{IN}, R_1, R_2, R_3 and R_g. This relationship is:

$$V_{OUT} = V_{IN} \left[\frac{R_3}{R_3 + R_g} - \frac{R_2}{R_1 + R_2} \right]$$

Equation No. 11

When $(R_1/R_2) = (R_g/R_3)$, V_{OUT} becomes zero and the bridge is balanced. If we could adjust one of the resistor values, R_2 for example, then we could balance the bridge for various values of the other resistors. Figure 16 shows a schematic of this concept.

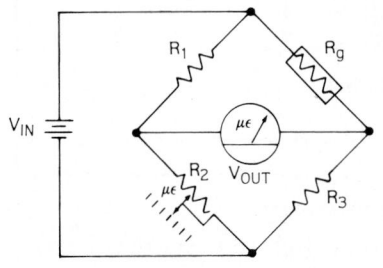

Figure 16: Bridge Circuit with Provision for Balancing the Bridge

Referring to the gage factor equation,

$$GF = \frac{\Delta R/R}{\epsilon}$$

Equation No. 10

we see that the quantity we need to measure is the fractional change in gage resistance from the unstrained value to the strained value. If, when the gage is unstrained, we adjust R_2 until the bridge is balanced and then apply strain to the gage, the change in R_g due to the strain will unbalance the bridge and V_{OUT} will become nonzero. If we adjust the value of R_2 to once again balance the bridge, the amount of the change required in resistance R_2 will equal the change in R_g due to the strain. Some strain indicators work on this principal by incorporating provisions for inputting the gage factor of the gage being used and indicating the change in the variable resistance, R_2, directly in micro-strain.

In the previous example the bridge becomes unbalanced when the strain is applied. V_{OUT} is a measure of this imbalance and is directly related to the change in R_g, the quantity of interest. Instead of rebalancing the bridge we could install an indicator, calibrated in micro-strain, that responds to V_{OUT}. Refer to Figure 16. If the resistance of this indicator is

much greater than that of the strain gage, its loading effect on the bridge circuit will be negligible, i.e., negligible current will flow through the indicator. This method often assumes: 1) a linear relationship between V_{OUT} and strain, 2) a bridge that was balanced in the initial, unstrained, state, 3) a known value of V_{IN}. In a bridge circuit the relationship between V_{OUT} and strain is nonlinear but for strains up to a few thousand micro-strain the error is usually small enough to be ignored. At large values of strain, corrections must be applied to the indicated reading to compensate for this nonlinearity.

The majority of commercial strain indicators use some form of balanced bridge for measuring resistance strain gages. In multichannel systems the number of manual adjustments required for balanced bridge methods becomes cumbersome to the user. Multichannel systems, under computer control, eliminate these adjustments by using an unbalanced bridge technique.

Unbalanced Bridge Strain Gage Measurement

The equation for V_{OUT} can be rewritten in the form of the ratio of V_{OUT} to V_{IN}:

$$\frac{V_{OUT}}{V_{IN}} = \left[\frac{R_3}{R_3 + R_g} - \frac{R_2}{R_1 + R_2} \right]$$

Equation No. 12

This equation holds for both the unstrained and the strained condition. Defining the unstrained value of gage resistance as R_g and the change due to strain as ΔR_g, the strained value of gage resistance is $R_g + \Delta R_g$. The actual effective value of resistance in each bridge arm is the sum of all the resistances in that arm and may include such things as lead wires, printed circuit board traces, switch contact resistance, interconnects, etc. As long as these resistances remain unchanged between the strained and unstrained readings, the measurement will be valid. Let's define a new term, V_r, as the difference of the ratios of V_{OUT}

to V_{IN} from the unstrained to the strained state:

$$V_r = \left[\left(\frac{V_{OUT}}{V_{IN}}\right)_{strained} - \left(\frac{V_{OUT}}{V_{IN}}\right)_{unstrained}\right]$$

Equation No. 13

By substituting the resistor values that correspond to the two (V_{OUT}/V_{IN}) terms into this equation, we can derive an equation for $\Delta R_g/R_g$. This new equation is:

$$\frac{\Delta R_g}{R_g} = \frac{-4V_r}{1 + 2V_r}$$

Equation No. 14

Note that it was assumed in this derivation that ΔR_g was the only change in resistance from the unstrained to the strained condition. Recalling the equation for gage factor:

$$GF = \frac{\Delta R_g/R_g}{\epsilon}$$

Equation No. 10

and combining these two equations we get an equation for strain in terms of V_r and GF.

$$\epsilon = \frac{-4V_r}{GF(1 + 2V_r)}$$

Equation No. 15

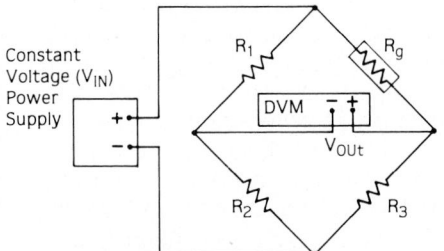

Figure 17: Instrumentation for Unbalanced Bridge Strain Gage Measurement

The schematic in Figure 17 shows how we can instrument the unbalanced bridge.

A constant voltage power supply furnishes V_{IN} and a digital voltmeter (DVM) is used to measure V_{OUT}. The DVM for this application should have a high (greater than 10^9 ohms) input resistance and 1 microvolt or better resolution. The gage factor is supplied by the gage manufacturer. In practice we would use a computer to have the DVM read and store V_{OUT} under unstrained conditions, then take another reading of V_{OUT} after the specimen was strained. Since the values for gage factor and the excitation voltage, V_{IN}, are known, the computer can calculate the strain value indicated by the change in bridge output voltage. If the value of V_{IN} is unknown or subject to variations with time, we can have the DVM measure it at the time V_{OUT} is measured to get a more precise value for V_r. This "timely" measurement of V_{IN} greatly reduces the stability requirements of the power supply, allowing a lower cost unit to be used. Note that in the preceding ¼ bridge example the bridge was not assumed to be balanced nor its output approximated as truly linear. Instead we just derived the equation for strain in terms of quantities that are known, or can be measured, and let the computer solve the equation to obtain the exact strain value.

In the preceding example we made some assumptions that impact the accuracy of the strain measurement:

• resistance in the three inactive bridge arms remained constant from unstrained to strained readings

• DVM accuracy, resolution, and stability were adequate for the required measurement

• resistance change in the active bridge arm was due only to change in strain

• V_{IN} and gage factor were both known quantities

Appendix B shows schematics of several configurations of bridge circuits, using strain gages, and gives the equation for strain as a function of V_r for each.

Multichannel Wheatstone Bridge Measurements

In the preceding example the measurement accuracy was dependent upon the resistances of all the bridge arms remaining constant from the time of the unstrained reading to the time of the strained reading, except for the change in the gage resistance due to strain. If any of the brige arm resistances changed during that time span there would be a corresponding change in bridge output voltage which would be interpreted as strain induced, so we would see an error. The same would be true of any other variation that changed the bridge output voltage. Any switching done in the bridge arms can cause a change in resistance due to variations in the

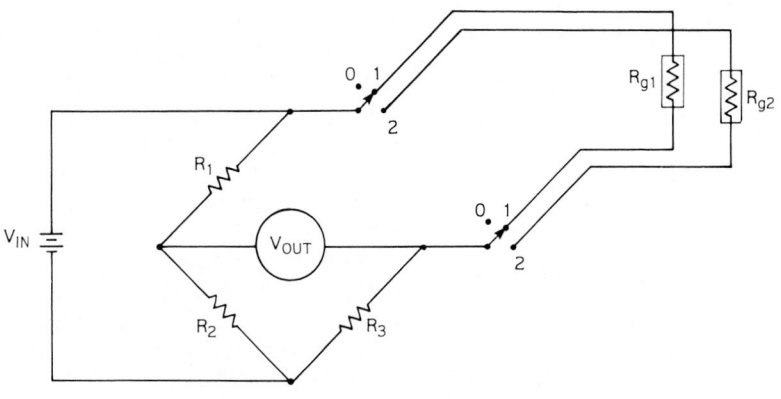

Figure 18: Switching Inside Bridge Arms

Measurement Methods (continued)

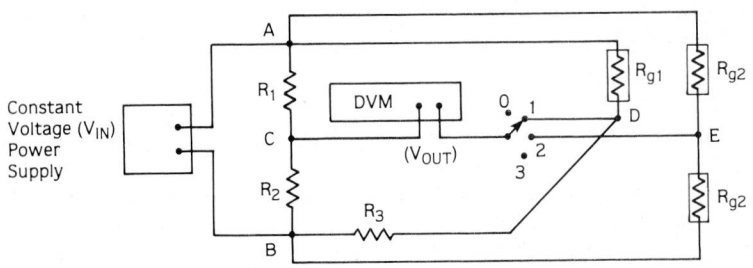

Figure 19: Schematic of Bridge Circuit with Shared Internal Half Bridge and Power Supply

Four-Wire Ohm Strain Gage Measurement

As we mentioned before, we can measure the change in absolute value of gage resistance to compute strain. This can be done quite accurately using a four-wire ohms measurement technique with a high resolution (e.g., 1 milliohm per least significant digit) digital multimeter (DMM). Figure 20 depicts the four-wire ohms method of resistance

switch or relay contact resistance and affect the bridge output voltage. For that reason it is not desirable to do switching inside the bridge arms for multichannel systems but rather allow those interconnections to be permanently wired and switch the DVM from bridge to bridge. Since a DVM has extremely high input impedance compared to the bridge arms, it doesn't load the bridge and switching the DVM has no effect on the bridge output voltage level. Figures 18 and 19 show schematics of these two methods of switching. We can see that switching inside the bridge arms allows the same bridge completion resistors to be used for multiple gages but that the power to the gage is removed when it is not being read. Also, any variations in switch contact resistance will appear in series with the gage resistance and will be indistinguishable from resistance changes due to strain.

Figure 19 shows a multiple channel arrangement that switches the DVM and also shares the power supply and internal half-bridge. This circuit is known as a "Chevron Bridge" and is often used for strain measurement on rotating machine elements to minimize the number of slip rings. One channel is shown as a ¼ bridge and the other as a ½ bridge (two active gages). The midpoint of the internal half-bridge for either of these configurations serves as a voltage reference point for the DVM and isn't affected by strain. Since the bridge completion resistors must have excellent stability specifications, they are relatively expensive and there is a cost advantage to

sharing the internal half bridge in multichannel systems.

For this method to function properly, the circuit must be designed and constructed such that a change in current due to strain in one arm does not change the current in any of the other arms. Also, the excitation voltage, V_{IN}, must be measured across points A-B and it may be desirable to measure this voltage each time a new set of readings is taken from this group of channels. The DVM is switched between points C-D, C-E, etc., to read the output voltages of the various channels in the group. This method keeps all of the gages energized at all times which minimizes dynamic heating and cooling affects in the gages and eliminates the need for switching inside the bridge arms. If the DVM has good low level measurement capability, the power supply voltage can be maintained at a low level thereby keeping the gage self heating effects to a minimum. For example, using a 2 volt power supply for the bridge yields a power dissipation, in a 350 ohm gage, of only 3 milliwatts. Yet even with this low power, 1 micro-strain sensitivity is still maintained with a ¼ bridge configuration (assuming GF=2), when using a DVM with 1 microvolt resolution. Since several channels are dependent upon one power supply and one resistor pair, a failure of one of these components will cause several channels to become inoperative. However the measurement of the excitation voltage permits the power supply to drift, be adjusted, or even replaced with no loss in measurement accuracy.

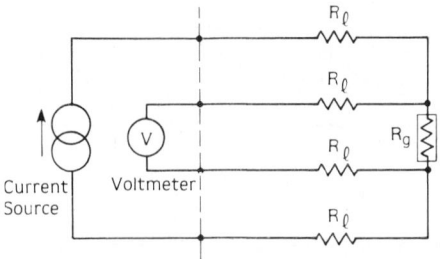

Figure 20: Schematic of Four-wire Ohm Circuit

measurement. The current source is connected internally in the DMM to the ohms source terminals while the voltmeter is connected to the ohms sense terminals of the DMM. When a measurement is being taken, the current source supplies a known fixed value of direct current through the circuit from the ohms source terminals while the voltmeter measures the d.c. voltage drop across the gage resistance. The absolute resistance value is computed from the values of current and voltage by the DMM and displayed or output to a computer. The lead resistances, R_ℓ, from the ohms source terminals to the gage are in series with the gage resistance but do not affect the accuracy of the measurement, since the voltage is read directly across the gage. The input impedance to the sense terminals is extremely high so the current flow in that loop is negligible. The source current value is typically very low which means the power dissipated in the strain gage is also very low and selfheating effects are virtually eliminated. For example, 1 milliamp is a typical value for the source current and this corresponds

to a power dissipation of 120 microwatts in a 120 ohm gage or 350 microwatts in a 350 ohm gage.

A technique for voltage offset compensation can be used with four-wire ohms measurements to correct for these effects. This is accomplished by first measuring the voltage across the gage without current flow from the source terminals and subtracting this value from the voltage read with source current flow. The resulting net voltage is then used to compute the gage resistance. Offset compensated four-wire ohms measurements can be made automatically by the DMM if it has that capability or the offset compensation can be accomplished by the computer controlling the instrumentation.

To use four-wire ohms for measuring strain we first make a resistance measurement of the gage in the unstrained condition and store this reading. Then we apply the strain to the specimen and make another measurement of gage resistance. The difference of these two readings divided by the unstrained reading is the fractional change in resistance that we use in the gage factor equation to compute strain. Of course the DMM can input these readings directly to a computer which calculates strain using the gage factor for the particular gage. This technique also lends itself to multichannel systems since variations in switch resistance in the circuit have the same effect as lead resistances and do not affect the accuracy of the measurement.

Constant Current Techniques

In the discussion of bridge circuits we assumed that the bridge excitation was furnished by a constant voltage source. We could have assumed constant current excitation for those discussions and derived the corresponding equations for strain as a function of voltage out and current supplied. In the example of Figure 19 the constant voltage supply which is shared by multiple bridges cannot be directly replaced by a constant current source since we wouldn't know how the current was divided between the various bridge circuits. In some cases the bridge output is more nearly linear when using constant current rather than constant voltage excitation but that is of little consequence if we solve an equation for strain versus output voltage with a computer. The use of a constant current source for a full bridge configuration does eliminate the need to sense the voltage at the bridge which eliminates the need for two wires to the bridge. In general, there is no real measurement advantage to using constant current rather than constant voltage excitation for bridge circuits as applied to strain gage measurements.

The four-wire ohms measurement discussed in the preceding section used a constant current source for excitation and we noted that the lead wires had no affect on the measurement. That method required four wires to be connected to the gage. Constant current excitation is sometimes used with a two-wire gage connection for dynamic strain measurements where temperature drift effects are negligible or can be filtered out from the strain data. In the circuit of Figure 21, changes in gage resistance result in proportional changes in V_{OUT}. Note

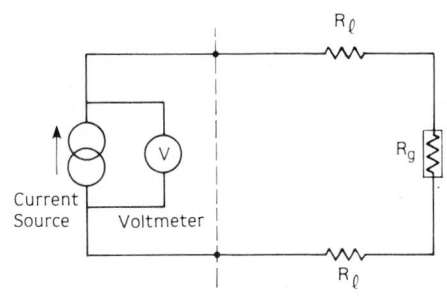

Figure 21: Constant Current Circuit Dynamic Strain Measurement

that V_{OUT} is also affected by changes in the lead resistances, R_ℓ. By measuring only the time varying component of V_{OUT}, the dynamic strain can be observed while slowly changing effects, such as temperature, are rejected.

The use of very sensitive DMMs to measure the bridge imbalance voltage or the gage resistance directly with four-wire ohms limits the speed at which the measurement can be made and only low frequency dynamic strains may be measured with these methods. Higher speed analog to digital converters typically have lower sensitivities so higher signal levels are needed when measuring higher frequency dynamic or transient strains. One way to achieve this is to amplify the bridge output voltage to an acceptable level. Another method is to use a semiconductor strain gage and exploit its large gage factor. A semiconductor gage can be used in a bridge circuit (such as Figure 19) with a DVM having lower resolution and higher speed than that required with metal gages. A semiconductor gage can also be used in a circuit similar to that for four-wire ohms (see Figure 22). In this case, the cur-

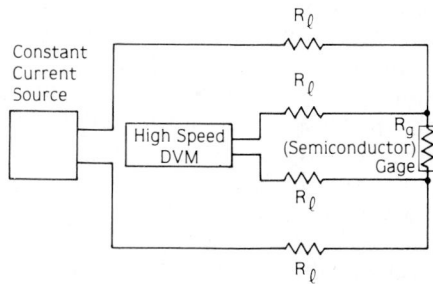

Figure 22: Circuit for Semiconductor Gage and High Speed Digital Voltmeter

rent source and the DVM should be separate instruments to allow the current level to be adjusted to obtain the best output voltage for the expected maximum strain level.

The lead wires do not affect the measurement since the voltage, as in four-wire ohms, is measured directly across the gage. This arrangement also allows the use of a less sensitive, higher speed DVM while maintaining reasonable strain resolution. For example, a DVM with 100 microvolt sensitivity gives a strain resolution of 6 $\mu\epsilon$ with a 0.44 milliamp current source (350 ohm semiconductor gage with GF = 100).

Practical Strain Measurement

Shielding and Guarding—Interference Rejection

The low output level of a strain gage makes strain measurements susceptible to interference from other sources of electrical energy. Capacitive and magnetic coupling to long cable runs, electrical leakage from the specimen through the gage backing, and differences in grounding potential are but a few of the possible sources of difficulty. The results of this type of electrical interference can range from a negligible reduction in accuracy to rendering the data invalid.

The Noise Model

In Figure 23, the shaded portion includes the Wheatstone bridge strain gage measuring circuit seen previously in Figures 15 and 17. The single active gage R_g shown mounted on a test specimen — e.g., an airplane tail section. The bridge excitation source V_{IN}, bridge completion resistors R_1, R_2 and R_3, and the DVM represent the measurement equipment located a significant distance (e.g., 100 feet) from the test specimen. The strain gage is connected to the measuring equipment via three wires having resistance R_ℓ in each wire. The electrical interference which degrades the strain measurement is coupled into the bridge through a number of parasitic resistance and capacitance elements. In this context, the term "parasitic" implies that the elements are unnecessary to the measurement, are basically unwanted, and are to some extent unavoidable. The parasitic elements result from the fact that lead wires have capacitance to other cables, gages have capacitance to the test specimen, and gage adhesives and wire insulation are not perfect insulators — giving rise to leakage resistance.

Examining the parasitic elements in more detail, the active gage R_g is shown made up of two equal resistors with C_{iso} connected at the center. C_{iso} represents the capacitance between the airplane tail section and the gage foil. Since the

capacitance is distributed uniformly along the gage grid length, we approximate the effect as a "lumped" capacitance connected to the gage's midpoint. R_{iso} and C_{iso} determine the degree of electrical isolation from the test specimen which is often electrically grounded or maintained at some "floating" potential different than the gage. Typical values of R_{iso} and C_{iso} are 1000 megohms and 100 pF respectively. Elements C_c and R_c represent the wire-to-wire capacitance and insulation resistance between adjacent power or signal cables in a cable vault or cable bundle. Typical values for C_c and R_c are 30 pF and 10^{12} ohms per foot for dry insulated conductors in close proximity.

The power supply exciting the bridge is characterized by parasitic elements C_{ps} and R_{ps}. A line powered, "floating output" power supply usually has no deliberate electrical connection between the negative output terminal and earth via the third wire of its power cord. However, relatively large amounts of capacitance usually exist between the negative output terminal circuits and the chassis and between the primary and secondary windings

of the power transformer. The resistive element R_{ps} is due to imperfect insulators and may be reduced several decades by ionic contamination or moisture due to condensation or high ambient humidity. If the power supply does not feature floating output, R_{ps} may be a fraction of an ohm. It will be shown that use of a non-floating or grounded output power supply drastically increases the mechanisms causing electrical interference in a practical, industrial environment. Typical values for C_{ps} and R_{ps} for floating output, laboratory grade power supplies are 0.01 μf and 100 megohms respectively. It is important to realize that neither the measuring equipment nor the gages have been "grounded" at any point. The entire system is "floating" to the extent allowed by the parasitic elements.

To analyze the sources of electrical interference we must first establish a reference potential. Safety considerations require that the power supply, DVM, bridge completion, etc., cabinets all be connected to earth ground through the third wire of their power cords. In Figure 23 this reference potential is designated as the measurement

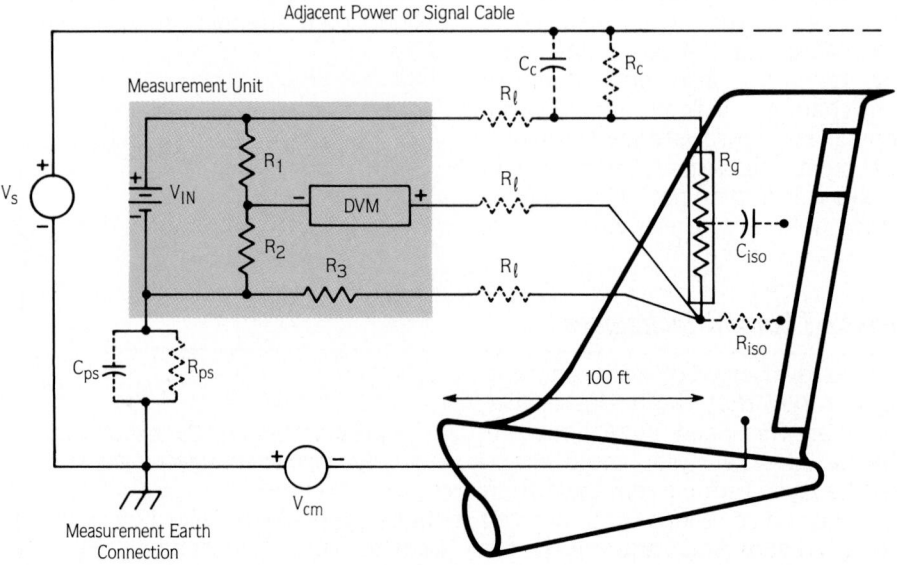

Figure 23: Remote Quarter Bridge Measurement Illustrating Parasitic Elements and Interference Sources

earth connection. The test specimen is often grounded (for safety reasons) to the power system at a point some distance away from the measurement equipment. This physical separation often gives rise to different grounding potentials as represented by the voltage source V_{cm}. In some cases, functional requirements dictate that the test specimen be "floated" or maintained many volts away from power system ground by electronic power supplies or signal sources. In either case, V_{cm} may contain dc and time varying components — most often at power line related frequencies. Typical values of V_{cm}, the common mode voltage, range from millivolts due to IR drops in "clean" power systems to 250 volts for specimens floating at power line potentials, for example parts of an electric motor. The disturbing source, V_s, is shown connected to measurement earth and represents the electrical potential of some cable in close proximity but unrelated functionally to the gage wires. In many applications, these adjacent cables may not exist or may be so far removed as to not affect the measurement. They will be included here to make the

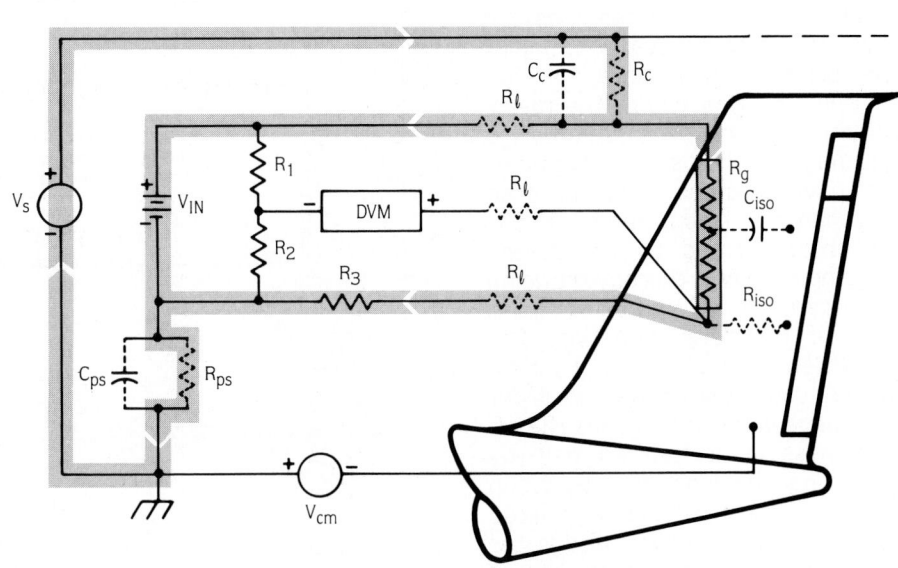

Figure 24: Current Leakage from Adjacent Cable Flows Through Gage Wires Causing Measurement Error

analysis general and more complete.

Shielding of Measurement Leads

The need for using shielded measurement leads can be seen by examining the case shown in Figure 24. Here an insulation failure (perhaps due to moisture) has reduced parasitic R_c to a few thousand ohms, and d.c. current is flowing through the gage measurement leads as a result of the source V_s. Negligible current flows through the DVM because of its high impedance. The currents through R_g and R_ℓ develop error-producing IR drops inside the measurement loops.

In Figure 25, a shield surrounds the three measurement leads and the current has been intercepted by the shield and routed to the point where the shield is connected to the bridge. The DVM reading error has been eliminated. Capacitive coupling from the signal cable to unshielded measurement leads will produce similar voltage errors, even if the coupling occurs equally to all three leads. In the case where V_s is a high voltage sine wave power cable, the DVM error will be substantially reduced if the voltmeter integrates the input for a time equal to an integer number of periods (e.g., 1, 10, or 100) of the power line wave form. The exact amount of the error reduction depends upon the DVM's normal mode rejection, which can be as large as 60-140 dB or 10^3:1 - 10^7:1 If the DVM is of a type having a very short sampling period, i.e., less than 100 μsec, it will measure the instan-

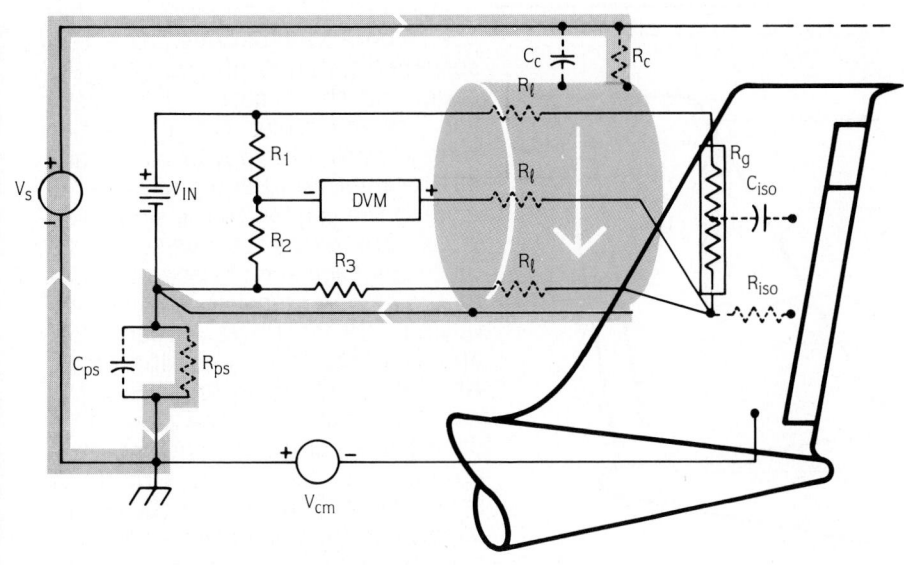

Figure 25: Addition of a Metal Shield Around the Gage Wires Keeps Current Due to V_s Out of Measurement Leads

Practical Strain Measurement (continued)

taneous value of d.c. signal (due to strain) plus interference. Averaging the proper number of readings can reduce the error due to power line or other periodic interference.

In the situation where the measurement leads run through areas of high magnetic fields, near high current power cables, etc., twisted measurement leads minimize the loop areas formed by the bridge arms and the DVM thereby reducing measurement degradation as a result of magnetic induction. The flat, three conductor side-by-side, molded, cable commonly used for strain gage work approaches the effectiveness of a twisted pair by minimizing the loop area between wires. The use of shielded, twisted leads and a DVM which integrates over one or more cycles of the power line wave form should be considered whenever leads are long, traverse a noisy electromagnetic environment, or when highest accuracy is required.

Guarding the Measuring Equipment

Figure 26 shows the error-producing current paths due to the common mode source, V_{cm}, entering the measurement loop via the gage parasitic elements, C_{iso} and

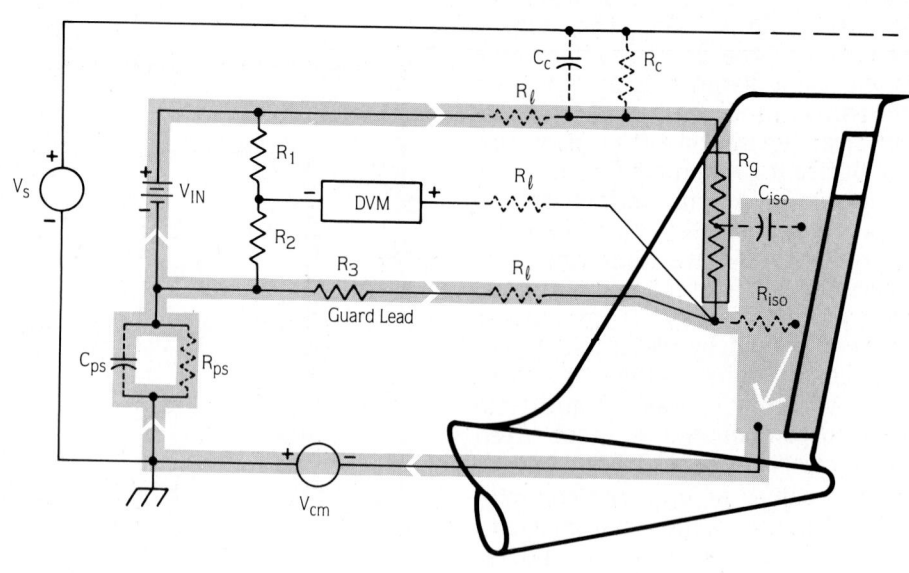

Figure 26: Error-producing Common Mode Current Path

R_{iso}. In the general case, both a.c. and d.c. components must be considered. Again current flow through gage and lead resistances result in error voltages inside the bridge arms. Tracing either loop from the DVM's negative terminal to the positive terminal will reveal unwanted voltages of the same polarity in each loop. The symmetry of the bridge structure in no way provides cancellation of the effects due to current entering at the gage.

Whereas shielding kept error-producing currents out of the measurement loop by intercepting the current, guarding controls current flow by exploiting the fact that no current will flow through an electrical component having both of its terminals at the same potential.

In Figure 27, a "guard" lead has been connected between the test specimen (in close proximity to the gage) and the negative terminal of the power supply. This connection forces the floating power supply and all the measuring equipment — including the gage — to the same electrical potential as the test specimen. Since the gage and the specimen are at the same potential, no error producing current flows through R_{iso} and C_{iso} into the measuring loops. Another way of interpreting the result is to say that the guard lead provides an alternate current path around the measuring circuit. It should be observed that if the power supply and the rest of the measuring circuits could not float above earth or chassis potential, the guarding technique would reduce the interference by factors of only 2:1 or 4:1. Proper guarding with a floating

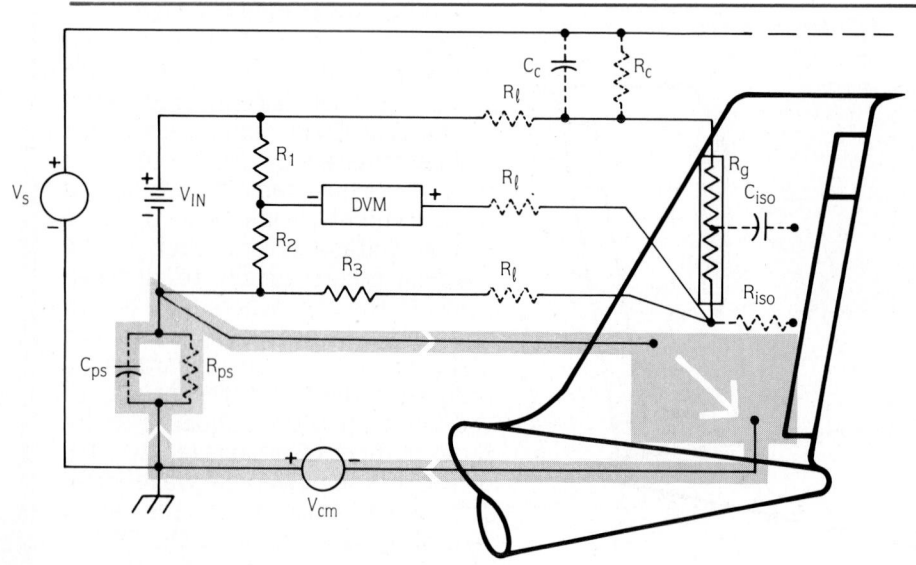

Figure 27: Guard Wire Diverts Common Mode Current Away from Gage Wires

supply should yield improvements on the order of 10^5:1 or 100 dB.

In situations where it is possible to ground the test specimen at measurement earth potential, the common mode source, V_{cm}, will be essentially eliminated.

Extension to Multichannel Measurements

Figure 28, on the following page, shows the extension of the guarding technique to a multi-channel strain gage measurement using a shared power supply and internal half bridge completion resistors. For simplicity, only the capacitive parasitic elements are shown. In ordinary practice, capacitive coupling is usually more significant and more difficult to avoid than resistive coupling. For generality we've used two test specimens at different potentials with respect to measurement earth. The switching shown in the figure allows simultaneous selection of the DVM and the associated guard connection.

Figure 29 illustrates the currents flowing due to the specimen potentials V_{cm1} and V_{cm2}. Note that regardless which channel is selected,

Figure 28: Multichannel Strain Measurement Including Two Separate Test Specimens

the guard line (also functioning as the shield for the wires to the gage) keeps the common mode current

out of the gage leads selected for the measurement. Common mode current flows harmlessly through the gage leads of the unselected channel. It should be noted that each lead wire shield is "grounded" at only a single point. The common mode current through each combined guard and shield is limited by the relatively high impedance of the parasitic element C_{ps} and should not be confused with the "heavy" shield current which might occur if a shield were grounded at both ends, creating a "ground loop".

CMR Limitations

The schematics and discussion of guarding presented thus far might convey the impression that infinite rejection of common mode interference is possible. It seems reasonable to ask what if anything limits common mode rejection? Figure 30 includes a new parasitic element, C_{ug}, the unguarded capacitance to chassis associated with the DVM and multiplexer. In practice, the DVM and multiplexer are usually realized as guarded instruments [Reference 13] featuring three wire switching

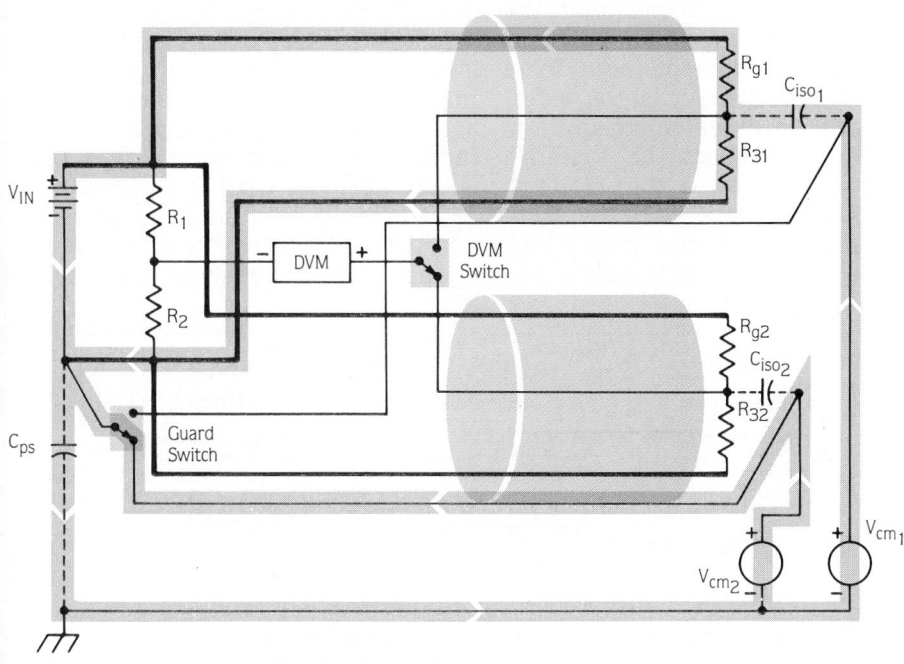

Figure 29: Multichannel Guard Switching Keeps Common Mode Current Out of Selected Gage Leads

Practical Strain Measurement (continued)

and measurements, but the guard isolation is not perfect. Capacitance ranging from 15 pF – 20 μf can be found between the instrument low connection and chassis. In Figure 30, this capacitance causes a portion of the common mode current in the selected channel to flow through the internal half bridge resistors R_1 and R_2 giving rise to a measurement error. In a multichannel system, all of the unselected channels (gages) sharing the same power supply also contribute current, but this current exits the bridge via the power supply and returns through the guard wire causing no additional errors.

In Figure 30, the a.c. interference voltage presented to the terminals of the DVM causes an error because the d.c. measuring voltmeter does not totally reject the a.c. A DVM's ability to measure d.c. voltage in the presence of a.c. interference is called the normal mode rejection ratio NMRR and is usually stated for 50 and 60 Hz interference.

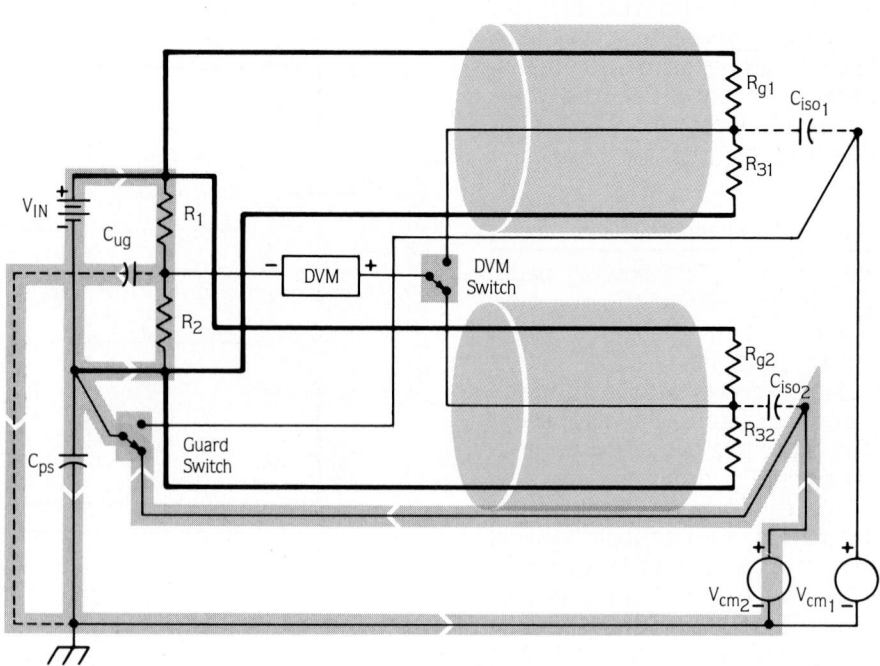

Figure 30: Unguarded Capacitance of Multiplexer and DVM Result in Measurement Error Due to V_{cm2} of Selected Channel

$$NMRR = 20 \log \frac{V_{NM} (a.c.)}{V_{DVM} (d.c.)}$$

Equation No. 16

A d.c. voltmeter's NMRR is a function of input filtering and the analog to digital conversion technique employed.

Additionally, the DVM and multiplexer system reject a.c. interference via guarding and design control of parasitics. The quantitative measure of a system's ability to reject common mode a.c. voltage is the common mode rejection ratio, CMRR, defined as:

$$CMRR = 20 \log \frac{V_{cm} (a.c.)}{V_{DVM} (a.c.)}$$

Equation No. 17

where V_{cm} and V_{DVM} are both sinusoids at the power line frequency of interest – 50, 60, or 400 Hz. Note that V_{DVM} is an a.c. wave form presented to the terminals of a d.c. voltmeter. Thus CMRR is an a.c. voltage transfer ratio from the common mode source to the DVM terminals. Caution must be exercised in comparing CMRR specifications to insure that identical procedures were employed in arriving at the numerical result.

The overall figure of merit for a measurement system is the effective common mode rejection ratio ECMRR and reflects the system's ability to measure d.c. voltage (strain) in the presence of a.c. common mode interference. If all measurements are made at the same frequency,

Thus ECMRR describes how well the parasitics are controlled in the system and the sampling characteristics of the DVM, i.e., integrating or instantaneous sampling.

Reference 10 provides additional information on the subject of floating, guarded measurements and rejection ratios. Appendix D contains measurement sensitivity data which can be used to compute measurement error (in $\mu\epsilon$) as a function of DVM, power supply, and bridge completion resistor specifications.

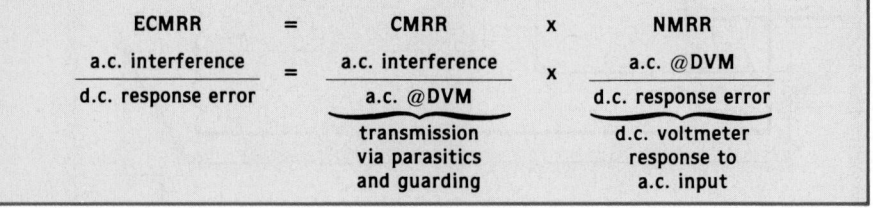

Equation No. 18

and if the rejection ratios are expressed in dB,

$$ECMRR(dB) = CMRR(dB) + NMRR(dB)$$

Equation No. 19

Bridge Excitation Level

The bridge excitation voltage level affects both the output sensitivity and the gage self heating. From the measurement standpoint a high ex-

citation level is desirable but a lower level reduces gage self heating. The electrical power in the gage is dissipated as heat which must be transferred from the gage to the surroundings. In order for this heat transfer to occur the gage temperature must rise above that of the specimen and the air. The gage temperature is therefore a function of the ambient temperature and the temperature rise due to power dissipation.

An excessive gage temperature can cause various problems. The carrier and adhesive materials are no longer able to faithfully transmit the strain from the specimen to the grid if the temperature becomes too high. This adversely affects hysteresis and creep and may show up as instability under load. Zero or unstrained stability is also affected by high gage temperatures. Temperature compensated gages suffer a loss of compensation when the temperature difference between the gage grid and the specimen becomes too large. When the gage is mounted on plastics, excessive power dissipation can elevate the temperature of the specimen under the gage to the point that the material properties of the specimen change.

The power that must be dissipated as heat by the gage in a bridge circuit with equal resistance arms is given by the following equation:

$$P = V^2/4R_g = (I^2)R_g$$

Equation No. 20

where P is the power in watts, R_g is the gage resistance, I is the current through the gage and V is the bridge excitation voltage. From equation (20) we see that lowering the excitation voltage (or gage current) or increasing the gage resistance will decrease the power dissipation. When self-heating may be a problem, higher values of gage resistance should be used. Table 3 illustrates the relationship between voltage, gage resistance and power dissipation.

The temperature rise of the grid is difficult to calculate because many factors influence the heat balance. Unless the gage is submerged in a liquid, most of the heat transfer will occur by conduction to the specimen. Generally, cooling of the gage by convection is undesirable because of the possibility of creating time variant thermal gradients on the gage. These gradients can generate voltages due to the thermocouple effect at the lead wire junctions causing errors in the bridge output voltage. Heat transfer from the gage grid to the specimen is via conduction. Therefore the grid surface area and the materials and thicknesses of the carrier and adhesive influence gage temperature. The heat sink characteristics of the specimen are also important.

POWER DENSITY is a parameter used to evaluate a particular gage size and excitation voltage level for a particular application. Power density is the power dissipated by the gage divided by the gage grid area and has units of watts/in.^{2}. Recommended values of power density vary, depending upon accuracy requirements, from 2-10 for good heat sinks, such as heavy aluminum or copper sections, to 0.01-0.05 for poor heat sinks such as unfilled plastics. Stacked rosettes create a special problem in that the temperature rise of the bottom gage adds to the two gages above it and that of the center gage adds to the top gage. These may require a very low voltage or different voltages for each of the three gages to have the same temperature at each gage. [6]

One way we can determine the maximum excitation voltage that can be tolerated is by increasing the voltage until a noticeable zero instability occurs. We then reduce the voltage until the zero is once more stable and without a significant offset relative to the zero point at a low voltage. The bridge completion resistors also dissipate power and in practice may be more susceptible to drift from self heating effects than the strain gage. The stability of the bridge completion resistors is related to load-life, and maintaining only a fraction of rated power in them will give better long term stability. If the above method of finding the maximum voltage level is used, care should be exercised to insure that the power rating of the completion resistors is not exceeded as the voltage is increased.

Reducing the bridge excitation voltage dramatically reduces gage power, since power is proportional to the square of voltage. However, bridge output voltage is proportional to excitation voltage, so reducing it lowers sensitivity. If the DVM used to read the output voltage has 1 microvolt resolution, 1 micro-strain resolution can be maintained, with a ¼ bridge configuration, using a 2 volt bridge excitation level. If the

STRAIN GAGE POWER DISSIPATION				
Bridge Excitation Voltage	Gage Power in Milliwatts			
	1000 Ohm	500 Ohm	350 Ohm	120 Ohm
0.1	0.0025	0.005	0.007	0.021
0.2	0.010	0.020	0.029	0.083
0.5	0.0625	0.125	0.179	0.521
1.0	0.250	0.500	0.714	2.083
2.0	1.000	2.000	2.857	8.333
3.0	2.250	4.500	6.429	18.750
4.0	4.000	8.000	11.429	33.333
5.0	6.250	12.500	17.857	52.083
10.0	25.000	50.000	71.400	208.300

Table 3

Practical Strain Measurement (continued)

DVM has 0.1 microvolt resolution the excitation voltage can be lowered to 0.2 volts while maintaining the same strain resolution. From Table 3 we see that, at these excitation levels, the power dissipated by a 350 ohm gage goes from 2.857 to 0.029 milliwatts. So, using a sensitive DVM for measuring the bridge output permits the use of low excitation voltages and low gage self heating while maintaining good measurement resolution.

The four-wire ohms technique is also a good way to keep the power in the gage extremely low. This is due to the low value of constant current supplied to the gage by the DMM, typically 1 milliamp. This current (1 milliamp) corresponds to a power dissipation of 0.12 milliwatts in a 120 ohm gage and 0.35 milliwatts in a 350 ohm gage. With four-wire ohms a gage is energized only when it is selected and is actually being measured by the DMM. As mentioned previously, resolution will be lower using four-wire ohms than with a bridge, but will be adequate for many applications.

Lead Wire Effects

In the preceding chapter reference was made to the effects of lead wire resistance on the strain measurement for the various configurations. In a bridge circuit the lead wire resistance can cause two types of errors. One error is due to resistance changes in the lead wires that are indistinguishable from resistance changes in the gage. The other error is known as LEAD WIRE DESEN-

SITIZATION and becomes significiant when the magnitude of the lead wire resistance exceeds 0.1% of the nominal gage resistance. The significance of this source of error is shown in Table 4.

LEAD WIRE DESENSITIZATION (Refer to Figure 32)		
¼ and ½ bridge, 3-wire connections		
AWG	R_g=120 Ohms	R_g=350 Ohms
18	.54%	.19%
20	.87	.30
22	1.38	.47
24	2.18	.75
26	3.47	1.19
28	5.52	1.89
30	8.77	3.01

Magnitudes of computed strain values will be low by the above percent per 100 feet of hard drawn solid copper lead wire at 25°C (77°F)

Table 4

If the resistance of the lead wires is known, the computed values of strain can be corrected for LEAD WIRE DESENSITIZATION. In a prior section, we developed equations for strain as a function of the measured voltages for a ¼ bridge configuration:

$$\Delta R_g / R_g = -4V_r / (1 + 2V_r)$$

Equation No. 14

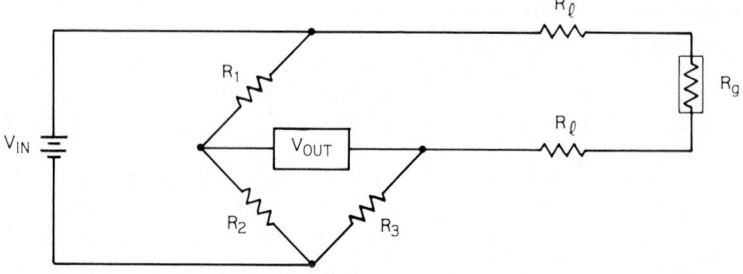

Figure 31: Two-wire ¼ Bridge Connection

$$\epsilon = -4V_r / GF(1 + 2V_r)$$

Equation No. 15

These equations are based on the assumptions that V_r is due solely to the change in gage resistance, ΔR_g, and that the total resistance of the arm of the bridge that contained the gage was R_g. Referring to Figure 32 we see that one of the lead wire resistances, R_ℓ, is in series with the gage so the total resistance of that bridge arm is actually $R_g + R_\ell$. If we substitute this into equation 14 it becomes:

$$\frac{\Delta R_g}{R_g} = \left(\frac{-4V_r}{1 + 2V_r} \right) \left(\frac{R_g + R_\ell}{R_g} \right)$$

Equation No. 21

Rewriting the equation for strain we see that the previous strain equation is in error by a factor of the ratio of the lead wire resistance to the nominal gage resistance.

$$\epsilon = \frac{-4V_r}{GF(1 + 2V_r)} \bullet \underbrace{\left(1 + \frac{R_\ell}{R_g} \right)}_{\textbf{Error Term}}$$

Equation No. 22

This factor is lead wire desensitization and we see from equation (22) and from Table 4 that the effect is reduced if the lead wire resistance is small and/or the nominal gage resistance is large. If ignoring this term $(1 + R_\ell / R_g)$ will cause an unacceptable error then it should be added to the computer program such that the strains computed with equation 15 are multiplied by this factor. Appendix B gives the equations for various bridge configurations and the lead wire resistance compensation terms that apply to them. Appendix A has a table containing the resistance, at room temperature, of some commonly used sizes of copper wire.

The most common cause of

changes in lead wire resistance is temperature changes. The copper used for lead wires has a nominal temperature coefficient of resistance, at 25°C, of 0.00385 ohms/ohm °C. For the 2-wire circuit in Figure 31, this effect will cause an error if the temperature during the unstrained reading is different than the temperature during the strained reading. An error occurs because any change in resistance in the gage arm of the bridge during this time is assumed to be due to strain. Also, both lead wire resistances are in series with the gage in the bridge arm further contributing to the lead wire desensitization error.

The THREE-WIRE method of connecting the gage, shown in Figure 32, is the preferred method of wiring strain gages to a bridge circuit. This method compensates for the effect of temperature on the lead wires. For effective compensation the lead wires must have approximately the same nominal resistance, the same temperature coefficient of resistance and be maintained at the same temperature. In practice this is effected by using the same size and length wires and keeping them physically close together.

Temperature compensation is accomplished because the resistance changes occur equally in adjacent arms of the bridge and therefore the net effect on the output voltage of the bridge is negligible. This technique works equally well for ¼ and ½ bridge configurations. The lead wire desensitization effect is reduced over the two-wire connection because only one lead wire resistance is in series with the gage. The resistance of the signal wire to the DVM doesn't affect the measurement because the current flow in this lead is negligible due to the high input impedance of the DVM.

Mathematical correction for lead wire desensitization requires the resistances of the lead wires to be known. The values given in wire tables can be used, but for temperature extremes, measurement of the wires after installation is required for utmost accuracy. Two methods for arriving at the resist-

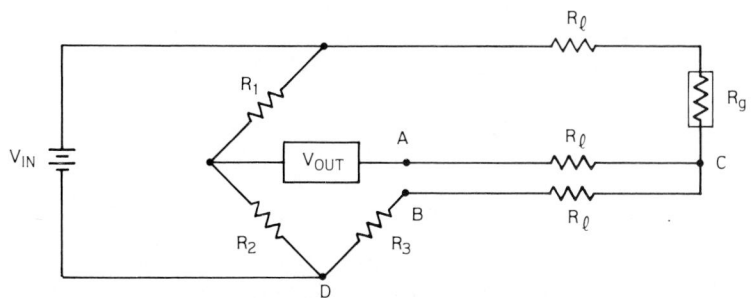

Figure 32: Three-wire ¼ Bridge Connection

ance of the lead wires from the instrumentation side of the circuit in Figure 32 follow:

(1) If the three wires are the same size and length, the resistance measured between points A and B, before the wires are connected to the instrumentation, is $2R_\ell$.

(2) Measure the voltage from A-B (which is equivalent to B-C) and the voltage from B-D. Since R_3 is typically a precision resistor whose value is well known, the current in the C-D leg can be computed using ohms law. This is the current that flows through the lead resistance so the value of R_ℓ can be computed, since the voltage from B-C is known. The equation for computing R_ℓ is:

$$R_\ell = \frac{V_{AB}}{V_{BD}} \cdot R_3$$

Equation No. 23

These measured values for lead resistance should be retained for later calculations.

Diagnostics

To insure strain data that is as error free as possible, various diagnostic checks can be performed on the gage installation and instrumentation. In a stress analysis application the entire gage installa-

tion can't be calibrated as can be done with certain transducers. Therefore potential error sources should be examined prior to taking data.

Mounted Gage Resistance

The unstrained resistance of the gage should be measured after the gage is mounted but before the wiring is connected to the instrumentation. This test will help locate gages damaged during installation. Under laboratory conditions with room temperature cure adhesives, the mounted resistance value of metal foil gages should usually fall within the package tolerance range for the gage. Under field conditions the shift in gage resistance will usually be less than 2%. Greater shifts may indicate damage to the gage. The farther the gage resistance value deviates from the nominal value, the larger the unstrained bridge output voltage. This limits the strain range at maximum resolution when using the unbalanced bridge technique. The easiest, accurate way to measure this resistance is with the four-wire ohms function of a DMM.

Gage Isolation

The isolation resistance from the gage grid to specimen, if the specimen is conductive, should also be measured before connecting the lead wires to the instrumentation. This check should not be made with a high-voltage insulation tester, because of possible damage to the

Practical Strain Measurement (continued)

gage, but rather with an ohmmeter. A value of isolation resistance of less than 500 megohms usually indicates the presence of some type of surface contamination. Contamination often shows up as a time varying high resistance shunt across the gage which causes an error in the strain measurement. For this reason an isolation resistance value of at least 150 megohms should be maintained. A properly mounted gage with fully cured adhesive will usually have 1000 megohms or higher isolation resistance so any gages with low values should be suspect.[2]

Diagnostic Bridge Measurements

Additional errors occur when voltages are induced in the measurement circuit by sources other than strain. These voltages may be in the form of static offsets such as a thermally induced voltage or time varying disturbances such as a magnetically induced voltage. Other sources of interference are capacitive coupling of signals to the gage or wiring, resistive leakage paths to the gage or from the wiring to adjacent signal carriers, a leakage path in the excitation supply, a poor connection to guard or a damaged shield. Since error producing interference can arise from so many unexpected sources, what can be done to detect the presence of unwanted voltages?

The first step is to disconnect the excitation supply from the bridge and power up all equipment that is to be operating during the test. This insures that all the interference sources are activated. Next, take several consecutive bridge output voltage readings for each strain gage channel. The voltages should be very nearly zero. If there is an offset voltage it could be thermally induced or due to a resistive leakage path. A time varying cyclic voltage could be caused by resistive, magnetic or capacitive coupling to the interfering source. Erratic voltage readings could be due to an open input to the DVM. An integrating voltmeter which samples over an integer number of power line cycles greatly increases rejection of magnetic induction and other interference sources at power line frequency. When using non-integrating voltmeters several readings can be averaged to minimize the effect on static strain readings.

Thermally induced voltages are caused by thermocouple effects at the junctions of dissimilar metals within the measurement circuits, in the presence of temperature gradients. These may occur at connectors, where the lead wire meets the gage metal, in switches or in the DVM. Magnetically induced voltages occur when the wiring is located in a time varying magnetic field. Magnetic induction can be controlled by using twisted lead wires and forming minimum but equal loop areas in each side of the bridge. These loops should be arranged as shown in Figure 33 to have minimum effect on bridge output. In severe magnetic fields, magnetic shielding for the wiring may be required.

The next step is to connect the excitation supply to the bridge. A

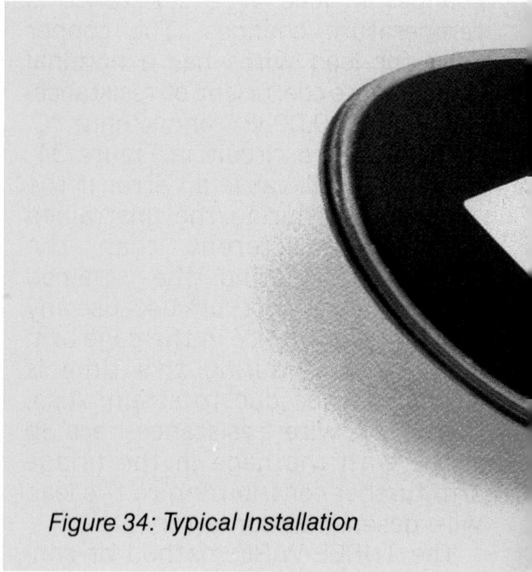

Figure 34: Typical Installation

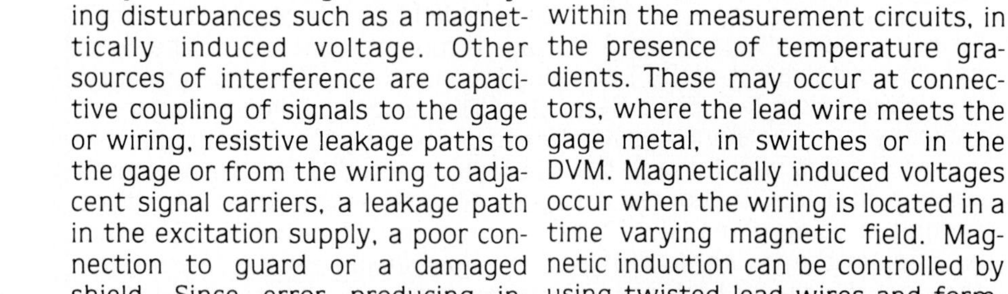

series of readings taken by the DVM of the excitation voltage is a good verification that the excitation supply is set to the correct voltage level and is stable enough to allow the accuracy expected. Some thermally induced voltages may be due to heating effects from power dissipated in the bridge circuit so a check should be made with the power applied. This is done by taking a sequence of readings of the bridge output then reversing the polarity of the excitation supply and repeating the sequence. One half the difference in the absolute values of the bridge output voltages is the thermally induced voltage. If the temperature and power levels will remain at this level during the test then subsequent voltage readings could be corrected, by this offset voltage amount. To monitor the thermally induced voltages the bridge power can be connected with switches so that the voltage readings may be taken with both power supply polarities. If the measured thermally induced voltages are more than a few microvolts the source should be found and eliminated rather than trying to correct the voltage readings. If, after a reasonable time for the gage and bridge resistors to reach steady state temperatures, the voltage is still drifting the excitation level may be too high.

Another test on the gage, particularly on the gage bond, can be

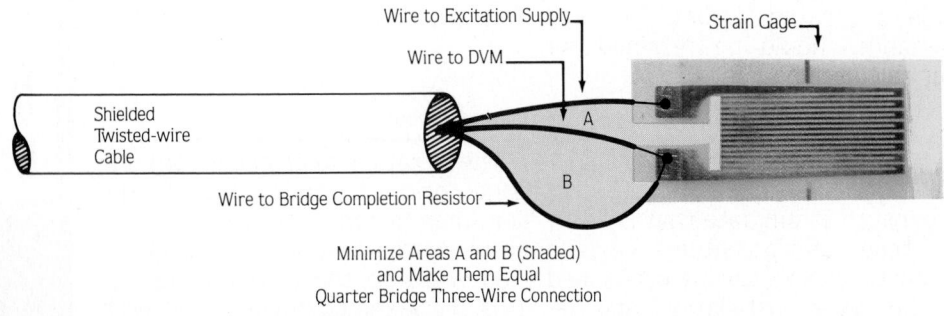

Figure 33: Gage Wiring to Minimize Magnetic Induction

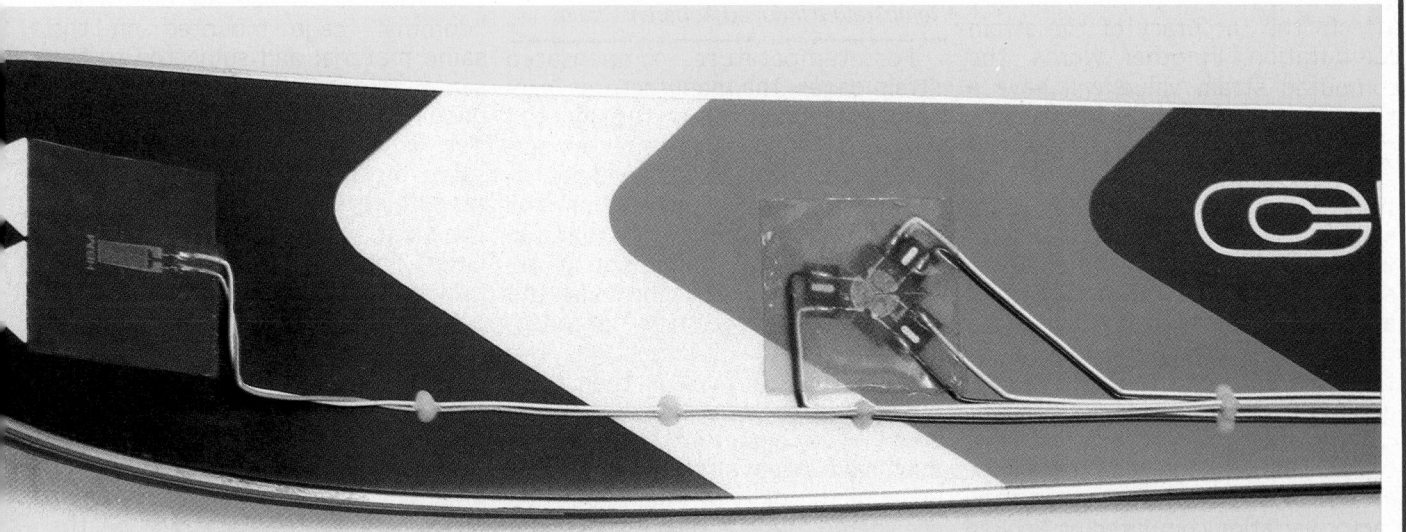

performed at this time. While monitoring the bridge output with the DVM, press lightly on the strain gage with a pencil eraser. The output voltage should change slightly but then return to the original value when the pressure is removed. If the output voltage doesn't return to the original value or becomes erratic the gage is probably imperfectly bonded or is damaged and should be replaced.

The unstrained bridge output voltage level also has diagnostic value. A shorted or open gage will give an output of approximately one half the excitation voltage. In many cases the unstrained bridge output should be 2 millivolts or less per excitation volt. For example, if each of the four bridge arms had a tolerance of ±1% the unstrained output would at most be, 10 millivolts per excitation volt. So, if the unstrained output is more than a few millivolts per volt of excitation the installation should be inspected. If the test entails some type of temperature cycle and a temperature compensated gage is utilized, recording the unstrained output over the temperature cycle is a method of verifying the adequacy of the compensation.

Shunt Calibration (Verification)

When using the unbalanced bridge method of strain measurement with instrumentation under computer control, there are no adjustments for bridge balance or span. Since shunt calibration was originally used to adjust the span of balanced bridge instruments, what is the role of shunt calibration with an imbalanced bridge? Shunt calibration with this technique might more correctly be termed "shunt verification" since the instrumentation won't actually be calibrated by shunt calibration. Shunt verification is the placing in parallel with one of the bridge arm resistors, or gages, a resistor of known value. This will change the bridge output voltage a predictable amount and if we measure this output change, just as if it were caused by strain, we can compute the equivalent strain value. Since we already know the change in resistance from the parallel combination of resistors, we can compute the equivalent strain value for a given gage factor, i.e., $\epsilon = (1/GF)(\Delta R/R)$. By using the same program subroutines and instrumentation which will be used in the actual test, we verify most of the system and gain confidence in the test setup.

The value of the shunt resistor is often in the 10-500 kilohm range so the current through it is low: less than 1 milliamp. This resistor is also outside the bridge arms so the effects of switching and lead wires are not as important as for the gage. Any of the bridge arms for any bridge configuration may be

shunted and a corresponding value of equivalent strain computed.

Temperature Effects

We have examined ways to compensate for the effects of temperature on the lead wires to the gage. Now let's look at some methods to compensate for the temperature effects on gage resistance and gage factor. Some of these methods require the temperature to be measured at the gage. This can be accomplished by several different temperature sensors such as thermocouples, thermistors, and resistance temperature detectors (RTDs). Since we want to sense the temperature of the strain gage itself, problems can arise when large thermal gradients exist or when the temperature is rapidly changing. We need a sensor that has adequate thermal response and need to locate it such that it senses the same temperature that exists at the gage.

Gage Factor versus Temperature

The gage manufacturer supplies a nominal gage factor and tolerance with each gage. If this gage factor is per NAS 942, Reference [9], it is the nominal gage factor and tolerance as measured at room temperature, in a uniaxial stress field, on a material with a Poisson's ratio of 0.285, for that particular lot of gages. The

PRACTICAL STRAIN GAGE MEASUREMENTS

Practical Strain Measurement (continued)

tolerance on the gage factor directly affects the accuracy of the strain computation, in other words, the computed strain value will have a tolerance at least as great as the gage factor tolerance. A plot showing how gage factor varies with temperature is also furnished with the gage. This plot is in the form of % gage factor variation (%ΔGF) versus temperature (T). The temperature at which these variations become significant depends upon the gage alloy and the accuracy required.

In practice the temperature must be measured at the gage during the strained measurement and the gage factor variation computed or "looked up". The actual gage factor is then computed using this variation and the nominal gage factor,

$$GF_A = GF \frac{(1 + \% \Delta GF)}{100}$$

Equation No. 24

This actual gage factor, GF_A, is then used in the equation for computing strain, e.g., equation 15, instead of GF. The value of strain thus computed is compensated for the effect of temperature on the gage factor.

For most metallic gage alloys, commonly used for static strain measurement, the gage factor variation with temperature is nearly linear over a broad temperature range and is less than ±1% for temperature excursions of ±100°C. For example, the equation for gage factor variation versus temperature in °C for a typical temperature compensated constantan alloy gage, as taken from the plot enclosed by the manufacturer, was found to be: %ΔGF=0.007T-0.1. For gage alloys with nonlinear characteristics, we need to use a point by point correction or some type of curve fitting routine to approximate the temperature dependence. In general, gage factor temperature compensation is required only for large temperature extremes or for tests requiring the utmost accuracy.

Temperature Induced Apparent Strain

For temperature compensated strain gages, the manufacturer supplies a plot of temperature-induced APPARENT STRAIN versus temperature. This plot is obtained by installing a sample of gages from the lot on a piece of unstrained material having a thermal coefficient of expansion matching that for which the compensated gage was intended, and varying the temperature. The apparent strain value is then computed and plotted versus temperature. The apparent strain curve may have been plotted by using a gage factor of +2. This should be considered when using this plot since the actual gage value may be different and temperature dependent. A fourth- or fifth-order polynominal may be used to describe the apparent strain curve and can be obtained from the manufacturer or derived from the plot. Thermally-induced apparent strain occurs because perfect temperature compensation over a broad range can't be achieved. It results from the interaction of the thermal coefficient of resistance of the gage and the differential thermal expansion between the gage and the specimen. Also, the specimen will seldom be the exact alloy used by the gage manufacturer in determining the apparent strain curve. Apparent strain is, of course, zero for the temperature at which the gage is mounted. If that temperature were maintained for the duration of the test no correction would be required, but if the temperature varies during the course of the test, compensation for the apparent strain may be required depending upon the temperature changes, the gage alloy and the accuracy required.

If the temperature changes between the time of the unstrained and strained readings, errors may be incurred as can be seen from the apparent strain plot. These errors are in the form of a strain offset. If the gage temperature and the apparent strain characteristics are known, this offset can be calculated and the strain value compensated accordingly. Another way of achieving compensation is to use an unstrained "dummy" gage mounted on the same material and subjected to the same temperature as the active gage. This dummy gage and the active gages that are to be compensated should all be from the same manufacturer's lot so they all have the same apparent strain characteristics. The dummy can be used in a bridge arm adjacent to the active gage thereby effecting electrical cancellation of the apparent strain. For multichannel systems where many gages are mounted in an area of uniform temperature, it is more efficient to read the dummy gage directly. The value of strain read from the dummy gage will be the value of the apparent strain. The strain readings from the active gages that are mounted on the same material, at the same temperature, can then be corrected by subtracting this amount from them.

There are some cases where it is desirable to generate a thermally induced apparent strain curve for the particular gage mounted on the test specimen. Such would be the case if a compensated gage weren't available to match the thermal coefficient of expansion of the specimen material or if the compensation weren't adequate for the desired accuracy. Any time the temperature varies during the test the accuracy of the apparent strain compensation can be improved by using the actual characteristics of the mounted gage. To accomplish this the mounted but mechanically unstrained gage must be subjected to temperature variations and the apparent strain computed at appropriate values of measured temperature. With computer controlled instrumentation, the data can be taken automatically while the temperature is varied. If the temperatures of the actual test are known, the apparent strain values can be recorded at only those temperatures and used as a "look up" table for correction of the test data. The temperature compensated gage factor of the mounted gage should be used for computing these apparent strain values. If the test temperatures at which data will be taken are not known, then it will be

necessary to generate the equation for the apparent strain curve over the temperature range of interest. Curve-fitting computer programs are available to generate an equation that approximates the measured characteristics. [5,6]

Data: Input, Output, Storage

When using unbalanced bridge techniques with computer control, data storage becomes an important consideration. Storage of the unstrained bridge imbalance voltage ratio is especially critical since for some tests it may be impossible to return to the unstrained condition. This unstrained data should be stored in nonvolatile media such as magnetic tape or disc with a redundant copy if the test is critical or of long duration. Storage of the subsequent strained readings may be done during or after the test as required for data reduction or archival purposes. Large amounts of data can be stored quickly and inexpensively with the media available today, and frequent storage of data is good insurance against power interruptions and equipment failures.

Previously we discussed using one power supply for several different channels of strain gages and measuring it with an accurate DVM. This enables us to use an inexpensive supply and also allows its replacement should it fail, with no loss in measurement accuracy. We also discussed a circuit that used a common internal half-bridge for several channels of strain gages. For very expensive and/or long term tests when using this technique it may be desirable to have some type of "backup" for this resistor pair since

UNSTRAINED RAW DATA

CHAN	Vout	Vin	Ratio
0	-0.000589	1.980	-0.000298
1	0.000528	1.980	0.000267
2	0.000065	1.980	0.000033
3	-0.000101	1.980	-0.000051
4	-0.000128	1.980	-0.000065
5	-0.000418	1.980	-0.000211
6	-0.000275	1.980	-0.000139
7	-0.001345	1.980	-0.000679
8	-0.000276	1.980	-0.000139
9	-0.000244	1.980	-0.000123

Unstrained Data Should be Stored in Nonvolatile Media

several data channels will be lost should a resistor fail. This can be accomplished by reading the voltage across each of the two resistors and

the power supply voltage, and storing these voltages in a nonvolatile medium. Should the resistor pair fail, it would be replaced with a new pair and a new set of voltage readings taken. These two sets of readings would then be used to com-

STRAIN READINGS

CHANNEL	MICROSTRAIN
0	-286
1	410
2	1165
3	417
4	291
5	776
6	257
7	142
8	351
9	117

Strain Readings from 10 Channels

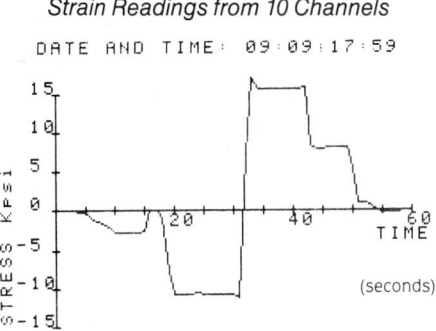

DATE AND TIME: 09:09:17:59

Plot of Stress vs. Time Computated from Strain Gage Data taken on a Cantilever Beam

pute an offset voltage to compensate for the difference in the ratio of the two pairs of resistors. This offset voltage would be added to all strained imbalance voltage readings taken with the new pair of resistors. This technique can result in as little as ±10 micro-strain loss in measurement accuracy.

Use of a computer to control instrumentation, data manipulation, and storage gives us almost unlimited data output capability. With the wide varity of printers, displays and plotters available, the test data can be reduced and output by the computer in almost any conceivable format, often while the test is in process. With computational power and "smart" instrumentation, we can greatly increase the speed and accuracy of the measurement while eliminating the tedious manual-adjustment process. Now we have more time to concentrate on the test results.

"Courtesy of Radio Shack, Division of Tandy Corp."

"Courtesy of IBM"

"Courtesy of Apple Computer Inc."

"Courtesy of Hewlett Packard, Personal Computer Division"

Figure 35: A Desktop Computer with a μMEGA Can Be Used as an Instrumentation Controller

Appendices and Bibliography

Appendix A: Tables

WIRE RESISTANCE Solid Copper Wire		
AWG	Ohms/Foot (25°C)	Diameter (in.)
18	0.0065	0.040
20	0.0104	0.032
22	0.0165	0.0253
24	0.0262	0.0201
26	0.0416	0.0159
28	0.0662	0.0126
30	0.105	0.010
32	0.167	0.008

AVERAGE PROPERTIES OF SELECTED ENGINEERING MATERIALS Exact values may vary widely			
Material	Poisson's Ratio, ν	Modulus of Elasticity, E psi x 10^6	Elastic Strength (a) Tension (psi)
ABS (unfilled)	–	0.2-0.4	4500-7500
Aluminum (2024-T4)	0.32	10.6	48000
Aluminum (7075-T6)	0.32	10.4	72000
Red Brass, soft	0.33	15	15000
Iron-Gray Cast	–	13-14	–
Polycarbonate	0.285	0.3-0.38	8000-9500
Steel-1018	0.285	30	32000
Steel-4130/4340	0.28-0.29	30	45000
Steel-304 SS	0.25	28	35000
Steel-410 SS	0.27-0.29	29	40000
Titanium alloy	0.34	14	135000

(a) Elastic strength may be represented by proportional limit, yield point, or yield strength at 0.2 percent offset.

Appendix B: Bridge Circuits

STRAIN GAGE BRIDGE CIRCUITS AND EQUATIONS

Equations compute strain from unbalanced bridge voltages: sign is correct for V_{IN} and V_{OUT} as shown
GF = Gage Factor: ν = Poisson's ratio:

$V_r = [(V_{OUT}/V_{IN})\text{strained} - (V_{OUT}/V_{IN})\text{unstrained}]$:
ϵ = Strain; Multiply by 10^6 for micro-strain: tensile is (+) and compressive is (−)

Quarter Bridge Configurations:

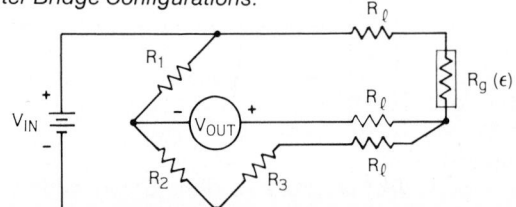 OR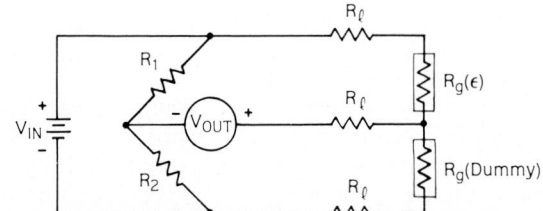

$$\epsilon = \frac{-4V_r}{GF(1+2V_r)} \cdot \left(1 + \frac{R_\ell}{R_g}\right)$$

Half Bridge Configurations: (AXIAL)   (BENDING)

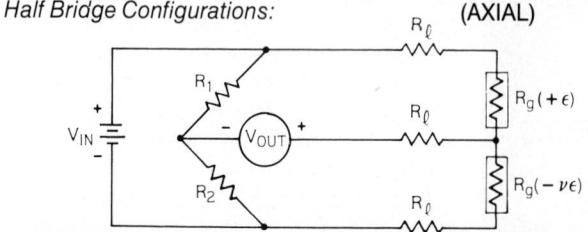   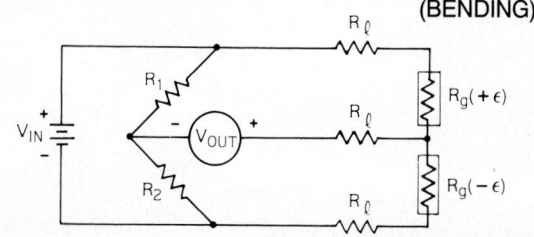

$$\epsilon = \frac{-4V_r}{GF[(1+\nu)-2V_r(\nu-1)]} \cdot \left(1 + \frac{R_\ell}{R_g}\right) \qquad \epsilon = \frac{-2V_r}{GF} \cdot \left(1 + \frac{R_\ell}{R_g}\right)$$

Full Bridge Configurations: (BENDING)   (AXIAL)

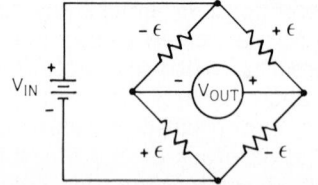

$$\epsilon = \frac{-V_r}{GF} \qquad\qquad \epsilon = \frac{-2V_r}{GF(\nu+1)} \qquad\qquad \epsilon = \frac{-2V_r}{GF[(\nu+1)-V_r(\nu-1)]}$$

Appendix C: Equations

BIAXIAL STRESS STATE EQUATIONS

$$\epsilon_x = \frac{\sigma_x}{E} - \nu\frac{\sigma_y}{E} \qquad \epsilon_z = -\nu\frac{\sigma_x}{E} - \nu\frac{\sigma_y}{E} \qquad \sigma_y = \frac{E}{1 - \nu^2}(\epsilon_y + \nu\,\epsilon_x)$$

$$\epsilon_y = \frac{\sigma_y}{E} - \nu\frac{\sigma_x}{E} \qquad \sigma_x = \frac{E}{1 - \nu^2}(\epsilon_x + \nu\,\epsilon_y) \qquad \sigma_z = 0$$

ROSETTE EQUATIONS

Rectangular Rosette:

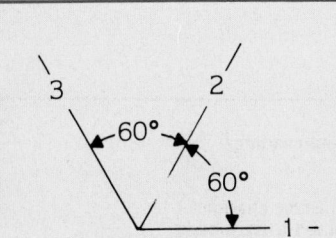

$$\epsilon_{p,q} = \frac{1}{2}\left[\epsilon_1 + \epsilon_3 \pm \sqrt{(\epsilon_1 - \epsilon_3)^2 + (2\epsilon_2 - \epsilon_1 - \epsilon_3)^2}\right]$$

$$\sigma_{p,q} = \frac{E}{2}\left[\frac{\epsilon_1 + \epsilon_3}{1 - \nu} \pm \frac{1}{1 + \nu}\sqrt{(\epsilon_1 - \epsilon_3)^2 + (2\epsilon_2 - \epsilon_1 - \epsilon_3)^2}\right]$$

$$\theta_{p,q} = \frac{1}{2}\,\text{TAN}^{-1}\frac{2\epsilon_2 - \epsilon_1 - \epsilon_3}{\epsilon_1 - \epsilon_3}$$

Delta Rosette:

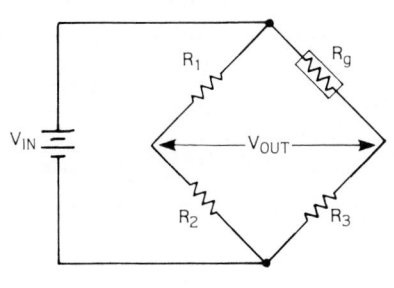

$$\epsilon_{p,q} = \frac{1}{3}\left[\epsilon_1 + \epsilon_2 + \epsilon_3 \pm \sqrt{2[(\epsilon_1 - \epsilon_2)^2 + (\epsilon_2 - \epsilon_3)^2 + (\epsilon_3 - \epsilon_1)^2]}\right]$$

$$\sigma_{p,q} = \frac{E}{3}\left[\frac{\epsilon_1 + \epsilon_2 + \epsilon_3}{1 - \nu} \pm \frac{1}{1 + \nu}\sqrt{2[(\epsilon_1 - \epsilon_2)^2 + (\epsilon_2 - \epsilon_3)^2 + (\epsilon_3 - \epsilon_1)^2]}\right]$$

$$\theta_{p,q} = \frac{1}{2}\,\text{TAN}^{-1}\frac{\sqrt{3}(\epsilon_2 - \epsilon_3)}{2\epsilon_1 - \epsilon_2 - \epsilon_3}$$

WHERE: $\epsilon_{p,q}$ = Principal strains; $\sigma_{p,q}$ = Principal stresses; and $\theta_{p,q}$ = the acute angle from the axis of gage 1 to the nearest principal axis. When positive, the direction is the same as that of the gage numbering and when negative, opposite.

NOTE: Corrections may be necessary for transverse sensitivity, refer to gage manufacturers literature.

Appendix D: Instrumentation Accuracy

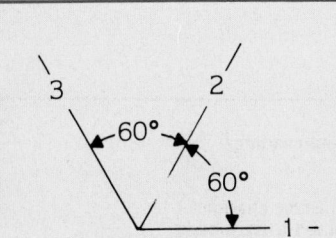

¼ Bridge Circuit

Measurement error (in $\mu\epsilon$) due to the instrumentation is often difficult to determine from published specifications. However, accuracy can be computed using the following simplified error expressions. For the ¼ bridge, add equations 1-6 (N = 1). For the ½ bridge with two active arms, add equations 2-6 (N = 2). For the full bridge with four active arms, add equations 3-6 (N = 4).

The total error for a measurement must also include gage, lead wire, and, if applicable, bridge nonlinearity errors. These are discussed in the body of this application note. Additionally, other equipment imperfections which vary from instrument to instrument must occasionally be considered (e.g., offsets caused by leakage currents due to humidity or ionic contamination on p.c. boards and connectors).

(1) R_3 change from unstrained to strained reading (due to temperature, load life, etc.)

$$\epsilon_{error} \approx -\frac{\Delta R_3/R_3}{GF}$$

PRACTICAL STRAIN GAGE MEASUREMENTS

Appendices and Bibliography (continued)

(2) $\frac{R_1}{R_2}$ change from unstrained to strained reading (due to temperature, load life, etc.)

$$\epsilon_{error} \approx \frac{\Delta\frac{R_1}{R_2} \quad \frac{R_1}{R_2}}{GF \cdot N}$$

Digital voltmeters and A/D converters are specified in terms of a ± gain error (% of reading) and a ± offset error (number of counts, in volts). Since strain calculations require two measurements, a repeatable offset error, e.g., due to relay thermal EMF, etc., will cancel, but offset due to noise and drift will not. Assuming that noise and drift dominate, the offset on two readings will be the root sum of squares of the two offsets. This is incorporated into the formulas.

(3) DVM offset error on bridge measurement

$$\epsilon_{error} \stackrel{<}{\approx} \frac{-4}{V_{IN} \cdot GF \cdot N} \cdot \sqrt{(\text{Offset Error}_{strained})^2 + (\text{Offset Error}_{unstrained})^2}$$

Error terms 4-6 can usually be ignored when using high accuracy DVMs (e.g., 5½ digit). These error terms are essentially the product of small bridge imbalance voltages with small gain or offset terms. For equations 4-6, V_{OUT}, the bridge imbalance voltage, is a measured quantity which varies from channel to channel. To calculate worst case performance, the equations use resistor tolerances and measured strain, eliminating the need for an exact knowledge of V_{OUT}.

(4) DVM gain error on bridge measurement

$$\epsilon_{error} \approx \frac{-4}{GF \cdot V_{IN} \cdot N} \cdot [(V_{OUT}) \cdot (\text{Gain Error})_{strained \ reading} - (V_{OUT}) \cdot (\text{Gain Error})_{unstrained \ reading}]$$

$$\stackrel{<}{\approx} - \epsilon_{measured} \cdot (\text{Gain Error})_{strained \ reading} - \frac{\sum \text{tolerances on } R_1/R_2, R_3, R_g}{GF \cdot N} \cdot \left(\begin{array}{c}\text{Gain Error change} \\ \text{strained-unstrained}\end{array}\right)$$

The bridge excitation supply can be monitored with a DVM or preset using a DVM and allowed to drift. In the first case, supply related errors are due only to DVM gain and offset terms, assuming a quiet supply. In the second case, since power supply accuracy is usually specified in terms of a ± gain and a ± offset from the initial setting, identical equations can be used. Also for the second case, note that the strained reading gain error is the sum of the DVM and excitation supply gain errors, while the strained reading offset error is the root sum of squares of the DVM and excitation supply offset errors.

(5) Offset error on supply measurement (or on supply drift)

$$\epsilon_{error} \approx \frac{4}{GF \cdot V_{IN}^2 \cdot N} \cdot [(V_{OUT}) \cdot (\text{Offset Error})_{strained \ reading} - (V_{OUT}) \cdot (\text{Offset Error})_{unstrained \ reading}]$$

$$\stackrel{<}{\approx} \frac{\epsilon_{measured}}{V_{IN}} \cdot (\text{Offset Error})_{strained \ reading} + \frac{\sum \text{tolerances on } R_1,/R_2, R_3, R_g}{V_{IN} \cdot GF \cdot N} \cdot \sqrt{(\text{Offset Error}_{strained})^2 + (\text{Offset Error}_{unstrained})^2}$$

(6) Gain error on supply measurement (or on supply drift)

$$\epsilon_{error} \approx \frac{4}{GF \cdot V_{IN} \cdot N} \cdot [(V_{OUT}) \cdot (\text{Gain Error})_{strained \ reading} - (V_{OUT}) \cdot (\text{Gain Error})_{unstrained \ reading}]$$

$$\stackrel{<}{\approx} \epsilon_{measured} \cdot (\text{Gain Error})_{strained \ reading} + \frac{\sum \text{tolerances on } R_1/R_2, R_3, R_g}{GF \cdot N} \cdot \left(\begin{array}{c}\text{Gain error change} \\ \text{strained-unstrained}\end{array}\right)$$

EXAMPLE

Evaluate the error for a 24-hour strain measurement with a ±5°C instrumentation temperature variation. This includes the DVM and the bridge completion resistors but not the gages. The hermetically sealed resistors have a maximum TCR of ±3.1 ppm/°C, and have a ±0.1% tolerance. The DVM/Scanner combination, over this time and temperature span, has a 0.004% gain error and a 4 μV offset error on the 0.1 volt range where the bridge output voltage, V_{OUT}, will be measured. The excitation supply is to be set at 5 V using the DVM. The DVM has a 0.002% gain error and a 100 μV offset error on the 10 volt range. Over the given time and temperature span, the supply has a 0.015% gain error and a 150 μV offset error and will not be remeasured. The mounted gage resistance tolerance is assumed to be ±0.5% or better. The strain to be measured is 3000 $\mu\epsilon$ and the gage factor is assumed to be +2.

Notice that the temperature, as given, can change by as much as ±10°C between the unstrained and strained measurements. This is the temperature change that must be used to evaluate the resistor changes due to TCR. The R_1/R_2 ratio has the tolerance and TCR of two resistors included in its specification so the ratio tolerance is ±0.2% and the ratio TCR is ±6.2 ppm/°C. **The gain error change on the bridge output measurement, and on the excitation measurement, can be as much as twice the gain error specification.** The following table shows the total error and the contribution of the individual error equations 1-6.

BIBLIOGRAPHY AND CREDITS

OMEGA ENGINEERING, INC. gratefully acknowledges **THE HEWLETT PACKARD COMPANY** for permission to reproduce their article **Application Note 290-1—Practical Strain Gage Measurements.**

1. Higdon, Ohlsen, Stiles, Weese and Riley: MECHANICS OF MATERIALS, 3rd Edition, John Wiley & Sons, Inc., New York, 1976.

2. C. C. Perry and H. R. Lissner: THE STRAIN GAGE PRIMER, McGraw-Hill, Inc., New York, 1962.

3. I. S. Sokolnikoff: TENSOR ANALYSIS (Theory and Applications to Geometry and Mechanics of Continua), Second Edition, John Wiley & Sons, New York, 1964.

4. Hornsey, McFarland, Muhlbauer, and Smith: MECHANICS OF MATERIALS (An Individualized Approach), Houghton Mifflin Company, Boston, 1977.

5. MANUAL ON EXPERIMENTAL STRESS ANALYSIS, Third Edition, Society for Experimental Stress Analysis, Westport, Ct., 1978.

6. James W. Dally and William F. Riley: EXPERIMENTAL STRESS ANALYSIS, Second Edition, McGraw-Hill, Inc., New York, 1978.

7. William M. Murray and Peter K. Stein: STRAIN GAGE TECHNIQUES, 1958.

8. Peter K. Stein: ADVANCED STRAIN GAGE TECHNIQUES, Stein Engineering Services, Inc., Phoenix, Arizona, 1962.

9. National Aerospace Standard 942, Revision 2, 1 July 1964: STRAIN GAGES, BONDED RESISTANCE, Aerospace Industries Association of America, Inc., Washington D.C.

10. Hewlett-Packard Co., Application Note 123: FLOATING MEASUREMENTS AND GUARDING, Hewlett-Packard Co., Palo Alto, California, 1970.

Equation	¼ Bridge	½ Bridge	Full Bridge
(1) R_3	15.5	—	—
(2) R_1/R_2	31.0	15.5	—
(3) V_{OUT} offset	2.3	1.1	0.6
(4) V_{OUT} gain	0.4	0.4	0.3
(5) V_{IN} offset	0.3	0.2	0.2
(6) V_{IN} gain	1.3	1.1	1.0
Sum	±50.8 $\mu\epsilon$	±18.3 $\mu\epsilon$	±2.1 $\mu\epsilon$

CONCLUSIONS

Based upon this example, several important conclusions can be drawn:
- Surprisingly large errors can result even when using state of the art bridge completion resistors and measuring equipment.
- Although typical measurements will have a smaller error, the numbers computed reflect the guaranteed instrumentation performance.
- Measuring the excitation supply for both the unstrained and strained readings not only results in smaller errors but allows the use of an inexpensive supply.
- Bridge completion resistor drift limits quarter and half bridge performance. Changes due to temperature, moisture absorption, and load life, require the use of ultra-stable hermetically sealed resistors.

STRAIN GAGES **E**

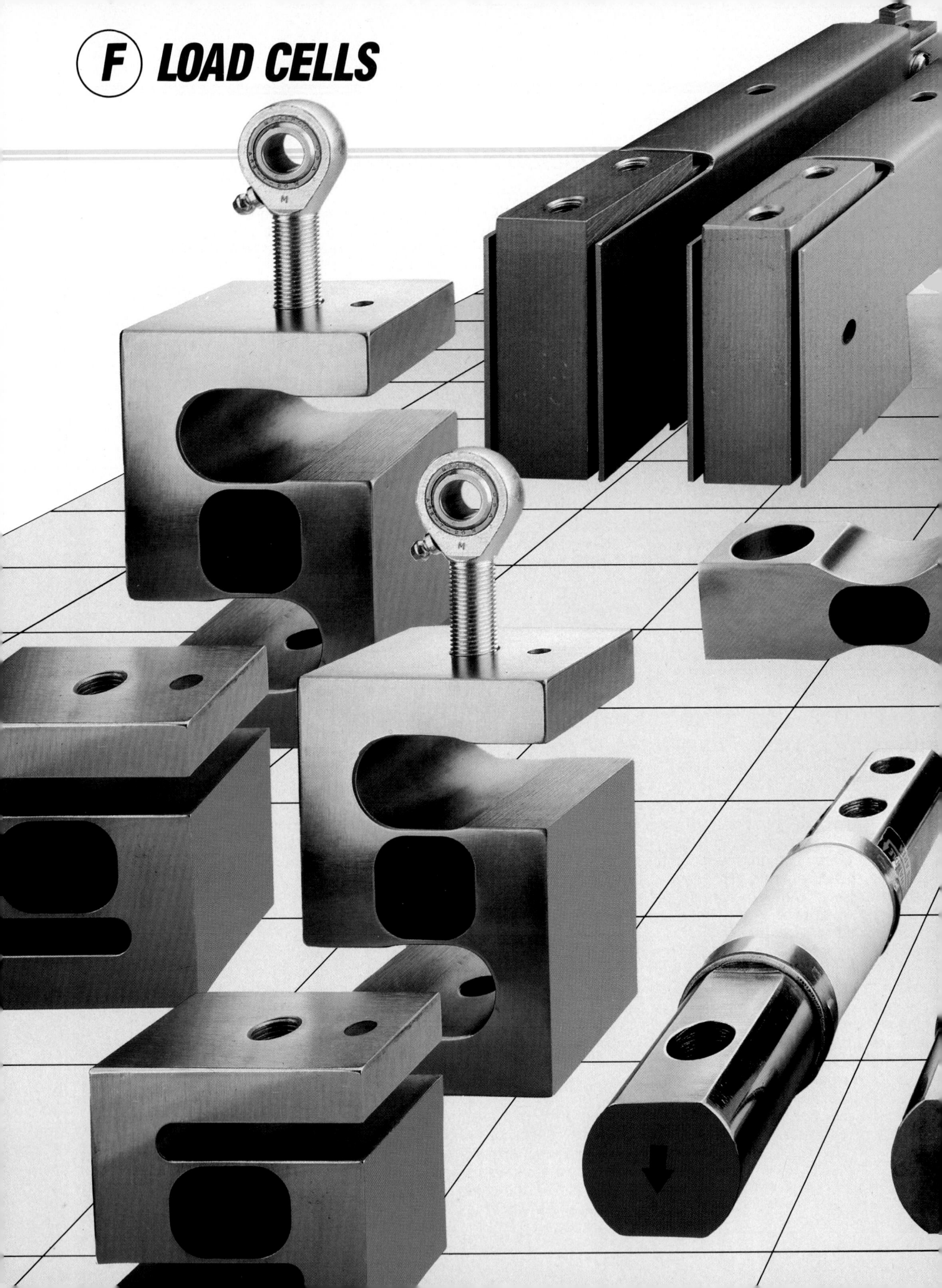

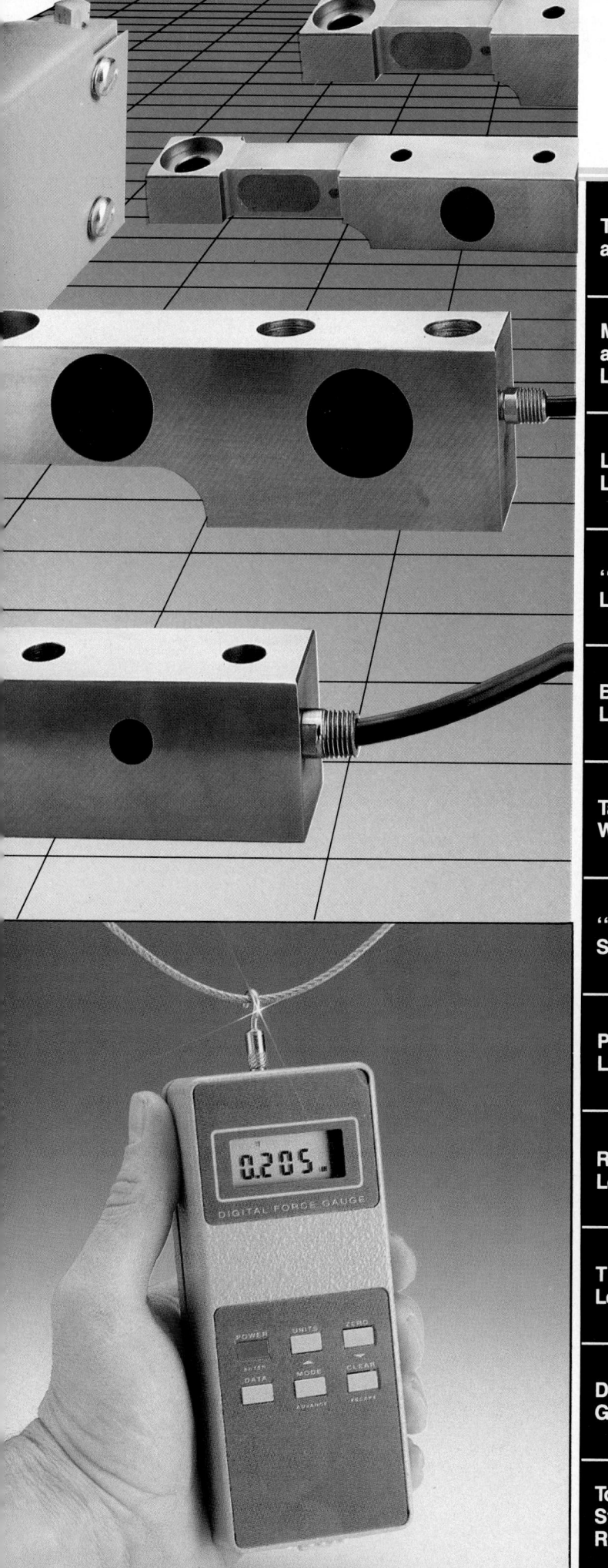

Technical Articles and Selection Guide		F-3
Miniature Beam and Compression Load Cells		F-7 to F-10
Load Bolts and Load Washers		F-11
"S" Shaped Load Cells		F-13
Beam Type Load Cells		F-15 to F-19
Tank and Bin Weighing Assemblies		F-20
"J" Box Summing Box		F-22
Platform Load Cell		F-23
Rod Ends, Load Buttons		F-24
Thin Beam O.E.M. Load Cells		F-25 to F-28
Digital Force Gages		F-29
Torque Cells Stationary and Rotating		F-30 to F-32

BASIC LOAD CELL PRINCIPLES

OMEGA® Load Cells

A load cell is a transducer that converts a load acting on it into an analog electrical signal. This conversion is achieved by the physical deformation of strain gages which are bonded to the load cell beam and wired in a Wheatstone Bridge configuration. (Figure 1).

Weight applied to the load cell either through compression or tension produces a deflection of the beam which introduces strain to the gages. The strain will produce an electrical resistance change proportional to the load. OMEGA load cells require excitation and an output device, i.e., digital readout, recorder, controller, etc.

Four Strain Gages in A Bridge

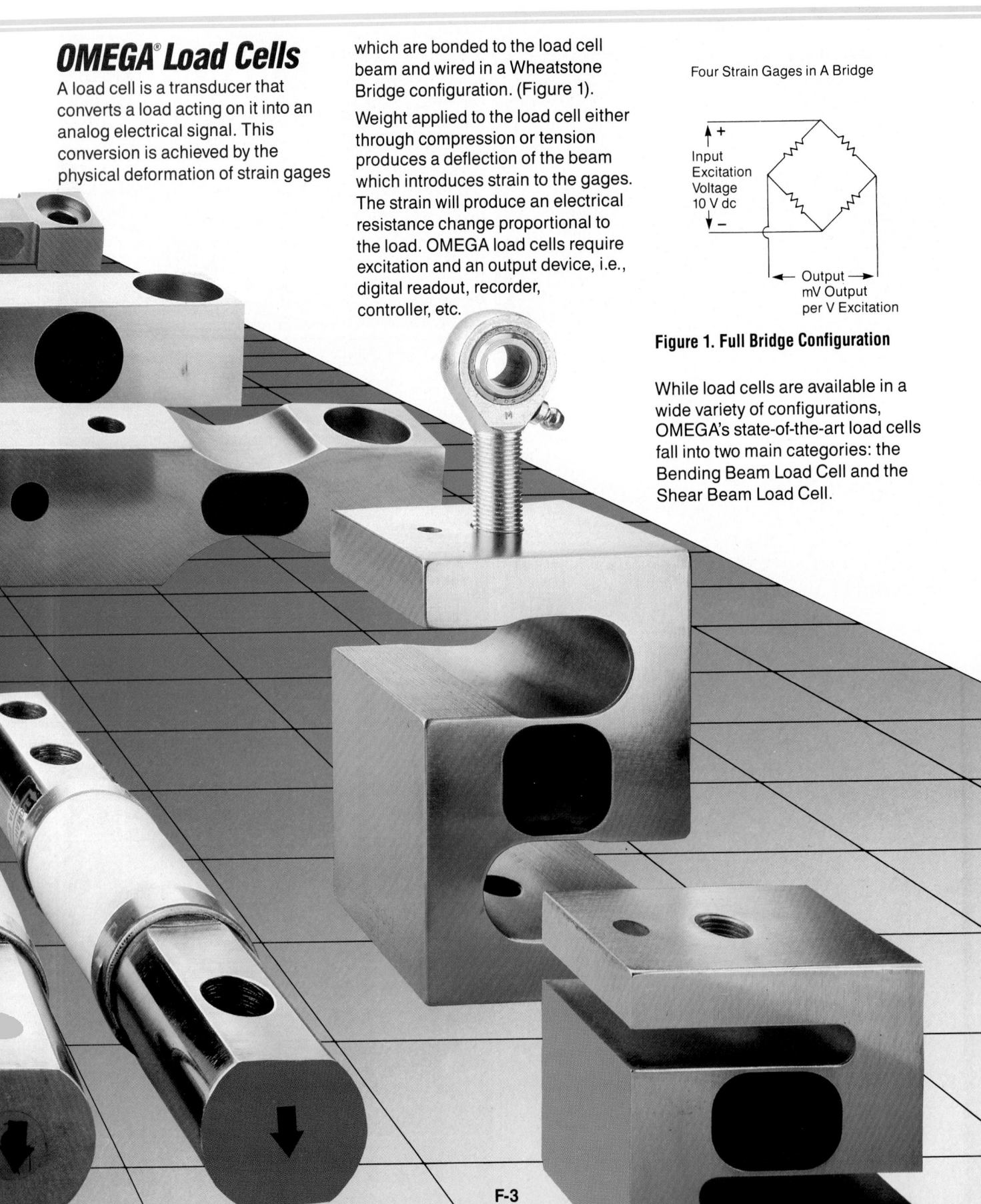

Input Excitation Voltage 10 V dc

Output mV Output per V Excitation

Figure 1. Full Bridge Configuration

While load cells are available in a wide variety of configurations, OMEGA's state-of-the-art load cells fall into two main categories: the Bending Beam Load Cell and the Shear Beam Load Cell.

Bending Beam Load Cells

The Bending Beam Load Cell is the most popular type in use today due to its simple design and low cost. The Bending Beam Load Cell principle states that a force applied on a rectangular block of steel mounted as a cantilever beam will produce shear stresses and bending stresses at the cross section (a-a) as shown in Figure 2.

To measure the applied force (F), strain gages are mounted to the top and bottom of the beam. These strain gages are actually measuring the bending stresses of the beam which are proportional to the load (F).

Because the strain gages are mounted on the outer surface of the bending beam, the Bending Beam Load Cell requires a protective cover and explicit handling instructions.

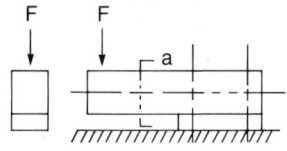

At Section a-a

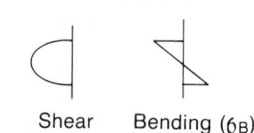

Shear Stresses (τ) Bending (6_B) Stresses

Figure 2. Bending Beam Load Cell Principle

Shear Beam Load Cells

The weight applied to a cantilever beam can also be found by the measurement of the shear forces produced by the applied load. Figure 2, above, demonstrates that

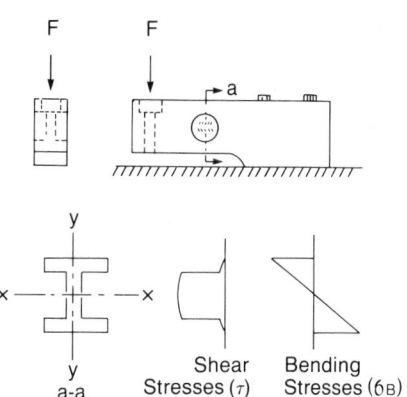

Figure 3. Shear Beam Load Cell Principle

the shear stresses on a Bending Beam Load Cell are constantly changing along the cross section. However, the I-beam cross section of a Shear Beam Load Cell, depicted in Figure 3, produces a uniform shear stress that can be measured very readily by strain gages mounted on the web of the beam.

The Shear Beam Load Cell has a number of distinct advantages over the Bending Beam Load Cell because of web-mounting of the strain gages. These advantages and a comparison of the two types of Omega Load Cells appear below.

While more than one load cell may appear suitable for a given application, only the design engineer can make the final decision as to which model will meet all of his requirements.

Installation Hints

1. Load Cells should be loaded in the specified direction of loading only. Lateral forces, bending, or torsional moments should be avoided.

2. Leveling operations are important to the accuracy of the system. These include horizontal leveling, vertical positioning of the container or weight, and uniform distribution of the load between multiple load cells.

3. The system should be checked for unintentional force shunts. The container or weight must not rest on any supporting frame. Undesired force shunts may be detected by applying and removing very small weights (about 0.1% of the total weight). The indicator or the electrical measuring equipment should respond.

4. Do not overload the load cell during the mounting procedure. Even very transient overloads can damage a load cell. The use of dummies during installation may alleviate this problem.

5. Electrically bypass the load cell with stranded copper wire to protect it against damage by welding currents or lightning.

6. The load cell must be protected against strong radiant heat, particularly on one side.

Load Cell Selection Guide

Shear Beam Load Cells

High side load rejection
Lower creep
Faster return to Zero after load removal
Higher tolerance of dynamic forces and vibrations
Better sealing and environmental protection

Bending Beam Load Cells

Lower Cost
Simple Construction

LOAD CELL AND TORQUE SENSOR SELECTION GUIDE

SERIES	PAGE	PRICES START AT	ACCURACY	RANGES (LBS)	FEATURES/APPLICATIONS
LCK LCG	F-7 F-8	$460	.26%	1kg to 1K 100 to 50K	Miniature and subminiature compression load cells with an intergral load button design. Ideal mounting where space is restricted. Excellent long term stability.
LCF	F-9	$750	.17%	1kg-500 lb	Miniature tension/compression load cell. Ideal for space restricted areas. Threaded ends facilitate easy installation.
LCH	F-10	$765	.13%	50 to 50K	Low profile tension/compression load cell. Mounting holes and female threads provide easy installation. Used frequently in research and industrial in-line force monitoring.
LCCA LCCB	F-13 F-14	$350	.04%	25 to 20K 50 to 10K	S-shaped tension/compression load cells. Applications include tank level hoppers, truck scales. Superior side load rejection.
LCJA LCJB	F-15 F-16	$330	.04% .03%	500 to 20K 1K to 10K	Bending beam load cells. Used in multiple load cell applications. Tank weighing, industrial process control. Low profile construction for integration into restricted areas.
LCDA LCDB	F-17 F-18	$320	.04% .04%	25 to 500 50 to 1K	Bending beam load cell. Used in multiple load cell systems. Accessories available for different mounting configurations.
LCTB	F-19	$755	.03%	5K to 150K	Double ended shear beam load cell. Center loaded design ideal for tank weighing in a wet corrosive environment due to its high accuracy low profile.

LOAD CELL AND TORQUE SENSOR SELECTION GUIDE

SERIES	PAGE	PRICES START AT	ACCURACY	RANGES (LBS)	FEATURES/APPLICATIONS
LCS	F-11	$245	.60%	2K to 40K	Load bolt for static tension or compression loads. Used to control bolt preloads, bolt pattern loads, or bolt load analysis. Bolt diameters from ¼″ to 1″. Full wheatstone bridge circuit design.
LCW	F-12	$375	.25%	200 to 200K	Combination load washer and compression load cell. Used as a washer to measure bolt loading characteristics, or as a compression load cell when used in conjunction with the load buttons. Full wheatstone bridge circuit design.
LCAA	F-23	$495	.04%	5 to 50	Platform load cell. Used to construct commercial and industrial weighing systems. Upper and lower tapped holes facilitate easy installation.
LCL	F-25	$69	.22%	¼-40	Thin beam load cell. Ideal for small load measurements used frequently for high volume applications. Thermally matched, full strain gage bridge, laminated to the beam to provide excellent stability and reliability.
DFG51	F-29	$1170	.20%	2 to 100	Handheld microprocessor based digital force gage. Provides fast and highly accurate readings in pounds, kilograms or Newtons. Standard RS232, analog, and open collector outputs. Peak memory for tensile or compressive loads.
TQ102	F-30	$420	.37	200-5K In-Lb	Socket extension reaction torque sensor. Available in ¼, ⅜, ½, and ¾″ square drives. Ideal for drive/socket systems to monitor or verify bolt torque. Measures torque in both clockwise and counterclockwise directions.
TQ101 TQ501	F-31 F-32	$1525	.18%	10 to 100K 100 to 10K In-Lb	Reaction and rotary torque sensors. Reaction torque sensor is flange mounted. Rotary torque sensor is key mounted. Industrial construction for a wide range of applications. Measures torque in both clockwise and counterclockwise directions.

SUBMINIATURE COMPRESSION LOAD CELL

NIST | MADE IN USA

LCK Series
0-1kg to 0 to 1000 lb

- **Ideal for Load Measurement Where Space is Restricted**
- **Rugged All Stainless Steel Construction**
- **Temperature Compensation 60°F to 160°F**

From $550

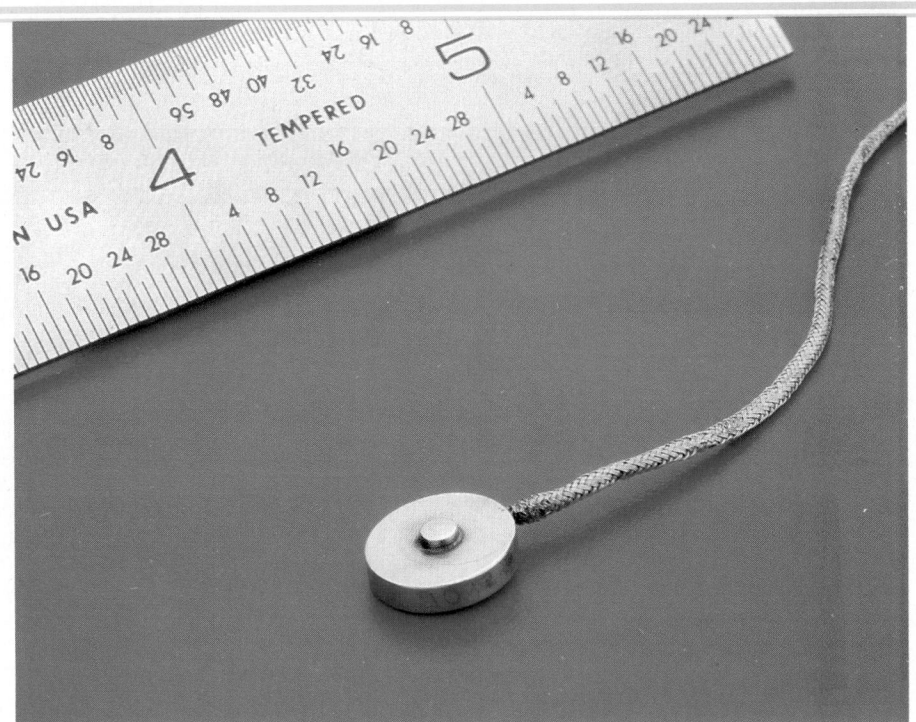
Shown Larger Than Actual Size

Small in size, but not in performance the OMEGA LCK Series compression load cells are designed to measure load ranges from 1 kg to 1000 lbs. Rugged all stainless steel construction along with a bonded foil strain gage assure superior linearity and hysteresis. Temperature compensation is achieved through a miniature circuit board which is included in the load cells lead cable. These units are designed to be mounted on a smooth, flat surface.

SPECIFICATIONS

Signal Output: 2 mV/V nominal
Linearity and Hysteresis: ±0.25% full scale
Repeatability: ±0.1% full scale
Zero Balance: ±2%
Compensated Temperature Range: 60°F to 160°F
Operating Temperature Range: −65°F to 250°F
Temperature Effect: Zero 0.01% full scale/°F Span 0.01% of reading/°F
Bridge Resistance: 350 ohm bonded foil gage
Excitation Voltage: 5 Vdc, 7 Vdc max
Full Scale Deflection: 0.001″ to 0.003″
Safe Overload: 150%
Construction: Stainless steel
Electrical: 5 ft. four conductor cable
Weight: < 0.5 oz.

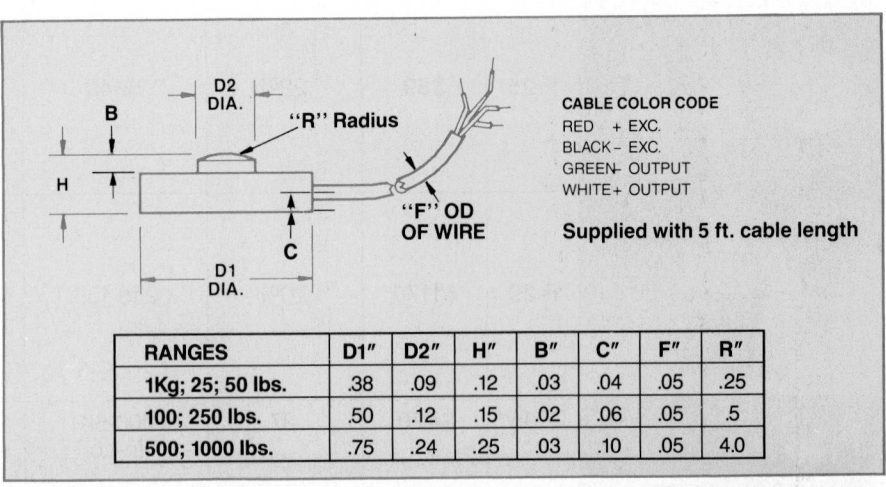

CABLE COLOR CODE
RED + EXC.
BLACK − EXC.
GREEN − OUTPUT
WHITE + OUTPUT

Supplied with 5 ft. cable length

RANGES	D1″	D2″	H″	B″	C″	F″	R″
1Kg; 25; 50 lbs.	.38	.09	.12	.03	.04	.05	.25
100; 250 lbs.	.50	.12	.15	.02	.06	.05	.5
500; 1000 lbs.	.75	.24	.25	.03	.10	.05	4.0

To Order (Specify Model Number)

MODEL	LOAD RANGE	PRICE	COMPATIBLE METER
LCK-1KG	1kg	$585	DP87, DP41-S, DP2000S5
LCK-25	25 lb	550	DP87, DP41-S, DP2000S3
LCK-50	50 lb	550	DP87, DP41-S, DP2000S4
LCK-100	100 lb	550	DP87, DP41-S, DP2000S5
LCK-250	250 lb	550	DP87, DP41-S, DP2000S3
LCK-500	500 lb	550	DP87, DP41-S, DP2000S4
LCK-1000	1000 lb	550	DP87, DP41-S, DP2000S5

HIGHLIGHTED MODELS IN STOCK FOR FAST DELIVERY

MINIATURE COMPRESSION LOAD CELL

LCG COMPRESSION LOAD CELL
0-500 to 0-50,000 lb

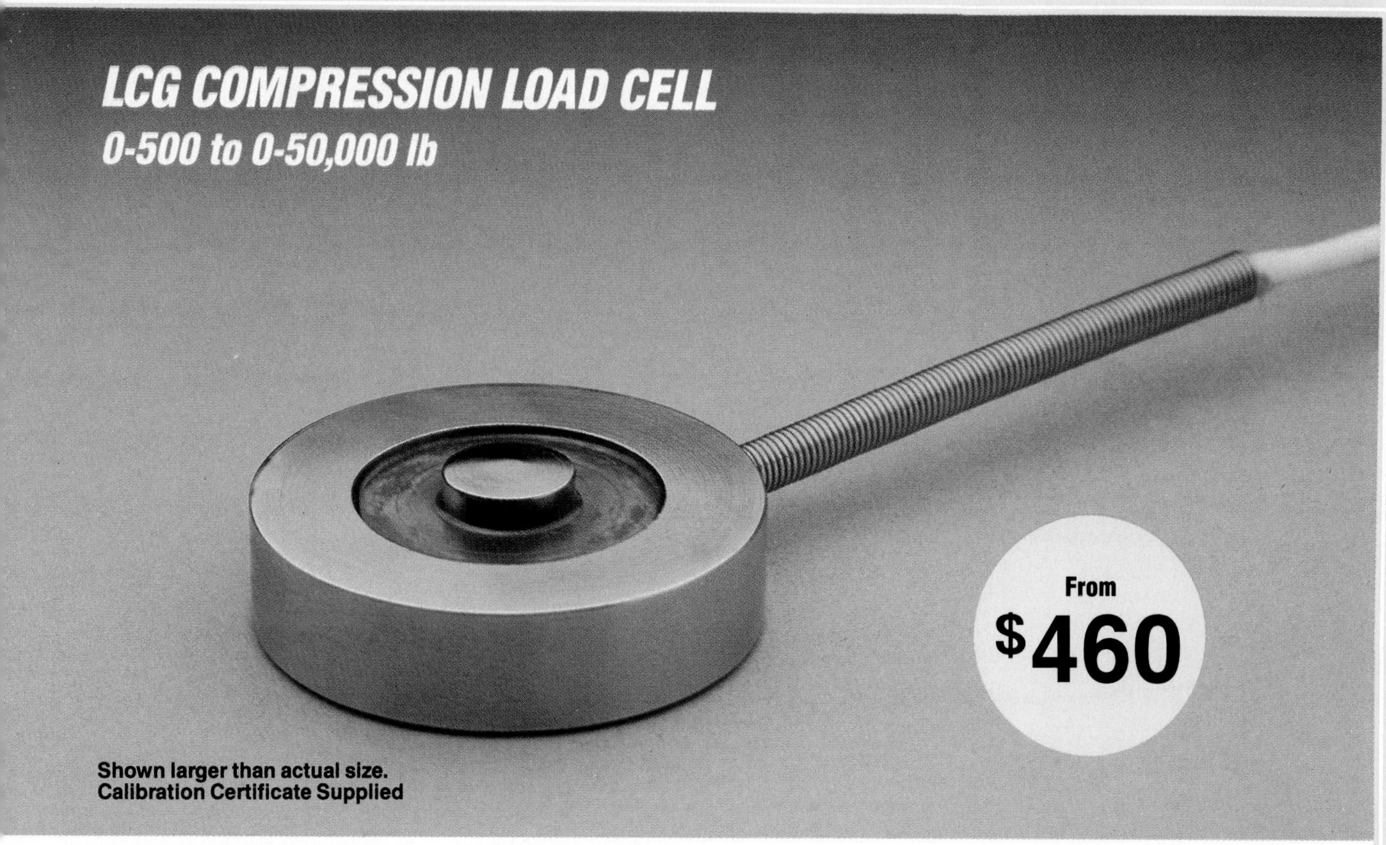

From
$460

Shown larger than actual size.
Calibration Certificate Supplied

The OMEGA® LCG Series bonded foil strain gage load cells are compression only units that are highly cost effective. To ensure excellent long term stability and reliability in severe environments, the LCG Series utilizes high quality strain gages, precision gaging techniques and all stainless steel construction. These units are designed to operate by mounting on a flat surface and have a load button machined as an integral part of the basic load cell.

SPECIFICATIONS

Signal Output: 2 mV/V nom.
Linearity: .2%
Hysteresis: .2%
Repeatability: ±0.05% FS
Zero Balance: ±1%
Compensated Temperature Range: 60°F to 160°F
Temperature Effect, Zero: ±0.005% F.S./°F; span: ±0.01% reading/°F
Bridge Resistance: 350 ohm foil strain gage
Excitation Voltage: 10 V
Safe Overload: 150% of full scale
Deflection: .004
Electrical Connection: 5 feet of shielded cable with pigtail end
Operating Temperature Range: −65°F to 250°F

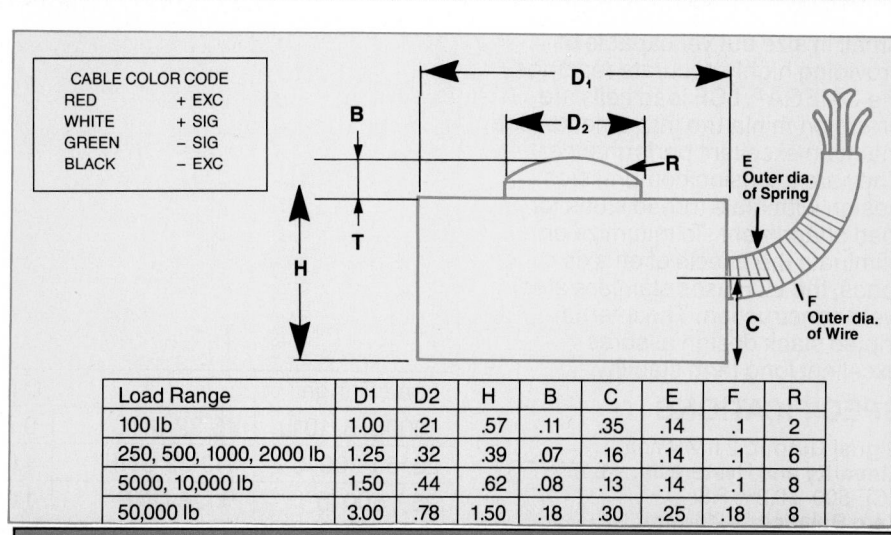

CABLE COLOR CODE
RED + EXC
WHITE + SIG
GREEN − SIG
BLACK − EXC

E Outer dia. of Spring
F Outer dia. of Wire

Load Range	D1	D2	H	B	C	E	F	R
100 lb	1.00	.21	.57	.11	.35	.14	.1	2
250, 500, 1000, 2000 lb	1.25	.32	.39	.07	.16	.14	.1	6
5000, 10,000 lb	1.50	.44	.62	.08	.13	.14	.1	8
50,000 lb	3.00	.78	1.50	.18	.30	.25	.18	8

To Order *(Specify model number)*

Model No.	Load Range	Price	Compatible Meter
LCG-100	100 lb	$590	DP41-S, DP350
LCG-250	250 lb	490	DP41-S, DP350
LCG-500	500 lb	460	DP41-S, DP350
LCG-1K	1,000 lb	460	DP41-S, DP350
LCG-2K	2,000 lb	460	DP41-S, DP350
LCG-5K	5,000 lb	525	DP41-S, DP350
LCG-10K	10,000 lb	525	DP41-S, DP350
LCG-50K	50,000 lb	695	DP41-S, DP350

MINIATURE TENSION AND COMPRESSION LOAD CELL

LCF Tension/Compression Load Cell
0-1 Kg to 0-500 lb

$750

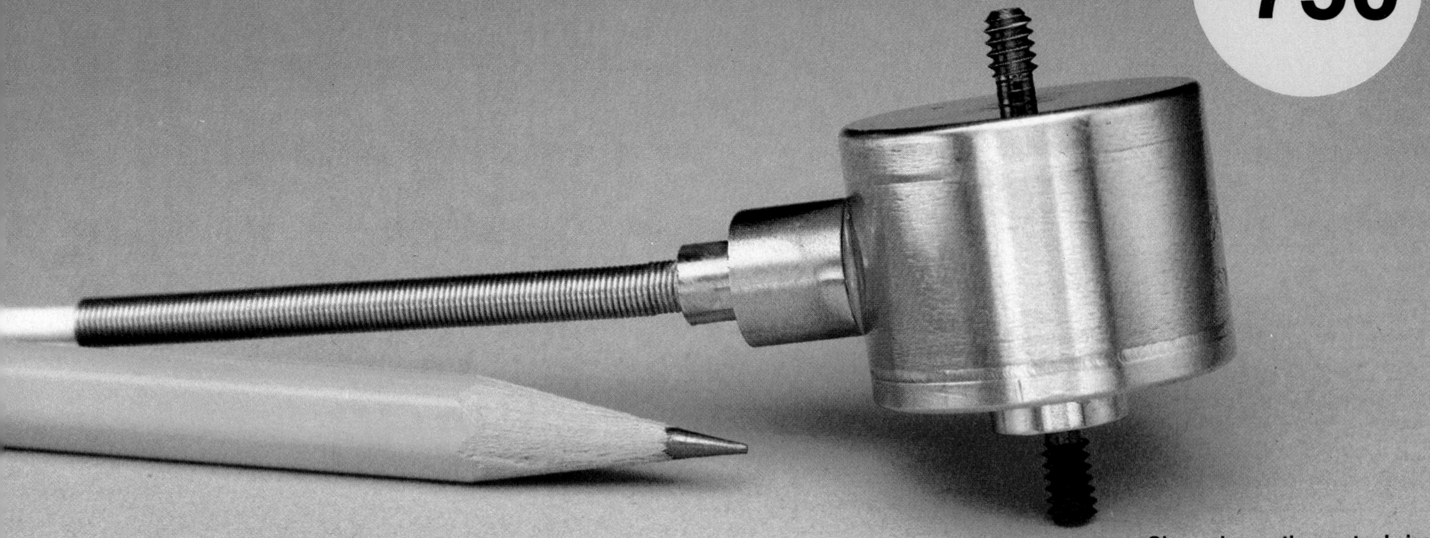

Shown larger than actual size.
Calibration Certificate Supplied

For Rod End Accessories, see page F-24.

Small in size but yet capable of providing highly accurate readings, the OMEGA® LCF load cells are precision miniature instruments that maintain excellent performance. They are a tension/compression design with male thread studs for load attachment. To minimize or eliminate the effects of off axis loads, the LCF uses stainless steel weld construction. The internal tripled stack design assures excellent long term stability.

SPECIFICATIONS

Signal Output: 2 mV/V nom.
Linearity and Hysteresis: ±0.15% F.S., LCF-500 ±0.2% F.S.
Zero Balance: ±2% max.
Repeatability: ±0.05% F.S.
Compensated Temperature Range: 60°F to 160°F
Temperature Effect of Zero and Span: ±0.005% F.S./°F
Bridge Resistance and Gage Type: 350 ohm foil
Excitation Voltage: 1000g thru 10 lb 5.0 Vdc; 20 lb thru 500 lb 10.0 Vdc
Safe Overload: 150% F.S.
Deflection: .001" to .003"
Electrical Connection: 5 feet of cable with pigtail end

▶ *HIGHLIGHTED MODELS STOCKED FOR FAST DELIVERY* ◀

F-9

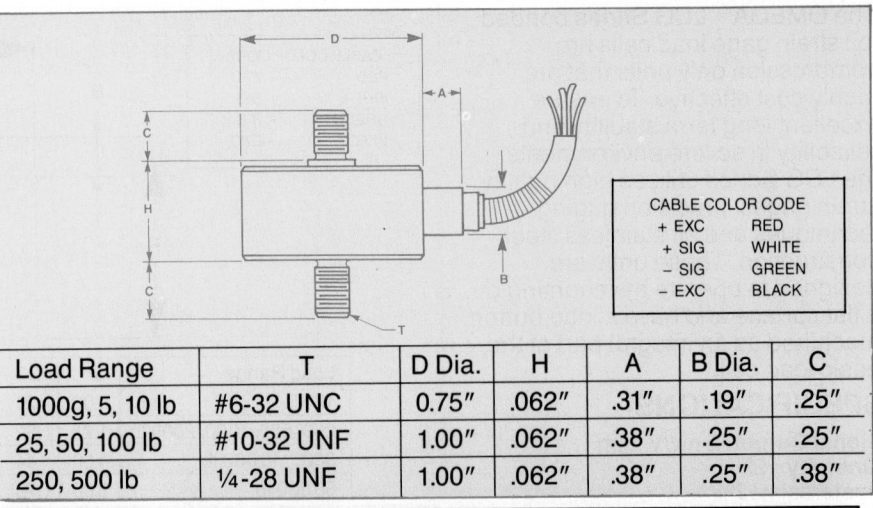

CABLE COLOR CODE
+ EXC	RED
+ SIG	WHITE
− SIG	GREEN
− EXC	BLACK

Load Range	T	D Dia.	H	A	B Dia.	C
1000g, 5, 10 lb	#6-32 UNC	0.75"	.062"	.31"	.19"	.25"
25, 50, 100 lb	#10-32 UNF	1.00"	.062"	.38"	.25"	.25"
250, 500 lb	¼-28 UNF	1.00"	.062"	.38"	.25"	.38"

To Order *(Specify model number)*

Model No.	Load Range	Price	Compatible Meter	Rod End
LCF-250G	250 g	**$1075**	DP41-S, DP350	REC-006F
LCF-500G	500 g	1075	DP41-S, DP350	REC-006F
LCF-1KG	1000 g	750	DP41-S, DP350	REC-006F
LCF-5	5 lb	750	DP41-S, DP350	REC-006F
LCF-10	10 lb	750	DP41-S, DP350	REC-006F
LCF-25	25 lb	750	DP41-S, DP350	REC-010F
LCF-50	50 lb	750	DP41-S, DP350	REC-010F
LCF-100	100 lb	750	DP41-S, DP350	REC-010F
LCF-500	500 lb	750	DP41-S, DP350	REC-014F

Accessories

LOW PROFILE TENSION AND COMPRESSION LOAD CELL

LCH Series 0-50 to 0-50,000 lb

- ✔ **All Stainless Steel Construction**
- ✔ **Dual Stabilizing**
- ✔ **Diaphragms Reduce Off-Center Loading Effects**
- ✔ **High Accuracy ±.25%**
- ✔ **Mating Connector Included**

The OMEGA LCH Series low profile tension and compression load cells are rated for both impressive accuracy and performance. These bonded foil strain gage load cells are available in the ranges from 0-50 to 0-50,000 lb measurements.

From

$765

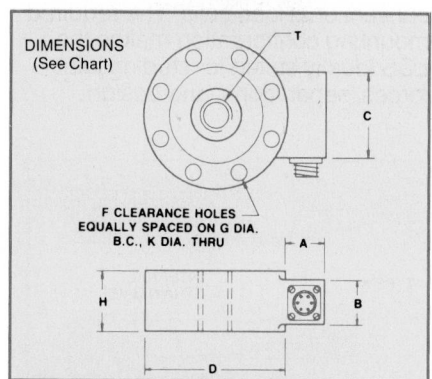

DIMENSIONS (See Chart)

F CLEARANCE HOLES EQUALLY SPACED ON G DIA. B.C., K DIA. THRU

Ranges (lbs.)	D″	H″	F″	G″ Dia. B.C.	K″ Dia. Thru	T	A″	B″	C″
50;100;500;1000	3.00	1.00	6	2.250	.28	3/8-24 UNF	.82	.75	1.25
5000	3.50	1.00	6	2.625	.34	1/2-20 UNF	.82	.75	1.25
10,000	5.50	1.80	8	4.500	.40	1-14 UNF	1.25	1.50	2.00
20,000; 50,000	6.00	1.80	8	4.875	.53	1-1/2-12 UNF	125	1.50	2.00

▶ *HIGHLIGHTED MODELS IN STOCK FOR FAST DELIVERY* ◀

To Order (Specify Model Number)

Model	Load Range	Price	Compatible Meter
LCH-50	50 lb	**$765**	DP2000S2,DP350,DP3002-S
▶LCH-100	100 lb	765	DP2000S3,DP350,DP3002-S◀
LCH-500	500 lb	765	DP2000S3,DP350,DP87
▶LCH-1K	1000 lb	765	DP2000S3,DP350,DP87◀
▶LCH-5K	5000 lb	765	DP87, DP3002-S, DP41-S◀
LCH-10K	10000 lb	935	DP87,DP3002-S,DP41-S
LCH-20K	20000 lb	1075	DP87,DP41-S
LCH-50K	50000 lb	1075	*DP87,DP41-S

*Counts by tens

SPECIFICATIONS

Signal Output: 3 mV/V nominal
Linearity: ±0.1% full scale
Hysteresis: ±0.08% full scale
Repeatability: ±0.03% full scale
Zero Balance: ±2%
Operating Temperature: −65 to 250°F
Compensated Temperature Range: 60°F to 160°F
Temperature Effect: Zero 0.002% full scale/°F; Span 0.002% of reading/°F
Bridge Resistance: 350 ohm bonded foil strain gage
Deflection Full Scale: 0.003″
Excitation Voltage: 10 Vdc (15 Vdc max.)
Safe Overload: 150%
Construction: 17-4 PH stainless steel
Mating Connector: PT06F-10-6S up to 5k (included), MS3106A-14S-6S 10k to 50k (included)

Allowable Extraneous Forces Without Damage % of Capacity			
Ranges	Side Load	Bending in lbs.	Torque in lbs.
≤500 lbs.	50%	40%	25%
≤ 5000 lbs.	30%	25%	25%
≤ 50K lbs.	20%	20%	15%

See page F-24 for Rod End's and Accessories.

LOAD CELLS

F

LOAD BOLTS FOR AXIAL STATIC TENSION LOADS

Shown With Model DP41-S Meter, $395

From
$245

LCS SERIES
0-2000 TO 0-39,000 lb.

✔ **N.I.S.T Calibration Certificate Included**
✔ **Full Wheatstone Bridge Configuration**
✔ **Bolt Diameters from ¼" up to 1"**
✔ **Accuracy of 0.60% Full Scale**

The OMEGA LCS Series load bolts offer a unique alternative to conventional load cells. The required mounting configuration makes the LCS ideally suited for studing joint forces, separations, and design.

SPECIFICATIONS

Rated Output: 1 to 2mV/V
Excitation: 10 Vdc, 15 Vdc maximum
Accuracy: 0.60% Full Scale
Linearity: 0.50% FS
Hysteresis: 0.25% FS
Repeatability: 0.10% FS
Zero Balance: 5% FS
Creep: 0.03% (in 20 minutes)
Operating Temperature: 50 to 150°F

Bridge Resistance: 350 ohms
Construction: Grade 8 bolt
Electrical: Teflon® insulated with polyvinyl over stainless steel overbraid. 9 conductor, 30 AWG
Thread Length: 2 (Bolt Dia.) + ¼"

Ordering Example: LCS-1/4-2L is a load bolt with a ¼"-20 bolt size (UNC) with a length of 2". Price: $245

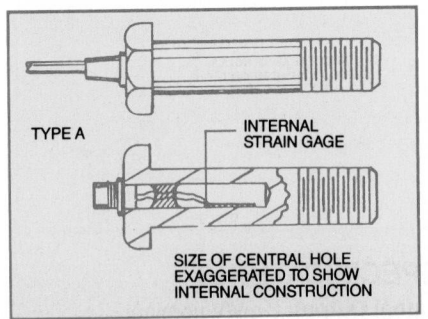

TYPE A — INTERNAL STRAIN GAGE

SIZE OF CENTRAL HOLE EXAGGERATED TO SHOW INTERNAL CONSTRUCTION

To Order (Specify Model Number)

MODEL	PRICE	BOLT SIZE UNC	LOAD CAPACITY	*AVAILABLE LENGTHS	COMPATIBLE METERS
LCS-¼-[*]L	$245	¼"-20	2,070 lbs	1¼", 2"	DP41-S, DP87, DP113-RO
LCS-⁵⁄₁₆-[*]L	245	⁵⁄₁₆"-18	3,410 lbs	1¼", 2"	DP41-S, DP87, DP113-RO
LCS-³⁄₈-[*]L	245	³⁄₈"-16	5,040 lbs	1¼", 2"	DP41-S, DP87, DP113-RO
LCS-⁷⁄₁₆-[*]L	245	⁷⁄₁₆"-14	6,910 lbs	1¼", 2"	DP41-S, DP87, DP113-RO
LCS-½-[*]L	245	½"-13	9,220 lbs	1¼", 2"	DP41-S, DP87, DP113-RO
LCS-⁹⁄₁₆-[*]L	245	⁹⁄₁₆"-12	11,800 lbs	1¼", 2"	**DP41-S, DP87, DP113-RO
LCS-⁵⁄₈-[*]L	255	⁵⁄₈"-11	14,700 lbs	2½", 6"	**DP41-S, DP87, DP113-RO
LCS-¾-[*]L	255	¾"-10	21,700 lbs	2½", 6"	**DP41-S, DP87, **DP113-RO
LCS-⅞-[*]L	265	⅞"-9	30,000 lbs	3½", 6"	**DP41-S, DP87, **DP113-RO
LCS-1-[*]L	265	1"-8	39,400 lbs	3½", 6"	**DP41-S, DP87, **DP113-RO

*Insert available length from chart.   ** User must scale in tons or 100 lb increments   National Institute of Standards and Technology (Formerly National Bureau of Standards)

COMBINATION LOAD WASHER AND COMPRESSION LOAD CELL

NIST | MADE IN USA | 1 YEAR WARRANTY

Typical Applications
- Clamping Forces
- Die Loads
- Bolt Stresses
- Weighing Systems
- Structural Loads

LCW-500 Shown $375
Includes Load Buttons and
Spherical Washers

LCW Series
0-200 to 0-200,000 lb

From
$375

- Compact Design
- Full Wheatstone Bridge Circuit Design
- Spherical Washers Included
- Recommended Use of Spherical Washers, When Used as Load Washers
- Recommended Use of Load Button, When Used as Compression Load Cell

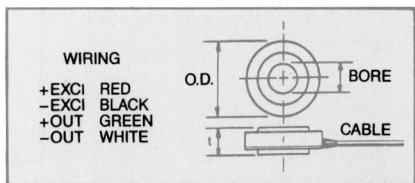

WIRING
+EXCI RED
−EXCI BLACK
+OUT   GREEN
−OUT   WHITE

SPECIFICATIONS

Rated Output: 2mV/V
Excitation: 10 Vdc, 15 Vdc maximum
Accuracy: 0.25% Full Scale
Linearity: 0.15% Full Scale
Hysteresis: 0.15% Full Scale
Repeatability: 0.15% Full Scale
Zero Balance: 2.0% Full Scale
Creep: 0.03% Full Scale (in 20 minutes)
Operating Temperature: 15 to 150°F
Storage Range: −15 to 170°F

Compensated Temperature: 15 to 150°F
Thermal Effects: Zero: 0.008% FS/°F
                    Output: 0.008% FS/°F
Maximum Load: Safe: 150%
                  Ultimate: 250%
Bridge Resistance: 350 ohms
Full Scale Deflection: 0.001″ nominal
Construction: 17-4 PH stainless steel, 44 RC
Electrical: 36″ Teflon® insulated with polyvinyl over SS overbraid. 4 conductor 30 AWG

Ranges (lbs.)	Bore	O.D.	T
LCW-200 to LCW-10K	.40	1.00	.35
LCW-20K	.50	1.20	.40
LCW-50K	.76	1.75	.50
LCW-100K	1.01	2.25	.70
LCW-200K	2.00	3.63	1.0

To Order (Specify Model Number)

MODEL NO.	PRICE	RATED CAPACITY	HT. OF BUTTON	WT. LBS.	COMPATIBLE METERS	SPHERICAL WASHERS PART NO.	BORE	** PRICE
LCW-200	$375	200	.37	1.0	DP350, DP2000-S5, DP41-S	SPW-2	$11/32$	$10
LCW-500	375	500	.42	1.0	DP350, DP2000-S3, DP41-S	SPW-2	$11/32$	10
LCW-1K	375	1,000	.55	1.0	DP350, DP2000-S4, DP41-S	SPW-2	$11/32$	10
LCW-2K	375	2,000	.55	1.0	DP350, DP2000-S5, DP41-S	SPW-2	$11/32$	10
LCW-5K	375	5,000	.55	1.0	DP41-S, DP87, DP113-RO	SPW-2	$11/32$	10
LCW-10K	445	10,000	.55	1.0	DP41-S, DP87, DP113-RO	SPW-2	$11/32$	10
LCW-20K	495	20,000	.76	1.5	DP41-S, DP87, DP113-RO	SPW-3	$13/32$	10
LCW-50K	535	50,000	1.0	2.0	DP87, *DP113-RO	SPW-5	$21/32$	15
LCW-100K	595	100,000	1.5	3.0	*DP87, *DP113-RO	SPW-7	$15/16$	15
LCW-200K	995	200,000	2.0	6.0	*DP87, *DP113-RO	SPW-7	$15/16$	15

*Must be scaled in tons, or count by ×10   **One set of spherical washers supplied with each load washer.

LOAD CELLS F

HIGH ACCURACY TENSION AND COMPRESSION
"S" BEAM LOAD CELLS

LCCA SERIES
250 TO 20000 lbs Capacity

**USE SUMMING J-BOX ON PAGE F-42
FOR MULTICELL INSTALLATIONS**

Shown smaller than actual size

✔ **Environmentally Protected For Washdown Applications**
✔ **Corrosion Resistant**
✔ **N.I.S.T. Certificate Supplied**
✔ **0.25% Interchangeable From**

$395

SPECIFICATIONS

Rated Output: 3mV/V ±0.0075mV/V (actual output supplied with each load cell)
Excitation: 10 Vdc (15 Vdc maximum)
Accuracy: 0.037% Full Scale
Linearity: 0.03% FS
Hysteresis: 0.02% FS
Repeatability: 0.01% FS
Zero Balance: 1% FS
Creep in 20 min: 0.03% FS
Operating Temperature: 0 to 150°F
Compensated Temperature: 0 to 150°F
Thermal effects: Zero - 0.0015% FS/°F Span - 0.0008% RDG/°F
Maximum Load: 200% FS
Bridge Resistance: 350 ohms nominal
Full Scale Deflection: 0.010″ to 0.020″
Construction: Nickel Plated Carbon Steel
Cable: 20′ 4-conductor shielded 22-gage wire

Highlighted Models Stocked for Fast Delivery!

DIMENSIONS (IN INCHES)

CABLE SEALING GLAND

4 CONDUCTOR SHIELDED CABLE. 20 FEET

A (thread dimension)

Capacity	A	B	C	D	E
50-200	¼-28	.75	.5	2.0	2.5
250	⅜-24	.75	.50	2.0	3.0
500-750 1,000-1,500	½-20	1.00	.75	2.0	3.0
2,000-3,000	½-20	1.25	1.00	2.0	3.0
5,000-10,000	¾-16	1.25	1.00	3.0	4.25
15,000	1-14	1.50	1.25	3.5	5.50
20,000	1¼-12	2.00	1.75	4.5	7.0

WIRING (TENSION)
RED: +INPUT
BLACK: −INPUT
GREEN: +OUTPUT
WHITE: −OUTPUT

To Order *(Specify Model Number)* / Accessories

MODEL	PRICE	RATED CAPACITY	WEIGHT	COMPATIBLE METERS	LOAD BUTTON MODEL	PRICE	ROD END MODEL	PRICE
▶LCCA-25	$395	25 lbs	2 lbs	DP3002-S, DP460-S, DP350	LBC-014	$ 40	REC-014M	$15
▶LCCA-50	395	50 lbs	2 lbs	DP3002-S, DP460-S, DP350	LBC-014	40	REC-014M	15
▶LCCA-100	395	100 lbs	2 lbs	DP3002-S, DP460-S, DP350	LBC-014	40	REC-014M	15
LCCA-150	395	150 lbs	2 lbs	DP3002-S, DP460-S, DP350	LBC-014	40	REC-014M	15
▶LCCA-200	395	200 lbs	2 lbs	DP3002-S, DP460-S, DP350	LBC-014	40	REC-014M	15
LCCA-250	395	250 lbs	2 lbs	DP41-S, DP3002-S, DP350	LBC-038	40	REC-038M	20
▶LCCA-500	395	500 lbs	2 lbs	DP41-S, DP3002-S, DP350	LBC-012	40	REC-012M	35
LCCA-750	395	750 lbs	2 lbs	DP41-S, DP3002-S, DP350	LBC-012	40	REC-012M	35
▶LCCA-1K	395	1000 lbs	2 lbs	DP41-S, DP3002-S, DP350	LBC-012	40	REC-012M	35
▶LCCA-2K	445	2500 lbs	3 lbs	DP41-S, DP3002-S, DP350	LBC-012	40	REC-012M	35
▶LCCA-3K	445	3000 lbs	3 lbs	DP41-S, DP87, DP113-R0	LBC-012	40	REC-012M	35
▶LCCA-5K	620	5000 lbs	3.5 lbs	DP41-S, DP87, DP113-R0	LBC-034	55	REC-034M	65
▶LCCA-10K	620	10000 lbs	3.5 lbs	DP41-S, DP87, DP113-R0	LBC-034	55	REC-034M	65
LCCA-15K	745	15000 lbs	6 lbs	DP41-S, DP87, DP113-R0	LBC-100	170	REC-100M	95
LCCA-20K	1145	20000 lbs	13 lbs	DP41-S, DP87, DP113-R0	—	—	REC-114M	95

National Institute of Standards and Technology (formerly National Bureau of Standards)

TENSION & COMPRESSION S TYPE LOAD CELL LCCB Series

From $350

Model LCCB-1K
$350

Model LCCB-100
$350

DP2000-S2
Meter Shown
$391

- ✔ N.I.S.T. Calibration Certificate Supplied
- ✔ 0.25% Interchangeable
- ✔ Water Resistant for Washdown Applications
- ✔ Ideal for Tank and Hopper Weighing

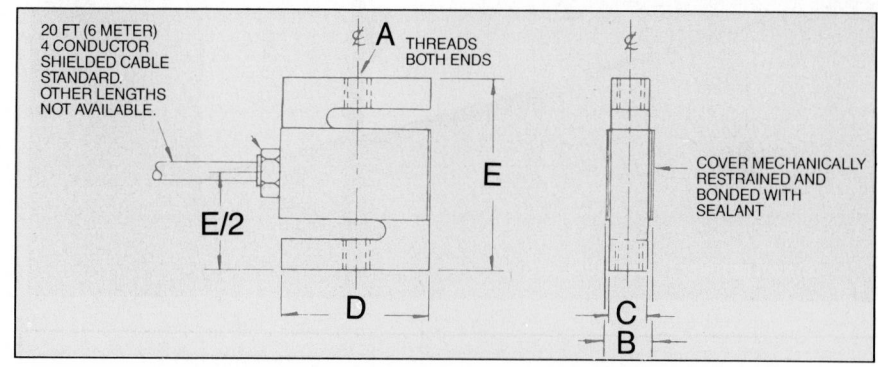

20 FT (6 METER) 4 CONDUCTOR SHIELDED CABLE STANDARD. OTHER LENGTHS NOT AVAILABLE.

THREADS BOTH ENDS

COVER MECHANICALLY RESTRAINED AND BONDED WITH SEALANT

SPECIFICATIONS

Rated Output: 3 mV/V ±0.0075 mV/V
(To eliminate .25% output end user must calibrate)
Excitation: 10 Vdc, 15 Vdc max.
Accuracy: 0.03% FS
Operating Temp. Range: −65 to 200°F
Compensated Temp. Range: 0 to 150°F
Thermal Effects: zero, 0.0015% FS/°F; output, 0.0008% Rdg/°F
Max. Load: Safe, 150%; ultimate, 300%; side load, 50%
Bridge Resistance: 350 Ohm
Construction: Nickel-plated steel
Electrical: 20′, 4-conductor shielded cable

WIRING (TENSION)

FUNCTION	COLOR
+EXCITATION	RED
−EXCITATION	BLACK
+OUTPUT	GREEN
−OUTPUT	WHITE
SHIELD	ORANGE

DIMENSIONS—INCH (MM)

CAPACITY	A	B	C	D	E
50-300	¼-28	.75	.50	2.0	2.5
50-1500	½-20	1.0	.75	2.0	2.5
2000	½-20	1.25	1.0	2.0	2.5
3000	½-20	1.25	1.0	3.0	4.0
5000-10000	¾-16	1.25	1.0	3.0	4.0

HIGHLIGHTED MODELS STOCKED FOR FAST DELIVERY

To Order (Specify Model Number)

Model No.	Price	Rated Capacity	FS Defl.	Wt. Lbs.	Compatible Meters	Load Button	Price	Rod End	Price
LCCB-50	$350	50 lbs.	0.013	0.8	DP350, DP2000-S2, DP87	LBC-014	$40	REC-014M	$15
LCCB-100	350	100 lbs.	0.013	0.8	DP350, DP2000-S3, DP41-S	LBC-014	40	REC-014M	15
LCCB-200	350	200 lbs.	0.013	0.8	DP350, DP2000-S4,	LBC-014	40	REC-014M	15
LCCB-300	350	300 lbs.	0.013	0.8	DP41-S, DP2000-S2, DP87	LBC-014	40	REC-014M	15
LCCB-500	350	500 lbs.	0.018	1.0	DP41-S, DP2000-S2, DP87	LBC-012	40	REC-012M	35
LCCB-1K	350	1000 lbs.	0.018	1.0	DP350, DP2000-S3, DP41-S	LBC-012	40	REC-012M	35
LCCB-2K	350	2000 lbs.	0.023	1.0	DP350, DP2000-S4, DP41-S	LBC-012	40	REC-012M	35
LCCB-5K	535	5000 lbs.	0.033	3.3	DP87, DP41-S	LBC-034	55	REC-034M	65
LCCB-10K	535	10,000 lbs.	0.033	3.3	DP87, DP41-S	LBC-034	55	REC-034M	65

See page F-38 for a complete selection of accessories.

National Institute of Standards and Technology (formerly National Bureau of Standards)

LOAD CELLS F

HEAVY DUTY SHEAR BEAM LOAD CELLS - 500 TO 20,000 LBS

LCJA SERIES

From **$370**

Shown smaller than actual size

✔ **Environmentally Protected For Washdown Applications**
✔ **Corrosion Resistant**
✔ **N.I.S.T. Certificate Supplied**
✔ **0.25% Interchangeable**
✔ **Exact Full Scale Output Stated For Easy Equipment Setup And System Calibration**

SPECIFICATION

Rated Output: 3mV/V ±0.0075mV/V (actual output supplied with each load cell)
Excitation: 10 Vdc (15 Vdc maximum)
Accuracy: 0.037% Full Scale
Linearity: 0.03% FS
Hysteresis: 0.02% FS
Repeatability: 0.01% FS
Zero Balance: 1% FS
Creep in 20 min: 0.03% FS
Operating Temperature: 0 to 150°F
Compensated Temperature: 0 to 150°F
Thermal effects: Zero - 0.0015% FS/°F Span - 0.0008% RDG/°F
Maximum Load: 200% FS
Side Load Rejection: 500:1
Bridge Resistance: 350 ohms nominal
Full Scale Deflection: 0.015″ to 0.025″
Construction: Nickel Plated Steel
Cable: 20' 4-conductor shielded 22-gage wire

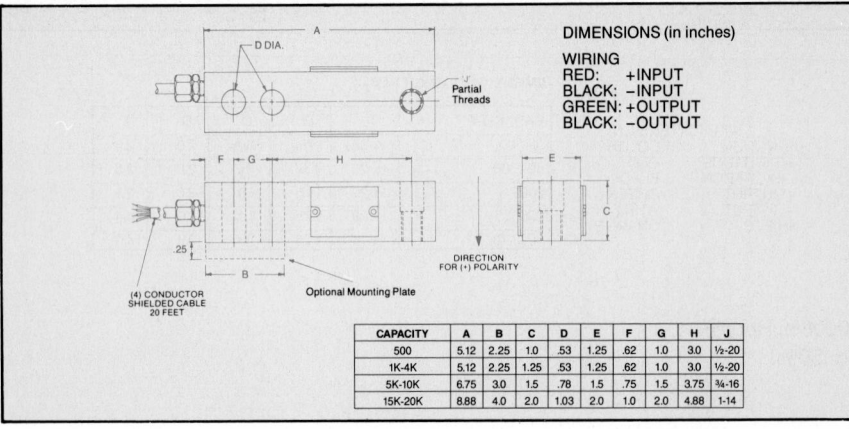

DIMENSIONS (in inches)

WIRING
RED: +INPUT
BLACK: –INPUT
GREEN: +OUTPUT
BLACK: –OUTPUT

Partial Threads

DIRECTION FOR (+) POLARITY

(4) CONDUCTOR SHIELDED CABLE 20 FEET

Optional Mounting Plate

CAPACITY	A	B	C	D	E	F	G	H	J
500	5.12	2.25	1.0	.53	1.25	.62	1.0	3.0	½-20
1K-4K	5.12	2.25	1.25	.53	1.25	.62	1.0	3.0	½-20
5K-10K	6.75	3.0	1.5	.78	1.5	.75	1.5	3.75	¾-16
15K-20K	8.88	4.0	2.0	1.03	2.0	1.0	2.0	4.88	1-14

To Order (Specify Model Number)

MODEL	PRICE	RATED CAPACITY	WEIGHT	COMPATIBLE METERS	LOAD BUTTON MODEL	PRICE	ROD END MODEL	PRICE	MOUNTING PLATES
LCJA-500	$370	500 lbs	4 lbs	DP41-S, DP3002-S, DP350	LBJ-2.5K	$24	REC-012M	$35	MFP-1
LCJA-1K	370	1000 lbs	4 lbs	DP41-S, DP3002-S, DP350	LBJ-2.5K	24	REC-012M	35	MFP-1
LCJA-2K	370	2000 lbs	4 lbs	DP41-S, DP3002-S, DP350	LBJ-2.5K	24	REC-012M	35	MFP-1
LCJA-2.5K	370	2500 lbs	4 lbs	DP41-S, DP3002-S, DP113-R0	LBJ-2.5K	24	REC-012M	35	MFP-1
LCJA-4K	370	4000 lbs	4 lbs	DP41-S, DP3002-S, DP113-R0	LBJ-10K	28	REC-012M	35	MFP-1
LCJA-5K	470	5000 lbs	3.5 lbs	DP41-S, DP87, DP113-R0	LBJ-10K	28	REC-034M	65	MFP-2
LCJA-10K	470	10000 lbs	3.5 lbs	DP41-S, DP87, DP113-R0	—	—	REC-034M	65	MFP-2
LCJA-15K	815	15000 lbs	9 lbs	DP41-S, DP87, DP113-R0	—	—	REC-100M	95	MFP-3
LCJA-20K	985	20000 lbs	9 lbs	DP41-S, DP87, DP113-R0	—	—	REC-100M	95	MFP-3

National Institute of Standards and Technology (formerly National Bureau of Standards)

▶ *HIGHLIGHTED MODELS IN STOCK FOR FAST DELIVERY!* ◀

RUGGED SHEAR BEAM LOAD CELL
1000 TO 10,000 LBS.
LCJB Series

- ✔ **0.25% Interchangeability Standard**
- ✔ **N.I.S.T. Certificate Supplied †**
- ✔ **Water Resistant for Washdown Applications**

OMEGA LCJB rugged low profile shear beam load cells are ideal for process weighing and also for use in low profile scales. These economical units are easy to install and durable in the field. Environmental protection is afforded through water resistant potting, compression seal and strain relief cable entry, and corrosion-resistant nickel plated steel.

From
$330

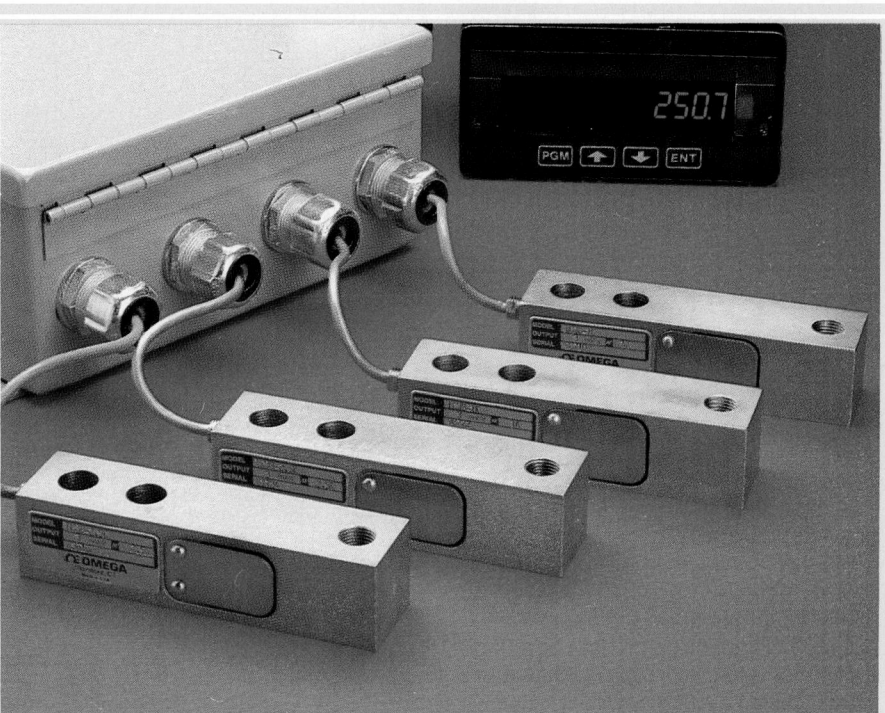

SPECIFICATIONS

Rated Output: 3 mV/V ±0.008 mV/V (To minimize tolerance end user must recalibrate)

Excitation: 10 Vdc, 15 Vdc max.

Accuracy: 0.03% FS

Repeatability: 0.01% FS

Zero Balance: 1% FS

Creep In 20 Min.: 0.03% Rdg

Operating Temp. Range: −65 to 200°F

Compensated Temp. Range: 0 to 150°F

Thermal Effects: Zero: 0.0015% FS/°F; Output: 0.0008% Rdg/°F

Max. Load: Safe: 150% FS; Ultimate: 400% FS; Side load: 100% FS

Bridge Resistance: Input 350 ±3.5 Ohms; Output 350 ±3.5 Ohms

Construction: Nickel-plated steel

Electrical: 20′, 4-conductor shielded cable

Weight: 2 lbs. (.9 kg) (5K, 10K model is 3.5 lbs.)

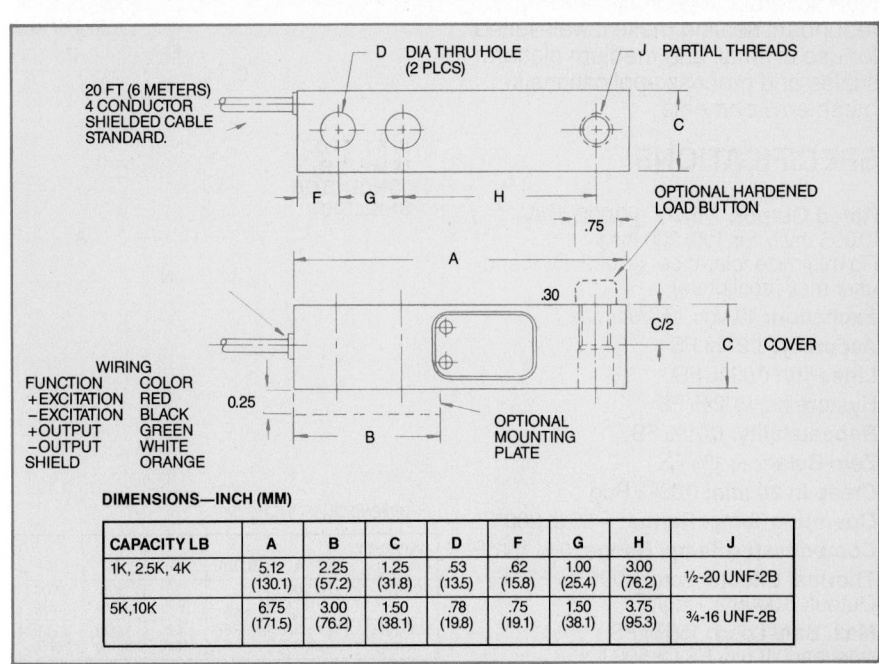

DIMENSIONS—INCH (MM)

CAPACITY LB	A	B	C	D	F	G	H	J
1K, 2.5K, 4K	5.12 (130.1)	2.25 (57.2)	1.25 (31.8)	.53 (13.5)	.62 (15.8)	1.00 (25.4)	3.00 (76.2)	½-20 UNF-2B
5K,10K	6.75 (171.5)	3.00 (76.2)	1.50 (38.1)	.78 (19.8)	.75 (19.1)	1.50 (38.1)	3.75 (95.3)	¾-16 UNF-2B

WIRING

FUNCTION	COLOR
+EXCITATION	RED
−EXCITATION	BLACK
+OUTPUT	GREEN
−OUTPUT	WHITE
SHIELD	ORANGE

To Order *(Specify Model Number)*

Model No.	Price	Rated Capacity	Full Scale Deflection	Compatible Meters	Load Button Part #	Price	Rod End Part #	Price	Mounting Plates
LCJB-1K	$330	1000 lbs.	0.016	DP350, DP2000-S3	LBC-012	$40	REC-012M	$35	MFP-1
LCJB-2.5K	330	2500 lbs.	0.03	DP87, DP41-S	LBC-012	40	REC-012M	35	MFP-1
LCJB-4K	330	4000 lbs.	0.04	DP87, DP41-S	LBC-012	40	REC-012M	35	MFP-1
LCJB-5K	415	5000 lbs.	.035	DP87, DP41-S	LBC-034	55	REC-034M	65	MFP-2
LCJB-10K	415	10,000 lbs.	0.42	DP87, DP41-S	LBC-034	55	REC-034M	65	MFP-2

See page F-22 for a complete selection of accessories.

†*National Institute of Standards and Technology (formerly National Bureau of Standards)*

STOCKED FOR FAST DELIVERY

LOAD CELLS **F**

RUGGED BEAM LOAD CELL FOR LOW CAPACITIES 50 to TO 1000 LBS.
LCDB SERIES

✔ **0.25% Interchangeable**
✔ **N.I.S.T. Certificate Supplied †**
✔ **Water Resistant for Washdown Applications**

From
$465

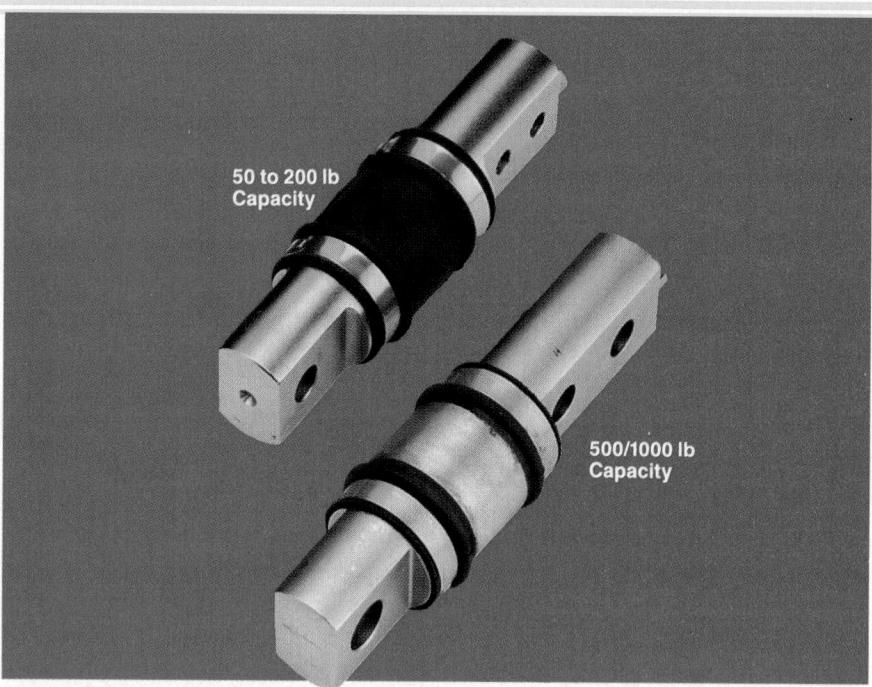

50 to 200 lb Capacity

500/1000 lb Capacity

The LCDB single-ended beam-type load cell is constructed as a bending beam for 200 lbs or less, and as a shear beam for above 200 lbs. Its high accuracy, low profile, and redundant sealing make it well-suited for use in small and medium platform scales and process applications in harsh environments.

SPECIFICATIONS

Rated Output: 2 mV/V ±0.002 mV/V (0.005 mV/V for 100, 200 lbs.) (To minimize tolerance ±0.002 mV/V end user may recalibrate)
Excitation: 10 Vdc, 15 Vdc max
Accuracy: .037% FS
Linearity: 0.03% FS
Hysteresis: 0.02% FS
Repeatability: 0.01% FS
Zero Balance: 1% FS
Creep in 20 min: 0.03% Rdg
Operating Temp. Range: −65 to 200°F
Compensated Temp. Range: 0 to 150°F
Thermal Effects: Zero, 0.0015% FS/°F; Output, 0.0008% Rdg/°F
Max. Safe Load: 150% FS; side load, 100% ($\geq$ 500 lbs.), 50% FS (1k)
Bridge Resistance: 350 Ohms ±4 Ohms
Full Scale Deflection: 0.070″ (500 lbs., 1000 lbs; 0.026″)
Construction: Nickel-plated steel, Neoprene boot secured by adhesive and stainless steel band. Bending beam <500 lbs., shear beam ≥500 lbs.
Electrical: 10′, four conductor shielded cable
Weight: 1.6 lbs. (.73 kg) (500 lbs., 1000 lbs.; 1.8 lbs [.82 kg])

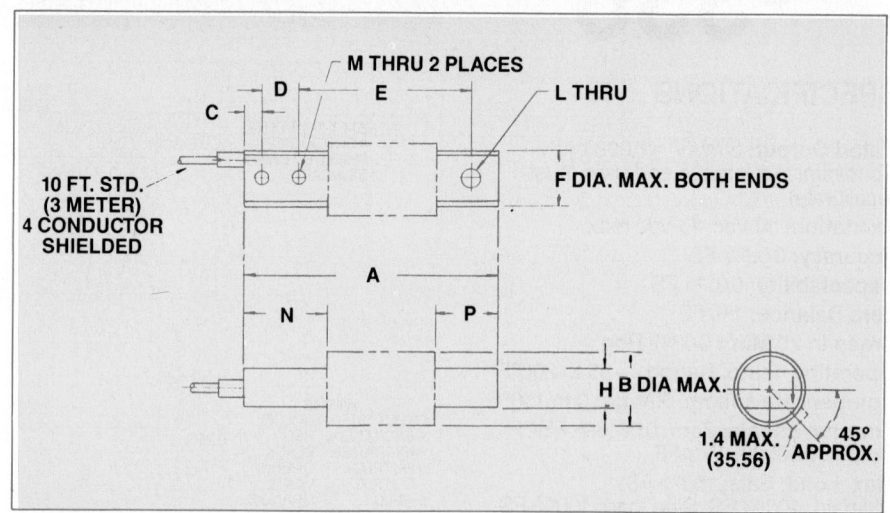

DIMENSIONS—INCH (MM)

CAPACITY lbs.	A	B DIA	C	D	E	F DIA	H	L DIA	M DIA	N	P
50-200	5.00 (127.0)	1.56 (39.6)	.38 (9.7)	.625 (15.9)	3.500 (88.9)	1.23 (31.2)	.750 (19.0)	.391 (9.9)	.266 (6.8)	1.50 (38.1)	1.25 (31.8)
500-1000	5.38 (136.7)		.62 (15.8)	1.000 (25.4)	3.250 (82.6)			.406 (10.3)	.406 (10.3)	2.07 (52.6)	1.20 (30.5)

To Order (Specify Model Number)

Model No.	Price	Rated Capacity	Compatible Meters
LCDB-50	**$465**	50 lbs.	DP350, DP2000-S2, DP3002-S
LCDB-100	465	100 lbs.	DP350, DP2000-S3, DP3002-S
LCDB-200	465	200 lbs.	DP350, DP2000-S3, DP3002-S
LCDB-500	540	500 lbs.	DP350, DP3002-S, DP113-RO
LCDB-1K	540	1000 lbs.	DP350, DP2000-S3, DP3002-S

† National Institute of Standards & Technology (Formerly National Bureau of Standards)

LOW PROFILE BENDING BEAM LOAD CELL

LCDA SERIES
25 to 500 lbs Capacity

✔ **High Quality Steel Provides Maximum Protection Against Adverse Loads**

✔ **Sealed For Washdown Areas**

✔ **0.25% Interchangability**

✔ **N.I.S.T Certificate Provided†**

✔ **Exact Full Scale Output Stated For Easy Setup And Calibration**

All Models
$320

The model LCDA is a versatile bending beam load cell for tension and compression loading. Compact and low in profile, the LCDA is ruggedly constructed of high quality alloy steel to provide maximum ruggedness for industrial applications. Each unit is nickel plated for corrosion resistance and sealed to resist moisture.

SPECIFICATIONS

Rated Output: 3mV/V ±0.0075mV/V (actual output supplied with each load cell)

Excitation: 10 Vdc (15 Vdc maximum)

Accuracy: 0.037% Full Scale

Linearity: 0.03% FS

Hysteresis: 0.02% FS

Repeatability: 0.01% FS

Zero Balance: 1% FS

Creep in 20 min: 0.03% FS

Operating Temperature: 0 to 150°F

Compensated Temperature: 0 to 150°F

Thermal Effects: Zero - 0.0015% FS/°F Span - 0.0008% RDG/°F

Maximum Load: 150% FS

Bridge Resistance: 350 ohms nominal

Full Scale Deflection: 0.020" to 0.025"

Construction: Nickel Plated Steel, neoprene boot with SS clamps

Cable: 20' 4-conductor shielded 22-gage wire

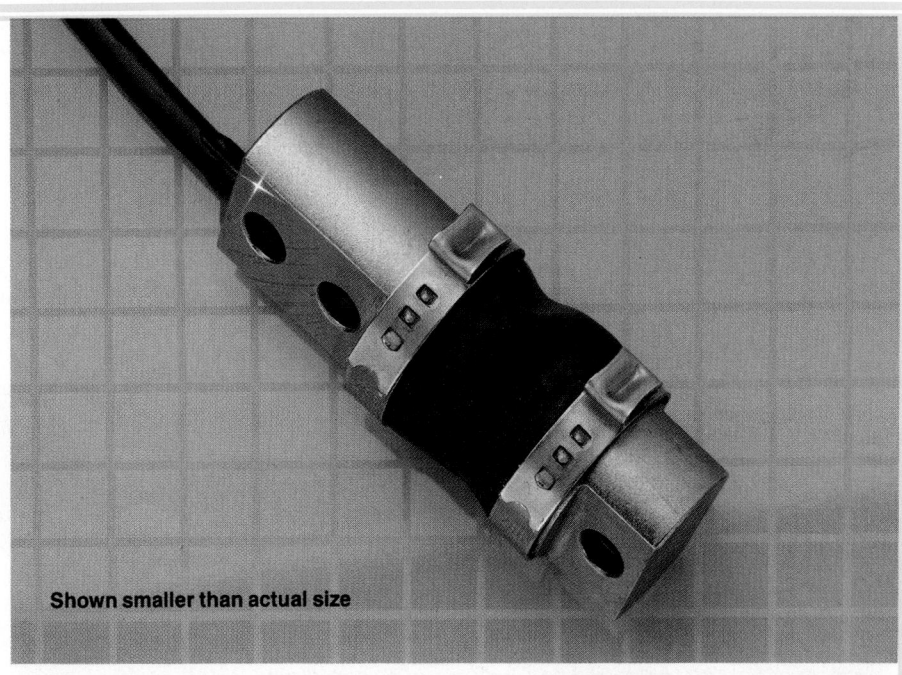

Shown smaller than actual size

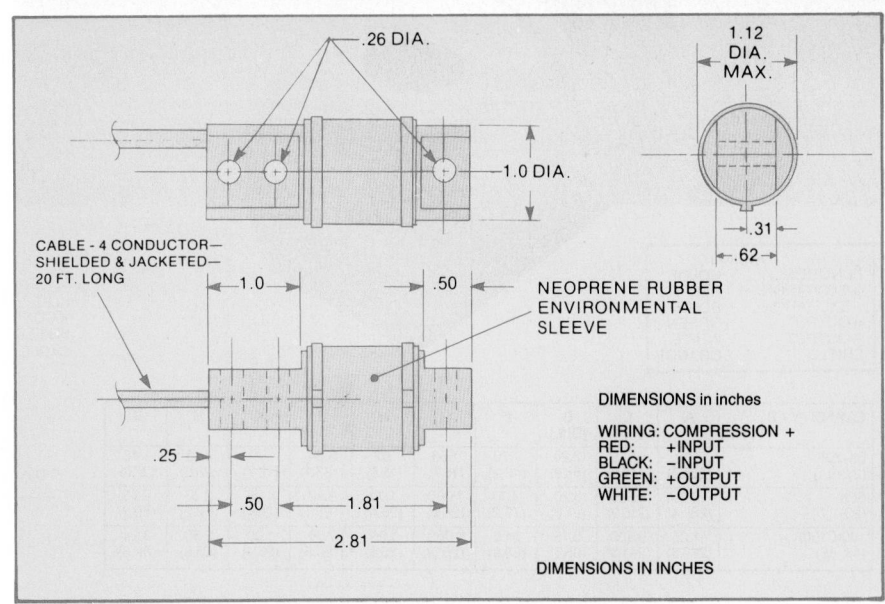

CABLE - 4 CONDUCTOR— SHIELDED & JACKETED— 20 FT. LONG

NEOPRENE RUBBER ENVIRONMENTAL SLEEVE

DIMENSIONS in inches

WIRING: COMPRESSION +
RED: +INPUT
BLACK: −INPUT
GREEN: +OUTPUT
WHITE: −OUTPUT

DIMENSIONS IN INCHES

HIGHLIGHTED MODELS STOCKED FOR FAST DELIVERY

To Order (Specify Model Number)

MODEL	PRICE	RATED CAPACITY	COMPATIBLE METERS
▶LCDA-25	$320	25 lbs	DP3002-S, DP87, DP41-S, DP350
▶LCDA-50	320	50 lbs	DP3002-S, DP87, DP41-S, DP350
LCDA-75	320	75 lbs	DP3002-S, DP87, DP41-S, DP350
▶LCDA-100	320	100 lbs	DP3002-S, DP87, DP41-S, DP350
LCDA-150	320	150 lbs	DP3002-S, DP87, DP41-S, DP350
▶LCDA-250	320	250 lbs	DP3002-S, DP87, DP41-S, DP350
▶LCDA-500	320	500 lbs	DP3002-S, DP87, DP41-S, DP350

†*National Institute of Standards and Technology (Formerly National Bureau of Standards)*

DOUBLE ENDED SHEAR BEAM LOAD CELLS
LCTB Series 5000 TO 150,000 lbs.
For Heavy Duty Weighing Applications

1 YEAR WARRANTY · **MADE IN USA** · **NIST**

- ✓ **0.1% Interchangeability**
- ✓ **Water Resistant for Washdown Applications**
- ✓ **Mounting Hardware Available**
- ✓ **Nickel-Plated Alloy Steel**
- ✓ **N.I.S.T. Certificate Supplied†**

From
$755

The OMEGA LCTB is a double-ended, shear beam load cell. The high accuracy, low profile, tolerance to non-axial loading, and redundant seal make these cells a good choice for tank, bin and weighing assemblies in wet, corrosive, environments. The redundant seal allows the cell to be submerged for extended periods without affecting accuracy.

WIRING	
FUNCTION	**COLOR**
+EXCITATION	RED
−EXCITATION	BLACK
+OUTPUT	GREEN
−OUTPUT	WHITE
SHIELD	ORANGE

10 FT (3 METER) 4 CONDUCTOR SHIELDED CABLE

P DIA. · G DIA. (2 PLACES) · A · C · E

D DIA. (2 PLACES) · H · DIMENSIONS—INCH (MM)

CAPACITY LB (TONS)	A	C	D (Dia.)	E	G	H	J	K	M	P
5K-20K (2.3-9.1)	8.12 (206.3)	6.875 (174.6)	2.20 (55.9)	1.70 (43.2)	.656 (16.7)	.62 (15.8)	5.24 (133.1)	.50 (12.7)	1.12 (28.5)	1.48 (37.6)
50K (23)	10.25 (260.4)	8.500 (215.9)	3.20 (81.3)	3.00 (76.2)	1.060 (26.9)	1.00 (25.4)	6.50 (165.1)	1.00 (25.4)	2.37 (60.2)	2.73 (69.3)
100K-150K (45, 68)	11.25 (285.8)	9.500 (241.3)	3.75 (95.3)	3.50 (88.9)	1.060 (26.9)	1.00 (25.4)	7.50 (190.5)	1.00 (25.4)	2.50 (63.5)	3.24 (82.3)

To Order (Specify Model Number)

Model No.	Price	Rated Capacity	FS Defl.	Wt. lbs.	Compatible Meters
LCTB-5K	$755	5000 lbs.	0.20	5	DP87, DP41-S
LCTB-10K	755	10,000 lbs.	0.025	5	DP87, DP41-S
LCTB-20K	755	20,000 lbs.	0.042	5	DP87, DP41-S
LCTB-30K	835	30,000 lbs.	0.020	16	DP87, DP41-S
LCTB-50K	955	50,000 lbs.	0.020	16	DP87*, DP41-S*
LCTB-100K	1596	100,000 lbs.	0.020	24	DP87*, DP41-S*
LCTB-150K	1596	150,000 lbs.	0.020	24	DP87*, DP41-S*

See page F-20 for detailed information on tank weighing assemblies.   † N.I.S.T. (National Institute of Standards and Technology)

* Note: with these meters, the user must use dummy zeros or count in tons.

SPECIFICATIONS
Rated Output: 3 mV/V ±0.003 mV/V
Excitation: 10 Vdc, 15 Vdc max.
Accuracy: 0.03% FS
Repeatability: 0.01% FS
Zero Balance: 1% FS
Creep in 20 min: 0.03% Rdg
Operating Temp. Range: −65 to 200°F
Compensated Temp. Range: 0 to 150°F
Thermal Effects: Zero: 0.0015% FS/°F; Output: 0.0008% Rdg/°F
Max. Load: Safe: 150% FS; ultimate, 300% FS; Side load: 100% FS
Bridge Resistance: 700 ±7 Ohms
Construction: Nickel-plated steel
Electrical: 10', 4-conductor shielded cable

HEAVY DUTY INDUSTRIAL WEIGHING ASSEMBLIES
CAPACITIES TO 150,000 POUNDS

TWA1 Assembly With LCJB Load Cell   TWA2 Assembly With LCTB Load Cell

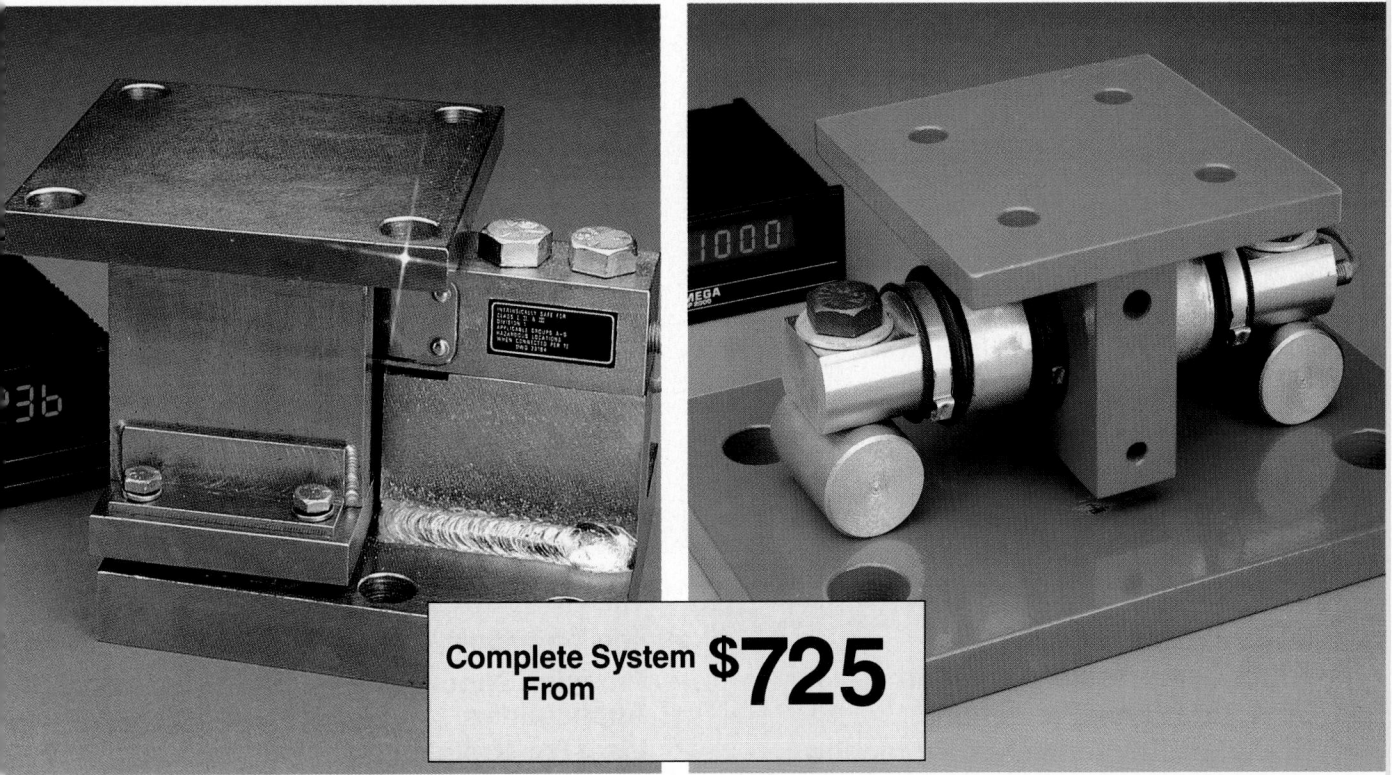

Complete System From $725

	DIMENSIONS - TWA1

4.00 SQ.
SYM ABOUT
0.62 DIA. MOUNTING HOLES (8 PLACES)
4.62
5.00 SQ.
.50
5.15 ± 0.15
.875 STOCK
0.62   2.00
5.90
ALL DIMENSIONS IN INCHES

DIMENSIONS - TWA2

	20K	50K	150K
A	5.5	7.8	10
B	3.0	5.1	7.5
D	.56	.69	.81
E	7.5	10	12
F	4.0	6	9
H	5.3	8.4	10.4
J	11	15	18
K	8	11.5	14
M	1.1	1.2	1.4
N	.50	.75	1.3
P	.75	1.0	1.3

$J_{K ± .005}$ $D_{DIA\ 4\ PLCS}$
$M_{DIA\ 4\ PLCS}$
$F_{± .005}$ $A_{(SQ)}$ $B_{(SQ)}$
E
N
H
P
1" UP TO 60K LBS
SUBPLATE RECOMMENDED   1½" UP TO 150K LBS

HIGHLIGHTED MODELS STOCKED FOR FAST DELIVERY!

To Order (Specify Load Cell and TWA Assembly)

LOAD CELL				TWA ASSEMBLY		
CAPACITY	**MODEL**	**PRICE**	**WT.**	**MODEL**	**PRICE**	**WT.**
1,000 lbs	LCJB-1K	$330	2 lbs	TWA1-4K	$395	17 lbs
2,500 lbs	LCJB-2.5K	330	2 lbs	TWA1-4K	395	17 lbs
4,000 lbs	LCJB-4K	330	2 lbs	TWA1-4K	395	17 lbs
5,000 lbs	LCTB-5K	755	5 lbs	TWA2-20K	395	22 lbs
10,000 lbs	LCTB-10K	755	5 lbs	TWA2-20K	395	22 lbs
20,000 lbs	LCTB-20K	755	5 lbs	TWA2-20K	395	22 lbs
30,000 lbs	LCTB-30K	835	16 lbs	TWA2-50K	825	80 lbs
50,000 lbs	LCTB-50K	955	16 lbs	TWA2-50K	825	80 lbs
100,000 lbs	LCTB-100K	1596	24 lbs	TWA2-150K	1195	170 lbs
150,000 lbs	LCTB-150K	1596	24 lbs	TWA2-150K	1195	170 lbs

Ordering Example: To order a system with a maximum capacity of 5000 lbs, specify: Load Cell **LCTB-5K $755** AND TWA2 Assembly **TWA2-20K $395** Total System Price = **$1150**

LOAD CELLS

F

TANK AND BIN WEIGHING SYSTEMS
CAPACITIES TO 2500 POUNDS

Complete System From **$495**

TWA3 ASSEMBLY WITH LCDA LOAD CELL

- ✓ **50 To 250 lbs Capacity**
- ✓ **150% Compression Overload**
- ✓ **50% Side Force Protection**
- ✓ **Complete Environmental Protection**

TWA4 ASSEMBLY WITH LCJA LOAD CELL

- ✓ **500 TO 2500 lbs Capacity**
- ✓ **Provides Shock Absorption For Industrial Applications**
- ✓ **Ideal For Multicell Installations**

TWA3 DIMENSIONS

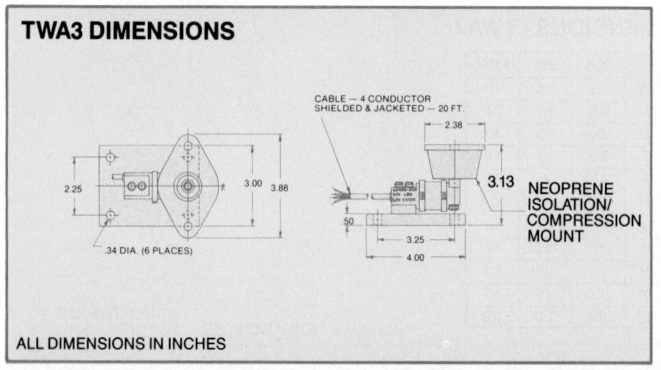

ALL DIMENSIONS IN INCHES

TWA4 DIMENSIONS (500 LBS CAPACITY)

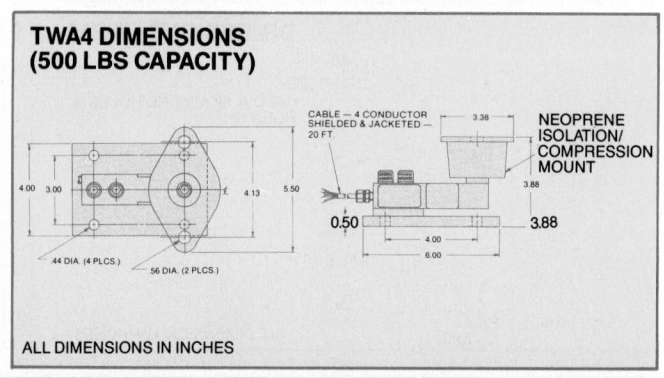

ALL DIMENSIONS IN INCHES

To Order (Specify Load Cell and TWA Assembly)

LOAD CELL				TWA ASSEMBLY		
CAPACITY	MODEL	PRICE	WT.	MODEL	PRICE	WT
50 lbs	LCDA-50	$320	1 lbs	TWA3-050	$175	5 lbs
75 lbs	LCDA-75	320	1 lbs	TWA3-075	175	5 lbs
100 lbs	LCDA-100	320	1 lbs	TWA3-100	175	5 lbs
150 lbs	LCDA-150	320	1 lbs	TWA3-150	175	5 lbs
250 lbs	LCDA-250	320	1 lbs	TWA3-250	175	5 lbs
500 lbs	LCJA-500	370	4 lbs	TWA4-500	290	6 lbs
1000 lbs	LCJA-1K	370	4 lbs	TWA4-1K	290	6 lbs
2000 lbs	LCJA-2K	370	4 lbs	TWA4-2K	290	6 lbs
2500 lbs	LCJA-2.5K	370	4 lbs	TWA4-2.5K	290	6 lbs

► *HIGHLIGHTED MODELS STOCKED FOR FAST DELIVERY!* ◄

Ordering Example: To order a system with a maximum capacity of 250 lbs specify: Load Cell **LCDA-250** $320 and TWA Assembly **TWA3-250** $175. Total System Price = **$495**

LOAD CELL SUMMING
J JUNCTION BOXES FOR MULTIPLE LOAD CELL INSTALLATIONS

1 YEAR WARRANTY

MADE IN USA

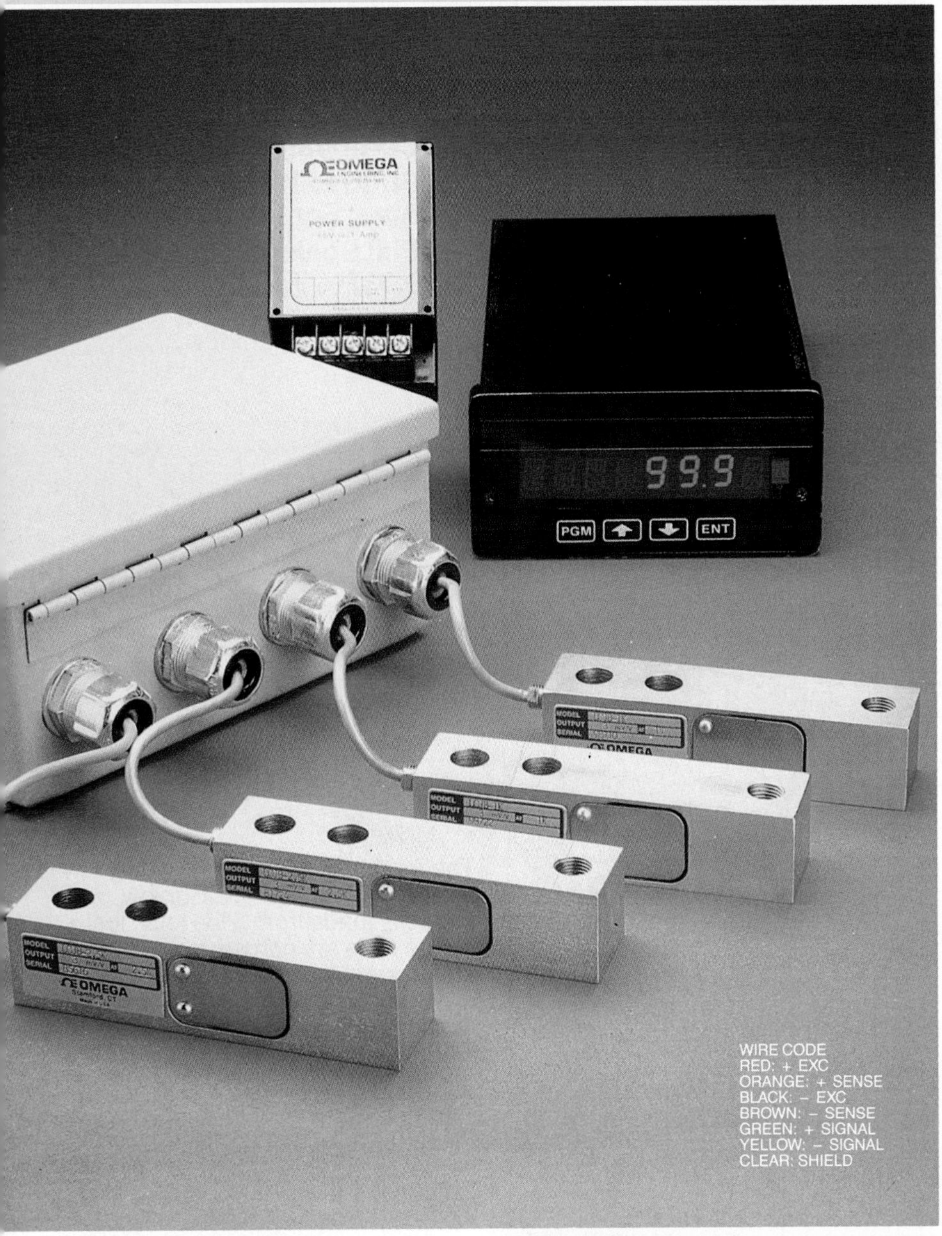

- ✔ **NEMA 4 Enclosure Standard**
- ✔ **Heavy Duty Case For Industrial Installations**
- ✔ **Models For 2 or 4 Load Cell Systems**
- ✔ **Internal Screw Terminations**

A J-BOX takes the input from multiple load cells and sums them in parallel to form a single output equal to the sum of the forces on the load cells. Summing is a common practice in industry as most tanks, bins, hoppers, and platforms are often supported by 2,3 or 4 load cells which are used to give the total weight being monitored. All load cells should be of the same capacity and have interchangeability rated outputs within 3.3% of each other. Omega load cells LCC, LCCA, LCCB, LCJ, LCJA, LCJB, LCD, LCDA, and LCDB have interchangeability specifications better than 3.3%. Load cells with larger interchangeability specifications can be used with the J-Boxes however, user supplied external resistors must be used.

From
$275

HIGHLIGHTED MODELS STOCKED FOR FAST DELIVERY!

WIRE CODE
RED: + EXC
ORANGE: + SENSE
BLACK: – EXC
BROWN: – SENSE
GREEN: + SIGNAL
YELLOW: – SIGNAL
CLEAR: SHIELD

SPECIFICATIONS

Weight: 15 lbs

Span: 3.3% Adjustment Larger Adjustment Requires External Resistors

Feedthroughs: Compression, .125″ to .25″ dia. wire

Lead Wire: 22FT - 6 Connector Shielded Jacketed Wire, 22 gage.

Case: Epoxy Coated Carbon Steel

Ordering Example
10,000 lbs system

4-LCJB-2.5K load cells	$330 ea.
1-JBOX-4 Summing Box	$315
1-PSS-10 Power Supply	$150
1-DP87 Digital Display	$629

DIMENSIONS

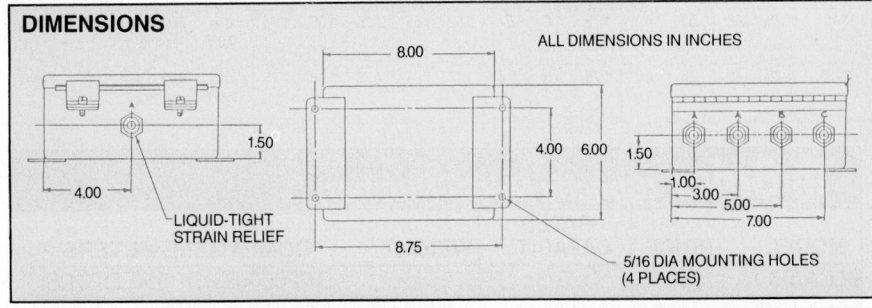

ALL DIMENSIONS IN INCHES

8.00
1.50
4.00
LIQUID-TIGHT STRAIN RELIEF
4.00 6.00
8.75
1.50
1.00
3.00
5.00
7.00
5/16 DIA MOUNTING HOLES (4 PLACES)

To Order *(Specify Model Number)*

MODEL	PRICE	DESCRIPTION
JBOX-2	$275	Sums 2 Load Cells
JBOX-4	315	Sums Up To 4 Load Cells

LOW CAPACITY PLATFORM LOAD CELLS
FOR USE IN INDUSTRIAL WEIGHING

MADE IN USA NIST 2 YEAR WARRANTY

LCAA SERIES
0-5 lbs to 0-50 lbs

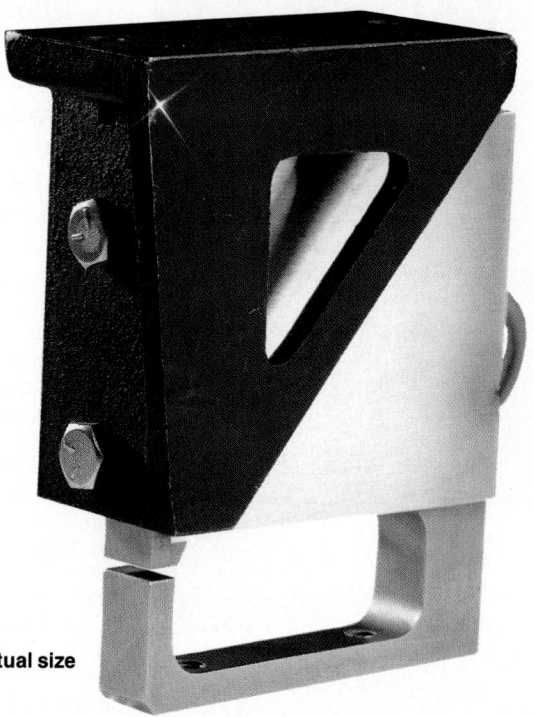

Shown smaller than actual size

✔ **Built In Overload Stops**
✔ **N.I.S.T Calibration Certificate Supplied** †
✔ **Rugged Heat Treated Steel For Long Life**
✔ **Full Scale Accuracy 0.037% Full Scale**

From
$495

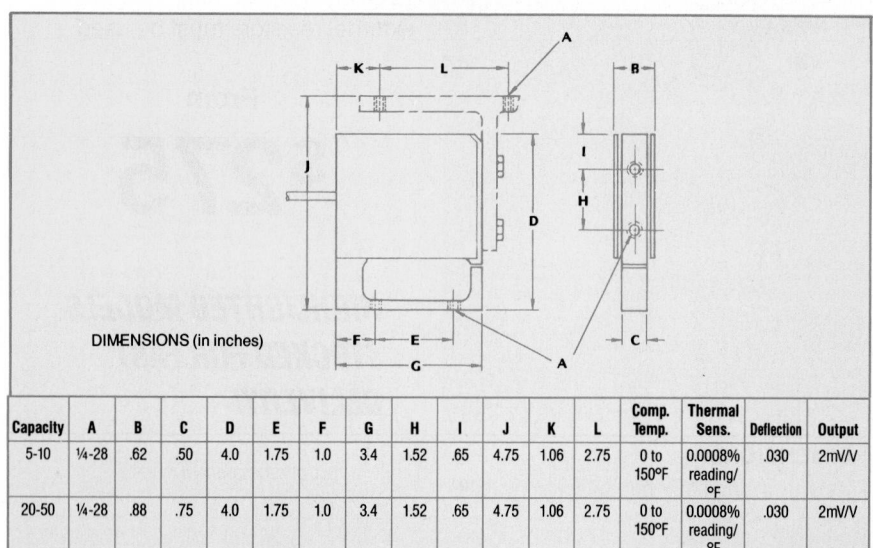

DIMENSIONS (in inches)

Capacity	A	B	C	D	E	F	G	H	I	J	K	L	Comp. Temp.	Thermal Sens.	Deflection	Output
5-10	¼-28	.62	.50	4.0	1.75	1.0	3.4	1.52	.65	4.75	1.06	2.75	0 to 150°F	0.0008% reading/°F	.030	2mV/V
20-50	¼-28	.88	.75	4.0	1.75	1.0	3.4	1.52	.65	4.75	1.06	2.75	0 to 150°F	0.0008% reading/°F	.030	2mV/V

To Order (Specify Model Number)

MODEL	PRICE	RATED CAPACITY	WEIGHT	COMPATIBLE METERS
▶LCAA-5	$495	5 lbs	1.5 lbs	DP2000-S3, DP350, DP41-S
▶LCAA-10	495	10 lbs	2.0 lbs	DP2000-S4, DP350, DP41-S
▶LCAA-20	535	20 lbs	2.0 lbs	DP2000-S5, DP350, DP41-S
▶LCAA-50	535	50 lbs	3.0 lbs	DP2000-S3, DP350, DP41-S

† *National Institute of Standards and Technology (Formerly National Bureau of Standards)*

▶ *HIGHLIGHTED MODELS STOCKED FOR FAST DELIVERY!* ◀

The model LCAA is a heavy duty low profile platform load cell for low capacity loads from 5 lbs to 50 lbs. These cells are constructed of nickel plated tool steel, heat treated for ruggedness and designed to provide maximum resistance to shock loading.

SPECIFICATIONS

Rated Output: 2mV/V nominal actual output supplied with each load cell
Excitation: 10 Vdc (15 Vdc maximum)
Accuracy: 0.037% Full Scale
Linearity: 0.03% FS
Hysteresis: 0.02% FS
Repeatability: 0.01% FS
Zero Balance: 2% FS
Creep in 20 min: 0.03% FS
Operating Temperature: 0 to 150°F
Compensated Temperature: 0 to 150°F
Thermal Effects: Zero - 0.0015% FS/°F Span - 0.0008% RDG/°F
Maximum Load: 150% FS
Platform Size: 5, 10 lbs 6" x 6" 20, 50 lbs 12" x 12"
Bridge Resistance: 350 ohms nominal
Full Scale Deflection: 0.02" ±0.005"
Construction: Nickel Plated Steel
Cable: 10' 4-conductor shielded 22-gage wire

LOAD CELL ACCESSORIES
ROD ENDS AND LOAD BUTTONS FOR ALL LOAD CELLS

Load Buttons For Compression Applications

Model LCCB Load Cells Shown with Accessory Load Button and Rod End

Corresponding accessory part numbers are specified on Load Cell pages. To match Load Cell and Accessory Parts match thread specifications between the accessory and the load cell.

Load Button Dimensions

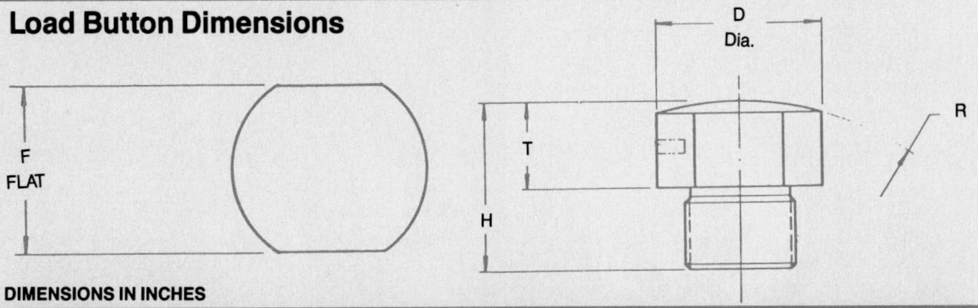

DIMENSIONS IN INCHES

To Order (Specify Load Button)

MODEL	PRICE	THREAD UNF-2A	H	T	D	F	R
LBC-014	$ 40	¼-28	.50	.20	.60	.50	2.0
LBC-038	40	⅜-24	.60	.30	.75	.63	2.0
LBC-012	40	½-20	.70	.30	.75	.63	4.0
LBC-034	55	¾-16	.90	.30	1.50	1.25	6.0
LBC-100	55	1-14	1.10	.30	1.50	1.25	8.0
LBC-114	60	1¼-12	1.50	.50	2.00	1.75	10.0
LBC-112	70	1½-12	2.25	1.00	2.50	2.25	14.0
HIGH HAT LOAD BUTTONS FOR LCJA ONLY							
LBJ-012	$ 40	½-20	1.5	.94	.50	.41	2.0
LBJ-034	40	¾-16	1.75	1.06	.75	.56	3.0
LBJ-100	50	1-14	2.0	1.40	.88	.75	6.0

Rod End Dimensions

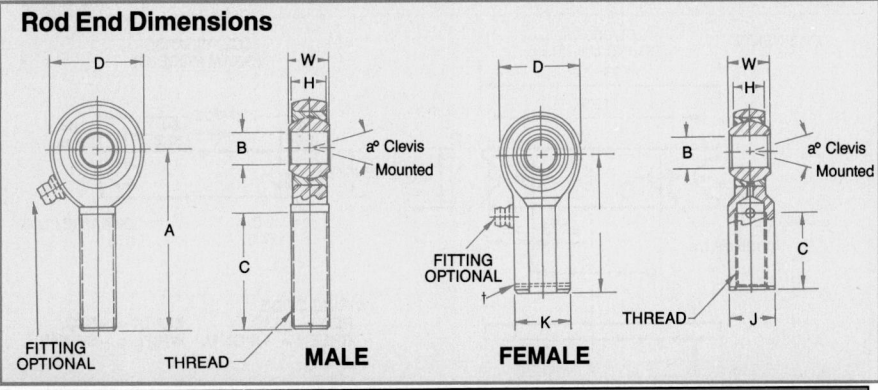

MALE   **FEMALE**

Rod Ends

To Order (Specify Rod End Model Number)

MALE ROD ENDS	PRICE	THREAD UNF-3A	B	W	H	A	D	C	a°	K	J	STATIC LOAD (LBS.)	WT. (LBS.)
REC-010M*	$ 10	10-32	.190	.312	.234	1.25	.625	.750	17	—	—	1,170	.03
REC-014M	15	¼-28	.190	.312	.250	1.562	.750	1.000	10	—	—	2,158	.04
REC-038M	20	⅜-24	.3125	.437	.344	1.938	1.000	1.250	12	—	—	5,323	.25
REC-012M	35	½-20	.4375	.562	.437	2.438	1.312	1.500	12	—	—	23,452	.25
REC-034M	65	¾-16	.6250	.750	.562	2.875	1.750	1.750	13	—	—	40,572	.60
REC-100M	95	1-14	1.000	1.375	1.000	4.125	2.750	2.125	14	—	—	43,541	2.1
REC-114M	95	1¼-12	1.250	1.093	.937	4.125	2.750	2.125	7	—	—	44,500	2.4
REC-112M	150	1½-12	1.500	1.312	1.125	5.375	3.500	3.000	6.5	—	—	138,826	4.8
FEMALE ROD ENDS		**UNF-2B**											
REC-006F*	$ 10	6-32†	.1250	.250	.187	.812	.500	.437	16	.312	.250	1,202	.02
REC-010F*	10	10-32	.190	.312	.234	1.062	.625	.500	17	.406	.312	2,028	.04
REC-014F	10	¼-28	.250	.375	.250	.375	.750	.687	21	.469	.375	3,114	.05

* Not available with grease fitting.
† UNC thread

STOCKED FOR FAST DELIVERY

LOAD CELLS

F

FULL BRIDGE THIN BEAM LOAD CELLS
FOR LOADS ¼ TO 40 LBS.

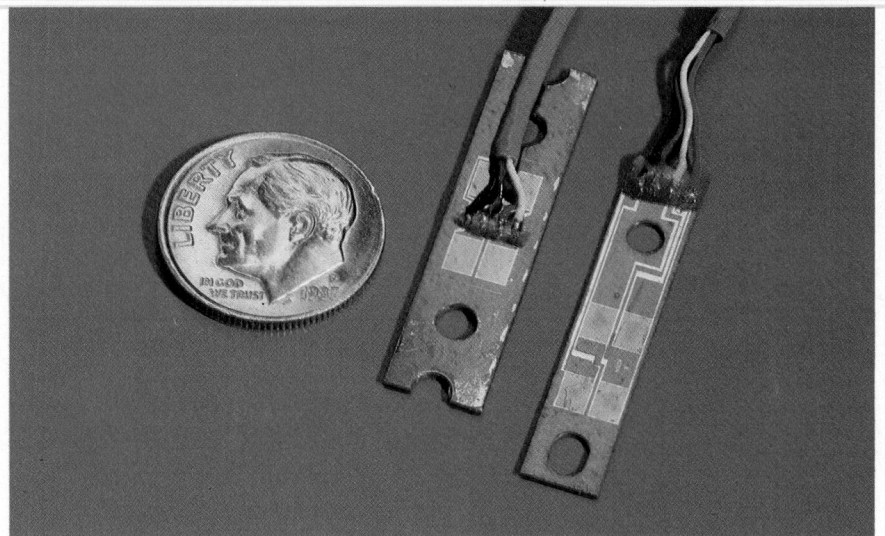

LCL Series

- **Measures Force, Pressure, Displacement**
- **Thermally Matched, Fully Active, Full Bridge Gage For Optimum Temperature Tracking**

All Models
$69

MADE IN
USA

When small load measurements are required, the OMEGA LCL Series thin beam load cells are exceptionally well suited. The LCL Series is designed to measure many different parameters found in medical instrumentation, home appliance, process control, robotics, automotive and many other high volume applications. A specially developed integrated strain gage includes all balancing, compensating and conductive elements and is laminated to the beam to provide excellent stability and reliability.

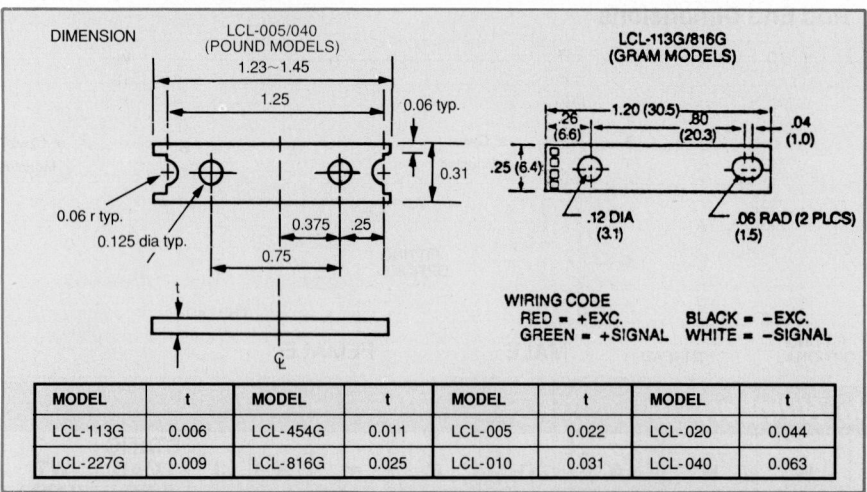

WIRING CODE
RED = +EXC.   BLACK = –EXC.
GREEN = +SIGNAL   WHITE = –SIGNAL

MODEL	t	MODEL	t	MODEL	t	MODEL	t
LCL-113G	0.006	LCL-454G	0.011	LCL-005	0.022	LCL-020	0.044
LCL-227G	0.009	LCL-816G	0.025	LCL-010	0.031	LCL-040	0.063

To Order *(Specify Model Number)*

MODEL	PRICE	RATED CAPACITY	COMPATIBLE METER
▶LCL-113G	$69	1/4 lb. (113 g)	DP2000S5, DP350, DP302-S ◀
▶LCL-227G	69	1/2 lb. (227 g)	DP2000S3, DP350, DP302-S ◀
▶LCL-454G	69	1 lb. (454 g)	DP2000S4, DP350, DP302-S ◀
LCL-816G	69	1.8 lb. (816 g)	DP2000S5, DP350, DP302-S
▶LCL-005	69	5 lb. (2.27 kg)	DP2000S4, DP350, DP302-S ◀
▶LCL-010	69	10 lb. (4.54 kg)	DP2000S5, DP350, DP302-S ◀
LCL-020	69	20 lb. (9.07 kg)	DP2000S5, DP350, DP302-S
LCL-040	69	40 lb. (18.14 kg)	DP2000S5, DP350, DP302-S

▶ *HIGHLIGHTED MODELS IN STOCK FOR FAST DELIVERY* ◀

SPECIFICATIONS

Excitation: 5 Vdc, 12 volts max.
Rated Output: 2 mV/V ±20% (to minimize ±20% tolerance end user must calibrate with a known weight)
Zero Balance: ±0.3 mV/V
Combined Error: 0.25% full scale
Operating Temperature: –65 to 200°F
Compensated Temp.: 20 to 120°F
Temperature Effects: Zero Balance 0.02% FS/°F; Output 0.02%/°F
Resistance: (Input and output) 1200 ohms ±300 ohms
Insulation Resistance: 1000 @ 50 Vdc
Seal: Urethane coated
Safe Overload: 150% FS
Full Scale Deflection: 0.010″ to 0.050″
Lead Wire: 9″ shielded PVC four conductor 30 AWG

ACCESSORIES

MODEL	PRICE	MOUNTING
LCL-CL1	$15	for LCL-113G thru LCL-816G
LCM-CL1	30	for LCL-005 thru LCL-040

INSTALLATION CONSIDERATIONS FOR THIN BEAM LOAD CELLS *LCL AND LCM SERIES*

Careful design considerations must be taken into account when mounting OMEGA's LCL and LCM Series thin beam load cells. The sensor's performance is dependent upon the mechanical interface. All thin beam load cells require mounting clamps to create a "double bend" during loading as shown in figure A. This illustration is exaggerated to show the clamp's effectiveness in producing opposing moments that create the double bend. An electrical output is generated as the double bend causes tension and compression on the sensor strain gage.

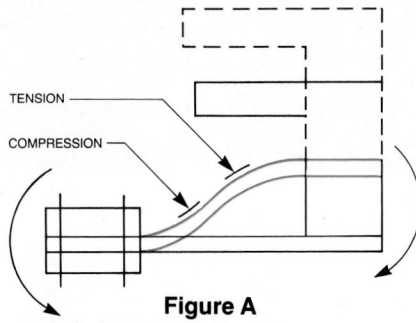

Figure A

Two typical mounting arrangements are shown below. For high accuracy applications, reinforcement plates should be slightly harder than the beam material, and the interfacing corners should be sharp. Due to low loads and sensor construction associated with the LCL-113G thru LCL-816G, in-line loading (Type 2) is not recommended.

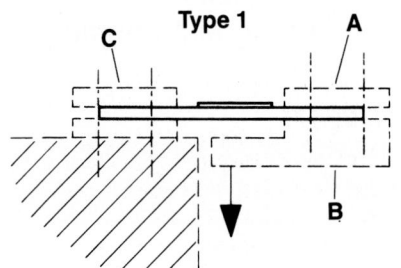

Type 1

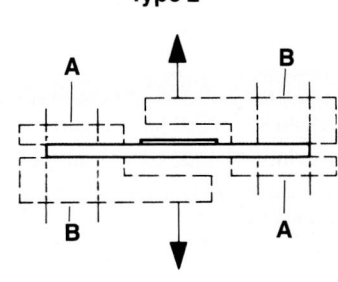

Type 2

LCL-CL1 Mounting Kit

Mounting Kit LCL-CL1 for thin beam sensors LCL-113G to LCL-816G. Type 1 mounting only. Kit includes: Mounting blocks A, B, and C.

DIMENSIONS IN INCHES

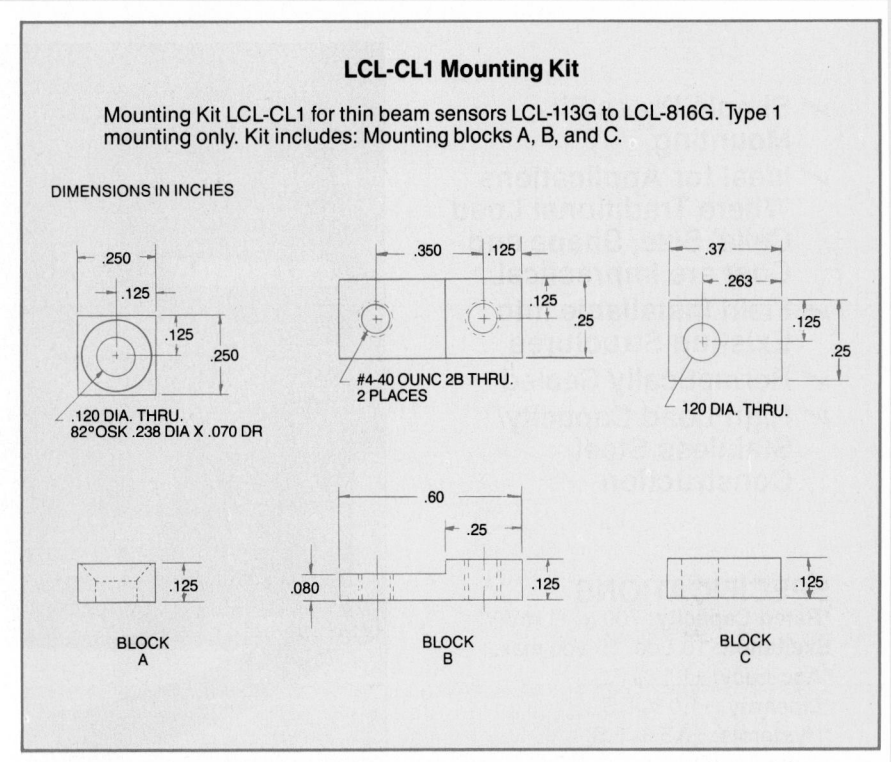

LCM-CL1 Mounting Kit

Mounting Kit LCM-CL1 mounting kit for thin beam sensors LCL-005 thru LCL-040 and LCM Series. Kit includes 4 mounting blocks, 2 of each block A & B.

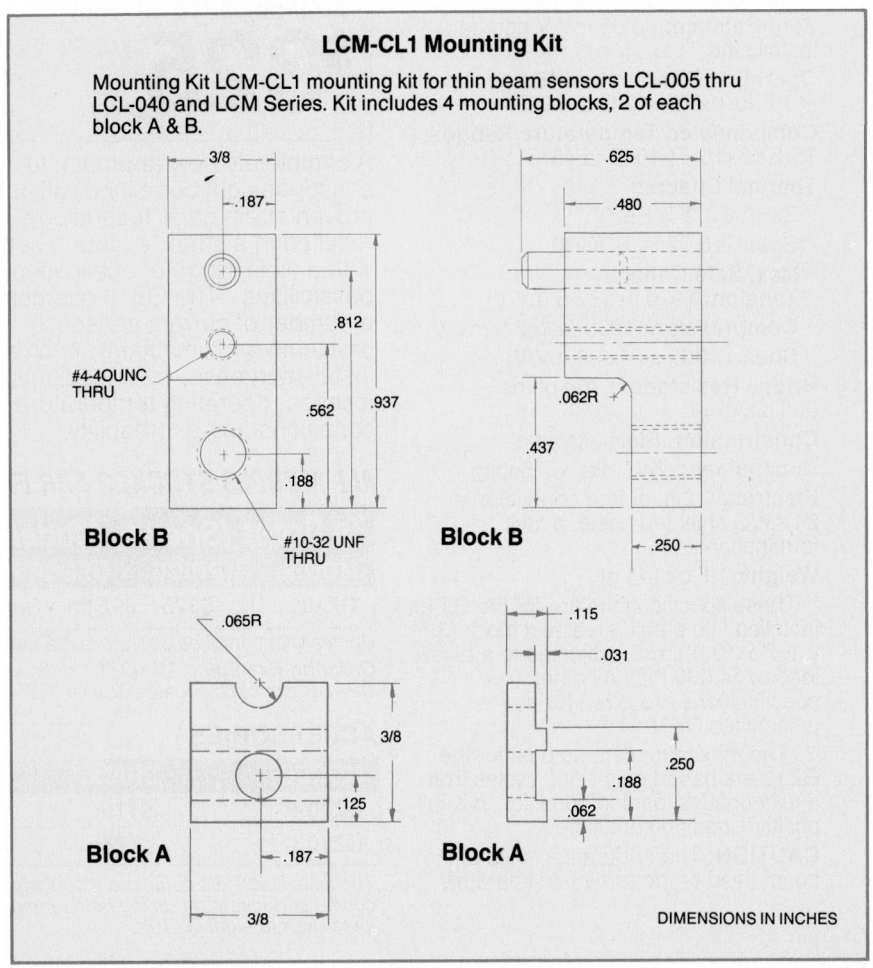

DIMENSIONS IN INCHES

LOAD CELLS

F

RUGGED PRESS FIT STRAIN SENSOR

NEW!

- ✔ **Simple Press Fit Mounting**
- ✔ **Ideal for Applications Where Traditional Load Cells' Size, Shape and Cost are Impractical**
- ✔ **Field Installable into Existing Structures**
- ✔ **Hermetically Sealed**
- ✔ **High Load Capacity/ Stainless Steel Construction**

SPECIFICATIONS

*Rated Capacity: 700 $\mu\epsilon$ (1 mV/V)
Excitation: 10 Vdc, 15 Vdc max.
*Accuracy: ±1.1 % F.S.
*Linearity: ±1.0 % F.S.
*Hystersis: ±0.5 % F.S.
*Repeatability: ±0.1 % F.S.
Zero Balance: ±0.05 mV/V prior to installation
Operating Temperature Range: -40°F to 150°F(-40°C to 60°C)
Compensated Temperature Range: 15°F to 115°F(-10°C to 45°C)
Thermal Effects:
  Zero ±0.2 % FS/°F
  Span ±0.02 % RDG/°F
**Max. Safe Capacity:
  Tension: 1920 $\mu\epsilon$ (±2.5 mV/V)
  Compression: 1900 $\mu\epsilon$ (±2.5 mV/V)
  Shear: 4000 $\mu\gamma$ (±4.0 mV/V)
Bridge Resistance: 700 ohms (full bridge)
Construction: Stainless steel
Dimensions: .746" dia. x .75 long
Electrical: 2 ft. of four conductor 24 AWG shielded cable, pigtail termination
Weight: 1.5 oz (45 g)
* These specifications are for the GZ10, installed into a mild steel test block (3.5" x 1.5" x 12.0") and subjected to a tensile load of 54,000 lbs. All other specifications are given for an uninstalled GZ10.
** The maximum safe outputs for the GZ10 are based on 10,000 cycles from a full negative loading condition to a full positive loading condition.
CAUTION: The endurance limits of the beam must be determined separately.

Model GZ10

$325

Model DP41-S Meter $395 Sold Separately. See Page D-7 for Details.

A completely new approach to sensor design, combined with proven strain gage technology, has resulted in a small, accurate sensor with a wide range of application possibilities. The GZ10 overcomes a number of current sensor problems and limitations, such as installation ease, size, load limit, location, operating temperature conditions and affordability.

Typical Applications
- ✔ **Tank Weighing Systems**
- ✔ **Structural Load Measuring**
- ✔ **Stamping Press Control**
- ✔ **Lift Trucks**
- ✔ **Rolling Mill Sensing**

ALL MODELS STOCKED FOR FAST DELIVERY!

To Order (Specify Model Number)

MODEL	PRICE	DESCRIPTION	COMPATIBLE METERS
GZ10	$325	Strain Sensor	DP41-S, DP3002-S, DP87

Comes with complete operator's manual.
Ordering Example: *The GZ10 strain sensor, GZ10-F installation kit for flat surfaces and a DP41-S compatible meter, $325 + 175 + 395 =* **$895.**

ACCESSORIES

MODEL	PRICE	DESCRIPTION
GZ10-F	$175	GZ10 installation kit for flat surfaces
GZ10-C	175	GZ10 installation kit for curved surfaces

The installation kits contain a mounting/drilling template, field installation tool (for flat or curved surfaces), mounting hole reamer, and a protective cover. Each kit can be used to install four to eight GZ10's.

PRINCIPLES OF OPERATION

The GZ10 is a unique press fit strain sensor, a close up view of its inside sensing device is shown left.

The GZ10 has unchallenged application versatility. Virtually any machine, device or structure can use the GZ10 as a cost effective, accurate solution to load sensing.

The GZ10 strain sensor operates on the principles of simple mechanics. When a physical structure is subjected to an external load, the structure eventually becomes deformed from the load. The deformity may be large and obvious, as in the case of a fishing rod bending to the weight of a hooked fish; or, as in the case of a bridge's stress from the weight of a motor vehicle, the deformity may be microscopic.

If a small hole is made in the structure, the hole will become oblong as the structure deforms, and in direct proportion with the load being applied to the structure. By inserting the GZ10 tightly into the hole, this deformity or strain can be measured very accurately. Thus, the GZ10 effectively converts the entire structure into a load, force or position transducer.

Because the GZ10 strain sensor is mounted into your machine or structure, the output of the GZ10 can be calibrated to meet your system needs. The maximum load is dependent on your structure. Full scale loads can vary from a few pounds to millions of pounds. It is

the mechanical integrity of your structure which determines the amount of strain which occurs under loading conditions. Before using the GZ10, it is recommended that a theoretical strain calculation is performed to ensure the feasibility of using the sensor.

"PLUG-IN" DESIGN ENHANCES APPLICATION VERSATILITY

The GZ10 strain sensor fits many applications where traditional transducers are considered impractical due to size, shape, cost or reliability. The GZ10's small size and shape allow it to be press-fit into a precision drilled hole. Redesigning or rebuilding an existing structure to accommodate a load cell is eliminated. By using compatible signal conditioning, the GZ10 can then be calibrated to read out weight, volume, strain or any other physical parameter.

Drilling the ¾" mounting hole in your member can alter its structural integrity. Therefore, it is important to ensure that the member is structurally sound after the hole is drilled. The addition of the ¾" hole is likely to decrease the load bearing capability of the structure. Therefore, the ultimate selection of the structural point of installation must be left to a qualified designer.

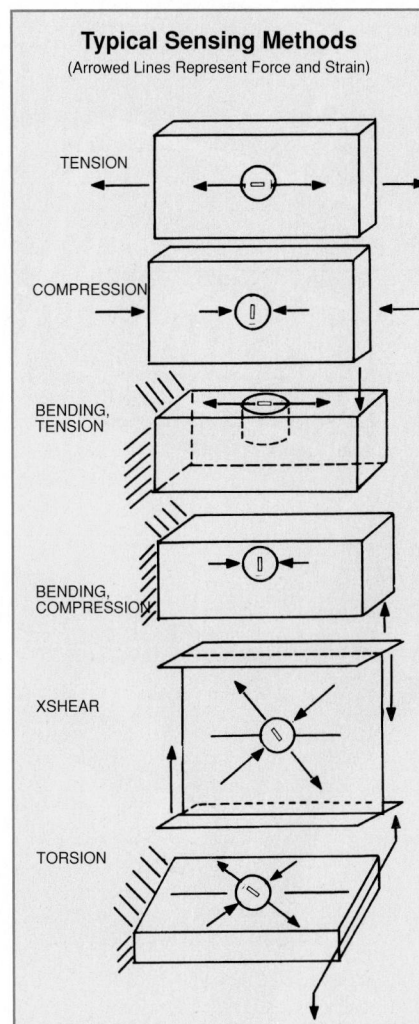

Typical Sensing Methods
(Arrowed Lines Represent Force and Strain)

TENSION

COMPRESSION

BENDING, TENSION

BENDING, COMPRESSION

XSHEAR

TORSION

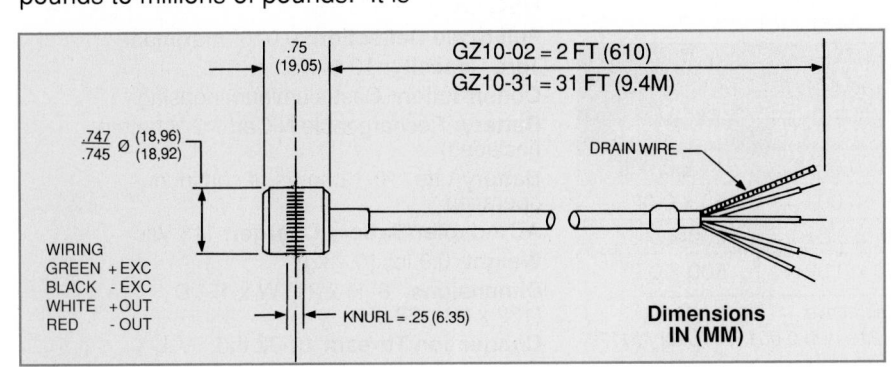

GZ10-02 = 2 FT (610)
GZ10-31 = 31 FT (9.4M)

.75 (19,05)

.747 / .745 Ø (18,96) (18,92)

DRAIN WIRE

WIRING
GREEN + EXC
BLACK - EXC
WHITE +OUT
RED   - OUT

KNURL = .25 (6.35)

Dimensions IN (MM)

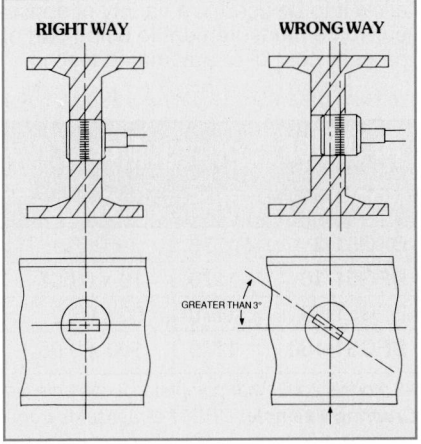

RIGHT WAY   WRONG WAY

GREATER THAN 3°

LOAD CELLS F

MICROPROCESSOR-BASED DIGITAL FORCE GAUGE
RANGES FROM 2 TO 100 LBS

NEW!

NIST | **1 YEAR WARRANTY** | **MADE IN USA**

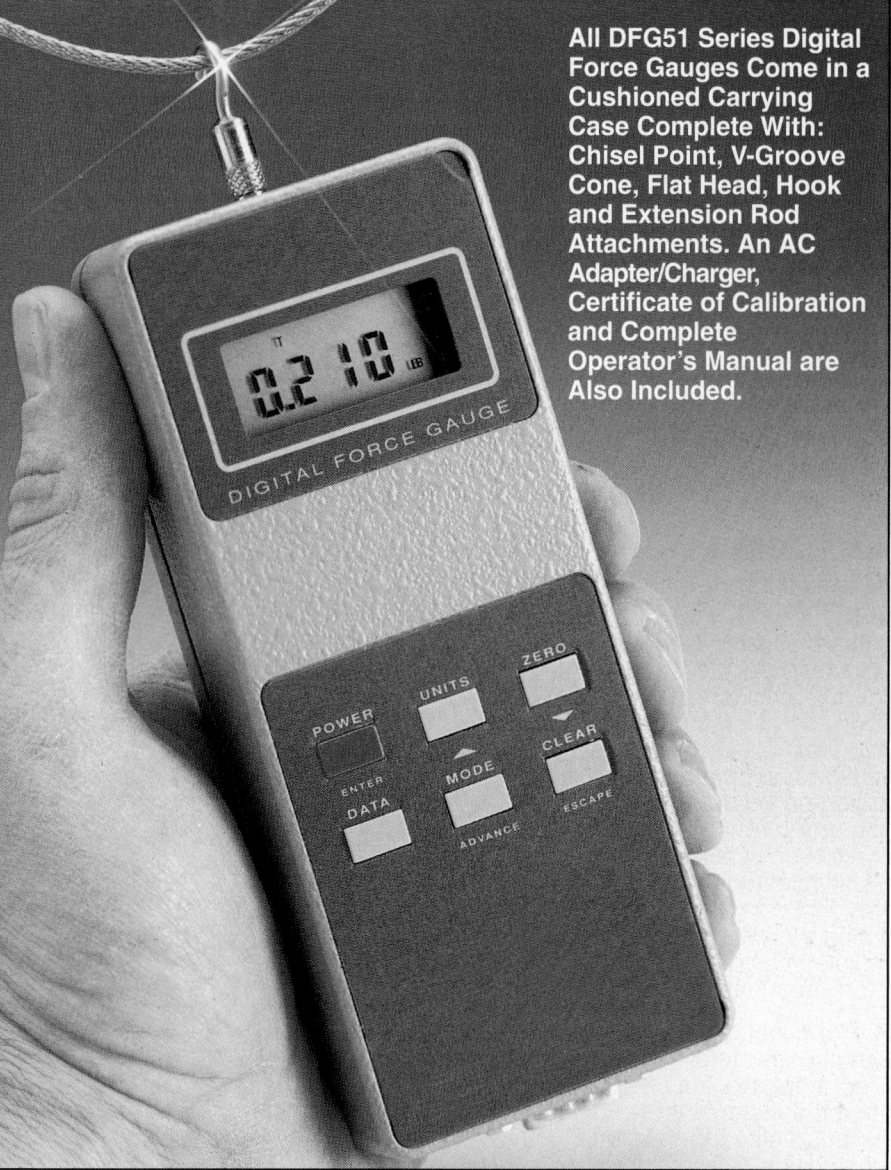

All DFG51 Series Digital Force Gauges Come in a Cushioned Carrying Case Complete With: Chisel Point, V-Groove Cone, Flat Head, Hook and Extension Rod Attachments. An AC Adapter/Charger, Certificate of Calibration and Complete Operator's Manual are Also Included.

DFG51
$1170

✔ **Standard RS-232, Analog, and Open Collector Outputs**

✔ **Peak Memory for Tensile and Compressive Loads**

✔ **Pushbutton Selectable Engineering Units In Lbs, KG, or N**

✔ **Programmable Analog and Digital Filtering**

✔ **External Trigger Mode for Slave Operation**

✔ **N.I.S.T. Calibration Certificate Supplied**

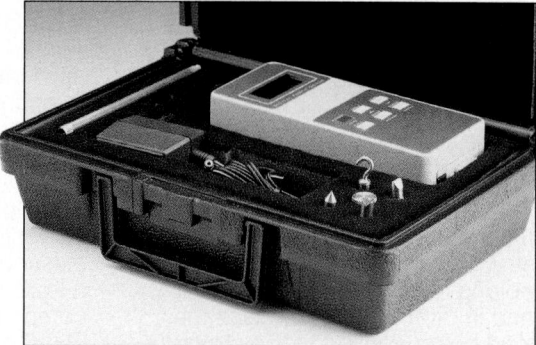

Specifications

Accuracy: ±0.20 % FS, ±1 LSC (least significant count)

Display: 4½ digit LCD with 0.3" high characters

Sample Rate: 65 samples per second

Analog Output: ±1 Vdc

Setpoint Outputs: Three open collector outputs standard

RS-232 : Standard

Operating Temp. Range: 40°F to 110°F (5°C to 45°C)

Thermal Effects: Zero 0.03 % F S/°C Span 0.01 % FS/°C

Max. Load: 150 % FS

Full Scale Deflection: 0.010" maximum

Tare Capacity: 10 % FS

Construction: Cast aluminum housing

Battery: Rechargeable NiCad 7.2 V battery (included)

Battery Life: 10-12 hours of continuous operation

AC Adapter/Battery Charger: 115 Vac

Weight: 0.9 lbs (0.4 kg)

Dimensions: 6" H x 2½" W x 1½" D (152 x 63 x 38 mm)

Connection Thread: 10-32 thd; ³⁄₁₆" L

The OMEGA DFG51 microprocessor-based digital force gauge is small, rugged and lightweight, which makes it an ideal instrument for portable handheld force measurement. The DFG51 has many features which allow it to be used in a variety of applications, ranging from simple push-pull force measurement to being part of a sophisticated system for process control or automated testing.

HIGHLIGHTED MODELS IN STOCK FOR FAST DELIVERY

To Order (Specify Model Number)

MODEL	PRICE	SCALE VS. RESOLUTION		
		POUNDS	**KILOGRAMS**	**NEWTONS**
DFG51-2	**$1170**	2 x 0.001	1 x 0.0005	10 x 0.005
DFG51-10	1170	10 x 0.005	5 x 0.002	50 x 0.02
DFG51-50	1170	50 x 0.02	25 x 0.01	250 x 0.1
DFG51-100	1170	100 x 0.05	50 x 0.02	500 x 0.2

All models come with complete kit contents indicated above.
Ordering Example: *DFG51-2 measures from 0 to 2lbs with 0.001 resolution, $1170.*

SOCKET EXTENSION REACTION TORQUE SENSOR
WITH ¼, ⅜, ½ AND ¾" SQUARE DRIVES

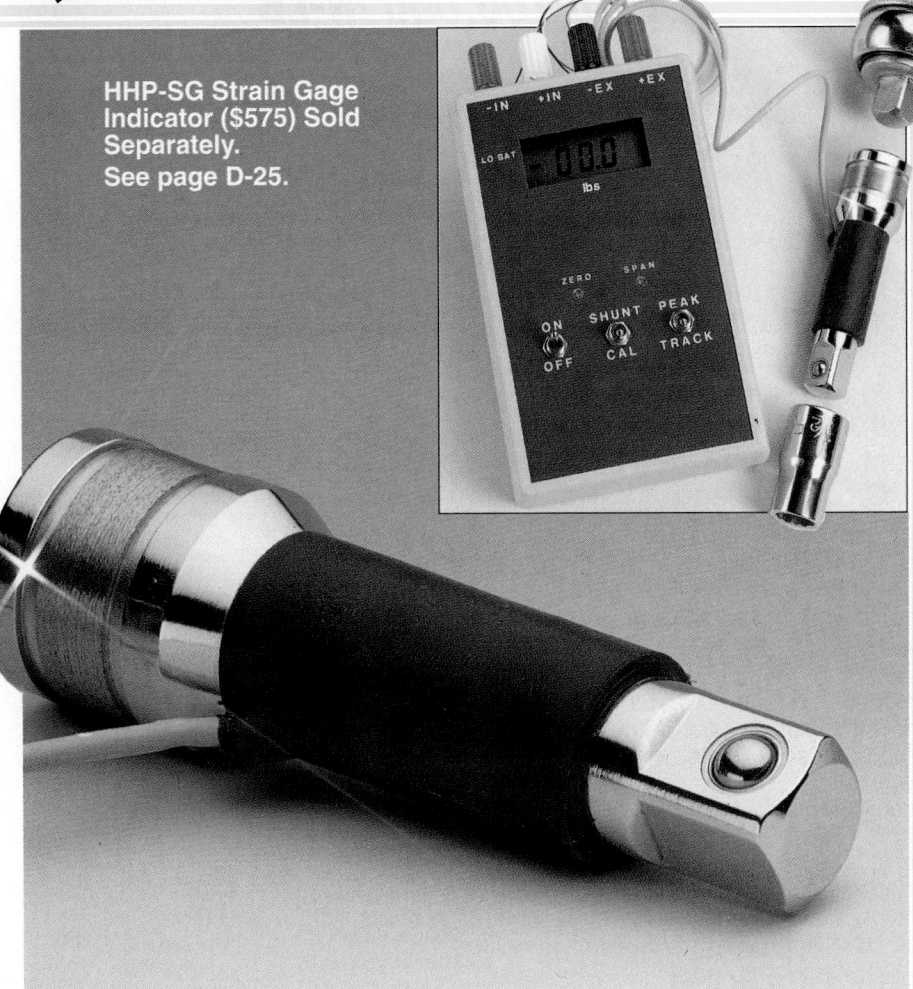

NEW!

1 YEAR WARRANTY

MADE IN USA

TQ102
$420

HHP-SG Strain Gage Indicator ($575) Sold Separately. See page D-25.

✔ **Ideal for Use with Drive/Socket Systems to Monitor or Verify Bolt Torque**

✔ **Measures Torque in Both Clockwise and Counterclockwise Directions**

✔ **Compact, Low Cost and Accurate**

✔ **Easily Inserted Between Socket and Drive**

✔ **Rugged Construction for Industrial Applications**

The OMEGA TQ102 Series socket extension torque sensor is installed between a socket and drive to measure or verify bolt torque. The sensor can measure torque in both clockwise and counterclockwise directions. This unique sensor's accuracy, cost and size make it ideal for a variety of industrial or laboratory applications.

SPECIFICATIONS
Rated Output: 3 mV/V nominal
Excitation: 10 Vdc, 20 Vdc maximum
Accuracy: 0.37 % FS
Linearity: 0.25 % FS
Hysteresis: 0.25 % FS
Repeatability: 0.1 % FS
Zero Balance: 0.1 % FS
Operating Temperature Range: -65 to 250°F (54 to 121°C)
Compensated Temperature Range: 32 to 170 °F(0 to 76°C)
Thermal Effects: 0.002 % FS/°F, zero; 0.002 % RDG/°F, span
Maximum Load: 150 % FS, safe; 300% FS, ultimate
Bridge Resistance: 350 ohms
Angular Deflection at FS: 3°
Construction: Nickel plated tool steel
Electrical: 2 ft of 4 conductor shielded cable, pigtail termination

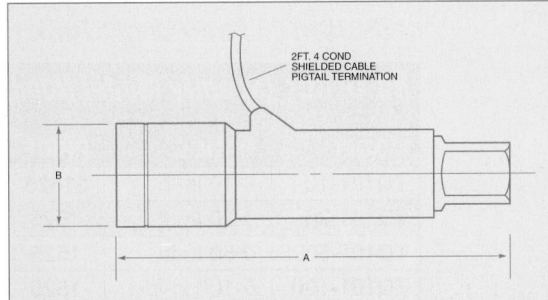

2FT. 4 COND SHIELDED CABLE PIGTAIL TERMINATION

WIRING
RED — + EXC
BLACK — - EXC
GREEN — + SIG
WHITE — - SIG

DIMENSIONS IN INCHES

MODEL NO.	A	B
TQ102-200	5.0	1 ½ DIA.
TQ102-400	3.5	⅞ DIA.
TQ102-1.5K	3.0	¹¹⁄₁₆ DIA.
TQ102-5K	3.0	½ DIA.

HIGHLIGHTED MODELS IN STOCK FOR FAST DELIVERY!

To Order *(Specify Model Number)*

MODEL NO.	PRICE	DRIVE	RANGE	* COMPATIBLE METERS
TQ102-200	$420	¼"	0-200 in-lb	HHP-SG, DS-350, DP41-S
TQ102-400	420	⅜"	0-400 in-lb	HHP-SG, DS-350, DP41-S
TQ102-1.5K	420	½"	0-1500 in-lb	HHP-SG, DS-350, DP41-S
TQ102-5K	420	¾"	0-5000 in-lb	HHP-SG, DS-350, DP41-S

The HHP-SG is a handheld meter, the DS-350 is a benchtop meter and the DP41 is a panel meter.
Comes with complete operator's manual.

Ordering Example: *TQ102-400 is a socket extension torque sensor for a ⅜" drive rachet with 0-400 in-lb range, with HHP-SG hand held strain gage Indicator (pictured above), $420 + 575 = $995.*

LOAD CELLS

F

FLANGE MOUNTED REACTION TORQUE SENSOR
0 TO 100,000 IN-LB

1 YEAR WARRANTY

MADE IN USA

Model TQ101 From

$1525

- ✔ Ideal for Monitoring Torque in Motor Pump and Machine Mounts
- ✔ Flange Mounted for Easy Installation
- ✔ Measures Torque in Clockwise and Counterclockwise Directions

The TQ101 Series reaction torque sensors are ideal for measuring reaction or restraining torques found in motor mounts, pump mounts, machine mounts, etc... They can also be used in limited rotation applications, such as the torque required to turn a nut or an actuator shaft. The TQ101 is designed with flanges, enabling easy installation or adaptation; it is rugged enough for factory use, yet accurate enough for the laboratory.

SPECIFICATIONS

Rated Output: 2.0 mV/V nominal
Excitation: 10 Vdc, 20 Vdc maximum
Accuracy: 0.18% FS
Linearity: 0.10 % FS
Hysteresis: 0.10 % FS
Repeatability: 0.10 % FS
Zero Balance: 1.0 % FS
Operating Temperature Range:
-65 to 250°F (-53 to 120°C)
Compensated Temp. Range:
32 to 170°F (0 to 76°C)
Thermal Effects:
Zero 0.002% FS/°F
Span 0.002% Rdg/°F
Max. Load:
Safe 150 % FS
Ultimate 300% FS
Bridge Resistance: 350 ohms nominal
Full Scale Angular Deflection: 1.2°
Construction: Nickel plated steel
Sensing Element: Aluminum (up to 500 in-lb), nickel plated steel (above 500 in-lb)
Cover: Aluminum (100, 200 and 500 in-lb) and nickel plated steel (all other ranges)
Electrical: Mating connector supplied

Shown Smaller Than Actual Size

HIGHLIGHTED MODELS IN STOCK FOR FAST DELIVERY!

To Order *(Specify Model Number)*

MODEL	RANGE	PRICE	WT (LBS)	COMPATIBLE METERS
TQ101-10	0-10 in-lb	$1525	3	DP41-S, DP302-S, DP2000-S4
TQ101-20	0-20 in-lb	1525	3	DP41-S, DP302-S, DP2000-S5
TQ101-50	0-50 in-lb	1525	3	DP41-S, DP3002-S, DP87
TQ101-100	0-100 in-lb	1525	5	DP41-S, DP302-S, DP2000-S4
TQ101-200	0-200 in-lb	1525	5	DP41-S, DP302-S, DP2000-S5
TQ101-500	0-500 in-lb	1525	5	DP41-S, DP3002-S, DP87
TQ101-1K	0-1,000 in-lb	2050	8	DP41-S, DP302-S, DP2000-S4
TQ101-2K	0-2,000 in-lb	2050	8	DP41-S, DP302-S, DP2000-S5
TQ101-5K	0-5,000 in-lb	2300	10	DP41-S, DP3002-S, DP87
TQ101-10K	0-10,000 in-lb	2300	10	DP41-S, DP3002-S, DP87
TQ101-15K	0-15,000 in-lb	3575	20	DP41-S, DP3002-S, DP87
TQ101-20K	0-20,000 in-lb	3575	20	DP41-S, DP3002-S, DP87
TQ101-50K	0-50,000 in-lb	3575	20	DP41-S, DP87, DP-760
TQ101-100K	0-100,000 in-lb	5275	30	DP41-S, DP87, DP-760

Comes with complete operator's manual.
Ordering Example: *TQ101-100 flange mounted reaction torque sensor, with 0 to 100 in-lb range, $1525.*

RUGGED IN-LINE ROTARY TORQUE SENSOR
WITH INTEGRAL SLIP RING ASSEMBLY

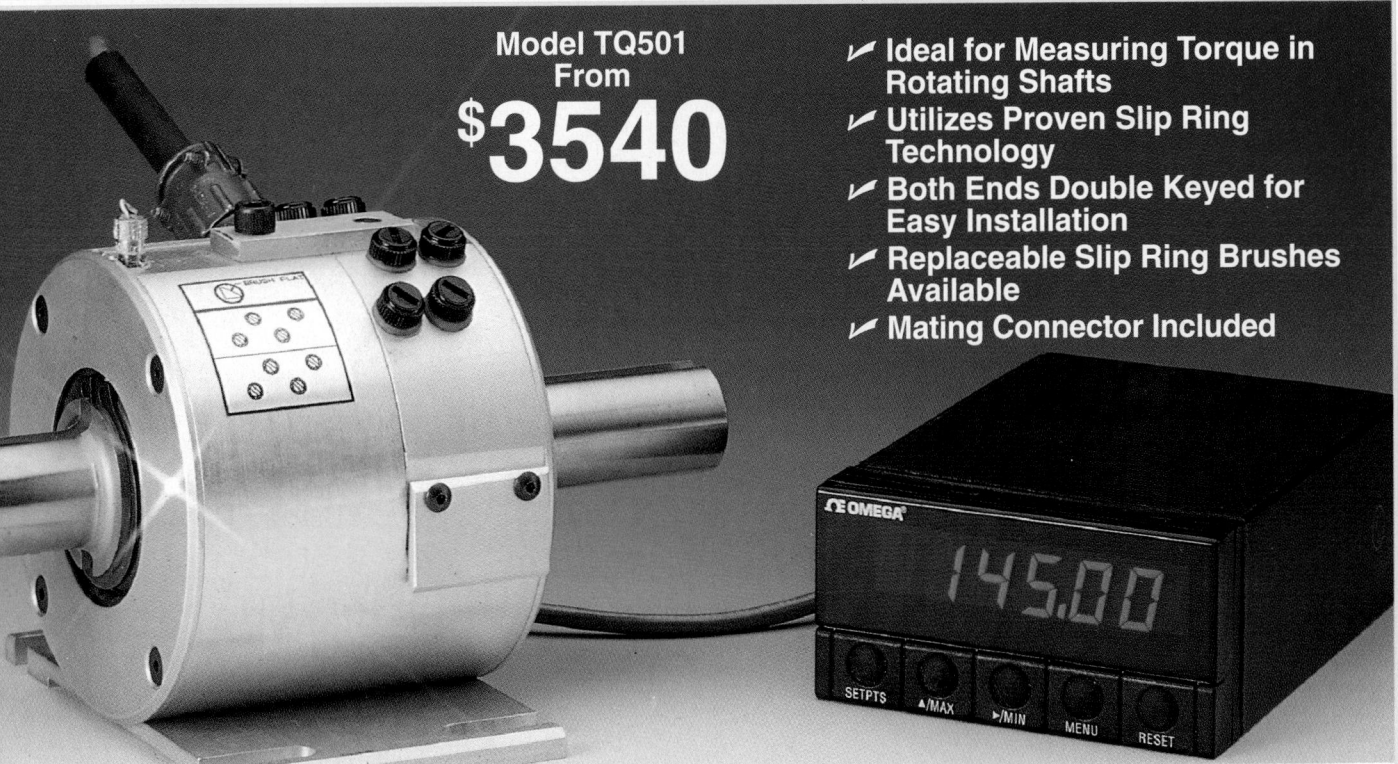

Model TQ501
From
$3540

- ✔ Ideal for Measuring Torque in Rotating Shafts
- ✔ Utilizes Proven Slip Ring Technology
- ✔ Both Ends Double Keyed for Easy Installation
- ✔ Replaceable Slip Ring Brushes Available
- ✔ Mating Connector Included

Model TQ501 Rotary Torque Sensor is Shown with Model DP41-S Meter ($395) and TX4-100 Wire ($28.50/per 100').

The TQ501 rotary torque sensor is ideal for measuring torque in rotating shafts. An integral slip ring assembly is used to transfer the electrical signal from rotating electronics to stationary electronics. The slip ring consists of silver graphite brushes which rub on the rotating ring, providing an electrical path for the incoming excitation and the outgoing signal voltage. Because of the low signal levels produced by a strain gage bridge, brushes should be periodically cleaned. For long term measurements, the brushes can be replaced.

SPECIFICATIONS
Rated Output: 2 mV/V nominal
Excitation: 10 Vdc, 20 Vdc maximum
Accuracy: 0.18% FS
Linearity: 0.10% FS
Hysteresis: 0.10% FS
Repeatability: 0.10% FS
Zero Balance: 1.0% FS
Operating Temp. Range: -65 to 250°F (-53 to 120°C)
Compensated Temp. Range: 32 to 170°F (0 to 77°C)
Thermal Effects: Zero 0.002% FS/°F Span 0.002% Rdg/°F
Max. Load: Safe 150 % FS. **Ultimate** 300 % FS
Bridge Resistance: 350 ohms nominal
Full Scale Angular Deflection: 1.2°
Construction: Nickel plated steel
Electrical: Mating connector supplied
Weight: 8 lbs (3.6 kg)

ACCESSORIES

MODEL	PRICE	DESCRIPTION
TX4-100	$28.50	100 ft of 4 conductor shielded wire

Comes with complete operator's manual.
Ordering Example: *TQ501-200 rotary torque sensor with integral slip ring assembly and 0 to 200 in-lb range, **$3975**.*

DIMENSIONS (INCHES)

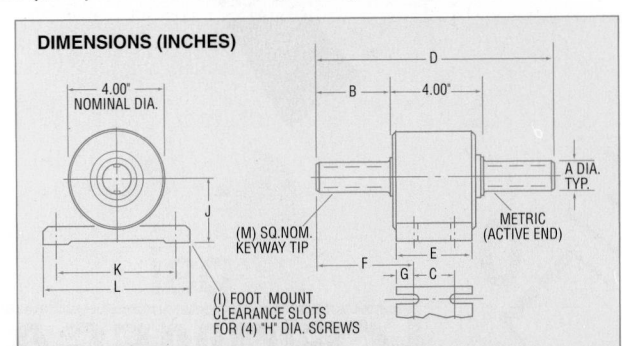

Model No.	A +.000 -.003	B	C	D	E	F	G	H	J +.000 -.010	K	L	M
TQ501-100	.750	2.25	1.56	8.50	3.26	3.26	0.86	14	2.125	4.000	4.75	3/16
TQ501-200												
TQ501-500												
TQ501-1K	1.000											1/4
TQ501-2K												
TQ501-5K	1.500	2.75	2.02	9.50	3.50	3.64	0.74	3/8	2.500	5.250	6.25	3/8
TQ501-10K												

HIGHLIGHTED MODELS IN STOCK FOR FAST DELIVERY!

To Order *(Specify Model Number)*

MODEL	RANGE	PRICE	COMPATIBLE METERS
TQ501-100	0-100 in-lb	$3540	DP41-S, DP302-S, DP2000-S4
TQ501-200	0-200 in-lb	3975	DP41-S, DP302-S, DP2000-S5
TQ501-500	0-500 in-lb	3975	DP41-S, DP3002-S, DP87
TQ501-1K	0-1,000 in-lb	3975	DP41-S, DP302-S, DP2000-S4
TQ501-2K	0-2,000 in-lb	3975	DP41-S, DP302-S, DP2000-S5
TQ501-5K	0-5,000 in-lb	3975	DP41-S, DP3002-S, DP87
TQ501-10K	0-10,000 in-lb	3975	DP41-S, DP3002-S, DP87

LOAD CELLS

F

G OMEGA® PRESSURE GAUGES

Selection Guide  G-3, G-4

2" and 2½" Commercial Grade Gauges G-5 Thru G-10

2½" and 3½" Panel Mount and General Service Gauges G-11, G-15

General Service and Liquid Filled Gauges G-16

Diaphragm Pressure Seals G-17, G-18

4½" and 6" Process Gauges G-19, G-20

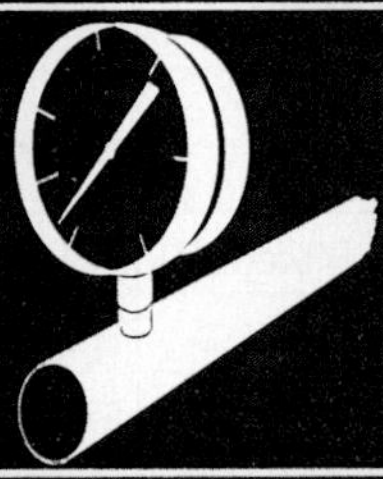

3½" Pocket Test Gauge 2½" Low Pressure Diaphragm G-21

4½" and 6" Test Gauges G-22 Thru G-26

OMEGA PRESSURE GAUGES

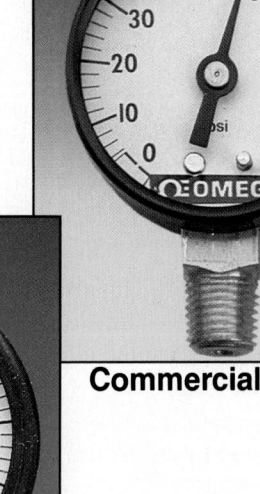

Commercial Gauge

Panel Gauge

Liquid-Filled Gauge

Low Pressure Gauge

SPECIFICATIONS	COMMERCIAL GAUGES TYPE C PAGES G-5 TO G-10	PANEL GAUGES TYPE P PAGES G-11 TO G-12	LOW PRESSURE GAUGES TYPE L PAGES G-19	LIQUID FILLED GAUGES TYPE F PAGE G-16
Prices Start At	$15	$27	$119	$32
Accuracy	3—2—3%	3—2—3%	2—1—2%	2—1—2%
Warranty	1-Year	1-Year	1-Year	1-Year
Dial Size (inches)	2 and 2½	2½	2½	2½
Bordon Tube	Bronze	Bronze	Brass Diaphragm	Bronze
Connection	¼ NPT Lower or Back	¼ NPT Lower or Back	¼ NPT Lower	¼″ NPT Male Lower or Back
Ranges	Vac. to 600 PSI	Vac. to 600 PSI	10 to 300 Inches H_2O	Vac to 6000 PSI
Case Material	Black Painted Steel	Black Painted Steel	Black Painted Steel	Stainless Steel
Window Material	Polycarbonate	Polycarbonate	Polycarbonate	Glass
Movement	Brass	Brass	Brass	Brass
Pointer	Fixed	Fixed	Adjustable	Fixed
Liquid Filled	N/A	N/A	N/A	Standard
Oxygen Service	N/A	N/A	N/A	N/A
Weather Resistant	No	No	No	N/A
Applications	Installation on pumps, portable compressors, industrial machinery, hydraulic and pneumatic systems	Instrument panels, air conditioning equipment, air and gas dryers compressors and test stands	Commercial heating, air conditioning burner service, gas distribution, filtration and cooling systems	Installation on pumps and industrial machinery, where vibration, shock or pulsation is present

QUICK SELECTION GUIDE

General Service Gauge

Pocket Test Gauge

Process Gauge

Differential Gauge

Test Gauge

DIFFERENTIAL GAUGES TYPE D PAGE G-17 TO 18	GENERAL SERVICE GAUGES TYPE S PAGES G-13 TO G-15	POCKET TEST GAUGE WITH COVER TYPE T PAGE G-21	PROCESS GAUGES TYPES H AND J PAGE G-19 TO G-20	TEST GAUGES TYPE T PAGES G-22 TO G-24
$567	$60	$33	$143	$227
2—1—2%	1% Full Scale	½% Full Scale	½% Full Scale	¼% Full Scale
1-Year	2-Year	1-Year	1-Year	1-Year
4½	2½ and 3½	2½ and 3½	4½ and 6	4½ and 6
Bronze	Stainless Steel	Stainless Steel	Stainless Steel	Stainless Steel
¼" NPT Male Lower or Back	¼ NPT Lower or Back	¼ NPT Lower	½ NPT Lower or Back	½ NPT Lower or Back
0 to 1000 PSID	Vac. to 10000 PSI	15 to 1000 PSI	Vac. to 20000 PSI	Vac. to 10000 PSI
Epoxy Coated Aluminum	Stainless Steel	Stainless Steel	Phenolic, Aluminum	Aluminum Alloy
Glass	Gasketed Polycarbonate	Glass	Double Strength Glass	Glass
Brass	Stainless Steel	Stainless Steel	Stainless Steel	Stainless Steel
Adjustable	Adjustable	Adjustable	Micrometer Adjustment	Adjustable
N/A	Optional	N/A	Optional	N/A
N/A	Optional	Optional	Optional	Optional
Yes	Yes	Yes	Yes	Yes
All types of industries, hydraulic and pneumatic systems	Hostile environments including corrosion, weather, and dust, steam boilers chemical and petrochemical plants	Portable test systems, tool boxes, field gauge testers, applications with media that are not compatible with brass	All types of industry including, process, plants power, petrochemical, chemical, aerospace, and laboratories	Instrument shops, laboratories, production testing, quality assurance, where performance, reliability and precision are required

COMMERCIAL GRADE GAUGES TYPE C

MADE IN
USA

- **Economically Priced**
- **Long Lasting Movement**
- **Durable Construction**
- **Stocked Ranges for Fast Delivery**

The OMEGA Spring Suspended Movement represents the new look of the future. Wearing parts have been reduced to a minimum. The entire movement is now suspended between two springs, the Bourdon tube above and the link below. For the user this means greater resistance to mechanical shock and vibration. This increased resistance to the effects of rough usage contributes to longer gauge life.

The conventional movement shown here is typical of those used by most manufacturers of commercial pressure gauges.

Prices start at $15

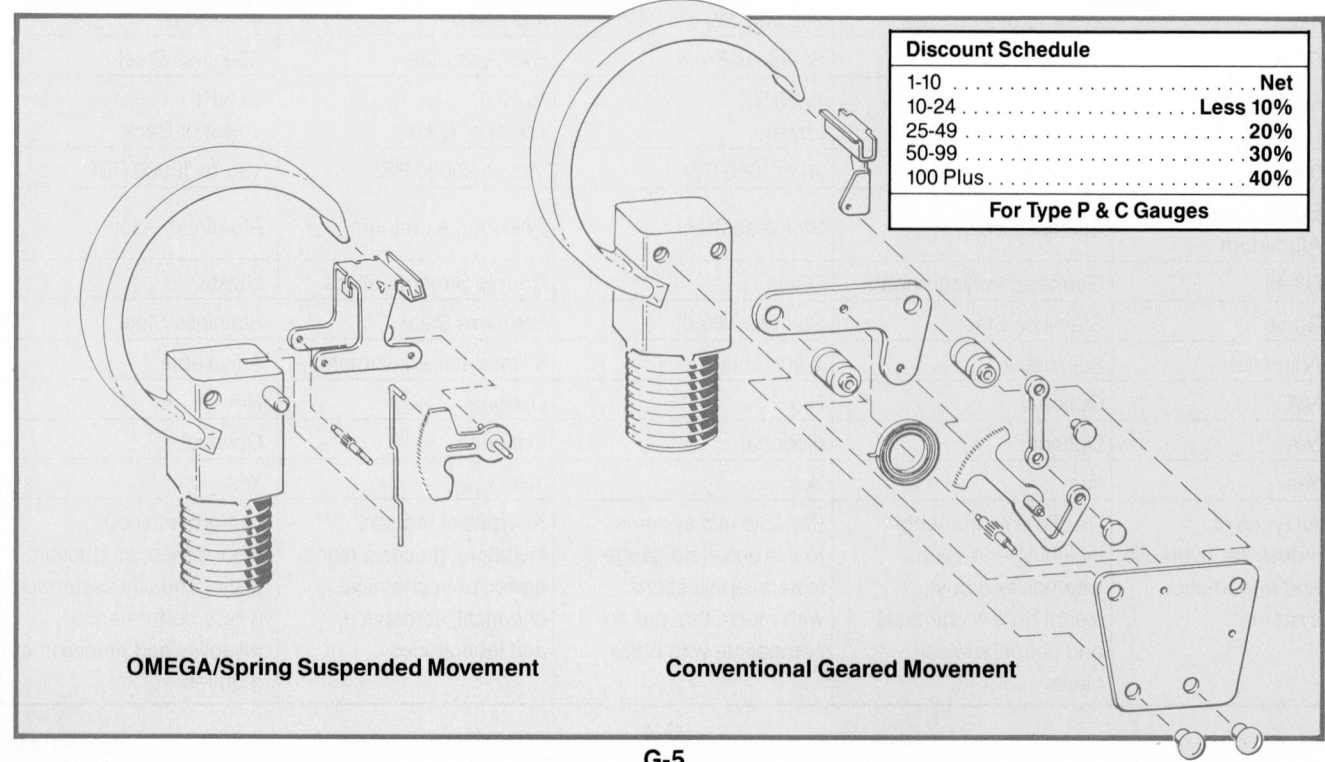

Discount Schedule	
1-10	Net
10-24	Less 10%
25-49	20%
50-99	30%
100 Plus	40%
For Type P & C Gauges	

OMEGA/Spring Suspended Movement   **Conventional Geared Movement**

MADE IN
USA

How To Order Type C— Commercial Grade Gauges

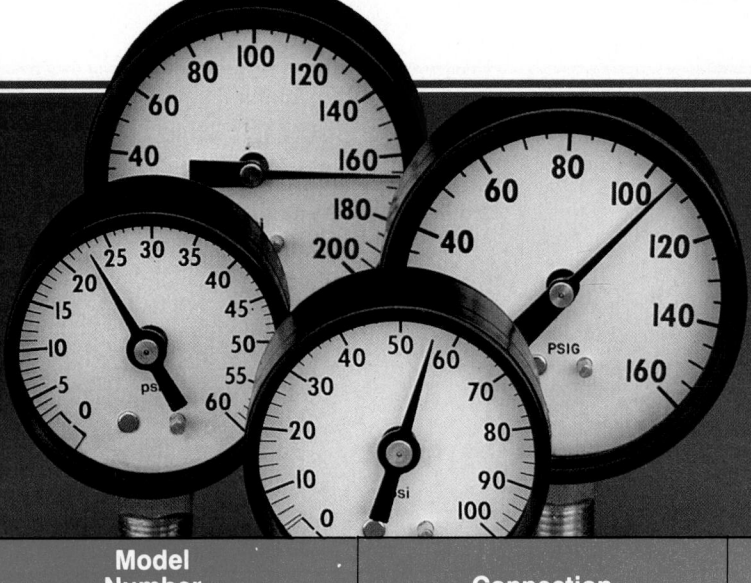

Dial Size	Model Number	Connection	Price
2"	PGC-20L-[*]	Lower	$15
	PGC-20B-[*]	Back	17
2½"	PGC-25L-[*]	Lower	17
	PGC-25B-[*]	Back	21

Insert Range Code from table.

Other Standard Ranges Available, refer to pg. G-7 and Consult Sales.

Ordering Example: PGC-20B-30 Commercial Pressure Gauge with 2" dial, back connection and 0/30 PSI range, **$17**.

HIGHLIGHTED MODELS STOCKED FOR FAST DELIVERY

Standard Case Case Style 1000
Specifications

Temperature: 150°F max
Case: Painted Steel
Window: Polycarbonate Plastic
Bourdon Tube: Bronze
Connection: Brass ¼" NPT
Ranges: Vacuum thru 600 PSI
Accuracy: 3-2-3% (3% over first & last, 10% of range, 2% over remaining range)

The high reliability of the OMEGA Commercial Gauge line is chiefly attributed to the unique OMEGA Spring Suspended Movement. The entire movement is now suspended between two springs, the Bourdon tube above and the link below. Wearing parts have been reduced to a minimum. Furthermore, these movement parts are ultrasonically cleaned and lubricated with silicone oil to ensure long cycle life. The spring suspended movement is largely resistant to the effects of shock, pulsation, and vibration. The result of this is longer gauge life. The numerous applications for OMEGA Commercial Gauges include installation on pumps, portable compressors, industrial machinery,

Stocked Ranges—Type P

Range Code	Range
30V/15	30 in Hg VAC to 15 PSI
30V/30	30 in. Hg VAC to 30 PSI
30V	30/0 in Hg VAC
15	0/15 PSI
30	0/30 PSI
60	0/60 PSI
100	0/100 PSI
160	0/160 PSI
300	0/300 PSI

STYLE L   **STYLE B**

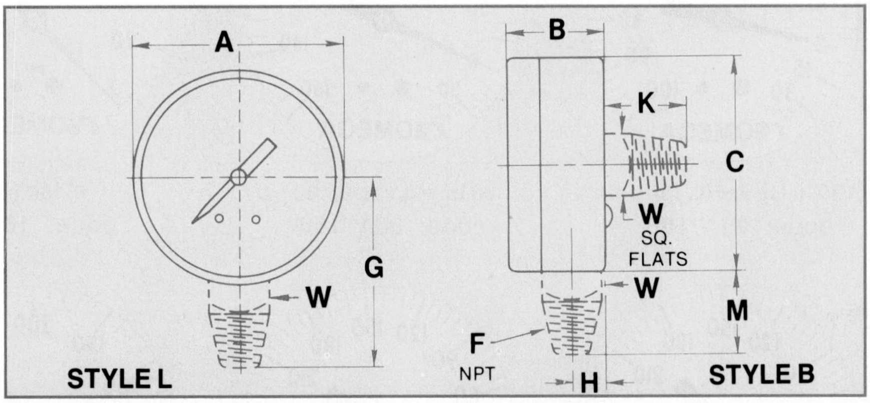

Size (in.)	A	B lower	B back	C	F NPT	G	H	K	M	W	Wgt. (ozs.)
2	2 ⁷⁄₆₄ (53)	1 ³⁄₆₄ (27)	1 ¹⁄₃₂ (26)	2 ⁷⁄₆₄ (54)	¼"	1 ²⁷⁄₃₂ (47)	⅜ (10)	⅞ (22)	²⁵⁄₃₂ (20)	⁹⁄₁₆ (14)	4½
2½	2 ²³⁄₃₂ (69)	1 ⅛ (29)	1 ⅛ (29)	2 ¹¹⁄₁₆ (68)	¼"	2 ⁵⁄₃₂ (55)	⅜ (10)	⅞ (22)	²⁵⁄₃₂ (20)	⁹⁄₁₆ (14)	6

hydraulic and pneumatic systems, instrumentation, and pressurized vessels.

STANDARD DIALS–TYPES C AND P
SINGLE SCALE PSI

Single Scale PSI*

30/0 in. Hg vac
code: 30 V

0/15 psi
code: 15

30 in. Hg vac/0/15 psi
code: 30 V/15

0/30 psi
code: 30

30 in. Hg vac/0/30 psi
code: 30 V/30

0/60 psi
code: 60

30 in. Hg vac/0/60 psi
code: 30 V/60

0/100 psi
code: 100

30 in Hg vac/0/100 psi
code: 30 V/100

30 in. Hg vac/0/160 psi
code: 30 V/160

0/160 psi
code: 160

0/200 psi
code: 200

0/300 psi
code: 300

30 in. Hg vac/0/300 psi
code: 30 V/300

0/400 psi
code: 400

0/600 psi
code: 600

See pages G-6 and G-12 for ordering information.

CUSTOM DIAL FACES
TYPES C AND P

Special Dials/Dual Scale PSI/kg/cm₂*

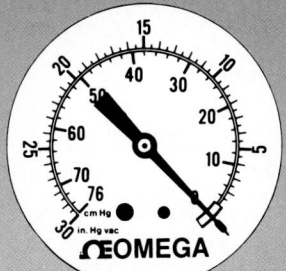

76/0 cm Hg
30/0 in. Hg vac

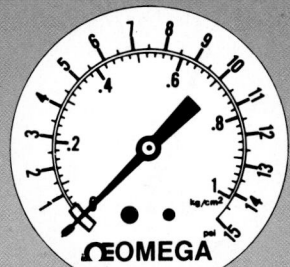

0/1 kg/cm²
0/15 psi

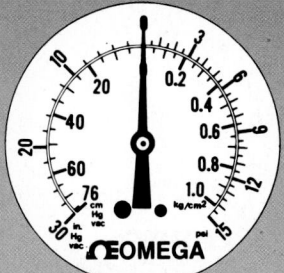

76 cm Hg vac/0/1.0 kg/cm²
30 in. Hg vac/0/15 psi

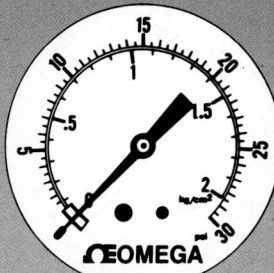

0/2 kg/cm²
0/30 psi

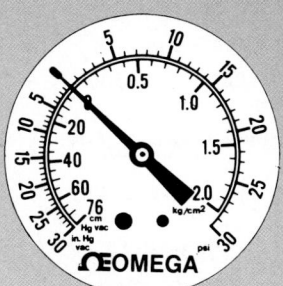

76 cm Hg vac/0/2.0 kg/cm²
30 in. Hg vac/0/30 psi

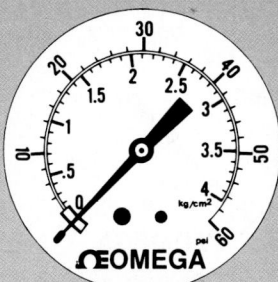

0/4 kg/cm²
0/60 psi

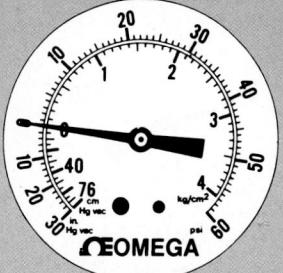

76 cm Hg vac/0/4 kg/cm²
30 in. Hg vac/0/60 psi

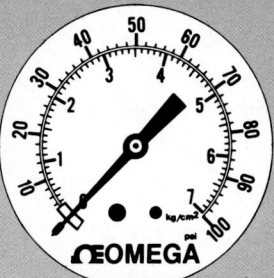

0/7 kg/cm²
0/100 psi

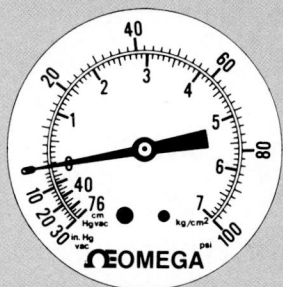

76 cm Hg vac/0/7 kg/cm²
30 in. Hg vac/0/100 psi

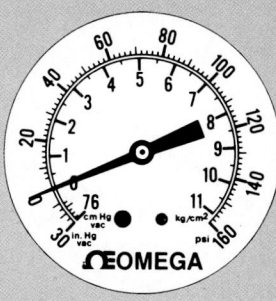

76 cm Hg vac/0/11 kg/cm²
30 in. Hg vac/0/160 psi

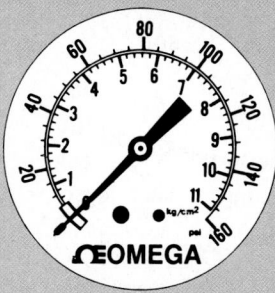

0/11 kg/cm²
0/160 psi

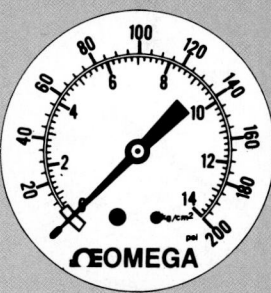

0/14 kg/cm²
0/200 psi

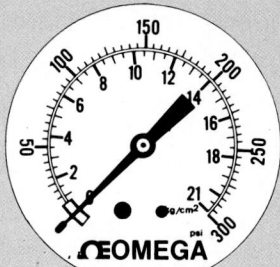

0/21 kg/cm²
0/300 psi

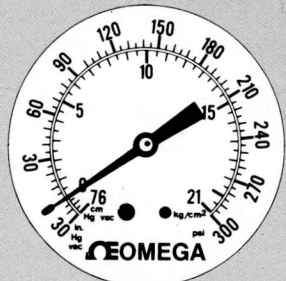

76 cm Hg vac/0/21 kg/cm²
30 in. Hg vac/0/300 psi

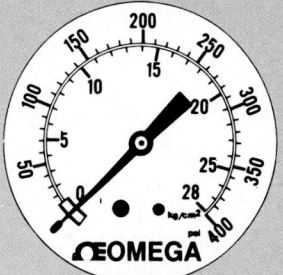

0/28 kg/cm²
0/400 psi

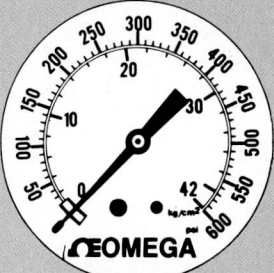

0/42 kg/cm²
0/600 psi

◄ NOTE:
To fulfill the varying needs of our customers, custom dial faces are available; however, these dial faces are subject to a $100 set-up fee for Type C and Type P. For each kind of custom dialface, there is a 10 piece minimum for Types C and P.

CUSTOM DIAL FACES
TYPES C AND P

Special Dials/Single Scale kPa*

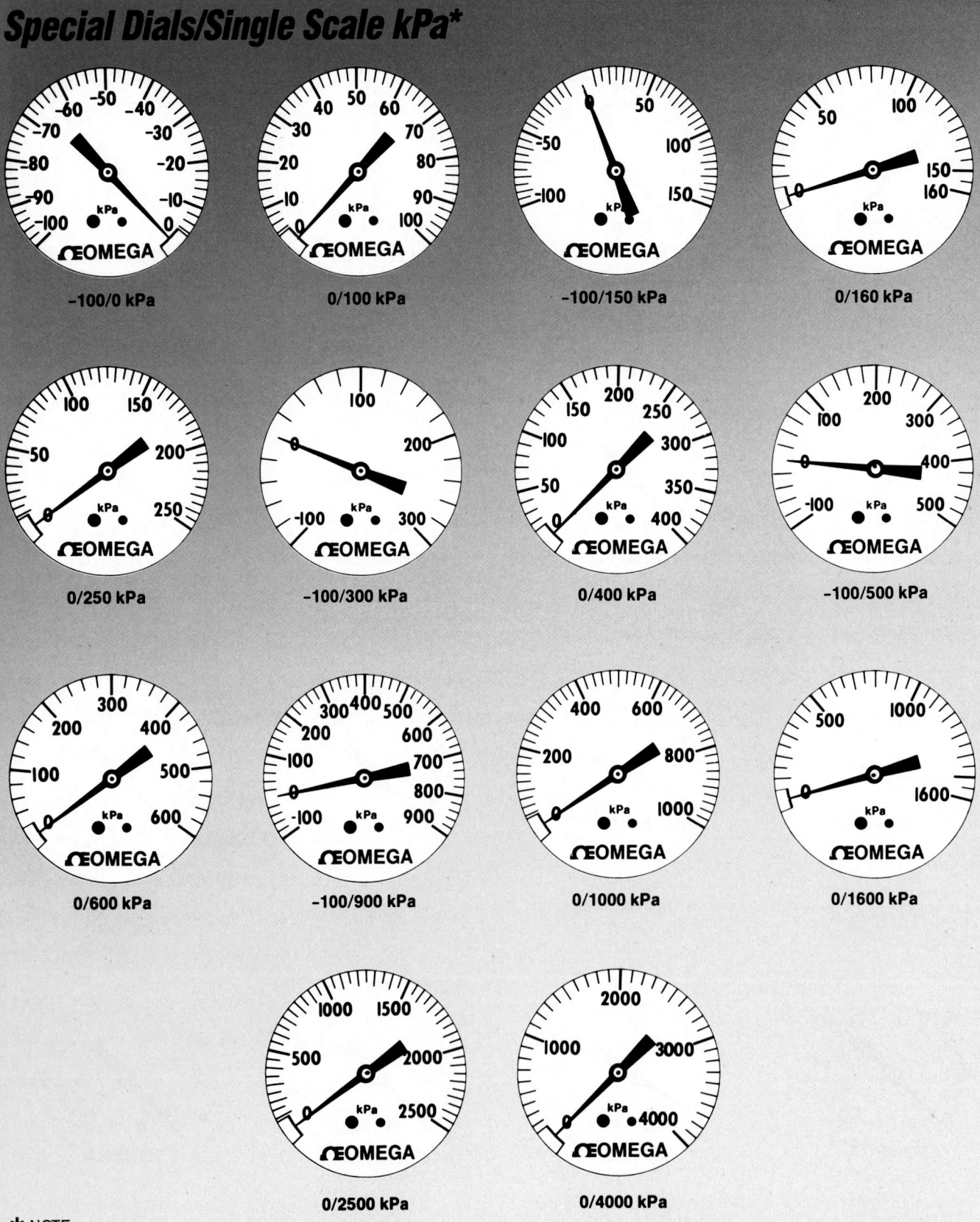

-100/0 kPa   0/100 kPa   -100/150 kPa   0/160 kPa

0/250 kPa   -100/300 kPa   0/400 kPa   -100/500 kPa

0/600 kPa   -100/900 kPa   0/1000 kPa   0/1600 kPa

0/2500 kPa   0/4000 kPa

★ NOTE:
To fulfill the varying needs of our customers, custom dial faces are available; however, these dial faces are subject to a $100 set-up fee for Type C and Type P. For each kind of custom dialface, there is a 10 piece minimum for Types C and P.

CUSTOM DIAL FACES
TYPES C AND P

Special Dials/Dual Scale PSI/kPa*

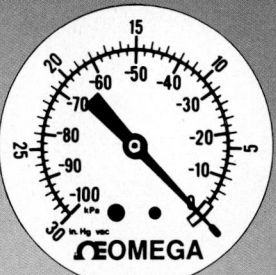

–100/0 kPa
30/0 in. Hg vac

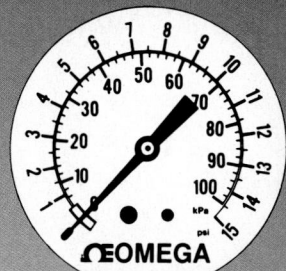

0/100 kPa
0/15 psi

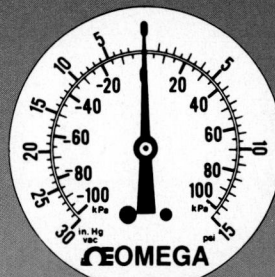

–100/0/100 kPa
30 in. Hg vac/0/15 psi

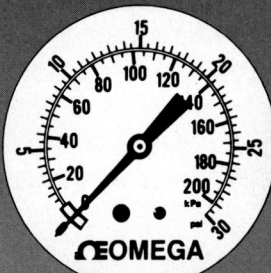

0/200 kPa
0/30 psi

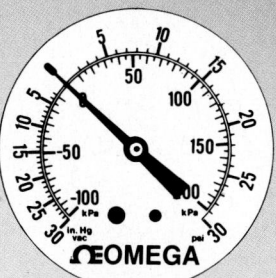

–100/0/200 kPa
30 in. Hg vac/0/30 psi

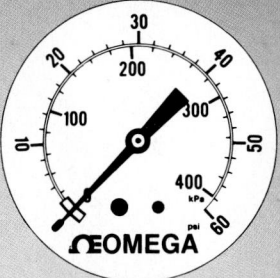

0/400 kPa
0/60 psi

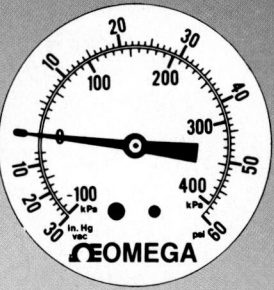

–100/0/400 kPa
30 in. Hg vac/0/60 psi

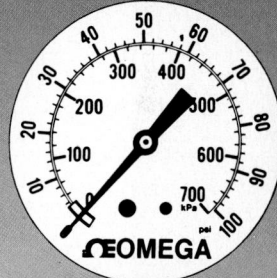

0/700 kPa
0/100 psi

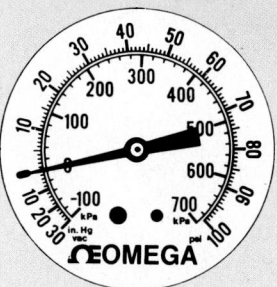

–100/0/700 kPa
30 in. Hg vac/0/100 psi

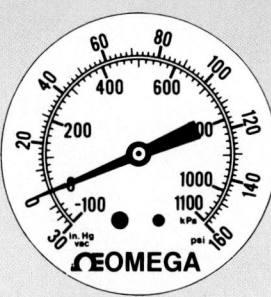

–100/0/1100 kPa
30 in. Hg vac/0/160 psi

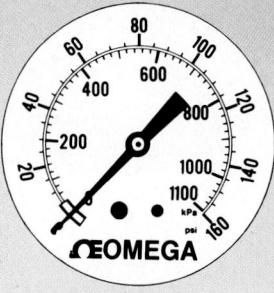

0/1100 kPa
0/160 psi

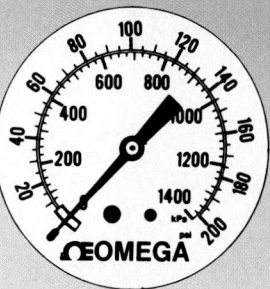

0/1400 kPa
0/200 psi

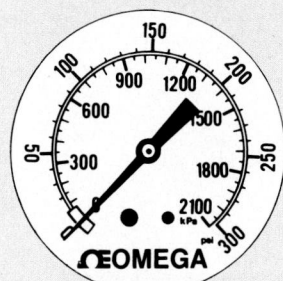

0/2000 kPa
0/300 psi

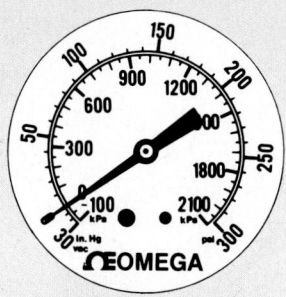

–100/0/2100 kPa
30 in. Hg vac/0/300 psi

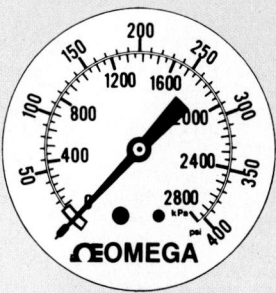

0/2800 kPa
0/400 psi

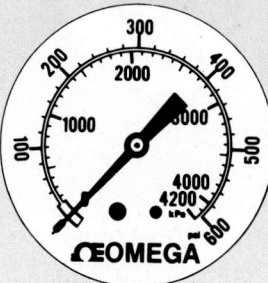

0/4000 kPa
0/600 psi

* NOTE:

To fulfill the varying needs of our customers, custom dial faces are available; however, these dial faces are subject to a $100 set-up fee for Type C and Type P. For each kind of custom dialface, there is a 10 piece minimum for Types C and P.

OMEGA® COMMERCIAL PANEL GAUGES
TYPE P

MADE IN
USA

- **Durable and Accurate Design**
- **U-Clamp Mount**
- **2½" Dials**
- **For Use in a Wide Variety of Applications**

Panel Mount Gauge

$27

OMEGA Panel Gauges, with a U-clamp mounting design, are durable gauges that feature long term gauge life and stability. The attractive black steel case gauges are designed for use in numerous panel gauge applications.

OMEGA® COMMERCIAL PANEL GAUGES

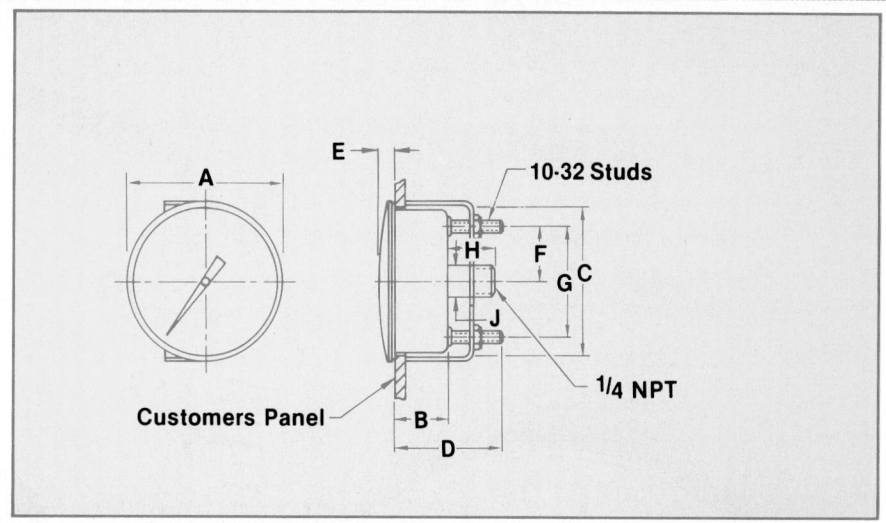

10-32 Studs
1/4 NPT
Customers Panel

Dial Size Inches	A	B	C	D	E	F	G	H	J
2½	2⅞ (73)	1 (25)	2¹¹⁄₁₆ (68)	2 (51)	⁷⁄₃₂ (7)	1 (25)	2 (51)	⅞ (22)	⁹⁄₁₆ SQ. (14)

Specifications

Case: Painted Steel
Window: Polycarbonate Plastic
Bourdon Tube: Bronze
Connection: Back
Fitting: ¼" NPT Brass
Dial Size: 2½"
Mounting: "U" Bracket
Ranges: Vacuum thru 600 PSI
Accuracy: 3-2-3%
Temperature: 150°F max

OMEGA Panel Gauges utilize a U-clamp mounting design. The attractive black painted steel case gauges are designed for use on instrument panels, air conditioning equipment, air and gas dryers, machine tools, air compressors, pressure test stands, and a wide variety of other panel gauge applications. The movement in the panel gauges is the unique OMEGA Spring Suspended Movement. The entire movement is suspended between two springs, the Bourdon tube above, and the link below. Wearing parts have reduced to a minimum.

Furthermore, these movement parts are ultrasonically cleaned and lubricated with silicone oil to ensure long cycle life. The spring suspended movement is resistant to the effects of shock, pulsation, and vibration, thus contributing to longer gauge life.

Warning: All gauge components should be selected considering media and ambient operating conditions to prevent misapplication. Improper application can be detrimental to the gauge, cause failure, and possible personal injury or property damage.

How To Order —Panel Mount Gauges

Dial Size	Model Number	Connection	Price
2½"	PGP-25B-[*]	Back	$27

*Insert Range Code from table below.
Ordering Example:
PGP-25B-100: Pressure Gauge, Commercial Panel Type, U-Clamp Mount, 2½" Dial, Back Connection, 0/100 PSI Range. Price $27

Stocked Ranges—Type P

Range Code	Range
30V/30	30 in. Hg VAC to 30 PSI
30V	30/0 in Hg VAC
15	0/15 PSI
30	0/30 PSI
60	0/60 PSI
100	0/100 PSI
160	0/160 PSI
200	0/200 PSI
300	0/300 PSI

▶ *HIGHLIGHTED MODELS STOCKED FOR FAST DELIVERY* ◀

OMEGA® GENERAL SERVICE GAUGES TYPE S

MADE IN USA

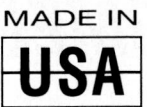

- 2½″ and 3½″ Dials
- Stem and Panel Mount Styles
- Weather Resistant Stainless Steel Case
- 316 SS Wetted Parts

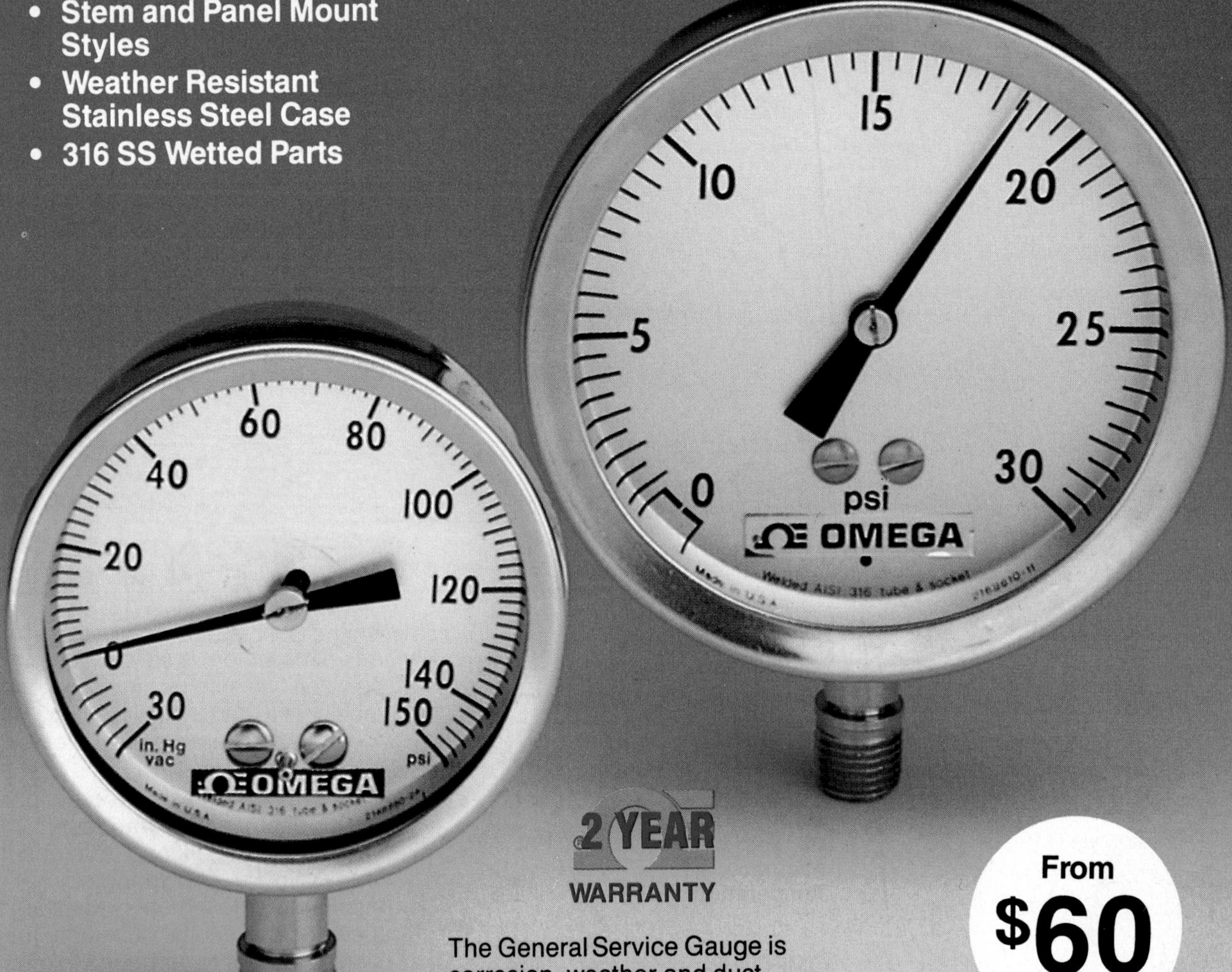

2 YEAR WARRANTY

From $60

The General Service Gauge is corrosion, weather and dust resistant for combating hostile environments. Mounting versatility, excellent readability and sustained accuracy make this stainless steel case-design a gauge leader. It can be stem, surface or flush mounted.

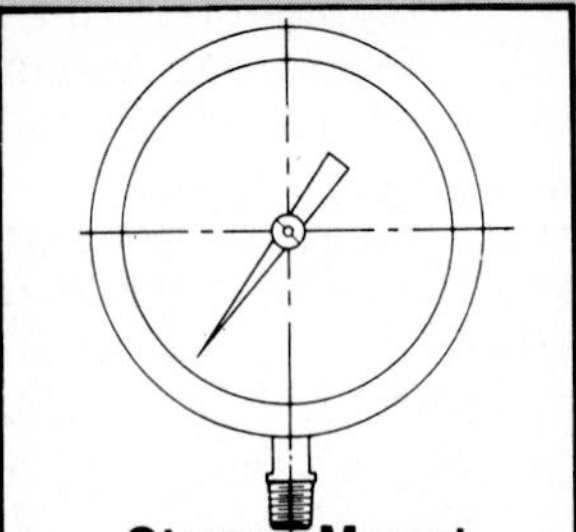

Stem Mount

STYLE L

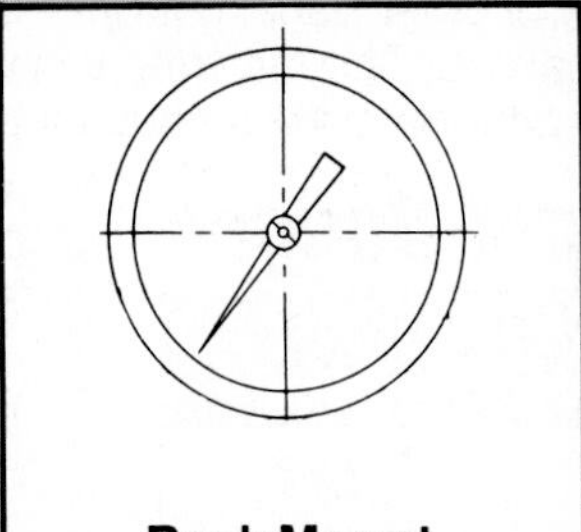

Back Mount

STYLE B

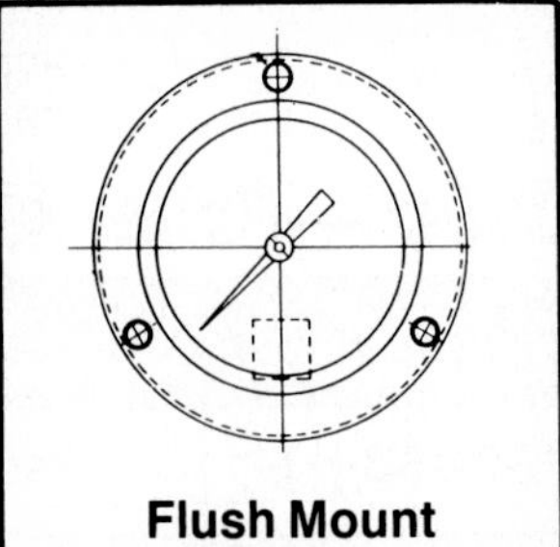

Flush Mount

STYLE B
With Flange Mtg Kit shown on Page G-14.

GENERAL SERVICE GAUGES TYPE S

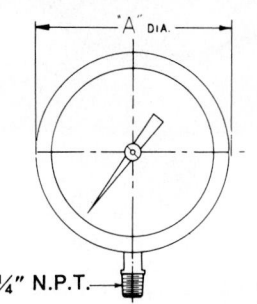

¼" N.P.T.

Stem Mount STYLE L

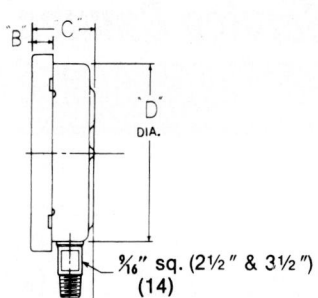

⁹⁄₁₆" sq. (2½" & 3½") (14)

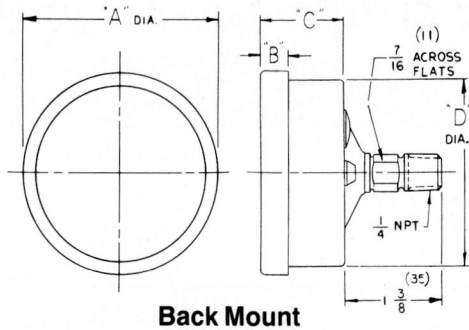

Back Mount STYLE B

SIZE (in.)	A	B	C	D
2½	2⁷⁄₈ (73)	³⁄₈ (10)	1⁵⁄₃₂ (29)	2²¹⁄₃₂ (67)
3½	3³¹⁄₃₂ (101)	1⁵⁄₃₂ (12)	1⁷⁄₃₂ (31)	3¹⁹⁄₃₂ (91)

Sustained accuracy and excellent readability are important user features of the OMEGA General Service Gauge line.

Meeting the requirements of many industrial applications, General Service Gauges may be used on steam boilers or other pressurized vessels; on pumps and compressors; on many types of industrial machinery; in the chemical, petrochemical and allied process industries, in power plants; in pulp and paper mills, plus in an unlimited number of low pressure applications using gauges with a bellows pressure element design.

The pressure gauge actuation systems that comprise the OMEGA General Service Gauge line is the standard 316 SS Bourdon tube system which is engineered to precise tolerances for consistent repeatability and response to pressure fluctuations.

SPECIFICATIONS

Max. Operating Temp: 150°F
Case: Polished Stainless Steel
Window: Polycarbonate Plastic with Neoprene Sealing Gasket
Bourdon Tube: 316 Stainless Steel
Connection: Back or Lower
Fitting: 316 SS, ¼" NPT
Dial Size: 2½" and 3½"
Mounting: Stem, Flange or "U" Bracket
Accuracy: 1% full scale

Warning: All gauge components should be selected considering media and ambient operating conditions to prevent misapplication. Improper application can be detrimental to the gauge, cause failure, and possible personal injury or property damage.

Accessories for Type S Gauges

MODEL NO.	DESCRIPTION	PRICE
UBK-25	U-Bracket Kit for 2½" Gage	$10
UBK-35	U-Bracket Kit for 3½" Gage	10
FMK-25	Flange Mount Kit for 2½" Gage	10
FMK-35	Flange Mount Kit for 3½" Gage	15

Model FMK Flange Kit

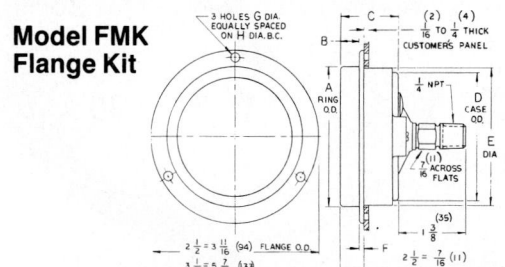

For a Complete Listing of Stocked General Service Gauges, Refer to pg. G-15

Model UBK U-Bracket

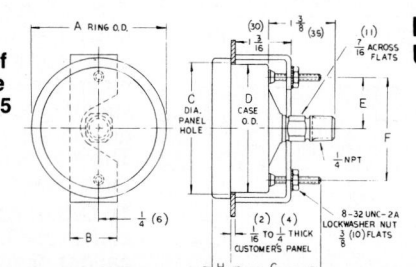

Size (in.)	A	B	C	D	E	F	G	H
2½	2⁷⁄₈ (73)	³⁄₈ (10)	1⁵⁄₃₂ (29)	2²¹⁄₃₂ (67)	2²³⁄₃₂ (69)	¹⁄₁₆ (2)	⁵⁄₃₂ (4)	3¹⁄₈ (79)
3½	3³¹⁄₃₂ (101)	1⁵⁄₃₂ (12)	1⁷⁄₃₂ (31)	3¹⁹⁄₃₂ (91)	3¹¹⁄₁₆ (94)	⁵⁄₃₂ (4)	⁷⁄₃₂ (6)	4⁹⁄₁₆ (116)

Size (in.)	A	B	C	D	E	F	G	H
2½	2⁷⁄₈ (73)	1¹⁄₈ (29)	2¹¹⁄₁₆ (68)	2²¹⁄₃₂ (67)	1¹⁄₃₂ (26)	2¹⁄₁₆ (52)	1²⁵⁄₃₂ (45)	³⁄₈ (10)
3½	3³¹⁄₃₂ (101)	1¹⁄₁₆ (27)	3²¹⁄₃₂ (93)	3¹⁹⁄₃₂ (91)	1⁷⁄₃₂ (31)	2¹³⁄₃₂ (61)	1¾ (44)	1⁵⁄₃₂ (12)

GENERAL SERVICE GAUGES TYPE S

How To Order Type S—General Service Gauges

Dial Size	Model Number	Connection	Price
2½"	**PGS-25L-[∗]** (to 600 PSI)	Lower	$60
	PGS-25L-[∗] (over 600 PSI)	Lower	66
	PGS-25B-[∗] (to 600 PSI)	Back	68
	PGS-25B-[∗] (over 600 PSI)	Back	74
3½"	**PGS-35L-[∗]** (to 600 PSI)	Lower	69
	PGS-35L-[∗] (over 600 PSI)	Lower	78
	PGS-35B-[∗] (to 600 PSI)	Back	81
	PGS-35B-[∗] (over 600 PSI)	Back	90

◆ **HIGHLIGHTED MODELS STOCKED FOR FAST DELIVERY** ◆

∗Insert Range Code from table below.
OPTION: X6B
Cleaned for oxygen service **$65**

Ordering Example:
PGS-25B-160: Pressure Gauge, General Service Type, 2½" Dial, Back Connection, 0/160 PSI Range   Price: **$68.**

Standard Ranges–Type S
pressure (PSI)

Range Code	Range	Figure Interval	Minor Graduation
15	0/15	1	0.2
30	0/30	5	0.5
60	0/60	5	1
100	0/100	10	1
160	0/160	20	2
200	0/200	20	2
300	0/300	30	5
400	0/400	50	5
600	0/600	50	10
800	0/800	100	10
1000	0/1000	100	10
1500	0/1500	200	20
2000	0/2000	200	20
3000	0/3000	300	50
5000	0/5000	500	50
6000	0/6000	1000	100
7500	0/7500	1000	100
10,000	0/10,000	1000	100
VACUUM			
30 V	30-0 inches Mercury	5 inches	0.5

Compound

Range Code	Range	Figure Interval		Minor Graduation	
		Inches Mercury	PSI	Inches Mercury	PSI
30 V/15	30" Hg Vac/0/ 15 PSI	5	3	1	0.5
30 V/30	30" Hg Vac/0/ 30 PSI	10	5	1	1
30 V/60	30" Hg Vac/0/ 60 PSI	10	10	2	1
30 V/100	30" Hg Vac/0/100 PSI	10	10	2	1
30 V/150	30" Hg Vac/0/150 PSI	10	20	5	2
30 V/300	30" Hg Vac/0/300 PSI	30	25	5	5

Pressure Range — Select a gauge with a full scale pressure range of approximately twice the normal operating pressure. The maximum operating pressure should not exceed approximately 75% of the full scale range. Failure to select a guage range within these criteria may ultimately result in fatigue failure of the Bourdon tube.

Also Available! Oil Filled Gauges
Type S Gauges are available on special order filled with silicone oil. The silicone oil is used to dampen the internal movement of the gauge when it is installed on vibrating equipment. The silicone oil has an operating range of − 40 to 150°F. The maximum storage temperature of the gauge is 180°F.

To Order: add suffix **F** to part number and an additional **$25.00** for 2½" gauges or an additional **$35.00** for 3½" gauges.
Example: PGS-25B-60-F: Pressure Gauge, General Service Type, 2½" Dial, 0/60 PSI Range, Silicone Oil Filled. Price: **$93.00**

Accessory — Min or max detection for PGS gauges.
PGS-25-MAX **$30** (2½" dial)
PGS-35-MAX **$35** (3½" dial)

VIBRATION RESISTANT LIQUID FILLED GAUGES

PGF Series Gauges
30" Hg TO 6000 PSI

✔ **Easy To Read 2½" Dial**

✔ **Superior Performance With Vibration, Pulsation, Shock**

✔ **Leakproof O-Ring Seal**

✔ **Lower and Back Mounts**

From **$32**

Liquid Filled for
Vibration Resistance

STANDARD RANGES

CODE PSI	FIGURE INTERV.	MINOR TICKS
15	1	0.5
30	5	0.5
60	5	1
100	10	1
200	20	5
300	30	5
400	50	10
600	50	10
1000	200	20
3000	500	100
5000	1000	100
VACUUM		
30V	5	0.5
in Hg	inchs	inchs

HIGHLIGHTED MODELS STOCKED FOR FAST DELIVERY!

Dimensions in Inches

GAUGE	B	C	D	G	H	T
Back	1¼	2⅞	½	2⁹⁄₃₂	N/A	⁹⁄₁₆
Lower	1¼	2²³⁄₃₂	¹³⁄₃₂	2⁹⁄₃₂	⅞	⁹⁄₁₆

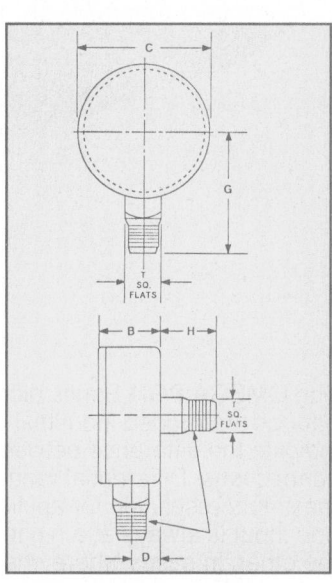

SPECIFICATIONS
Case: Stainless Steel
Wetted Parts: Brass/Bronze
Window: Shatter-Resistant Glass
Fill Fluid: Glycerine
Temperature: 150°F Max
Fitting: ¼" NPT Brass
Accuracy: 2-1-2%

To Order (Specify Model Number)

DIAL SIZE	MODEL	CONNECTION	PRICE VAC-600 PSI	PRICE 1000-6000 PSI
2½	**PGF-25B-[ ]**	Back	$39	$43
2½	**PGF-25L-[ ]**	Lower	41	45

[ ]—Insert Range Form Table
Ordering Example: *Model PGL-25B-100 is a back mount gauge with a pressure range to 100 PSI. Price: $41.*

NEW! DIFFERENTIAL PRESSURE DIAL GAUGES

PGD-45 SERIES
From
$567

✔ Heavy Duty Construction
✔ Double-Strength Break Resistant Glass
✔ 2-1-2₂% ANSI Grade A Accuracy

PGD Series Gauges are Available with Ports Located in the Back of the Gauge (Model Shown at Left), or in the Lower Six O'Clock Position (Shown Right).

The OMEGA PGD Series differential pressure gauges are rugged industrial gauges which indicate the difference between the two input connections. Differential ranges provide the maximum resolution for applications where one input is always at a higher pressure than the other. In cases where one input can be higher or lower than the other, a bi-directional differential range should be used.

The PGD Series is constructed with two independent bourdon tubes. The opposing bourdon tubes are linked to a single pinion gear which rotates a pointer for direct pressure readings. By using two independent bourdon tubes, the gauge can handle liquids or gases on either or both ports.

The large 4½" dial makes reading pressure easy. Each gauge is equipped with a micrometer adjustment for rezeroing the gauge. Gauges are available with ports located in the lower six o'clock position or in the rear for panel mounting.

SPECIFICATIONS
Accuracy: 2-1-2%, ANSI Grade A
Dial Size: 4½"
Dial Arc: 210°
Window: Double-strength glass
Connection: ¼" NPT male
Sensor Type: Bourdon tube
Wetted Parts: Tube/bronze; Fittings/brass
Case: Black epoxy coated aluminum
Operating Temperature: 150°F (65°C)
Weight: 3 lbs (1.4 kg)

WITH DIFFERENTIAL OR BI-DIRECTIONAL RANGES

1 YEAR WARRANTY

MADE IN USA

DIMENSIONS IN INCHES

NUTS & BOLTS NOT SUPPLIED

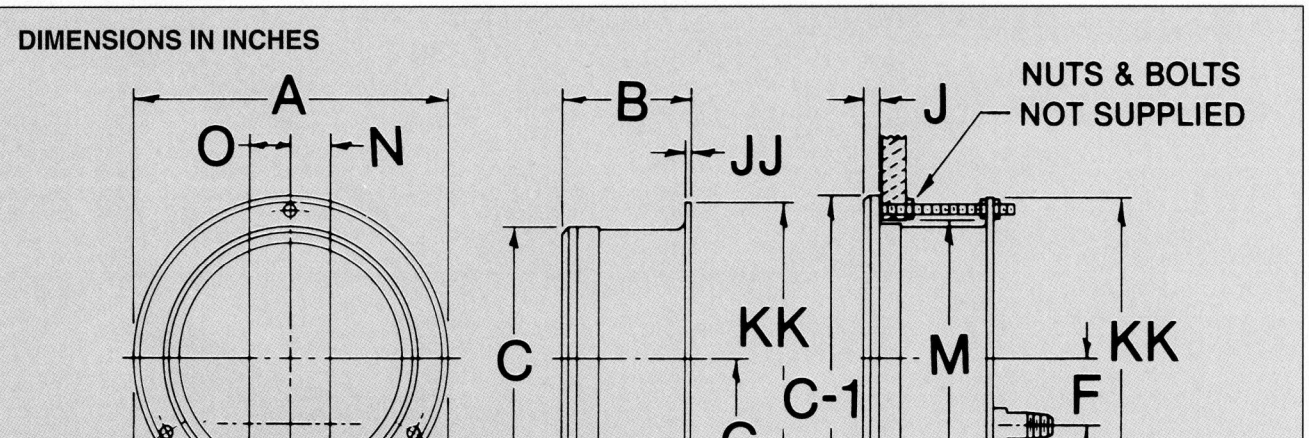

$^{19}/_{32}$" sq. FLATS (15)

¼" N.P.T.

3-**L** HOLES DIA. EQUALLY SPACED ON **E** DIA. BOLT CIRCLE

Note: Dimensions in Brackets ( ) are Millimeters

GAUGE SIZE	A	B	C	C1	D	E	F	G	H	J	K	L	M	N	O	JJ	KK
4½	5⅞ (149)	3¹/₃₂ (82)	4¹⁵/₁₆ (126)	5⅞ (149)	1¹/₁₆ (26)	5⅜ (137)	1¹/₁₆ (27)	3⁹/₁₆ (91)	1⁹/₁₆ (40)	³/₁₆ (5)	¹⁹/₃₂ (15)	⁷/₃₂ (6)	4¹⁵/₁₆ (125)	2¹/₃₂ (17)	2¹/₃₂ (17)	⅛ (3)	5¹³/₁₆ (148)

HIGHLIGHTED MODELS STOCKED FOR FAST DELIVERY!

AVAILABLE PRESSURE RANGES

RANGE CODE	RANGE (PSI)	FIGURE INTERVAL	MINOR GRADUATION	STATIC PRES LIMIT (PSI)*
20	0/20	5	0.2	30
30	0/30	5	0.5	60
60	0/60	10	1	120
100	0/100	10	1	200
200	0/200	20	2	300
600	0/600	100	10	900
1K	0/1000	100	10	1500
15/15	15/0/15	5	0.5	60
30/30	30/0/30	10	1	120
50/50	50/0/50	10	1	200
100/100	100/0/100	20	2	300
200/200	200/0/200	50	5	600
500/500	500/0/500	100	10	1500

Maximum pressure which can be applied to either port on the gauge.

To Order *(Specify Model Number)*

MODEL NUMBER	DIAL SIZE	CONNECTION	PRICE
PGD-45B-(*)	4½"	Back	**$567**
PGD-45L-(*)	4½"	Lower	572

* Insert range code from table below.

Ordering Example: *PGD-45B-30 is a 4½" differential pressure gauge with a back input connection and 0/30 PSI range, **$567**.*

G-18

INDUSTRIAL PROCESS GAUGES
Type H and J, 4½″ and 6″ Dials

- **.5% FS Accuracy**
- **PGH Gauge Ranges from 15 PSI to 20,000 PSI**
- **Double-Strength Break Resistant Glass**
- **Heavy Duty 316 SS Wetted Parts**
- **Compatible with Most Media**

From
$143

NOW HERMETICALLY SEALED!

Model PGH-45L-100 Shown

Model PGJ-45B-100 Shown

From
$176

SPECIFICATIONS

Dial Arc: 270°
Case: Lower Connection, Black Phenol; Back Connection, Aluminum
Window: Double-Strength Glass
Bourdon Tube: 316 Stainless Steel
Connection: ½ NPT Male—316SS
Mounting: Stem, Flush or Surface
Operating Temperature: 250°F Max.

Standard PSI Ranges

Range Code	Range	Figure Interval	Minor Grad.
15	0/15	1	0.1
30	0/30	5	0.2
60	0/60	5	0.5
100	0/100	10	1
160	0/160	20	1
200	0/200	20	2
300	0/300	50	2
400	0/400	50	5
600	0/600	50	5
800	0/800	100	10
1000	0/1000	100	10
1500	0/1500	200	10
2000	0/2000	200	20
3000	0/3000	500	20
5000	0/5000	500	50
10,000	0/10,000	1000	100
20,000	0/20,000	2000	200

HIGHLIGHTED MODELS STOCKED FOR FAST DELIVERY

To Order *(Insert Range Code [*] From Tables)*

DIAL	MODEL	CONNECTION	VACUUM TO 1000 PSI	1,500 THRU 10,000 PSI	15,000 AND 20,000 PSI
4½″	PGH-45L-[*]	Lower	$143	$179	$269
4½″	PGH-45B-[*]	Back	143	179	269
(Flush Aluminum Case)					
4½″	PGJ-45B-[*]	Back	176	194	291
6″	PGJ-60B-[*]	Back	256	282	378

* EXAMPLE: PGJ-45B-100 is 4½″ 0 to 100 PSI Style PGJ gauge with a back connection, $176..

Options (Add Suffix to Model Number)
-F Glycerine Oil Filled 4½″ Gauge $60, available only for PHG-45L Models

Vacuum

Range Code	Range	Figure Interval	Minor Grad.
30 V	30/0 In. Merc.	5 inches	0.2 inch
34 V	34/0 ft. water	5 feet	0.5 foot

Special Ranges

Compound

Range Code	Range	Figure Interval		Minor Graduation	
		Inches Mercury	PSI	Inches Mercury	PSI
30 V 15	30" Hg/0/15 PSI	5	3	0.5	0.2
30 V 30	30" Hg/0/30 PSI	10	5	1	0.5
30 V 60	30" Hg/0/60 PSI	10	10	1	1
30 V 100	30" Hg/0/100 PSI	10	10	2	1
30 V 150	30" Hg/0/150 PSI	10	20	5	2
30 V 300	30" Hg/0/300 PSI	30	25	5	2

Combination

Range Code	Range		Figure Interval		Minor Graduation	
	Inner Scale PSI	Outer Scale Ft. Water	PSI	Feet Water	PSI	Feet Water
15/34	0/15	0/34	3	5	0.5	0.5
30/70	0/30	0/70	5	10	0.5	1
60/140	0/60	0/140	5	20	0.5	5
100/230	0/100	0/230	10	20	1	2
160/370	0/160	0/370	20	50	2	5
200/480	0/200	0/480	20	50	5	5
300/690	0/300	0/690	25	100	5	10

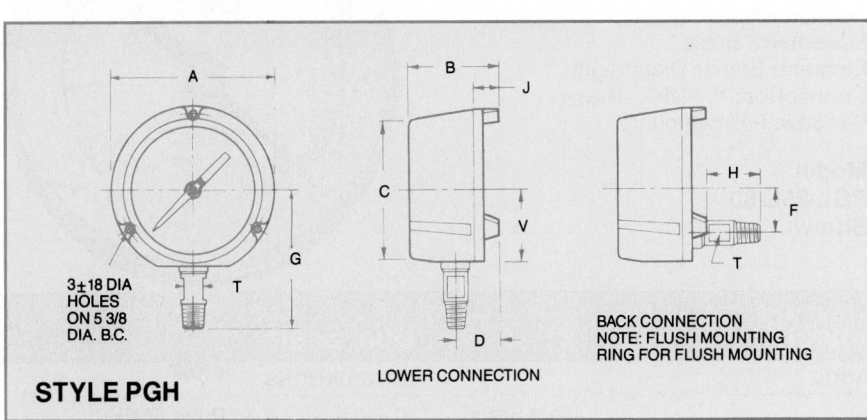

3±18 DIA HOLES ON 5 3/8 DIA. B.C.

BACK CONNECTION
NOTE: FLUSH MOUNTING RING FOR FLUSH MOUNTING

LOWER CONNECTION

STYLE PGH

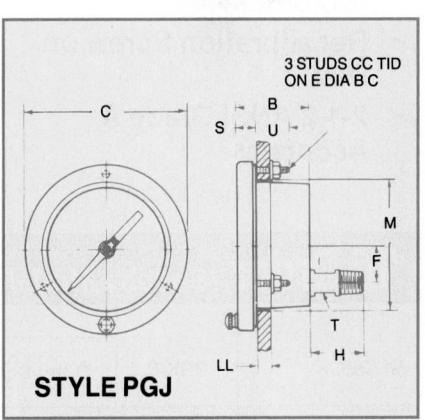

3 STUDS CC TID ON E DIA B C

STYLE PGJ

Style PGH

Dial Size Inches	A	B	D	F
4½	5¹³⁄₁₆ (148)	3⅜ (86)	1⅝ (41)	1⅝ (41)

G ½ NPT	H MAX.	V	Weight (lbs.)
4⁷⁄₁₆ (103)	1⅛ (29)	2⅝ (67)	3½

Style PGJ

Dial Size Inches	B	C	E	F	H Max.
4½		6¹⁄₁₆ (154)	5⅜ (137)	1⅝ (41)	1⅞ (48)
6	2⁹⁄₁₆ (65)	7⁹⁄₁₆ (192)	7 (178)	2⅛ (54)	

M	S	CC	LL	Weight (lbs.)
4⅞ (124)		#10-24		2¾
ρ½ (165)	⅝ (16)	¼-20	⅛/½ (3) (13)	3

TEST AND LOW PRESSURE DIAL GAUGES

POCKET TEST GAUGES WITH 3″ DIAL AND STAINLESS STEEL CASE

From
$119

To Order *(Specify Model Number)*

MODEL	PRICE	DIAL	RANGE	GRADUATIONS Figure Major	Minor
PGT-30L-15	$119	3″	0-15	1	0.1
PGT-30L-30	119	3″	0-30	2	0.2
PGT-30L-60	119	3″	0-60	5	0.3
PGT-30L-100	119	3″	0-100	10	1
PGT-30L-150	119	3″	0-150	10	1
PGT-30L-200	119	3″	0-200	20	2
PGT-30L-300	119	3″	0-300	20	2
PGT-30L-400	119	3″	0-400	50	2
PGT-30L-600	119	3″	0-600	50	5
PGT-30L-1000	119	3″	0-1000	100	10

◆ **HIGHLIGHTED MODELS STOCKED FOR FAST DELIVERY** ◆

- **Accuracy 0.5% Full Scale**
- **Ideal "Tool Box" Test Gauge**
- **All Stainless Steel Construction**

SPECIFICATIONS
Accuracy: 0.5% Full Scale
Case: Polished Stainless Steel
Dial: White Background with Mirrored Band
Pointer: Adjustable with Knife-Edge Tip
Movement: Stainless Steel
Element: 316 Stainless Steel
Connection. ¼″ NPT

LOW PRESSURE DIAPHRAGM GAUGES

✔ **Corrosion Resistant Bronze Diaphragm**
✔ **150% Overpressure Protection**
✔ **Recalibration Screw on Dial**
✔ **2-1-2 ANSI Grade A Accuracy**

SPECIFICATIONS
Dial Size: 2½″
Pointer: Black Aluminum
Movement: Brass
Element: Bronze Diaphragm
Connection: ¼″ NPT—Brass
Window: Polycarbonate

Model
PGL-25L-60
Shown

$33

To Order *(Specify Model Number)*

Dual Scale

MODEL	PRICE	RANGE Outer Scale	RANGE Inner Scale	GRADUATIONS Inner Scale Fig. Intervals	Inner Scale Minor Grad.	Outer Scale Fig. Intervals	Outer Scale Minor Grad.
PGL-25L-10	$33	0-10″ H$_2$O	—	1	0.1	—	—
PGL-25L-15	$33	0/15″ H$_2$O	0/9 oz/in^2	1	0.2	5	0.2
PGL-25L-35	33	0/35″ H$_2$O	0/20 oz/in^2	5	0.5	5	0.5
PGL-25L-60	33	0/60″ H$_2$O	0/35 oz/in^2	5	0.5	5	0.5
PGL-25L-100	33	0/100″ H$_2$O	0/60 oz^2	10	1	10	1
PGL-25L-160	33	0/160″ H$_2$O	—	20	2	—	—
PGL-25L-200	33	0/200″ H$_2$O	—	20	2	—	—
PGL-25L-300	33	0/300″ H$_2$O	—	50	5	—	—

OMEGA® TEST GAUGES   TYPE T
HIGH ACCURACY AND STAINLESS STEEL WETTED PARTS

- **High Accuracy–¼%**
- **Stem and Panel Mount**
- **Mirrored Scale**
- **316 SS Wetted Parts**
- **4½″ and 6″ Dial**

From
$227

The OMEGA® Test Gauge line consists of highly accurate gauges, designed for use in instrument shops, plants of all types, and laboratories throughout industry. Providing sustained accuracy to 0.25% full scale for most models. Performance, reliability and precision measurement are coupled with consistent accuracy in meeting the demanding service needs of numerous test gauge applications.

New 6″ Dial Models

Flush Mount

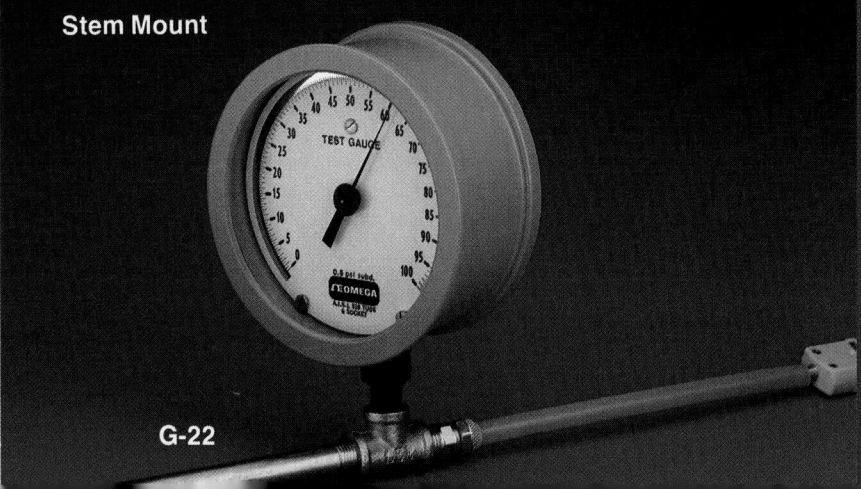
Stem Mount

G-22

TEST GAUGES—HIGH ACCURACY AND 316 STAINLESS STEEL WETTED PARTS

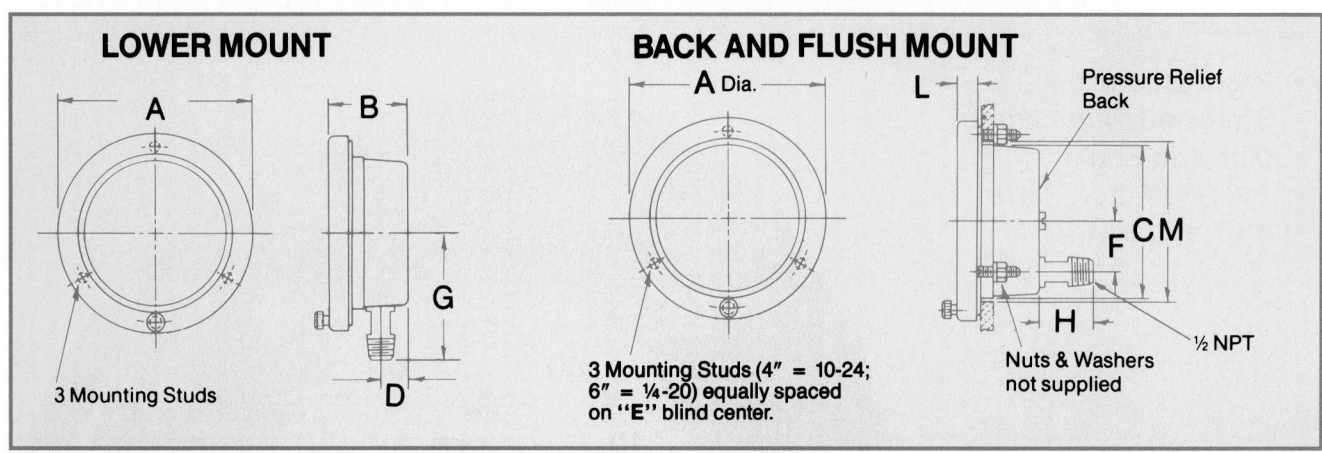

LOWER MOUNT

3 Mounting Studs

BACK AND FLUSH MOUNT

A Dia.

3 Mounting Studs (4" = 10-24; 6" = ¼-20) equally spaced on "E" blind center.

Pressure Relief Back

½ NPT

Nuts & Washers not supplied

Dial Size Inches	A	B	C	D	E	F	G	H	I	J	K	L	M
4½	6¹⁄₁₆ (154)	2⁹⁄₁₆ (65)	4¹³⁄₁₆ (122)	¹⁵⁄₁₆ (24)	5⅜ (129)	1⅝ (41)	3¹³⁄₁₆ (99)	1⅞ (48)	⅝ (16)	—	—	⅝ (16)	4⅞ (124)
6	7⁹⁄₁₆ (192)	2⁹⁄₁₆ (65)	6⁵⁄₁₆ (160)	¹⁵⁄₁₆ (24)	7 (178)	2⅛ (54)	4½ (114)	1⅞ (48)	⅝ (16)	—	—	⅝ (16)	6½ (165)

SPECIFICATIONS

Case: Solid Aluminum with Epoxy-coated Finish
Lower Connection: Green Finish
Back Connection: Black Finish
Window: Glass
Movement: Stainless Steel
Bourdon Tube: 316 Stainless Steel thru 3000 PSI; Monel, 5000 and 10,000 PSI ranges
Connection: 316 Stainless Steel
Fitting: ½" NPT
Dial Size: 4½" with White Background, black graduations and mirror band
Mounting: Stem: Lower Connection
 Panel or Stem: Back Connection
Accuracy: 0.25% FS
Ring: Lower Connection Model–Threaded Aluminum Back Connection Model–Mounting Flange With Hinged Cover Ring Secured By Knurled Screw
Safety Features: Solid Front With Pressure Relief Back
Temperature: 150°F (models will withstand continuous temperature up to 350°F, however, there will be discoloration of case and dial face)

The OMEGA Test Gauges are highly accurate gauges designed for use in instrument shops, plants of all types, and laboratories throughout industry. Performance, reliability, and precision measurement are coupled with consistent accuracy in meeting the demanding service needs of various test gauge applications such as for use as a master reference gauge, in test stand measurements, for production inspection, and for verifying accuracy of general service gauges. The dial has a stainless steel mirror ring for pointer reflection to prevent parallax error. This mirror surface reflects the pointer in any position and allows the gauge to be read with great accuracy. The lightweight, friction adjustable balanced pointer with knife edge tip, assures easy reading to the smallest subdivision. The accented dial graduations have a true width equivalent to 0.25 percent tolerance for quick and accurate gauge checking.

Warning: All gauge components should be selected considering media and ambient operating conditions to prevent misapplication. Improper application can be detrimental to the gauge, cause failure, and possible personal injury or property damage.

Ordering Example

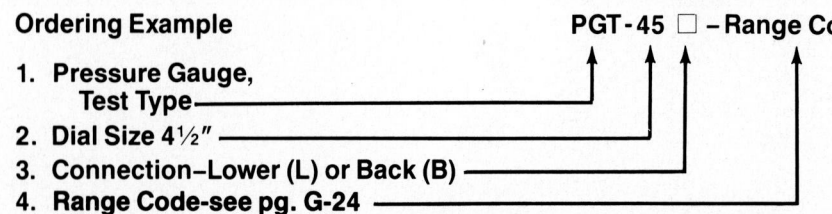

PGT-45 ☐ – Range Code

1. **Pressure Gauge, Test Type**
2. **Dial Size 4½"**
3. **Connection–Lower (L) or Back (B)**
4. **Range Code-see pg. G-24**

For Complete Listing of Stocked Test Gauges Refer to pg. G-24

TEST GAUGES 4½" AND 6" DIALS TYPE T

How To Order Type T — Test Gauges

Dial	Model	Connection	Vacuum to 1000 PSI	Price 1500 to 3000 PSI	5000 and 10000 PSI
4½"	PGT-45L-[*]	Lower	$227	$263	$297
	PGT-45B-[*]	Back	227	263	297
6"	PGT-60L-[*]	Lower	269	327	424
	PGT-60B-[*]	Back	269	327	424

Insert Range Code from table below.
Options: (Add suffix to part number)
-X6B Gauge cleaned for oxygen service, **$65**
Ordering Example: PGT-45B-300 Pressure Gauge, Test Type, 4½" Dial, Back Connection, 0/300 PSI, **$297.**
Precision test gauges cannot be oiled filled.

STYLE B

Standard PSI Ranges Type T

RANGE CODE	RANGE	FIGURE INTERVAL	MINOR GRADUATION
15	0/15	1	0.05
30	0/30	2	0.1
60	0/60	5	0.2
100	0/100	5	0.5
150	0/150	10	0.5
200	0/200	10	1
300	0/300	20	1
400	0/400	20	2
600	0/600	50	2
800	0/800	50	5
1000	0/1000(1)	50	5
1500	0/1500	100	5
2000	0/2000	100	10
3000	0/3000	200	10
5000	0/5000	500	10
10,000	0/10,000	1000	50
Vacuum			
30V	30/0" Hg	2" Hg	0.1" Hg
Compound			

Range Code	Range Inches Mercury	Range PSI	Figure Interval inches Hg	Figure Interval PSI	Minor Graduation inches Hg	Minor Graduation PSI
30V/15	30" Hg Vac/0/15 PSI		5	2	0.25	0.1
30V/30	30" Hg Vac/0/30 PSI		10	5	0.5	0.2
30V/60	30" Hg Vac/0/60 PSI		10	5	1	0.5
30V/100	30" Hg Vac/0/100 PSI		10	5	2	0.5
30V/150	30" Hg Vac/0/150 PSI		30	10	2	1
30V/200	30" Hg Vac/0/200 PSI		30	20	2	1
30V/300	30" Hg Vac/0/300 PSI		30	20	5	1
30V/400	30" Hg Vac/0/400 PSI		30	20	5	1

See page G-23 for special metric ranges.

STYLE L

◀ *HIGHLIGHTED MODELS STOCKED FOR FAST DELIVERY* ◀

SPECIAL METRIC RANGES
TYPE S AND TYPE T

TYPE S RANGE		DIAL GRADUATIONS		RANGE	DIAL GRADUATIONS		Outer Scale When Dual Range Specified PSI
kg/cm² (Kilograms per sq. cm.)	Bar	Figure Interval	Minor Graduation	kPa (Kilopascal)	Figure Interval	Minor Graduation	
Pressure							
0/1	0/1	0.1	0.01	0/100	10	1	0/14
0/1.6	0/1.6	0.2	0.02	0/160	20	2	0/22
0/2.5	0/2.5	0.5	0.05	0/250	50	5	0/35
0/4	0/4	0.5	0.05	0/400	50	5	0/55
0/6	0/6	0.5	0.1	0/600	50	10	0/85
0/10	0/10	1	0.1	0/1000	100	10	0/140
0/16	0/16	2	0.2	0/1600	200	20	0/220
0/25	0/25	5	0.5	0/2500	500	50	0/350
0/40	0/40	5	0.5	0/4000	500	50	0/550
0/60	0/60	5	1	0/6000	500	100	0/850
0/100	0/100	10	1	0/10,000	1000	100	0/1400
0/160	0/160	20	2	0/16,000	2000	200	0/2200
0/250	0/250	50	5	0/25,000	5000	200	0/3500
0/400	0/400	50	5	0/40,000	5000	500	0/5500
0/600	0/600	50	10	0/60,000	5000	500	0/8500
0/1000	0/1000	100	10	0/100,000	10,000	1000	0/14,000
Vacuum							
– 1/0	– 1/0	0.1	0.01	– 100/0 kPa	10	1	30/0″ Hg
Compound							
– 1/0/1.5	– 1/0/1.5	0.5	0.05	– 100/0/150 kPa	50	5	30″ Hg/0/20
– 1/0/3	– 1/0/3	0.5	0.05	– 100/0/300 kPa	50	5	30″ Hg/0/40
– 1/0/5	– 1/0/5	0.5	0.1	– 100/0/500 kPa	50	10	30″ Hg/0/70
– 1/0/9	– 1/0/9	1	0.1	– 100/0/900 kPa	100	10	30″ Hg/0/125
				– 100/0/1500 kPa	200	20	30″ Hg/0/215
				– 100/0/2400 kPa	500	20	30″ Hg/0/340

TYPE T RANGE		
kg/cm²	bar	kPa
Pressure		
0/1	0/1	0/100
0/1.6	0/1.6	0/160
0/2.5	0/2.5	0/250
0/4	0/4	0/400
0/6	0/6	0/600
0/10	0/10	0/1000
0/16	0/16	0/1600
0/25	0/25	0/2500
0/40	0/40	0/4000
0/60 (1)	0/60 (1)	0/6000 (1)
0/100	0/100	0/10,000
0/160	0/160	0/16,000
0/250	0/250	0/25,000
0/400	0/400	0/40,000
0/600	0/600	0/60,000
Vacuum		
–1/0	–1/0	–100/0
Compound		
–1/0/1.5	–1/0/1.5	–100/0/150
–1/0/3	–1/0/3	–100/0/300
–1/0/5	–1/0/5	– 100/0/500
–1/0/9	–1/0/9	–100/0/900

Ordering Special Ranges: Type S and T Custom Dials are available to fulfill the varying needs of our customers. There is a **$125 set-up fee and a 5 piece minimum order.**

See Pages G-10 to G-12 for Custom Dial Faces and Pricing.

BOURDON TUBE SELECTION MEDIA APPLICATION BASIS

Bourdon tube or bellows material

media application	brass or bronze	steel	AISI 316 stain. steel	monel	diaphragm seals **
Acetone			•	•	
Acetic Acid<40%			•		
Acetic Anhydride					•
Acetylene		•	•		
Acrolein					•
Air	•	•	•	•	
Alcohols	•		•	•	
Alkali Cleaners		•	•		
Alum. Chloride					•
Alum. Hydroxide					•
Alum. Sulfate<60%			•		
Ammonia Gas			•		
Ammonium Chloride					•
Ammonium Nitrate					•
Ammonium Sulfate					•
Aniline			•		
Argon	•	•	•	•	
Beer					•
Bauxite & Water			•		
Benzidine					•
Benzene				•	
Benzoic Acid					•
Black Liquor					•
Boric Acid					•
Brine				•	
Bromine					•
Butane	•	•	•	•	
Butyric Acid					•
Calcium Chloride					•
Calcium Hydroxide					•
Carbolic Acid			•		
Carbon Dioxide		•	•	•	
Carbon Monoxide		•	•	•	
Carbon Tet.			•		
Carbonated Water			•		
Caustic Soda					•
Caustic Potash					•
Cement Slurry					•
Chlorine Dioxide					•
Chlorine Dry				•	
Chlorine, Moist					•
Chloroform, Dry				•	

Bourdon tube or bellows material

media application	brass or bronze	steel	AISI 316 stain. steel	monel	diaphragm seals **
Chromic Acid					•
Cider			•		
Citric Acid			•		
Coffee			•		
Corn Oil			•		
Crude Oil (Sour)			•	•	•
Crude Oil (Sweet)			•	•	
Ethyl Acetate					•
Ethylene Oxide					•
Fatty Acids			•		
Ferric Chloride					•
Ferric Sulfate					•
Ferrous Chloride					•
Ferrous Sulfate					•
Fluorine Gas			•	•	
Formaldehyde			•		
Formic Acid					•
Freons	•	•	•	•	
Furfural					•
Gasoline	•		•		
Glycerine	•	•	•	•	
Hydrobromic Acid					•
Hydrochloric Acid					•
Hydrofluoric Acid					•
Hydrofluosilic Acid					•
Hydrogen ❷	•		•	•	
Hydrogen Peroxide					•
Hydrogen Sulphide (under 200°F)			•	•	
Hydroxy Acetic Acid					•
Kerosene	•	•	•	•	
Lacquers	•		•	•	
Lactic Acid					•
Linseed Oil			•	•	
Lime Water					•
Magnesium Chloride					•
Mercuric Chloride					•
Mercury			•	•	
Methylene Chloride					•
Milk			•		
Naphtha	•	•	•	•	
Naphthalene			•		
Nickel Chloride					•

Bourdon tube or bellows material

media application	brass or bronze	steel	AISI 316 stain. steel	monel	diaphragm seals **
Nitric Acid (75°F)			•		
Nitrogen	•	•	•		
Oleic Acid	•				
Oleum					•
Oxalic Acid					•
Oxygen ❶	•		•		
Palmitic Acid			•		
Perchloric Acid					•
Phosphoric Acid					•
Photographic Bleach			•		
Picric Acid					•
Propane	•	•	•	•	
Quinine					•
Rochelle Salt					•
Sea Water				•	
Silicate Solution			•	•	
Silver Nitrate					•
Soap			•		
Sodium Bicarbonate			•	•	
Sodium Bisulfate					•
Sodium Carbonate			•		
Sodium Chromate					•
Sodium Cyanide			•		
Sodium Phosphate			•		
Sodium Sulfide					•
Steam	•	•	•		
Stearic Acid			•		
Sulfur Chloride					•
Sulfur Dioxide					•
Sulfur Trioxide					•
Sulfuric Acid					•
Sulfurous Acid					•
Tall Oil					•
Tannic Acid			•	•	•
Tartaric Acid			•		
Tin Chloride					•
Toluene	•	•	•	•	
Turpentine			•	•	
Varnish		•	•	•	
Water	•		•	•	
Whisky			•		
Zinc Chloride					•
Zinc Sulphate<30%			•		

❶ Bronze and AISI 316 stainless steel are acceptable for oxygen service, provided the gauge has been cleaned for oxygen service and is free from oil.

❷ Over 1000 PSI — entire system must be AISI 316 stainless steel.

** Any standard Bourdon tube or bellows material may be used in conjunction with a diaphragm seal (with bellows use a Viton diaphragm) but the selection should take into consideration the corrosive environment in which it is to operate.

DIAPHRAGM PRESSURE SEALS
FOR ASSURED PROTECTION AND MEDIA COMPATIBILITY

Shown with
Model PGH-45L-200
Process Gauge

From
$170

- **Protects Pressure Instrumentation From Corrosive or Viscous Fluids, Clogging, and In-line Freezing of the Process Media**
- **Glycerine Fill Fluid is Standard, With Optional Fill Fluids Available**
- **Displacement of the Liquid Fill in the Pressure Seal Through Movement of the Diaphragm Transmits Process Pressure Directly to the Pressure Instrumentation**

OMEGA® Diaphragm Pressure Seals afford greater protection to sensitive pressure instrumentation from the damaging effects of corrosives, slurries, or viscous fluids that may be present in your pressure line. A variety of designs and styles are available to suit your application requirements.

100 Series

Distinguished by its 3-part design, the 100 series include a Teflon® coated diaphragm capsule which threads into the top housing assuring positive sealing at all surfaces and minimizes the possibility of any leakage of the filling fluid from the system.
The diaphragm capsule can be replaced without replacing the top housing. Continuous duty is assured, should the sensor be removed from the diaphragm seal, the process fluid is prevented from escaping. Easy cleaning and inspection of the diaphragm can be achieved during shutdown conditions by detaching the top and bottom housings. This design eliminates the need to refill the seal or recalibrate the instrument when the top and bottom housings are separated. A viton O-ring, compatible with all standard fill fluids, and a Teflon® back-up ring makes a seal between the diaphragm capsule and the top housing. The diaphragm is teflon coated to provide.an integral gasket, thus assuring a leaktight connection between the diaphragm and bottom housing. The 100 Series consists of a diaphragm capsule with a corrugated, metallic diaphragm edge welded to a sturdy back-up plate which threads into the top housing, once secured the top housing can be bolted to the bottom housing. The bottom housing has a standard ½" NPT fitting which easily threads to the process piping.

102 Series

Virtually identical to the 100 Series in both performance and design, the 102 Series includes a standard #150 raised face flange in place of a threaded female NPT process fitting. For more rugged applications an optional #300 raised face flange is also available.

302 Series

The 302 Series diaphragm seal includes both a Teflon® diaphragm and a teflon #150 raised face flange. This all teflon wetted construction provides both ruggedness and maximum corrosion resistance to acids, caustics, alkalies, ketones, hydrocarbons, and alcohols. All model 302 diaphragm seals include a top housing and diaphragm which are of the non-removable type. This non-removable designation means that a loss of fill fluid will result if the top housing is removed from the flange bottom housing.

OMEGA Diaphragm Pressure Seals are available to be used in conjunction with the following OMEGA pressure instrumentation:
- Pressure Transducer PX620 Series
- Dial Pressure Gauges PGH, PGJ, PGT Series
- Pressure Switches PSW-300, PSW-350, PSW-400 Series

MADE IN
USA

100 Series

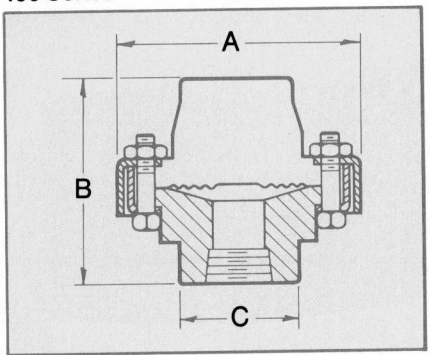

A		B		C	
in.	mm	in.	mm	in.	mm
3¾	95	2⅞	73	1¹³⁄₁₆	46

102 Series

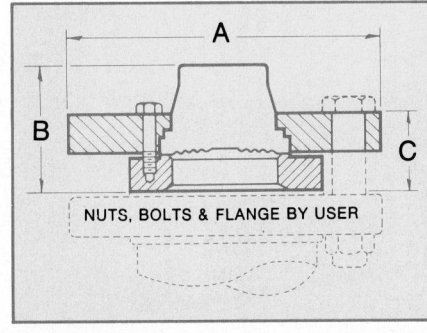

NUTS, BOLTS & FLANGE BY USER

FLANGE		A		B		C	
Size	Rating #	in.	mm	in.	mm	in.	mm
1½″	150	5	127	2⅜	61	1½	38
	300	6¼	159			1½	38
2″	150	6	152	1¹⁵⁄₁₆	49	1⅜	35
	300	6½	165			1½	38

302 Series

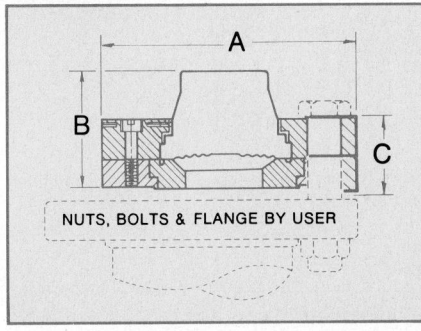

NUTS, BOLTS & FLANGE BY USER

FLANGE		A		B		C	
Size	Rating #	in.	mm	in.	mm	in.	mm
1″	150	4¼	100	2³⁄₁₆	56	1⅜	35
1½″	150	5	127	2⁵⁄₁₆	59	1¹³⁄₃₂	39
2″	150	6	152	2⅛	54	1⁹⁄₁₆	40

SPECIFICATIONS

Pressure: 15 to 2500 PSIG and vacuums greater than 30″ Hg; #150 flanges to 150 PSI, #300 flanges to 300 PSI

Temperature: See fill solution temperature range

NOTES:

1) PVC maximum 200 PSI @ 74°F, 125 PSI @ 125°F, 80 PSI @ 150°F

2) #150-RF Teflon flange maximum 150 PSI @ 150°F

Please Note: When diaphragm seals are connected to pressure instrumentation slight shifts in calibration will result. OMEGA recalibrates the instrument with the seal attached to negate calibration shifts. Please allow additonal lead time when ordering.

Ordering Examples:

1) PGT-45L-100/1-100-PM-½-CG
OMEGA test gauge and diaphragm seal with 1″ NPTF process connection. All Monel wetted parts and glycerine fill solution.

PGT-45L-100	**$227**
1-100-PM-½-CG	365
Total	**$592**

2) PG-45L-100/2-102-PM-½-CK-300-RF
OMEGA test gauge with 2″ #300 raised face flange diaphragm seal. All Monel wetted parts and silicone solution.

PGT-45L-100	**$227**
2-102-PM-½-CG-300-RM	
($365 + 35 + 70 + 50)	520
Total	**$747**

To Order *(Specify As Ordering Suffix to Pressure Instrument Model Number)*

ORDERING SUFFIX	PRICE	WETTED MATERIALS	
		DIAPHRAGM	BOTTOM HOUSING
½-100-SS-½-CG	**$275**	316L SS	316SS
½-100-PM-½-CG	365	K-Monel	Monel 400
½-100-GG-½-CG	865	Hastelloy B	Hastelloy B
½-100-HH-½-CG	865	Hastelloy C	Hastelloy C
½-100-SV-½-CG	190	316L SS	PVC (1)

▲ The 100 Series is available with ¼″, ½″, ¾″, 1″ process fittings at no additional charge. Please change the ordering suffix accordingly.

1½-102-SS-½-CG-150-RF	285	316L SS	316SS
1½-102-PM-½-CG-150-RF	365	K-Monel	Monel 400
1½-102-GG-½-CG-150-RF	585	Hastelloy B	Hastelloy B
1½-102-HH-½-CG-150-RF	585	Hastelloy C	Hastelloy C

▲ The 102 Series is available with a 2″ process connection, add $70. For a # 300-RF flange, add $50. Please change the ordering suffix accordingly.

1-302-TT-½-CG-150-RF	270	Teflon with 1″ process conn. (2)
1½-302-TT-CG-150-RF	320	Teflon with 1½″ process conn.(2)
2-302-TT-CG-150-RF	335	Teflon with 2″ process conn.(2)

Fill Solutions

TYPE	TEMP. RANGE	CODE	PRICE	USAGE
Glycerine	0 to 400°F	CG	**STD**	Gage Pressure
Silicone	−40 to 600°F	CK	$35	Gage/Vacuum Pressure
Halocarbon	−70 to 300°F	CF	35	Gage/Vacuum Pressure in Presence of Strong Oxidizing Agents (Oxygen, Chlorine, etc.)

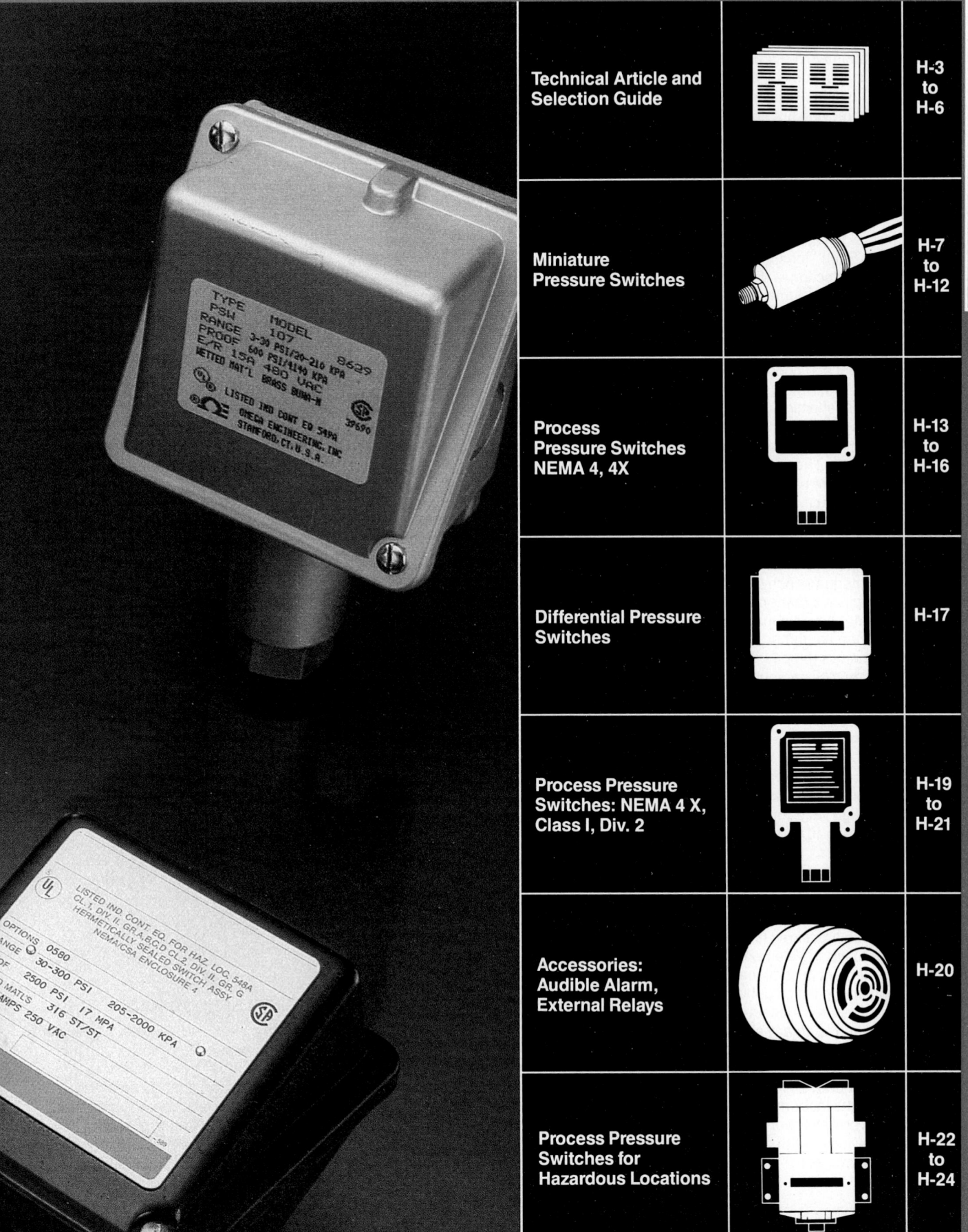

Technical Article and Selection Guide		H-3 to H-6
Miniature Pressure Switches		H-7 to H-12
Process Pressure Switches NEMA 4, 4X		H-13 to H-16
Differential Pressure Switches		H-17
Process Pressure Switches: NEMA 4 X, Class I, Div. 2		H-19 to H-21
Accessories: Audible Alarm, External Relays		H-20
Process Pressure Switches for Hazardous Locations		H-22 to H-24

PRESSURE CONTROL
AND EXPLOSION PROOF ENCLOSURES

Pressure controls may either (1) control—maintain the pressure of gas, liquid or solid at some specified value, or they may (2) limit — sensing that pressure is moving out of some safe range, alarm or shut down the malfunctioning equipment responsible for this deviation.

PRESSURE

Pressure is defined as the "force per unit area". Such "forces" always produce a deflection, a distortion, or some change in volume or dimension no matter how small or large the force. It is this resulting change to a sensing element that provides the basic measurement and controlling movement for pressure instruments. The proportional deflection of a sensing element may be used in a pressure controller to trip an electrical switch at a given pressure. The switch in the controller may be used, for example, to actuate and deactuate a compressor as needed to maintain a process pressure at a predetermined value.

The most common units of pressure are pounds per square inch (PSI), inches of water column in a manometer (WC), or inches of mercury in a manometer (Hg). The most popular metric unit of measurement is Kilopascal (Kpa). Pressure must be measured with respect to a given reference pressure, but is most commonly atmospheric pressure at sea level or absolute zero pressure.

Pressure is one of the most important industrial process variables, stretching from ultra high vacuum to positive pressures up to 10,000 PSI and above.

1. PRESSURE SENSING

The most important component of any instrument used to measure and/or control these pressures is the sensing/measuring element. It is this sensing element in combination with an opposing spring which determines the range of pressures measured and the sensitivity and accuracy of the measurement. The particular sensing element chosen also determines the overall ruggedness, life expectancy, size and cost of the instrument. OMEGA utilizes several styles of pressure sensing devices — the diaphragm, piston, bellows, and hi proof/low set diaphragm.

DIAPHRAGMS

OMEGA utilizes both flat and convoluted elastomer diaphragms (such as Buna N and Teflon®). The diaphragm is a deflecting mechanism that is installed with a back-up plate. When pressure is applied at the lower part, the diaphragm and plate will deflect, acting against a load spring which determines the range and basic sensitivity.

Diaphragms used on controls may sense pressures within 30″ Hg Vacuum to 6000 PSI. They feature a large effective area, hence, large forces, which make possible the sensing of low pressures with a relatively low cost mechanism. Teflon diaphragms combine economic corrosion resistance to many media with sensitivity to deflect with small pressure changes. As with bellows, the load spring is interchanged for altering ranges and sensitivities. The spring remains unchanged, except for vacuum service, where it is reversed.

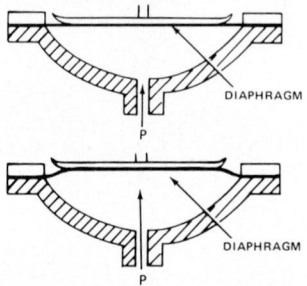

BELLOWS

A metallic bellows is a cylindrical element, generally closed at one end, with several deep folds or convolutions which expand or contract when subjected to pressure. They are commonly used for measuring vacuum (30″ Hg) and positive pressures up to 500 PSIG. The bellows material may be brass, phosphor bronze, or stainless steel, depending on the pressure range desired, sensitivity, corrosion resistance and cost area considered. Most controls are furnished with bellows elements. Since bellows life is increased when the axial travel is kept to a minimum, a load spring is employed to oppose this movement. A change in the load spring will change the range and sensitivity of the control.

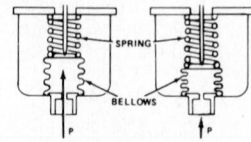

PISTON

A piston is designed for high pressure operation, for example, on hydraulic pressures up to 10,000 PSI. They are usually manufactured with a stainless steel smooth, piston rod that moves against a load spring to produce measurable movement. An O-ring is employed to seal the piston housing from the medium. The higher the pressure applied to the piston, the greater the O-ring squeezes the piston rod, and the less sensitive the pressure measurement/control device will be as pressure increases. The overall range of the piston sensor is determined by the selection of load spring opposing the piston movement. As with bellows and diaphragm elements, the load spring, acting against the piston, determines the range.

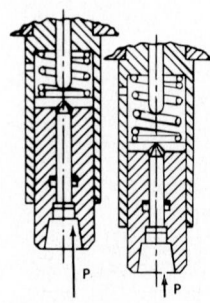

HI PROOF/LO SET

The hi-proof/lo set sensor assembly combines the sensitivity of a diaphragm with the ruggedness and high-proof pressures of a piston. It is designed for applications where low setpoints and high over-pressures up to 2500 PSI are anticipated.

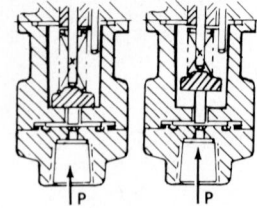

2. FROM SENSOR TO SWITCH

Once the pressure has been sensed and turned to measurable movement, this movement must be transferred to the actuating device, such as an on-off switch. For this function, a rod connects the bellows, diaphragm, or piston with the switch plunger. The plunger then moves to actuate or de-actuate the switch.

NEMA ENCLOSURE RATINGS

A setpoint can be obtained by threading in (higher setting) or out (lower setting) the plunger tip; or by positioning the switch(es) in relation to the plunger. The further away the switch is from the sensor plunger, the more the plunger must travel, and hence the higher the setting.

For "Force Balance" products, the setpoint adjustment positions an opposing spring that restricts the sensor movement until the pressure approaches the setpoint.

For models with knob/dial calibrations, the switch may be positioned in relationship to the sensor. Also, because a load spring usually opposes the movement of a bellows, diaphragm, or piston sensor, the moving of an adjustment thread or knob changes the amount of this spring tension against the sensor. If we increase the setting, we have increased the spring tension and hence the sensor requires a greater pressure to actuate the switch at the new setpoint.

3. THE SWITCH

The movement from the sensor actuates an electrical signal by changing the position of electrical contacts in a switch. The final component required for a simple pressure control device is the electric snap switch (on-off action). Most OMEGA controls utilize a Single Pole Double Throw (SPDT) switch. Such switches may be wired to either make or break an electrical circuit — they have both normally open, and normally closed. When wired normally open, the circuit is open when the switch is not actuated. When wired normally closed, the circuit is closed when the switch is not actuated.

Electric snap switches consist of a snap-acting mechanism built into a molded case. A lever is spring formed to provide positive snap action when the actuating plunger drives the lever to the transfer point. A quality switch has a beryllium copper lever with a silver contact tip that transfers from one stationary contact to the other. When the actuating force is relieved, the lever snaps back to its normal position.

Electric switches transfer a signal in response to the movement of the mechanical sensors covered in the preceding pages. Switches allow us to actuate a warning light (if lube oil pressure is falling), actuate a vacuum pump (if pressure is falling), and many other similar functions. In short, we can "make something happen" in response to our sensors.

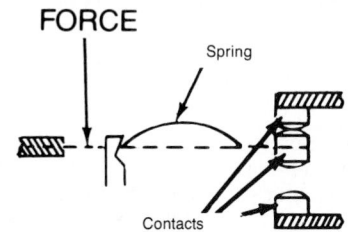

FORCE

Spring

Contacts

AN EXPLANATION OF NATIONAL ELECTRIC MANUFACTURING ASSOCIATION (NEMA) ENCLOSURES

TYPE NO. 4 Watertight & Dust-tight — An enclosure intended for indoor use to protect the enclosed control against splashing water, seepage of water, falling or hose-directed water, and severe external condensation. These enclosures have provision for watertight connectors and provisions for mounting external to the enclosure cavity.

TYPE NO. 4× Watertight, Dust-tight & Corrosion-Resistant - Same as Type 4 with Corrosion-Resistant construction.

EXPLOSION-PROOF ENCLOSURES

MEANING OF EXPLOSION-PROOF: Explosion-Proof means that the enclosure must be strong enough to withstand any internal pressures caused by an explosion and tight enough to prevent the issuance of flames. Explosion-proof does not mean that the equipment has to be gas tight. This is not feasible as any time the enclosure has to be opened the explosive atmosphere could enter the apparatus. It is in Class 1 locations only that explosion-proof electrical equipment is required.

HAZARDOUS LOCATIONS: These are defined by the National Electrical Code (ART. 500) as follows:

CLASS I: A location in which flammable gases or vapors exist in quantities sufficient to render the resultant atmosphere explosive or ignitable.

DIVISION I: Locations where hazardous concentrations of flammable gases or vapors exist:
1. Continuously, intermittently or periodically under normal conditions.

2. Exists frequently because of repair or maintenance operation or because of leakage.
3. Exists due to breakdown or faulty operation of equipment or processes, which might also cause simultaneous failure of electrical equipment.

DIVISION II: Locations in which flammable volatile liquid or flammable gases are handled, processed or used, but in which the hazardous liquids, vapors or gases will normally be confined within closed containers or closed systems from which they can escape only in case of accidental rupture or breakdown of such containers or systems or in case of abnormal operation of equipment.

GROUP A: Atmosphere containing Acetylene.

GROUP B: Atmospheres containing Hydrogen or gases or vapors of equivalent hazard such as Manufactured gas.

GROUP C: Atmospheres containing Ethyl-ether vapors, ethylene or cyclo-propane.

GROUP D: Atmospheres containing gasoline, petroleum, naptha, alcohols, acetone lacquer solvent and natural gas.

CLASS II: Location that is hazardous due to a quantity of combustible dust sufficient to explode if in suspension in the air or where an accumulated quantity of dust on electrical apparatus may cause apparatus to overheat and therefore cause a fire or explosion.

GROUP E: Atmospheres containing metal dust.

GROUP F: Atmospheres containing carbon black, coal or coke dust.

GROUP G: Atmospheres containing flour, starch or grain dusts.

CLASS III: Locations are those which are hazardous because of the presence of easily ignitable fibers or flyings are not likely to be in suspension in air in quantities sufficient to produce ignitable mixtures.

DIVISION I: Locations in which easily ignitable fibers or materials producing combustible flying are handled, manufactured or used.

DIVISION II: Locations in which easily ignitable fibers are stored or handled (except in process of manufacture).

PRESSURE SWITCH APPLICATION GUIDE

SERIES	PAGE	PRICE	RANGES	WETTED PARTS	FEATURES/APPLICATIONS
PSW-520 PSW-530 PSW-540 PSW-550	H-7	$74	Vacuum to 500 PSI	7-4PH, 303 SS, Buna-N O-ring on 5 Amp models	Miniature pressure switch able to handle a wide variety of media from vacuum to 500 PSI. Externally adjustable setpoint with locking ring, and fixed deadband. Available with 5A silver or 1A gold plated SPDT contacts.
PSW-560 PSW-570	H-8	$116	500 to 6000 PSI	17-4PH, 303 SS, Buna-N O-ring on 5 Amp models	Miniature pressure switch able to handle a wide variety of media from 500 to 6000 PSI. Externally adjustable setpoint with locking ring, and fixed deadband. Available with 5A silver or 1A gold plated SPDT contacts.
PSW-190	H-9	$68	10 to 3000 PSI	Buna-N, Brass, and stainless steel	General purpose pressure switch with slotted adjustment screw under sliding cover. Single setpoint, adjustable range, fixed deadband, and weather resistant construction. 5A SPDT contact rating with ½" NPTM conduit fitting.
PSW-800	H-10	$77	Vacuum to 7500 PSI	Buna-N, Brass, and stainless steel	General purpose pressure switch with ranges from vacuum to 7500 PSI. Features a simple external setpoint adjustment with locking set screw, and high overpressure rating. 5A SPDT contact rating with 1/2" NPTF conduit fitting.
PSW-170 PSW-180	H-11	$25	PSW-170, 1 to 68 PSIG PSW-180 1 to 45 PSID	Polyurethane, Brass, Buna-N, and Polysulphone	Miniature snap action pressure switches for gage (PSW-170) or differential (PSW-180) pressure. PSW-170 has ⅛" NPT or ⅛" hose barb, push on terminal wiring or PC board mounting and 4A SPDT contact rating. PSW-180 has NEMA-4 enclosure, terminal block wiring and 5A SPDT contact rating.
PSW-580	H-12	$30	Vacuum to 500 PSI	Buna-N, Aluminum, Zinc Alloy with Chromate Finish	Economical OEM type pressure switch. Externally adjustable setpoint with reference scale, fixed deadband, and screw terminal connections. UL rated heavy duty 15A SPDT switch standard.
PSW-100	H-13	$67	Vacuum to 3000 PSI	Buna-N, Brass, 316 SS, 303 SS, Phospher Bronze	General purpose pressure switch with internal reference scale and adjustable lock. Single setpoint, adjustable range, fixed or adjustable deadband, NEMA-4 die cast aluminum enclosure, diaphragm, bellows and piston type. 15A SPDT switch on a wide range selection.

SERIES	PAGE	PRICE	RANGES	WETTED PARTS	FEATURES/APPLICATIONS
PSW-300	H-15	$189	Vacuum to 3000 PSI	Buna-N or 316 SS	NEMA-4X watertight pressure switch for harsh or corrosive environments. Single or dual setpoint, adjustable range, fixed or adjustable deadband, and epoxy coated aluminum enclosure. 10A or 15A SPDT switch on a wide range selection.
PSW-350	H-17	$325	5" H$_2$O to 400 PSID	Buna-N or 316 SS	NEMA-4X watertight differential pressure switch for harsh or corrosive environments with a high static pressure rating. Single or dual setpoint, adjustable range, fixed or adjustable deadband, in an epoxy coated aluminum enclosure. 10A or 15A SPDT switch on a wide range selection.
PSW-150	H-18	$130	0 to 90 PSID	Brass, Phosphor Bronze, or 316 SS	General purpose differential pressure switch. Ideal for laboratory or industrial applications. Single setpoint, adjustable range, fixed deadband, cast aluminum enclosure. 15A SPDT switch rating on a wide range selection.
PSW-200	H-19	$199	Vacuum to 1700 PSI	Buna-N & 304 SS or 316 SS	Hermetically sealed pressure switch for Division 2 hazardous locations with internal reference scale and adjustable lock. Single setpoint, adjustable range, fixed deadband, rugged one piece epoxy coated aluminum body. BUNA-N or SS diaphragm for positive pressure, phospher bronze bellows for vacuum. 5A SPDT switch. Meets NEMA-4, 4X, and 9G classifications.
PSW-370	H-21	$345	5" H$_2$O to 3000 PSID	Teflon or Stainless Steel	NEMA-4X pressure switch for harsh environments with internal reference scale. Designed for industrial applications. Dual setpoint, adjustable range, fixed deadband, stainless steel construction, stainless steel or Teflon diaphragm. Two 15A SPDT switches on a wide range selection.
PSW-700	H-22	$360	Vacuum to 500 PSI	Brass for vacuum, or 316 SS for pressure	Heavy duty explosion-proof bellows type pressure switch with external setpoint dials. Ideal for division 1 hazardous locations. Dual setpoints, adjustable range, fixed deadband, cast aluminum enclosure rated for NEMA-4, 7 and 9 classifications. Two 15A SPDT switches on a wide range selection.
PSW-400	H-23	$364	Vacuum to 3000 PSI	Buna-N or 316 SS	Industrial pressure switch with dual chamber design for use in division 1 hazardous locations. Single or dual setpoint, adjustable range, fixed or adjustable deadband, epoxy coated aluminum enclosure. Meets NEMA 7 and 9 classifications. 10A or 15A SPDT switch on a wide range selection.

MINIATURE PRESSURE AND VACUUM SWITCHES

PSW-500 SERIES

From
$74

✔ **External Pressure Scale and Pointer for Easy Setpoint Adjustments**

✔ **5 Amp Model Switches With High Proof Pressures**

✔ **1 Amp Gold Plated Switches for TTL and Dry Contact Closures**

✔ **Stainless Steel Construction**

Shown Larger Than Actual Size

MODELS IN STOCK FOR FAST DELIVERY!

To Order *(Specify Model Number)*

MODEL	PRICE	ADJUSTABLE RANGE (PSIG)		DEADBAND (PSIG)	REPEATABILITY (PSI)	MAX. SYSTEM PRESSURE (PSI)*	SWITCH
		DECREASING	INCREASING				
PSW-521	$74	0.8 to 28.5	1.6 to 30	0.8 to 1.3	±0.6	30	1 AMP
PSW-522	74	2.0 to 48.0	3.0 to 50	1.0 to 1.7	±1.0	50	1 AMP
PSW-523	74	3.0 to 96.5	4.5 to 100	1.5 to 3.5	±2.0	100	1 AMP
PSW-524	74	7.5 to 242.5	9.7 to 250	2.2 to 9	±5.0	250	1 AMP
PSW-525	74	15 to 485	20 to 500	5.0 to 21	±10	500	1 AMP
PSW-531	110	0.5 to 16.3	1.2 to 20	0.6 to 3.7	±0.8	3000	5 AMP
PSW-532	110	0.5 to 42.5	1.4 to 50	0.8 to 7.5	±2.0	3000	5 AMP
PSW-533	110	1.2 to 91	3.0 to 100	1.1 to 9.0	±4.0	3000	5 AMP
PSW-534	110	3.0 to 222	5.0 to 250	2.2 to 28	±10	3000	5 AMP
PSW-535	110	6.0 to 432	9.0 to 500	3.5 to 68	±20	3000	5 AMP
MODEL	PRICE	ADJUSTABLE RANGE (IN. HG)		DEADBAND (IN. HG)	REPEATABILITY (IN. HG)	MAX. SYSTEM PRESSURE (IN. HG VAC/PSIG)*	SWITCH
		DECREASING	INCREASING				
PSW-541	$74	1.6 to 27.0	2.7 to 28.2	1.3 to 2.7	±1.2	28.2"Hg/0 PSIG	1 AMP
PSW-542	74	4.0 to 24.8	5.1 to 28.2	1.5 to 3.2	±2.0	28.2"Hg/0 PSIG	1 AMP
PSW-543	74	6.0 to 21.5	8.4 to 28.2	2.0 to 7.3	±4.0	28.2"Hg/0 PSIG	1 AMP
PSW-551	110	1.2 to 22.5	2.2 to 28.2	1.1 to 5.7	±1.6	29.9"Hg/3000 PSIG	5 AMP
PSW-552	110	1.2 to 21.8	2.7 to 28.2	1.4 to 6.4	±8.0	29.9"Hg/5000 PSIG	5 AMP

Exceeding these values may cause a shift in the set point.
Comes with complete operator's manual.
Ordering Example: *PSW-525 is a gage model switch for maximum system pressure of 500 PSI, **$74**.*

Shown Larger Than Actual Size

✔ **External Pressure Scale in PSI**
✔ **Pointer for Easy Setpoint Adjustments**
✔ **Heavy Duty Overpressure Protection**

**PSW-560 AND PSW-570 SERIES
PERFORMANCE TABLE**

MODEL	NOMINAL SETPOINT (PSI)	DEAD BAND 1 AMP/5AMP	REPEATABILITY (±PSI)
PSW-561 **PSW-571**	500	70/120	25
	1000	80/130	50
	1500	90/145	75
	2000	100/160	100
	2500	110/180	125
	3000	125/200	150
PSW-562 **PSW-572**	600	113/186	45
	1000	145/220	60
	1500	190/262	85
	2000	235/305	100
	2500	280/345	125
	3000	325/385	150
	3500	364/430	175
	4000	410/470	200
	5000	410/470	250
PSW-563 **PSW-573**	700	177/455	65
	1000	210/620	75
	1500	247/730	85
	2000	300/820	100
	3000	315/980	150
	4000	340/1000	200
	5000	355/1110	250
	6000	375/1280	300

SPECIFICATIONS

Approvals: UL (1 Amp switches PSW-520 and PSW-540 Series only)

Process Temp.: -65 to 225°F (-55 to 106°C) (2% setpoint shift can occur below -10°F or above 125°F)

Cycling: Not to exceed 20 cycles/min.

Warranty: 3 year/1 million cycles

Sensor: Piston (PSW-520 and 540 diaphragm)

Proof Pressure: 150% max. system pressure (PSW-530 and 550 proof pressure is the max. system pressure)

Wetted Parts: PSW-520 and 540 Series: 17-7 pH SS, 303 SS and loctite sealing compound #271; PSW-530 and 550 Series: 303 SS, 316 SS, Buna-N O-ring, loctite #271; PSW-560 and 570 Series: 17-7 PH SS, 303SS, Buna-N O-ring, and loctite #271

Enclosure: Body: 303 SS; internal switch housing and lock ring: zinc alloy chromate finish; cap: black valox

Dimensions: 2¹³⁄₁₆" L x 1⅛" dia. (71 x 28 mm)

(PSW-520 and PSW-540: 2⅝" L x ¹³⁄₃₂ " dia. [66 x 27 mm])

Pressure Port: ⅛-27 NPT

Electrical Connection: 20 AWG, three polyvinyl insulated, unjacketed, 12" pigtail leads

Wiring Code: Black is common, white is N.C., red is N.O.

Weight: 4 oz (113 g); PSW-520 and PSW-540 series 3 oz (85 g)

To Order (Specify Model Number)

1 AMP MODEL	5 AMP MODEL	PRICE	ADJUSTABLE RANGE (PSIG) DECREASING	ADJUSTABLE RANGE (PSIG) INCREASING	MAX. SYSTEM PRESSURE (PSIG)	PROOF PRESSURE (PSIG)
PSW-561	**PSW-571**	$116	500 to 2800	500 to 3000	3000	4500
PSW-562	**PSW-572**	116	600 to 4500	600 to 5000	5000	7500
PSW-563	**PSW-573**	116	700 to 5500	700 to 6000	6000	9000

Exceeding these values may cause a shift in the set point.

SWITCH RATING

MAX. RATING	AC/DC	VOLTS RESISTIVE	AMPS	AMPS INDUCTIVE CONTACTS
1 AMP SPDT	115/28	1/1	1/0.5	GOLD**
5 AMP SPDT	250/28	5/5	5/3	SILVER

***Use gold contacts for dry and TTL circuitry, ex. 5 Vdc @ 50 mA or less.*

Caution: Pressure switches are manufactured to the highest quality specifications. However, due to their economical construction, they should be used only for applications where, in the event of product failure, the risk of damage to equipment or personnel would be minimized.

3 YEAR WARRANTY
MADE IN USA

ECONOMICAL CYLINDRICAL PRESSURE SWITCH
PSW-190 SERIES

 **1 YEAR** WARRANTY

 **MADE IN USA**

Shown Larger Than Actual Size

From $68

The PSW-190 cylindrical pressure switch has an epoxy sealed electrical termination. This rugged design enables the switch to withstand harsh environments.

SPECIFICATIONS

Switch: SPDT, 5 amps at 250 Vac or 30 Vdc gold clad silver contacts for loads down to 5 mA at 6 Vdc, 2 mA at 12 Vdc and 1 mA at 24 Vdc

Operating Ambient Range: 0 to160°F (−18 to 77°C) with Buna-N construction; 0 to 180°F (−18 to 82°C) with Viton construction.

Media Temp: 160°F with Buna-N sensor. 250°F with Viton sensor

Wetted Parts: Brass, O-ring, and diaphragm

Repeatability:
PSW-191,192,195 and 196: ±1%
PSW-193,194,197 and 198: ±1.5%

Shock: Setpoint repeats after 50G's 10 msec duration

Vibration: Setpoint repeats after 10G's, 5-500CPS

Enclosure and Cover: Aluminum with irrate finish rated for 100 hr salt spray; potted and gasketed for outdoor use

Pressure Connection:
PSW-191,192,195 and 196: ⅛ NPT
PSW-193,194,197 and 198 ¼ NPT

Weight: 6.5 oz (128 g)

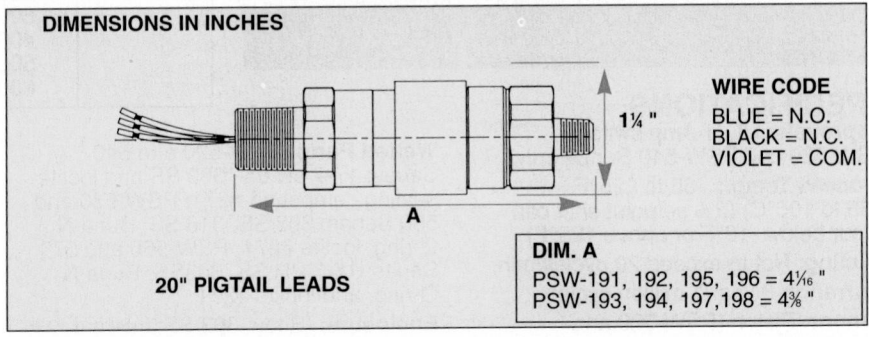

DIMENSIONS IN INCHES

1¼ "

WIRE CODE
BLUE = N.O.
BLACK = N.C.
VIOLET = COM.

A

20" PIGTAIL LEADS

DIM. A
PSW-191, 192, 195, 196 = 4¹⁄₁₆ "
PSW-193, 194, 197,198 = 4⅜ "

HIGHLIGHTED MODELS STOCKED FOR FAST DELIVERY!

To Order (Specify Model Number)

MODEL	PRICE	ADJUSTABLE RANGE	TYPICAL DEADBAND	PROOF PRESSURE	SWITCH
Models with Buna-N O-Ring and Diaphragm					
PSW-191	$68	10-150 PSI	2-70	3000	5A SPDT
PSW-192	68	30-600 PSI	8-40	3000	5A SPDT
PSW-193	68	100-1500 PSI	20-160	5000	5A SPDT
PSW-194	68	180-3000 PSI	50-280	5000	5A SPDT
Models with Viton O-Ring and Diaphragm					
PSW-195	$80	10-150 PSI	2-70	3000	5A SPDT
PSW-196	80	30-600 PSI	8-40	3000	5A SPDT
PSW-197	80	100-1500 PSI	20-160	5000	5A SPDT
PSW-198	80	180-3000 PSI	50-280	5000	5A SPDT

Comes with complete operator's manual.

Ordering Example: *PSW-192 is a cylindrical pressure switch with a Buna-N O-ring diaphragm and an adjustable range of 30 to 600 PSI,* **$68.**

GENERAL PURPOSE PRESSURE SWITCHES
FOR VACUUM TO 7500 PSI

  **MADE IN USA**  **NEW!**

PSW-800 Series
$77

- ✔ **Easy Adjustment with Locking Set Screw**
- ✔ **Rugged Industrial Design**
- ✔ **Standard ½" Female Conduit Fitting for Electrical Termination**

The PSW-800 Series are economical pressure switches which feature an easy to adjust setpoint with locking set screw. They utilize a sealed piston or diaphragm-piston design, which is ideally suited for harsh environments. All models come with 12" color coded leads and a ½" female conduit fitting for electrical connections.

SPECIFICATIONS
Set Point Repeatability:
Diaphragm Models: (PSW-801 to PSW-807): ±1% of span
Piston Models: (PSW-808 to PSW-811): ±1.5% of span
Hysteresis/Deadband:
See ordering matrix
Contact Rating: 5 amp max @ 125/250 Vac
Temp. Range: 0 to 165°F (-18 to 74°C) (vacuum range) -20 to 165°F (-29 to 74°C) (500 PSI and below); -40 to 165° F (-40 to 74°C) (600 PSI and above)
Thermal Effects: < 1% for 50°F change
Proof Pressure: See To Order chart
Burst Pressure: Two times proof pressure
Sensor Type: PSW-801 to PSW-807, diaphragm piston; PSW-808 to PSW-811, sealed piston
Wetted Parts:
500 PSI and below: brass, Buna-N
600 PSI and above: brass, Buna-N and stainless steel
Pressure Port: ¼" NPT male
Electrical Connection: 12" free leads with ½" female conduit fitting
Housing: Open type plastic housing
Weight: 0.95 lb (0.4 kg)

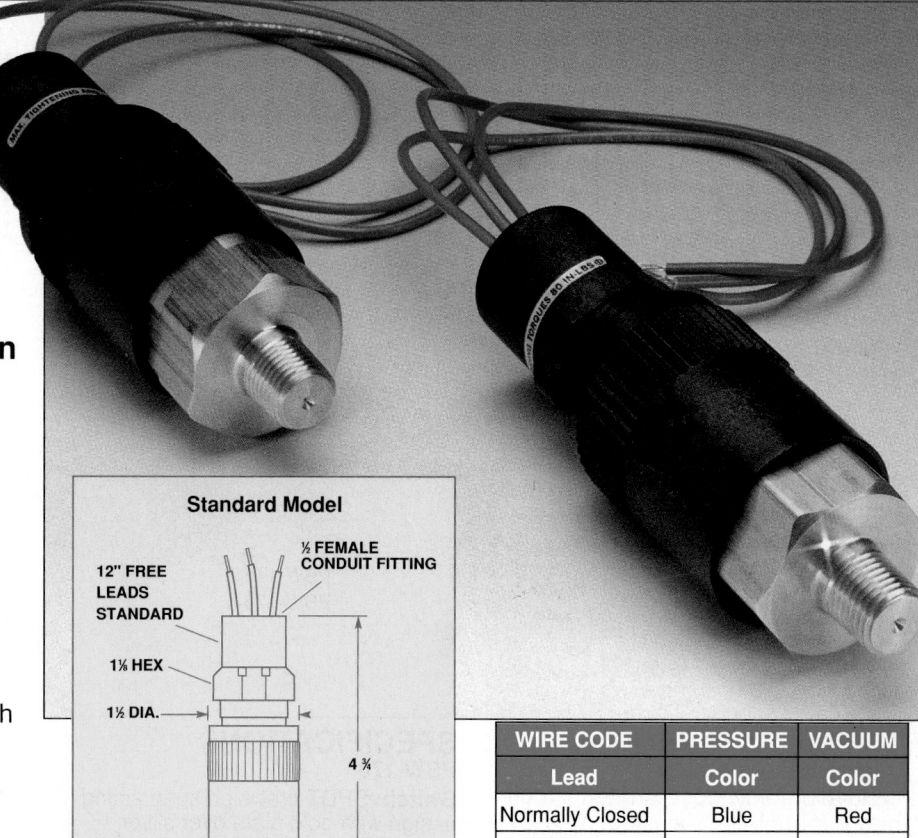

Standard Model

½ FEMALE CONDUIT FITTING
12" FREE LEADS STANDARD
1⅛ HEX
1½ DIA.
4 ¾
1¼ HEX
¼ NPR MALE PRESSURE PORT
DIMENSIONS IN INCHES

WIRE CODE	PRESSURE	VACUUM
Lead	Color	Color
Normally Closed	Blue	Red
Common	Purple	Purple
Normally Open	Red	Blue

HIGHLIGHTED MODELS IN STOCK FOR FAST DELIVERY!

To Order *(Specify Model Number)*

Model Number	Price	Increasing Min	Increasing Max	Decreasing Min	Decreasing Max	Dead Band Range	Proof Pressure
VACUUM MODELS (In. Hg)							
PSW-801	$77	1	28	4	30	1 to 4	30 PSI
GAGE PRESSURE MODELS (PSIG)							
PSW-802	77	2.5	12.8	3	15	.5 to 2.2	1000 PSI
PSW-803	77	5	31	6	35	1.0 to 4.0	1000 PSI
PSW-804	77	8.5	44	10	50	1.5 to 6.0	1000 PSI
PSW-805	77	22.5	112	25	125	2.5 to 13	1000 PSI
PSW-806	77	70.0	220	50	250	10 to 30	1000 PSI
PSW-807	77	110	440	130	500	20 to 60	1000 PSI
PSW-808	77	190	450	250	600	60 to 150	7000 PSI
PSW-809	77	360	1450	430	1700	70 to 250	7000 PSI
PSW-810	77	1450	3900	1650	4400	200 to 500	7000 PSI
PSW-811	77	3650	6700	4000	7500	350 to 800	12000 PSI

Pressure Setting Range spans the Increasing and Decreasing columns.

Comes with complete operator's manual.
***Ordering Example:** PSW-804 is a 10-50 PSI pressure switch with 1.5 to 6.0 PSI deadband range and 1000 PSI proof pressure, $77.*

ECONOMICAL GAGE AND DIFFERENTIAL PRESSURE SWITCHES

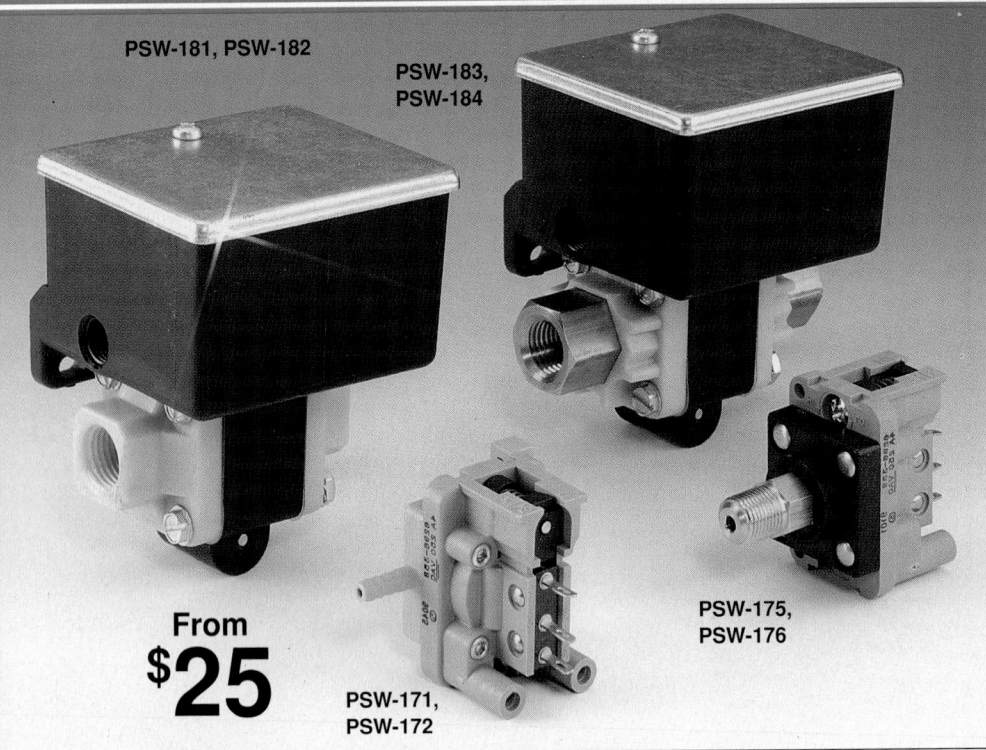

PSW-181, PSW-182

PSW-183, PSW-184

From $25

PSW-171, PSW-172

PSW-175, PSW-176

Operating Ambient Range: -20 to 130°F (-29 TO 54°C)

Max Media Temp: 140°F at 105 PSI, 160°F at 80 PSI max

Adjustment: Multi turn screw

Weight: 1.2 ounces with barb; 1.6 ounces with barb

PSW-180

Switch: SPDT rated at 5 amp at 250/125 Vac , 5 amps at 30 Vdc, gold clad contacts

Audible Alarm: Internal 9 Vdc battery powered, continuous tone 85dB

Repeatability: 1% of span

Ambient Temperature:
  Storage: -20 to 180°F (-29 to 82°C)
  Operating: 30 to 160°F (-1 to 71°C)

Max Media Temp: 200°F at 100PSI

Vibration: MIL STD 810C, 2.5G's 5-500CPS

Shock: 15G's, 10 msec duration.

System Operating Temp: 0-150 PSIG at up to 160°F air temperature

Working Differential Pressure: 0-150 PSID at up to 160°F air temperature

Diff Proof Pressure: 150 PSID at up to 160°F air temperature

Enclosure: NEMA-4, reinforced polyester body, zinc plated steel cover with neoprene gasket, terminal block wiring

Adjustment: multi-turn screw, accessible from outside enclosure

Pressure Port Choice:
¼ NPTF brass
¼ NPSF polysulfone

Weight: 6.5 oz (165 g)

The PSW-170 Series miniature gage pressure switch is a lightweight, low cost, printed circuit board mountable device in a small package. The PSW-170 is available with NPT or barbed pressure ports. The PSW-180 Series differential pressure switch offers a blend of small size, excellent performance and environmental protection. The PSW-180 is available with switch contacts or as an audible alarm.

SPECIFICATIONS
PSW-170

Switch: SPDT precision snap acting design with gold plate over silver contacts.Contact rating 4 amps at up to 250 Vac amps resistive, 3 amps inductive at 30 Vdc.

Terminals: 0.11" push-on; PC board insertible

Proof Pressure: 125 PSI

Burst Pressure: 160 PSI at 130°F (54°C) media temp, 130 PSI at 145°F (63°C)

To Order (Specify Model Number) — HIGHLIGHTED MODELS IN STOCK FOR FAST DELIVERY!

1/8" BARB POLYESTER	PRICE	1/8" NPT BRASS	PRICE	ADJUSTABLE RANGE (PSI) ON FALL MIN.	MAX.	ON RISE MIN.	MAX.	SWITCH	TYPICAL DEADBAND
PSW-170 SERIES MINIATURE PRESSURE SWITCH									
PSW-171	$25	PSW-175	$30	1	10	1.5	11	4A SPDT	0.8
PSW-172	25	PSW-176	30	6	65	8	68.5	4A SPDT	3.8

1/4" NPSF POLYSULFONE	PRICE	1/4" NPTF BRASS	PRICE	ADJUSTABLE RANGE (PSID) ON FALL MIN.	MAX	ON RISE MIN.	MAX.	SWITCH	TYPICAL DEADBAND
PSW-180 SERIES DIFFERENTIAL PRESSURE SWITCH									
PSW-181	$75	PSW-183	$80	1.0	9.0	2.0	10.0	5A SPDT	0.75
PSW-182	75	PSW-184	80	4.0	43.5	5.5	45.0	5A SPDT	1.0
PSW-180 SERIES WITH INTERNAL AUDIBLE ALARM									
PSW-185	$85	PSW-187	$90	1.0	9.0	2.0	10.0	N/A	0.75
PSW-186	85	PSW-188	90	4.0	43.5	5.5	45.0	N/A	1.0

Comes with complete operator's manual.

Ordering Example: *PSW-181 differential pressure switch with polysulfone process connection, $75.*

ECONOMICAL OEM PRESSURE SWITCH

PSW-580 Series

$30

✔ **External Scale for Easy Set Point Adjustments**

✔ **UL Rated Heavy Duty 15 AMP SPDT Switch Standard**

SPECIFICATIONS

Switch: 15 Amp SPDT silver contacts
Approvals: UL
Process Temp.: -31 to 185°F (-35 to 85°C) 2% set point shift can occur below -10°F or above 125°F
Proof Pressure: 600 PSIG
Cycling: Not to exceed 60 cycles/min
Warranty: 3 years/1 million cycles
Sensor: Aluminum diaphragm
Wetted Parts: Buna N, aluminum, zinc alloy chromate finish, and loctite sealing compound #271
Enclosure: Switch actuator and bracket steel irridite finish; adjusting cap and body zinc alloy chromate finish; switch shield mylar
Pressure Port: ¼" NPT male
Electrical Conn.: Screw terminals
Size: 3⅝" H x 2⅜" W x 1⅝" Dia.
Weight: 7.4 oz (210 grams)

Caution: Pressure switches are manufactured to the highest quality specifications. However, due to their economical construction, they should be used only for applications where in the event of product failure, the risk of damage to equipment or personnel would be minimized.

The PSW-580 Series comes with complete operator's manual.

Shown Larger Than Actual Size

HIGHLIGHTED MODELS STOCKED FOR FAST DELIVERY!

To Order *(Specify Model Number)*

MODEL	PRICE	ADJUSTABLE RANGE	DEADBAND	REPEATABILITY	PROOF PRESSURE
PSW-581	$30	6 to 28 in Hg 1.5 to 3.5 PSIG	3 to 14 in Hg 0.5 to 1.7 PSIG	±1.2 in Hg ±0.15 PSIG	29.9 in Hg 600 PSIG
PSW-582	30	3 to 40 PSIG	2 to 5 PSIG	±1.0 PSIG	600 PSIG
PSW-583	30	30 to 150 PSIG	5 to 30 PSIG	±5.0 PSIG	600 PSIG
PSW-584	30	100 to 500 PSIG	30 to 120 PSIG	±20 PSIG	600 PSIG

Comes with complete operator's manual.
Ordering Example: *PSW-582 is an economical pressure OEM pressure switch with an adjustable range of 3 to 40 PSIG and 600 PSIG proof pressure, $30.*

GENERAL PURPOSE PRESSURE SWITCHES
NEMA-4 ENCLOSURE

RANGE 30-300 PSI / 205-2000 KPA
PROOF 2500 PSI / 172 MPA
E/R 15A 480 VAC
WETTED MAT'L 316 S/S
(UL) LISTED IND CONT EQ 549A

Model PSW-121

- **Ranges From 3 to 3000 PSI**
- **SPDT Switch Output**
- **Internal Reference Scales and Adjustment Lock**
- **Safe, Easy Wiring Access**

Omega's affordable, general purpose pressure switches offer distinct advantages over most similar style switches, including calibrated reference scales and DPDT or adjustable deadband switches, as well as a wide selection of adjustable ranges from 3 to 3000 psi.

From
$80

Gasketed Cover
Long Life Switch
Vibration Resistant Set Point and Scale
Rugged NEMA-4 Enclosure

SPECIFICATIONS
Approval: UL listed, CSA certified
Storage Temp: −65 to +160°F
Process Temp: SS 0-160°F; Buna-N 0-150°F
Ambient Temperature: −40 to +160°F, (except models PSW-107 to 117; 0 to 160°F). Setpoint typically shifts less than 1% of range for a 50°F (28°C) ambient temperature change.
Shock: Set point repeats after 15G, 10ms duration
Vibration: Set point repeats after 2.5G, 5-500 CPS
Enclosure: NEMA 4 Classification
Set Point Repeatability: PSW-107 to 117 and 129 to 131 ±1% of adjustable range; PSW118 to 129 and 132 to 133 ±1.5% of adjustable range
Switch Output: 1 SPDT. Switch may be wired "normally open" or "normally closed"
Electrical Rating: Std. 15 amp 125/250/480 V ac Resistive
External Manual Reset: 15A 125/250 V ac Resistive
Double Pole Double Throw: 10A 125/250 V ac Resistive
Enclosure: Die Cast Aluminum, (max. 0.06% copper). Light grey aluminum lacquer finish, gasketed
Weight: Approximately 2 lb
Electrical Connection: ½″ NPT, (2) 7/8″ diameter knockouts
Pressure Connection: ¼ NPTF (except Models 118 to 126 ½″ NPTF).

2 YEAR WARRANTY — **MADE IN USA**

To Order *(Specify Model Number)*

MODEL	PRICE	ADJUSTABLE RANGE ENGLISH	ADJUSTABLE RANGE METRIC	DEAD BAND ENGLISH UNITS	PROOF PRESSURE	SWITCH	ADDED FEATURE
Buna-N Diaphragm, "O" Ring and ¼" NPTF Brass Pressure Connection							
PSW-107	$ 80	3 to 30 PSI	20 to 210 kPa	1. to 2. PSI	600 PSI	15A SPDT	—
PSW-108	80	10 to 100 PSI	70 to 675 kPa	1. to 4. PSI	600 PSI	15A SPDT	—
PSW-109	135	10 to 100 PSI	70 to 675 kPa	—	600 PSI	15A SPDT	External Manual Reset
PSW-110	175	10 to 100 PSI	70 to 675 kPa	4. to 10. PSI	600 PSI	10A DPDT	DPDT Switch
PSW-111	130	10 to 100 PSI	70 to 675 kPa	3 to 7 PSI	600 PSI	15A SPDT	Adjustable Deadband
PSW-112	80	30 to 300 PSI	205 to 2000 kPa	1. to 5. PSI	600 PSI	15A SPDT	—
PSW-113	130	30 to 300 PSI	205 to 2000 kPa	4 to 11 PSI	600 PSI	15A SPDT	Adjustable Deadband
PSW-114	80	50 to 500 PSI	340 to 3400kPa	2 to 8 PSI	2500 PSI	15A SPDT	—
PSW-115	130	50 to 500 PSI	340 to 3400 kPa	5 to 12 PSI	2500 PSI	15A SPDT	Adjustable Deadband
PSW-116	135	50 to 500 PSI	340 to 3400kPa		2500 PSI	15A SPDT	External Manual Reset
PSW-117	105	100 to 1000 PSI	0.7 to 6.89 MPa	3. to 20. PSI	2500 PSI	15A SPDT	—
316SS Diaphragm and ½" NPTF Pressure Connection							
PSW-118	120	5 to 30 PSI	42 to 210 kPa	1. to 3. PSI	2500 PSI	15A SPDT	—
PSW-120	120	10 to 100 PSI	70 to 675 kPa	3. to 5. PSI	2500 PSI	15A SPDT	—
PSW-121	120	30 to 300 PSI	205 to 2000 kPa	3. to 6. PSI	2500 PSI	15A SPDT	—
PSW-123	180	30 to 300 PSI	205 to 2000 kPa	4 to 11 PSI	2500 PSI	15A SPDT	Adjustable Deadband
PSW-124	120	50 to 500 PSI	340 to 3400 kPa	4. to 7. PSI	2500 PSI	15A SPDT	—
PSW-125	120	200 to 1700 PSI	1.35 to 11.7 MPa	10. to 25. PSI	2500 PSI	15A SPDT	—
Phospher Bronze Bellow and ¼" NPTF Brass Pressure Connection							
PSW-127	90	30" Hg Vac to 0	−100 to 0 kPa	1 to 2" Hg	30 PSI	15A SPDT	—
PSW-128	190	30" Hg Vac to 0	−100 to 0 kPa	3 to 6.5" Hg	30 PSI	10A DPDT	DPDT Switch
PSW-129	120	20 to 200 PSI	140 to 1350 kPa	1 to 4. PSI	250 PSI	15A SPDT	—
316 SS Bellows and ½" NPTF Pressure Connection							
PSW-130	175	20 to 200 PSI	140 to 1350 kPa	1 to 3. PSI	250 PSI	15A SPDT	—
PSW-131	175	50 to 500 PSI	340 to 3400 kPa	1.5 to 5. PSI	575 PSI	15A SPDT	—
PSW-132	205	100 to 1700 PSI	7 to 11.7 MPa	9 to 23. PSI	2500 PSI	15A SPDT	—
303SS Piston and ¼" NPTF Pressure Connection with Buna-N O-Ring							
PSW-133	155	200 to 3000 PSI	1.4 to 20 MPa	40 to 180. PSI	10000 PSI	15A SPDT	—

Oxygen Clean: Option "X6B" -SS models only, add $35.

HIGHLIGHTED MODELS STOCKED FOR FAST DELIVERY

NEMA 4X WATERTIGHT PRESSURE SWITCH
FOR HARSH OR CORROSIVE ENVIRONMENTS

PSW-300 Series

- **Low Pressure Ranges 30″ Hg Vac to 150″ H₂0**
- **High Pressure Ranges 15 to 3000 PSI**
- **Buna-N or 316SS Diaphragm**
- **IOA SPDT Switch**
- **Tamper/vibration resistant setpoint adjustment 20 to 100% range**
- **Fixed or Adjustable deadband**

Ideal for use in harsh and corrosive environments, the PSW-300 Series Pressure Switches feature stainless steel or Buna-N diaphragm-sealed piston or diaphragm actuators that provide repeatability of ±1% of range. Standard design allows easy access to switches. For versatility, single setpoint with fixed deadband, single setpoint with adjustable deadband or dual independently adjustable setpoints may be chosen.

Corrosion Resistant NEMA 4X Enclosure

Watertight Neoprene Gasket

Wiring Diagram

¾″ NPT Conduct Connection

Screw Terminals

Easy to Ready Setpoint Scale

Setpoint Adjustment

SPECIFICATIONS
Approval: UL listed, CSA certified
Storage Temp: −20 to 150°F
Ambient Temp. Limits: −20 to 150°F. Set point typically shifts ±1% of range per 50°F of temperature change.
Enclosure: NEMA, 4X watertight and corrosion resistant
Setpoint Repeatability: ±1% of range
Switch Output: 1 or 2 SPDT switch may be wired "normally open" or "normally closed"
Electrical Rating: 10 A: 125/250 V ac; 0.5 A, 125 V dc, 0.25 A. 250 V ac, 15 A: 125/250 Vac
Enclosure: Epoxy coated aluminum, gasketed
Weight: 2 lb
Electrical Connection: ¾ NPT female
Pressure Connection: ¼ NPT female; for vacuum to 600 PSI: ½″ NPT Male/¼ NPT female for 1000 and 3000 PSI
Connection Material: Vac through in. H₂0 ranges; carbon steel: All PSI ranges; 316SS
Oxygen Service: Specify Option X6B for special cleaning.

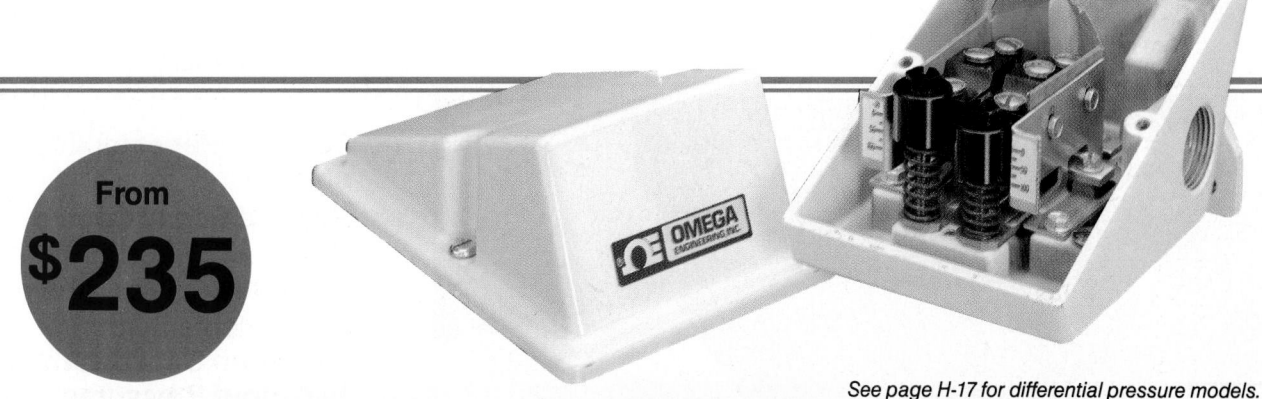

From
$235

See page H-17 for differential pressure models.

To Order *(Specify Model Number)*

MODEL	PRICE	ADJUSTABLE RANGE		DEAD BAND ENGLISH UNITS	PROOF PRESSURE	SWITCH
		ENGLISH	**METRIC**			
Single Set Point, Adjustable Deadband Buna-N Diaphragm, O-Ring, ¼ NPTF Connection						
PSW-301	$235	−6 to −30 IN Hg Vac	−20 to −100kPa	6 to 24	250 PSI	10A SPDT
▶ PSW-302	235	6 to 30 IN H₂0	1.5 to 7.5 kPa	4 to 27	20 PSI	10A SPDT ◀
PSW-303	235	12 to 60 IN H₂0	3 to 15 kPa	5 to 54	20 PSI	10A SPDT
▶ PSW-304	235	30 to 150 IN H₂0	7.4 to 37 kPa	18 to 135	20 PSI	10A SPDT ◀
PSW-305	205	3 to 15 PSI	20 to 100 kPa	2.5 to 13	500 PSI	10A SPDT
PSW-306	205	6 to 30 PSI	40 to 200 kPa	3 to 18	500 PSI	10A SPDT
▶ PSW-307	205	20 to 100 PSI	140 to 700 kPa	10 to 90	1000 PSI	10A SPDT ◀
PSW-308	205	40 to 200 PSI	280 to 1400 kPa	18 to 180	1000 PSI	10A SPDT
PSW-309	205	80 to 400 PSI	.56 to 2.8 MPa	45 to 360	2400 PSI	10A SPDT
PSW-310	260	200 to 1000 PSI	1.4 to 7 MPa	160 to 900	12000 PSI	10A SPDT
PSW-311	260	600 to 3000 PSI	4.2 to 21 MPa	400 to 2600	12000 PSI	10A SPDT
Dual Set Point, Fixed Deadband Buna-N Diaphragm, O-Ring and ¼ NPTF Connection						
PSW-321	$265	−6 to −30 IN Hg Vac	−20 to −100kPa	.7 to 1.4	250 PSI	TWO 15A SPDT
PSW-322	265	6 to 30 IN H₂0	1.5 to 7.5 kPa	.7 to 1.4	20 PSI	TWO 15A SPDT
PSW-323	265	12 to 60 IN H₂0	3 to 15 kPa	.7 to 1.8	20 PSI	TWO 15A SPDT
PSW-324	265	30 to 150 IN H₂0	7.4 to 37 kPa	2.1 to 4.2	20 PSI	TWO 15A SPDT
PSW-325	230	3 to 15 PSI	20 to 100 kPa	.7 to 1.4	500 PSI	TWO 15A SPDT
▶ PSW-326	230	6 to 30 PSI	40 to 200 kPa	.7 to 2.1	500 PSI	TWO 15A SPDT ◀
▶ PSW-327	230	20 to 100 PSI	140 to 700 kPa	1.4 to 3.5	1000 PSI	TWO 15A SPDT ◀
PSW-328	230	40 to 200 PSI	280 to 1400 kPa	1.4 to 5.6	1000 PSI	TWO 15A SPDT
PSW-329	230	80 to 400 PSI	.56 to 2.8 MPa	6 to 11	2400 PSI	TWO 15A SPDT
PSW-330	285	200 to 1000 PSI	1.4 to 7 MPa	10 to 42	12000 PSI	TWO 15A SPDT
PSW-331	285	600 to 3000 PSI	4.2 to 21 MPa	42 to 98	12000 PSI	TWO 15A SPDT
Dual Set Point, Fixed Deadband 316SS Diaphragm, and ¼ NPTF						
PSW-345	$290	3 to PSI	20 to 100kPa	.7 to 1.4	500 PSI	TWO 15A SPDT
PSW-346	290	6 to 30 PSI	40 to 200 kPa	1.7 to 2.8	500 PSI	TWO 15A SPDT
PSW-347	290	20 to 100 PSI	140 to 700 kPa	2.8 to 5.6	1000 PSI	TWO 15A SPDT
PSW-348	290	40 to 200 PSI	280 to 1400 kPa	4.2 to 11.2	1000 PSI	TWO 15A SPDT

ressure Switch Options:
(Add Suffix to Part Number) Hermetically Sealed 5A 125/250 Vac Switch for Extra Protection in Severe Environments.
-P Single Set Point **$75.00**
-PP Dual Set Point **$150.00**
316 Stainless Steel Welded Pressure Activator -S 15 to 600 PSI, **$54.00**

NEMA 4X DIFFERENTIAL PRESSURE SWITCH

MADE IN
USA

PSW-350 Series

- ✔ **Setpoint Repeatability of ±1%**
- ✔ **Rugged Epoxy Coated NEMA 4X Watertight Enclosure**
- ✔ **Dependable Switch Actuation Between the Two Input Pressures**
- ✔ **High Static Pressure**

From
$350

▶ *HIGHLIGHTED MODELS STOCKED FOR FAST DELIVERY* ◀

To Order *(Specify Model Number)*

Model	Price	Adjustable Range	Deadband English Units	Static Working Pressure	Proof Pressure	Switch
Single Setpoint, Adjust. Deadband, Buna-N Diaphragm and O-Ring, ¼ NPTF						
PSW-351	$350	5 to 30" H_2O	4 to 27	5.4 PSI	21.6 PSI	10A SPDT
PSW-352	350	9 to 60" H_2O	5 to 54	5.4 PSI	21.6 PSI	10A SPDT
PSW-353	350	15 to 100" H_2O	8.5 to 90	5.4 PSI	21.6 PSI	10A SPDT
PSW-354	350	23 to 150" H_2O	18 to 135	5.4 PSI	21.6 PSI	10A SPDT
PSW-355	405	5 to 30 PSID	3 to 27	500 PSI	2000 PSI	10A SPDT
PSW-356	405	9 to 60 PSID	5 to 54	500 PSI	2000 PSI	10A SPDT
PSW-357	405	30 to 200 PSID	18 to 180	1000 PSI	4000 PSI	10A SPDT
PSW-358	405	60 to 400 PSID	45 to 360	1000 PSI	8000 PSI	10A SPDT
Dual Setpoint, Fixed Deadband, Buna-N Diaphragm and O-Ring, ¼ NPTF						
PSW-361	$375	5 to 30" H_2O	0.7 to 1.4	5.4 PSI	21.6 PSI	15A SPDT*
PSW-362	375	9 to 60" H_2O	0.7 to 2.0	5.4 PSI	21.6 PSI	15A SPDT*
PSW-363	375	15 to 100" H_2O	1.4 to 2.8	5.4 PSI	21.6 PSI	15A SPDT*
PSW-364	375	23 to 150" H_2O	2.4 to 4.2	5.4 PSI	21.6 PSI	15A SPDT*
PSW-365	430	5 to 30 PSID	1.0 to 2.1	500 PSI	2000 PSI	15A SPDT*
PSW-366	430	9 to 60 PSID	1.4 to 2.8	500 PSI	2000 PSI	15A SPDT*
PSW-367	430	30 to 200 PSID	1.4 to 5.6	1000 PSI	4000 PSI	15A SPDT*
PSW-368	430	60 to 400 PSID	5.6 to 11	1000 PSI	8000 PSI	15A SPDT*

Two switches.

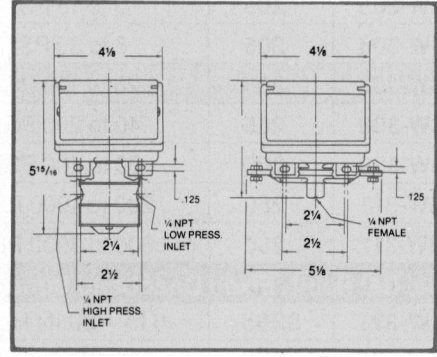

SPECIFICATIONS

See page H-11 for additional specifications.

Process Fluid: 0 to 150°F Buna-N and Teflon® diaphragms; 20 to 300°F for Viton® diaphragms

Pressure Connection: ¼ NPTF; brass plated carbon steel for PSID ranges; carbon steel for H_2O ranges.

Options:

Ordering Suffix	Add'l. Cost	Description
-Viton	$35	Viton diaphragm and O-ring
-Teflon	35	Teflon diaphragm and O-ring
-SS	60	SS Diaphram (PSI Units Only)

GENERAL-PURPOSE DIFFERENTIAL PRESSURE SWITCH

PSW-150 Series

✔ **15 Amp SPDT**
✔ **Easy Adjustments**
✔ **Vibration Resistant Setpoints**

From

$170

The PSW-150 Series differential switches are ideally suited for laboratory and industrial applications where a rugged, repeatable, and dependable switch is required. For ease of installation ports are tagged high and low, and the setpoint adjusts over the entire range.

SPECIFICATIONS

Approvals: UL listed
Repeatability: ±1% range
Ambient Switch Shift: 0.02% range/°F
Storage Temp.: −65 to 165°F
Ambient Switch Temp.: −40 to 160°F
Process Temp.: Brass, 250°F; phosphor bronze, 250°F; 316SS, 500°F
Shock: Setpoint repeats after 1.5 *g* at 10 ms duration
Vibration: setpoint repeats after 2.5 at 5-500 Hz
Output: (1) SPDT, 15 Amp 125/250/480 Vac
Enclosure: Cast aluminum, gray enamel finish
Electrical: ⅞″ Dia. conduit port, screw terminals
Pressure Port: ¼ NPTF
Weight: 2 lbs

Model PSW-153 Shown

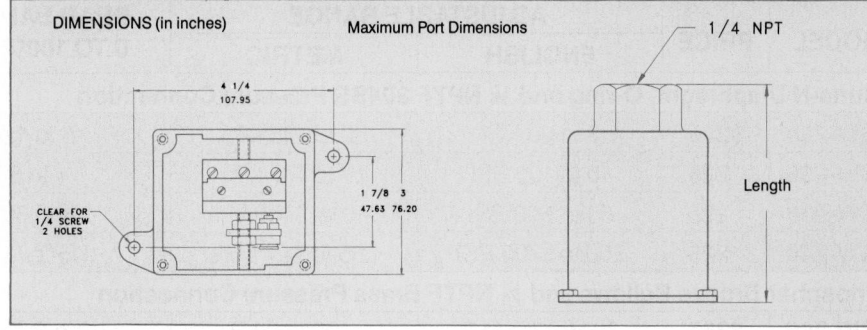

DIMENSIONS (in inches)   Maximum Port Dimensions

▶HIGHLIGHTED MODELS STOCKED FOR FAST DELIVERY!◀

To Order *(Specify Model Number)*

Model	Price	Pressure Range	Length	Deadband	Proof Pressure	Static Pressure	Bellows Materials
▶PSW-151	$225	0-6 PSID	2.54	0.1 to 0.4	6 PSI	30″ Hg Vac to 30 PSI	Brass
▶PSW-152	180	0-25 PSID	1.81	0.6 to 1.0	25 PSI	30″ Hg Vac to 110 PSI	Phospho Bronze
▶PSW-153	235	0-40 PSID	2.54	0.3 to 0.7	40 PSI	30″ Hg Vac to 180 PSI	Brass
▶PSW-154	265	0-70 PSID	1.94	2.0 to 4.0	70 PSI	30″ Hg Vac to 350 PSI	316SS
▶PSW-155	170	0-90 PSID	1.88	2.0 to 4.0	90 PSI	30″ Hg Vac to 200 PSI	Phospho Bronze

PRESSURE SWITCH PSW-200 SERIES
FOR HARSH INDUSTRIAL ENVIRONMENTS

MADE IN USA

From
$225

PSW-200 Series

- ✓ **Rugged One Piece Epoxy Coated Aluminum body**
- ✓ **Meets NEMA 4, 4X, 9G Classifications**
- ✓ **UL Listed: CSA Certified**
- ✓ **Stainless Steel Nameplate**
- ✓ **Internal Reference Scale With Adjustable Lock**
- ✓ **Hermetically Sealed Switch**

Approvals:
UL Listed
Class 1 Division 2, Groups
A, B, C, D
Class II Groups G
Class III CSA Certified

SPECIFICATIONS

Approvals: UL listed, CSA certified
Storage Temperature: −65 to 160°F
Ambient Temperature Limits: −40 to 160°F, except Models PSW-234-240, 0 to 160°F. Setpoint typically shifts less than 1% of range for a 50°F ambient temperature change.
Shock: Setpoint repeats after 15G, 10ms duration
Vibration: Setpoint repeats after 2.5G. 5 to 500 CPS
Enclosure Classification: NEMA 4, 4X
Setpoint Repeatability: PSW-234-240, PSW-241-245 ±1.5% of adjustable range.

Switch Output: Hermetically sealed. 1 SPDT. Switch may be wired "normally open" or "normally closed"
Electrical Output: 5A 125/250 V ac resistive
Enclosure: Die cast aluminum, epoxy coated, gasketed
Weight: 2 lb
Electrical Connection: ½" NPT (2) 7/8" diameter knockouts
Pressure Connection: ¼ NPTF except models PSW-241-245 ½" NPT

To Order *(Specify Model Number)*

MODEL	PRICE	ADJUSTABLE RANGE		DEAD BAND FIXED 0 TO 100% RANGE		PROOF PRESS	SWITCH*
		ENGLISH	METRIC				
Buna-N Diaphragm, O-ring and ¼ NPTF 304SS Pressure Connection							
PSW-234	$225	3 to 20 PSI	20 to 135 kPa	.5 to 1.5 PSI		1000 PSI	5A SPDT
PSW-236	225	10 to 100 PSI	70 to 675 kPa	1 to 5 PSI		1000 PSI	5A SPDT
PSW-238	225	50 to 500 PSI	340 to 3400 kPa	4 to 30 PSI		2500 PSI	5A SPDT
PSW-240	225	200 to 1700 PSI	1.35 to 11.7 MPa	15 to 80 PSI		2500 PSI	5A SPDT
Phospher Bronze Bellows and ¼ NPTF Brass Pressure Connection							
PSW-246	$265	30 Hg Vac to 0	−100 to 0 kPa	1 to 3 Hg Vac		30 PSI	5A SPDT
316 Stainless Steel Diaphragm and ½ NPTF Pressure Connection							
				0 To 75% RANGE	100% RANGE		
PSW-241	$265	6 to 30 PSI	42 to 210kPa	1 to 4 PSI	5 PSI	2500 PSI	5A SPDT
PSW-242	265	10 to 100 PSI	70 to 675 kPa	1 to 8 PSI	15 PSI	2500 PSI	5A SPDT
PSW-243	265	30 to 300 PSI	205 to 2000 kPa	3 to 18 PSI	25 PSI	2500 PSI	5A SPDT
PSW-244	265	50 to 500 PSI	340 to 3400 kPa	4 to 30 PSI	45 PSI	2500 PSI	5A SPDT
PSW-245	265	200 to 1700 PSI	1.35 to 11.7 MPa	5 to 60 PSI	80 PSI	2500 PSI	5A SPDT

Deadbands are fixed, nonadjustable and tend to increase linearly with increased setpoint.
*Hemetically Sealed

PRESSURE SWITCH ACCESSORIES

AUDIBLE ALARM

The OMEGA Model 70A audible alarms are the latest development in solid sound production. When 120 Vac is applied to them, a piezoelectric transducer operates as a solid state oscillator, resulting in a loud, audible alarm tone. Only a 1⅛" diameter hole is required for panel mounting.

To Order (Specify Model Number)

MODEL NO.	PRICE	TONE TYPE
70A-1	$18	Continuous tone
70S-2	24	Fast pulse tone
70A-3	24	Slow pulse tone
70A-4	18	Warble tone

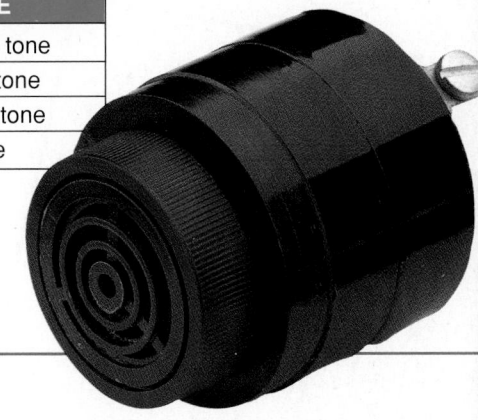

ALL MODELS STOCKED FOR FAST DELIVERY!

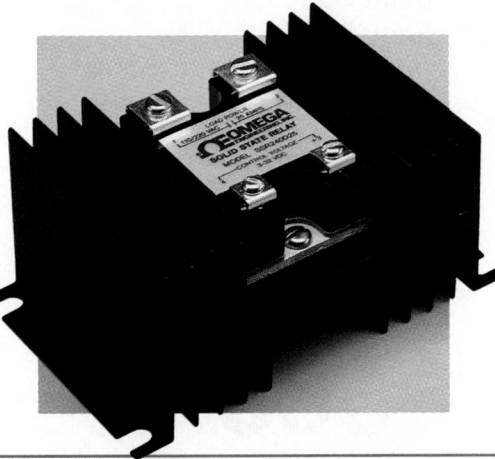

HIGH RELIABILITY SOLID STATE RELAYS

Solid state relays are used for switching large loads, and in conjunction with pressure switches, they extend the power rating of the switch.

To Order (Specify Model Number)

MODEL NO.	PRICE	CONTROL SIGNAL	MAX AC OUTPUT
SSR240AC10	$27	ac	10A
SSR240AC25	37	Control Signal	25A
SSR240AC45	50	(30 to 280 Vac)	45A
SSR240DC10	27	dc	10A
SSR240DC25	26	Control Signal	25A
SSR240DC45	47	(3 to 32 Vdc)	45A
FHS-2	17	Finned heat sink	

To Order (Specify Model No.)

MODEL NO.	PRICE	SSR OUTPUT
SSRL2	$65	120 Vac @5 amps
SSRL3	84	220 Vac @ 5 amps

LATCHING 5 AMP SOLID STATE RELAYS

External dry contacts provide the controlling signal for this SSRL. Latching relays are used to extend the hysteresis or deadband range of the pressure switch.

(SSRL Series relays are not failsafe; we recommend a third level switch independent of the SSRL for alarm of overfill or overdrain conditions.)

NEW!

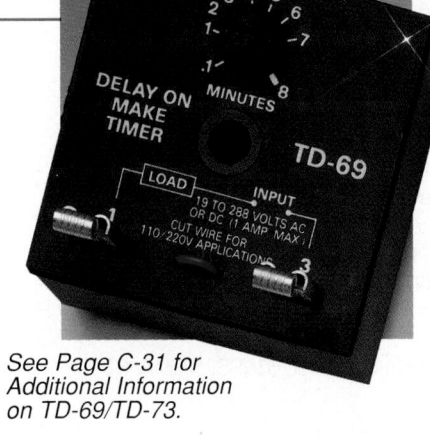

See Page C-31 for Additional Information on TD-69/TD-73.

DELAY RELAYS

Delay relays are used to eliminate false pressure transients from sound high alarms (Model TD-69). The TD-73 is used to prevent furnaces and compressors from quick restarts.

To Order (Specify Model Number)

MODEL NO.	PRICE	ADJUSTABLE TIME DELAY	TYPE
TD-69	$25	6 seconds to 8 minutes	Delay-on-make
TD-73	25	6 seconds to 5 minutes	Delay-on-break

ALL STAINLESS STEEL PRESSURE SWITCH
FOR HARSH ENVIRONMENTS
DUAL 15A SPDT SWITCHES

Shown Smaller Than Actual Size

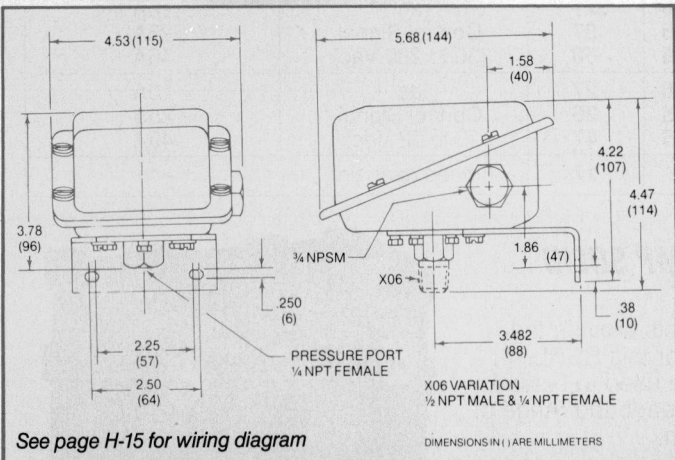

See page H-15 for wiring diagram

DIMENSIONS IN ( ) ARE MILLIMETERS

PSW 370 Series

✔ **All-Stainless NEMA 4X Case Resists Industrial Corrosion**

✔ **Designed for Tough Industrial Application With Long Life UL and CSA Rated Switches**

✔ **Ranges from 30″ H₂O to 3000 PSI**

✔ **Easy to Adjust With Internal Reference Scale**

✔ **Teflon or Stainless Steel Diaphragms**

From
$365

To Order (Specify Model Number)

MODEL	PRICE	DIAPHRAGM MATERIAL	ADJUSTABLE RANGE	DEAD BAND ENGLISH UNITS	PROOF PRESSURE
▶PSW370	$425	TEFLON	5 to 30″ H₂0	2.5 to 5.9	20 PSI
▶PSW371	425	TEFLON	22 to 150″ H₂0	8.4 to 19.2	20 PSI
PSW372	365	ST STEEL	3 to 15 PSI	2.4 to 3.6	500 PSI
PSW373	365	ST STEEL	6 to 30 PSI	2.4 to 6.8	500 PSI
▶PSW374	365	ST STEEL	20 to 100 PSI	8.5 to 15.3	1000 PSI
PSW375	365	ST STEEL	40 to 200 PSI	17 to 34	1000 PSI
▶PSW376	365	ST STEEL	80 to 400 PSI	37.4 to 71.4	2400 PSI
PSW377	365	ST STEEL	120 to 600 PSI	37.4 to 119	2400 PSI
PSW378	375	TEFLON	150 to 1000 PSI	84 to 216	12000 PSI
PSW379	375	TEFLON	450 to 3000 PSI	301 to 418	12000 PSI

HIGHLIGHTED MODELS STOCKED FOR FAST DELIVERY

SPECIFICATIONS

Electrical Rating: 15A, 125/250/480 Vac; 1/2A, 125 Vdc; 1/4A 250 Vdc

Switch Output: Two SPDT switches can be wired "normally open", or "normally closed"

Setpoint Repeatability: ±1% range

Ambient & Storage Temperature: −20 to 150°F

Setpoint: Typically shifts ±1% of range per 50°F

Electrical Connections: ¾ NPSM, 316SS Fitting

Pressure Connections: ¼ NPT Female, 304SS

Wetted Parts: Inches of water and 1000 and 3000 PSI ranges: Teflon and stainless steel. 15 PSI to 600 PSI ranges: stainless steel.

Enclosure: Gasketed 316SS, NEMA 4X rated.

HEAVY DUTY INDUSTRIAL DESIGN
EXTERNAL SETPOINT ADJUSTMENTS

PSW-700 Series
30" Hg Vacuum to 500 PSI

- ✔ **Division I Rating**
- ✔ **Tamper Resistant Set Points**
- ✔ **Heavy Duty Enclosure Rated NEMA 4, 7, 9, IP66**
- ✔ **Terminal Block Wiring**

From

$389

The PWS-700 Series pressure switch is built for the rugged industrial setting. The external setpoints allow adjustments while keeping the electronics isolated from the environment. The external setpoints also have a range scale allowing fast and easy set up.

MADE IN USA · UL · CSA · 1 YEAR WARRANTY

SPECIFICATIONS

Approvals: UL listed, CSA Class I, Division 1 & 2 Groups B, C, and D; Class II, Groups E, F, and G Class III

Repeatability: ±1% Range

Switch Temp Coef: .02% Range/°F

Ambient Temp Range: −40 to 160°F

Process Temp Range: Brass to 250°F 316SS to 500°F

Shock: Setpoint repeats after 15g, 10ms duration

Vibration: Setpoint repeats after 2.5g at 5 to 500Hz

Output: (2) SPDT 15A 125/250/480 Vac

Enclosure: Low copper cast aluminum

Electrical Connection: ¾ NPT Conduit; internal screw terminals

Weight: approx. 4 lbs

Options: Oxygen Cleaning - add suffix "X6B" $30.00 **Example: PSW-703-X6B** is a 30 PSI switch cleaned for oxygen service. Price = **$515**

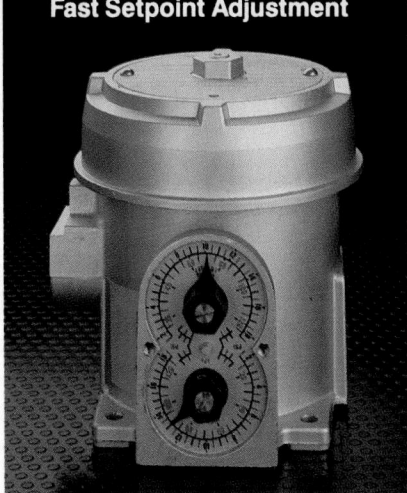

Fast Setpoint Adjustment

> ►*HIGHLIGHTED MODELS STOCKED FOR FAST DELIVERY*◄

To Order (Specify Model Number)

MODEL	PRICE	RANGE	DEAD BAND (PSI)	PROOF PRES.	DIAL GRADU-ATIONS	MATERIAL	CONNECTION
PSW-701	$389	30" to 0 HG Vac	.2 to .9" HG	30" HG	0.5" HG	Brass	¼ NPTF
PSW-702	485	0 to 20 PSI	.1 to .45	25 PSI	0.5 PSI	316SS	½ NPTF
PSW-703	485	0 to 30 PSI	.1 to .6	40 PSI	0.5 PSI	316SS	½ NPTF
PSW-704	495	0 to 100 PSI	.2 to .8	125 PSI	2 PSI	316SS	½ NPTF
PSW-705	435	0 to 200 PSI	1.5 to 8	250 PSI	5 PSI	316SS	¼ NPTF
PSW-706	435	0 to 300 PSI	2 to 9	350 PSI	10 PSI	316SS	¼ NPTF
PSW-707	435	0 to 500 PSI	3 to 12	575 PSI	10 PSI	316SS	¼ NPTF

HEAVY DUTY INDUSTRIAL PRESSURE SWITCH

PSW-400 Series

Mounting Bracket

- **Dual Chamber Design**
- **Isolates Electronics From Pressure Media**
- **Heavy Duty Cast Aluminum Enclosure With Corrosion Resistant Epoxy Coating**
- **Meets NEMA 7 and 9 Classifications**
- **Gasketed Covers**
- **Tamper/Vibration Resistant Setpoint Adjustment**
- **Surface Mounting Bracket Standard**

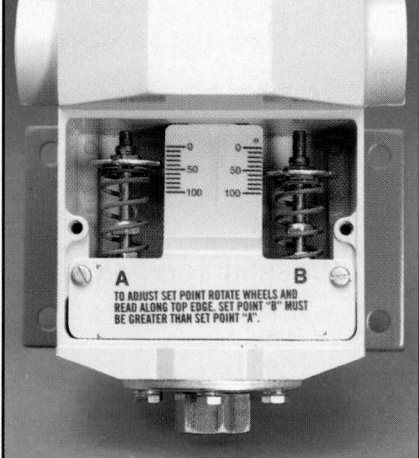

Set Point Chamber With Two Adjustable Scales.

Definition of Division I: Locations where hazardous concentrations exist continuously, intermittently or periodically under normal operating conditions.

Designed for applications in hazardous atmospheres, the PSW-400 Series Pressure Switches offer complete reliability due to a rugged die cast aluminum enclosure with waterproof gaskets and two separate chambers for electronics and actuator. Single or dual setpoints are available with all critical parts of stainless steel. In addition, the PSW-400 Series employs vibration resistant setpoints and a calibrated scale.

SPECIFICATIONS

Approval: UL listed, Class I Division 1 and 2, Groups B, C, D. Class II Division 1 and 2, Groups E, F, G CSA certified

Storage Temp.: −20 to 150°F

Ambient Temp. Limits: −20 to 150°F

Process Temp. Limits: SS, 300°F; Buna-N, 150°F

Enclosure Classification: NEMA, 7, 9 hazardous location, explosion proof, dust ignition proof.

Setpoint Repeatability: ±1% of range

Switch Output: 1 or 2 SPDT switch may be wired "normally open" or "normally closed"

Electrical Rating: 10 A: 125/250 Vac; 0.5 A: 125 Vdc; 0.25 A: 250 Vdc; 15 A: 125/250 Vac. Optional hermetically sealed 5 A: 125/250 Vac

Enclosure: Dual chamber epoxy coated cast aluminum, gasketed

Weight: 6 lb

Electrical Connection: 2 ea. ¾" NPT electrical conduit hubs

Pressure Connection: ¼" NPT female; vacuum to 600 PSI; ½" NPT Male/¼" NPT female for 1000 to 3000 PSI

Connection Material: Vacuum thru inches H_2O ranges; carbon steel. All PSI ranges; 316 SS.

Oxygen Service: Specify Option X6B for special cleaning. Add $62 only 316 SS.

Pressure Switch Options: (Add suffix to part number) Hermetically sealed 5 A 125/250 Vac switch for extra protection in severe environments.
-P Single SetPoint $75.00
-PP Dual SetPoint $150.00
316 Stainless Steel Welded Pressure Activator
-S 15 to 600 PSI Only $54.00

DUAL CHAMBER DESIGN

¾ NPT Electrical Chamber Isolated From Working Fluid

Top View Shown

From

$390

To Order *(Specify Model Number)*

MODEL	PRICE	ADJUSTABLE RANGE		DEAD BAND ENGLISH UNITS	PROOF PRESSURE	SWITCH
		ENGLISH	METRIC			
Single Setpoint, Adjustable Deadband Buna-N Diaphragm, O-Ring, ¼ NPTF Connection						
PSW-401	$415	−6 to −30 IN Hg Vac	−20 to −100kPa	3 to 27	250 PSI	10A SPDT
PSW-402	425	6 to 30 IN H₂0	1.5 to 7.5 kPa	3 to 27	20 PSI	10A SPDT
PSW-403	425	12 to 60 IN H₂0	3 to 15 kPa	3 to 54	20 PSI	10A SPDT
PSW-404	425	30 to 150 IN H₂0	7.4 to 37 kPa	15 to 135	20 PSI	10A SPDT
▶ PSW-405	390	3 to 15 PSI	20 to 100 kPa	2 to 13	500 PSI	10A SPDT ◀
PSW-406	390	6 to 30 PSI	40 to 200 kPa	2 to 27	500 PSI	10A SPDT
PSW-407	390	20 to 100 PSI	140 to 700 kPa	5 to 90	1000 PSI	10A SPDT
PSW-408	390	40 to 200 PSI	280 to 1400 kPa	13 to 180	1000 PSI	10A SPDT
▶ PSW-409	390	80 to 400 PSI	.56 to 2.8 MPa	20 to 360	2400 PSI	10A SPDT ◀
PSW-410	445	200 to 1000 PSI	1.4 to 7 MPa	100 to 900	12000 PSI	10A SPDT
PSW-411	445	600 to 3000 PSI	4.2 to 21 MPa	200 to 2800	12000 PSI	10A SPDT
Dual Setpoint, Fixed Deadband Buna-N Diaphragm, and ¼ NPTF Connection						
PSW-421	$435	−6 to −30 IN Hg Vac	−20 to −100kPa	.5 to 1 in Hg	250 PSI	TWO 15A SPDT
PSW-422	435	6 to 30 IN H₂0	1.5 to 7.5 kPa	.5 to 1 in H₂0	20 PSI	TWO 15A SPDT
PSW-423	435	12 to 60 IN H₂0	3 to 15 kPa	.5 to 1.3	20 PSI	TWO 15A SPDT
PSW-424	435	30 to 150 IN H₂0	7.4 to 37 kPa	1.5 to 3	20 PSI	TWO 15A SPDT
PSW-425	405	3 to 15 PSI	20 to 100 kPa	.5 to 1 PSI	500 PSI	TWO 15A SPDT
PSW-426	405	6 to 30 PSI	40 to 200 kPa	.5 to 1.5	500 PSI	TWO 15A SPDT
PSW-427	405	20 to 100 PSI	140 to 700 kPa	1 to 2.5	1000 PSI	TWO 15A SPDT
PSW-428	405	40 to 200 PSI	280 to 1400 kPa	1 to 4	1000 PSI	TWO 15A SPDT
▶ PSW-429	405	80 to 400 PSI	.56 to 2.8 MPa	4 to 8	2400 PSI	TWO 15A SPDT ◀
PSW-430	455	200 to 1000 PSI	1.4 to 7 MPa	7 to 30	1200 PSI	TWO 15A SPDT
PSW-431	455	600 to 3000 PSI	4.2 to 21 MPa	30 to 70	1200 PSI	TWO 15A SPDT
Dual Setpoint, Fixed Deadband 316SS Diaphragm and ¼ NPTF						
PSW-445	$465	3 to PSI	20 to 100kPa	.5 to 1	500 PSI	TWO 15A SPDT
PSW-446	465	6 to 30 PSI	40 to 200 kPa	1 to 2	500 PSI	TWO 15A SPDT
▶ PSW-447	465	20 to 100 PSI	140 to 700 kPa	2 to 4	1000 PSI	TWO 15A SPDT ◀
PSW-448	465	40 to 200 PSI	280 to 1400 kPa	3 to 8	1000 PSI	TWO 15A SPDT

▶ *HIGHLIGHTED MODELS STOCKED FOR FAST DELIVERY* ◀   **H-24**

J LVDT DISPLACEMENT TRANSDUCERS

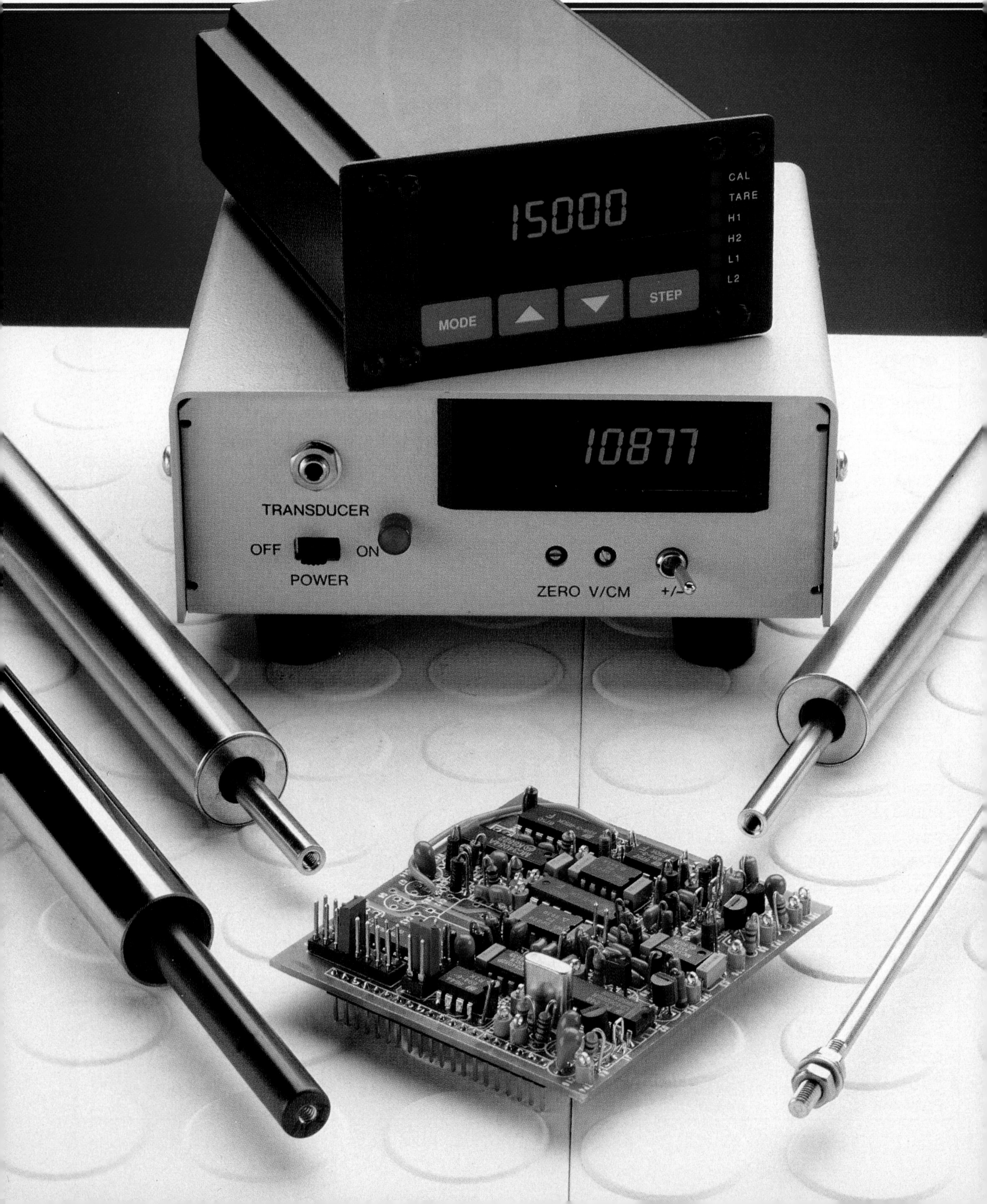

LVDT Displacement Transducers Selection Guide		J-3
High Speed Displacement System		J-5
AC LVDT Transducers		J-7 to J-10
DC LVDT Transducers		J-11 to J-16
AC LVDT Instrumentation	1492	J-17 to J-20

DISPLACEMENT J

LINEAR DISPLACEMENT MEASUREMENT SELECTION GUIDE

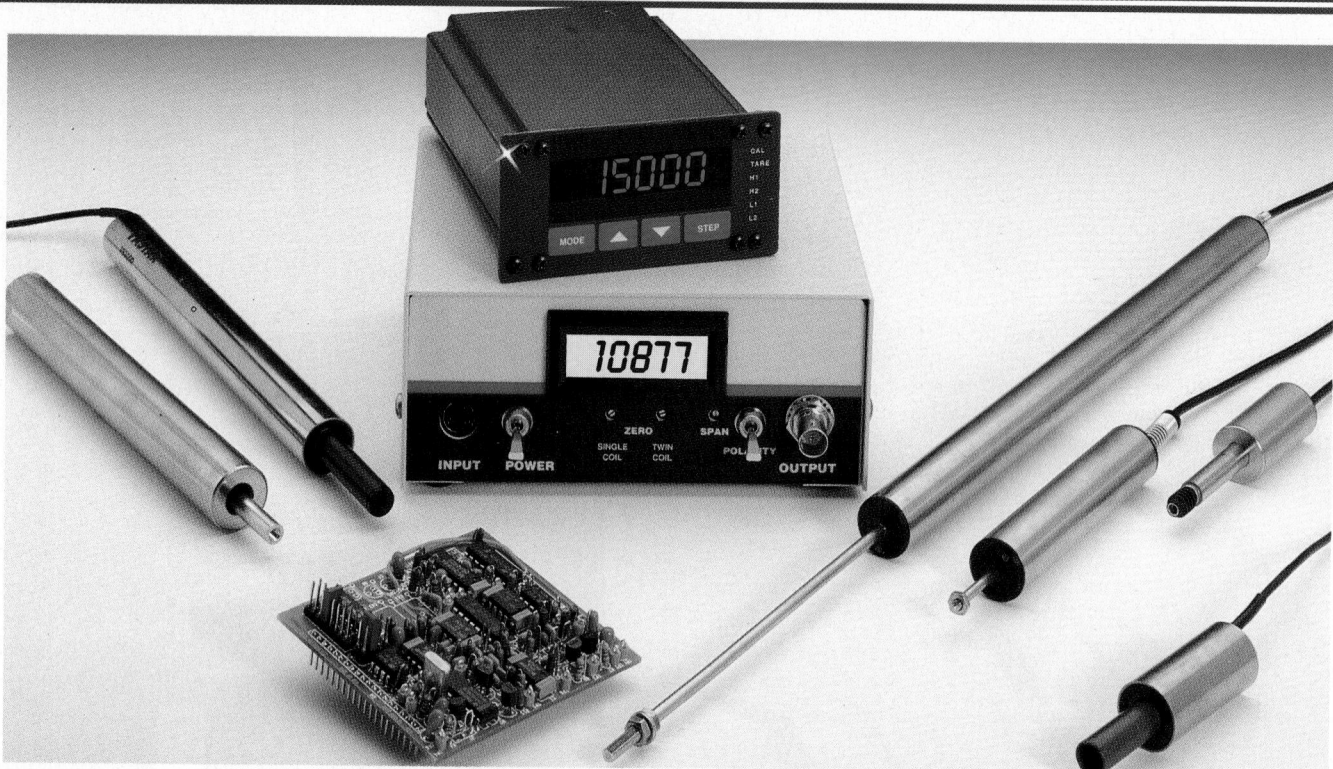

INSTRUMENTS

DP-LVDT - High Performance Display For AC LVDT Transducers.
- ✓ 5 Digit Display
- ✓ 5 KHz Excitation
- ✓ Analog Output
- ✓ Min - Max Values
- ✓ Optional Alarm Relays and RS232 Communications

To Order Specify: DP-LVDT $795

LDX-2 - Loop Powered Transmitter For AC LVDT Transducers
- ✓ Wide Sensitivity 30 to 530 mV/V
- ✓ Rugged Sealed Metal Housing
- ✓ High Accuracy 0.02%
- ✓ Provides AC Excitation and Standard 4 to 20mA output

To Order Specify: LDX-2 $265

LDX-3 - Line Powered Signal Conditioning Module For AC LVDT Transducers
- ✓ Energizes Transducer And Provides 0 to 5 Vdc Output
- ✓ High Accuracy 0.10%
- ✓ Adjustable Zero And Span
- ✓ Rugged Metal Case

To Order Specify: LDV-2 $326

LDX-4 - DC Powered Signal Conditioning Module For AC LVDT Transducers
- ✓ Selectable ±5V, ±10V, or ±20mA Outputs
- ✓ Adjustable Zero And Span

- ✓ High Accuracy Modulator/Demodulator Provides 3V @ 5KHz Excitation

To Order Specify: LDX-4 $326

SP300 - High Speed Signal Conditioning Module For LD100 Series Transducers
- ✓ 4½ Digit Display
- ✓ 0 to 15KHz Analog Frequency Response
- ✓ Output Scalable to ±10V
- ✓ Provides 115KHz Excitation to LD100 Series Transducers
- ✓ Also Available Without Display Or As Circuit Board For OEM Designers

To Order Specify: SP300 $785

LD100 WITH SP300A SIGNAL CONDITIONING DISPLAY MODULE

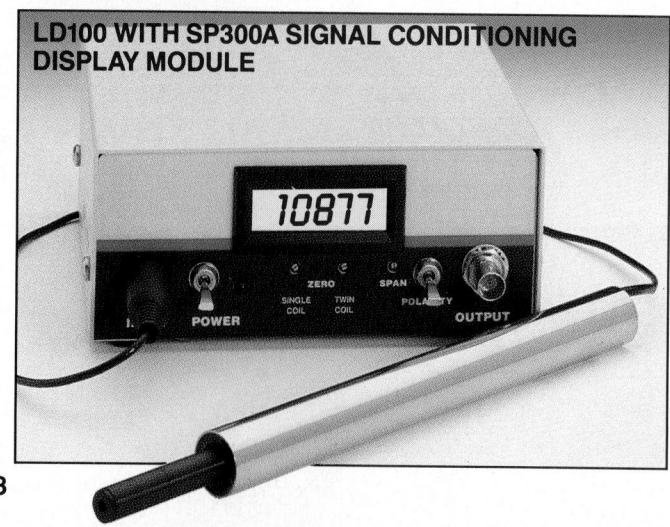

LDX-4 SIGNAL CONDITIONER WITH LD200 AND DP2000 DISPLAY

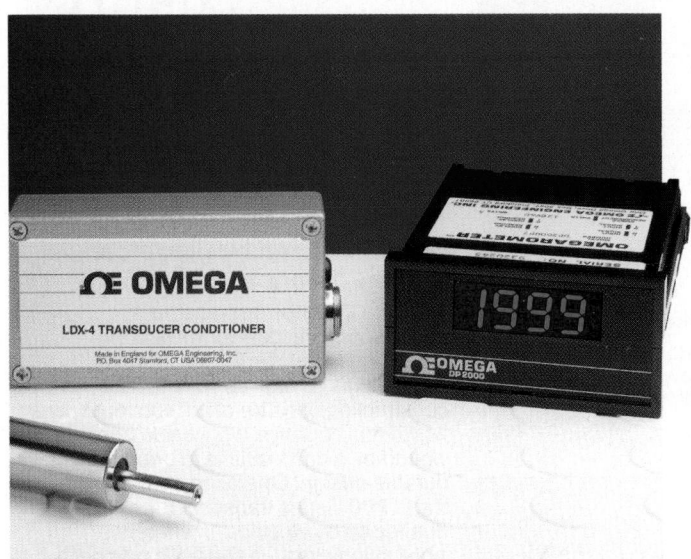

LD500 GAUGING TRANSDUCERS

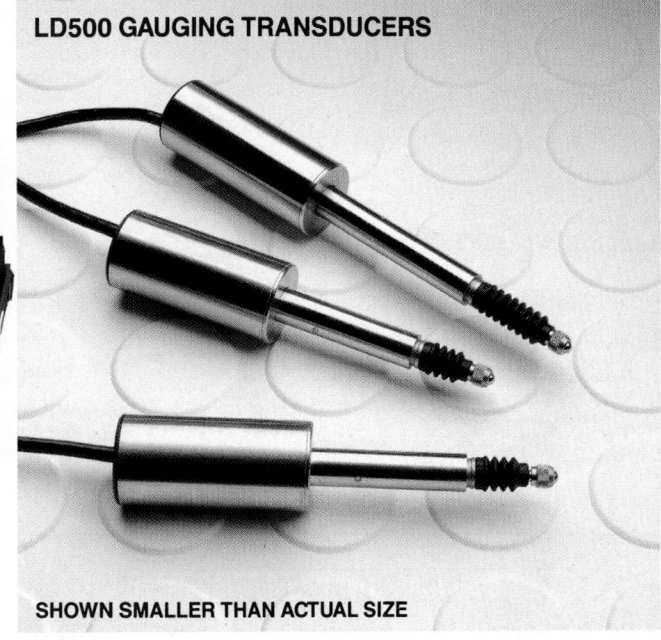

SHOWN SMALLER THAN ACTUAL SIZE

TRANSDUCERS

MODEL	PRICE	OUTPUT	LINEARITY	RANGE	FEATURES
LD100	From $195	DC Up to 10V	0.15%	+ 0.75" (20mm) to + 10" (250mm)	**HIGH SPEED -** Frequency response flat 0 to 15KHz. Transducers require dedicated signal conditioning modules, SP150, SP200A or SP300A. Excellent in high vibration areas such as engine analysis.
LD200	From $89	AC mV/V/mm	0.25%	± 0.05" (1.25mm) to ± 0.40" (10.0mm)	**RUGGED -** Designed for use on machine tools and vehicles where infinite resolution and high repeatability are very important characteristics.
LD300	From $320	AC mV/V/mm	0.25%	± 0.60 (15mm) to ± 12" (300mm)	**LONG STROKE AC -** High accuracy and our longest stroke up to ±12". Armatures are spring loaded up to 6" length. AC operation provides the highest accuracy and performance.
LD400	From $198	DC mV/mm	0.25%	± 0.04" (1.0mm) to ± 0.20 (5.0mm)	**MINIATURE DC -** Supplied with Delrin bearings, these miniature transducers provide near frictionless motion to detect the smallest displacement.
LD500	From $489	DC mV/mm	< 0.15μm (Repeatability)	± 0.04" (1.0mm) to ± 0.20" (5.0mm)	**PRECISION GAUGING -** Designed for industrial automation, these transducers have hardened steel shafts, O-ring seals and titanium push rods to give highly repeatable readings.
LD600	From $465	DC mV/mm	0.25%	± 0.60" (15mm) to ± 12" (300mm)	**LONG STROKE DC -** These transducers include a custom hybrid IC which provides a mV/mm output. This enables extremely simple setup and operation with standard DC amplifiers.

HIGH SPEED DISPLACEMENT SYSTEMS
IDEAL FOR OSCILLATING DISPLACEMENT MEASUREMENT
RUGGED, VIBRATION-RESISTANT DESIGN

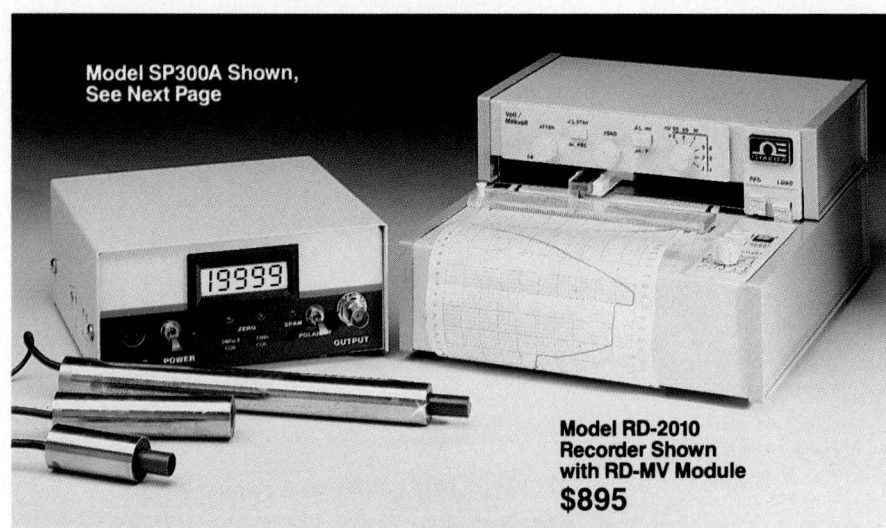

Model SP300A Shown,
See Next Page

Model RD-2010
Recorder Shown
with RD-MV Module
$895

From
$195  **NEW!**

- ✔ **High Speed**
- ✔ **All Stainless Steel**
- ✔ **Vibration Resistant**
- ✔ **Operates up to 175°F**
- ✔ **Unaffected by Electrical Interference**

The LD100 Series displacement transducers are ideal for measuring oscillating linear displacement with frequencies as high as 15 kHz. The construction consists of an aluminum core which moves inside a polymide bobbin wound by a coil resulting in a rugged and durable design. Operating from 112 kHz, the LD100 Series transducers are unaffected by electrical interference. Applications include hydraulic cylinders, vibration analysis, robotics, automated production systems, etc.

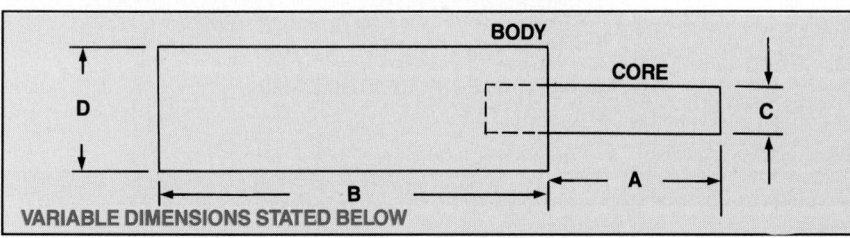

BODY
CORE
D
C
B
A
VARIABLE DIMENSIONS STATED BELOW

Model	Resolution	Linearity
LD100-20	.000013 in. (.00033 mm)	±0.15%
LD100-50	.00004 in. (.0010 mm)	±0.15%
LD100-100	.0001 in (.0025 mm)	±.015%
LD100-150	.0001 in. (.0025 mm)	±0.15%
LD100-200	.0002 in (.004 mm)	±.015%
LD100-250	.0002 in. (.004 mm)	±0.15%

DIMENSIONS, in. (mm)

MODEL	LINEAR RANGE	A, LENGTH*	B, LENGTH	C, DIA.	D, DIA.
LD100-20	0.75 (20)	1.45 (36.8)	1.75 (45)	0.37 (9.4)	0.75 (19)
LD100-50	2.00 (50)	2.70 (68.6)	3.34 (85)	0.37 (9.4)	0.75 (19)
LD100-100	4.00 (100)	4.82 (122.4)	5.30 (134.6)	0.37 (9.4)	0.75 (19)
LD100-150	6.00 (150)	6.70 (170.2)	7.27 (185)	0.37 (9.4)	0.75 (19)
LD100-200	8.00 (200)	8.73 (221.7)	9.12 (231.6)	0.37 (9.4)	0.75 (19)
LD100-250	10.00 (250)	10.70 (271.8)	10.90 (277)	0.37 (9.4)	0.75 (19)

* Note: Core fully extended

SPECIFICATIONS
ELECTRICAL
Non-Linearity: ±0.15% full scale
Excitation Frequency: 112 kHz
Frequency Response: 15 kHz
Thermal Effect: zero: 0.02%/°F (0.04%/°C); sensitivity: 0.02%/°F (0.04%/°C)
Compensated Temperature Range: 25 to 175°F (−5 to 80°C)
Operable Temperature Range: −60 to 175°F (−5 to 80°C)
Phase Shift: Lags −1.1°/100 Hz (30 μS delay) motion to output
Electrical Connection: 0.1 in. diameter (2.5 mm), 9 ft. (3 m) coaxial cable
MECHANICAL
Core Mass: LD100-20 (0.2 oz.); LD100-50 (0.4 oz.); LD100-100 (0.5 oz.); LD100-150 (0.7 oz.); LD200-200 (0.9 oz.); LD250 (1.0 oz.)
Threaded Core: 6-32 in. (STD); M4x7 mm (metric)
Core Material: Aluminum
Radial Core Clearance: 0.02 nominal
Case Material: nickel-plated steel
Vibration Resistance: Meets MIL-STD 810c, Figure 514-4, Curve AM, Time Schedule II, Random Vibration Test (overall g rms 29.3 min)
Shock Resistance: 50 g peak (5 msec)

HIGHLIGHTED MODELS STOCKED FOR FAST DELIVERY!

To Order *(Specify Transducer and Signal Conditioner)*

TRANSDUCERS

MODEL	PRICE	DESCRIPTION
LD100-20	$195	+.75" (20 mm) High speed transducer and core
LD100-50	235	+2" (50 mm) High speed transducer and core
LD100-100	285	+4" (100 mm) High speed transducer and core
LD100-150	330	+6" (150 mm) High speed transducer and core
LD100-200	365	+8" (200 mm) High speed transducer and core
LD100-250	395	+10" (250 mm) High speed transducer and core

SIGNAL CONDITIONERS *(Required to Operate LD100 Transducers)*

SP150	$435	Circuit board
SP200A	565	Benchtop processor unit with analog output
SP300A	785	Benchtop processor unit with display and analog output

Note: *SP150, SP200A and SP300A are dedicated signal conditioners for LD100 sensors.*

SIGNAL CONDITIONING
FOR LD100 SERIES
DISPLACEMENT TRANSDUCERS

AC POWERED HIGH SPEED CIRCUIT BOARD SIGNAL CONDITIONDER

The SP150 circuit board is powered by either 115 or 230 Vac. The SP150 provides all user adjustments and connections. The unit provides both 0-10 V and 4-20 mA outputs.

The board drives the LD100 with a 112 kHz current source. A displacement at frequencies up to 15 kHz can be measured with the SP150 circuit board.

SP150 CIRCUIT BOARD
$435

HIGH SPEED SIGNAL CONDITIONER

The transducer plugs into a jack on the front of the SP200A. A BNC connector on the back of the unit is used to transmit an output signal of up to 0 to ±10 V for a unidirectional displacement and from ±2 to ±10 V for bidirectional displacement. The processor has two 15 turn potentiometers for zero and scale adjustment. Plus, a polarity reverse switch allows you to change polarity of the output signal. Displacement changing at frequencies up to 15 kHz can be measured with the SP200A processor.

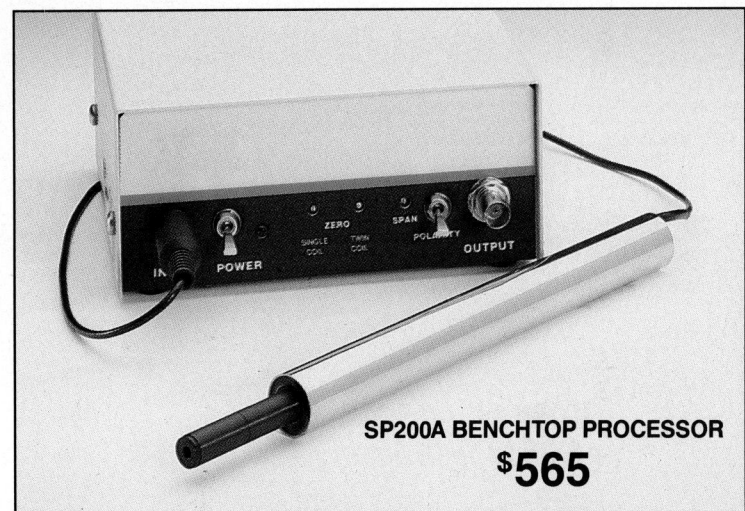

SP200A BENCHTOP PROCESSOR
$565

HIGH SPEED DISPLAY & CONDITIONER

This unit has a 4½ digit LCD display which will display the output voltage of up to 0 to ±10 V for unidirectional displacements and between ±2 to ±10 V for bidirectional output . The transducer plugs into a jack on the front of the unit and has a BNC connector on the back for the output voltage transmission. The processor has two 15 turn potentiometers for zero and scale adjustment. It also features a polarity switch that allows you to change polarity of the output signal. Displacements changing at frequencies up to 15 kHz can be measured with the SP300A processor. The display has a sample rate of 2 readings per second.

**SP300A BENCHTOP PROCESSOR
WITH 4½ DIGIT DISPLAY**
$785

Note: These signal conditioners will only work with OMEGA's LD100 Series Displacement Transducers

DISPLACEMENT J

J-6

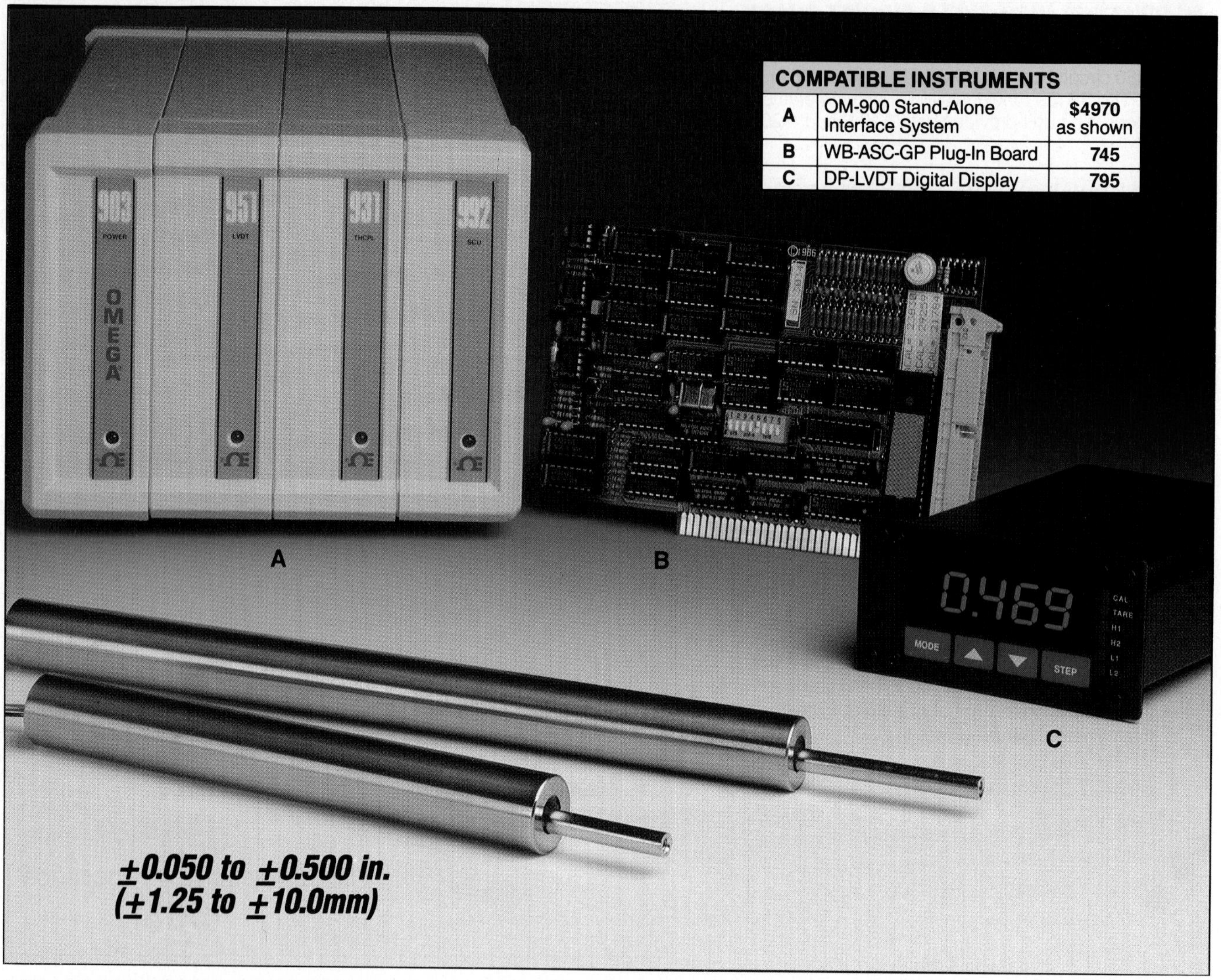

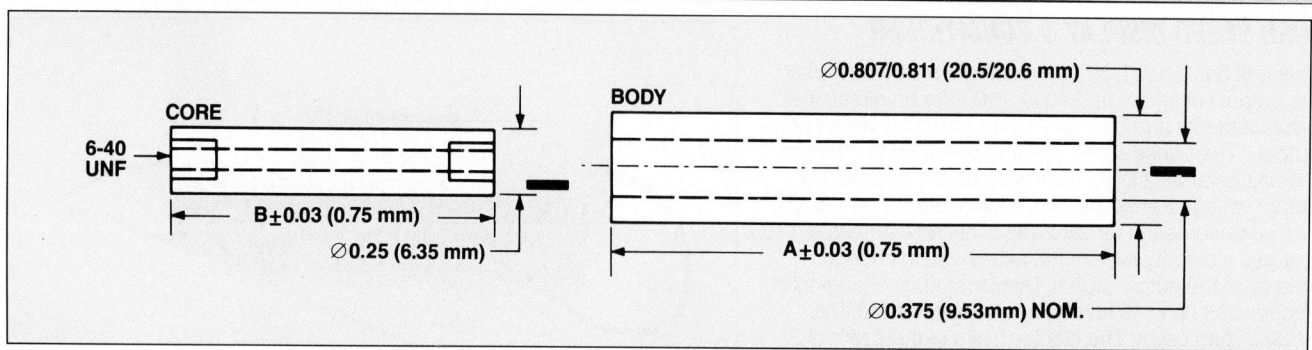

COMPATIBLE INSTRUMENTS		
A	OM-900 Stand-Alone Interface System	$4970 as shown
B	WB-ASC-GP Plug-In Board	745
C	DP-LVDT Digital Display	795

±0.050 to ±0.500 in.
(±1.25 to ±10.0mm)

CORE

6-40 UNF

B±0.03 (0.75 mm)

⌀0.25 (6.35 mm)

BODY

⌀0.807/0.811 (20.5/20.6 mm)

A±0.03 (0.75 mm)

⌀0.375 (9.53mm) NOM.

DIMENSIONS, in. (mm)			
MODEL	LINEAR STROKE ± IN. (mm)	A	B
LD200-1.25	0.05 (1.25mm)	1.12 (28.57)	0.80 (20.00)
LD200-2.5	0.10 (2.50 mm)	1.81 (45.97)	1.10 (28.00)
LD200-5	0.20 (5.00 mm)	2.50 (63.50)	1.85 (47.00)
LD200-7.5	0.30 (7.50 mm)	3.19 (81.00)	1.97 (50.00)
LD200-10	0.40 (10.0 mm)	4.31 (109.60)	2.95 (75.00)

LD200 Series
From $89

- ✓ Low Cost—High Linearity
- ✓ Rugged Construction for Machine Tools and Vehicles
- ✓ Large Core Clearance for Easy Installation
- ✓ Compatible with Standard AC Signal Conditioners and Displays
- ✓ Cores are Reversible and Interchangeable

The LD200 Series of ac powered LVDT transducers provide an economically priced range of displacement sensors with outstanding rugged construction and high performance. The series covers a broad measurement range from ±0.050 to ±0.500″ (±1.25 to ±10.0mm). These transducers can be used for displacement measurements in applications where high resolution and repeatability characteristics are very important.

The coils are wound on a rugged glass-filled nylon bobbin housed within a stainless steel case. Its epoxy-bonded construction makes the device suitable for operation in wet or oily environments and in applications where high levels of mechanical stress (vibration, shock, etc.) are encountered. The armature assembly (core and push rod) has friction free movement within the sensor due to the generous radial clearance of the bore.

This series offers good linearity, low levels of residual voltage and good temperature coefficients making it ideal for most displacement measurement applications, particularly machine tooling and production automation.

SPECIFICATIONS
ELECTRICAL
Linearity: see above chart
Sensitivity: (mV/V/mm) see above chart
Excitation: 1 to 10 V rms
Excitation Frequency: 1 kHz to 10 kHz
Energizing Current: < 40 mA

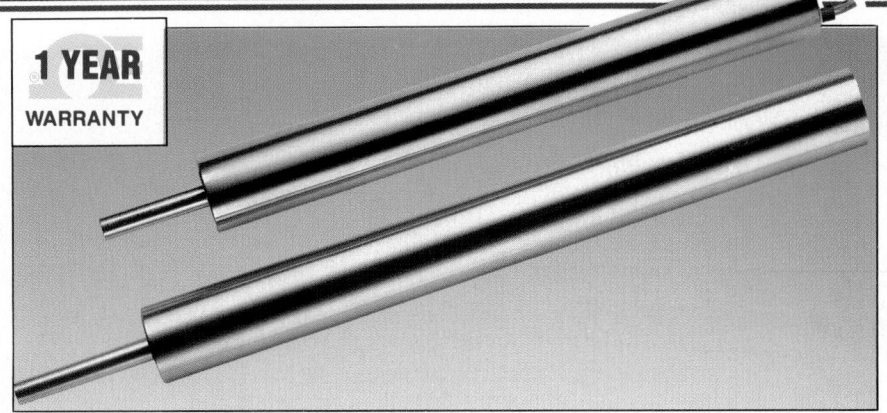

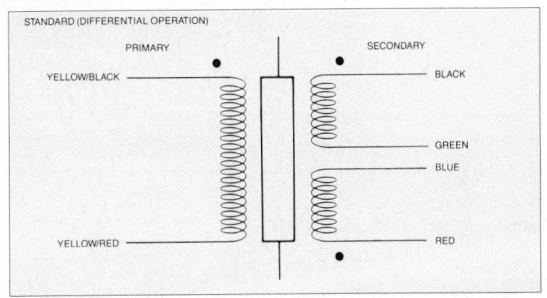

Frequency Response: 10% of excitation frequency
Zero Offset: 0.5% FS
Thermal Effect: zero: 0.014%/°F (0.025%/°C) sensitivity: 0.011%/°F (0.020%/°C)
Compensated Temperature Range: −67 to 300°F (−55 to 150°C)
Operable Temperature Range: −67 to 300°F (−55 to 150°C)
Electrical Connection: 12″ leads

MECHANICAL
Core Mass: LD200-1.25 (0.13 oz.); LD200-2.5 (0.22 oz.); LD200-5 (0.32 oz.); LD200-7.5 (0.40 oz.); LD200-10 (0.50 oz.)

Threaded Core: 6-40 UNF
Core Material: NiFe - Radio Metal 50
Radial Core Clearance: 0.062 in.
Case Material: 400 Series stainless steel
Weight: LD200-1.25 (1.16 oz.); LD200-2.5 (1.52 oz.); LD200-5 (1.73 oz.) LD200-7.5 (2.5 oz.); LD200-10 (2.61 oz.)

CONNECTION
Electrical Connections
Yellow/Black: Excitation
Yellow/Red: Excitation
Black: + Signal
Red: Signal ground
Connect blue and green together

MODEL	NOMINAL RANGE		LINEARITY-TYPICAL 2.5 kHz % OF FULL RANGE				SENSITIVITY @ 2.5kHz-NOMINAL	
	mm	in.	50%	100%	125%	150%	mV/V/mm	mV/V/0.001″
LD200-1.25	±1.25	±0.05	0.10	0.25	0.25	0.50	250	6.35
LD200-2.5	±2.50	±0.10	0.10	0.25	0.25	0.50	180	4.50
LD200-5	±5.00	±0.20	0.10	0.25	0.25	0.50	100	2.54
LD200-7.5	±7.50	±0.30	0.10	0.25	0.25	0.50	57	1.40
LD200-10	±10.00	±0.40	0.10	0.15	0.25	0.40	35	0.90

HIGHLIGHTED MODELS STOCKED FOR FAST DELIVERY!

To Order (Specify Model Number)

MODEL	PRICE	COMPATIBLE INSTRUMENTS
LD200-1.25	$89	DP-LVDT, LDX-2, LDX-3, LDX-4, RD2000
LD200-2.5	130	DP-LVDT, LDX-2, LDX-3, LDX-4, RD2000
LD200-5	170	DP-LVDT, LDX-2, LDX-3, LDX-4, RD2000
LD200-7.5	185	DP-LVDT, LDX-2, LDX-3, LDX-4, RD2000
LD200-10	205	DP-LVDT, LDX-2, LDX-3, LDX-4, RD2000

HIGH ACCURACY AC LONG STROKE
DISPLACEMENT TRANSDUCERS LD300 SERIES

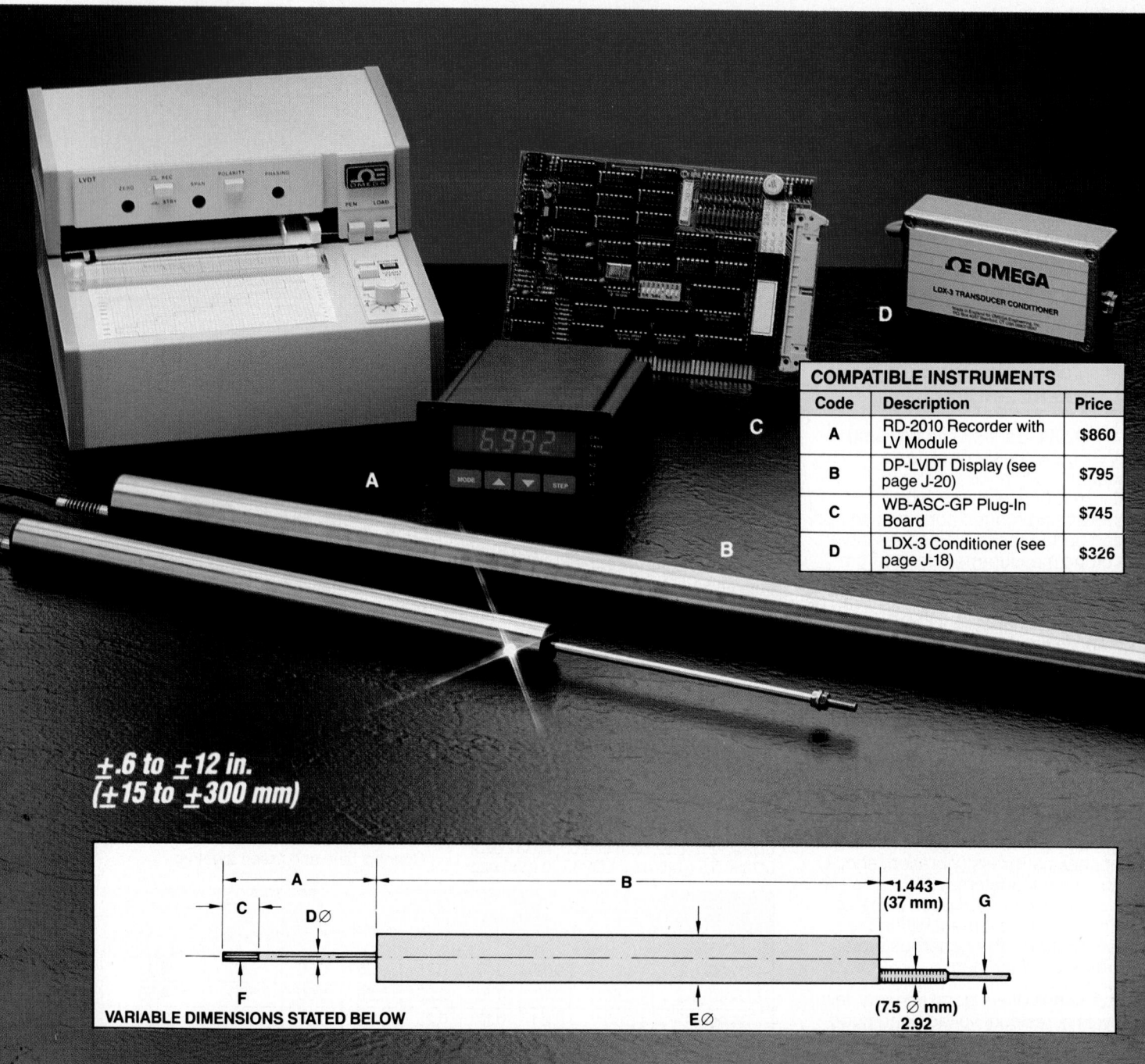

**±.6 to ±12 in.
(±15 to ±300 mm)**

COMPATIBLE INSTRUMENTS		
Code	**Description**	**Price**
A	RD-2010 Recorder with LV Module	$860
B	DP-LVDT Display (see page J-20)	$795
C	WB-ASC-GP Plug-In Board	$745
D	LDX-3 Conditioner (see page J-18)	$326

1.443 (37 mm)

(7.5 Ø mm) 2.92

VARIABLE DIMENSIONS STATED BELOW

MODEL	LINEAR STROKE ±in. (mm)	DIMENSIONS, in. (mm), at Electrical Zero						
		A	**B**	**C**	**D**	**E**	**F**	**G**
LD300-15	0.6 (15)	1.76 (45)	3.78 (97)	.78 (20)	.12 (3.17)	.75 (19)	M3	.14 (3.5)
LD300-25	1.0 (25)	2.34 (60)	6.08 (156)	.78 (20)	.16 (4.0)	.75 (19)	M4	.14 (3.5)
LD300-50	2.0 (50)	3.32 (85)	10.92 (280)	.78 (20)	.16 (4.0)	.75 (19)	M4	.14 (3.5)
LD300-100	4.0 (100)	5.66 (145)	17.55 (450)	.78 (20)	.19 (4.75)	1.00 (25)	M5	.18 (4.5)
LD300-150	6.0 (150)	7.68 (197)	21.53 (552)	.75 (19)	.19 (4.75)	1.00 (25)	M5	.18 (4.5)
LD300-250	10.0 (250)	11.62 (298)	29.45 (755)	.75 (19)	.19 (4.75)	1.00 (25)	M5	.18 (4.5)
LD300-300	12.0 (300)	13.61 (349)	33.42 (857)	.75 (19)	.19 (4.75)	1.00 (25)	M5	.18 (4.5)

1 YEAR
WARRANTY

LD300 Series
From

$**320**

- ✔ **Rugged Stainless Steel Case**
- ✔ **LVDT - Infinite Resolution**
- ✔ **0.25% Linearity**
- ✔ **Spring Loaded Armature**
- ✔ **Works with Standard AC Signal Conditioning Modules**

This series provides our longest stroke length — to a total of ±300mm (12 inches) based on the established linear variable differential transformer principle, which is intrinsically ac operating. LVDT's, that are ac powered, ultimately produce the best accuracy using remote electronics. Special winding techniques are used to ensure the best possible linearity. They are then packaged in a rugged housing and the transformer core is provided with an extension rod and very low friction nylon bearings that act as guides. The transducer is provided with a spring return armature, and is easily adapted to most industrial measurement situations.

Due to their inherent long life, infinite resolution, versatility, and excellent repeatability, these units are highly suitable for many varied and demanding industrial applications.

SPECIFICATIONS

ELECTRICAL
Linearity: 0.25% FS

Sensitivity: (mV/V/mm) See chart below

Excitation: 1 to 10 V rms

Excitation Frequency: 1 kHz to 10kHz

Energizing Current: See chart below

Frequency Response: 2 mS

Zero Offset: 0.5% FS

Thermal Effect: zero: 0.003%/°F (0.005%/°C), sensitivity: 0.005%/°F (0.008%/°C)

Compensated Temperature Range; −40 to 212°F (−40 to 100°C)

Operable Temperature Range: −40 to 212°F (−40 to 100°C)

Electrical Connection: 9′ shielded cable

Calibration: calibrated at 5 V, 5 kHz with 100k ohm load at 20°C

MECHANICAL
Threaded Core: LD300-15 (M3); LD300-25, -50 (M4); LD300-100, -150, -250, -300 (M5)

Core Material: Ni/Fe - Radio Metal 50

Case Material: 400 series stainless steel

Weight: See chart below

CONNECTIONS
Electrical Connections

Red and Blue: Excitation (ac)

White: Signal

Green: Signal Ground

Red and White: In phase for inward displacement

To Order *(Specify Model Number)*

MODEL	LINEAR STROKE, ±in. (mm)	PRICE	COMPATIBLE INSTRUMENTS
LD300-15	0.6 (15)	$320	DP-LVDT, LDX-2, LDX-3, LDX-4
LD300-25	1.0 (25)	330	DP-LVDT, LDX-2, LDX-3, LDX-4
LD300-50	2.0 (50)	425	DP-LVDT, LDX-2, LDX-3, LDX-4
LD300-100	4.0 (100)	510	DP-LVDT, LDX-2, LDX-3, LDX-4
LD300-150	6.0 (150)	595	DP-LVDT, LDX-3, LDX-4
LD300-250	10.0 (250)	665	DP-LVDT, LDX-2, LDX-3, LDX-4
LD300-300	12.0 (300)	750	DP-LVDT, LDX-3, LDX-4

HIGHLIGHTED MODELS STOCKED FOR FAST DELIVERY!

MODEL	MAXIMUM STROKE, ±in.(mm)	WEIGHT	CORE ASSEMBLY	SPRING RATE	FORCE*	SENSITIVITY, mV/V/mm	ENERGIZING CURRENT	OUTPUT IMPED.	I/O PHASE
LD300-15	.886 (22)	60 g	10 g	3.30 g/mm	110	34.0	6 mA	220 Ω	7°
LD300-25	1.378 (35)	96 g	18 g	2.34 g/mm	150	20.0	4 mA	210 Ω	9°
LD300-50	2.441 (62)	170 g	25 g	1.95 g/mm	185	9.3	4 mA	160 Ω	10°
LD300-100	4.921 (125)	600 g	54 g	1.19 g/mm	120	5.0	6 mA	160 Ω	7°
LD-300-150	7.007 (178)	900 g	78 g	1.00 g/mm	120	3.5	5 mA	150 Ω	7°
LD-300-250	10.884 (279)	1300 g	106 g	CANNOT BE		2.1	6 mA	110 Ω	5°
LD-300-300	12.992 (330)	1600 g	122 g	SPRING LOADED		1.7	9 mA	90 Ω	2°

* At electrical zero, grams

MINIATURE DC DISPLACEMENT TRANSDUCERS WITH DELRIN BEARINGS

LD400 Series

NEW!

6 5 4 3
TYPE:
RANGE:
LOOP
SUPPLY
1 2
A
4328.65
1
2
3
4
SETPTS
▲MAX
►MIN
MENU
RESET
B
C

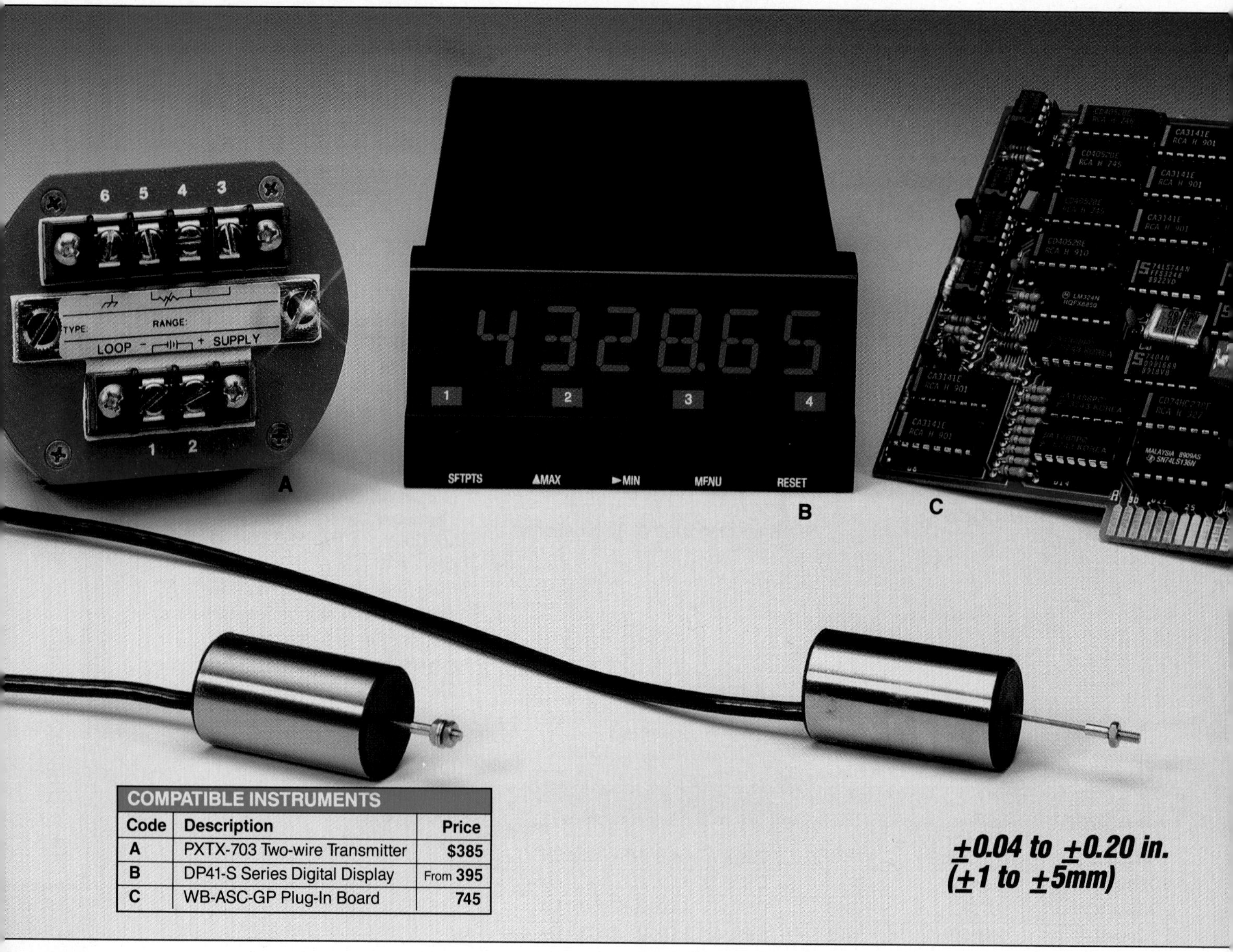

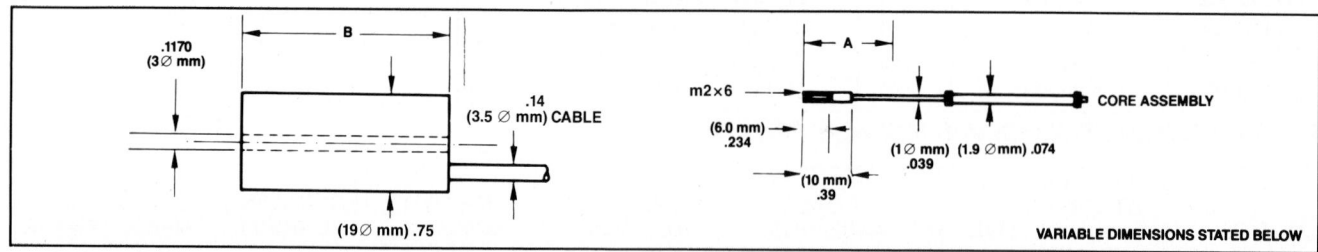

COMPATIBLE INSTRUMENTS		
Code	**Description**	**Price**
A	PXTX-703 Two-wire Transmitter	**$385**
B	DP41-S Series Digital Display	From **395**
C	WB-ASC-GP Plug-In Board	**745**

±0.04 to ±0.20 in. (±1 to ±5mm)

B
.1170
(3∅ mm)
.14
(3.5 ∅ mm) CABLE
(19∅ mm) .75
A
m2×6
CORE ASSEMBLY
(6.0 mm)
.234
(1∅ mm)
.039
(1.9 ∅mm) .074
(10 mm)
.39
VARIABLE DIMENSIONS STATED BELOW

MODEL	LINEAR STROKE, ±in. (mm)*	DIMENSIONS, in. (mm)*		WEIGHT, oz.(g)	
		A	B	BODY	CORE (guided)
LD400-1	.04 (1)	.88 (22.5)	1.44 (37)	1.01 (26)	.04 (1.0)
LD400-2.5	.10 (2.5)	.93 (23.5)	1.44 (37)	1.01 (26)	.04 (1.0)
LD400-5	.20 (5)	.79 (20)	1.68 (43)	1.17 (30)	.04 (1.0)

* *At electrical zero*

1 YEAR WARRANTY

LD400 Series
From
$198

- ✓ **High Output Miniature Transducers**
- ✓ **Delrin Bearings for Precise Motion**
- ✓ **Infinite Resolution**
- ✓ **Rugged Low Mass Construction**
- ✓ **Compatible with Standard DC Signal Conditioning Modules and Instruments**

The LD400 Series miniature dc-dc transducers provide a method of measuring displacements up to 0.20 in. (5mm) with very high accuracy and infinite resolution. They have a free guided armature incorporating Delrin bearings, providing near frictionless motion to detect the smallest movement the associated instrumentation is capable of identifying.

These transducers utilize a precision linear variable differential transformer (LVDT) as the measuring source together with hybrid IC's which include an oscillator, demodulator and filter; providing a self-contained unit that accepts a dc input and provides a dc output relative to armature position. High linearity and low mass of moving parts is ideally suited to applications in civil, mechanical, chemical and production engineering.

SPECIFICATIONS
ELECTRICAL
Linearity: 0.25% FS
Sensitivity: (mV/V/mm) see chart below
Excitation: 10 to 24 Vdc regulated
Engergizing Current at 10 Vdc: LD400-1 (10 mA); LD400-2.5 (10 mA); LD400-5 (13 mA)
Response Time: 1.5 mS
Output Ripple: <1% FS

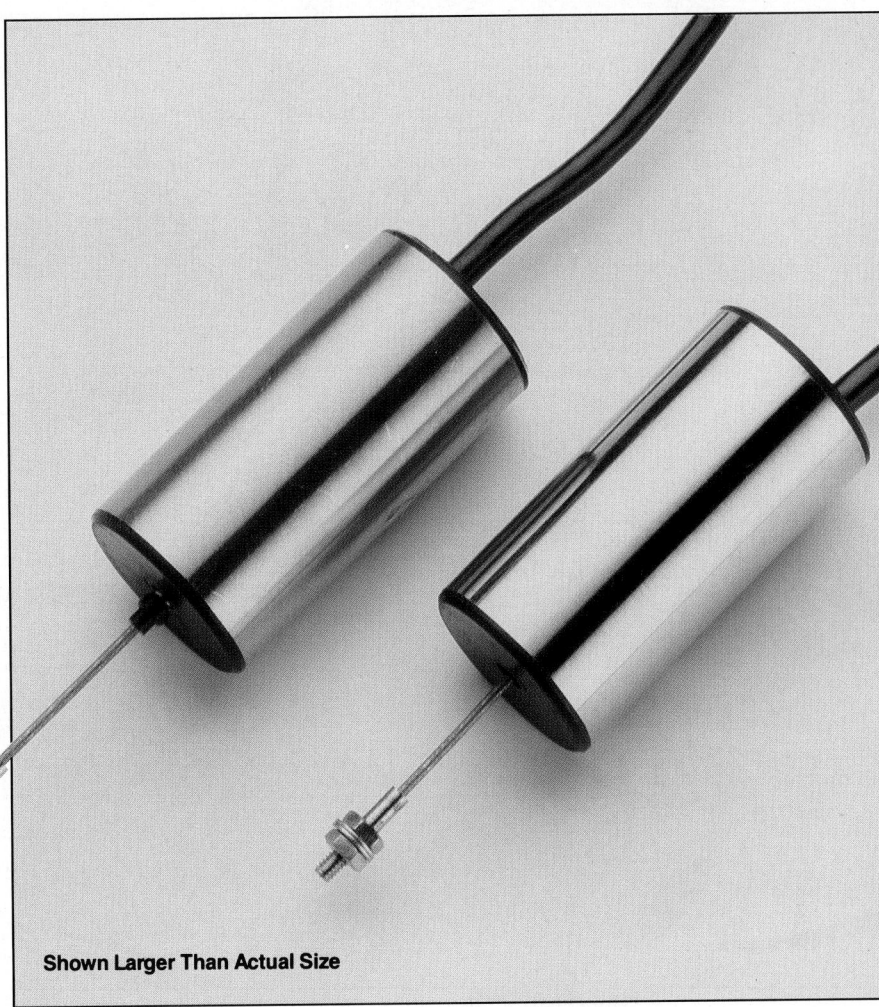

Shown Larger Than Actual Size

Thermal Effect: zero: 0.003%/°F (0.005%/°C); sensitivity: 0.003%/°F (0.005%/°C)
Compensated Temperature Range: −4 to 175°F (−20 to 80°C)
Operable Temperature Range: −4 to 175°F (−20 to 80°C)
Electrical Connection: 9′ shielded cable
Calibration: Provided with a transducer output impedance of 2.4 kohms into a calibration load of 20 kohms at 20°C. Variations in these parameters will change performance.

MECHANICAL
Threaded Core: M2 thread
Core Material: Ni/Fe - Radio Metal 50
Case material: 400 series stainless steel
Weight: See chart, previous page

CONNECTIONS
Electrical Connections
Red: +Excitation
Blue: −Excitation
White: + Signal*
Green: − Signal
*White and Red in phase for positive inward displacement

To Order *(Specify Model Number)*				
MODEL	STROKE, ± mm	PRICE	SENSITIVITY	COMPATIBLE METERS
LD400-1	1.0	$198	78 mV/V/mm	DP41-S, DP354, DP3002-P
LD400-2.5	2.5	225	78 mV/V/mm	DP41-S, DP354, DP3002-P
LD400-5	5.0	235	56 mV/V/mm	DP41-S, DP354, DP3002-P

HIGHLIGHTED MODELS STOCKED FOR FAST DELIVERY!

DISPLACEMENT   J

PRECISION DC GAUGING TRANSDUCERS
FOR QUALITY CONTROL OR AUTOMATION TOOLING
LD500 Series

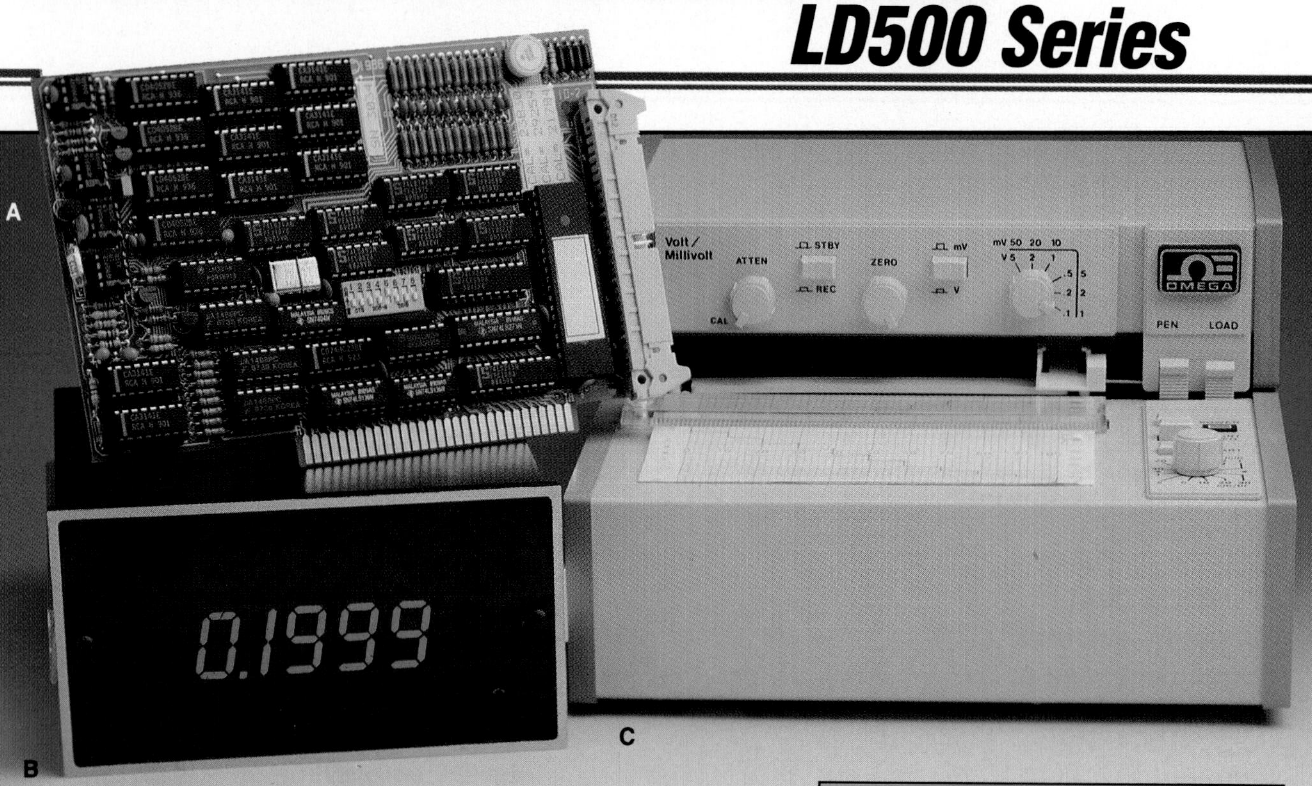

A
B
C
0.1999
Volt / Millivolt
ATTEN
STBY
REC
ZERO
mV
V
CAL
OMEGA
PEN
LOAD

LD500 Series

From **$489**

COMPATIBLE INSTRUMENTS		
Code	**Description**	**Price**
A	WB-ASC-GP Plug-In Board	**$745**
B	DP772 Display	**740**
C	RD2010 Recorder with RD-MV Module	**895**

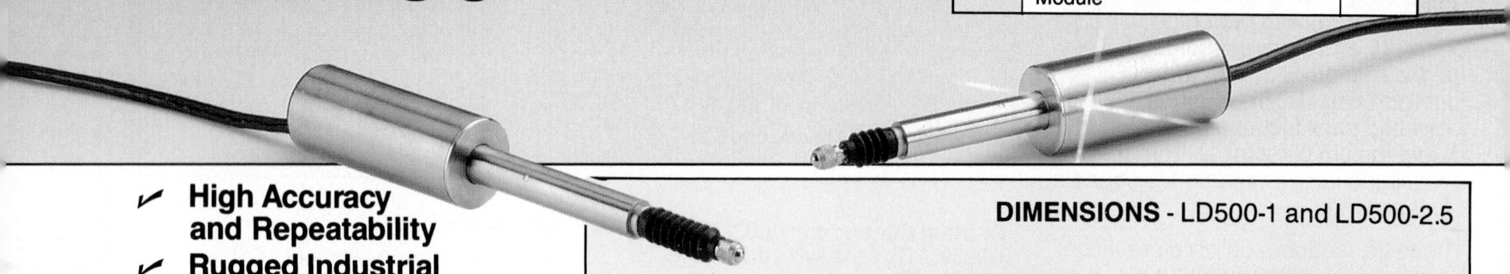

- **High Accuracy and Repeatability**
- **Rugged Industrial Construction**
- **Replaceable Tips**
- **Repeatability Better Than 0.15 μm**
- **Linear Ball Bearing Actuator**

These precision manufactured displacement transducers can be mounted to most production lines to do automatic gauging for quality, sorting, or go/no go applications. The hardened steel shaft, O-ring seals and titanium pushrod can withstand most industrial situations. The hybrid IC module provides a linear mV/V/mm (inch) output which will interface with most standard dc input meters, recorders, data interfaces and industrial controllers.

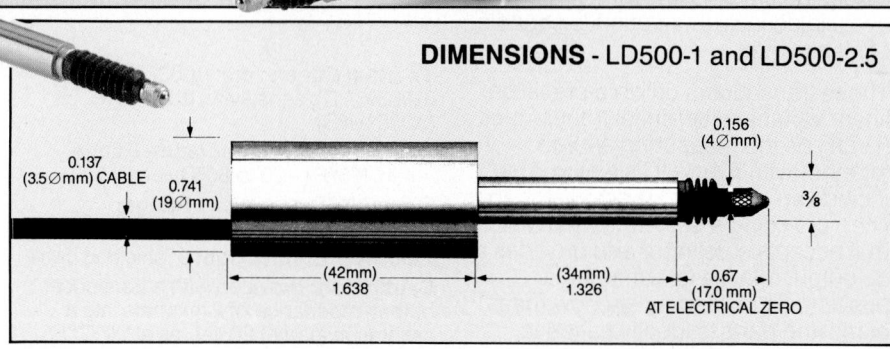

DIMENSIONS - LD500-1 and LD500-2.5

0.137
(3.5∅mm) CABLE
0.741
(19∅mm)
(42mm)
1.638
(34mm)
1.326
0.156
(4∅mm)
3/8
0.67
(17.0 mm)
AT ELECTRICAL ZERO

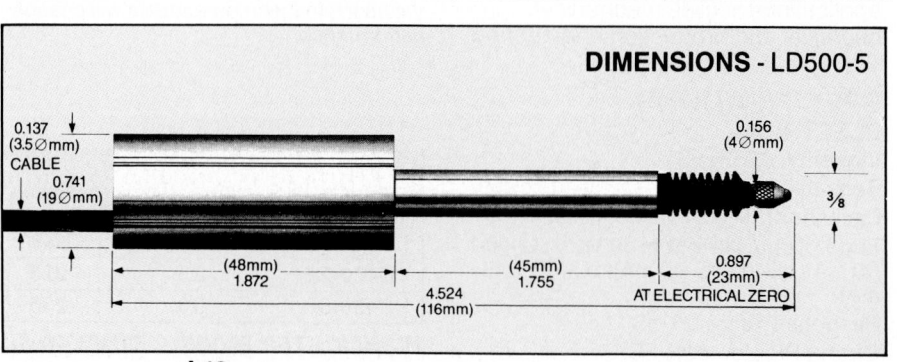

DIMENSIONS - LD500-5

0.137
(3.5∅mm)
CABLE
0.741
(19∅mm)
(48mm)
1.872
(45mm)
1.755
4.524
(116mm)
0.156
(4∅mm)
3/8
0.897
(23mm)
AT ELECTRICAL ZERO

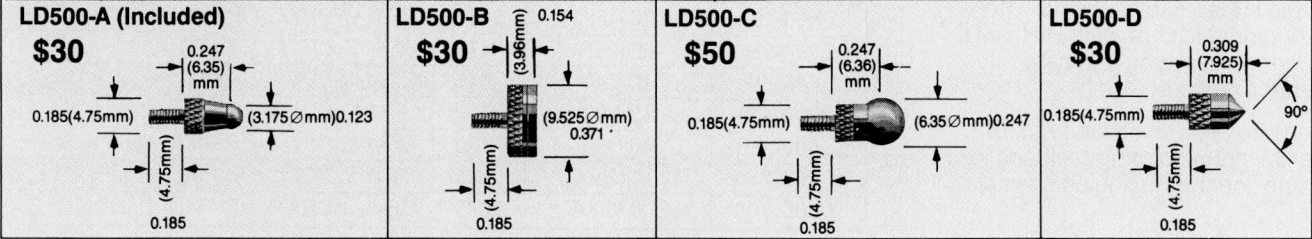

GAUGING TRANSDUCERS

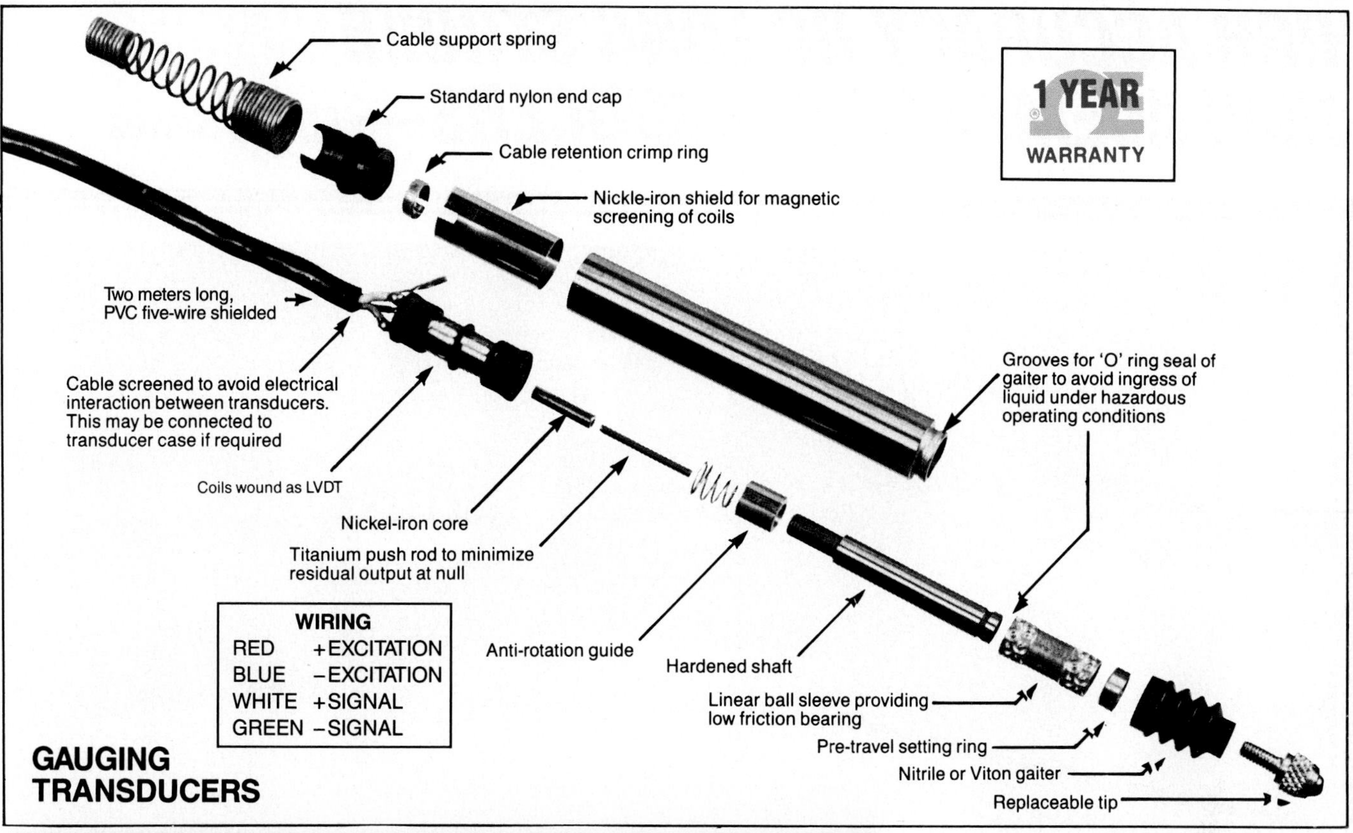

Cable support spring

Standard nylon end cap

Cable retention crimp ring

Nickle-iron shield for magnetic screening of coils

Two meters long, PVC five-wire shielded

Cable screened to avoid electrical interaction between transducers. This may be connected to transducer case if required

Coils wound as LVDT

Nickel-iron core

Titanium push rod to minimize residual output at null

Grooves for 'O' ring seal of gaiter to avoid ingress of liquid under hazardous operating conditions

Anti-rotation guide

Hardened shaft

Linear ball sleeve providing low friction bearing

Pre-travel setting ring

Nitrile or Viton gaiter

Replaceable tip

1 YEAR WARRANTY

WIRING

RED	+EXCITATION
BLUE	−EXCITATION
WHITE	+SIGNAL
GREEN	−SIGNAL

To Order *(Specify model number)*

MODEL	PRICE	STROKE, in (mm)	COMPATIBLE METERS
LD500-1	$489	.04 (1.0)	DP41-S, DP-354, DP772
LD500-2.5	525	.10 (2.5)	DP41-S, DP-354, DP772
LD500-5	565	.20 (5.0)	DP41-S, DP-354, DP773

Note: LD500-A tip included.

◆ HIGHLIGHTED MODELS STOCKED FOR FAST DELIVERY! ◆

SPECIFICATIONS

MECHANICAL

MODEL	LINEAR STROKE ±in. (mm)	SPRING RATE	REPEATABILITY	TEMPERATURE RANGE	TEMPERATURE COEFFICIENT		LINEARITY
					ZERO	SENSITIVITY	
LD500-1	±.04 (1.0)	13g/mm	<0.15µm (6µin)	−20 to 80°C	<.01%/°C	<.01%/°C	0.25%
LD500-2.5	±.10 (2.5)	13g/mm	<0.15µm (6µin)	−20 to 80°C	<.005%/°C	<.01%/°C	0.25%
LD500-5	±.20 (5.0)	10g/mm	<0.10µm (4µin)	−20 to 80°C	<.005%/°C	<.01%/°C	0.25%

ELECTRICAL

MODEL	CURRENT	INPUT VOLTAGE	OUTPUT RIPPLE (TYPICAL)	RESPONSE TIME	FREQUENCY RESPONSE	SENSITIVITY	CABLE
LD500-1	10 mA	10 to 24 Vdc	<1% FS	1.5 ms	100 Hz for - 3dB	78 mV/V/mm (1.98 mV/V/.001″)	Two meters long, PVC five-wire shielded
LD500-2.5	10 mA	10 to 24 Vdc	<1% FS	1.5 ms	100 Hz for-3dB	78 mV/V/mm (1.98mV/V/.001″)	Two meters long, PVC five-wire shielded
LD500-5	13 mA	10 to 24 Vdc	<1% FS	1.5 ms	100 Hz for-3dB	56 mV/V/mm (1.42 mV/V/.001″)	Two meters long, PVC five-wire shielded

REPLACEMENT TIPS

LD500-A (Included)
$30
0.247 (6.35) mm
(3.175 Ø mm)0.123
0.185(4.75mm)
(4.75mm)
0.185

LD500-B
$30
0.154 (3.96)
(9.525 Ø mm) 0.371
(4.75mm)
0.185

LD500-C
$50
0.247 (6.36) mm
(6.35 Ø mm)0.247
0.185(4.75mm)
(4.75mm)
0.185

LD500-D
$30
0.309 (7.925) mm
90°
0.185(4.75mm)
(4.75mm)
0.185

HIGH ACCURACY DC LONG STROKE DISPLACEMENT TRANSDUCERS— *LD600 Series*

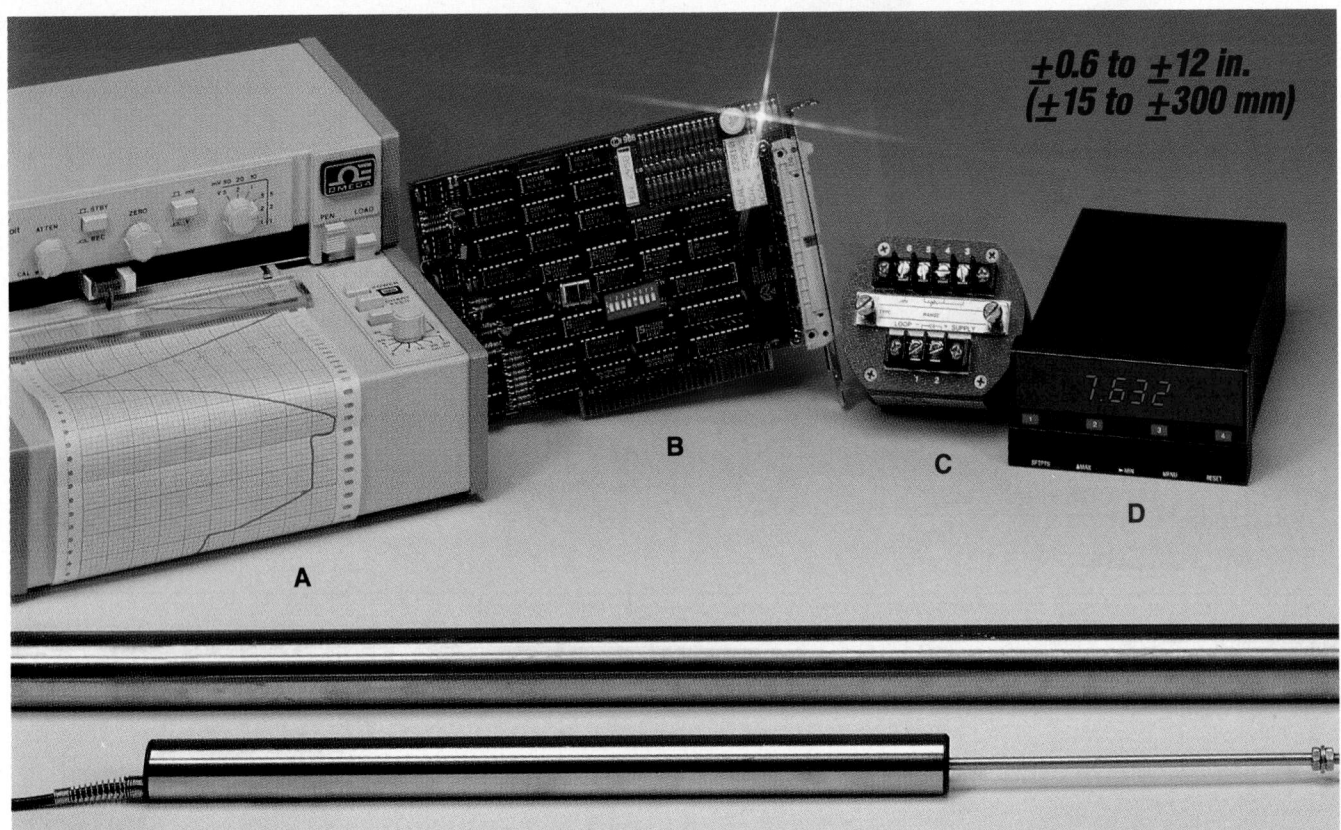

±0.6 to ±12 in.
(±15 to ±300 mm)

A

B

C

D

- ✔ **Rugged Stainless Steel Case**
- ✔ **Custom Built-In Hybrid IC Gives Linear DC Output**
- ✔ **0.25% Linearity**
- ✔ **Spring Loaded Armature**
- ✔ **Compatible With Standard DC Signal Conditioning Module**

The LD600 Series provides our longest stroke length (for dc powered transducers) to a total of ±300mm (12 inches). Our custom hybrid IC composed of an oscillator/demodulator and filter requires dc excitation and provides a linear mV signal proportional to displacement. The built-in electronics enables extremely simple systems to be set up. The mV/V output is compatible with all dc metering, recording and data interface devices.

Long stroke transducers require special manufacturing methods to ensure linearity, including special winding techniques that are used to make the coils. These windings are then packaged in a rugged housing and the transformer core is provided with an extension rod and low friction nylon bearings to guide it. The transducers are provided with a spring return armature for easy installation.

The inherent long life, infinite resolution and excellent repeatability of the LD600 Series transducers makes them highly suitable for many varied and demanding applications.

LD600 Series
From
$465

COMPATIBLE INSTRUMENTS

Code	Description	Price
A	RD-2000 Series Recorder	from $1600
B	WB-ASC-GP Plug-In Board	745
C	PXTX-703 Two-Wire Transmitter	385
D	DP41-S Series Digital Display	from 395

HIGHLIGHTED MODELS IN STOCK FOR FAST DELIVERY!

To Order *(Specify Model Number)*			
MODEL	LINEAR STROKE ±in. (mm)	PRICE	COMPATIBLE METERS
LD600-15	0.6 (15)	$465	DP41-S, DP773, DP3700
LD600-25	1.0 (25)	475	DP41-S, DP773, DP3700
LD600-50	2.0 (50)	545	DP41-S, DP773, DP3700
LD600-100	4.0 (100)	630	DP41-S, DP773, DP3700
LD600-150	6.0 (150)	730	DP41-S, DP773, DP3700
LD600-250	10.0 (250)	935	DP41-S, DP773, DP3700
LD600-300	12.0 (300)	1075	DP41-S, DP773, DP3700

1 YEAR WARRANTY

SPECIFICATIONS
ELECTRICAL
Linearity: 0.25% FS

Sensitivity: (mV/V/mm) see chart below

Excitation: Vdc regulated (see ranges in chart below)

Energizing Current: see chart below

Response Time: 0.4 mS

Output Ripple: <1% FS

Thermal Effect: zero: 0.003%/°F (0.005%/°C); sensitivity: 0.009%/°F (0.015%/°C)

Compensated Temperature Range: −4 to 175°F (−20 to 80°C)

Operable Temperature Range: −4 to 175°F (−20 to 80°C)

Electrical Connection: 9′ shielded cable

Calibration: Provided with a transducer output impedance of 2.0 kohms into a calibration load of 20 kohms at 20°C. Variations in these parameters will change performance

Shown with DP41-S Digital Panel Meter, $395.

MECHANICAL
Threaded Core: see chart below

Core Material: Ni/Fe - Radio Metal 50

Case Material: 400 series stainless steel

Weight: see chart below

CONNECTIONS
Electrical Connections

Red: +Excitation

Blue: − Excitation

White: +Signal*

Green: − Signal

* Polarity is for inward displacement

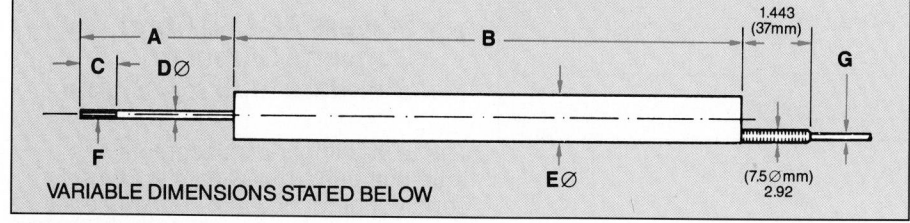

VARIABLE DIMENSIONS STATED BELOW

U.S. AND CANADA

for placing orders, call: 1-800-82-66342™
1-800-TC-OMEGA

DISPLACEMENT **J**

MECHANICAL

MODEL	LINEAR STROKE ±in. (mm)	DIMENSIONS, in. (mm), at Electrical Zero						
		A	B	C	D	E	F	G
LD600-15	0.6 (15)	1.76 (45)	3.78 (97)	.78 (20)	.12 (3.17)	.74 (19)	M3	.14 (3.5)
LD600-25	1.0 (25)	2.34 (60)	6.08 (156)	.78 (20)	.16 (4.0)	.74 (19)	M4	.14 (3.5)
LD600-50	2.0 (50)	3.32 (85)	10.92 (280)	.78 (20)	.16 (4.0)	.74 (19)	M4	.14 (3.5)
LD600-100	4.0 (100)	5.66 (145)	17.55 (450)	.78 (20)	.19 (4.75)	.98 (25)	M5	.18 (4.5)
LD600-150	6.0 (150)	7.68 (197)	21.53 (552)	.74 (19)	.19 (4.75)	.98 (25)	M5	.18 (4.5)
LD600-250	10.0 (250)	11.62 (298)	29.45 (755)	.74 (19)	.19 (4.75)	.98 (25)	M5	.18 (4.5)
LD600-300	12.0 (300)	13.61 (349)	33.42 (857)	.74 (19)	.19 (4.75)	.98 (25)	M5	.18 (4.5)

MODEL	MAXIMUM STROKE, ±in.(mm)	WEIGHT	ARMATURE ASSEMBLY	SPRING RATE	FORCE*	SENSITIVITY, mV/V/mm	CURRENT @ 10 mV, mA	INPUT VOLTAGE RANGE
LD600-15	.886 (22)	60 g	10 g	3.30 g/mm	110	28.00	10	9 to 24 V
LD600-25	1.378 (35)	96 g	18 g	2.34 g/mm	150	16.50	18	9 to 24 V
LD600-50	2.441 (62)	170 g	25 g	1.95 g/mm	185	6.00	40	9 to 24 V
LD600-100	4.921 (125)	600 g	54 g	1.19 g/mm	120	2.00	40	9 to 15 V
LD600-150	7.007 (178)	900 g	78 g	1.00 g/mm	120	1.33	40	9 to 15 V
LD600-250	10.884 (279)	1300 g	106 g	Cannot Be Spring Loaded		0.80	40	9 to 15 V
LD600-300	12.992 (330)	1600 g	122 g			0.66	40	9 to 15 V

* At electrical zero, grams

LOOP POWERED DIPSLACEMENT TRANSMITTER WITH EXCITATION FOR AC LVDTs WORKS WITH LD200 AND LD300 SERIES TRANSDUCERS

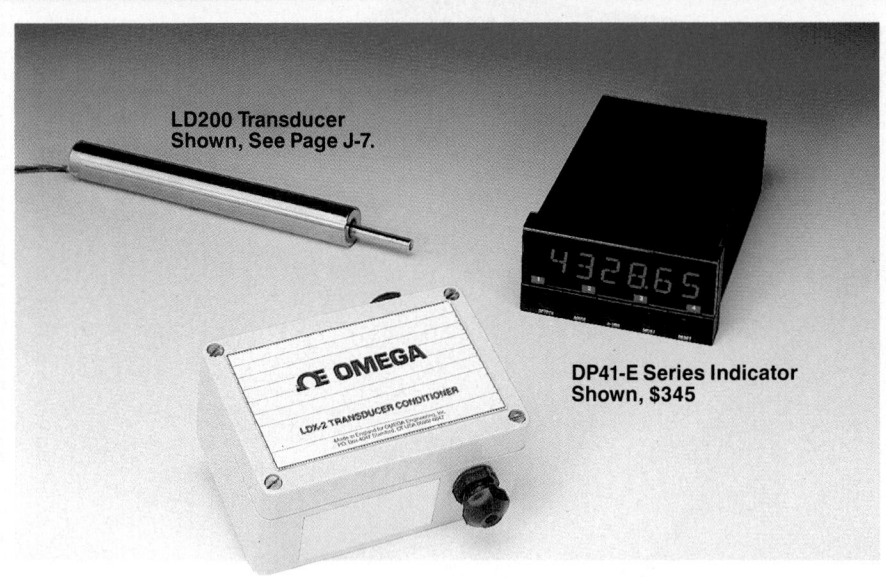

LD200 Transducer Shown, See Page J-7.

DP41-E Series Indicator Shown, $345

NEW!

Model LDX-2
$265

- ✔ **Wide Input Range of 30 to 530mV/V**
- ✔ **Rugged Sealed Housing**
- ✔ **2-Wire 4-20 mA Signal for Remote Locations**
- ✔ **0.02% Accuracy of Reading**
- ✔ **Powers AC LVDT and Converts Signal to Standard 4-20 mA Signal**

The LDX-2 linear displacement transmitter is a two-wire, 4 to 20mA conditioner for ac LVDT transducers. It is designed for use where long signal transmission distances are required before interfacing with a controller or meter. A feature of the two-wire operation is the low susceptibility to noise and cable resistance, making it ideal for industrial environments.

The two-wire operation enables both power and signal to use the same pair of wires. The position of the transducer is indicated by the amount of current, from 4 to 20mA full scale. If a cable break occurs, zero current is indicated, thereby showing a fault.

The LDX-2 is housed in an ABS impact-resistant plastic case with two water resistant cable ports for the transducer cable and supply cable. The box is sealed to IP65 standard and is supplied with mounting nuts for a DIN 46277-1 rail, or may be bolted to any surface without affecting the seal.

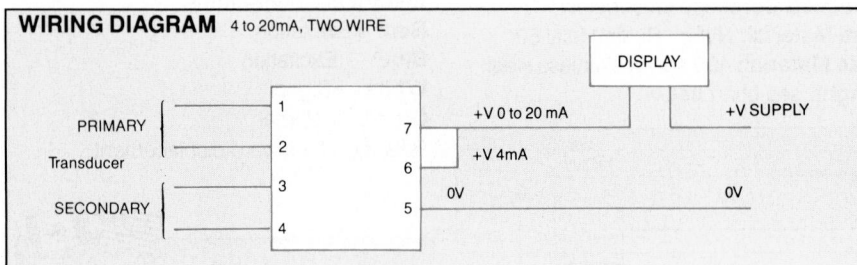

WIRING DIAGRAM 4 to 20mA, TWO WIRE

PRIMARY Transducer — 1, 2

SECONDARY — 3, 4

7 → +V 0 to 20 mA

6 → +V 4mA

5 → 0V

DISPLAY

+V SUPPLY

0V

SPECIFICATIONS

ELECTRICAL

Power Supply: 13 to 48 Vdc, up to 30mA

Supply Protection: Reverse polarity protected

Transducer Drive: 0.9V rms at 5kHz nominal, 13Hz switchable

Oscillator Protection: Open and short circuit protected

Transducer Sensitivity Range: 30 to 530mV/V in 2 coarse gain positions

Range of Gain Control: 3.5 to 1 switched, 5 to 1 adjustable

Range of Zero Control: Up to 100% on max gain

Output Current: 4 to 20mA 2 wire or 0 to 20mA 3 wire

Output Impedance: Effectively infinite

Output Protection: Open and short circuit protected

Output Ripple: <50A pk to pk at 10kHz

Output Filter: Cut off frequency −3dB at 25Hz second order

Linearity: <0.02%

Temperature Range: 0 to 70°C operating; −40 to +80°C storage

Temperature Coefficient: Zero, better than 0.01% FS/°C; Gain, better than 0.01% FS/°C

Long Term Stability: Zero, 0.2%/year typical; Gain, 0.3%/year typical

Effect of Supply Change: Negligible

Terminations: Screw terminals. Access through two cable ports for wires 1 to 5 mm in diameter

MECHANICAL

Weight: 220g

Mounting: Through holes in base by 2 screws and nuts; can be mounted to DIN 46277-1

Acessories Included: 2 fixing screws and nuts

Environment: Sealed to IP65

Dimensions: 2.13″ H X 3.12″ W X 4.21″ L (54.5 x 80 x 108mm)

AC POWERED SIGNAL CONDITIONER FOR AC LVDTS
PROVIDES TRANSDUCER EXCITATION & 0 TO ±5 VDC ANALOG OUTPUT
WORKS WITH LD200 AND LD300 SERIES TRANSDUCERS

1 YEAR WARRANTY

DP41 Series Indicator Shown, From $295

Model LDX-3
$326

LD200 Transducer Shown, See Page C-117.

✓ **Oscillator/Demodulator Provides 0.1% Accuracy of Reading**

✓ **Selectable Outputs of ±5V or ±20mA Interfaces With Standard Laboratory Instruments**

✓ **Adjustable Zero and Span Controls**

✓ **Rugged Metal Case**

A compact oscillator/demodulator unit with adjustable span and zero controls for use with any of OMEGA's, and most other manufacturer's, LVDT ac transducers. The unit is housed in a die-cast aluminum box providing a high degree of mechanical and environmental protection. The LDX-3 incorporates its own regulation for operation from ac power of 120 volts. 9 foot ac power cable is standard.

The unit gives output from 0 to ±5V into 2000 ohms, or 0 to ±20mA into 100 ohms max. This, together with a 10:1 range of span controls, makes the LDX-3 a very versatile single channel conditioner for a wide range of transducers.

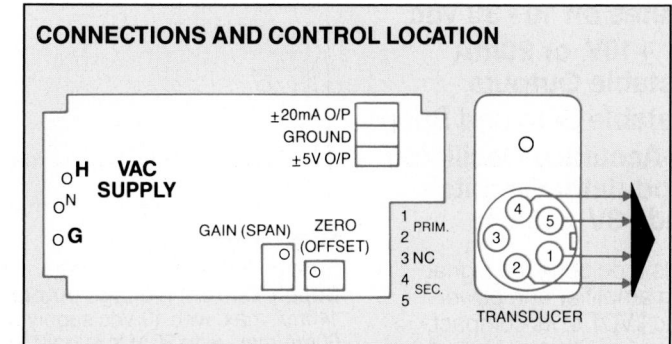

CONNECTIONS AND CONTROL LOCATION

±20mA O/P
GROUND
±5V O/P

H
N
G
VAC SUPPLY

GAIN (SPAN)   ZERO (OFFSET)

1 PRIM.
2
3 NC
4 SEC.
5

TRANSDUCER

SPECIFICATIONS
MECHANICAL
Weight: 300g
Mounting: 2 fixing straps and screws
Accessories Included: Amphenol plug, mountings

ELECTRICAL
Power Supply: 120 Vac 60Hz (210V optional)
Transducer Drive: 3V rms at 5kHz max. rated 20mA

Oscillator Protection: Open and short circuit protected
Range of Zero Control: ±100% of linear output voltage
Output Voltage: ±5V into 2000 Ω minimum
Output Current: ±20mA into 100 Ω max.
Output Protection: Open and short circuit protected
Output Ripple: 2mV pk to pk at 5kHz (typical)

Output Filter: Cut off frequency −3dB at 500Hz second order
Linearity: <0.01%
Temperature Range: 0 to 60°C
Temperature Coefficient: Zero, (offset), better than 0.02% FS/°C; Gain, (span), better than 0.02% FS/°C
Terminations: 5 pin DIN connector
Dimensions: 1.22″ H x 2.36″ W x 4.33″ L (31 x 60 x 110 mm)

DISPLACEMENT

J

DC POWERED SIGNAL CONDITIONER
PROVIDES TRANSDUCER EXCITATION AND SELECTABLE ANALOG OUTPUTS
WORKS WITH LD200 AND LD300 SERIES TRANSDUCERS

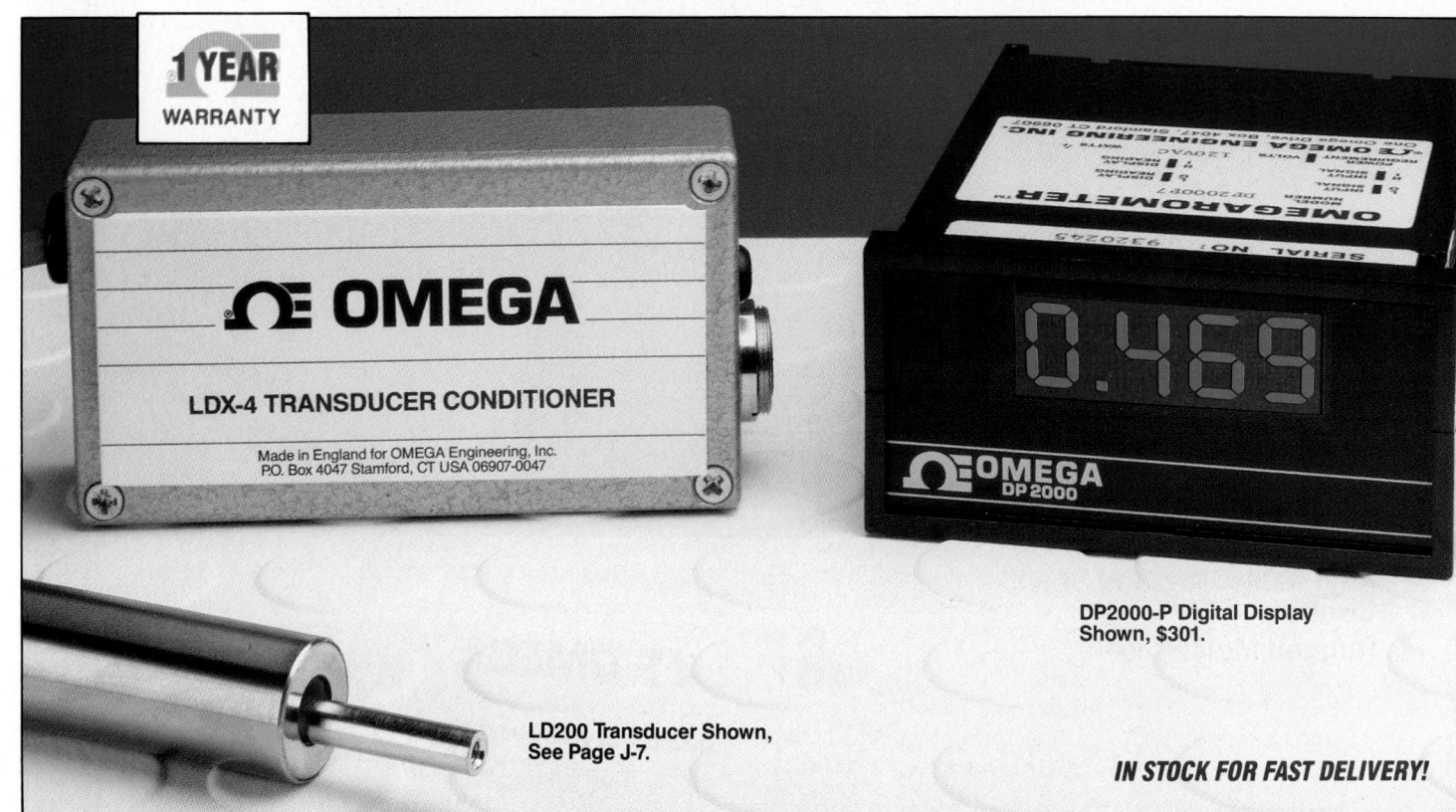

1 YEAR WARRANTY

Ω OMEGA

LDX-4 TRANSDUCER CONDITIONER

Made in England for OMEGA Engineering, Inc.
P.O. Box 4047 Stamford, CT USA 06907-0047

Ω OMEGA DP 2000

DP2000-P Digital Display
Shown, $301.

LD200 Transducer Shown,
See Page J-7.

IN STOCK FOR FAST DELIVERY!

Model LDX-4
$326

- ✔ **Operates on 10 - 30 Vdc**
- ✔ **±5V, ±10V, or 20mA Selectable Outputs**
- ✔ **Adjustable Zero and Span**
- ✔ **High-Accuracy Oscillator/ Demodulator Circuits Provide 3V @ 5kHz**

The LDX-4 is a dc powered signal conditioning amplifier and power supply for ac LVDT's. Its compact, rugged case can withstand industrial installations and protect the laboratory grade electronics. Complete zero and span adjustments allow the LDX-4 to be used with any LVDT with an output between 45 and 450mV/V full scale. Selectable outputs of ± 5V or ± 10V interface with recorders, displays, and other instruments. Also, when using the ± 5V output range, a second 0 - 20mA signal is available for retransmitting the signal over long distances.

CONNECTIONS AND CONTROL LOCATIONS

V out · 0V · I out

5 V · 10V

0V

Zero Span

1 **PRIMARY**
2
3 **NC**
4
5 **SECONDARY**

TRANSDUCER

SPECIFICATIONS

Supply Voltage: 10 - 30 Vdc
Supply Current (voltage output): 140mA max. with 10 Vdc supply voltage; 60mA max. with 30 Vdc supply voltage
Supply Current (current output): 180mA max. with 10 Vdc supply voltage; 70mA max. with 30 Vdc supply voltage
Noise on Power Supply (typical): 20mVpp @ 100kHz
Input Protection: Over voltage, reverse connection
Transducer Energization: 3V rms @ 5kHz
Transducer Range: 45 to 450mV/V full scale
Output Voltage (selectable): ± 5Vdc or ± 10Vdc full scale

Load Resistance: 1kΩ minimum
Analog Output Current: ± 20mA full scale into 150Ω maximum (only with 5V range selected)
Offset Range: 0 - 100%
Gain Temperature Coefficient: < 200ppm/°C
Output Temperature Coefficient: < 200ppm/°C
Output Noise: < 20mVpp @ 10 to 100kHz
Non-Linearity: < 0.1% BSL
Temperature Range: 0 to +60°C
Weight (approx.): 300g
Dimensions: 1.57″ H x 2.56″ W x 4.72″ L (40 x 65 x 120 mm)

HIGH PERFORMANCE INDICATOR
WITH 5 kHz EXCITATION FOR AC LVDT TRANSDUCERS
WORKS WITH LD200 AND LD300 SERIES TRANSDUCERS

Model DP-LVDT
$795

✔ **5 Digit Display**
✔ **0-2 V Analog Output for Recorders**
✔ **Min-Max Values Stored**
✔ **Scalable in Engineering Units**
✔ **AC Transducer Excitation**

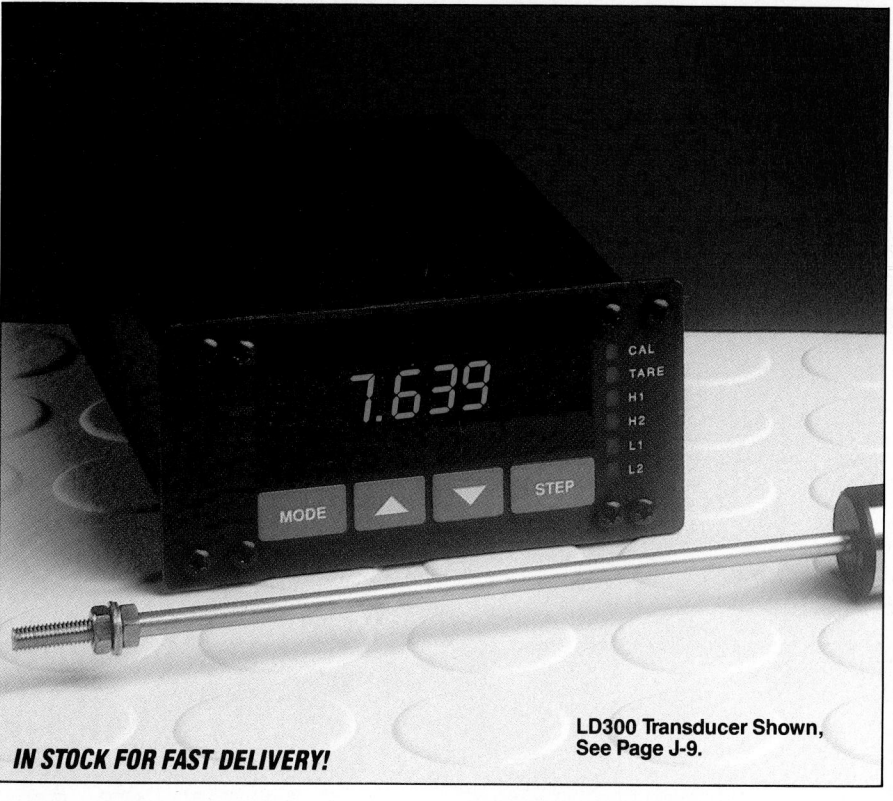

IN STOCK FOR FAST DELIVERY!

LD300 Transducer Shown,
See Page J-9.

The DP-LVDT is a high-performance, high-accuracy, single channel transducer conditioning device combined with a microprocessor controlled 5 digit DPM.

A ±25,000 count charge balance converter is used to provide a maximum read-out capability of ±99999, on 0.4" high-efficiency LED display.

Four front panel push buttons allow simple calibration of the unit. The same controls are used to initiate zero, full scale and trip setpoints. All calibration values are stored in nonvolatile memory to minimize setting up procedures after a power failure. It's also used to store the max. and min. readings.

For the industrial user, the system will provide facilities for diverse applications such as automatic processing, testing, etc., requiring direct readout to 1/10000 inch or mm.

SPECIFICATIONS
ENVIRONMENTAL
Operating Temperature: 0 to 55°C
Storage Temperature: −10 to 85°C

MECHANICAL
⅛ DIN Hard Anodized Aluminum Case:
Case size - 1.72" x 3.56" x 5.0"
(44 x 90 x 127mm).
Splash-proof front panel; Panel cutout—
1.65 x 3.58" (42 x 91mm). Screw
terminal power and signal connections.

To Order (Specify Model Number)		
MODEL	**PRICE**	**COMPATIBLE TRANSDUCERS**
DP-LVDT	$795	LD200, LD300

Options —add suffix to model number

ORDERING SUFFIX	PRICE	DESCRIPTION
-RC	165	Relays & Serial Communication

*Ordering Example: DP-LVDT-RC meter/signal conditioner with relays and communication, $795 + 165 = **$960**.*

ELECTRICAL (Standard Device)
Display: 5 digit 0.4" high efficiency LED polarity indicated for negative only
Transducer Excitation Voltage: 5V; 5kHz (ac LVDT) @ 35mA
Sensitivity: Internally preset 0.5 to 750mV/V

A to D SPECIFICATIONS
Resolution: 1 part in 25000
Linearity: ±0.01% rdg; ±lsb
Update Time: 200 mS; 5 reading per sec
Serial Output (optional): RS232, 300, 1200, 2400, 4800, or 9600 baud, factory selectable. Half-duplex transmit only. Handshake DSR, DTR & TXD.

DISPLACEMENT J

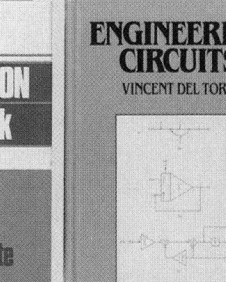

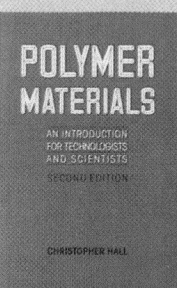
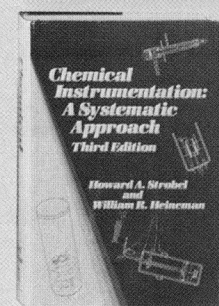

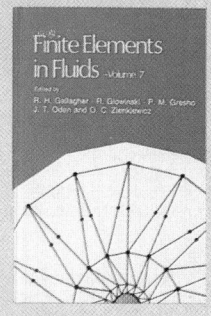

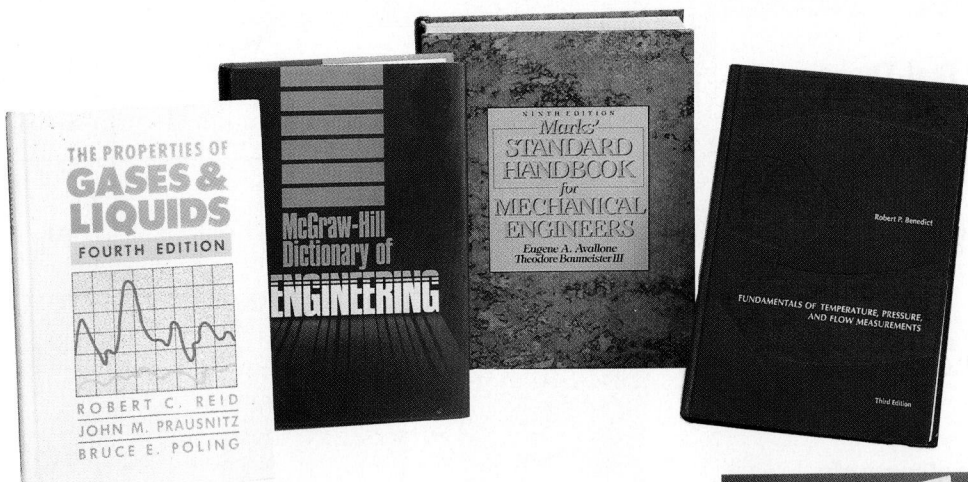

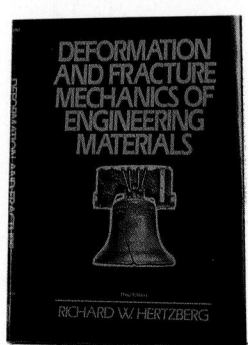

TECHNICAL AND SCIENTIFIC BOOKS

HEAT EXCHANGER DESIGN, 2ND ED.
Fraas
WILEY
ISBN 0-471-62868-9
ORDER NO. ME-0208 **$74.50**

GAS TURBINE THEORY
Cohen, Rogers
WILEY
ISBN 0-470-20705-1
ORDER NO. ME-0709 **$49.95**

FUNDAMENTALS OF ENGINEERING THERMODYNAMICS
Moran, Shapiro
WILEY
ISBN 0-471-89576-8
ORDER NO. GE-0528 **$57.50**

APPLIED THERMODYNAMICS
Eastop, McConkey
WILEY
ISBN 0-470-20666-7
ORDER NO. ME-0737 **$36.95**

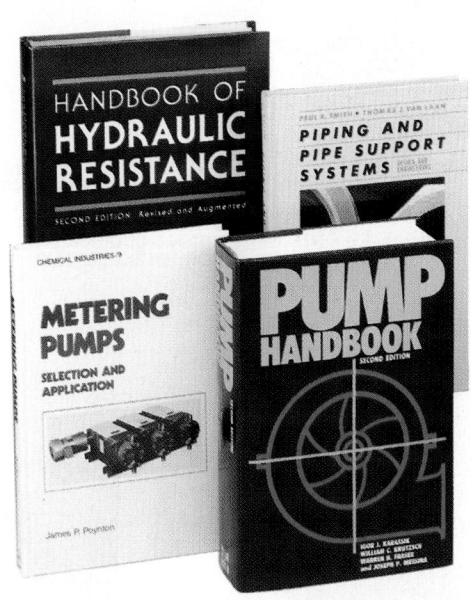

HANDBOOK OF HYDRAULIC RESISTANCE
Idelchik
HEMISPHERE
ISBN 0-89116-284-4
ORDER NO. ME-0614 **$105.00**

METERING PUMPS
Poynton
MARCEL DEKKER
ISBN 0-8247-1759-7
ORDER NO. MS-0919 **$99.75**

PIPING AND PIPE SUPPORT SYSTEMS
Smith, Laan
MCGRAW-HILL
ISBN 0-07-058931-3
ORDER NO. ME-0715 **$54.00**

PUMP HANDBOOK, 2ND ED.
Karassik, Krutzsch, Fraser, Messina
MCGRAW-HILL
ISBN 0-07-033302-5
ORDER NO. ME-0341 **$99.50**

MECHANICAL ENGINEERS' HANDBOOK
Kutz
WILEY
ISBN 0-471-08817-X
ORDER NO. ME-0013 **$89.95**

ON-LINE ELECTRICAL TROUBLESHOOTING
Lundquist
MCGRAW-HILL
ISBN 0-07-039110-6
ORDER NO. EE-1075 **$34.50**

Mechanical Engineering

**VIBRATION WITH CONTROL,
MEASUREMENT AND STABILITY**
Inman
PRENTICE HALL
ISBN 0-130942798-8
ORDER NO. ME-0832 **$59.00**

**MACHINERY NOISE AND
DIAGNOSTICS**
Lyon
BUTTERWORTHS
ISBN 0-409-90101-6
ORDER NO. ME-0809 **$42.95**

OPTICAL METROLOGY
Gasvik
WILEY
ISBN 0-471-91246-8 **$99.00**
ORDER NO. ME-0733

GAS TURBINE THEORY
Cohen, Rogers
WILEY
ISBN 0-470-20705-1
ORDER NO. ME-0709 **$69.95**

**MECHANICAL ENGINEERS'
HANDBOOK**
Kutz
WILEY
ISBN 0-471-08817-X
ORDER NO. ME-0013 **$135.00**

**FIBER-REINFORCED COMPOSITES
MATERIALS, MANUFACTURING,
AND DESIGN**
Mallick
MARCEL DEKKER
ISBN 0-8247-7796-4
ORDER NO. MM-0961 **$65.00**

ON-LINE PROCESS ANALYZERS
Nichols
WILEY
ISBN 0-471-86608-3
ORDER NO. ME-0481 **$67.95**

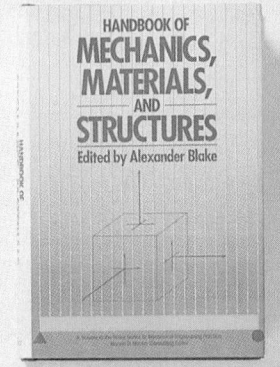

**HANDBOOK OF MECHANICS,
MATERIALS, AND STRUCTURES**
Blake
WILEY
ISBN 0-471-86239-8
ORDER NO. ME-0003 **$94.95**

**STRESS CONCENTRATION
FACTORS**
Peterson
WILEY
ISBN 0-471-68329-9
ORDER NO. ME-0090 **$81.95**

PRINCIPLES OF DYNAMICS
Greenwood
PRENTICE HALL
ISBN 0-13-709981-9
ORDER NO. ME-0830 **$70.00**

**THEORY OF VIBRATION WITH
APPLICATIONS**
Thomson
PRENTICE HALL
ISBN 0-13-914532-X
ORDER NO. ME-0831 **$66.00**

ΩE OMEGA Recommended

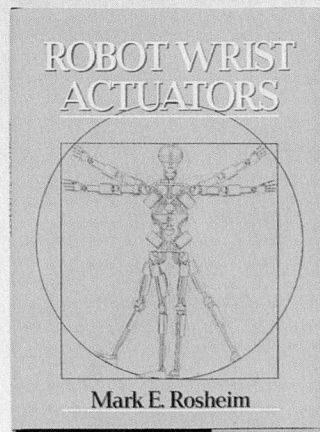

ROBOT WRIST ACTUATORS
Rosheim
WILEY
ISBN 0-471-61595-1
ORDER NO. MS-0933 **$64.95**

DYNAMICS OF MULTIBODY SYSTEMS
Shabana
WILEY
ISBN 0-471-61494-7
ORDER NO. GE-0556 **$64.95**

ADVANCED COMPOSITE MOLD MAKING
Morena
VAN NOSTRAND REINHOLD
ISBN 0-442-26414-3
ORDER NO. ME-0823 **$55.95**

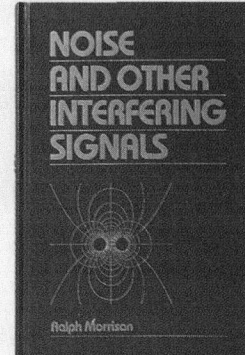

NOISE AND OTHER INTERFERING SIGNALS
Morrison
WILEY
ISBN 0-471-54288-1
ORDER NO. CS-2016 **$36.95**

DEFORMATION AND FRACTURE MECHANICS OF ENGINEERING MATERIALS
Hertzberg
WILEY
ISBN 0-471-63589-8
ORDER NO. MM-0013 **$67.95**

FLUID MECHANICS FOR ENGINEERING TECHNOLOGY
Granet
PRENTICE HALL
ISBN 0-13-322876-2
ORDER NO. ME-0828 **$55.00**

MARKS' STANDARD HANDBOOK FOR MECHANICAL ENGINEERS
Avallone, Baumeister
MCGRAW-HILL
ISBN 0-07-004127-X
ORDER NO. ME-0301 **$92.00**

COMBUSTION
Classman
ACADEMIC PRESS
ISBN 0-12-285851-4
ORDER NO. ME-0708 **$53.00**

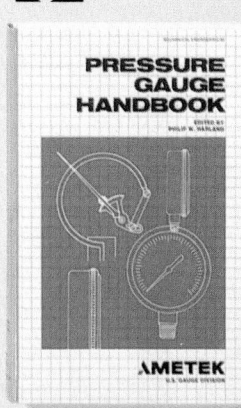

PRESSURE GAUGE HANDBOOK
Harland
MARCEL DEKKER
ISBN 0-8247-7433-7
ORDER NO. CH-4051 **$79.95**

DESIGN FOR ASSEMBLY
Swift
SPRINGER-VERLAG
ISBN 0-387-18929-7
ORDER NO. GE-0547 **$85.00**

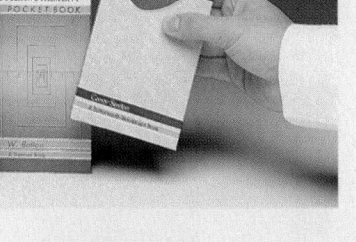

NEWNES ELECTRONIC CIRCUITS POCKETBOOK
Marsden
BUTTERWORTHS
ISBN 0-7506-0132-9
ORDER NO. CS-2021 **$26.95**

NEWNES INSTRUMENTATION & MEASUREMENT POCKETBOOK
Bolton
BUTTERWORTHS
ISBN 0-7056-0039-X
ORDER NO. CS-2022 **$28.95**

NEWNES C POCKETBOOK
Sexton
BUTTERWORTHS
ISBN 0-7506-0221-X
ORDER NO. CS-2023 **$26.96**

NEWNES MECHANICAL ENGINEER'S POCKETBOOK
Timings and May
BUTTERWORTHS
ISBN 0-434-91988-8
ORDER NO CS-2024 **$32.95**

ΩE OMEGA Recommended

Mechanical Engineering

**OBJECT-ORIENTED PROGRAMMING
FOR WINDOWS®**
Tellow
WILEY
ISBN 0-471-52957-5
ORDER NO. CS-2003   **$49.95**

**OBJECT ORIENTATION: CONCEPTS,
LANGUAGES, DATABASES, USER
INTERFACES**
Koshafian, Avnous
WILEY
ISBN 0-471-51801-8
ORDER NO. CS-2015   **$32.95**

**OBJECT-ORIENTED PROGRAMMING
WITH THE X WINDOW SYSTEM
TOOLKITS**
Smith
WILEY
ISBN 0-471-53260-6
ORDER NO. CS-2018   **$46.95**

**FRACTURE AT HIGH
TEMPERATURES**
Riedel
SPRINGER-VERLAG
ISBN 0-387-17271-8
ORDER NO. MM-0637   **$85.00**

RESIDUAL STRESS
Noyan
SPRINGER-VERLAG
ISBN 0-387-96378-2
ORDER NO. MM-0639   **$70.00**

**INTRODUCTION TO RELIABILITY
ENGINEERING**
Lewis
WILEY
ISBN 0-471-81199-8
ORDER NO. ME-0734   **$67.95**

**INDUSTRIAL AND MARINE FUELS
REFERENCE BOOK**
Clark
BUTTERWORTHS
ISBN 0-408-01488-1
ORDER NO. ME-0808   **$150.00**

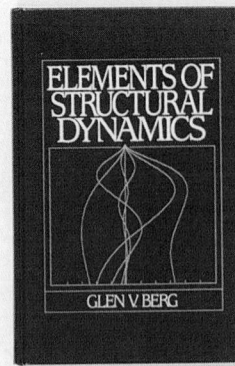

**ELEMENTS OF STRUCTURAL
DYNAMICS**
Berg
PRENTICE HALL
ISBN 0-13-272493-6
ORDER NO. ME-0826   **$54.00**

APPLIED THERMODYNAMICS
Eastop, McConkey
WILEY
ISBN 0-470-20666-7
ORDER NO. ME-0737   **$48.95**

Mechanical Engineering

PRESTRESSED CONCRETE
Nawy
PRENTICE HALL
ISBN 0-13-698375-8
ORDER NO. ME-0829 **$71.00**

HEAT EXCHANGER DESIGN, 2ND ED
Fraas
WILEY
ISBN 0-471-62868-9
ORDER NO. ME-0208 **$74.50**

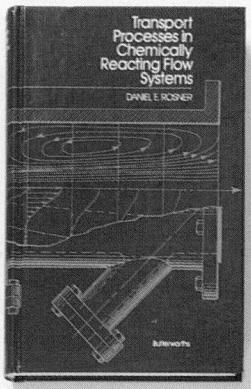

**TRANSPORT PROCESSES IN
CHEMICALLY REACTING FLOW
SYSTEMS**
Rosner
BUTTERWORTHS
ISBN 0-409-95178-1
ORDER NO. ME-0810 **$65.00**

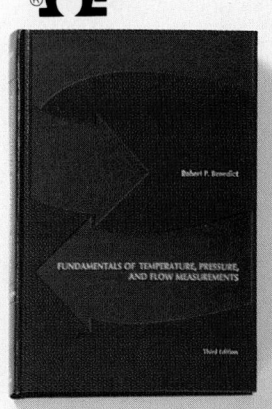

**FUNDAMENTALS OF
TEMPERATURE, PRESSURE, AND
FLOW MEASUREMENTS**
Benedict
WILEY
ISBN 0-471-89383-8
ORDER NO. OP-6 **$89.95**

FLEXIBLE MANUFACTURING
Lenz
MARCEL DEKKER
ISBN 0-8247-7683-6
ORDER NO. MS-0917 **$89.75**

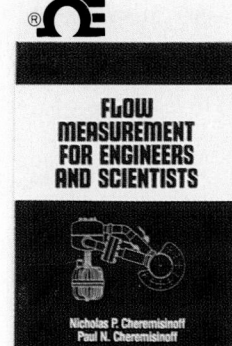

**FLOW MEASUREMENT FOR
ENGINEERS AND SCIENTISTS**
Cheremisinoff, Cheremisinoff
MARCEL DEKKER
ISBN 0-8247-7831-6
ORDER NO. MS-0918 **$140.00**

**ENGINEERING MECHANICS STATICS
AND DYNAMICS**
Sandor
PRENTICE HALL
ISBN 0-13-279092-0
ORDER NO. ME-0827 **$62.00**

**ROTOR DYNAMICS OF
TURBOMACHINERY**
Vance
WILEY
ISBN 0-471-80258-1
ORDER NO. ME-0842 **$71.95**

**ELECTRONIC PRODUCT DESIGN
FOR AUTOMATED MANUFACTURING**
Stillwell
MARCEL DEKKER
ISBN 0-8247-7937-1
ORDER NO. EE-1057 **$99.75**

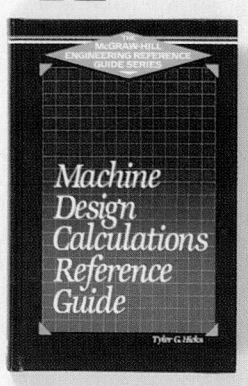

**MACHINE DESIGN CALCULATIONS
REFERENCE GUIDE**
Hicks
MCGRAW-HILL
ISBN 0-07-028799-6
ORDER NO. ME-0713 **$34.50**

**DESIGN OF REINFORCED
CONCRETE STRUCTURES**
Cowan
PRENTICE HALL
ISBN 0-13-201443-2
ORDER NO. ME-0825 **$54.00**

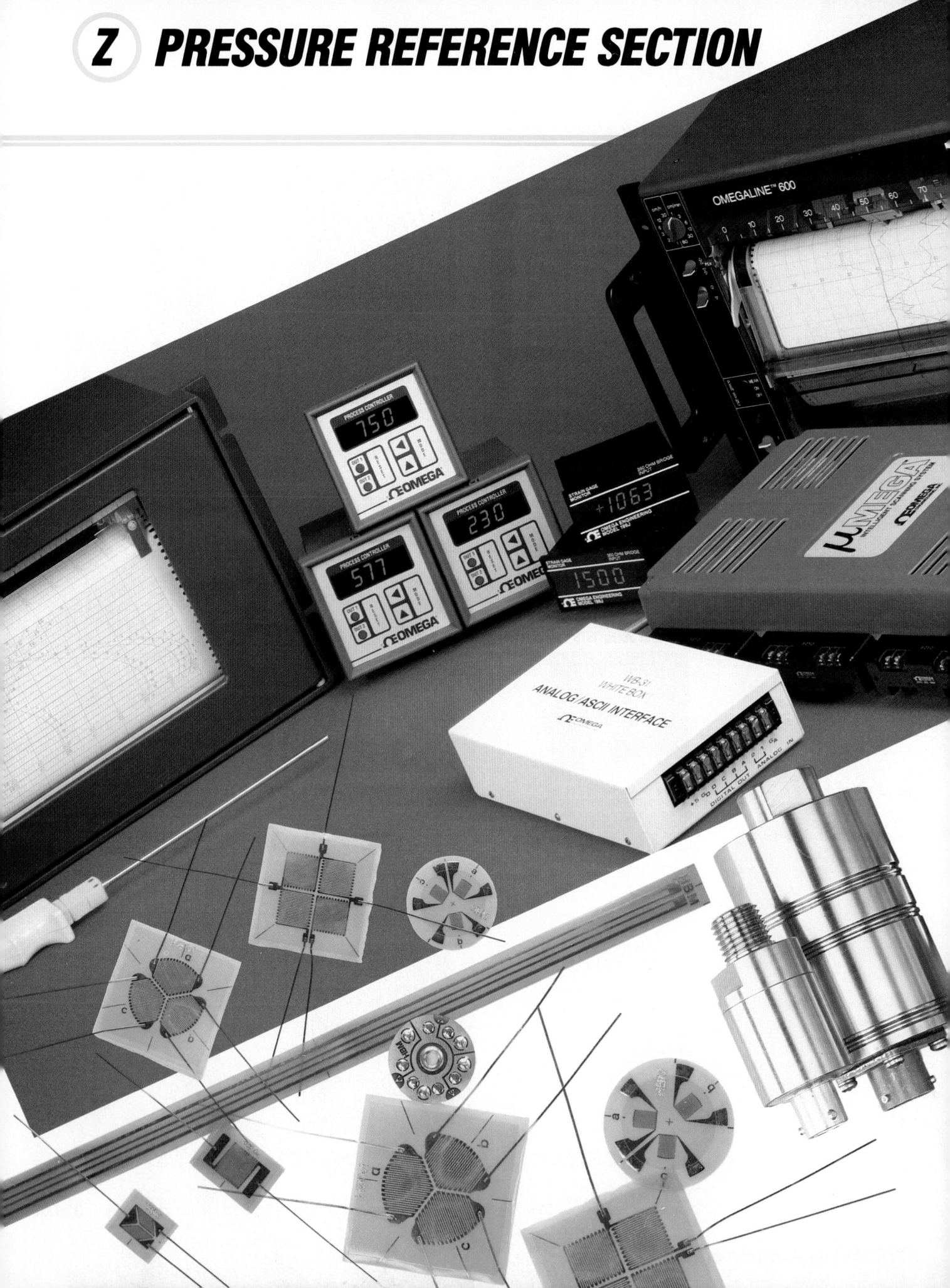

TABLE OF CONTENTS

Pressure Reference Section (Glossary)	Z-3 to Z-6
Pressure Reference Section, Pressure Measurement (Describes how sensors are built)	Z-7 to Z-13
Pressure Transducer Application Considerations	Z-14 to Z-26
Pressure Reference Section, Technical Data Section Conversion Charts)	Z-27 to Z-28
Hazardous Location Classifications	Z-29 to Z-30
Pressure Transducers Installation and Use	Z-31 to Z-33
Waterhammer	Z-34 to Z-35
Mounting and Installing Load Cells	Z-36 to Z-37
Beam Diagrams and Formulas	Z-38 to Z-62
Torsional Members Diagrams and Formulas	Z-63
Circular Flat Plates Diagrams and Formulas	Z-64 to Z-71
LVDT Glossary	Z-72 to Z-73
The LD100, A Fast Linear Displacement Transducer	Z-74 to Z-76
The Linear Variable Displacement Transformer	Z-77 to Z-83
Chemical Resistance Chart	Z-84 to Z-95
Piping Data	Z-96
Tubing Data	Z-97
NPT and Straight Thread Data	Z-98

A

Absolute pressure transducer: A transducer which measures pressure in relation to zero pressure (a vacuum on one side of the diaphragm).

Accuracy: The total of all deviations from a specified straight line. Usually the sum of nonlinearity, repeatability, and hysteresis is expressed as a percent of full scale output.

Ambient conditions: The conditions around the transducer (pressure, temperature, etc.)

Ambient pressure: The pressure of the medium surrounding the transducer.

Amplifier: A device which draws power from a source other than the input signal and which produces as an output an enlarged reproduction of the essential features of its input.

Analog output: A voltage or current signal that is a continuous function of the measured parameter.

B

Best fit straight line (BFSL): A line midway between two parallel straight lines enclosing all output vs. pressure values.

Breakdown voltage rating: The dc or ac voltage which can be applied across insulation portions of a transducer without arcing or conduction above a specific current value.

Bridge resistance: See Input impedance and Output impedance.

Burst pressure: The maximum pressure applied to a transducer sensing element or case without causing leakage.

C

Calibration: A test during which known process values are applied to the transducer and corresponding output readings are recorded under specified conditions.

Calibration curve: A graphic representation of the calibration record.

Calibration cycle: Calibration in ascending and descending directions.

Compensation: An addition of specific materials or devices to counteract a known error.

D

Dead volume: The volume of the pressure port of a transducer at room temperature and ambient barometric pressure.

Diaphragm: The sensing element consisting of a membrane which is deformed by the pressure differential applied across it.

Digital output: An output signal which represents the size of an input in the form of a series of discrete quantities.

Differential transducer: A transducer designed to accept two independent sources simultaneously. The output is proportional to the difference between the two sources.

Drift: An undesired change in output over a period of time which is not a function of the measurand.

Duty cycle: The pulse width times the frequency.

Dynamic calibration: Calibration in which the input varies over a specific length of time and the output is recorded vs. time.

E

End points: The end points of a full scale calibration curve.

Environmental conditions: All conditions in which a transducer may be exposed during shipping, storage, handling, and operation.

Error: The difference between the value indicated by the transducer and the true value of the measurand being sensed. Usually expressed in percent of full scale output.

Error band: The allowable deviations of output from a specific reference norm. Usually expressed as a percentage of full scale.

Excitation: The external application of electrical voltage current applied to a transducer for normal operation.

F

Flow: Flow or travel of liquids or gases in connection with pressure sensing devices.

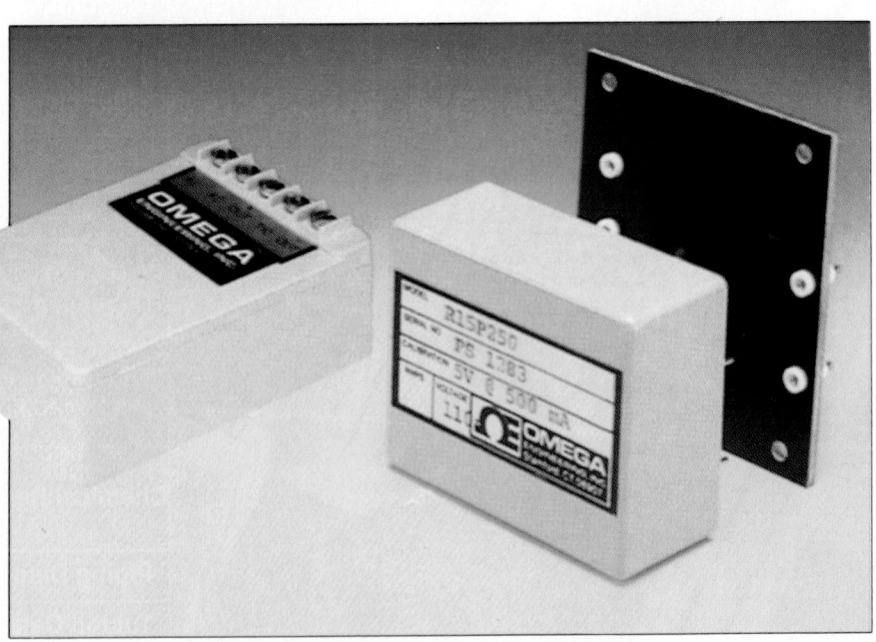

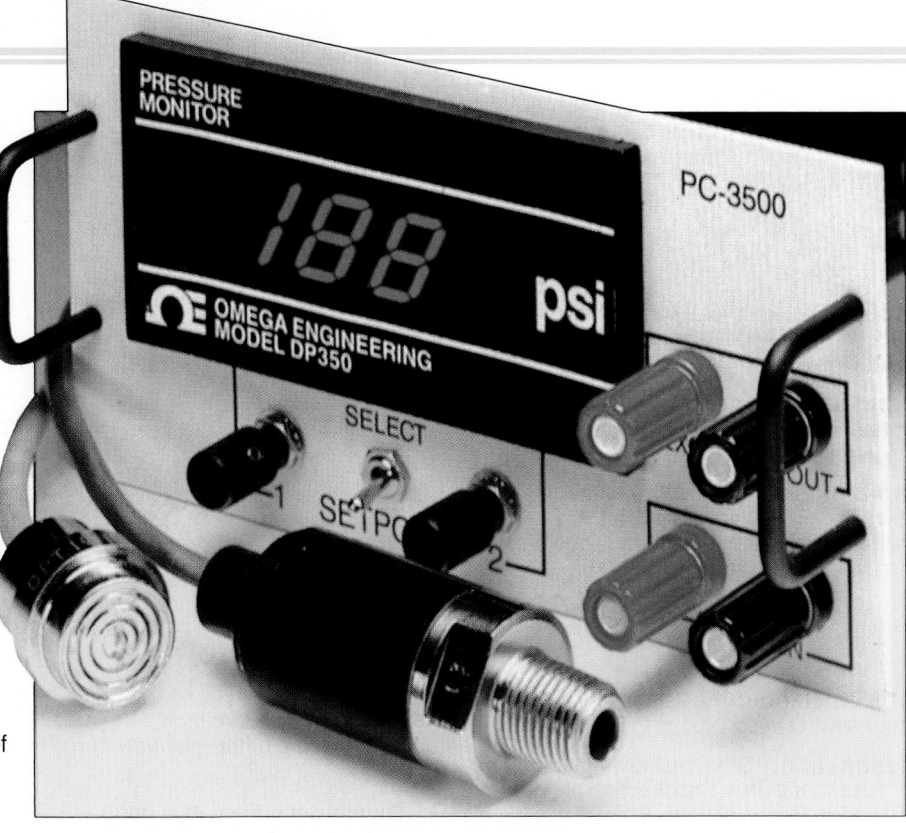

Frequency-modulated output: A transducer output which is obtained in the form of a deviation from a center frequency, where the deviation is proportional to the applied stimulus.

Frequency, natural: The frequency of free (not forced) oscillations of the sensing element of a fully assembled transducer.

Frequency output: An output in the form of frequency which varies as a function of the applied measurand.

Full bridge: A Wheatstone bridge configuration utilizing four active elements or strain gages.

Full scale output: The algebraic difference between the minimum output and maximum output.

G

Gage factor: A measure of the ratio of the relative change of resistance to the relative change in length of a piezoresistive strain gage.

Gage length: The distance between two points where the measurement of strain occurs.

Gage pressure transducer: A transducer which measures pressure in relation to the ambient pressure.

H

Half bridge: Two active elements or strain gages.

Hooke's Law: Defines the basis for the measurement of mechanical stresses via the strain measurement. The gradient of Hooke's line is defined by the ratio of which is equivalent to the Modulus of Elasticity E (Young's Modulus).

Hysteresis: The difference in output when the pressure value is first approached with increasing pressure and then with decreasing pressure. Expressed in percent of full scale during any one calibration cycle.

I

Input impedance: The resistance measured across the excitation terminals of a transducer.

Insulation resistance: The resistance measured between two insulated points on a transducer when a specific dc voltage is applied at room temperature.

L

Leakage rate: The maximum rate at which a fluid is permitted or determined to leak through a seal. The type of fluid, the differential pressure across the seal, the direction of leakage, and the location of the seal must be specified.

Least-squares line: The straight line for which the sum of the squares of the residuals (deviations) is minimized.

Life cycle: The minimum number of pressure cycles the transducer can endure and still remain within a specified tolerance.

Linearity: The closeness of a calibration curve to a specified straight line. Linearity is expressed as the maximum deviation of any calibration point on a specified straight line during any one calibration cycle.

Linearity (end point): Linearity referred to a straight line between end points.

Load impedance: The impedance presented to the output terminals of a transducer by the associated external circuitry.

M

Maximum elongation: The strain value where a deviation of more than $\pm 5\%$ occurs with respect to the mean characteristic (diagram of resistance change vs strain).

Maximum excitation: The maximum value of excitation voltage or current that can be applied to the transducer at room conditions without causing damage or performance degradation beyond specified tolerances.

Measurand: A physical quantity, property, or condition which is measured.

Mechanical hysteresis: The difference of the indication with increasing and decreasing strain loading, at identical strain values of the specimen.

Mounting error: The error resultant from installing the transducer, both electrical and mechanical.

N

Normal (axial) stress: The force per unit area on a given plane within a body

$$\alpha = F/A$$

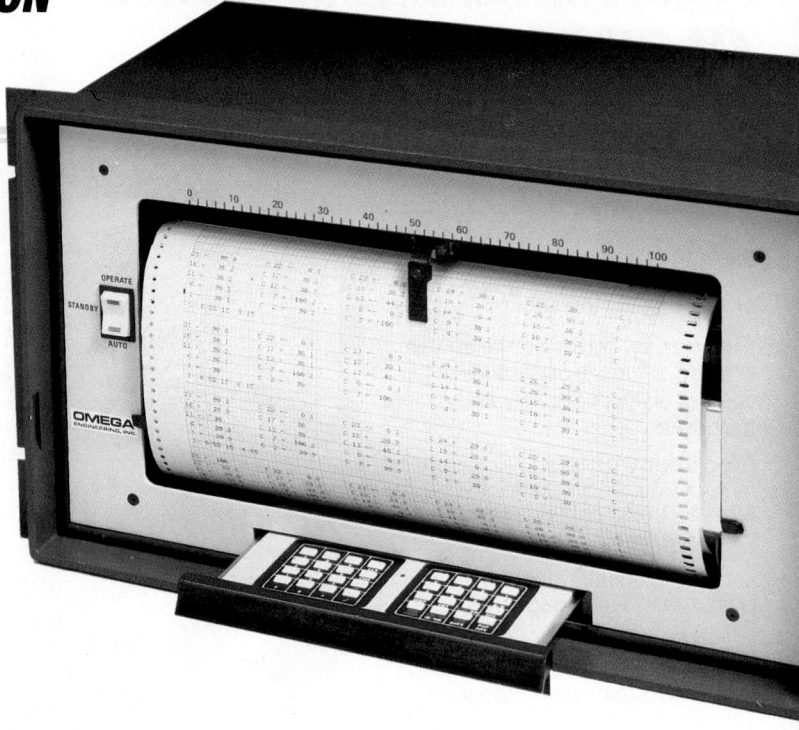

Null: A condition, such as balance which results in a minimum absolute value of output.

O

Output: The electrical signal which is produced by an applied input to the transducer.

Output impedance: The resistance as measured on the output terminals of a pressure transducer.

Output noise: The RMS, peak-to-peak (as specified) ac component of a transducer's dc output in the absence of a measurand variation.

P

Piezoresistance: Resistance that changes with stress.

Poisson ratio: The ratio between the strain of expansion in the direction of force and the strain of contraction perpendicular to that force $\nu = -E_t/E_1$.

Principal axes: The axes of maximum and minimum normal stress.

Proof pressure: The specified pressure which may be applied to the sensing element of a transducer without causing a permanent change in the output characteristics.

PSIA: Pounds per square inch absolute. Pressure referenced to a vacuum.

PSID: Pounds per square inch differential. Pressure difference between two points.

PSIG: Pounds per square inch gage. Pressure referenced to ambient air pressure.

PSIS: Pounds per square inch standard. Pressure referenced to a standard atmosphere.

Pulse width modulation: An output in the form of duty cycle which varies as a function of the applied measurand.

R

Range: The measurand values, over which a transducer is intended to measure, specified by their upper and lower limits.

Recovery time: The length of time which it takes a transducer to return to normal after applying a proof pressure.

Repeatability: The ability of a transducer to reproduce output readings when the same measurand value is applied to it consecutively, under the same conditions, and in the same direction. Repeatability is expressed as the maximum difference between output readings.

Resolution: The magnitude of output step changes as the measurand is continuously varied over the range. This term applies primarily to potentiometric transducers. Resolution is best specified as average and maximum resolution; it is usually expressed in percent of full scale output.

Resonant frequency: The measurand frequency at which a transducer responds with maximum amplitude.

Response time: The length of time required for the output of a transducer to rise to a specified percentage of its final value as a result of a step change of measurand.

Room conditions: Ambient environmental conditions under which transducers must commonly operate.

S

Self heating: Internal heating of a transducer as a result of power dissipation.

Sensing element: That part of the transducer which reacts directly in response to the measurand.

Sensitivity: The ratio of change in transducer output to a change in the value of the measurand.

Sensitivity shift: A change in slope of the calibration curve due to a change in sensitivity.

Shearing strain: A measure of angular distortion also directly measurable, but not as easily as axial strain.

Shear modulus: The ratio of the shear stress and the angular shear distortion.

Shear stress: Where normal stress is perpendicular to the designated plane, shear stress is parallel to the plane.

PRESSURE REFERENCE SECTION
GLOSSARY

Signal conditioning: To process the form or mode of a signal so as to make it intelligible to, or compatible with, a given device, including such manipulation as pulse shaping, pulse clipping, compensating, digitizing, and linearizing.

Smallest bending radius: The smallest radius that a strain gage can withstand in one direction, without special treatment, without suffering visible damage.

Span: The algebraic difference between the limits of the range.

Stability: The ability of a transducer to retain all its performance throughout its life span.

Static calibration: A calibration recording pressure versus output at fixed points at room temperature.

Static error band: The error band applicable at room temperature.

Strain: The ratio of the change in length to the initial unstressed reference length.

Strain gage: A measuring element for converting force, pressure, tension, etc., into an electrical signal.

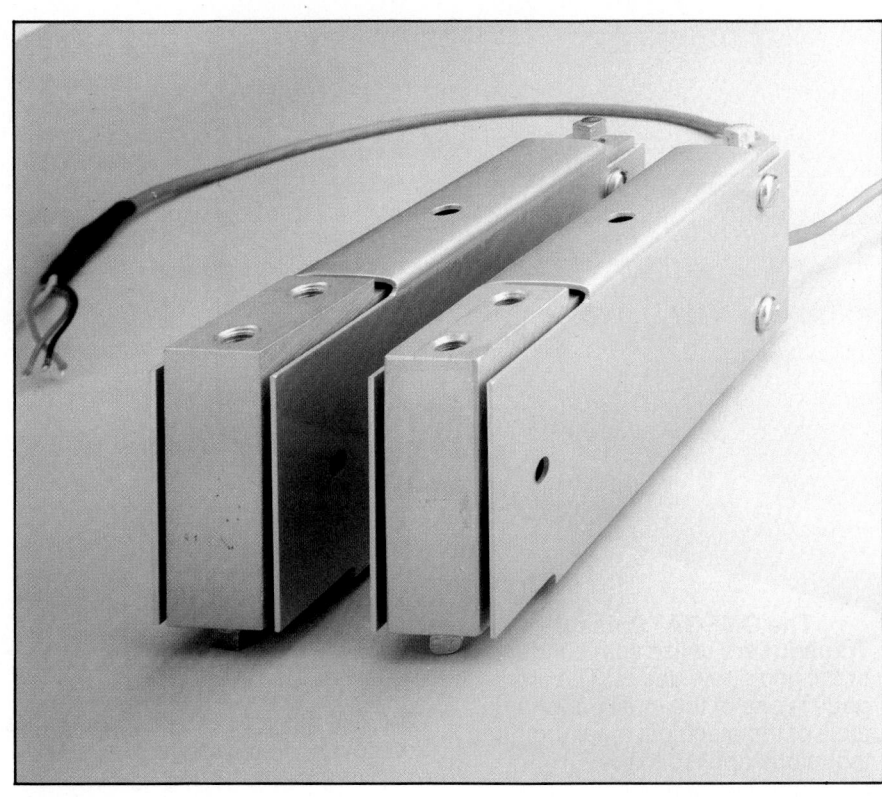

T

Temperature error: The maximum change in output, at any measurand value within the specified range, when the transducer temperature is changed from room temperature to specified temperature extremes.

Temperature range, operable: The range of ambient temperatures, given by their extremes, within which the transducer may be operated. Exceeding compensated range may require recalibration.

Temperature range, compensated: The range of ambient temperatures within which all tolerances specified for Thermal Zero Shift and Thermal Sensitivity Shift are applicable (temperature error).

Thermal coefficient of resistance: The change in resistance of a semiconductor per unit change in temperature over a specific range of temperature.

Thermal sensitivity shift: The sensitivity shift due to changes of the ambient temperature from room temperature to the specified limits of the compensated temperature range.

Thermal zero shift: An error due to changes in ambient temperature in which the zero pressure output shifts. Thus, the entire calibration curve moves in a parallel displacement.

Transducer: A device (or medium) that converts energy from one form to another. The term is generally applied to devices that take physical phenomenon (pressure, temperature, humidity, flow, etc.) and convert it to an electrical signal.

Typical: Error is within plus or minus one standard deviation (± 1) of the nominal specified value, as computed from the total population.

V

Vacuum: A pressure less than atmospheric pressure.

Vibration error: The maximum change in output of a transducer when a specific amplitude and range of frequencies are applied to a specific axis at room temperature.

Vibration error band: The error recorded in output of a transducer when subjected to a given set of amplitudes and frequencies.

Y

Young's Modulus: Young's Modulus (the Modulus of Elasticity) is equivalent to the ratio of normal stress to strain.

PRESSURE

199.9

OMEGA ENGINEERING

242PC100G
8331

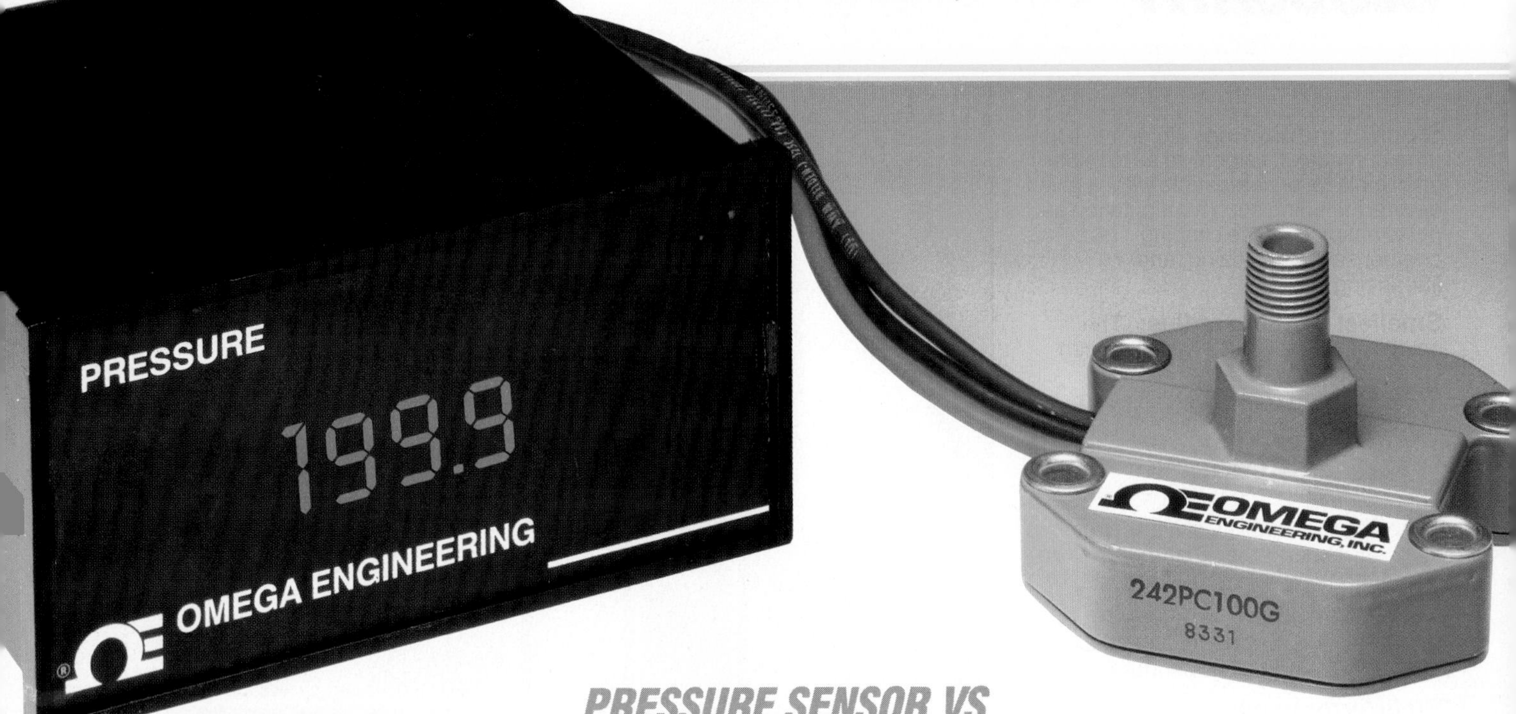

The OMEGA® Pressure Transducers utilize semiconductor or foil grid strain gages. The strain gage is one of the most important tools of the electrical measurement technique applied to the measurement of mechanical quantities. As their proper name indicates, they are used for the measurement of strain. As a technical term "strain" is comprised of tensile and compressive strain, distinguished by a positive or negative sign. Thus, strain gages can be used to pick up expansion as well as contraction.

The strain of a body is always caused by an external influence or an internal effect. Strain might be caused by forces, pressures, heat, or structural changes of the material. If certain conditions are fulfilled, the amount or the value of the influencing quantity can be derived from the measured strain value. In experimental stress analysis, this feature is widely used. Experimental stress analysis uses the strain values measured on the surface of a specimen or structural part to state the stress in the material and also to predict its safety and endurance. Special tranducers can be designed for the measurement of forces or other derived quantities, e.g. moments, pressures, accelerations, displacements, vibrations and others. The tranducer generally contains a pressure sensitive diaphragm with strain gages bonded to it.

PRESSURE SENSOR VS PRESSURE TRANSDUCER

OMEGA® Pressure Transducers are composed of pressure sensors (diaphragm and strain gages) coupled with compensation networks. The pressure sensor, by itself, is incomplete; it is a subcomponent for a calibrated transducer.

Within the last several years, pressure sensors in the form of integrated circuits with etched pressure-sensitive diaphragms have been introduced. These sensors are frequently called transducers, and users expect them to accurately measure pressure directly without additional network compensation, but they will not do so (see Figure 1 and Table 1). The calibration and compensation of pressure sensors are the most expensive steps in the transducer manufacturing process. This process requires special equipment, technical skills, proprietary knowledge about the chip, and a program to calibrate for the extreme parameters of the chips to be purchased.

In order to be complete, the sensor must have either intrinsic in its design or added to it the following properties:

1. An integral pressure interface (diaphragm) that isolates and couples the measurand to the sensing elements (strain gages)

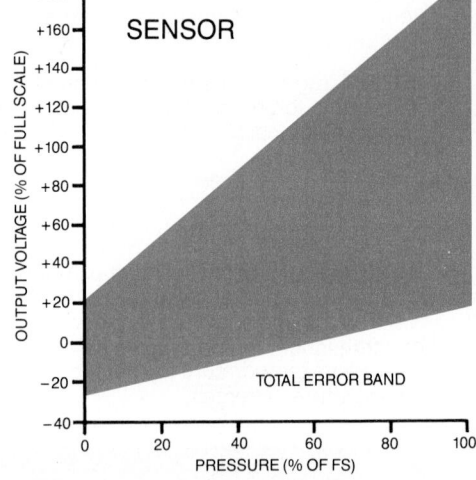

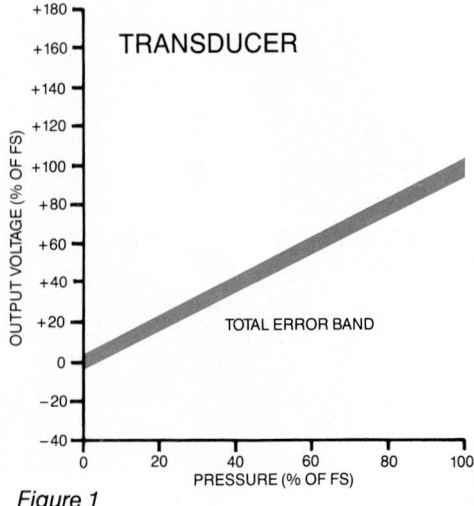

Figure 1

2. **Minimal thermal coefficients** of expansion and contraction of all sensor parts (or alternatively self-compensating parts) between the sensor and all mechanical interfaces;

3. **Excellent linearity,** hysteresis, and repeatability.

Regardless of complexity, no procedure would yield a satisfactory calibrated transducer if its sensor did not have these properties. Sensors having these properties are now ready to be compensated.

The objective in calibration is to:

1. **Make the sensor into a transducer** that is interchangeable from unit to unit without readjustment;

2. **Compensate for the nonlinear** characteristics of the strain gage.

The typical specifications shown in Table 1 illustrate that the sensor output for a given pressure input must be calibrated to make it useful. Figure 2, while not illustrating all of the calibration and compensation methods available to the user or the transducer manufacturer, serves to illustrate the scope of the tasks involved in transforming a sensor into a calibrated transducer.

The ideal sensor application:

There is a stable (constant) operating temperature

OR

the drift due to temperature is tolerable

AND

the pressure media will be compatible with the input side of the chamber.

AND

interchangeability is not a requirement — zero and gain adjustments are accessible.

Operating temperature is seldom stable and drift with temperature is very extensive. The sensor must be compensated over the operating temperature range both at zero and full pressure to be stable.

If temperature is not a factor, then only sensitivity and zero balances must be set (see Table 2). The values for trim resistors will vary from unit to unit.

If temperature is a factor, adjust for A, B, C, and D according to Table 2. Each adjustment has some effect upon the others, and the cycle may have to be repeated for close tolerances of $\pm 2\%$.

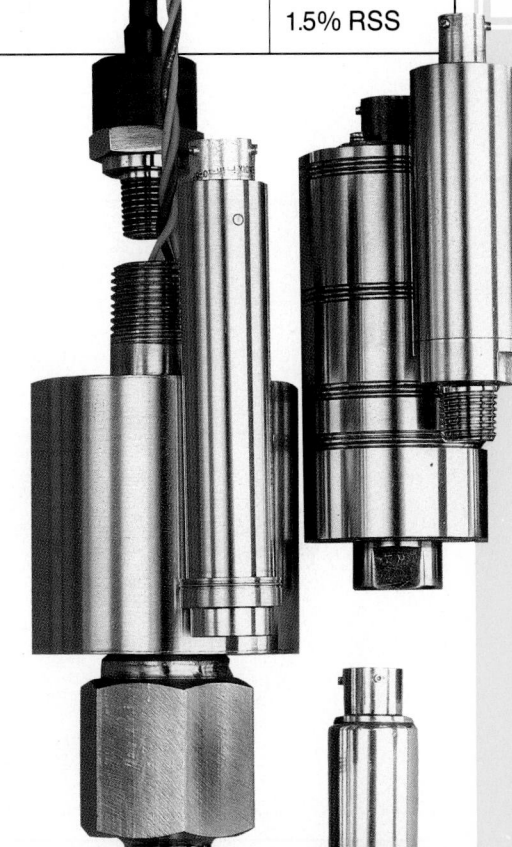

TABLE 1
COMPARING OPERATING SPECIFICATIONS

Typical Sensor	Parameter	Typical Transducer
$\pm 50\%$	Sensitivity	$\pm 1\%$
$\pm 20\%$	Zero balance (null)	$\pm 1\%$
$\pm 0.5\%$	Nonlinearity and hysteresis	$\pm 0.5\%$
$\pm 10\%$	Thermal pressure coefficient	$\pm 0.5\%$
$\pm 5\%$	Thermal zero coefficient	$\pm 0.5\%$
to be calibrated	Total error band	1.5% RSS

TABLE 2
COMPENSATION PROCEDURES

Compensation	Added Components	Equipment Needed	Required Knowledge	Interaction
A Sensitivity	Potentiometer or Fixed Resistor	Calibrated Pressure Source and Readout	Bridge Resistance	**C** Thermal Effect on Sensitivity
B Zero Balance	Potentiometer (2) or Fixed Resistors (2)	Power Supply and Readout	Bridge Resistance	**D** Thermal Effect on Zero
C Thermal Effect on Sensitivity	Resistor and Thermistor	Calibrated Pressure Source Temperature Chamber and Readout	Bridge Temperature Coefficient of Resistance; Bridge Temp. Coefficient of Sensitivity	**A** Sensitivity
D Thermal Effect on Zero	Fixed Resistor	Temperature Chamber, and Readout	Gage Temperature Coefficent of Resistance; Bridge Temp. Coefficient of Resistance	**A** Sensitivity **B** Zero Balance **C** Thermal Effect on Sensitivity

SENSOR + COMPENSATION PROCEDURES = TRANSDUCER

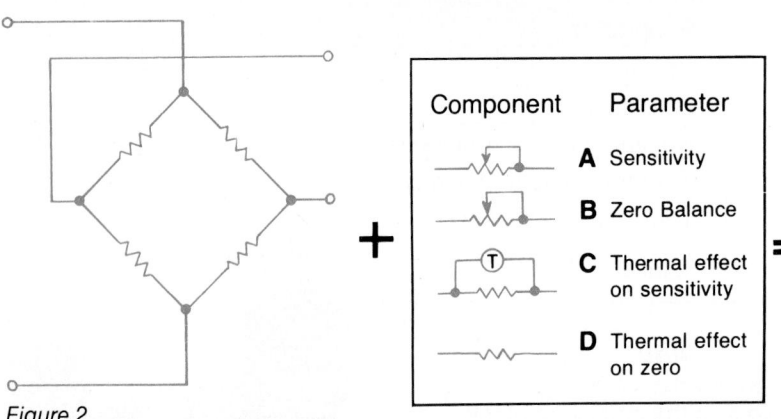

Figure 2

Component	Parameter
A	Sensitivity
B	Zero Balance
C	Thermal effect on sensitivity
D	Thermal effect on zero

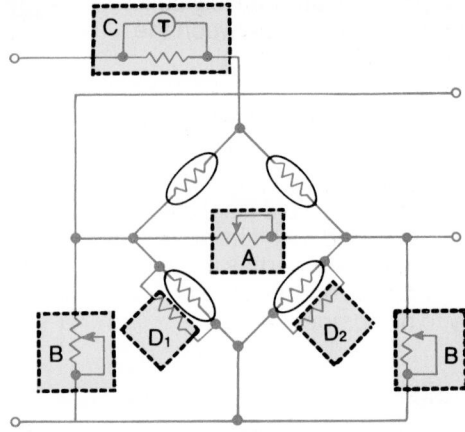

D_1 use if zero T.C. $\frac{\Delta EO}{\Delta T}$ is positive

D_2 use if zero T.C. $\frac{\Delta EO}{\Delta T}$ is negative

External Zero Balance Circuit

OMEGA transducers are fully compensated for zero balance, span and temperature. However, as with all transducers, the long-term effects of component aging require that the user provide some type of external zero balance to recalibrate the system (see Figure 3), or the zero offset can be compensated with instrumentation.

CONCLUSION

The ideal pressure transducer should be:

* **interchangeable**
* **accurate over a wide temperature range**
* **operable at temperature extremes**
* **durable within the external environment**
* **durable within the pressure environment**
* **compatible with various measurand (gases, liquids, slurries, etc.)**
* **isolated from the measurand**

Calibrating and compensating a sensor to make a calibrated transducer is not easy. It requires skill, equipment, and intimate knowledge of sensor characteristics. All OMEGA pressure transducers are fully compensated.

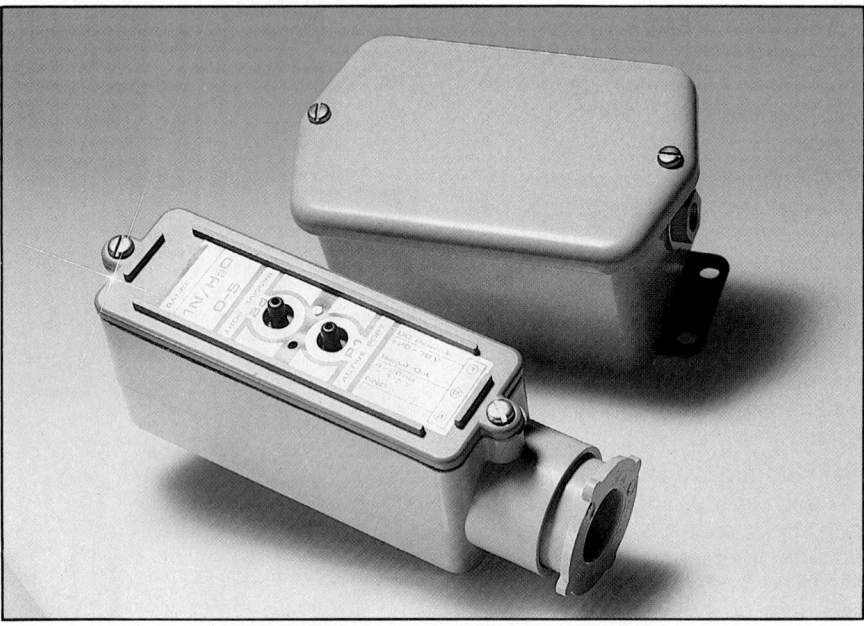

Figure 3

NOTES:
1. CIRCUIT PROVIDES APPROXIMATELY 50% FULL SCALE ZERO BALANCE
2. "C" ARE CALIBRATION ADJUSTMENT RESISTORS INSIDE TRANSDUCER

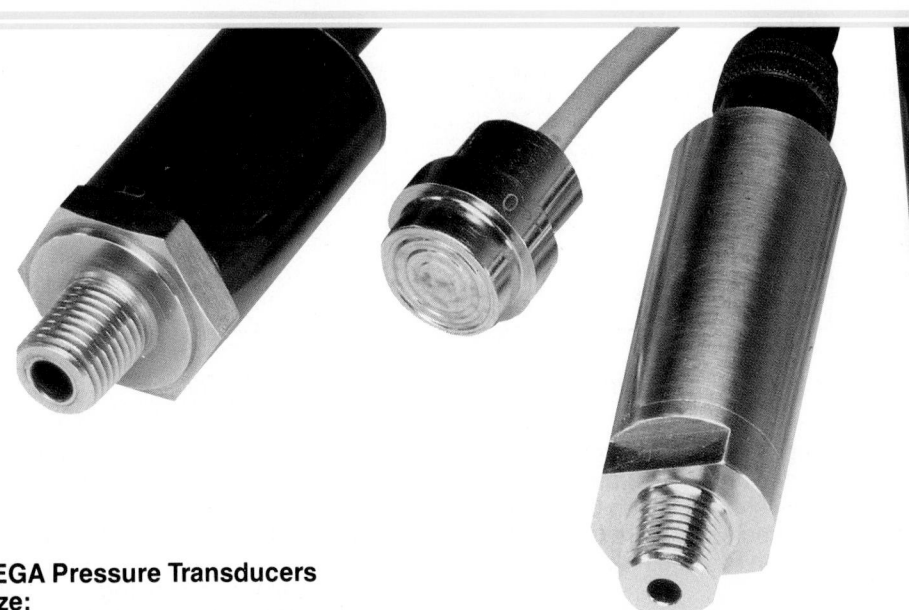

OMEGA Pressure Transducers utilize:

1. Semiconductor strain gages bonded to a silicon diaphragm (piezoresistive);

2. Semiconductor strain gages bonded to a stainless steel diaphragm;

3. Foil grid strain gages bonded to a stainless steel diaphragm.

PIEZORESISTIVE (SILICON) DIAPHRAGMS

Operating Principle

Piezoresistance of a semiconductor can be described as the change in resistance that is caused by an applied strain of the diaphragm. Thus, solid state resistors can be used as pressure sensors, much like wire strain gages, but with several important differences and advantages.

The high sensitivity, or gage factor, is perhaps 100 times that of wire strain gages. Piezoresistors are diffused into a homogeneous single crystalline silicon medium. The diffused resistors are thus integrated into the silicon force sensing member. Typically, other types of strain gages are bonded to force sensing members of dissimilar material, resulting in thermo-elastic strain and complex fabrication processes. Most strain gages are inherently unstable due to degradation of the bond, as well as temperature sensitivity and

hysteresis caused by the thermo-elastic strain.

Silicon is an ideal material for receiving the applied force. Silicon is a perfect crystal and does not become permanently stretched. After being strained, it returns to the original shape. Silicon wafers are better than metal for pressure sensing diaphragms, as silicon has extremely good elasticity within its operating range. Silicon diaphragms normally fail only by rupturing.

Technical Description

The sensing element consists of four nearly identical piezoresistors buried in the surface of a thin circular silicon diaphragm. Gold pads attached to the silicon diaphragm surface provide connection to the piezoresistors, and serve as pads for probe type resistance measurements, or for bonding of wire leads. The thin

diaphragm is formed by chemically etching a circular shaped cavity into the surface opposite the piezoresistors. The unetched portion of the silicon slice provides a rigid boundary constraint for the diaphragm and a surface for mounting to some other member. Figure 4 is a cross-sectional view of the sensing element with wire leads bonded to the metal contacts.

A pressure causes the thin diaphragm to bend, inducing a stress or strain in the diaphragm and also in the buried resistor. The resistor values will change depending on the amount of strain they undergo, which depends on the amount of pressure applied to the diaphragm. Hence, a change in pressure (mechanical input) is converted to a change in resistance (electrical output). The sensing element converts (transduces) energy from one form to another.

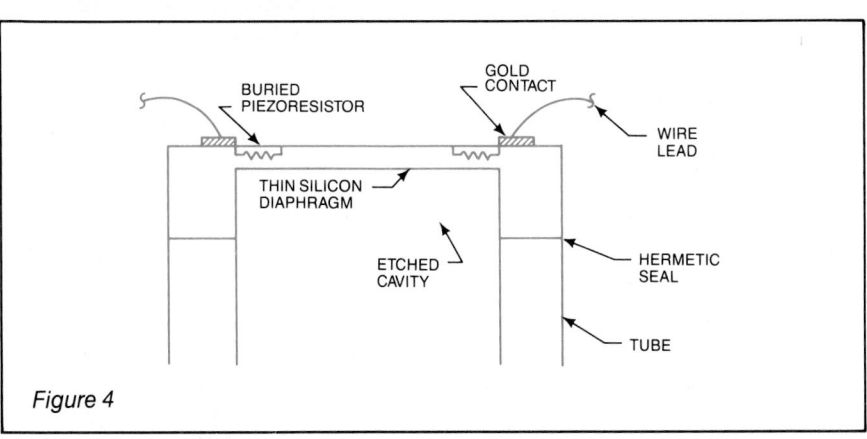

Figure 4

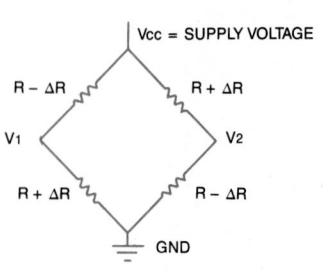

Figure 5

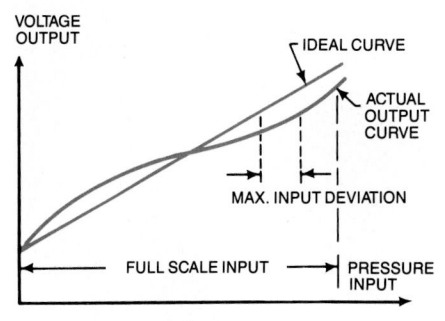

Figure 6

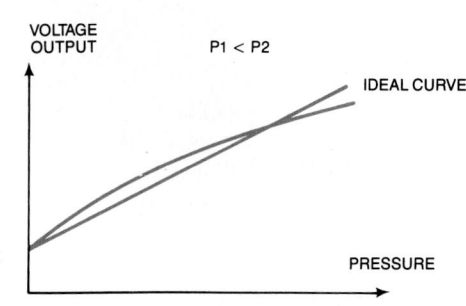

Figure 8

The resistors can be connected in either a half-bridge or a full Wheatstone bridge arrangement. For a pressure applied to the diaphragm using a full bridge arrangement, the resistors can theoretically be approximated as shown in Figure 5 (non-amplified units)

$R + \Delta R$ and $R - \Delta R$ represent the actual resistor values at the applied pressure. R represents the resistor value for the undeflected diaphragm, pressure equals zero where all four resistors are nearly equal in value. ΔR represents the change in resistance due to an applied pressure. All four resistors will change by approximately the same value. Note that two resistors increase and two decrease depending on their orientation with respect to the crystalline direction of the silicon material.

The signal voltage generated by the full bridge arrangement is proportional to the amount of supply voltage (Vcc) and the amount of pressure applied which generates the resistance change ΔR.

The nonlinearity of the voltage output curve is of considerable importance, since it can represent a significant source of error in the transducer measuring device. A convenient way of defining nonlinearity is to express it as a percentage of the full scale input (pressure). Thus:

$$\% \text{ Nonlinearity} = \frac{\text{Maximum Input Deviation}}{\text{Full-Scale Input}} \times 100$$

Figure 6 illustrates the maximum input deviation.

Diaphragms of different thicknesses produce different transducer output curve shapes, when the diaphragm is deflected by a pressure greater at P1 than P2 (see Figure 7).

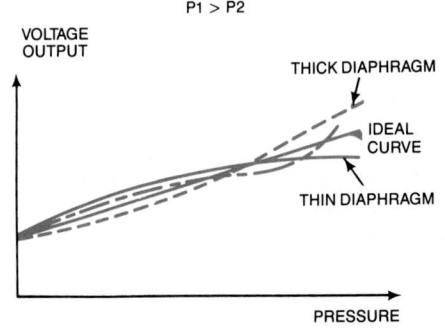

Figure 7

Diaphragms deflected in the opposite direction (P1 < P2) exhibit nonlinearity curves of one shape only, regardless of diaphragm thickness as shown in Figure 8.

When the diaphragm is deflected in both directions, the nonlinearity curve shape will be a combination of Figures 7 and 8. (See Figure 9.)

Zero pressure does not produce zero output. There is some voltage through the unit, even with zero scale reading. This is called the null offset or null voltage, and represents the beginning point of the transducer response graph.

Transducer Types

Pressure may be applied to both sides of the sensing chip. P1 is the termination side and only clean dry gases such as air are recommended as measurands on this side. Fewer restrictions apply to the P2 side, except that media incompatible with polyester, silicon, or silicone based adhesive should not be used.

In absolute devices, P2 is sealed with a vacuum representing a fixed reference. The difference in pressure between the vacuum reference and the measurand applied at P1 causes the deflection of the diaphragm, producing the output voltage change.

Differential and gage devices measure one pressure with respect to another. In differential devices, measurands are applied to both ports. In gage devices, P1 is vented to atmospheric pressure, and the measurand is applied to the P2 port.

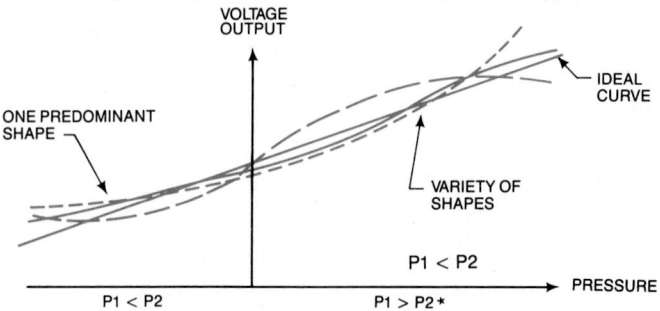

The deflection results in the lower % of Full Scale Output tolerance for Linearity and Hysteresis.

Z-11

STAINLESS STEEL DIAPHRAGM (WITH SEMICONDUCTOR STRAIN GAGES)

Operating Principle

OMEGA also offers pressure transducers which utilize semiconductor strain gages that are epoxy bonded to a stainless steel diaphragm. Pressure applied to the diaphragm through the pressure port produces a minute deflection which introduces strain to the gages. The strain produces an electrical resistance change proportional to the pressure. Four gages (or two gages with fixed resistors) form a Wheatstone Bridge (see Figure 10).

The differential resistance is measured by applying a constant voltage to the bridge. Diaphragm deflection results in an analog (millivolt) output which is proportional to the pressure.

Fixed resistors are used for bridge completion (in half bridge units), temperature compensation, zero balance and to achieve full scale output.

Various output voltages can be provided through amplifier or other signal conditioning circuits internal or external to the transducer. Also other supply voltages are accommodated by using appropriate internal circuitry.

Semiconductor Gage Characteristics

Semiconductor gage characteristics provide overall accuracy and performance. OMEGA manufactures semiconductor strain gages to its own specifications of resistance, strain levels and thermal characteristics. They are manufactured from pure single crystal silicon wafers which are processed through steps of oxidation, wafer alignment, photo etching and diffusion. Gold wire welded to the gage ends is used as a conductor to the solder tabs to provide maximum conductivity and thus constant resistance values.

The initial resistance values as manufactured are measured and closely controlled. Then the resistance at 70°F, 30°F and 130°F is measured. The gages are assembled in sets which have thermal

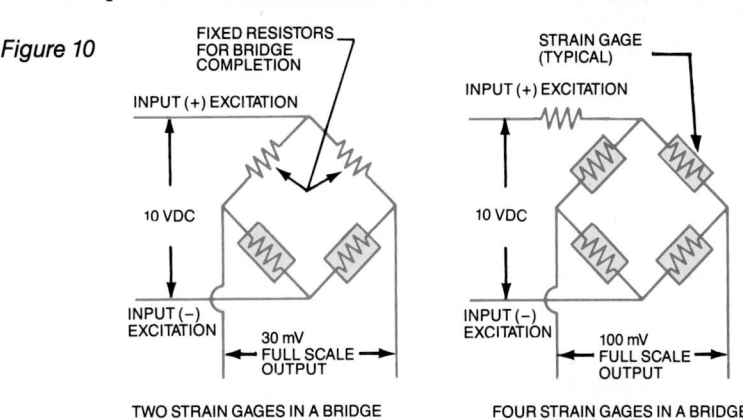

Figure 10

FIXED RESISTORS FOR BRIDGE COMPLETION

INPUT (+) EXCITATION

10 VDC

INPUT (−) EXCITATION

30 mV FULL SCALE OUTPUT

TWO STRAIN GAGES IN A BRIDGE (HALF BRIDGE UNIT)

STRAIN GAGE (TYPICAL)

INPUT (+) EXCITATION

10 VDC

INPUT (−) EXCITATION

100 mV FULL SCALE OUTPUT

FOUR STRAIN GAGES IN A BRIDGE (FULL BRIDGE UNIT)

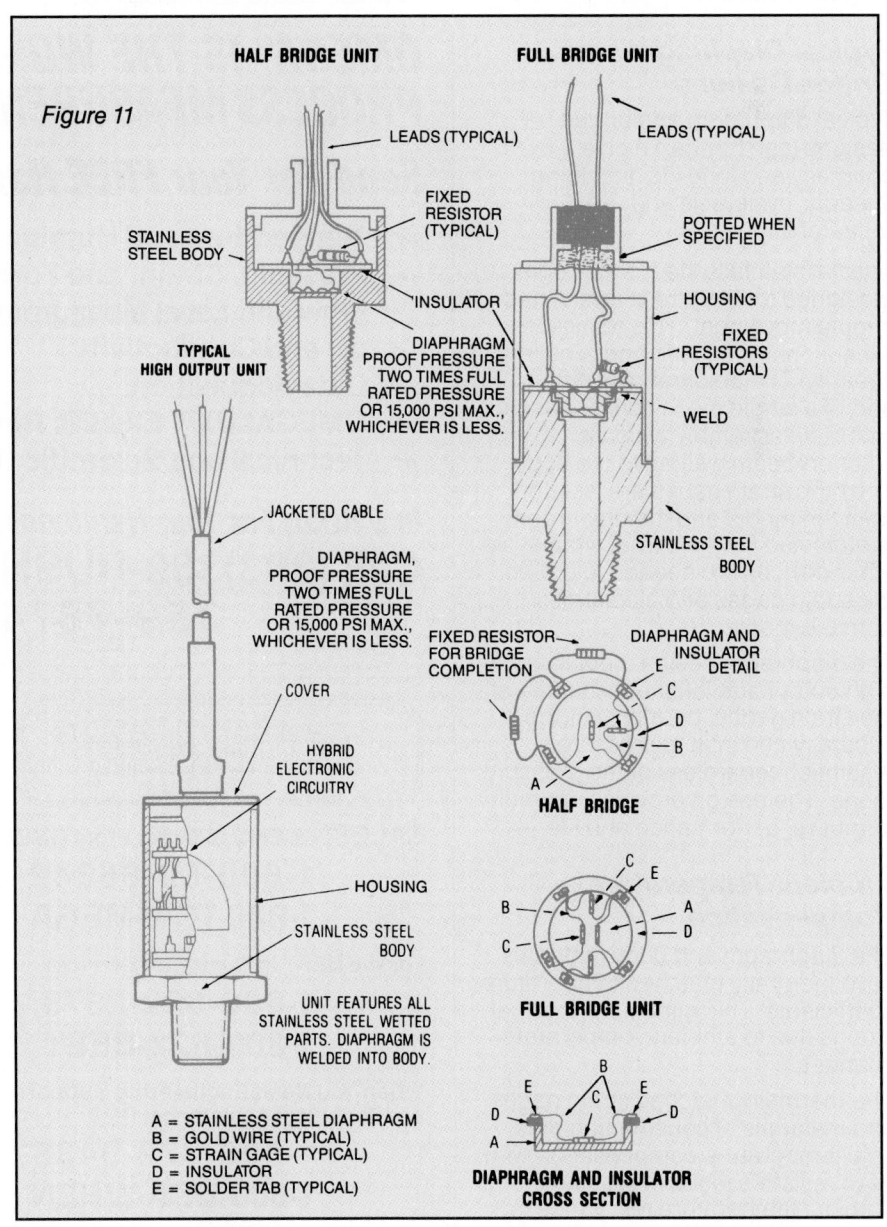

Figure 11

HALF BRIDGE UNIT

FULL BRIDGE UNIT

LEADS (TYPICAL)

LEADS (TYPICAL)

STAINLESS STEEL BODY

FIXED RESISTOR (TYPICAL)

INSULATOR

TYPICAL HIGH OUTPUT UNIT

POTTED WHEN SPECIFIED

HOUSING

FIXED RESISTORS (TYPICAL)

WELD

DIAPHRAGM PROOF PRESSURE TWO TIMES FULL RATED PRESSURE OR 15,000 PSI MAX., WHICHEVER IS LESS.

STAINLESS STEEL BODY

JACKETED CABLE

DIAPHRAGM, PROOF PRESSURE TWO TIMES FULL RATED PRESSURE OR 15,000 PSI MAX., WHICHEVER IS LESS.

COVER

HYBRID ELECTRONIC CIRCUITRY

HOUSING

STAINLESS STEEL BODY

UNIT FEATURES ALL STAINLESS STEEL WETTED PARTS. DIAPHRAGM IS WELDED INTO BODY.

FIXED RESISTOR FOR BRIDGE COMPLETION

DIAPHRAGM AND INSULATOR DETAIL

HALF BRIDGE

FULL BRIDGE UNIT

A = STAINLESS STEEL DIAPHRAGM
B = GOLD WIRE (TYPICAL)
C = STRAIN GAGE (TYPICAL)
D = INSULATOR
E = SOLDER TAB (TYPICAL)

DIAPHRAGM AND INSULATOR CROSS SECTION

characteristics within close tolerances. This controlled procedure is important in order to provide the strain gage characteristics necessary to consistently produce transducers that meet catalog specifications.

Bonding

The strain gages are epoxy bonded to a precision metal diaphragm, the thickness of which determines the pressure range of the transducer. The proprietary bonding method, coupled with the diaphragm design and metal finish, results in excellent long term stability.

Typical Diaphragm and Bridge Designs

Typical diaphragm and bridge designs (see Figure 11) give ±0.5% accuracy and long life (including linearity, hysteresis and repeatability).

The flat stainless steel diaphragm (designed for low stress levels) has minute movement. This results in exceptionally long life and excellent linearity. The diaphragm is either part of a single piece construction or part of an assembly which is electron-beam welded to the body. Thus the strain gages are isolated from the media and the diaphragm is protected from external strains. No other devices are needed to protect the strain gages and electronics from the media.

The diaphragm design, coupled with high output and infinite resolution of the strain gages, permits uniform accuracy and infinite pressure resolution regardless of the pressure range. The design provides optimum output vs. performance and life.

Ambient Temperature Compensation

The diaphragm and body materials have thermally matched temperature coefficients. This minimizes thermal strains due to ambient temperature changes.

The thermally matched strain gages and materials of construction plus final temperature compensation with fixed resistors result in excellent ambient temperature resistance in industrial environments.

Vibration and Shock Resistance

The rigid sensing diaphragm with bonded semiconductor strain gages and low mass, provide a no moving parts transducer with excellent resistance to shock and vibration. This makes OMEGA units particularly suited for industrial applications such as engines, compressors and over-the-road equipment which may be subject to vibration or shock.

SS DIAPHRAGM
(WITH FOIL STRAIN GAGE)

In addition to relative low cost and good accuracy, the pressure transducers (with foil strain gages on a stainless steel diaphragm) have good temperature stability and can be bonded to corrosion resistant materials. They do, however, have a low output (about 3 mV/V) which makes more amplification necessary. OMEGA offers both amplified and non-amplified transducers.

PRESSURE TRANSDUCER APPLICATION CONSIDERATIONS

PRESSURE REFERENCE TYPES

OMEGA® pressure transducers measure absolute, differential, or gage pressure. Absolute pressure is measured with respect to a perfect vacuum, an example of which is the measurement of barometric pressure. Differential pressure is the difference between two pressures. For instance, the measurement of pressure drop across an orifice or venturi, used to compute flow rate. Gage pressure is a form of differential pressure measurement in which atmospheric pressure is used as the reference. Measurement of auto tire pressure, where a pressure above atmospheric is needed to maintain tire performance characteristics, is an example.

Figure 12 compares absolute and gage pressures at sea level. Note that the zero references are different.

TRANSDUCER EFFECTS

Pressure tranducer output is given by $V_O = V1 + S(P)$ for a regulated transducer, and $V_O = Vs [k1 + k2(P)]$ for a ratiometric transducer. A ratiometric transducer is one in which the output is related to the supply voltage by a ratio. For a particular supply voltage (Vs), $V1 + Vs (k1)$ and $S = Vs (k2)$ making the two equivalent. Pressure versus output relation is illustrated in Figure 13.

Null (V1) has an initial tolerance and a temperature coefficient, as does the sensitivity (S). The null temperature error will cause the whole curve to shift along the voltage axis (see Figure 14).

The sensitivity temperature error will cause a change in slope (see Figure 15). Other important effects include linearity, repeatability, and hysteresis. Linearity refers to how closely the transducer output adheres to a straight line over the desired pressure range. One method of computing linearity error is the method of least squares, which mathematically provides a "best fit" line to the data (see Figure 16).

Repeatability refers to the ability of the transducer to reproduce the same output with the same measurand applied in the same direction consecutively, as in Figure 17.

Hysteresis refers to the ability of a transducer to reproduce the same output with the same measurand applied consecutively, first with increasing pressure, then with decreasing pressure (see Figure 18).

Temperature Hysteresis refers to the ability of a transducer to reproduce the same output with the same measurand applied, at a given temperature, before and after a temperature cycle.

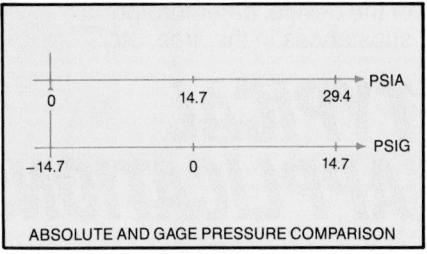

ABSOLUTE AND GAGE PRESSURE COMPARISON

Figure 12

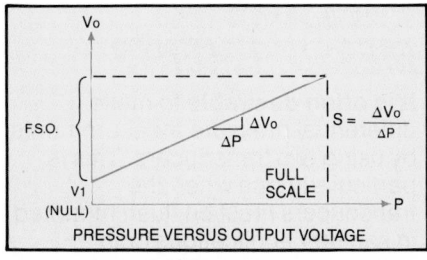

PRESSURE VERSUS OUTPUT VOLTAGE

Figure 13

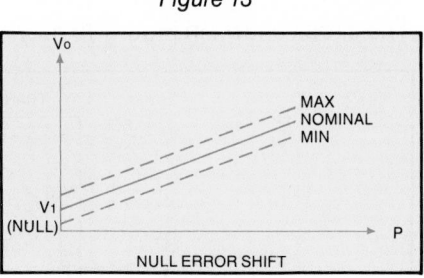

NULL ERROR SHIFT

Figure 14

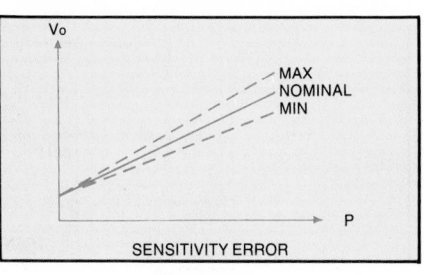

SENSITIVITY ERROR

Figure 15

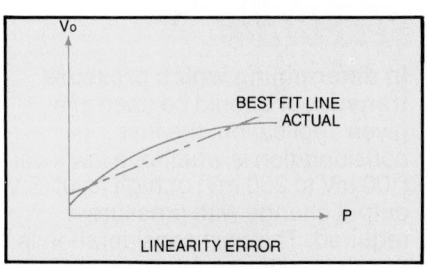

LINEARITY ERROR

Figure 16

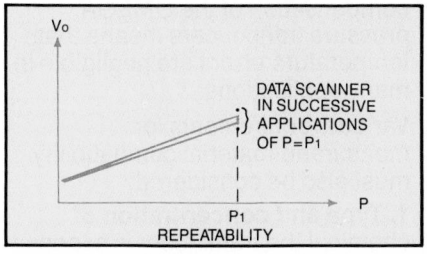

REPEATABILITY

Figure 17

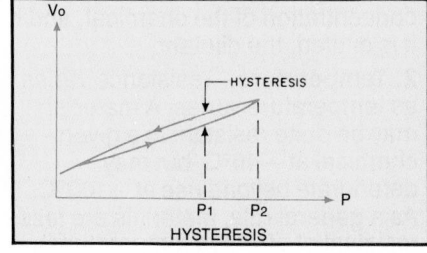

HYSTERESIS

TOTAL ERROR

When choosing a transducer, the total error contribution is important. A realistic approach for computation of the total error due to several independent sources, is the root-sum-square (R.S.S.) method. To assess the total error of a transducer over a 40°C range, for example, the following calculations can be made (values for example only):

Temperature Error =
$$\frac{40°C}{80°C} \times 1\% = 0.5\%$$

Linearity = 0.75%

Repeatability and Hysteresis = 0.15%

R.S.S. Error =
$$\sqrt{(0.5)^2 + (0.75)^2 + (0.15)^2} = 0.9\%$$

An alternate approach yielding the worst-case error is to compute the algebraic sum (using the same specifications).

Worst Case Error =
$$\pm0.5 \pm0.75 \pm 0.15 = \pm1.4\%.$$

TRANSDUCER SELECTION

In determining which pressure transducer should be used in a given application, the first consideration is whether a low level (100 mV to 250 mV) or high level (5 V) output change with pressure is required. The next consideration is the allowed temperature error. The built-in, individually adjusted compensation of the OMEGA pressure transducers means that temperature errors are negligible in many applications.

Various requirements for measurand/material compatibility must also be considered:

1. Type and concentration of chemical the transducer is exposed to. Material resistance to a chemical is usually quite sensitive to the concentration of the chemical, and if it is diluted, the dilutant.

2. Temperature—resistance varies as temperature varies. A material may be quite resistant to a given chemical at −40°C, but may deteriorate beyond use at +100°C. As a general rule, materials are less resistant at elevated temperatures.

3. Exposure Time—the length of time a material is to be exposed to the chemical must be known. Continuous versus intermittent exposure can have a noticeable effect on performance.

4. Type of Exposure—immersion, splash, spray or fumes. Material/product performance varies depending upon the type of exposure.

5. Criteria for Failure—material may increase in volume, distort, or otherwise change in appearance, but still perform functionally. It is important to be specific on what the user considers to be a failure.

6. General Information—application environment, protection of the device, other foreign substances in the area, etc.

TYPICAL APPLICATIONS

DIFFERENTIAL PRESSURE MEASUREMENTS

It is often desirable to make differential pressure measurements by using two transducers. This is particularly true when the transducers must be flush mounted in sanitary applications or to maximize frequency response.

The circuit shown in Figure 19 may be used with OMEGA PX-102 pressure transducers.

Set-up Procedure

1. With no pressure applied, set zero balance using potentiometer R_1.

2. Apply full scale pressure to both transducers simultaneously. Adjust potentiometer R_2 for zero output.

3. System is now ready for use. Output will be approximately 50 mV for full scale differential and will operate bi-directionally.

HIGH TEMPERATURE PRESSURE MEDIA

Frequently it is necessary to measure the pressure of fluids which are at temperatures either above or below the operating range of available transducers. The expense of a special transducer can often be avoided if the pressure transducer is isolated from the pressure source by a short length of pipe or tubing.

The curves (see Figure 20) suggest tubing lengths of various sizes and materials to limit the temperature at the transducer to a range of 0°F to 200°F for fluid temperatures between −400°F and +1700°F. These curves are based on the following assumptions:

1. The pressure vessel is insulated to limit radiant heat transfer to the transducer. Thus, the major source of thermal input is via the connecting tubing.

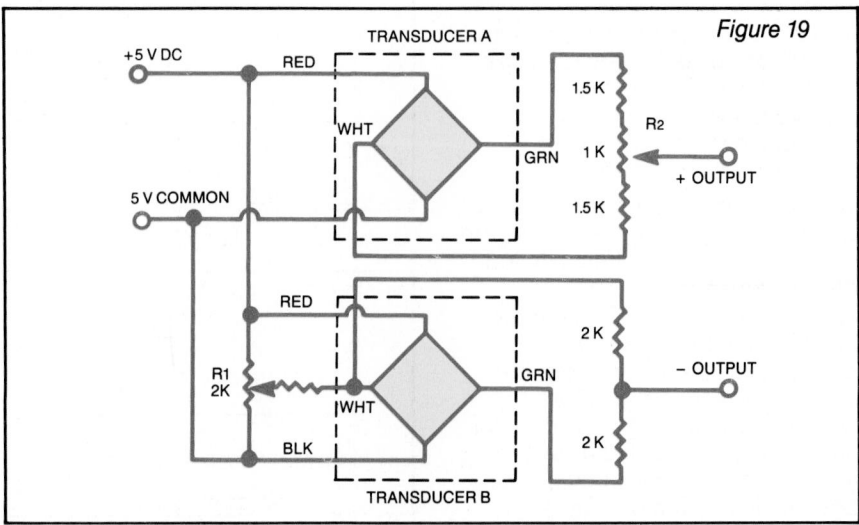

Figure 19

2. The pressure medium has a coefficient of thermal conductivity less than 0.4 BTU/hr/ft/°F. This figure encompasses a wide range of liquids and·gases.

3. The ambient temperature around the transducer is 100°F.

4. The heat transfer rate (convection) from the tubing to still air is 1.44/BTU/ft/hr/°F.

Deviation from these conditions will require some slight adjustments in the length of tubing selected. Or, if there is any doubt, a thermocouple on the transducer will readily verify proper operating conditions.

Note that a 6" length of 1/4" stainless steel tubing will effectively protect a transducer from a 1000°F pressure source. Thus, pressure transducers capable of operating at 200°F can measure the pressure of fluids having much higher temperatures.

APPLICATION FLEXIBILITY

OMEGA PX-102, PX-510, PX-440 pressure transducers may all be used interchangeably in a wide variety of adaptors. These adaptors are simple two-piece fittings which house the transducer. They not only interface with the working system, but also shield the transducer from the mechanical environment.

Nine standard types are available to adapt to almost any application.

Several thread types, case materials and pressure ratings allow the basic pressure transducer to be used in a variety of areas from marine to medical and from low pressures to over 20,000 psi. Several other custom designs exist to accommodate flush mount and integral pressure port requirements.

AUTOMOTIVE DIAGNOSTICS

Application: Measurement of fuel injection, transmission hydraulics, and coolant pressures on production line European luxury automobile.

Problem: Automobiles manufactured in Europe are designed and built for European drivers, driving conditions, and pollution standards. Changes in performance characteristics and operating standards to accommodate American drivers and U.S. EPA regulations must be made—product monitoring to this end is necessary.

Among variable pressures requiring measurement in this program are cooling system, hydraulic transmission, and fuel injection. It is necessary to log these parameters, along with speed engine rpm, etc., as the car is driven under a variety of operating conditions.

Automotive engines are hot, vibrate to significant "g" levels, and have a great deal of electrical noise.

Solution: OMEGA PX-102 transducers with OMEGA AD-1SS adaptors are mounted directly on the engine or its auxiliary fluid systems. In some cases, small "standoffs" are used where engine temperatures exceed 210°F. A customer designed signal conditioner is powered by the car's battery and receives the 0-100

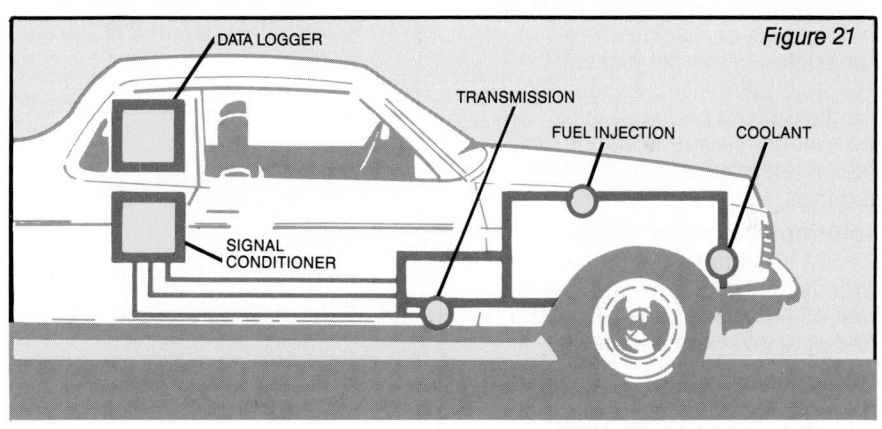

Figure 21

mV transducer output from under the hood, amplifies it, and transmits the resulting signal to a data logger (see Figure 21).

Incoming cars are routinely tested on a sampling basis in this fashion to insure that factory adjustments to U.S. conditions are uniform and meet performance standards.

Environments: Operating temperatures 150° to 250°F; vibration ±3 g's 20-50 Hz; humidity 90%.

Pressure Characteristics: Fuel injection, coolant, and hydraulic transmission pressures are all in the 0-100 psi range, subject to abrupt step changes with superimposed ripple.

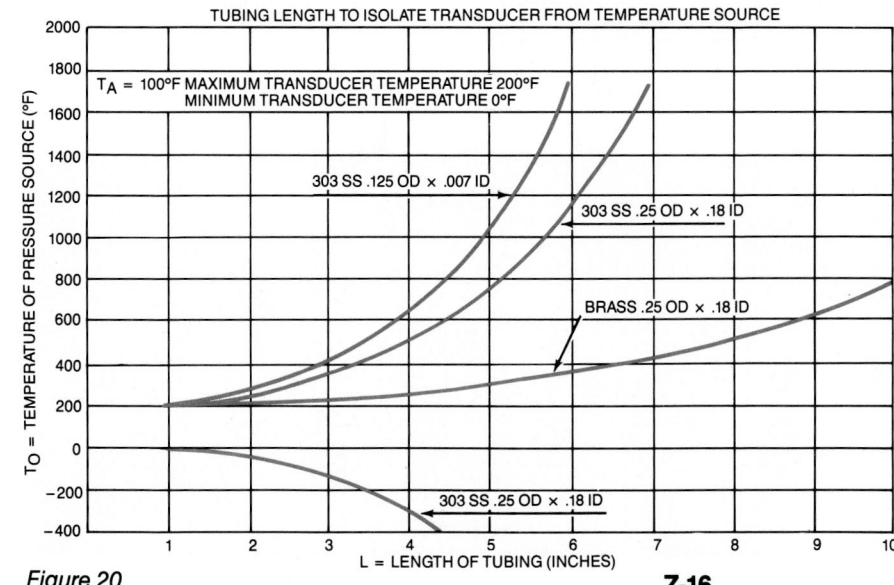

Figure 20

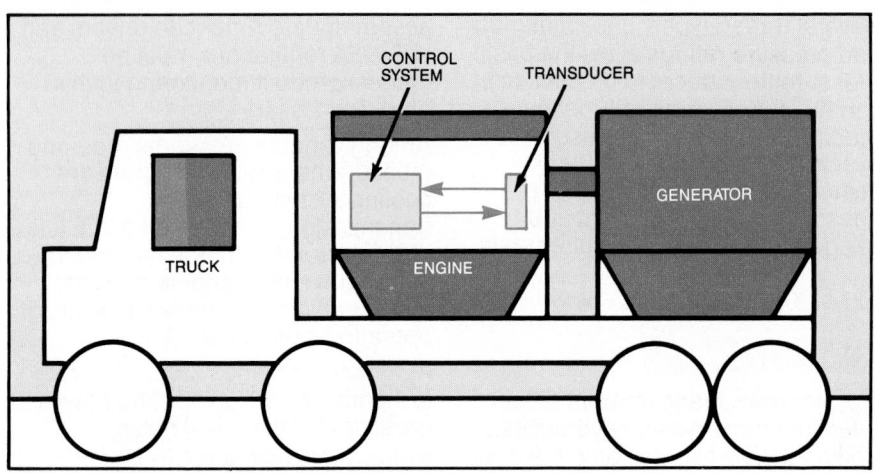

Figure 22

DIESEL ENGINE SAFETY SYSTEMS

Application: Measurement of lube oil pressure in diesel engine generator sets.

Problem: Diesel engine generator sets are used either for emergency standby power generation (typically in hospitals) or full time power generation in remote locations. Absolute reliability is essential; should lube oil pressure fail for any reason, the engine would destroy itself if not stopped within 30-45 seconds.

Solution: A modified OMEGA PX-102 transducer is mounted directly on the engine and senses lube oil pressure, generally at the 70-80 psi level (see Figure 22).

The 0-100 mV signal transmitted to customer supplied electronics activates a control circuit that will stop the engine if lube oil pressure falls below a preset limit.

Environments: Operation in diesel engine environments calls for several modifications of our standard transducer:

(1) Special high temperature cable and adhesives are used to insure operation at temperatures approaching 300°F.

(2) An integral pressure port is welded to the transducer to aid in ease of installation and to insure continued operation in 5-500 Hz environments.

(3) Special testing is required to insure accuracy and interchangeability of 1% over the working temperature range of 150° to 250°F.

Pressure Characteristics:
Pressures are initially quite high during cold weather startups and transducer can be over-ranged. Pressure is generally steady state and the sensor is not subjected to spikes or periodic fluctuations.

GEOPHYSICAL PROSPECTING

Application: Level control of seismic streamers.

Problem: Seismic streamers are long waterproof arrays of sonic detection apparatus which receive and transmit echoes from the ocean floor to a shipboard analyzer.

Proper analysis of these echoes requires that the streamer be parallel to the ocean surface — each end must be at the same depth. A streamer is quite long and towed at some distance from the ship. Should it lose forward speed it may sink to depths considerably lower than its design usage before it can be reeled aboard.

Solution: An OMEGA transducer is mounted at each end of the array and measures sea water pressure (level). The ends of the streamer are at identical depths when both sensor

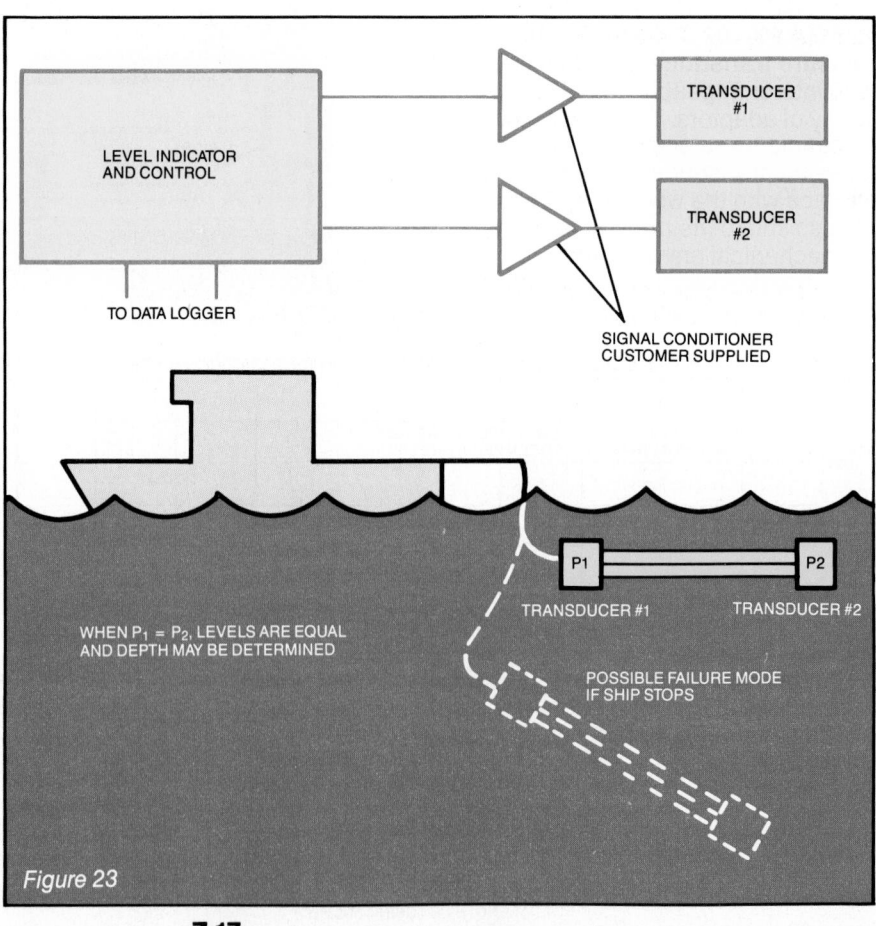

Figure 23

outputs are observed and noted to be equal. This is possible due to the high accuracy and stability of the OMEGA transducers. (In case you were wondering, streamer design does not permit the use of a differential pressure device and requires the use of two independent transducers instead.) See Figure 23.

In addition to their operating peformance, OMEGA pressure transducers are desirable in view of their five times over-range capability. If a streamer sinks, the transducer can see five times design depth without damage or loss of calibration.

Customer supplied electronics transmit level information back to the ship for monitoring, logging, and control.

Environments: The streamer sees all marine environments from arctic to tropical. The transducer is exposed to sea air and water as well as shipboard shock. Severe overpressures may be experienced.

Pressure Characteristics: Other than overpressures, pressures are mildly modulating to steady.

SEWAGE LEVEL CONTROL

Application: Regulation of sewage pumps to maintain tank level in unattended treatment stations.

Problem: Sewage is held in agitated holding tanks. Its liquid level is maintained between predetermined points by a sensor which turns a high volume pump "on" (high level) or "off" (low level).

Sewage will foul, clog or corrode conventional level sensors. It may also contain solid objects as large as cinder blocks or 2 × 4's. Because of its composition, there is always the risk that the pump may be damaged or the line clogged, and sewage may not actually move from the tank in spite of control commands. A positive indication of movement is necessary to insure system and equipment safety. A pressure measurement in the lines to and from the pump is used to detect fluid movement.

As a consequence of the pump's operation, transient high pressure

pulses (or spikes) are generated at its discharge side. These can be eight or ten times the normal running pressure and, while lasting only several milliseconds, could damage an unprotected transducer.

When the pump is turned off, a check valve within the pump will close. As sewage falls back to this valve, a "water hammer" (short duration pressure pulses or shock generated by a rapid change in flow rate) effect occurs.

In short, this application has two difficult measurements—the first being one of level, and the second being one of pump discharge pressure. Both measurements involve difficult media.

Solution: The measurement of liquid level is accomplished by mounting a PX-102-15 psig pressure transducer on the discharge side of a highly reliable commercial aquarium air pump. The pressure required to bubble air through an immersed pipe is directly related to liquid level (see Figure 24). By using

a large pipe, the possibility of clogging is reduced and the system is made relatively self-cleaning. This method also safeguards the transducer since it need not be immersed while sensing liquid level. A nylon adaptor with a "T" threaded into its front is used to mount the transducer.

Normal pump discharge pressure was rated at 20 psi. In view of the eight to ten times greater than normal pressure spikes, a 0-100 psig transducer was used to sense flow from the pump. Since it could be over-ranged to 200 psig without damage (10 times normal working pressure), it was determined that this gave maximum reliability coupled with maximum practical sensitivity of flow detection. The ability of the transducer to withstand vacuum "underpressures" is also important because falling heads after the pump is turned off can create partial vacuums at the transducer on the inlet side.

The discharge transducer is

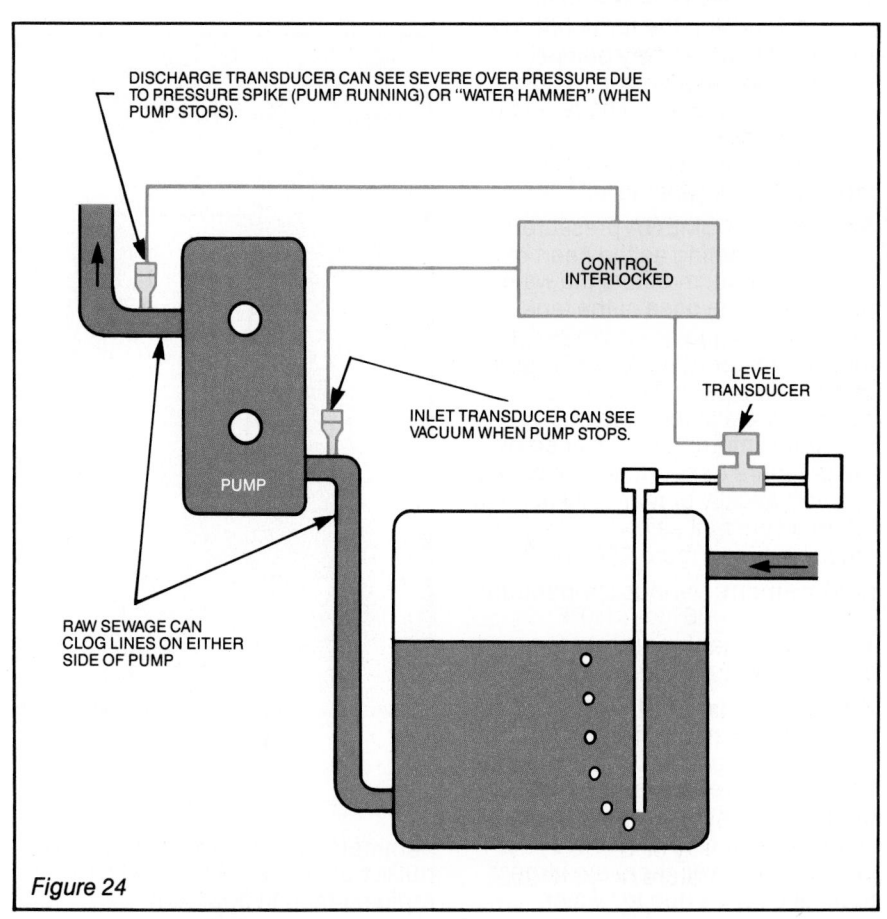

DISCHARGE TRANSDUCER CAN SEE SEVERE OVER PRESSURE DUE TO PRESSURE SPIKE (PUMP RUNNING) OR "WATER HAMMER" (WHEN PUMP STOPS).

CONTROL INTERLOCKED

LEVEL TRANSDUCER

INLET TRANSDUCER CAN SEE VACUUM WHEN PUMP STOPS.

PUMP

RAW SEWAGE CAN CLOG LINES ON EITHER SIDE OF PUMP

Figure 24

mounted in an AD-1SS adaptor in a "drain" position. (Pressure "snubbers" cannot be used to dampen pressure spikes over prolonged periods of time due to the clogging nature of the media.)

Environments: Both level and discharge transducers are mounted in enclosures and do not see weather extremes. Atmospheres are mildly corrosive, generally humid, and, on occasion, explosive.

Pressure Characteristics: Level transducer: pressure constantly changes from 2-12 psig with random ripple resulting from surging sewage. Pump transducers: pressure ranges from partial vacuum to 20 psi with random spikes to 200 psi.

WATER LEVEL CONTROL

Application: To monitor and control water level in water towers.

Problem: Municipal and private water towers must have a control system to govern the turn-on/turn-off function of their supply pumps. Often these towers are in remote unmanned locations. The task is to maintain a constant safe volume of water in the tank without manually monitoring the water level.

Solution: An OMEGA pressure transducer, acting as the heart of the control system, monitors the water pressure at the base of the tank. The transducer signal is processed and then telemetered back to a control center miles away. The control decisions are made here based on the status information provided by the pressure transducer. The control is automatically or manually done to retain a constant safe water level in the tank. (See Figure 25A and 25B.)

Environment: Various temperature ranges from −20° to +110°F. Transducer diaphragm is also subject to water freeze-ups.

Pressure Characteristics: Pressure ranges are dependent upon height of water storage tank. Typically the water pressure is 35 psi. Often it is lower. For smaller tanks, it is under 10 psi. Pressure changes are gradual; however, there are large pressure spikes due to "water

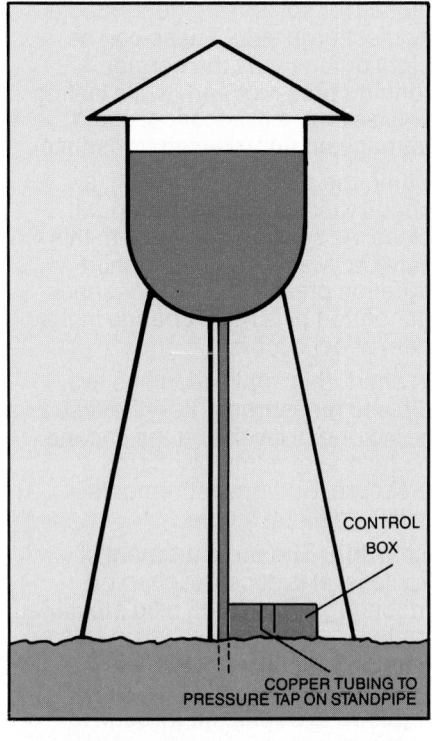

CONTROL BOX

COPPER TUBING TO PRESSURE TAP ON STANDPIPE

Figure 25A

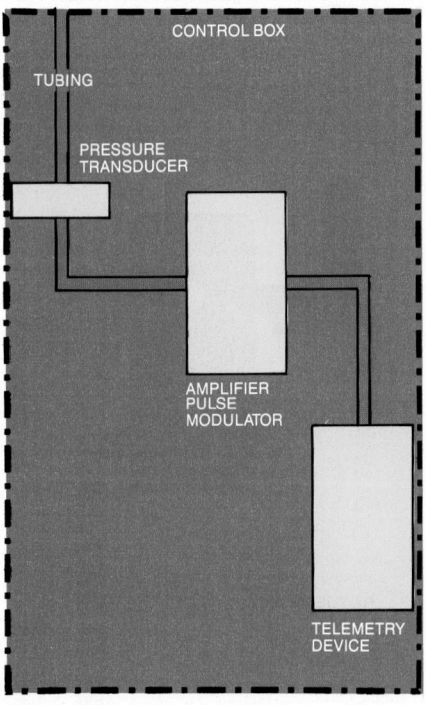

CONTROL BOX

TUBING

PRESSURE TRANSDUCER

AMPLIFIER PULSE MODULATOR

TELEMETRY DEVICE

Figure 25B

hammer" (short duration pressure pulses or shocks generated by a rapid change in flow rate).

DEEP SEA DIVING BELLS

Application: Measurement of pressures internal to, and external to, deep sea diving bells used in underwater construction of off-shore platforms and pipelines.

Problem: If divers can be held at deep sea pressures upon their return to the surface, their subsequent productivity can be increased greatly through the elimination of lengthy decompression procedures.

Solution: A diver enters his bell which is then lowered to working depth. Internal pressures on the first dive are increased to remain equal with external pressures. The diver leaves through a bottom lock, works and then returns. The lock is then sealed and the bell is raised. Internal pressures are maintained while external pressures decrease to atmospheric at the surface.

The diver then leaves the bell through another lock and enters a high pressure living chamber. He remains there until ready for the next dive when he re-enters the bell which is now already at (the same) high pressure. That these two pressures are equal is literally a matter of life or death.

Two OMEGA pressure transducers are mounted within the diving bell. The "outside" sensor measures the pressure in the ocean outside over a 0-1000 psis range. Its sealed construction permits safe operation and accurate readings. When it is back on deck and reads 0 psis, there may be as much as 1000 psig within the bell and on its outside case. The "inside" transducer measures the bell's internal pressure and must also be sealed. (See Figure 26.)

Both sensors must be extremely accurate if the diver is able to leave the bell without danger of its flooding, and to enter and leave his living chamber without an abrupt and hazardous pressure change.

A Signal Conditioner accepts the transducer output and converts it to 4-20 mA for safe transmission back to the ship.

Environments: The transducer sees typical marine environments: high humidity, salt air, shipboard

shock, small temperature changes during use, and no vibration.

Pressure Characteristics: Pressure changes are slow and consistent with the physiological system. The application is unique in that ambient pressures may be much higher than those measured—hence the need for a psis unit.

OIL TANKER PUMPS

Application: Monitoring of loading and unloading pumps mounted on deck of ocean going tanker.

Problem: Remote measurement of discharge pressure in loading and unloading operations provides crew with positive and centralized indication of pump performance.

Signal must be transmitted almost the length of the ship in extreme environments. Conditions are such to require Coast Guard approval for this equipment's usage in potentially explosive situations.

On-board tanks are sometimes at partial vacuum as they are emptied. The sensor must indicate this condition as well as normal pressures above ambient.

Solution: OMEGA PX-440 two wire transmitters are mounted in pipe "T"'s on the discharge side of the pumps. They are wired back to the bridge in deck conduit where they are powered through an isolating barrier. A readout on the bridge reads pump pressures.

PX-440 absolute transducers are used — at normal atmospheric pressure they read 15% of full scale, thus permitting measurements into the vacuum region. The all-welded construction of the unit permits deck-top operation. See figure 27.

Environments: Brutal! Salt spray, occasional seawater, tropic to arctic temperatures, occasional shock, no significant vibration.

Pressure Characteristics: Pressure is steady with no significant spikes or surges.

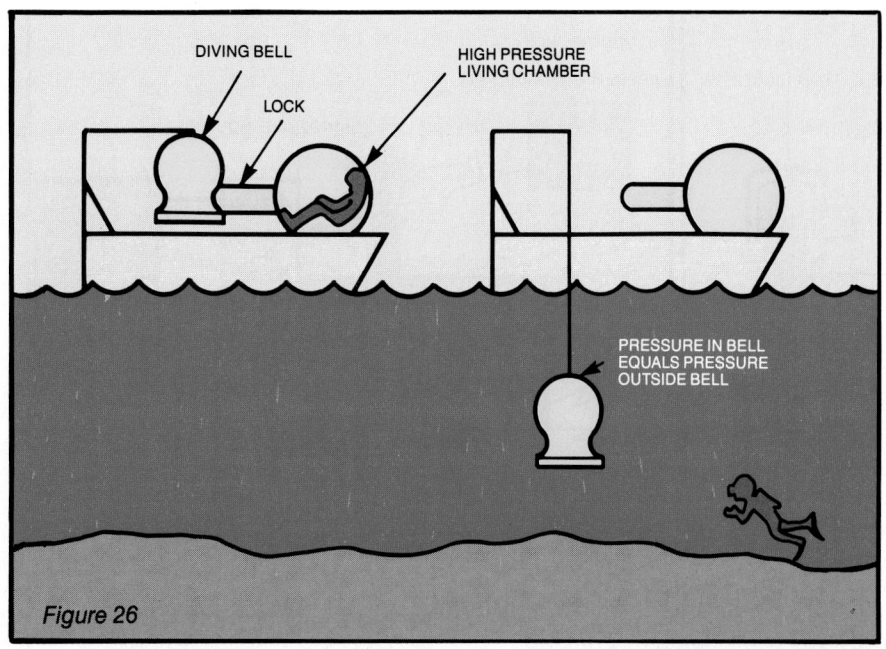

Figure 26

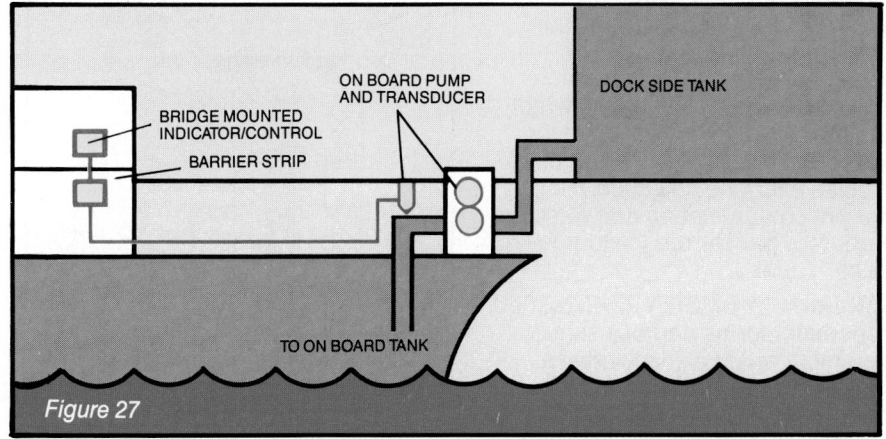

Figure 27

OIL WELL RE-CONDITIONING

Application: Customer "flushing" of old oil wells.

Problem: The bottom of a well and its surrounding strata can become clogged with residues which impede the flow of oil. By injecting various materials at high pressure (acid and/or steam, for example) the system is purged and the flow of product is restored.

The system can become plugged and pressure can rapidly build to dangerous levels. An automatic shutoff prior to rupture is necessary to insure the safety of operators and equipment.

Solution: An OMEGA PX-510 transducer is mounted in a "T" on the discharge of a high pressure, high volume, diesel driven pump.

Customer electronics permit presetting a maximum allowable pressure beyond which the pump is automatically turned off. The transducer's 0-5 V dc output permits signal transmission over long lines and remote location of the control box and system operator. See fig. 28.

Environments: The sensor assembly may be exposed to marine, desert, or arctic environments. Vibration is excessive due both to pump mounting and transportation by truck or helicopter. Media may contain sand, steam, acid, and petroleum wastes.

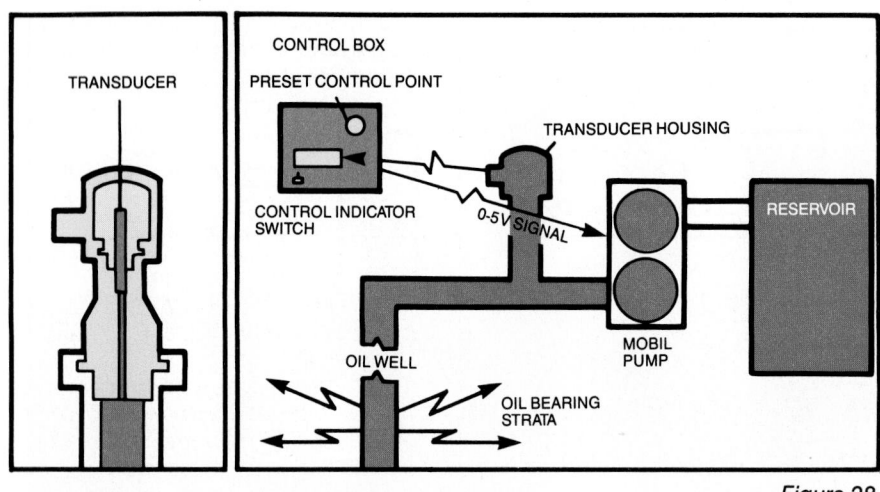

Figure 28

PIPELINE INSTRUMENTATION

Application: Liquid interface detector for pipelines.

Problem: Each liquid has unique "speed of sound" characteristics which will vary with both pressure and temperature. A "speed of sound" detector can differentiate between liquids in a pipeline when its readings are compensated for both pressure and temperature. Precise interface detection will prevent contamination and waste as product is transferred to storage tanks.

Solution: An OMEGA PX-102-2,000 transducer forms part of a sensor assembly which also includes a sound velocity and temperature transducer. The manufacturer's electronics package receives all three signals, "massages" the inputs, and produces an amplified and compensated "sound velocity" output for transmission to the receiver downstream. When a change in output is noted, operators are alerted to the imminent arrival of liquid interface. (See Figures 29A and 29B.)

Environments: Sensor assembly is mounted in outdoor environments from arctic to tropical (−60° to +60°C). It will see rain, snow, dust, and salt spray, but no particular shock or vibration.

Pressure Characteristics: Range 0-2000 psi with generally steady readings (no surge or spikes). Petroleum products (heavy oils, gasoline, kerosene) and seawater are the measured media.

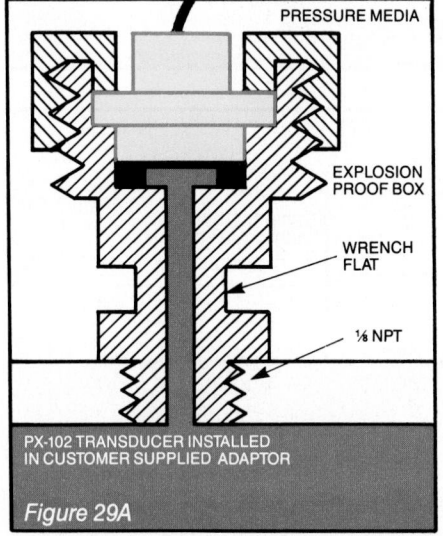

Figure 29A

SUBSEA PRODUCTION

Application: Measurement of wellhead pressures in subsea environments.

Problem: Oil wells on the ocean bottom are capped by a subsea production tree — an array of remotely operated valves and manifolds which control the wells' safety and production commonly referred to as a "Christmas Tree." Valves are hydraulically operated.

Pressures at the wellhead that must be monitored continuously include those within the tubing, annulus, and hydraulic system. They provide indication of the well's performance and also signal conditions which require automatic corrective action. Production trees are not available for routine servicing, and all measurements and systems must maintain reliable operation for years at the ocean's bottom.

For example, a rapid buildup in tubing pressure could signal a condition— unless counteracted—which could result in loss of product and hazardous surface conditions should a rupture occur.

Again, hydraulic system pressures must be known and maintained to produce correct valve operation with resulting proper safety and production.

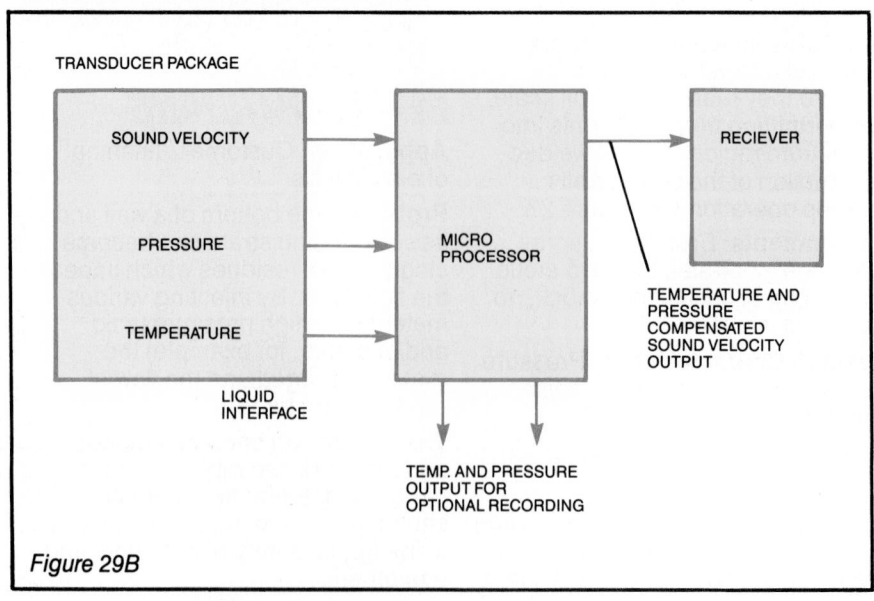

Figure 29B

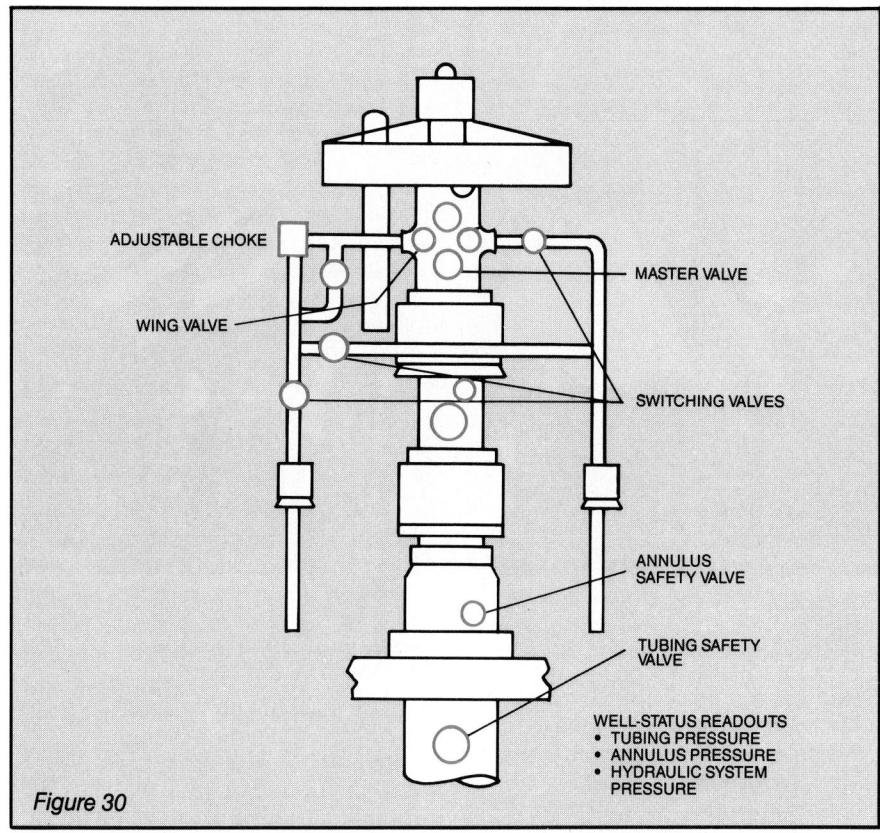

ADJUSTABLE CHOKE

WING VALVE

MASTER VALVE

SWITCHING VALVES

ANNULUS
SAFETY VALVE

TUBING SAFETY
VALVE

WELL-STATUS READOUTS
• TUBING PRESSURE
• ANNULUS PRESSURE
• HYDRAULIC SYSTEM
  PRESSURE

Figure 30

Solution: OMEGA PX-102 transducers are wet-lined directly to the annulus, tubing, and hydraulic supply. They are mounted in an enclosure that is otherwise hermetically sealed. Customer supplied electronics provide alarm, logging, and control functions. (See Figure 30.)

The two times over-range capabilities of the OMEGA PX-102 and its drift-free stability make it ideally suited for this demanding application.

Pressure Media: Hydraulic fluid, crude petroleum, seawater.

Environments: Sensors operate in a relatively stable and benign environment—even though at the bottom of the ocean.

BEVERAGE CAN COATING

Application: Control of paint spraying operation to insure uniform coating of inside of steel beverage cans.

Problem: Part of the steel beverage can-making operation includes spraying a lacquer coating inside of

cans to prevent rusting and flavor change. Present visual method of inspection is inadequate because the coating is performed at the rate of 12,000 cans per hour. By the time a problem is observed, many cans have been miscoated. Two spraying problems occur: a clogged nozzle which stops spray altogether or sprays in blobs, and a worn nozzle which permits overcoating. With the

present system, an additional bank of spraying machines is necessary to insure that every can is coated. This second coating adds time and expense to the operation.

Solution: A pressure transducer is inserted near the tip of a spray gun nozzle to monitor spraying pressures. Transducer output is fed into a multi-channel data acquisition/controller with one channel per spray head. (Typically five spray machines operate simultaneously.) The controller provides adjustable upper and lower set points with the upper limit set to indicate a clogged nozzle and the lower limit set to indicate a worn nozzle. When limits are exceeded, the system is immediately shut down. OMEGA controllers, modified with solid state switches to insure long life under high cyclic rates, are used in the system. (See Figure 31.)

Environment: High level electrical and environmental noise from surrounding machinery.

Pressure Characteristics: 0 to 1000 psi range. Upper control limit set at approximately 650 psi and lower limit at 550 psi.

Paint system is of the constant flow type with spray occurring when an electrical solenoid opens the nozzle. Because pressure in the nozzle drops after every spray pulse, the lower limit is constantly tripped. A microprocessor controls the system and permits shutdown only if limits are exceeded during actual spraying time (35 milliseconds).

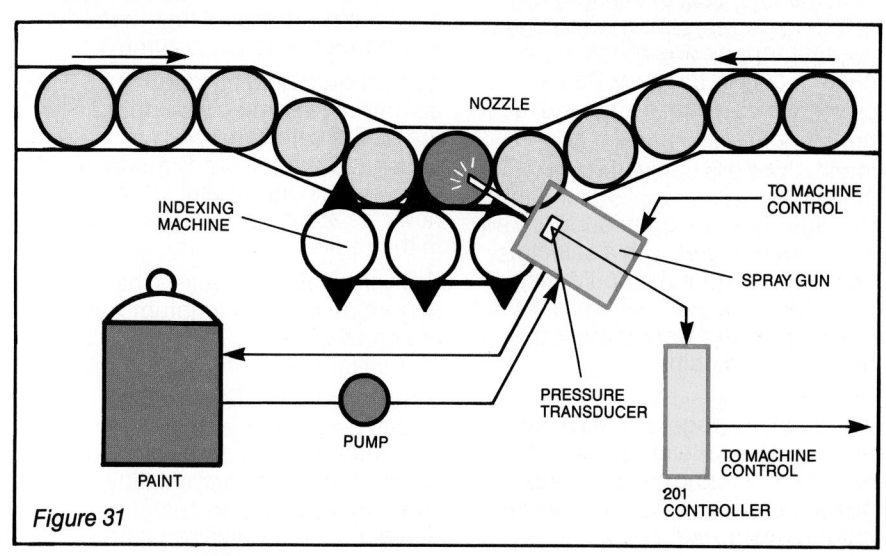

NOZZLE

INDEXING
MACHINE

TO MACHINE
CONTROL

SPRAY GUN

PRESSURE
TRANSDUCER

PAINT

PUMP

201
CONTROLLER

TO MACHINE
CONTROL

Figure 31

IN THE PLASTICS INDUSTRY

Application: Measurement of pressures in the clamp mechanism and other hydraulic systems in plastic injection molding machines.

Problem: Customer had been using Bourdon-type pressure gages with the following problems:

(1) Gages were mounted at three locations on the machine which were selected for convenience of installation. Since the machines are twenty feet long, the operators did not walk around them to read the gages.

(2) In order to get the operators to read the pressures, the gages were all brought to the front of the machine by adding piping. This greatly increased the installation cost.

(3) Because the pressures were cycling at approximately 1 Hz, the Bourdon-type gages rapidly wore out. To save the gages, the manufacturer put a valve upstream of each one. The valve was to be turned off when the gage was not being read.

(4) Experience showed that the operators were either leaving the valves open or shut all the time. As a result, they were either wearing out the gages anyway or were not controlling the pressure properly. Also, the total cost of the system including gages, piping, valves, and frequent repairs was much more than the cost of the gage itself.

Solution: Two OMEGA PX-102 transducers and a special two-channel power supply and signal conditioner were supplied for each machine. The customer supplied a single panel meter with a selector switch so the operator could read either transducer at will. The switch and panel meter were mounted on the easily accessible control console.

In addition to longer life, the PX-102 system offered the industrial designers an opportunity to improve the appearance of the machine with better looking instrumentation.

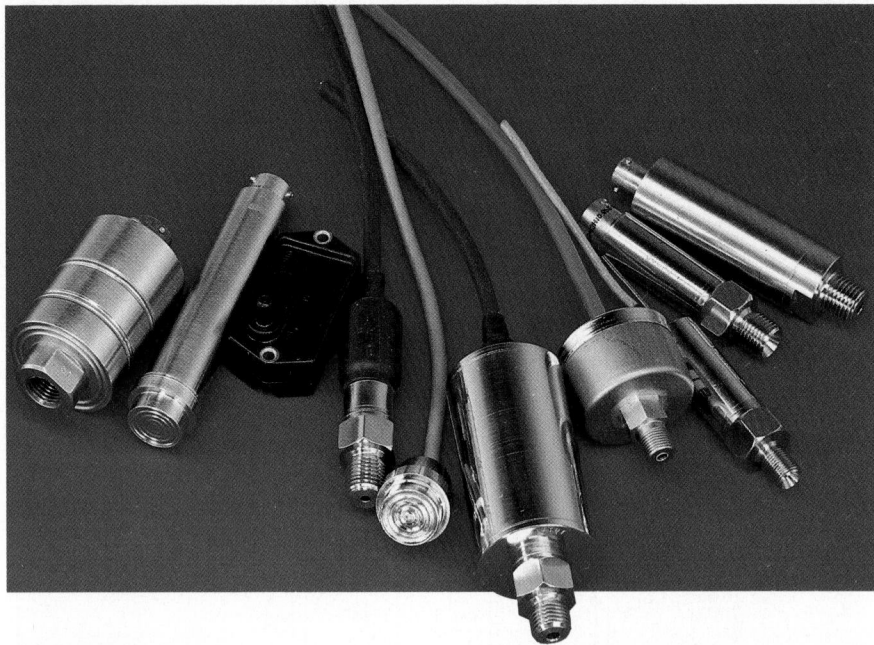

Advantages:
1. Simpler installation
2. Remote reading
3. Ability to withstand millions of cycles without wearing out
4. Modern appearance of readout

LIQUID CHROMATOGRAPHS

Application: Control of liquid flow — high pressure, minimum volume.

Problem: Liquid is passed through a column packed with solid absorbent under conditions of high pressure and constant flow. This liquid consists of the sample to be analyzed and another carrier. The two liquids are mixed together prior to introduction to the column.

As the liquid goes through the column, the sample's components are selectively absorbed for subsequent analysis. Separation efficiency is dependent upon liquid flow rate at high pressures, typically in the region of 5000 psi.

Precise analysis requires that the system be kept to minimum volumes of known values. Liquids are often corrosive, sometimes extremely so.

Solution: An OMEGA PX-102 15,000 psi sensor is mounted in a customer designed flow chamber which is shown schematically. Transducer output to customer designed electronics regulates speed of metering pumps and hence flow rate from the chamber.

Note that: (1) the chamber is designed for minimum volume; (2) clamping is accomplished on the outer rim (non-responsive) of the transducer face; and (3) mixing of the sample and carrier take place at the transducer's face. (See Figures 32A and 32B.)

The materials normally encountered in this process are entirely compatible with the 15-5 ph stainless steel from which the PX-102 is made. Inconel-X transducers (psi specials) have been used successfully in some severely corrosive applications.

Environments: Environments are benign and have no vibration or shock. Temperatures are those of an air-conditioned laboratory.

Pressure Characteristics: Steady state with minimum "ripple".

WATER PIPE PRESSURE

Application: Monitoring of automatic sprinkler systems.

Problem: Under normal conditions a sprinkler system is under relatively steady static pressure. In the event the system "goes off", the pressure drops to a lower value as water is sprayed. A pressure drop in a particular segment of a total

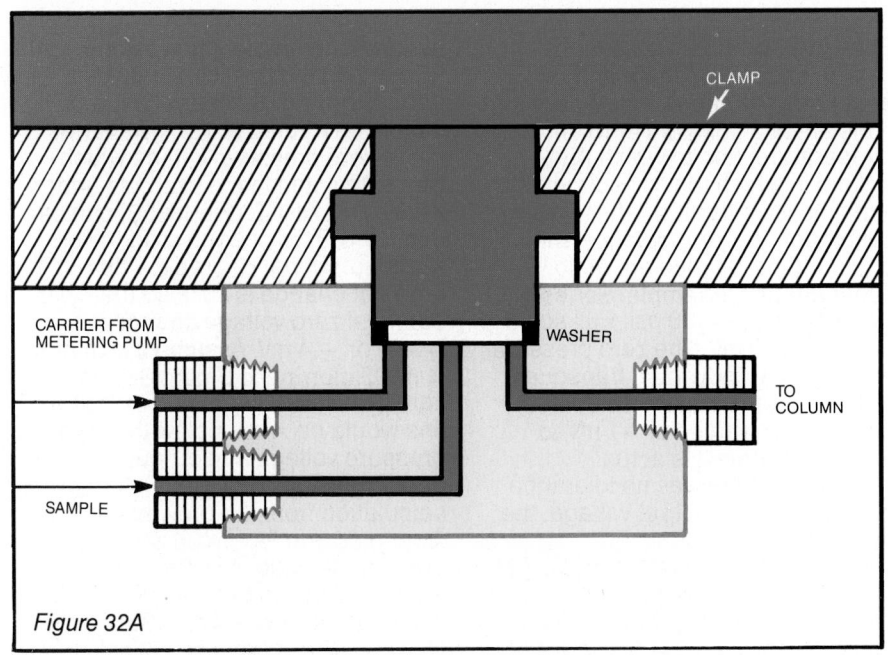

CARRIER FROM
METERING PUMP

CLAMP

WASHER

TO
COLUMN

SAMPLE

Figure 32A

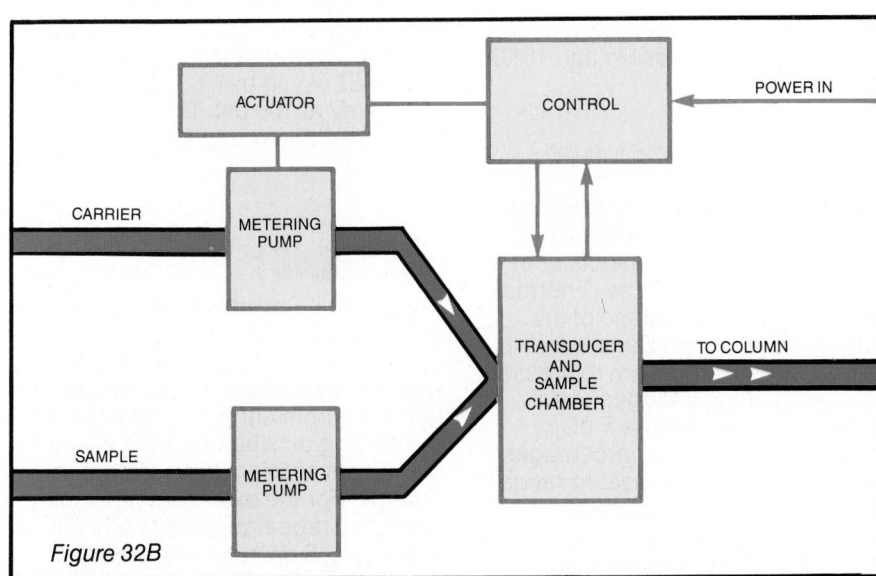

ACTUATOR

CONTROL

POWER IN

CARRIER

METERING
PUMP

SAMPLE

METERING
PUMP

TRANSDUCER
AND
SAMPLE
CHAMBER

TO COLUMN

Figure 32B

Automated production and testing of the OMEGA pressure transducers have made the selling price of these units such that the sales price of the customer's total package is economically acceptable.

Environments: Transducer will operate from −40° to +200°F although usage is generally within 0° to 150°F. Unit is enclosure mounted and sees no vibration or direct weather. Having a 0-200 psi range, it may see 350 psi without damage and up to 875 psi without bursting. These requirements are necessary due to the possibility of a "water hammer".

Pressure Characteristics: Normally steady rate to mildly fluctuating pressures are noted with occasional exposure to severe over-ranging resulting from a "water hammer".

HYDROELECTRIC TURBINE SYSTEMS

Application: Measurement of lube oil pressure in hydroelectric turbine generators.

Problem: Continual and steady flow of lube oil to turbine generators is necessary to insure efficient and safe operation. Remote indication and alarm are needed since turbines are often unattended.

Solution: OMEGA PX-440 pressure transducers are mounted in oil lines to turbine's main bearings and lube system. Signal conditioners power the transducers and transmit a 4-20 mA signal to the control room. Customer supplied indicator/alarm system will alert the operator immediately if oil pressure and flow depart from preset limits. Corrective action can then be initiated before the equipment is endangered.

Environments: Sensors are installed in the benign environments found in hydroelectric power stations.

Pressure Characteristics: Pressures generally range 50-60 psi, are steady and characteristic of those produced by a positive displacement pump. The only exceptions are in the rare event of leaking or breaking oil line (pressure drop) or plugged outlet (pressure rise).

building's system relative to the pressure in other segments will indicate a fire and its location—independent of fluctuations in normal building or municipal water pressure.

Scanning of pressure sensors in any particular building is done from a centralized scanner. When a particular transducer reports a lower reading, the scanner will show its building and station and thus direct firefighters to the correct location.

Due to the large number of stations and economic factors determining

total system price, low cost is an important criterion in transducer selection.

Solution: An OMEGA pressure transducer is used as the basic pressure sensor in the customer's alarm package. Signal output is amplified and transmitted to a central system panel. When the panel is scanned, all sensor outputs are within nominal values of being identical if there is no water flow. If certain outputs fall, the scanner will sound an alarm and indicate specific transducer location for firefighters.

HOW TO INTERPRET THE SPECIFICATIONS

In some cases the standard methods of specifying transducer performance may be difficult to translate into usable data. This section is for the purpose of clarifying this data to make it more useful.

AMBIENT TEMPERATURE REFERENCE

All specifications are referenced to an ambient temperature of 75°F. This means that the unit was calibrated at 75°F at the factory. As long as the ambient temperature remains at 75°F, there are no thermal effects.

ZERO BALANCE AND FULL SCALE OUTPUT

If, from one transducer to another at 75°F ambient temperature there was no tolerance on the output voltage at either zero or full rated pressure, the output line would start at zero with zero pressure and proceed to the full output voltage at full pressure. This is shown as a dotted line in Figure 33. Since there is a tolerance on the zero pressure voltage (called zero balance), the actual voltage at zero pressure can be above or below zero as depicted by the two solid lines on Figure 33.

There is also a tolerance on the voltage at full rated pressure (Full scale output voltage.) This results from a change in the slope of the output line (sensitivity) as illustrated in Figure 34.

Each individual transducer has particular zero pressure and full pressure voltages which remain constant at a constant ambient temperature, and to which the system in which the transducer is installed is calibrated. After system calibration the zero balance shift and output tolerance are of no consequence. Example, Series PX-301 Unit: 0—100 psi. Full scale output is 100 mV. The zero pressure output of any individual transducer will be at some constant value between the values of +1 mV to −1 mV. Assume it is actually +.05 mV. If there was no tolerance on the full scale output voltage, the output at 100 psi would be 100.05 mV. The tolerance on the full scale output, however, is ±1%. Therefore, the full output at 100 psi could be between 99.05 and 101.05 mV. Assume it is 101.05 mV. The system would then be calibrated to +.05 mV at zero pressure and 101.05 mV at 100 psi.

THERMAL EFFECTS

Thermal effects are the effects of ambient temperature changes. Ambient temperature affects both the zero pressure voltage (Thermal Zero Effect) and the slope of the output line (Thermal Sensitivity Effect). These effects are expressed in ± percentage changes of full scale output per degree F of ambient change. The percentages apply over the compensated range of +30° to +130°F. Figure 35 illustrates how these percentages relate to the total compensated range.

Figure 36 illustrates that with an ambient temperature change the zero pressure voltage and output line at 75° (from Figure 34) are changed. This is the Thermal Zero Effect. A corresponding change in the voltage at full pressure also occurs. At the same time a change in the output line slope occurs. This is called Thermal Sensitivity Effect as illustrated by Figure 37.

EXAMPLES
OMEGA Series PX-301 Unit:
0—100 psi. Full scale output 100 mV.

Assume the ambient temperature is 95°F when the unit is put into use and calibrated. Since the unit was factory calibrated at 75°F, a change in the zero pressure voltage which was calculated in the example under ZERO BALANCE (Figure 33) can be expected. This change is .02% full scale output per degree F. The ambient change is 20°F so the potential zero voltage change is ±.4% or ±.4 mV. Assume it is minus .4 mV. Referring to Figure 36, the zero pressure voltage and output line would be .4 mV below the zero pressure voltage and output line from Figure 34. Using the calculation from the previous examples, the Figure 36 zero pressure voltage is (+.05 −.4) or −.35, and the voltage at 100 psi would be (101.05 −.4) or 100.65. However, the voltage at 100 psi is also affected by the Thermal Sensitivity Effect. Assume this to be +.4 mV. Therefore the final value Figure 37 would be (100.65 +.40) or 101.05 mV at 100 psi. The zero pressure value would still be −.35 mV.

ACCURACY

Figure 38 illustrates that the combined effects of linearity, hysteresis and repeatability are related to the output lines that are achieved from either Figure 34 or 37 depending on whether there is any significant ambient temperature change. For the examples previously used, the repeatability is ±.5% full scale or ±.5 mV around the output line from Figure 37.

CONCLUSION

This section has been written to promote a better understanding of the use of the specifications. Although it is possible for the worst case to occur where all the factors accumulate in the same direction, this is very rare; in fact, experience shows that in the vast majority of cases the changes described tend to be more cancelling than additive. The result is a transducer which in all respects consistently meets the needs of the industrial market.

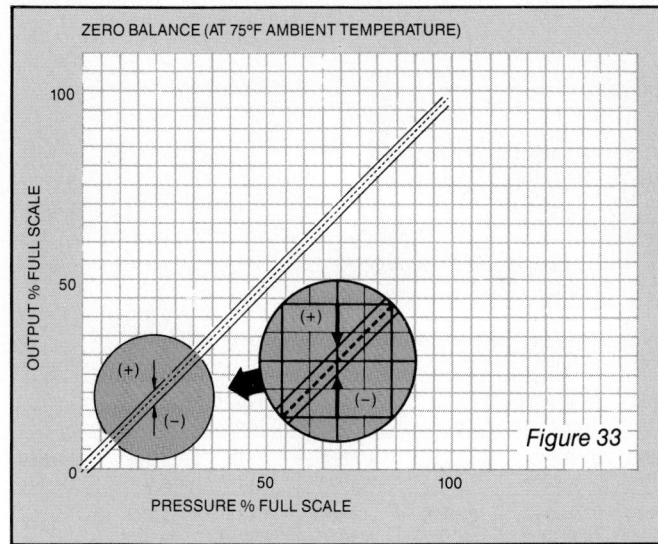

Figure 33

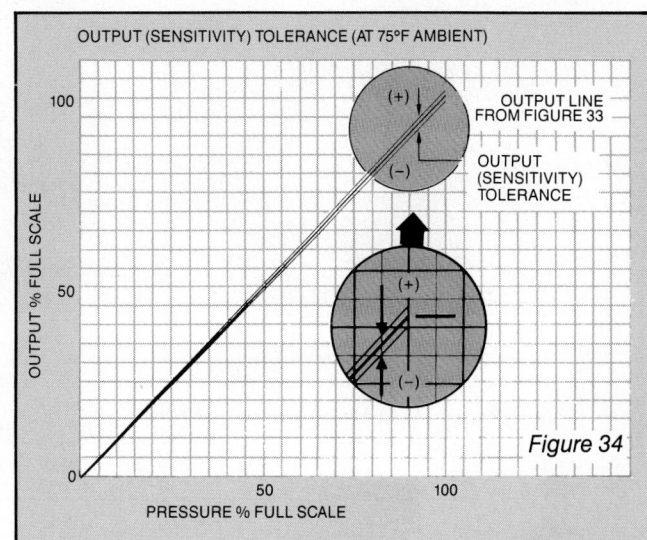

Figure 34

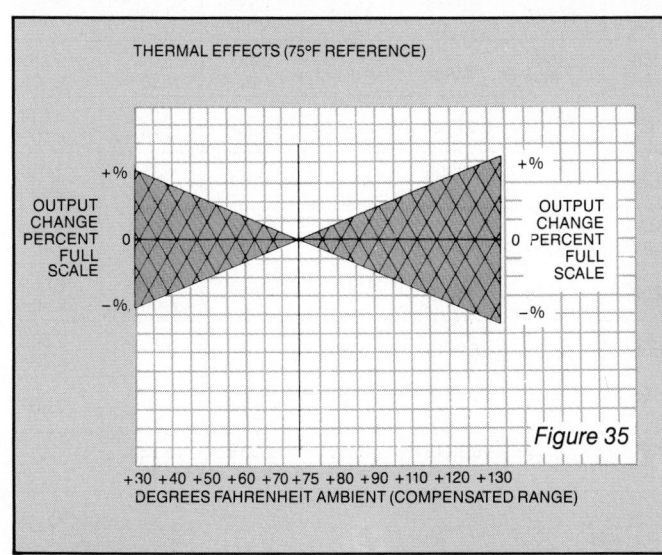

Figure 35

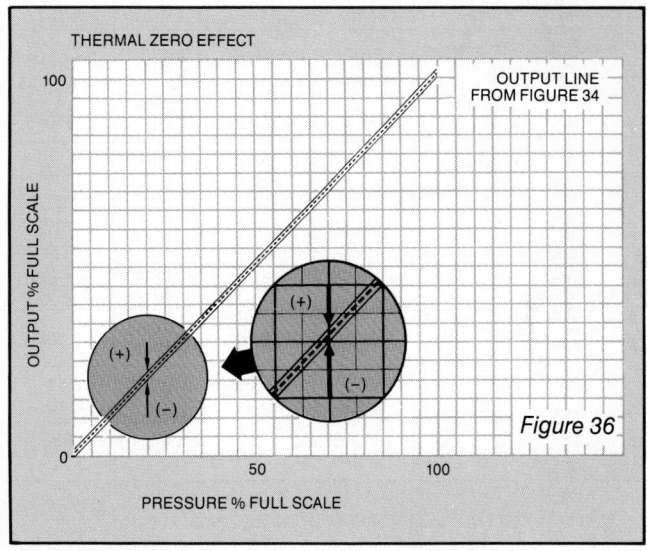

Figure 36

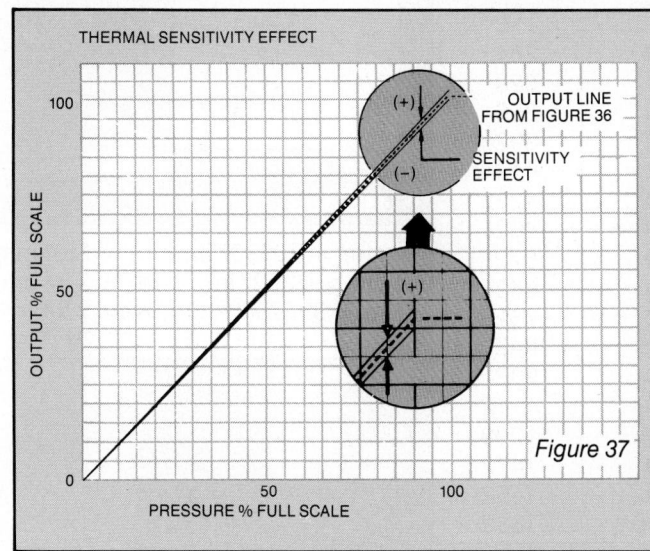

Figure 37

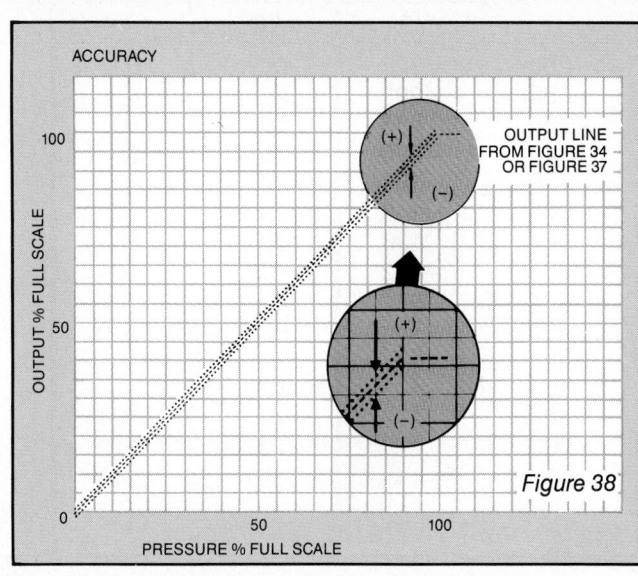

Figure 38

PRESSURE REFERENCE SECTION
TECHNICAL DATA SECTION

PRESSURE CONVERSION TABLE TO HELP IN APPLYING OMEGA® PRESSURE TRANSDUCERS

multiply no. of → to obtain ↓	by →	Atmos	Bars	Dynes/ cm²	In of Hg (0°C)	In of H₂O (4°C)	K grams/ meter²	Lb/In² psi	Lb/ft²	mm of Hg torr	Microns	Pascals
Atmos		1	9.86923 × 10⁻¹	9.86923 × 10⁻⁷	3.34207 × 10⁻²	2.458 × 10⁻³	9.678 × 10⁻⁵	0.068046	4.7254 × 10⁻⁴	1.316 × 10⁻³	1.316 × 10⁻⁶	9.869 × 10⁻⁶
Bars		1.01325	1	10⁻⁶	3.3864 × 10⁻²	2.491 × 10⁻³	9.8067 × 10⁻⁵	6.8948 × 10⁻²	4.788 × 10⁻⁴	1.333 × 10⁻³	1.333 × 10⁻⁶	10⁻⁵
Dynes/ cm²		1.01325 × 10⁶	10⁶	1	3.386 × 10⁴	2.491 × 10³	98.067	6.8948 × 10⁴	478.8	1.333 × 10³	1.333	10
In of Hg (0°C)		29.9213	29.53	2.953 × 10⁻⁵	1	7.355 × 10⁻²	2.896 × 10⁻³	2.036	0.014139	3.937 × 10⁻²	3.937 × 10⁻⁵	2.953 × 10⁻⁴
In of H₂O (4°C)		406.8	401.48	4.0148 × 10⁻⁴	13.60	1	3.937 × 10⁻²	27.68	0.1922	0.5354	5.354 × 10⁻⁴	4.014 × 10⁻³
K grams/ meter²		1.033227 × 10⁴	1.0197 × 10⁴	1.0197 × 10⁻²	345.3	25.40	1	7.0306 × 10²	4.882	13.59	13.59 × 10⁻³	1.019 × 10⁻¹
Lb/in² psi		14.695595	14.504	1.4504 × 10⁻⁵	0.4912	3.6126 × 10⁻³	1.423 × 10⁻³	1	6.9444 × 10⁻³	1.934 × 10⁻²	1.934 × 10⁻⁵	1.450 × 10⁻⁴
Lb/ft²		2116.22	2088.5	2.0885 × 10⁻³	70.726	5.202	0.2048	144.0	1	2.7844	2.7844 × 10⁻³	2.089 × 10⁻²
mm of Hg torr		760	750.06	7.5006 × 10⁻⁴	25.400	1.868	7.3558 × 10⁻²	51.715	0.35913	1	10⁻³	7.502 × 10⁻³
Microns		760 × 10³	750.06 × 10³	0.75006	2.54 × 10⁴	1.868 × 10³	73.558	51.715 × 10³	359.1	1 × 10³	1	7.502
Pascals		1.01325 × 10⁵	1 × 10⁵	10⁻¹	3.386 × 10³	2.491 × 10²	9.8067	6.8948 × 10³	4.788 × 10¹	1.333 × 10²	1.333 × 10⁻¹	1

TEMPERATURE CONVERSION CHART

°C	°F	°C	°F	°C	°F
– 200	– 328	0	32	140	284
– 180	– 292	5	41	160	320
– 160	– 256	10	50	180	356
– 140	– 220	15	59	200	392
– 120	– 184	20	68	212	414
– 100	– 148	25	77	220	428
– 90	– 130	30	86	250	482
– 80	– 112	40	104	300	572
– 70	– 94	50	122	350	662
– 60	– 76	60	140	400	752
– 50	– 58	70	158	450	842
– 40	– 40	80	176	500	932
– 30	– 22	90	194	600	1112
– 20	– 4	100	212	700	1292
– 10	+ 14	120	248	800	1472
				900	1652
				1000	1832

TEMPERATURE

$$°C = \frac{(F - 32)}{1.8}$$

$$°F = 1.8C + 32$$

METRIC

mm = 0.03937 in.	in. = 25.4 mm
cm = 0.3937 in.	in. = 2.54 cm
m = 39.37 in.	in. = 2.54 × 10⁻² m

PRESSURE VS ALTITUDE

| Altitude | Pressure | | |
(Feet)	In of Hg	mm of Hg	psi
− 1,000	31.02	787.9	15.25
− 500	30.47	773.8	14.94
0	29.921	760.0	14.70
500	29.38	746.4	14.43
1,000	28.86	732.9	14.18
1,500	28.33	719.7	13.90
2,000	27.82	706.6	13.67
2,500	27.31	693.8	13.41
3,000	26.81	681.1	13.19
3,500	26.32	668.6	12.92
4,000	25.84	656.3	12.70
4,500	25.36	644.2	12.45
5,000	24.89	632.3	12.23
10,000	20.58	522.6	10.10
15,000	16.88	428.8	8.28
20,000	13.75	349.1	6.75
30,000	8.88	225.6	4.36
40,000	5.54	140.7	2.72
50,000	3.426	87.30	1.689
60,000	2.132	54.15	1.048
70,000	1.322	33.59	0.649
80,000	0.820	20.83	0.403

SI: The Modernized Metric System

SI—the International System of Units—establishes the pascal (Pa) as the standard unit for Pressure or Stress in the modernized Metric System adopted by the American National Standards Institute.

To Convert to pascals	Multiply by
atmosphere	1.013×10^5
bar	1.000×10^5
dyne/centimeter^2	1.000×10^{-1}
inch of mercury (0°C)	3.386×10^3
inch of water (4°C)	2.491×10^2
kilogram/meter^2	9.807
pound/inch^2 (psi)	6.895×10^3
pound/foot^2	4.788×10^1
torr (mm of mercury 0°C)	1.333×10^2

PRESSURE CONVERSION CHART

psi	in. of H_2O	in. of Hg	mm of H_2O	mm of Hg	bar	mbar
.01	.2768	.0204	7.031	.5171	.0007	.6895
.02	.5536	.0407	14.06	1.034	.0014	1.379
.03	.8304	.0611	21.09	1.551	.0021	2.068
.04	1.107	.0814	28.12	2.068	.0028	2.758
.05	1.384	.1018	35.15	2.586	.0034	3.447
.06	1.661	.1222	42.18	3.103	.0041	4.137
.07	1.938	.1425	49.22	3.620	.0048	4.826
.08	2.214	.1629	56.25	4.137	.0055	5.516
.09	2.491	.1832	63.28	4.654	.0062	6.205
.10	2.768	.2036	70.31	5.171	.0069	6.895
.20	5.536	.4072	140.6	10.34	.0138	13.79
.30	8.304	.6108	210.9	15.51	.0207	20.68
.40	11.07	.8144	281.2	20.68	.0276	27.58
.50	13.84	1.018	351.5	25.86	.0345	34.47
.60	16.61	1.222	421.8	31.03	.0414	41.37
.70	19.38	1.425	492.2	36.20	.0483	48.26
.80	22.14	1.629	562.5	41.37	.0552	55.16
.90	24.91	1.832	632.8	46.54	.0620	62.05
1.0	27.68	2.036	703.1	51.71	.0690	68.95
2.0	55.36	4.072	1406	103.4	.1379	137.9
3.0	83.04	6.108	2109	155.1	.2068	206.8
4.0	110.7	8.144	2812	206.8	.2758	275.8
5.0	138.4	10.18	3515	258.6	.3447	344.7
6.0	166.1	12.22	4218	310.3	.4137	413.7
7.0	193.8	14.25	4922	362.0	.4826	482.6
8.0	221.4	16.29	5625	413.7	.5516	551.6
9.0	249.1	18.32	6328	465.4	.6205	620.5
10.0	276.8	20.36	7031	517.1	.6895	689.5
14.7	406.9	29.93	10340	760.2	1.014	1014
15.0	415.2	30.54	10550	775.7	1.034	1034
20.0	553.8	40.72	14060	1034	1.379	1379
25.0	692.0	50.90	17580	1293	1.724	1724
30.0	830.4	61.08	21090	1551	2.068	2068
40.0	1107	81.44	28120	2068	2.758	2758
50.0	1384	101.8	35150	2586	3.447	3447
100.0	2768	203.6	70310	5171	6.895	6895
150.0	4152	305.4	105500	7757	10.34	10340
200.0	5538	407.2	140600	10340	13.79	13790
250.0	6920	509.0	175800	12930	17.24	17240

Example: To convert 21.5 psi to mm/Hg. find the conversion factors for 20 psi (1034), 1.0 psi (51.71), and 0.5 psi (25.86). The sum of these factors is the mm/Hg value for 21.5 psi (1111.57/mm Hg).

CONVERSION FACTORS

PRESSURE

psi = in. of H_2O × (3.6127×10^{-2})
psi = in. of Hg × (0.49118)
psi = mm of H_2 × (1.4223×10^{-3})
psi = mm of Hg × (1.9339×10^{-2})
psi = cm of H_2O × (14.223×6^{-3})
psi = kg/cm^2 × (14.223)
psi = bar × (14.503)
psi = mbar × (1.4503×10^{-2})
psi = Pa × (1.4503×10^{-4})
psi = kPa × (1.4503×10^{-1})

in. of H_2O = pxi × 27.68
in. of Hg = psi × 2.036
mm of H_2O = psi × 703.1
mm of Hg = psi × 51.71
cm of H_2O = psi × 70.3
kg/cm^2 = psi × .0703
bar = psi × .0689
mbar = psi × 68.95
Pa = psi × 6895
kPa = psi × 6.895

INTRINSIC SAFETY

Hazardous (Classified) Locations in Accordance with Article 500, National Electrical Code-1990

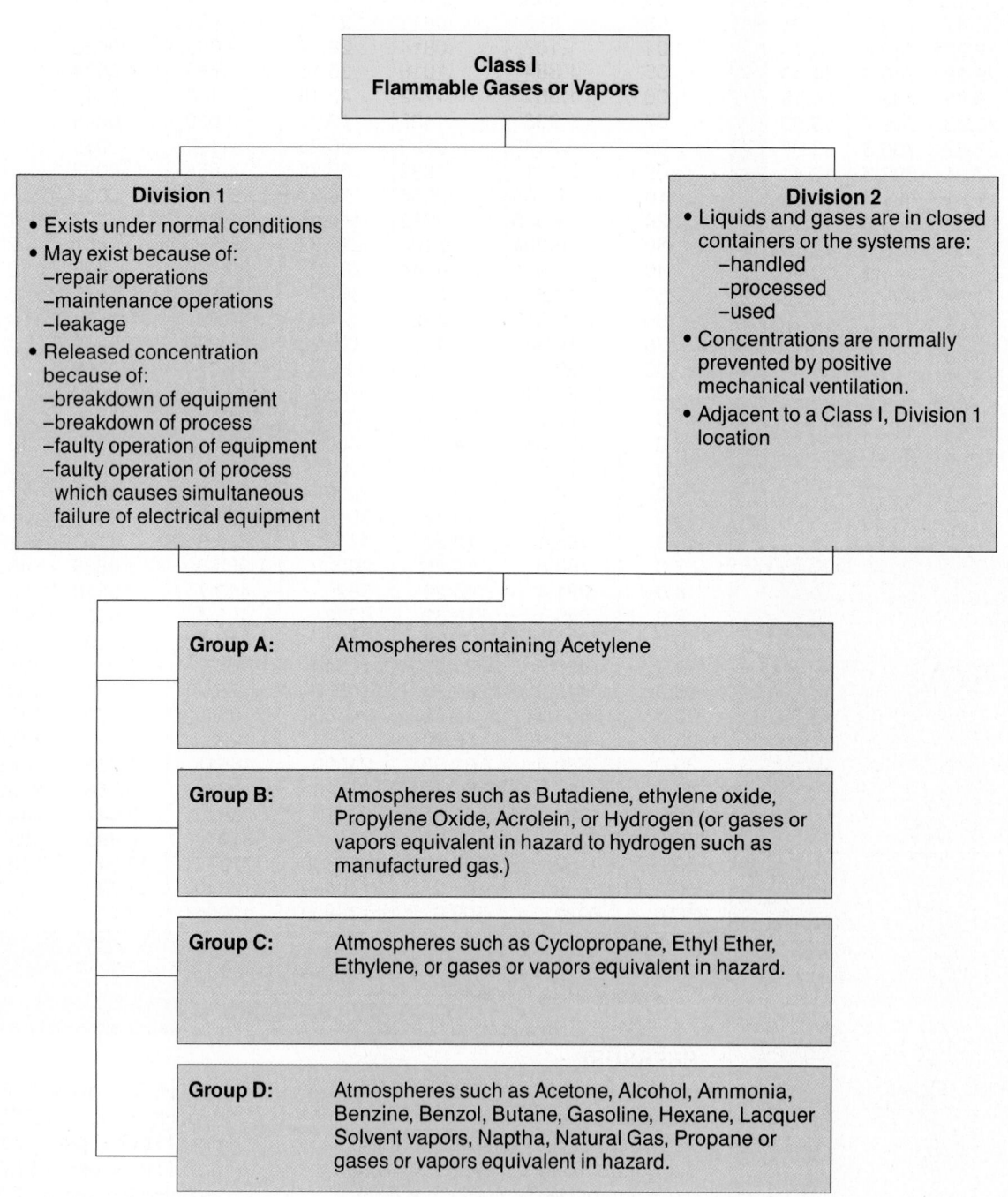

Class I
Flammable Gases or Vapors

Division 1
- Exists under normal conditions
- May exist because of:
  - repair operations
  - maintenance operations
  - leakage
- Released concentration because of:
  - breakdown of equipment
  - breakdown of process
  - faulty operation of equipment
  - faulty operation of process which causes simultaneous failure of electrical equipment

Division 2
- Liquids and gases are in closed containers or the systems are:
  - handled
  - processed
  - used
- Concentrations are normally prevented by positive mechanical ventilation.
- Adjacent to a Class I, Division 1 location

Group A: Atmospheres containing Acetylene

Group B: Atmospheres such as Butadiene, ethylene oxide, Propylene Oxide, Acrolein, or Hydrogen (or gases or vapors equivalent in hazard to hydrogen such as manufactured gas.)

Group C: Atmospheres such as Cyclopropane, Ethyl Ether, Ethylene, or gases or vapors equivalent in hazard.

Group D: Atmospheres such as Acetone, Alcohol, Ammonia, Benzine, Benzol, Butane, Gasoline, Hexane, Lacquer Solvent vapors, Naptha, Natural Gas, Propane or gases or vapors equivalent in hazard.

Courtesy of R. Stahl, Inc.

**Class II
Combustible Dusts**

Division 1
- Exists under normal conditions
- Combustible mixture produced by:
  - mechanical failure of equipment or machinery
  - abnormal operation of equipment and provide source of ignition from:
  - simultaneous failure of electrical equipment
  - simultaneous failure of operation of protection devices
  - other causes
- electrically conductive dusts may be present

Division 2
- Not normally in the air.
- Accumulations normally sufficient to interfere with normal operation of electrical equipment or other apparatus.
- In the air as a result of infrequent malfunctioning of:
  - handling equipment
  - process equipment
- Accumulations are sufficient to interfere with the safe dissipation of heat from electrical equipment
- Accumulations may be ignitible by abnormal or failure of electrical equipment.

Group E: Atmospheres containing combustible metal dusts (regardless of resistivity), dusts of similarly hazardous characteristics (< 100kΩ/cm) or electrically conductive dusts.

Group F: Atmospheres containing combustible Carbon Black, Charcoal or Coke Dusts which have > 8% total volatile material or if these dusts are sensitized so that they present an explosion hazard and having a resistivity > 100K Ω/cm but ≤ 100 MΩ/cm

Group G: Atmospheres containing combustible dusts having a resistivity > 100K Ω/cm or electrically nonconductive dusts.

**Class III
Ignitible Fibers or Flyings**

Division 1
- Fibers or materials producing combustible flyings are manufactured, stored or handled.

Not Grouped
- Manufacturers such as textile mills, cotton-related mills or clothing plants.
- Fibers and flyings including Rayon, Cotton, Sisal, Hemp, Jute and Spanish Moss

Division 2
- Fibers are handled except during the process of manufacture or are stored except during the process of manufacture.

PRESSURE TRANSDUCERS
INSTALLATION AND USE

INTRODUCTION
Common problems or questions concerning the use of pressure transducers are:

1. Transducer outputs and their wiring configurations;
2. Wiring one transducer to multiple readouts, recorders, computers. etc.;
3. Wiring multiple transducers to one readout, recorder, computer, etc.;
4. Using a milliamp signal with voltage input instrumentation;
5. Determining how many transducers can be excited from one power supply.

Each of these problems, or questions are discussed in detail in the following article.

TRANSDUCER OUTPUTS AND THEIR WIRING CONFIGURATIONS
OMEGA transducers have three main types of electrical outputs; millivolts (mV), volts (V), and current (mA). It is important for the user to know which output suits his application to ensure proper selection of a transducer. The following will describe the advantages, disadvantages, and wiring for millivolt, volt and current output transducers.

Transducers with an amplified voltage output are generally used in a light industrial environment and computer interface systems, where a higher level dc signal is required. Due to the built-in signal conditioning, they are higher cost and larger in size than the millivolt output transducers. Amplified voltage signals can travel up to medium distances and are much better in their immunity to stray electrical interference than the millivolt signal. Typical wiring configurations are shown in Figure 2.

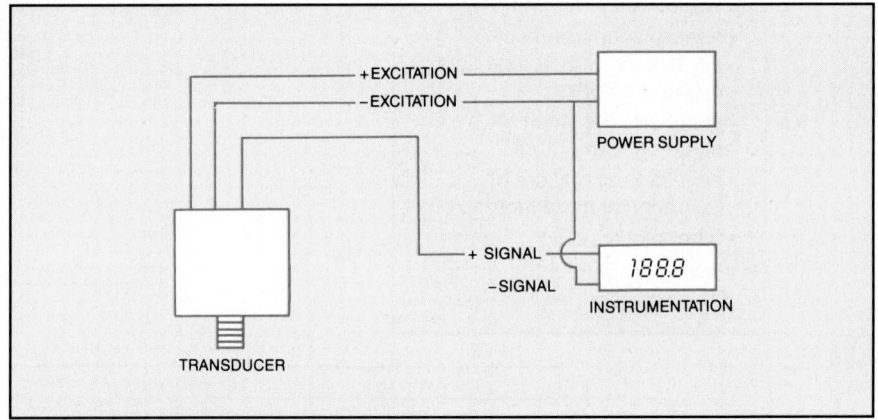

FIGURE 2. TYPICAL WIRING CONFIGURATION FOR VOLTAGE OUTPUT TRANSDUCER (–EXCITATION AND –SIGNAL ARE COMMON)

signal conditioning, the transmitters are higher cost and larger in size than the millivolt output transducers. Unlike the millivolt and voltage output transducers, a current signal is immune to any stray electrical interference, a valuable asset in the factory. A current signal also can be transmitted long distances. Typical wiring configurations are shown in Figure 3.

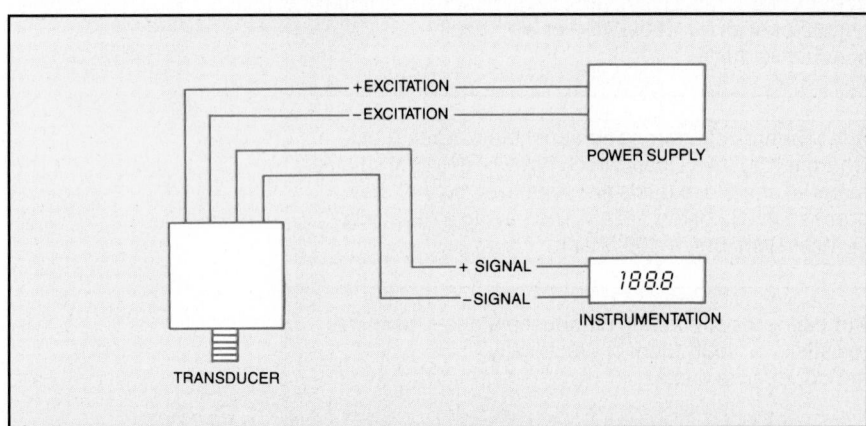

FIGURE 1. TYPICAL WIRING CONFIGURATION FOR MILLIVOLT OUTPUT TRANSDUCER

Transducers with a millivolt output are generally used in laboratory applications. They are low cost, small in size, and require a regulated power supply. Remembering that the millivolt signal is very low level, it is limited to short distances (up to 200 feet is usually considered the limit) and is very prone to stray electrical interference from other nearby electrical signals (other instrumentation, high ac voltage lines, etc.). Typical wiring configurations are shown in Figure 1.

Transducers with a current output are generally used in heavy industrial environments, and are the most common type used in process control. Transducers with a current output are generally called transmitters. The difference between a transducer and a transmitter is a commonly asked question. A transducer produces millivolts, amplified voltage, or current output. A transmitter produces current output only. Again, due to the built-in

WIRING ONE TRANSDUCER TO MULTIPLE READOUTS, RECORDERS, COMPUTERS, ETC
One of the great advantages of a current signal is the simplicity in setting up a multi-instrument system. Long distance transmission from instrument to instrument without electrical interference make multi-instrument systems easy. For example, a material test center may have one control room for all the different test labs, enabling operation from one central location. Instrument calibration and troubleshooting are simple in a multi-instrument current loop. The only limitation for the number of instruments is the amount of voltage from the power supply driving the current loop. The minimum voltage required is determined by Ohms law, V=IR (voltage equals current times resistance). This is shown and explained in Figure 4.

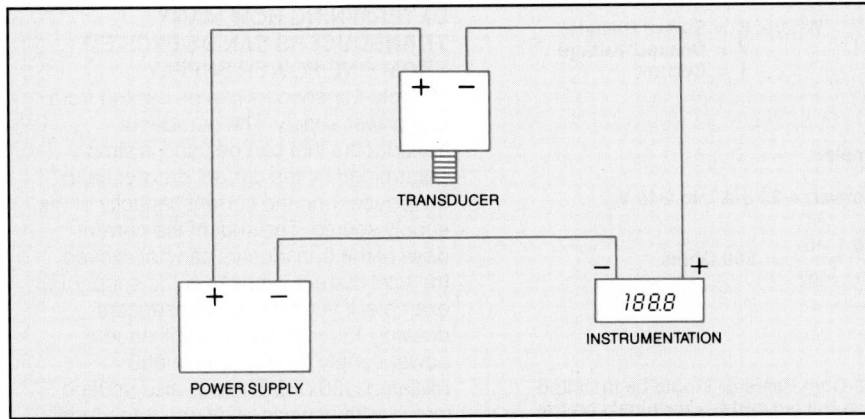

FIGURE 3. TYPICAL WIRING CONFIGURATION FOR CURRENT OUTPUT TRANSDUCER

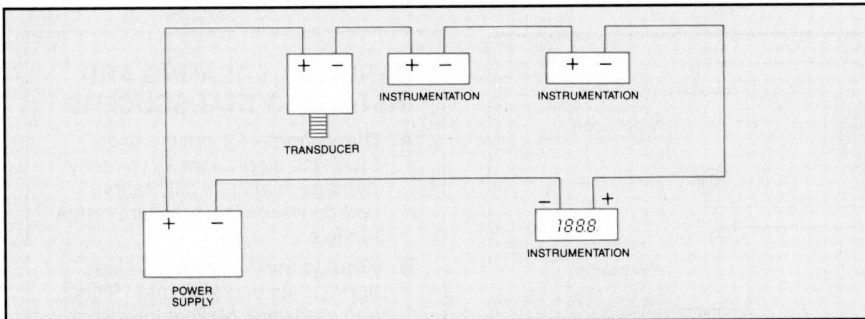

FIGURE 4. MULTI-INSTRUMENT 4-20 mA CURRENT LOOP (PANEL METERS, CHART RECORDER, COMPUTERS, ETC)

$$MINIMUM\ VOLTAGE\ REQ'D = (0.20\ AMPS)(R_{LINE} + R_{LOAD}) + Vs_{TRANSDUCER}$$

WHERE:

R_{LINE} = RESISTANCE DUE TO WIRE

R_{LOAD} = COMBINED INSTRUMENTATION RESISTANCES

$Vs_{TRANSDUCER}$ = MINIMUM SUPPLY VOLTAGE FOR TRANSDUCER

For example, let's assume you have the following:

1. Pressure transmitter (4-20 mA) with 12-30 Vdc supply voltage;
2. Panel meter with a 10 ohm input impedance;
3. Recorder with a 25 ohm input impedance;
4. Computer with a 200 ohm input impedance;
5. Lead wire resistance of 5 ohms.

Minimum voltage required = (.020) (5+10+25+200)+12 = 16.8 volts 24 volts is the most common power supply in a 4-20 mA current loop.

the case, an analog output can be used instead to retransmit the signal.

WIRING MULTIPLE TRANSDUCERS TO ONE READOUT, RECORDER, COMPUTER, ETC.

In measuring multiple pressures, it is a common mistake trying to use multiple transducers, a switching device, and just one panel meter, thus saving money on multiple panel meters (or any other instrumentation). The problem is that each transducer has a unique zero point and the readout only has one zero screw. The net result is that the total accuracy increases to about 3%, even though each sensor is 0.5% accurate. In most cases, this large error is intolerable.

The correct method of using multiple transducers with one readout device is to use transducers that have built-in zero and span adjustments screws, the same output (voltage or current), and the same pressure range. Each transducer is adjusted by applying a known pressure, so that they all have identical outputs. When they all have identical outputs, the meter is scaled and a switch can be used.

Another solution to using multiple transducers with one readout is to use a scanner instead of a meter and a switch. There are many types of scanners. The type of scanner that works with multiple

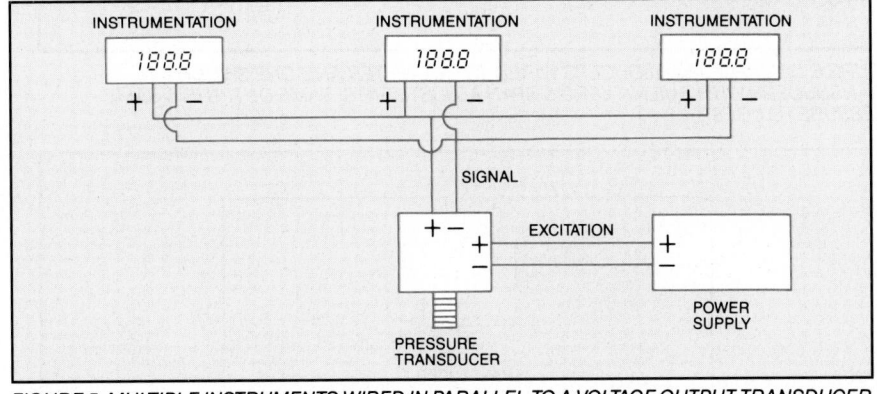

FIGURE 5. MULTIPLE INSTRUMENTS WIRED IN PARALLEL TO A VOLTAGE OUTPUT TRANSDUCER

Wiring a voltage or millivolt signal to multiple instruments also can be done, but is not as easy and does not have the calibration and troubleshooting advantages inherent in a current loop system. The voltage or millivolt signal can be wired in parallel to multiple instruments as shown in Figure 5. This method assumes a very high input impedance in the instruments being wired. If this is not

pressure transducers must have independent scaling on each channel.

Some scanners, besides having independent scaling on each channel, also offer independent current, voltage, or millivolt inputs to each channel. These types of scanners enable you to use transducers with different outputs as well as different pressure ranges with the same instrument.

PRESSURE TRANSDUCERS (Continued)

USING A MILLIAMP SIGNAL WITH VOLTAGE INPUT INSTRUMENTATION

Most instrumentation is set up to receive voltage. A commonly asked question is how to use a current signal with instrumentation set up for voltage. This is simply done by installing a resistor across the input terminals of the instrumentation. The value of the resistor is determined by Ohms law (V=IR). For example, installing a 500 ohm resistor will convert 20 mA to 10 volts (V=IR=.020x500). This is shown in Figure 7. The only other consideration is the zero offset. Since most current loops have a low end of 4 mA, there will be a zero offset. Using the same value resistor as above, 4 mA will convert to 2 volts.

$$R = \frac{V}{I} \qquad \text{Where: } R = \text{Size of Resistor}$$
$$V = \text{Desired Voltage}$$
$$I = \text{Current}$$

Example:

To Convert 4-20 mA into 2-10 V

$$R = \frac{V}{I} = \frac{10}{.02} = 500 \text{ Ohms}$$

A 500 Ohm Resistor Would be Installed Across the (+) and (−) Terminals on the Instrumentation.

DETERMINING HOW MANY TRANSDUCERS CAN BE EXCITED FROM ONE POWER SUPPLY

Multiple transducers can be excited from one power supply. The number of transducers that can be used is simply determined by the current draw of each transducer and the current capacity of the supply source. The sum of the current draw of the transducers can not exceed the total current capacity of the supply. For example, if you have 50 transducers drawing 13 milliamps, you will need a power supply having at least 650 milliamps (50x13). There is also nothing wrong with powering just one transducer with a power supply having high current capacity. **Œ**

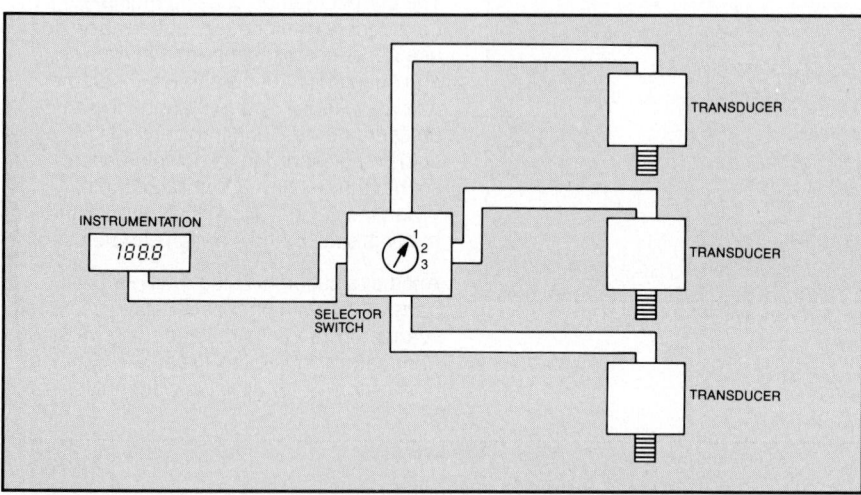

FIGURE 6. MULTIPLE TRANSDUCERS WIRED TO ONE METER AND ONE SWITCH (TRANSDUCERS WITH BUILT-IN ZERO & SPAN ADJUSTMENTS, SAME OUTPUTS & SAME PRESSURE RANGES)

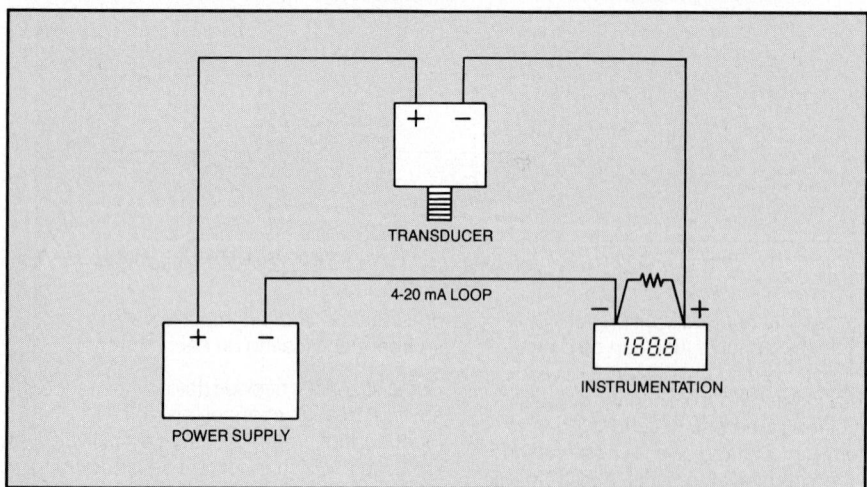

FIGURE 7. CONVERTING CURRENT INTO VOLTAGE FOR INSTRUMENTATION SET UP FOR VOLTAGE

HANDLING, LOCATING AND INSTALLING TRANSDUCERS

A. **Diaphragm**—Do not press or touch the diaphragm as you may damage or alter its calibration, particularly on low pressure range models.

B. **Fittings and Hardware**—Use appropriate pressure rated fittings and hardware. Make sure you have the correct thread type and size fitting. Use pressure limiters, capacity chambers, snubbers, etc., if needed.

C. **Operate at Ambient Temperatures**—Locate the transducer where it can be readily inspected and serviced. Ambient temperature should be within the transducer specifications. The temperature coefficient effects on the overall accuracy of the transducer can be minimized the closer the ambient temperature is to 25°C. Avoid locations with excessive vibration.

D. **Installation**—Installation should be made only by qualified personnel familiar with safety practices and knowledgeable with all industry accepted standard relating to pressure systems.

Transducer calibration and/or zero may shift if it is over-torqued when installing. Check for a zero shift after installing.

When installing transducers, refer to standard industry torque data for thread size and material type.

WATERHAMMER
A COMPLEX PHENOMENON WITH A SIMPLE SOLUTION

Waterhammer is an impact load that is the most misunderstood force known to pressure transducers today. A waterhammer is created by stopping and/or starting a liquid flow suddenly. The results of a waterhammer or impulse load are devastating to a pressure sensor. The impulse load occurs suddenly, in the millisecond time frame, but the effects of it last a life time. Waterhammers occur in almost all pressure systems and usually can not be stopped without extensive time, energy and studies.

A common example of a waterhammer occurs in most homes everyday. Simply turning off a shower quickly sends a loud thud trough the house; this is a perfect example of a waterhammer. Dishwashers and washing machines make these same sounds, because inside them small solenoid valves are being opened and closed quickly, producing this pulse noise. The key phrase in the examples above was turning on or off the water "quickly" verses turning it off slowly. In the shower example, if you turn the water off slowly, the waterhammer will not occur. Common industrial hardware like relief valves, solenoid valves, valves in general, centrifugal pumps, positive displacement pumps, and regulators can and will cause heavy hammer effects. A simple solution to this devastating effect is to protect each sensor with a pressure snubber. Snubbers are low ticket items that will insure that this hammer effect will not render your costly sensor useless. All pressure sensors should utilize snubbers for all installations.

The hammer occurs because an entire train of water is being stopped so fast that the end of the train hits up against the front end and sends shock waves through the pipe. This is similar to a real train, instead of slowing to a stop, it hits into a mountain side. The back of the train continues forward even though the front can not go anywhere. Since the water flow is restricted inside the pipe, a shock wave of incompressible water travels back down the pipe deflecting everything in its path. An unprotected transducer in the path of this monstrous wake is, without question, going to sustain heavy damage.

To understand the damage caused by the waterhammer forces, it is necessary to understand the principles behind the sensor. Most pressure sensors utilize a rigid diaphram as the primary sensing element. The diaphram deflects due to the pressure, and its' deflection is transformed to an electrical output via various methods. The key component is the rigid diaphram. The rigid diaphram deflects only on the order of a thousanth of an inch. With a large wake of fluid hitting the sensor, it is no wonder the diaphram is bent beyond its' elastic limit and permanent damage is done. Remember that a snubber eliminates this effect and therefore should always be installed on every pressure system.

> ## "The results of a waterhammer or impulse load are devastating to a pressure sensor."

Snubbers are chosen by the media that they will be used on such as liquids, gases or dense liquids like motor oils, and their physical mounting fittings. Snubbers only let so much fluid pass through per unit time, eliminating the surge from hitting the diaphram. Liquids possess a large hammer effect because they are incompressible , but gases can also possess a hammer effect large enough to render a sensor useless. A practical analogue to a snubber is a sponge in the drain of a sink. The sponge ensures that the sink empties slowly, instead of all at once. A lot of common questions are asked about hammer effects; the following are just a few.

WILL A SNUBBER EFFECT THE RESPONSE TIME OF MY PRESSURE TRANSDUCER?

In most cases, the transducer is connected to a meter of a recorder that updates at 2 to 3 times a second; therefore a snubber will not effect it at all.

WHAT ARE THE SYMPTOMS THAT MY SENSOR HAS BEEN DAMAGED BY A FLUID HAMMER?

Most sensors will exhibit a higher then normal output at zero pressure (a zero shift). This occurs because the diaphram can not return to zero. In severe cases no output occurs or the output does not change with an increase in pressure.

IF MY SENSOR HAS A LARGE ZERO OFFSET CAUSED BY THIS HAMMER EFFECT CAN IT BE REPAIRED?

Most sensors are non-repairable. The diaphram is the main building block of the sensor. When building a sensor the diaphram is first built and then all other components are chosen to achieve the rated specification. When a diaphram bends beyond its elastic limit, it can not be bent back to original shape or replaced because of the unique components associated with the original diaphram. If a diaphram does have a slight zero shift, less then 10%, it probably is still linear and can be used. Before reinstalling it in the system, please acquire a snubber or the hammer effect will occur again and possibly damage the unit further.

WILL A SNUBBER STOP AN OVERPRESSURE?

Snubbers stop spikes only, they do not perform miracles. An overpressure will not be stopped by a snubber. A spike lasts only on the order of milliseconds; any overpressure for more than that time will damage the sensor.

HOW IS A SNUBBER INSTALLED IN A PRESSURE SYSTEM?

The snubber would screw on to the front end of the transducer and then thread into the piping system. The snubber is located between the piping under pressure and the pressure transducer.

The following brief equations summarize the hammer effect and is followed by an example of waterhammers destructive forces.

WATERHAMMER *(Continued)*

The following equation determines the maximum pressure change that occurs during a fluid hammer. The equation assumes that the piping is inelastic.

$$\Delta P = \frac{\rho c \Delta v}{g}$$

where

$$c \text{ for liquids} = \left(\frac{Eg}{\rho}\right)^{1/2}$$

$$c \text{ for gases} = (KgRT)^{1/2}$$

where

ΔP is the change in pressure resulting from the fluid hammer (pounds per square foot)

ρ is the fluid density (pound mass per cubic foot)

c is the speed of sound in the fluid (feet per second)

Δv is the change in velocity of the fluid (feet per second)

g is the gravitational constant (32.2 feet per second per second)

E is the bulk modulus of the fluid media (listed in PSI but must be converted to PSF)

k is the ratio of specific heats ($k=1.4$ for air)

R is the specific gas constant (foot pounds per pound mass per degree Rankine)

T is the absolute temperature in Rankine

Example of waterhammer occurring in typical house piping. Assuming you have one inch water piping, how much of a change in pressure will be created from a waterhammer?

Assume that the water is flowing at 10 gallons per minute and the temperature is about room temperature (70°F). A 1 inch schedule 40 pipe has an internal area equal to 0.00600 ft².

Fluid velocity V = Q/A = 10 gpm (1/448.83 gpm/cfs)/.006 ft² = 3.71 ft/sec

Where Q is the flow rate, and A is the internal area in the pipe.

$$c = \left(\frac{Eg}{\rho}\right)^{1/2} = \left[\frac{(320 \times 10^3 \text{ lbs/in}^2)(144 \text{ in}^2/\text{ft}^2)(32.2 \text{ ft/sec}^2)}{62.3 \text{ lbs/ft}^3}\right]^{1/2} = 4880 \text{ ft/sec}$$

$$\Delta P = \frac{\rho c \Delta v}{g} = \frac{(62.3 \text{ lb/ft}^3)(4880 \text{ ft/sec})(3.71 \text{ ft/sec})}{32.2 \text{ ft/sec}^2} = 3502g \text{ lbs/ft}^2 = 243 \text{ lbs/in}^2$$

In this example, a 1 inch pipe with a flow rate of 10 gpm had a hammer effect resulting in an increase in pressure of 243 PSI above normal operating conditions. Considering normal city water pressure of 50 PSI, most end users would select a sensor of approximately 100 PSI full scale to be on the safe side. A 100 PSI sensor usually has an over pressure of 200% associated with it, meaning it will be able to withstand 200 PSI. Now the hammer increases the system from 50 PSI to 293 PSI (50 + 243), which is overpressurizing the transducer and causing damage to it. Most end users are puzzled as to how a system that is supplied with only 60 PSI is capable of producing over 200 PSI. After reading this article it should be evident that fluid hammers are a complex phenomena with a simple solution: installing snubbers on all pressure transducers.

PROPERTIES OF WATER AT ATMOSPHERIC PRESSURE

Temp. °F	Density lbm/ft³	Density slug/ft³	Viscosity lbf-sec/ft²	Kinematic Viscosity ft²/sec	Surface Tension lbf/ft	Vapor Pressure Head ft	Bulk Modulus lbf/in²
32	62.42	1.940	3.746 EE-5	1.931 EE-5	0.518 EE-2	0.20	293 EE3
40	62.43	1.940	3.229 EE-5	1.664 EE-5	0.514 EE-2	0.28	294 EE3
50	62.41	1.940	2.735 EE-5	1.410 EE-5	0.509 EE-2	0.41	305 EE3
60	62.37	1.938	2.359 EE-5	1.217 EE-5	0.504 EE-2	0.59	311 EE3
70	62.30	1.936	2.050 EE-5	1.059 EE-5	0.500 EE-2	0.84	320 EE3
80	62.22	1.934	1.799 EE-5	0.930 EE-5	0.492 EE-2	1.17	322 EE3
90	62.11	1.931	1.595 EE-5	0.826 EE-5	0.486 EE-2	1.61	323 EE3
100	62.00	1.927	1.424 EE-5	0.739 EE-5	0.480 EE-2	2.19	327 EE3
110	61.86	1.923	1.284 EE-5	0.667 EE-5	0.473 EE-2	2.95	331 EE3
120	61.71	1.918	1.168 EE-5	0.609 EE-5	0.465 EE-2	3.91	333 EE3
130	61.55	1.913	1.069 EE-5	0.558 EE-5	0.460 EE-2	5.13	334 EE3
140	61.38	1.908	0.981 EE-5	0.514 EE-5	0.454 EE-2	6.67	330 EE3
150	61.20	1.902	0.905 EE-5	0.476 EE-5	0.447 EE-2	8.58	328 EE3
160	61.00	1.896	0.838 EE-5	0.442 EE-5	0.441 EE-2	10.95	326 EE3
170	60.80	1.890	0.780 EE-5	0.413 EE-5	0.433 EE-2	13.83	322 EE3
180	60.58	1.883	0.726 EE-5	0.385 EE-5	0.426 EE-2	17.33	313 EE3
190	60.36	1.876	0.678 EE-5	0.362 EE-5	0.419 EE-2	21.55	313 EE3
200	60.12	1.868	0.637 EE-5	0.341 EE-5	0.412 EE-2	26.59	308 EE3
212	59.83	1.860	0.593 EE-5	0.319 EE-5	0.404 EE-2	33.90	300 EE3

MOUNTING & INSTALLING LOAD CELLS
A LOOK AT THE EFFECT OF VARIOUS INSTALLATION CRITERIA

By LaVar Clegg

Most load cell data sheets provide performance information in terms of output, non-linearity, hysteresis, creep, and temperature sensitivity. Such parameters are based on application of ideal or axial loads. In this article we will discuss the response of load cells to non-axial loads and the effects of imperfect mounting conditions.

ANGULAR LOAD

An angular load is one which is applied at the intended point but at an angle with respect to the primary axis. There are at least two ways in which an angular load can originate. First, it can be the result of an axial load plus a side load. Second, it can be caused by a vertical load acting on a beam that is not mounted perfectly level.

An unlevel cell mounting is not an unusual condition in practice. To analyze this condition, refer to Figure 1. The angular load P can be resolved trigonometrically into an axial load as a side load. The load cell, of course, responds to the axial component Pcos0. Assuming that the response of the cell to the side load is small and well-behaved (such an assumption is a good one), it is apparent that the error resulting from an angular load, as opposed to an axial load, is easily accounted for in a calibration process. There is no contribution to non-linearity; therefore the error is not an error at all as far as measurement accuracy is concerned. This is comforting to know because it would be impractical to do precision leveling on an installation and then maintain it. There is a serious source of measurement error which pertains to angular loading. It is the condition of an inconsistent angle. If the angle varies with respect to load, non-linearity and possibly hysteresis errors will result. They will not be removable by calibration.

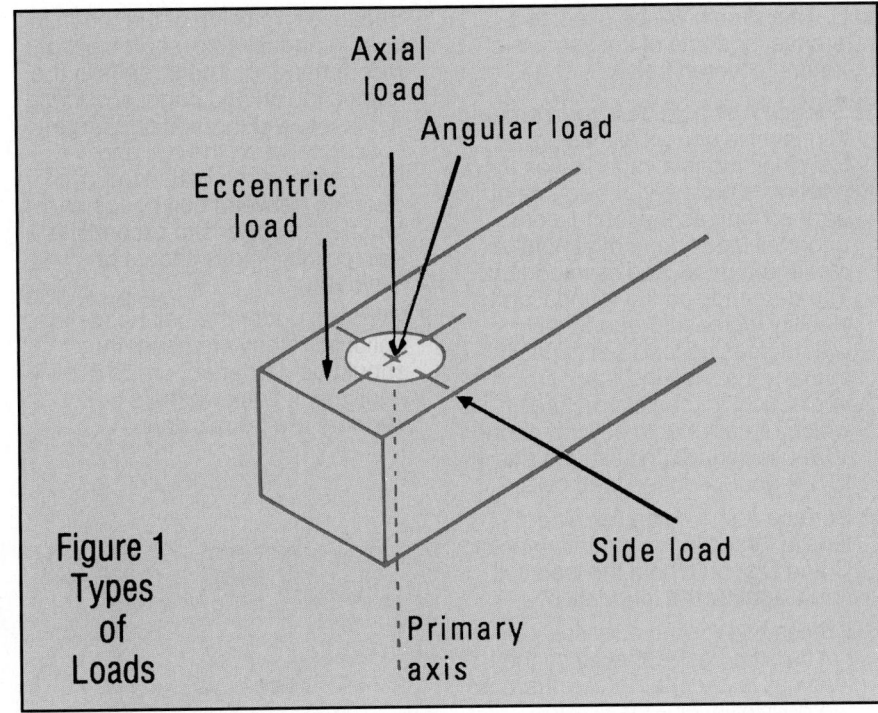

Figure 1
Types
of
Loads

Axial load, Angular load, Eccentric load, Side load, Primary axis

For example, consider a case in which the load cell mounting has some compliance because it is due to inadequate support. At no load 0 = 0, at half load 0 = 1°, and at full load 0 = 2°. This situation would produce a non-linearity of 0.023% full scale (in addition to any other sources of non-linearity errors) as given by the formula:
%FS = (cos1°-cos2°)(1/2) = 0.00023

ECCENTRIC LOAD

An eccentric load is one that is applied in parallel with the primary axis but not concentric with it. It would be desirable for a cell to respond to an eccentric load with the same sensitivity as to an axial load. Such is not normally the case. However, just as an angular load with constant angle is not a source of error, an eccentric load with constant eccentricity is not a source of error. It is when the load position moves between weighments that a source of error exists.

SIDE LOAD

Any force acting at 90° from the primary axis and on the point of axial load application is called a side load. Side loads are common as they are induced by dynamic loads, expansion and contraction of structures, and

various mounting anomalies. Pure side loads are difficult to generate in the laboratory and therefore the response of load cells to pure side loads is difficult to measure. The response is very low relative to axial load response, and if the test load is not applied at exactly 90° from the primary axis, the small component load in the axial direction will create response overshadowing that of the large side component of the load.

MOUNTING

The preceding information on axial and non-axial loads pertains primarily to the manner of load application to the live end of the beam. Now, let's look at the attachment of the dead end of the beam.

There is no single, correct way to mount single-ended beams. Users seem to learn by experience and skill what works best for their particular application and economic constraints. Nevertheless, good mounting practices are worth enumerating.

Figure 2 illustrates a mounted single-ended bream. It is attached to a foundation on surface A by means of mounting bolts C and D. A load is applied

at E. This sketch will be used as a reference for some of the aspects of mounting covered below.

1. Surface A should be level in order to minimize non-axial loading. However, modest imperfection in leveling is not a serious source of error so long as the foundation under all loads, from minimum to maximum rated load, is important. The demands on the foundation for stability increase proportionally with increasing load cell capacity. In many installations it is impractical to create structures which remain stable beyond about 10,000 lbs, in which case it is easier to use double-ended load cells.

2. Surface A should be flat. The tensile forces in the mounting bolts C and D should hold the load cell firmly against the foundation.

   If these two mating surfaces are not flat, the position taken by the load cell is uncertain. Also, there is the possibility of undesirable bending stresses being induced in the beam, causing non-linearity or hysteresis or both in the load cell output. The mounting surface of load cells is typically flat within 0.002 inch. Surface A should be equally flat.

3. Bolts C and D should be grade 8 or equivalent high-strength bolts.

   With a load at point E the bolts are in tension. The tendency of such a load is to stretch the bolts and lift the load cell off surface A. Of course, the cell must remain in firm contact with surface A in order to avoid angular load errors. Therefore the bolts must be adequately tightened and only high strength bolts are capable of such tightening.

4. By reasoning of the above point, the mounting bolts should be seated to recommended torque. While the necessary torque is actually determined by the bolt size, the cell capacity, and the cell dimensions, it is convenient to generalize as follows:

Bolt Dia.	Torque (ft-lbs)
¼″	12
½″	100
¾″	350

5. Because stretching of the mounting bolts is undesirable, short bolts are recommended. The threads in the foundation should begin at surface A. Recesssed threads or a large spacer between the cell and foundation which cause the distance between bolt heads and foundation threads to exceed the load cell thickness should be avoided.

6. Washers under the bolt heads are optional. If they are used, they should be hardened, grade 8, or equivalent. Lock washers or flat washers are permissible.

7. With high capacity cells starting at about the 5000-lb range, point B begins to show deformation under repeated loading. In such cases it is recommended that the foundation be hardened steel. The body of high capacity single-ended beams is typically relatively hard, about Rockwell C-45, so a slightly lower hardness than that would be appropriate for a foundation.

By understanding the possible sources of error and by using good mounting practices, loading conditions can be managed to contribute negligible effect on weighing accuracy in practical installations.

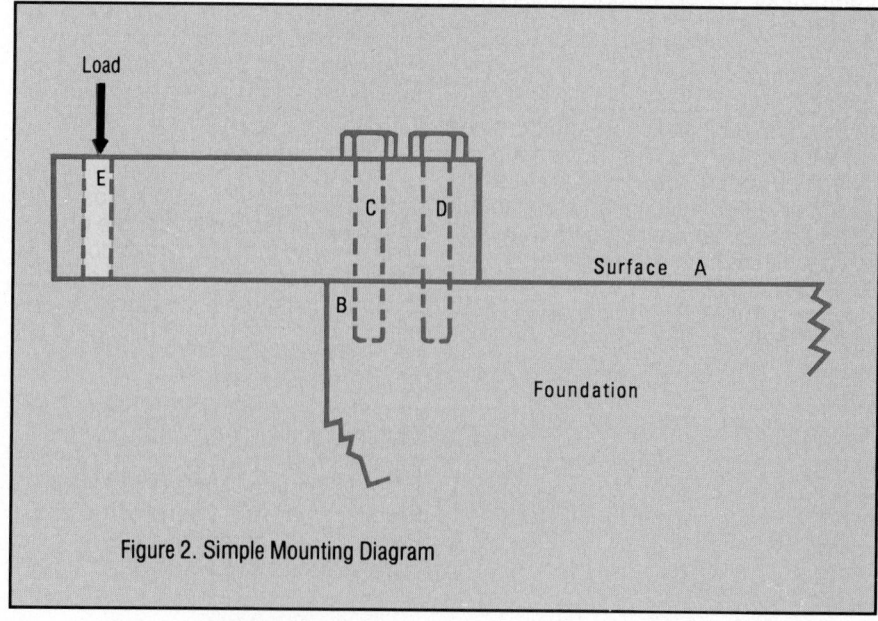

Figure 2. Simple Mounting Diagram

APPLICATION FORMULAS FOR INDUSTRIAL STRAIN MEASUREMENTS

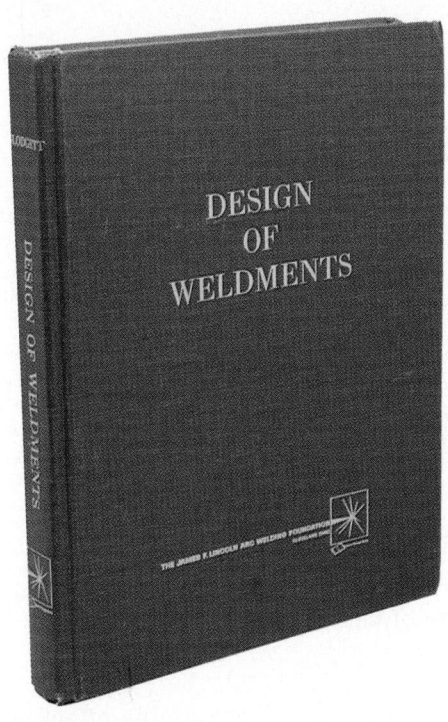

OMEGA ENGINEERING, Inc. gratefully acknowledges the James F. Lincoln Arc Welding Foundation, for permission to reprint "Beam Diagrams and Formulas". Originally printed in the textbook Design of Weldments.

Beam Diagrams and Formulas

The following beam diagrams and formulas have been found useful in the design of steel weldments.

Proper signs, positive (+) and negative (–), are not necessarily indicated in the formulas. The following are suggested:

Shear diagram above reference line is (+)

Shear diagram below reference line is (–)

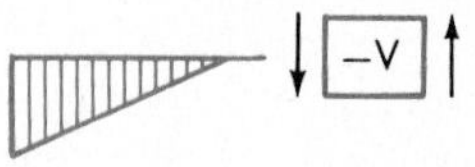

Reaction to left of (+) shear is upward (+)

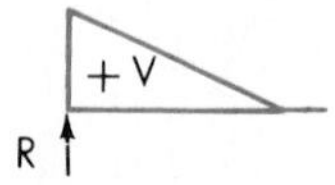

Reaction to left of (–) shear is downward (–)

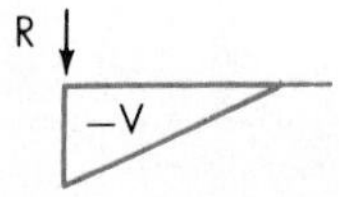

Reaction to right of (+) shear is downward (–)

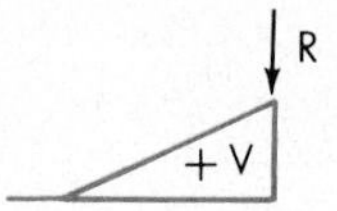

Reaction to right of (–) shear is upward (+)

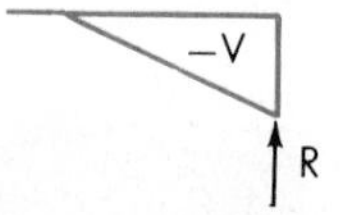

Moment above reference line is (+)
Compressive bending stresses on top fibers
also tends to open up a corner connection

Moment diagram on same side as compressive stress

Moment below reference line is (–)
Compressive bending stresses on bottom fibers
also tends to close up a corner connection

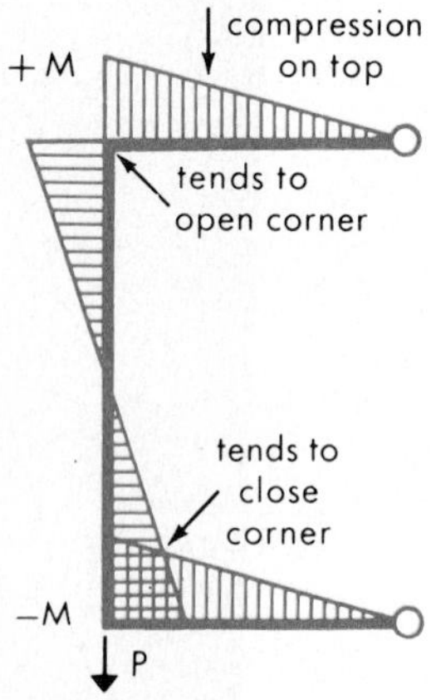

Angle of slope, θ
     clockwise rotation (–), counter-clockwise rotation (+)

On the next page is a visual index to the various beam diagrams and formulas. As indicated, these are keyed by number to the type of beam and by capital letter to the type of load.

For some conditions, influence curves are included to illustrate the effect of an important variable. These are keyed to the basic beam diagram and are positioned as close as practical to the diagram.

VISUAL INDEX TO FORMULAS ON FOLLOWING PAGES
FOR VARIOUS BEAM–LOAD CONDITIONS

Type of BEAM \ Type of LOAD	Concentrated force (A)	Uniform load entire span (B)	Uniform load partial span (C)	Varying load (D)	Couple (E)
① Cantilever (free — fixed)	1Aa, 1Ab	1B	1C	1Da, 1Db	1E
② (guided — fixed)	2A	2B			
③ Simply supported (supported)	3Aa, 3Ab, 3Ac, 3Ad	3B	3C	3Da, 3Db, 3Dc	3Ea, 3Eb, 3Ec
④ (fixed — fixed)	4Aa, 4Ab, 4Ac	4Ba, 4Bb	4C	4D	4E
⑤ (supported — fixed)	5Aa, 5Ab	5B	5C	5Da, 5Db	5E
⑥ Single span with overhang	6Aa, 6Ab	6Ba, 6Bb	6Ca, 6Cb		
⑦ Continuous two span	7Aa, 7Ab	7B		7D — See adjacent to ③D	For other multi-span load conditions, see discussion under ⑦

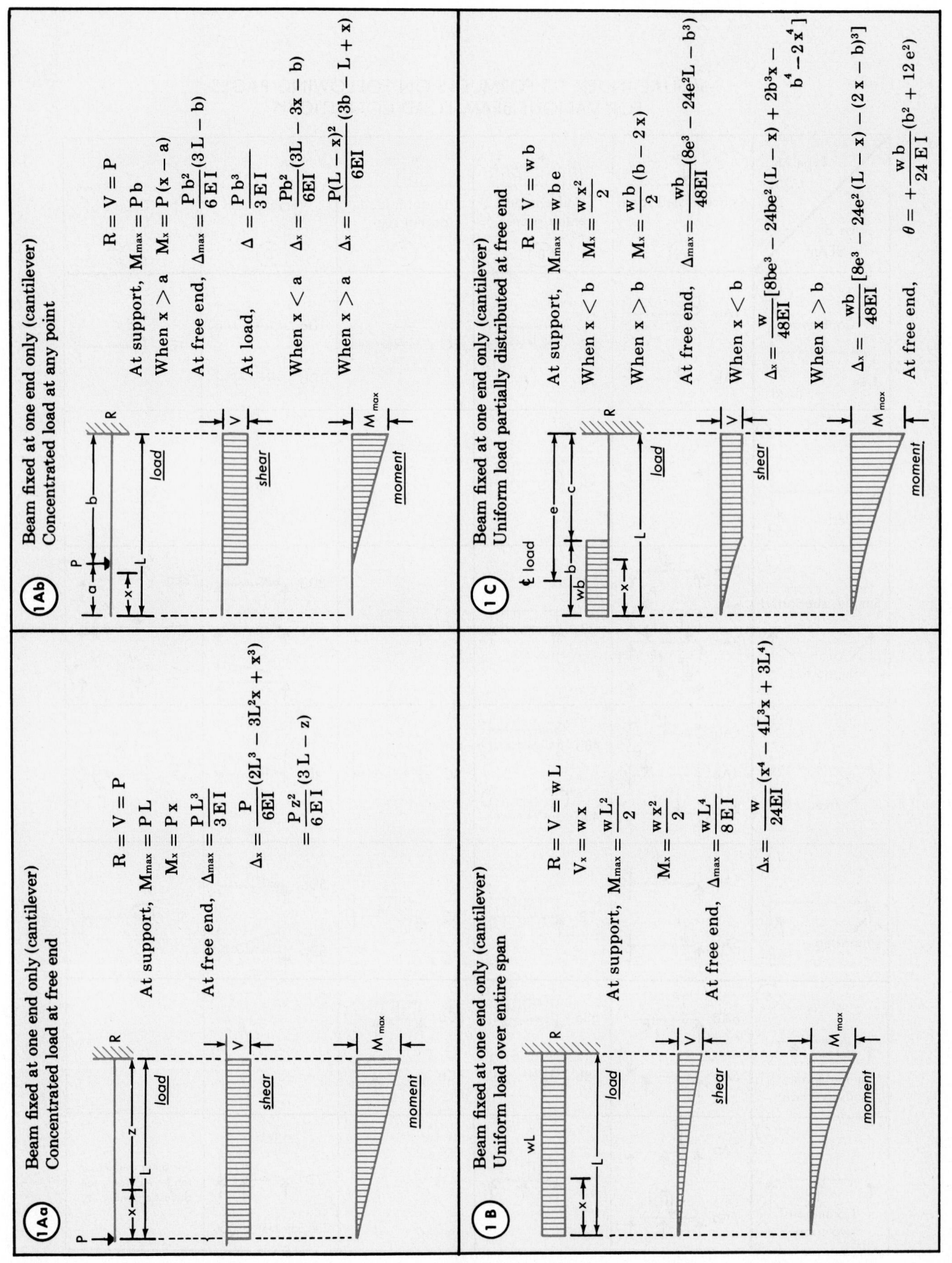

1Aa Beam fixed at one end only (cantilever)
Concentrated load at free end

$$R = V = P$$

At support, $M_{max} = PL$

$$M_x = Px$$

At free end, $\Delta_{max} = \dfrac{PL^3}{3EI}$

$$\Delta_x = \dfrac{P}{6EI}(2L^3 - 3L^2x + x^3)$$
$$= \dfrac{Pz^2}{6EI}(3L - z)$$

load   *shear* M_{max} *moment*

1Ab Beam fixed at one end only (cantilever)
Concentrated load at any point

$$R = V = P$$

At support, $M_{max} = Pb$

When $x > a$, $M_x = P(x - a)$

At free end, $\Delta_{max} = \dfrac{Pb^2}{6EI}(3L - b)$

At load, $\Delta = \dfrac{Pb^3}{3EI}$

When $x < a$, $\Delta_x = \dfrac{Pb^2}{6EI}(3L - 3x - b)$

When $x > a$, $\Delta_x = \dfrac{P(L - x)^2}{6EI}(3b - L + x)$

load   *shear* M_{max} *moment*

1B Beam fixed at one end only (cantilever)
Uniform load over entire span

$$R = V = wL$$
$$V_x = wx$$

At support, $M_{max} = \dfrac{wL^2}{2}$

$$M_x = \dfrac{wx^2}{2}$$

At free end, $\Delta_{max} = \dfrac{wL^4}{8EI}$

$$\Delta_x = \dfrac{w}{24EI}(x^4 - 4L^3x + 3L^4)$$

load   *shear* M_{max} *moment*

1C Beam fixed at one end only (cantilever)
Uniform load partially distributed at free end

$$R = V = w\,b\,e$$

At support, $M_{max} = w\,b\,e$

When $x < b$, $M_x = \dfrac{w\,x^2}{2}$

When $x > b$, $M_x = \dfrac{w\,b}{2}(b - 2x)$

At free end, $\Delta_{max} = \dfrac{wb}{48EI}(8e^3 - 24e^2L - b^3)$

When $x < b$,
$$\Delta_x = \dfrac{w}{48EI}\big[8be^3 - 24be^2(L - x) + 2b^3x - b^4 - 2x^4\big]$$

When $x > b$,
$$\Delta_x = \dfrac{wb}{48EI}\big[8e^3 - 24e^2(L - x) - (2x - b)^3\big]$$

At free end, $\theta = +\dfrac{wb}{24EI}(b^2 + 12e^2)$

load   *shear* M_{max} *moment*

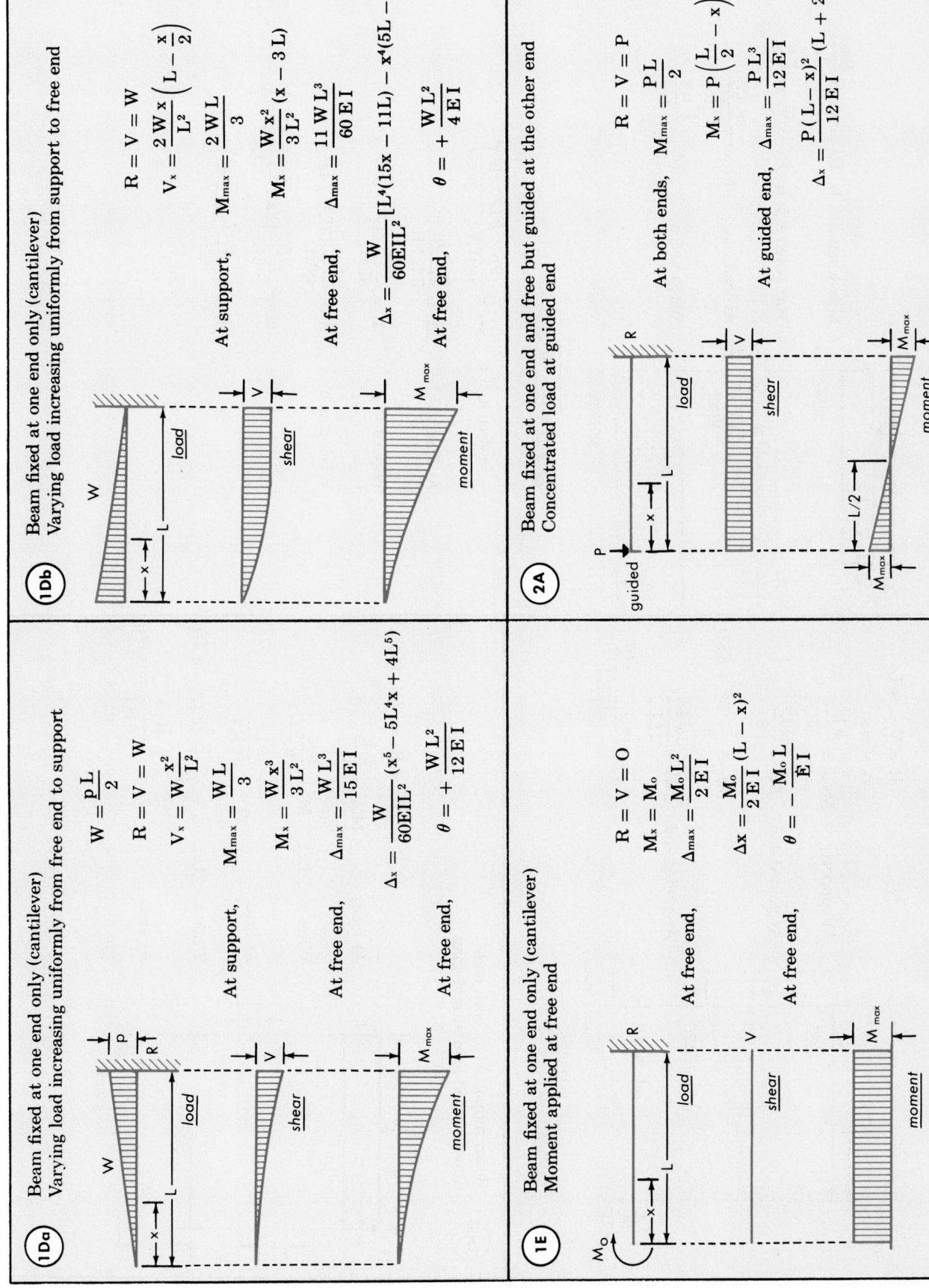

1Da

Beam fixed at one end only (cantilever)
Varying load increasing uniformly from free end to support

$$W = \frac{pL}{2}$$

$$R = V = W$$

$$V_x = W\frac{x^2}{L^2}$$

At support, $\quad M_{max} = \frac{WL}{3}$

$$M_x = \frac{Wx^3}{3L^2}$$

At free end, $\quad \Delta_{max} = \frac{WL^3}{15EI}$

$$\Delta_x = \frac{W}{60EIL^2}(x^5 - 5L^4x + 4L^5)$$

At free end, $\quad \theta = +\frac{WL^2}{12EI}$

1Db

Beam fixed at one end only (cantilever)
Varying load increasing uniformly from support to free end

$$R = V = W$$

$$V_x = \frac{2Wx}{L^2}\left(L - \frac{x}{2}\right)$$

At support, $\quad M_{max} = \frac{2WL}{3}$

$$M_x = \frac{Wx^2}{3L^2}(x - 3L)$$

At free end, $\quad \Delta_{max} = \frac{11WL^3}{60EI}$

$$\Delta_x = \frac{W}{60EIL^2}[L^4(15x - 11L) - x^4(5L - x)]$$

At free end, $\quad \theta = +\frac{WL^2}{4EI}$

1E

Beam fixed at one end only (cantilever)
Moment applied at free end

$$R = V = O$$

$$M_x = M_o$$

At free end, $\quad \Delta_{max} = \frac{M_o L^2}{2EI}$

$$\Delta_x = \frac{M_o}{2EI}(L - x)^2$$

At free end, $\quad \theta = -\frac{M_o L}{EI}$

2A

Beam fixed at one end and free but guided at the other end
Concentrated load at guided end

$$R = V = P$$

At both ends, $\quad M_{max} = \frac{PL}{2}$

$$M_x = P\left(\frac{L}{2} - x\right)$$

At guided end, $\quad \Delta_{max} = \frac{PL^3}{12EI}$

$$\Delta_x = \frac{P(L - x)^2}{12EI}(L + 2x)$$

2B Beam fixed at one end and free but guided at the other end
Uniform load over entire span

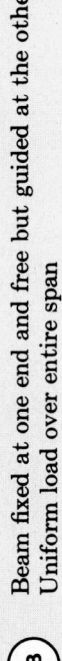

$$R = V = wL$$

$$V_x = w\,x$$

At support, $\quad M_{max} = \dfrac{wL^2}{3}$

At guided end, $\quad M_1 = \dfrac{wL^2}{6}$

$$M_x = \dfrac{w}{6}\left(L^2 - 3x^2\right)$$

At guided end, $\quad \Delta_{max} = \dfrac{wL^4}{24\,EI}$

$$\Delta_x = \dfrac{w\left(L^2 - x^2\right)^2}{24\,EI}$$

3Ab Beam supported at both ends
Concentrated load at any point

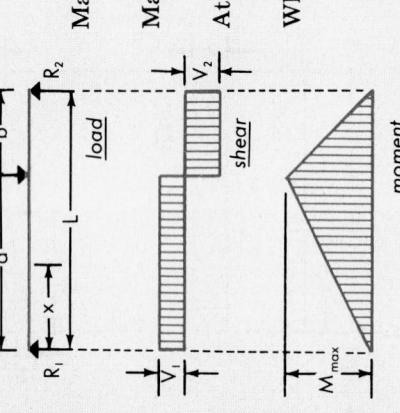

Max when $a < b$ $\quad R_1 = V_1 = \dfrac{P\,b}{L}$

Max when $a > b$ $\quad R_2 = V_2 = \dfrac{P\,a}{L}$

At load, $\quad M_{max} = \dfrac{P\,a\,b}{L}$

When $x < a$ $\quad M_x = \dfrac{P\,b\,x}{L}$

At $x = \sqrt{\dfrac{L^2 - b^2}{3}}$

when $a > b$ $\quad \Delta_{max} = \dfrac{Pb}{3EIL}\sqrt{\left(\dfrac{L^2 - b^2}{3}\right)^3}$

At load, $\quad \Delta = \dfrac{P\,a^2\,b^2}{3\,EIL}$

When $x < a$ $\quad \Delta_x = \dfrac{Pbx}{6EIL}\left(L^2 - b^2 - x^2\right)$

$$\Delta_{\mathfrak{c}} = \dfrac{Pa}{48EI}\left(3L^2 - 4a^2\right)$$

When $x < b$

At ends, $\quad \Big\{$

$$\theta_1 = -\dfrac{P}{6EI}\left(2aL + \dfrac{a^3}{L} - 3a^2\right)$$

$$\theta_2 = +\dfrac{P}{6EI}\left(aL - \dfrac{a^3}{L}\right)$$

3Aa Beam supported at both ends
Concentrated load at mid-span

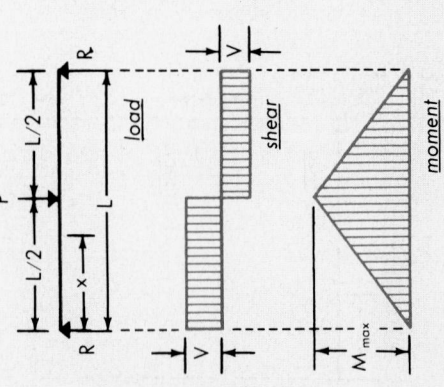

$$R_1 = R_2 = V = P/2$$

At load, $\quad M_{max} = \dfrac{P\,L}{4}$

When $x < L/2$ $\quad M_x = \dfrac{P\,x}{2}$

At load, $\quad \Delta_{max} = \dfrac{PL^3}{48\,EI}$

When $x < L/2$ $\quad \Delta_x = \dfrac{P\,x}{48\,EI}\left(3L^2 - 4x^2\right)$

At end, $\quad \theta_1 = -\dfrac{PL^2}{16\,EI} = -\theta_2$

3c Beam supported at both ends
Uniform load partially distributed over span

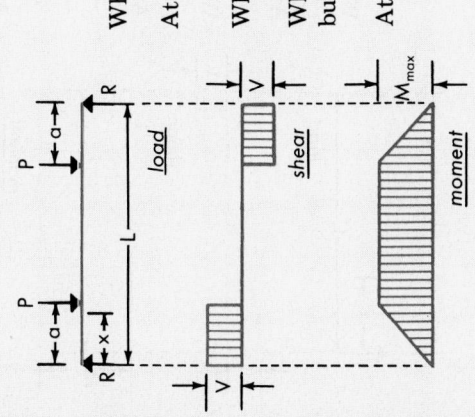

$$\text{Max when } a < c \quad R_1 = V_1 = \frac{wb}{2L}(2c + b)$$

$$\text{Max when } a > c \quad R_2 = V_2 = \frac{wb}{2L}(2a + b)$$

$$\text{When } x > a \text{ but } x < (a + b) \quad V_x = R_1 - w(x - a)$$

$$\text{At } x = a + \frac{R_1}{w} \quad M_{max} = R_1\left(a + \frac{R_1}{2w}\right)$$

$$\text{When } x < a \quad M_x = R_1 x$$

$$\text{When } x > a \text{ but } x < (a + b) \quad M_x = R_1 x - \frac{w}{2}(x - a)^2$$

$$\text{When } x > (a + b) \quad M_x = R_2(L - x)$$

When $a = c$

$$R = V = \frac{wb}{2}$$

$$V_x = w\left(a + \frac{b}{2} - x\right)$$

$$\text{At center,} \quad M_{max} = \frac{wb}{2}\left(a + \frac{b}{4}\right)$$

$$\text{When } x < a \quad M_x = \frac{wbx}{2}$$

$$\text{When } x > a \text{ but } x < (a + b) \quad M_x = \frac{wbx}{2} - \frac{w}{2}(x - a)^2$$

$$\text{At center,} \quad \Delta_{\text{c}} = \frac{wb}{384EI}(-8L^3 + 4b^2L - b^3)$$

3Ac Beam supported at both ends
Two equal concentrated loads, equally spaced from ends

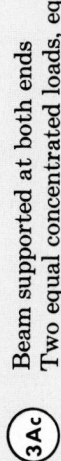

$$R = V = P$$

$$M_{max} = Pa$$

$$M_x = Px$$

$$\text{When } x < a$$

$$\text{At center,} \quad \Delta_{max} = \frac{Pa}{24EI}(3L^2 - 4a^2)$$

$$\text{When } x < a \quad \Delta_x = \frac{Px}{6EI}(3La - 3a^2 - x^2)$$

$$\text{When } x > a \text{ but } x < (L - a) \quad \Delta_x = \frac{Pa}{6EI}(3Lx - 3x^2 - a^2)$$

$$\text{At ends,} \quad \theta = \frac{Pa}{2EI}(L - a)$$

3Ad Beam supported at both ends
Two unequal concentrated loads, unequally spaced from ends

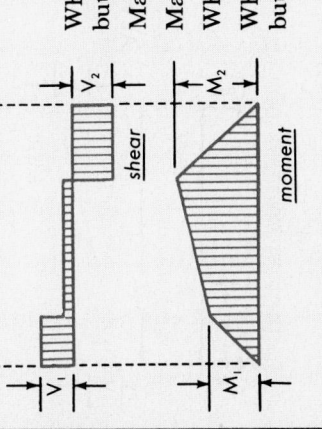

$$R_1 = V_1 = \frac{P_1(L - a) + P_2 b}{L}$$

$$R_2 = V_2 = \frac{P_1 a + P_2(L - b)}{L}$$

$$V_x = R_1 - P_1$$

$$M_1 = R_1 a \qquad M_2 = R_2 b$$

$$M_x = R_1 x$$

$$\text{When } x > a \text{ but } x < (L - b)$$

$$\text{Max when } R_1 < P_1$$

$$\text{Max when } R_2 < P_2$$

$$\text{When } x < a \quad M_x = R_1 x$$

$$\text{When } x > a \text{ but } x < (L - b) \quad M_x = R_1 x - P_1(x - a)$$

Also see formulas on page 8

3Da Beam supported at both ends
Varying load, increasing uniformly to one end

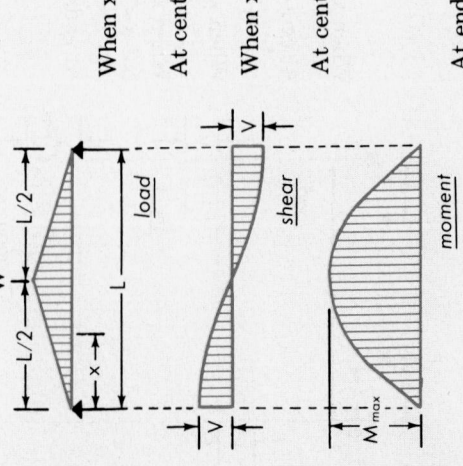

$$W = \frac{PL}{2}$$

$$R_1 = V_1 = \frac{W}{3}$$

$$R_2 = V_{2(max)} = \tfrac{2}{3}W$$

$$V_x = \frac{W}{3} - \frac{Wx^2}{L^2}$$

At $x = L/\sqrt{3} = .5744L$

$$M_{max} = \frac{2WL}{9\sqrt{3}} = .1283\,WL$$

$$M_x = \frac{Wx}{3L^2}(L^2 - x^2)$$

At $x = L\sqrt{1 - \sqrt{8/15}} = .5193L$

$$\Delta_{max} = .01304\,\frac{WL^3}{EI}$$

$$\Delta_x = \frac{Wx}{180\,EIL^2}(3x^4 - 10L^2x^2 + 7L^4)$$

At center, $\Delta_{c} = \dfrac{5WL^3}{384EI}$

At ends, $\theta_1 = -\dfrac{7WL^2}{180EI}$

   $\theta_2 = +\dfrac{8WL^2}{180EI}$

3B Beam supported at both ends
Uniform load over entire span

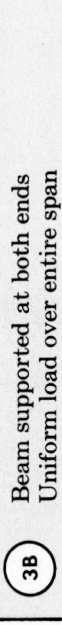
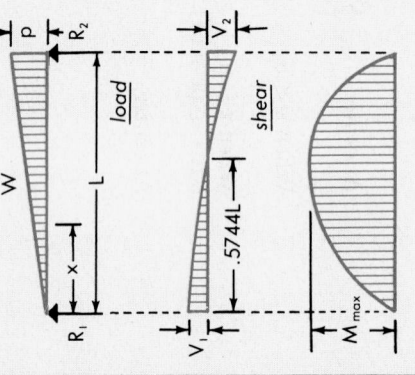

$$R = V = \frac{wL}{2}$$

$$V_x = w\left(\frac{L}{2} - x\right)$$

At center, $M_{max} = \dfrac{wL^2}{8}$

$$M_x = \frac{wx}{2}(L - x)$$

At center, $\Delta_{max} = \dfrac{5wL^4}{384\,EI}$

$$\Delta_x = \frac{wx}{24EI}(L^3 - 2Lx^2 + x^3)$$

At ends, $\theta = \dfrac{wL^3}{24\,EI}$

3Db Beam supported at both ends
Varying load, increasing uniformly to center

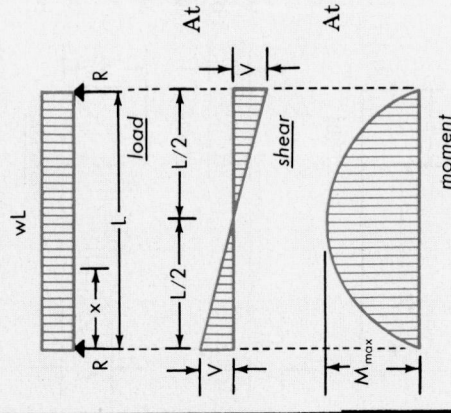

$$R_1 = R_2 = V = \frac{W}{2}$$

When $x < L/2$, $V_x = \dfrac{W}{2L^2}(L^2 - 4x^2)$

At center, $M_{max} = \dfrac{WL}{6}$

When $x < L/2$, $M_x = Wx\left(\dfrac{1}{2} - \dfrac{2x^2}{3L^2}\right)$

At center, $\Delta_{max} = \dfrac{WL^3}{60\,EI}$

$$\Delta_x = \frac{Wx}{480EIL^2}(5L^2 - 4x^2)^2$$

At ends, $\theta = \dfrac{5WL^2}{96\,EI}$

BEAM FORMULAS APPLIED TO SIDE OF TANK, BIN OR HOPPER
(p = pressure, psi; m = width of panel considered)

3Da

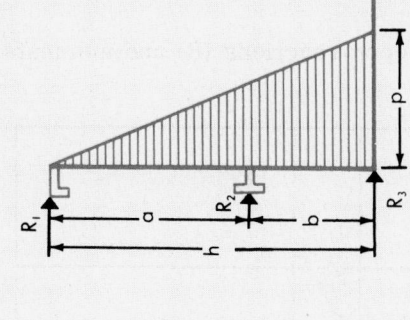

$$R_1 = \frac{p\,h\,m}{6} \qquad R_2 = \frac{p\,h\,m}{3} = V_{max}$$

$$M_{max} = \frac{p\,h^2\,m}{9\sqrt{3}} = .0642\,p\,h^2\,m$$

$$M_x = \frac{p\,x\,m}{6\,h}(h^2 - x^2)$$

$$\Delta_{4} = \frac{5\,h^4\,m}{768\,E\,I}$$

$$\Delta_x = \frac{p\,x\,m}{360\,E\,I\,h}(3\,x^4 - 10\,h^2\,x^2 + 7\,h^4)$$

$$\Delta_{max} = .00652\,\frac{p\,h^4\,m}{E\,I}$$
$$(\text{at } x = .5193\,h)$$

3Dc

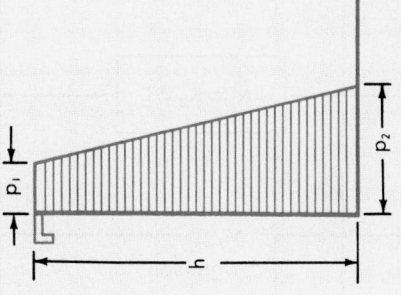
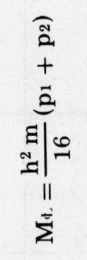

$$M_{4.} = \frac{h^2\,m}{16}(p_1 + p_2)\ *$$

$$\Delta_{4.} = \frac{5\,h^4\,m}{768\,E\,I}(p_1 + p_2)\ *$$

$$V_{max} = \frac{m\,h}{6}(p_1 + 2\,p_2)$$

(* These values are within 98% of maximum.)

7D

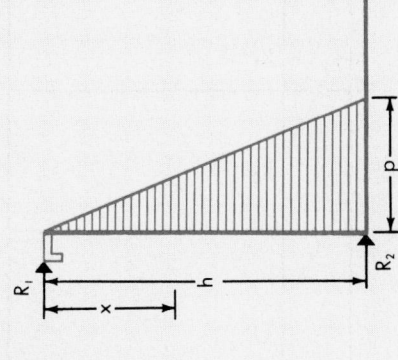

Maximum bending moment is least when

$$a = .57\,h$$
$$b = .43\,h$$

$$M_{max} = .0147\,p\,h^2\,m$$
(negative moment at middle support, 2)

$$R_1 = +.030\,p\,h\,m$$
$$R_2 = +.320\,p\,h\,m$$
$$R_3 = +.150\,p\,h\,m$$

$$V_{max} = +.188\,p\,h\,m$$
(at middle support, 2)

Also see formulas on page 7

7D Influence Lines

Effect of location of middle support (2) upon reactions (R) and moments (M)

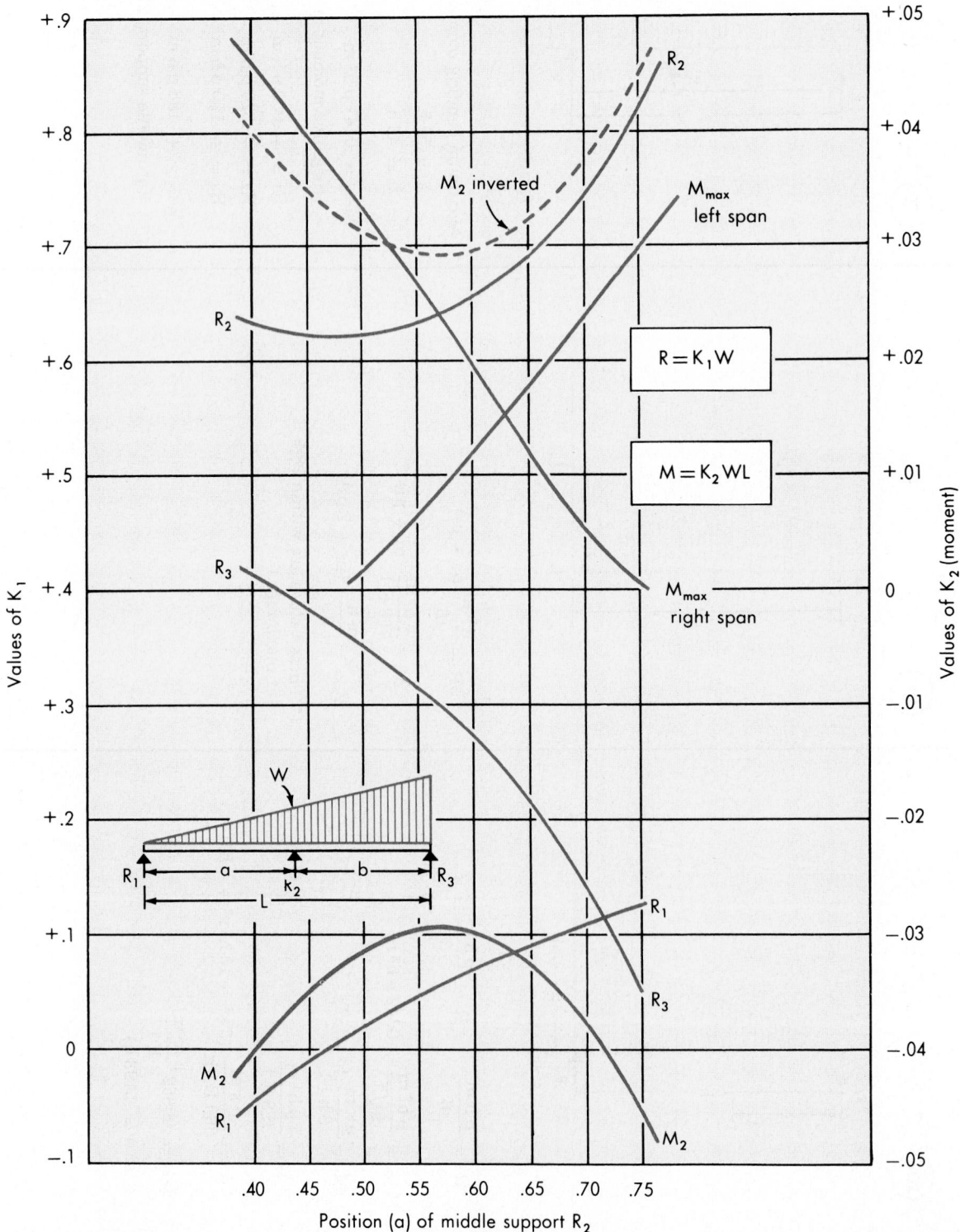

$$R = K_1 W$$

$$M = K_2 WL$$

Z-47

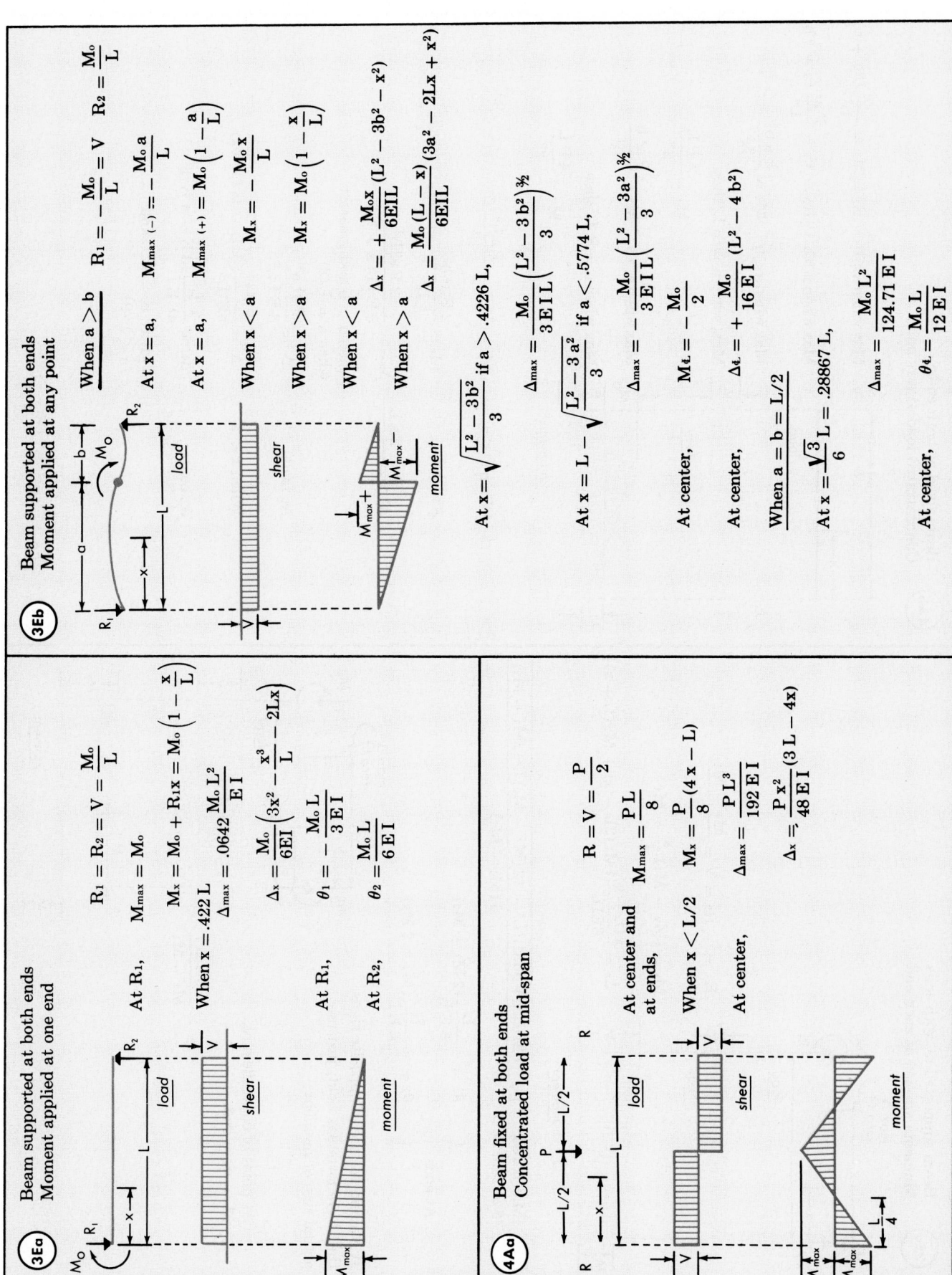

3Ea

Beam supported at both ends
Moment applied at one end

$$R_1 = R_2 = V = \frac{M_o}{L}$$

At R_1, $\quad M_{max} = M_o$

$$M_x = M_o + R_1 x = M_o\left(1 - \frac{x}{L}\right)$$

$$\Delta_{max} = .0642\,\frac{M_o L^2}{EI}$$

When $x = .422\,L$,

$$\Delta_x = \frac{M_o}{6EI}\left(3x^2 - \frac{x^3}{L} - 2Lx\right)$$

At R_1, $\quad \theta_1 = -\frac{M_o L}{3EI}$

At R_2, $\quad \theta_2 = \frac{M_o L}{6EI}$

3Eb

Beam supported at both ends
Moment applied at any point

When $a > b$ $\quad R_1 = -\frac{M_o}{L} = V \quad R_2 = \frac{M_o}{L}$

$$= -\frac{M_o a}{L}$$

At $x = a$, $\quad M_{max\,(-)} = -\frac{M_o a}{L}$

At $x = a$, $\quad M_{max\,(+)} = M_o\left(1 - \frac{a}{L}\right)$

When $x < a$ $\quad M_x = -\frac{M_o x}{L}$

When $x > a$ $\quad M_x = M_o\left(1 - \frac{x}{L}\right)$

When $x < a$ $\quad \Delta_x = +\frac{M_o x}{6EIL}(L^2 - 3b^2 - x^2)$

When $x > a$ $\quad \Delta_x = \frac{M_o(L-x)}{6EIL}(3a^2 - 2Lx + x^2)$

At $x = \sqrt{\dfrac{L^2 - 3b^2}{3}}$ if $a > .4226\,L$,

$$\Delta_{max} = \frac{M_o}{3EIL}\left(\frac{L^2 - 3b^2}{3}\right)^{3\!/\!2}$$

At $x = L - \sqrt{\dfrac{L^2 - 3a^2}{3}}$ if $a < .5774\,L$,

$$\Delta_{max} = -\frac{M_o}{3EIL}\left(\frac{L^2 - 3a^2}{3}\right)^{3\!/\!2}$$

At center, $\quad M_{\xi} = -\frac{M_o}{2}$

At center, $\quad \Delta_{\xi} = +\frac{M_o}{16EI}(L^2 - 4b^2)$

When $a = b = L/2$

At $x = \dfrac{\sqrt{3}}{6}L = .28867\,L$,

$$\Delta_{max} = \frac{M_o L^2}{124.71\,EI}$$

At center, $\quad \theta_{\xi} = \frac{M_o L}{12EI}$

4Aa

Beam fixed at both ends
Concentrated load at mid-span

$$R = V = \frac{P}{2}$$

At center and
at ends, $\quad M_{max} = \frac{PL}{8}$

When $x < L/2$ $\quad M_x = \frac{P}{8}(4x - L)$

At center, $\quad \Delta_{max} = \frac{PL^3}{192\,EI}$

$$\Delta_x = \frac{P x^2}{48\,EI}(3L - 4x)$$

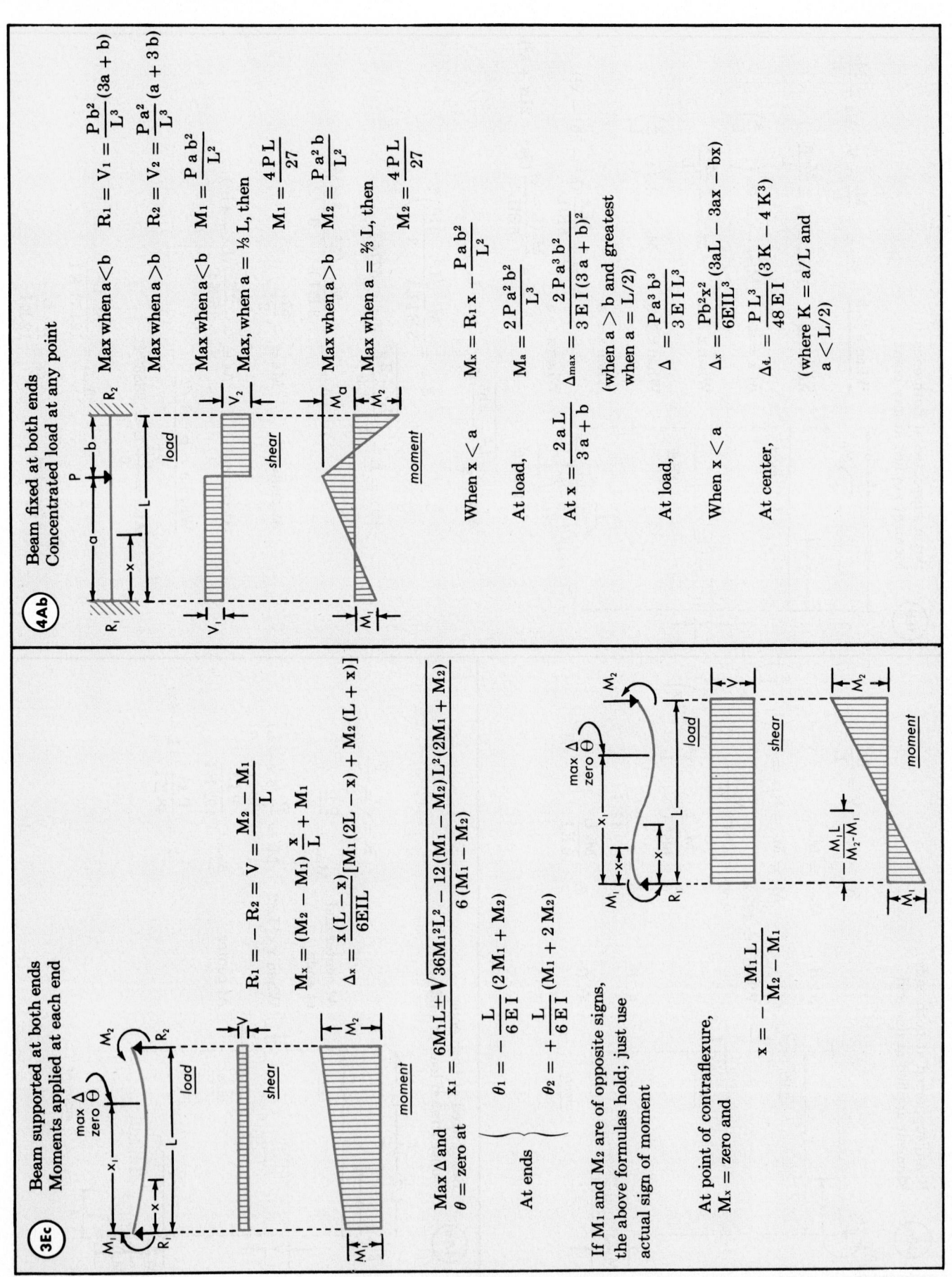

4Ab Beam fixed at both ends
Concentrated load at any point

$R_1 = V_1 = \dfrac{Pb^2}{L^3}(3a+b)$ Max when $a<b$

$R_2 = V_2 = \dfrac{Pa^2}{L^3}(a+3b)$ Max when $a>b$

$M_1 = \dfrac{Pab^2}{L^2}$ Max when $a<b$

$M_1 = \dfrac{4PL}{27}$ Max, when $a = \tfrac{1}{3}L$, then

$M_2 = \dfrac{Pa^2b}{L^2}$ Max when $a>b$

$M_2 = \dfrac{4PL}{27}$ Max when $a = \tfrac{2}{3}L$, then

When $x<a$, $M_x = R_1x - \dfrac{Pab^2}{L^2}$

At load, $M_a = \dfrac{2Pa^2b^2}{L^3}$

At $x = \dfrac{2aL}{3a+b}$ $\Delta_{max} = \dfrac{2Pa^3b^2}{3EI(3a+b)^2}$

(when $a>b$ and greatest when $a=L/2$)

At load, $\Delta = \dfrac{Pa^3b^3}{3EIL^3}$

When $x<a$, $\Delta_x = \dfrac{Pb^2x^2}{6EIL^3}(3aL-3ax-bx)$

At center, $\Delta_{L} = \dfrac{PL^3}{48EI}(3K-4K^3)$

(where $K = a/L$ and $a<L/2$)

3Ec Beam supported at both ends
Moments applied at each end

$R_1 = -R_2 = V = \dfrac{M_2-M_1}{L}$

$M_x = (M_2-M_1)\dfrac{x}{L}+M_1$

$\Delta_x = \dfrac{x(L-x)}{6EIL}[M_1(2L-x)+M_2(L+x)]$

Max Δ and θ = zero at $x_1 = \dfrac{6M_1L \pm \sqrt{36M_1^2L^2 - 12(M_1-M_2)L^2(2M_1+M_2)}}{6(M_1-M_2)}$

At ends $\theta_1 = -\dfrac{L}{6EI}(2M_1+M_2)$

$\theta_2 = +\dfrac{L}{6EI}(M_1+2M_2)$

If M_1 and M_2 are of opposite signs, the above formulas hold; just use actual sign of moment

At point of contraflexure, M_x = zero and

$x = -\dfrac{M_1L}{M_2-M_1}$

(4Ab) Influence Lines

Effect of position of force (F) upon moments M_a, M_1, M_2 and upon Δ_{max}

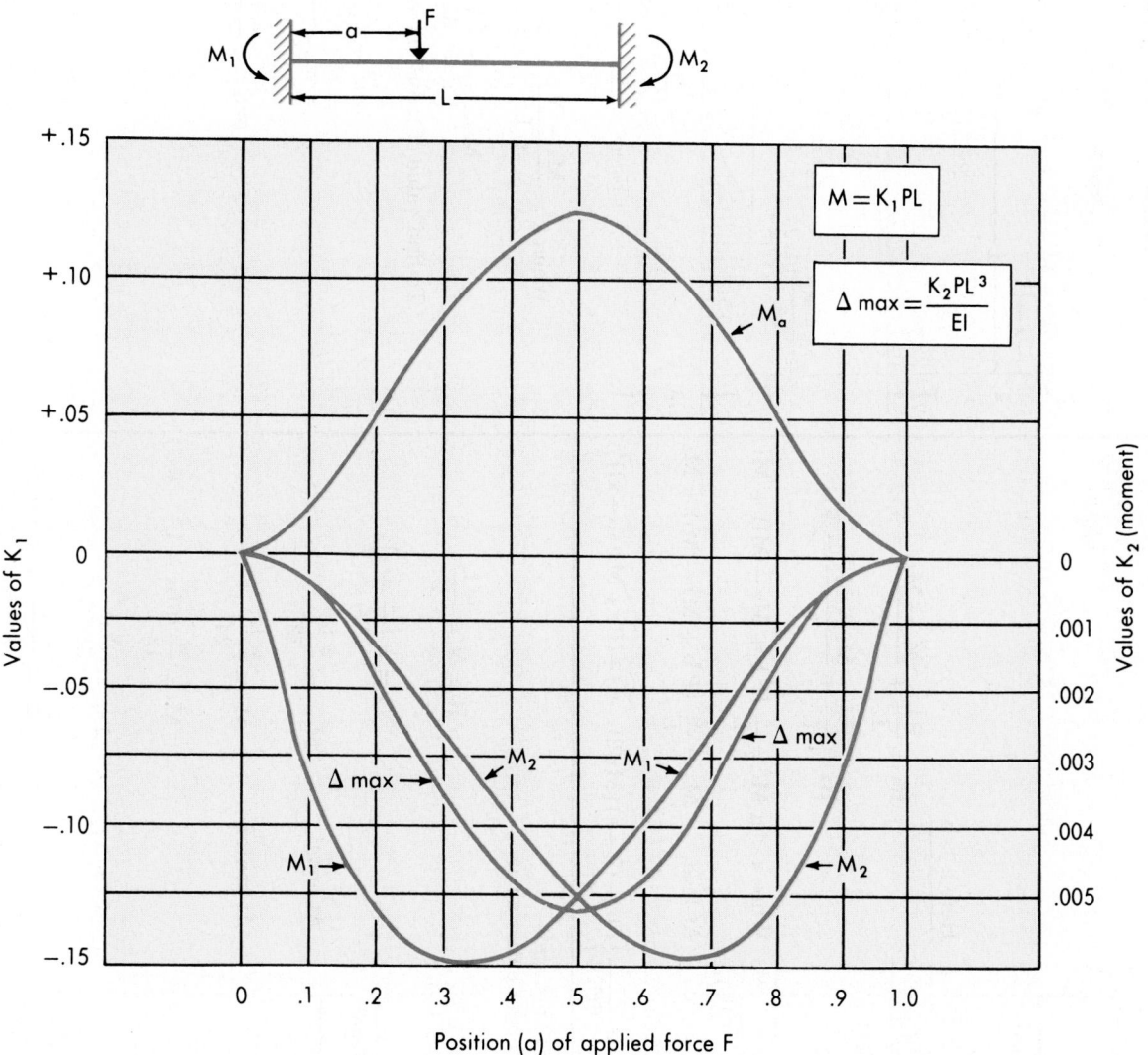

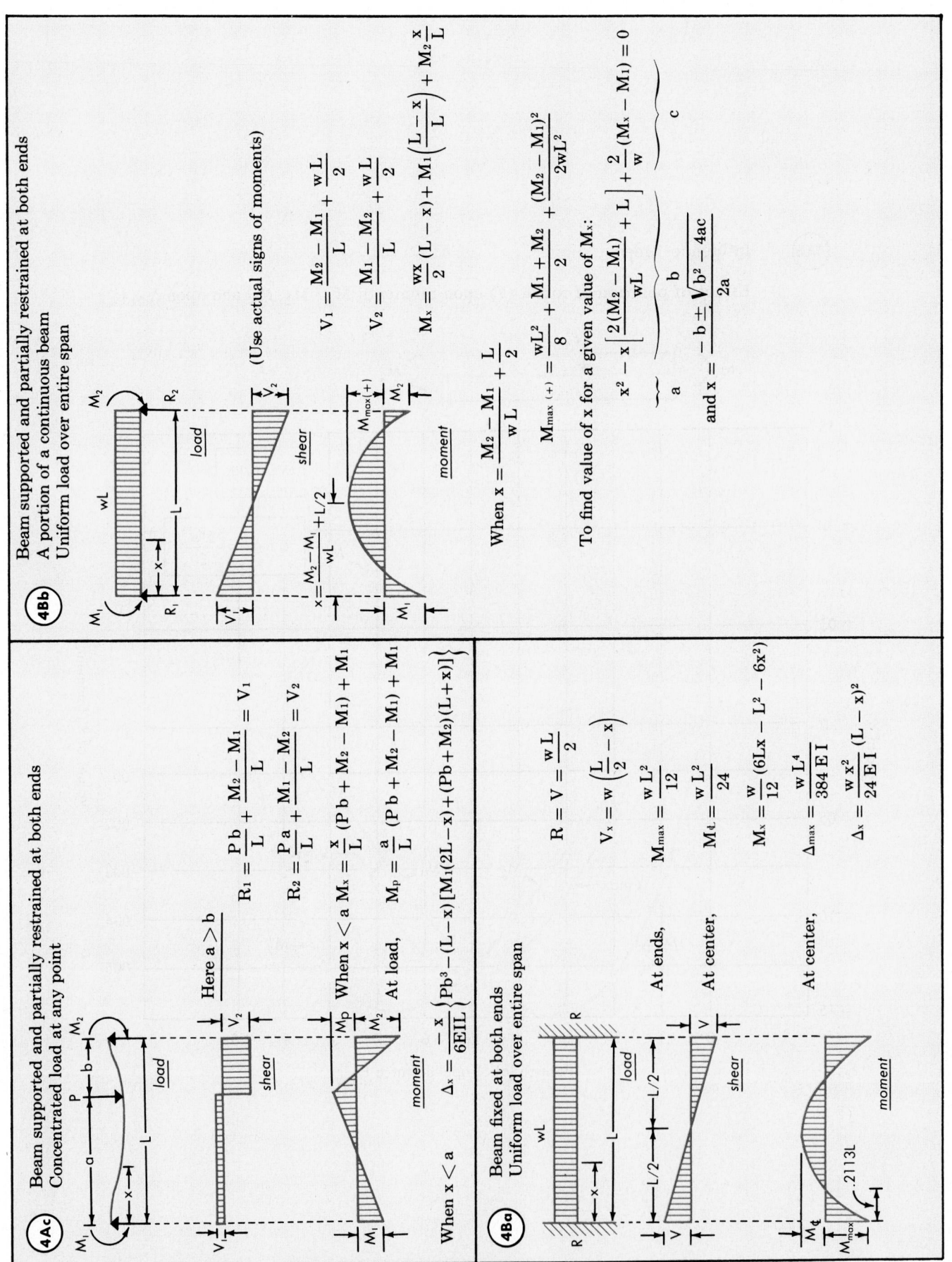

4Bb — Beam supported and partially restrained at both ends
A portion of a continuous beam
Uniform load over entire span

(Use actual signs of moments)

$$V_1 = \frac{M_2 - M_1}{L} + \frac{wL}{2}$$

$$V_2 = \frac{M_1 - M_2}{L} + \frac{wL}{2}$$

$$M_x = \frac{wx}{2}(L-x) + M_1\left(\frac{L-x}{L}\right) + M_2\frac{x}{L}$$

When $x = \dfrac{M_2 - M_1}{wL} + \dfrac{L}{2}$

$$M_{max\,(+)} = \frac{wL^2}{8} + \frac{M_1 + M_2}{2} + \frac{(M_2 - M_1)^2}{2wL^2}$$

To find value of x for a given value of M_x:

$$\underbrace{x^2}_{a} - x\underbrace{\left[\frac{2(M_2 - M_1)}{wL} + L\right]}_{b} + \underbrace{\frac{2}{w}(M_x - M_1)}_{c} = 0$$

and $x = \dfrac{-b \pm \sqrt{b^2 - 4ac}}{2a}$

4Ac — Beam supported and partially restrained at both ends
Concentrated load at any point

$$R_1 = \frac{Pb}{L} + \frac{M_2 - M_1}{L} = V_1$$

$$R_2 = \frac{Pa}{L} + \frac{M_1 - M_2}{L} = V_2$$

Here a > b

When $x < a$ $M_x = \dfrac{x}{L}(Pb + M_2 - M_1) + M_1$

At load, $M_p = \dfrac{a}{L}(Pb + M_2 - M_1) + M_1$

When $x < a$ $\Delta_x = \dfrac{-x}{6EIL}\left\{Pb^3 - (L-x)[M_1(2L-x) + (Pb+M_2-M_1)(L+x)]\right\}$

4Ba — Beam fixed at both ends
Uniform load over entire span

$$R = V = \frac{wL}{2}$$

$$V_x = w\left(\frac{L}{2} - x\right)$$

At ends, $M_{max} = \dfrac{wL^2}{12}$

At center, $M_{\mathfrak{c}} = \dfrac{wL^2}{24}$

$$M_x = \frac{w}{12}(6Lx - L^2 - 6x^2)$$

At center, $\Delta_{max} = \dfrac{wL^4}{384\,EI}$

$$\Delta_x = \frac{wx^2}{24\,EI}(L-x)^2$$

.2113L

4E Beam fixed at both ends
Moment applied at any point

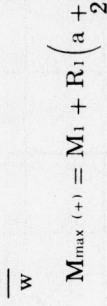

$$R_1 = -\frac{6 M_o a b}{L^3} = V$$

$$R_2 = +\frac{6 M_o a b}{L^3}$$

$$M_1 = -\frac{M_o b}{L^2}(L - 3a)$$

$$M_2 = -\frac{M_o a}{L^2}(2L - 3a)$$

When $x < a$,
$$M_x = -\frac{M_o}{L^2}\left[\frac{6abx}{L} + b(L - 3a)\right]$$

When $x > a$,
$$M_x = \frac{M_o a}{L^2}\left(6b - \frac{6bx}{L} - 2L + 3a\right)$$

At $x = a$ (left side),
$$M_{max\,(-)} = M_{max\,(+)} - M_o$$

At $x = a$ (right side),
$$M_{max\,(+)} = M_o\left[-\frac{6a^2b}{L^3} - \frac{b}{L^2}(L - 3a) + 1\right]$$

At $x = \dfrac{-2M_1}{R_1} = -\dfrac{L(L - 3a)}{3a}$

if $a > L/3$ $\quad \Delta_{max\,(+)} = +\dfrac{M_o b(L - 3a)^3}{54\,E\,I\,a^2}$

At $x = L/3b$
if $a < 2L/3$ $\quad \Delta_{max\,(-)} = -\dfrac{M_o a(2L - 3a)^3}{54\,E\,I\,b^2}$

When $x < a$
$$\Delta_x = -\frac{M_o b x^2}{2EIL^2}\left(L - 3a + \frac{2ax}{L}\right)$$

When $x > a$
$$\Delta_x = \frac{M_o a(L - x)^2}{2EIL^2}\left(3a - 2L + 2b - \frac{2bx}{L}\right)$$

At center,
$$M_{\mathcal{L}} = -\frac{M_o}{L^2}[3ab + b(L - 3a)]$$

At center,
$$\Delta_{\mathcal{L}} = -\frac{M_o b}{8EI}(L - 2a)$$

Greatest maximum deflection Δ
when $a = .2324\,L,\ \Delta_{max} = -\dfrac{.01615\,M_o\,L^2}{EI}$

4C Beam fixed at both ends
Uniform load partially distributed over span

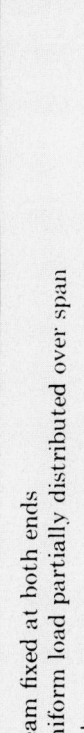
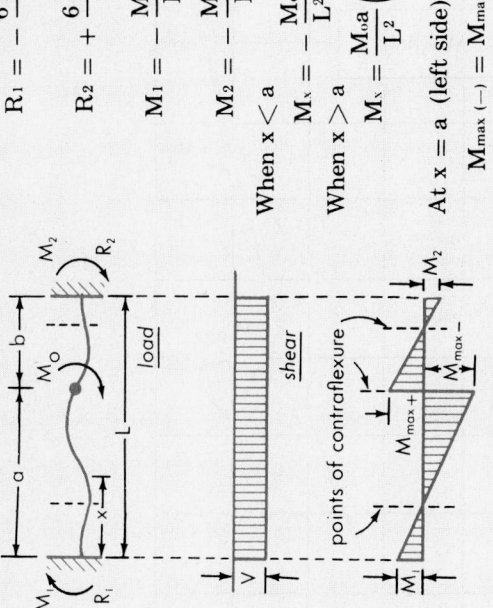

$$R_1 = V_1 = \frac{wb}{4L^3}[4e^2(L + 2d) - b^2(c - a)]$$

$$R_2 = V_2 = wb - R_1$$

$$M_1 = \frac{wb}{24L^2}\{b^2[L + 3(c - a)] - 24e^2d\}$$

$$M_2 = R_1 L - wbe + M_1$$

At $x = a + \dfrac{R_1}{w}$
$$M_{max\,(+)} = M_1 + R_1\left(a + \frac{R_1}{2w}\right)$$

When $x < a$ $\qquad M_x = M_1 + R_1 x$

When $x > a$
but $x < (a + b)$ $\qquad M_x = M_1 + R_1 x - \dfrac{w}{2}(x - a)^2$

When $x < a$ $\qquad \Delta_x = \dfrac{1}{6EI}(3M_1 x^2 + R_1 x^3)$

When $x > a$
but $x < (a + b)$ $\qquad \Delta_x = \dfrac{1}{24EI}[12M_1 x^2 + 4R_1 x^3 - w(x - a)^4]$

Effect of position of moment (M_O) upon M_1, M_2, M+ and M–

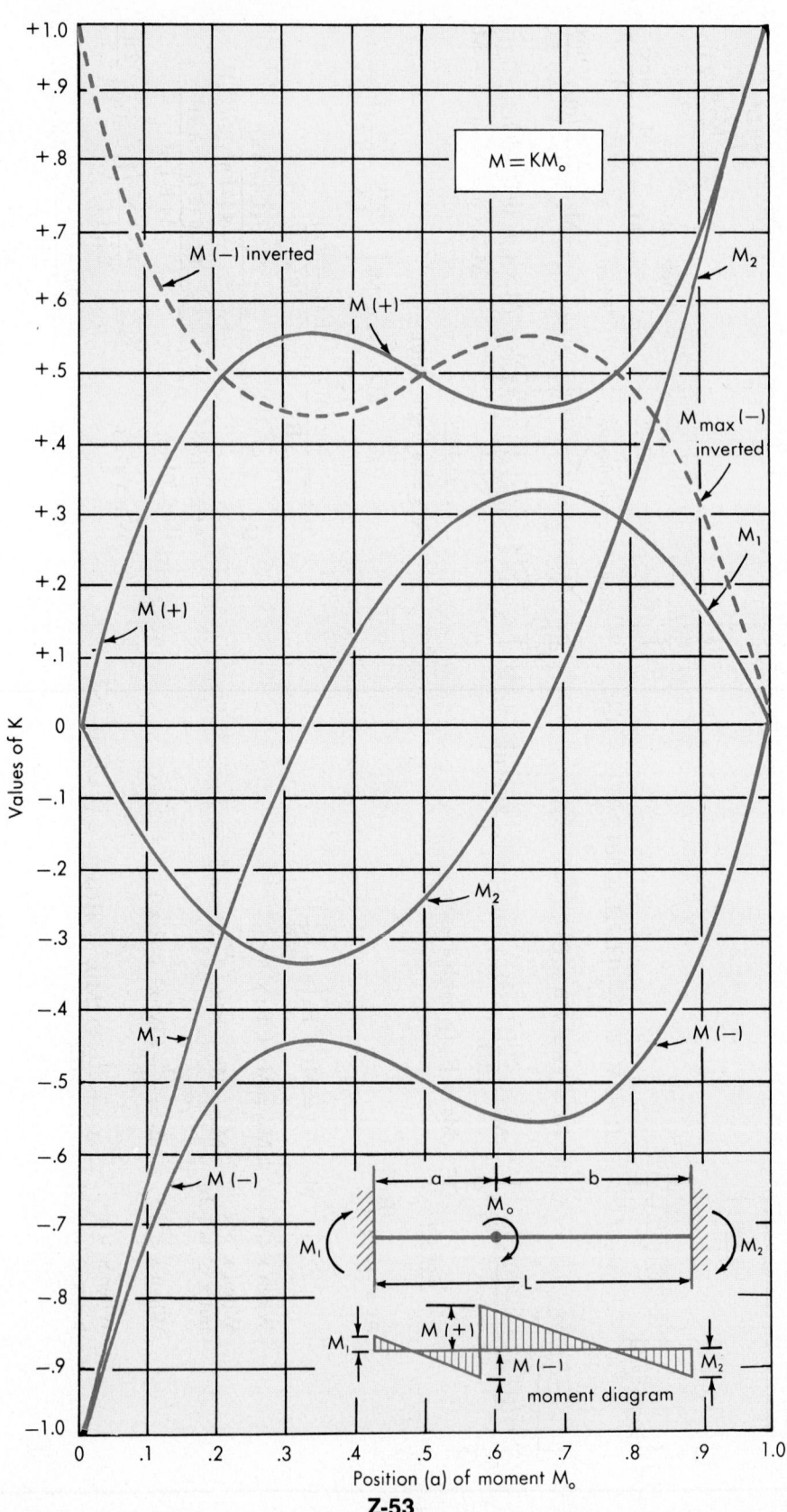

$M = KM_o$

M (–) inverted

M (+)

M_2

M_{max} (–) inverted

M_1

M (+)

M_1

M_2

M (–)

M (–)

a

b

M_o

M_1

M_2

L

M_1

M (+)

M (–)

M_2

moment diagram

Values of K

Position (a) of moment M_o

(4E) Influence Line for Maximum Deflection

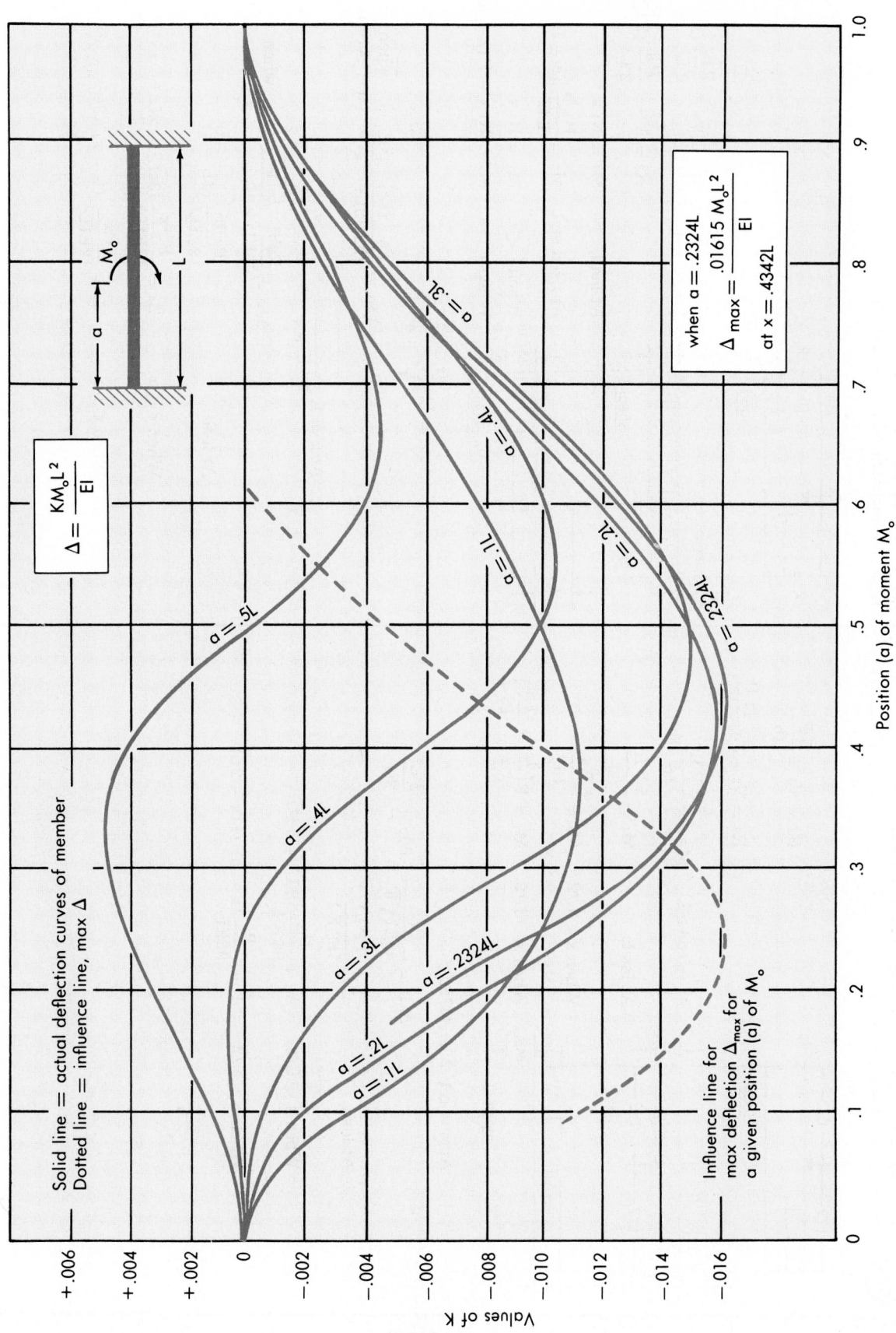

Solid line = actual deflection curves of member
Dotted line = influence line, max Δ

$$\Delta = \frac{K M_o L^2}{EI}$$

when a = .2324L
$$\Delta_{max} = \frac{.01615 \, M_o L^2}{EI}$$
at x = .4342L

Influence line for max deflection Δ_{max} for a given position (a) of M_o

Values of K

Position (a) of moment M_o

a = .5L
a = .4L
a = .3L
a = .2L
a = .1L
a = .2324L
a = .1L
a = .2L
a = .2324L
a = .3L
a = .4L

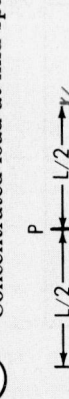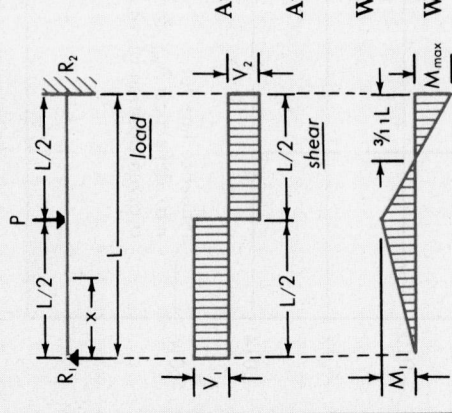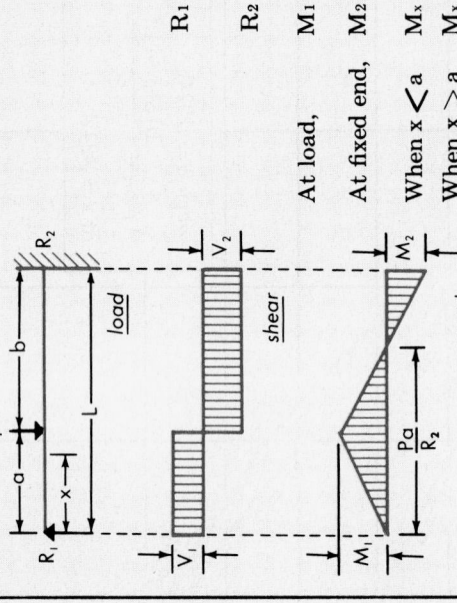

5Aa Beam fixed at one end and supported at the other end
Concentrated load at mid-span

$$R_1 = V_1 = \frac{5P}{16}$$

$$R_2 = V_{2\,max} = \frac{11P}{16}$$

At fixed end, $\quad M_{max} = \frac{3PL}{16}$

At load, $\quad M_1 = \frac{5PL}{32}$

When x < L/2 $\quad M_x = \frac{5Px}{16}$

When x > L/2 $\quad M_x = P\left(\frac{L}{2} - \frac{11x}{16}\right)$

At x = L√.2 = .4472 L,

$$\Delta_{max} = \frac{PL^3}{48EI\sqrt{5}} = .009317\frac{PL^3}{EI}$$

At load, $\quad \Delta = \frac{7PL^3}{768EI}$

When x < L/2 $\quad \Delta_x = \frac{Px}{96EI}(3L^2 - 5x^2)$

When x > L/2 $\quad \Delta_x = \frac{P}{96EI}(x-L)^2(11x - 2L)$

5Ab Beam fixed at one end and supported at the other end
Concentrated load at any point

$$R_1 = V_1 = \frac{Pb^2}{2L^3}(a+2L)$$

$$R_2 = V_2 = \frac{Pa}{2L^3}(3L^2 - a^2)$$

At load, $\quad M_1 = R_1 a$

At fixed end, $\quad M_2 = \frac{Pab}{2L^2}(a+L)$

When x < a $\quad M_x = R_1 x$

When x > a $\quad M_x = R_1 x - P(x - a)$

$$\Delta_{max} = \frac{Pa}{3EI}\frac{(L^2 - a^2)^3}{(3L^2 - a^2)^2} \quad \text{when}\atop a < .414 L$$

At x = $L\frac{L^2 + a^2}{3L^2 - a^2}$

$$\Delta_{max} = \frac{Pab^2}{6EI}\sqrt{\frac{a}{2L+a}} \quad \text{when}\atop a > .414 L$$

At x = $L\sqrt{\frac{a}{2L+a}}$

At load, $\quad \Delta = \frac{Pa^2b^3}{12EIL^3}(3L+a)$

When x < a $\quad \Delta_x = \frac{Pb^2x}{12EIL^3}(3aL^2 - 2Lx^2 - ax^2)$

When x > a $\quad \Delta_x = \frac{Pa}{12EIL^3}(L-x)^2(3L^2x - a^2x - 2a^2L)$

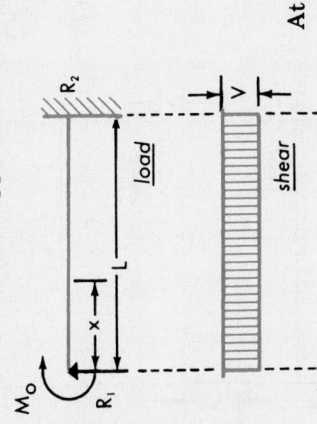

5B

Beam fixed at one end and supported at the other end
Uniform load over entire span

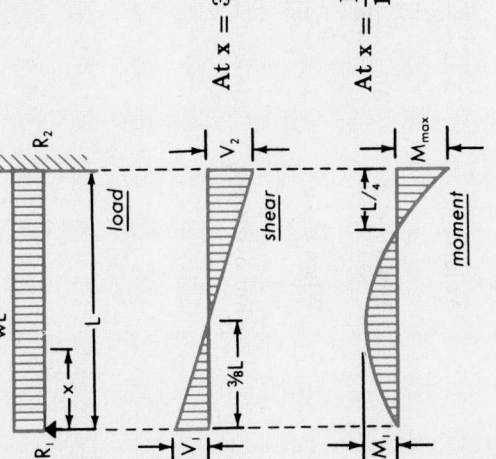

$$R_1 = V_1 = \frac{3\,w\,L}{8}$$

$$R_2 = V_2 = \frac{5\,w\,L}{8}$$

$$V_x = R_1 - w\,x$$

$$M_{max} = \frac{w\,L^2}{8}$$

At $x = 3/8\,L,$ $M_1 = \frac{9}{128}\,w\,L^2$

$$M_x = R_1\,x - \frac{w\,x^2}{2}$$

At $x = \frac{L}{16}(1 + \sqrt{33}) = .4215\,L,$

$$\Delta_{max} = \frac{w\,L^4}{185\,E\,I}$$

$$\Delta_x = \frac{w\,x}{48\,EI}\,(L^3 - 3Lx^2 + 2x^3)$$

$$\theta_1 = \frac{w\,L^3}{48\,E\,I}$$

5c

Beam fixed at one end and supported at the other end
Uniform load partially distributed over span

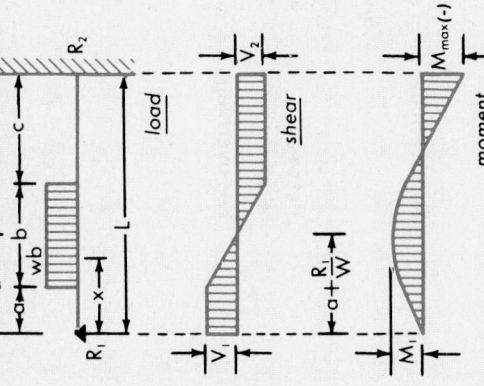

$$R_1 = V_1 = \frac{wb}{8L^3}\,(12e^2L - 4e^3 + b^2d)$$

$$R_2 = V_2 = wb - R_1$$

$$M_{max}\,(-) = \frac{wb}{8L^2}\,(12e^2L - 4e^3 + b^2d - 8eL^2)$$

$$M_1 = R_1\left(a + \frac{R_1}{2\,w}\right)$$

When $x < a$ $M_x = R_1\,x$

When $x > a$
but $x < (a+b)$ $M_x = R_1\,x - \frac{w}{2}\,(x - a)^2$

When $x > (a+b)$
but $x < L$ $M_x = R_1\,x - w\,b\,(x - d)$

When $x < a$ $\Delta_x = \frac{x}{24EI}\,[4R_1(x^2 - 3L^2) + wb\,(b^2 + 12e^2)]$

When $x > a$
but $x < (a+b)$ $\Delta_x = \frac{1}{24EI}\,[4R_1x(x^2 - 3L^2) + wbx\,(b^2 + 12e^2) - w\,(x - a)^4]$

When $x > (a+b)$
but $x < L$ $\Delta_x = \frac{1}{6EI}\,[3M_{max}(L - x)^2 + R_2(L - x)^3]$

5E

Beam fixed at one end and supported at the other end
Moment applied at the flexible end

$$R_1 = R_2 = V = \frac{3\,M_o}{2\,L}$$

$$M_1 = M_o$$

$$M_2 = 1/2\,M_o$$

$$M_x = \frac{M_o}{2\,L}\,(2\,L - 3x)$$

At $x = L/3,$ $\Delta_{max} = \frac{M_o\,L^2}{27\,EI}$

$$\Delta_x = \frac{M_o\,x}{4\,E\,I\,L}\,(L - x)^2$$

At supported end, $\theta = -\frac{M_o\,L}{4\,EI}$

6Ab Single span, simply supported beam, with overhang — Concentrated load at outer end

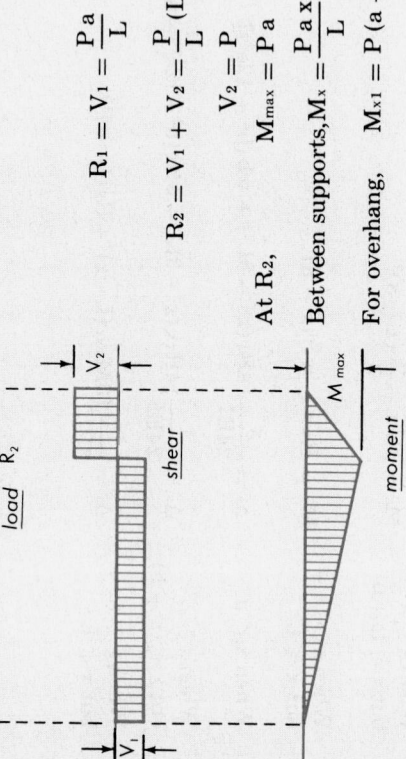

$$R_1 = V_1 = \frac{Pa}{L}$$

$$R_2 = V_1 + V_2 = \frac{P}{L}(L + a)$$

$$V_2 = P$$

At R_2, $M_{max} = Pa$

Between supports, $M_x = \frac{Pax}{L}$

For overhang, $M_{x1} = P(a - x_1)$

Between supports at $x = L/\sqrt{3}$,

$$\Delta_{max} = -\frac{PaL^2}{9\sqrt{3}\,EI}$$

For overhang $x_1 = a$,

$$\Delta_{max} = \frac{Pa^2}{3EI}(L + a)$$

Between supports,

$$\Delta_x = -\frac{Pax}{6EIL}(L^2 - x^2)$$

For overhang,

$$\Delta_{x1} = \frac{Px_1}{6EI}(2aL + 3ax_1 - x_1^2)$$

6Aa Single span, simply supported beam, with overhang — Concentrated load at any point between supports

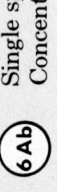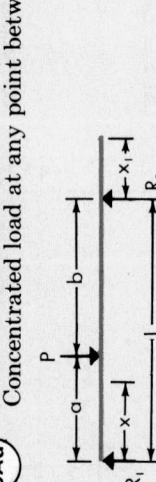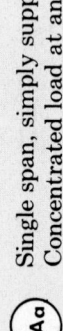

$$R_1 = V_1 \left(\begin{array}{c} max \\ when \end{array} a < b\right) = \frac{Pb}{L}$$

$$R_2 = V_2 \left(\begin{array}{c} max \\ when \end{array} a > b\right) = \frac{Pa}{L}$$

At load, $M_{max} = \frac{Pab}{L}$

When $x < a$, $M_x = \frac{Pbx}{L}$

At $x = \sqrt{\dfrac{a(a + 2b)}{3}}$

$$\Delta_{max} = \frac{Pab(a + 2b)\sqrt{3a(a + 2b)}}{27EIL} \quad \text{when } a > b$$

At load, $\Delta = \dfrac{Pa^2b^2}{3EIL}$

When $x < a$, $\Delta_x = \dfrac{Pbx}{6EIL}(L^2 - b^2 - x^2)$

When $x > a$, $\Delta_x = \dfrac{Pa(L - x)}{6EIL}(2Lx - x^2 - a^2)$

For overhang, $\Delta_{x1} = -\dfrac{Pabx_1}{6EIL}(L + a)$

(6Bb) Single span beam, overhanging at both ends
Uniform load over entire beam

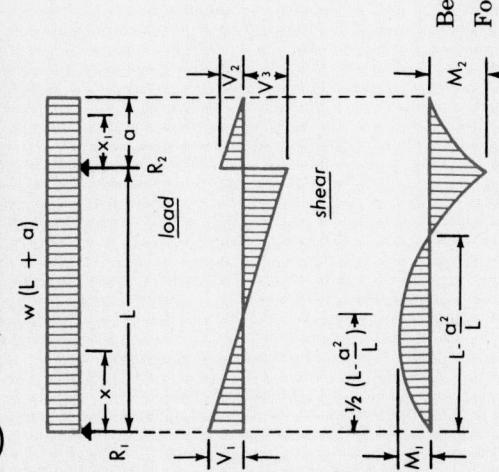

$$R = V_1 + V_2 = w(a + L/2)$$
$$V_{x1} = w x_1$$
$$V_x = w(x - L/2)$$

For overhang, $\quad M_{x1} = \dfrac{w x_1^2}{2}$

At support, $\quad M = \dfrac{w a^2}{2}$

Between supports, $M_x = \dfrac{w}{2}(L x - x^2 - a^2)$

At center, $\quad M_\ell = \dfrac{w}{8}(L^2 - 4 a^2)$

At ends, $\quad \Delta = \dfrac{wa}{24EI}(L^3 - 6a^2L - 3a^3)$

At center, $\quad \Delta_\ell = \dfrac{wL^2}{384EI}(5L^2 - 24a^2)$

When a = .207 × total length
or a = .354 L

$$M = M_\ell = \dfrac{w L^2}{16}$$

(6Ba) Single span, simply supported beam, with overhang
Uniform load over entire beam

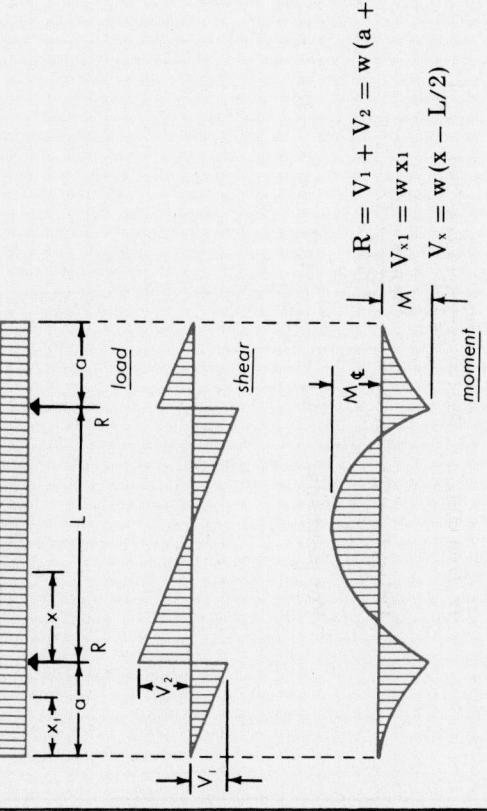

$$R_1 = V_1 = \dfrac{w}{2L}(L^2 - a^2)$$
$$R_2 = V_2 + V_3 = \dfrac{w}{2L}(L + a)^2$$
$$V_2 = wa$$
$$V_3 = \dfrac{w}{2L}(L^2 + a^2)$$

Between supports, $V_x = R_1 - w x$

For overhang, $\quad V_{x1} = w(a - x_1)$

At $x = \dfrac{1}{2}\left(L - \dfrac{a^2}{L}\right)$

$$M_1 = \dfrac{w}{8 L^2}(L^2 - a^2)^2$$

At R_2, $\quad M_2 = \dfrac{w a^2}{2}$

Between supports, $M_x = \dfrac{w x}{2 L}(L^2 - a^2 - x L)$

For overhang, $\quad M_{x1} = \dfrac{w}{2}(a - x_1)^2$

Between supports, $\Delta_x = \dfrac{w x}{24 E I L}(L^4 - 2L^2 x^2 + Lx^3 - 2a^2 L^2 + 2 a^2 x^2)$

For overhang, $\quad \Delta_{x1} = \dfrac{w x_1}{24 E I}(4a^2 L - L^3 + 6a^2 x_1 - 4 a x_1^2 + x_1^3)$

At free end, $\quad \Delta = \dfrac{w a}{24 E I}(3 a^3 + 4 a^2 L - L^3)$

When a = .414 L, $M_1 = M_2 = .08579\, w\, L^2$

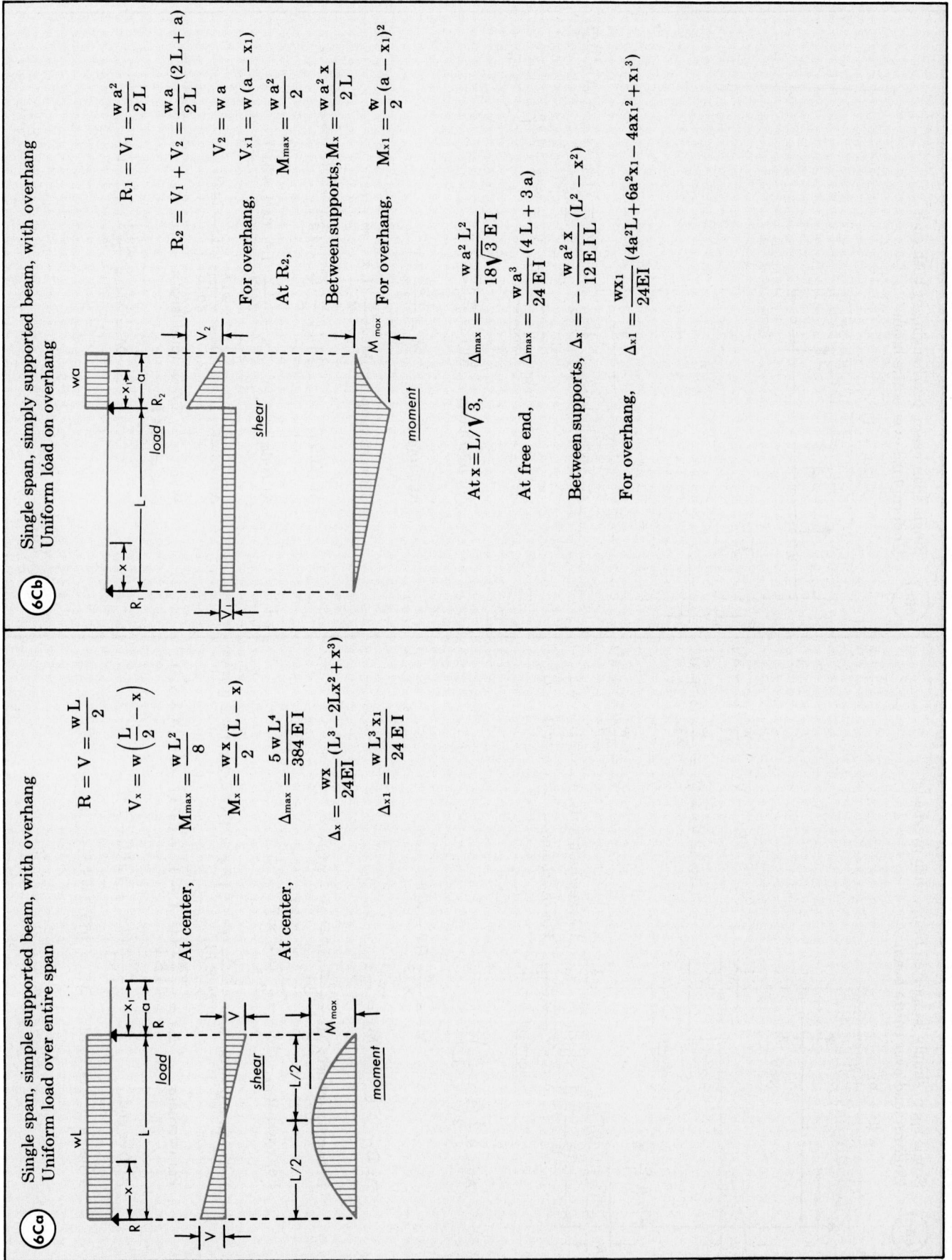

(6Ca) Single span, simple supported beam, with overhang
Uniform load over entire span

$$R = V = \frac{wL}{2}$$

$$V_x = w\left(\frac{L}{2} - x\right)$$

At center, $\quad M_{max} = \frac{wL^2}{8}$

$$M_x = \frac{wx}{2}(L - x)$$

At center, $\quad \Delta_{max} = \frac{5wL^4}{384\,E\,I}$

$$\Delta_x = \frac{wx}{24EI}(L^3 - 2Lx^2 + x^3)$$

$$\Delta_{x1} = \frac{wL^3 x_1}{24\,E\,I}$$

(6Cb) Single span, simply supported beam, with overhang
Uniform load on overhang

$$R_1 = V_1 = \frac{wa^2}{2L}$$

$$R_2 = V_1 + V_2 = \frac{wa}{2L}(2L + a)$$

$$V_2 = wa$$

For overhang, $\quad V_{x1} = w(a - x_1)$

At R_2, $\quad M_{max} = \frac{wa^2}{2}$

Between supports, $M_x = \frac{wa^2 x}{2L}$

For overhang, $\quad M_{x1} = \frac{w}{2}(a - x_1)^2$

At $x = L/\sqrt{3}$, $\quad \Delta_{max} = -\frac{wa^2 L^2}{18\sqrt{3}\,E\,I}$

At free end, $\quad \Delta_{max} = \frac{wa^3}{24\,E\,I}(4L + 3a)$

Between supports, $\Delta_x = -\frac{wa^2 x}{12\,E\,I\,L}(L^2 - x^2)$

For overhang, $\quad \Delta_{x1} = \frac{wx_1}{24EI}(4a^2L + 6a^2x_1 - 4ax_1^2 + x_1^3)$

(7) THEORY OF THREE MOMENTS

Consider the following continuous beam:

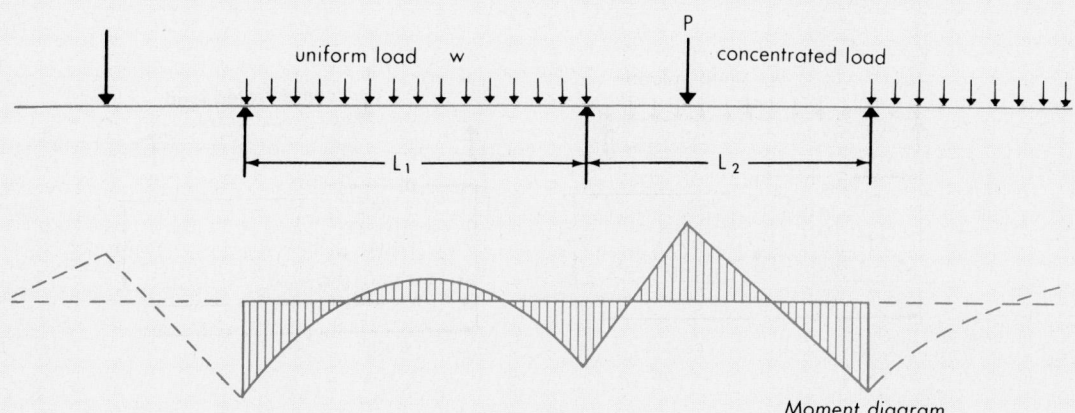

Moment diagram

The above moment diagram may be considered as made up of two parts: the positive moment due to the applied loads, and the negative moment due to the restraining end moments over the supports.

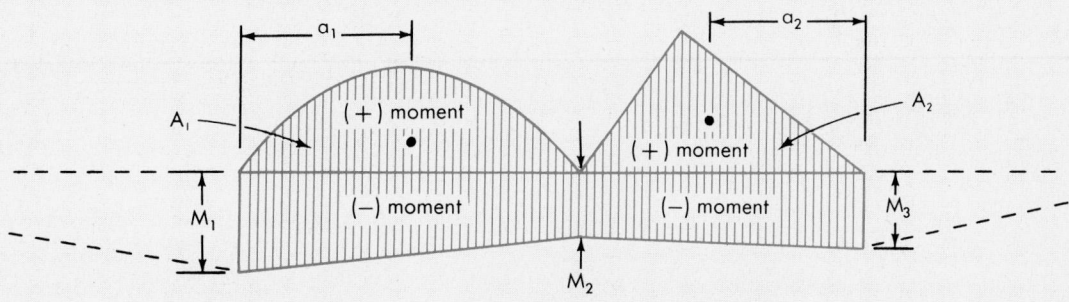

For any two adjacent spans, the following relationship is true:

$$+\frac{M_1 L_1}{6 E I_1} + \frac{M_2}{3 E}\left(\frac{L_1}{I_1} + \frac{L_2}{I_2}\right) + \frac{M_3 L_2}{6 E I_2} + \frac{A_1 a_1}{E I_1 L_1} + \frac{A_2 a_2}{E I_2 L_2} = 0$$

where:

M_1, M_2, and M_3 are the end moments at the 1st, 2nd, and 3rd supports.

L_1 and L_2 are the lengths of the 1st and 2nd span.

I_1 and I_2 are the moments of inertia of the 1st and 2nd span.

A_1 and A_2 are the areas under the positive moment diagrams of the 1st and 2nd span.

a_1 and a_2 are the distance of the centroids of the areas of the positive moment diagrams to the 1st and 3rd outer supports.

By writing this equation for each successive pair of spans, all of the moments may be found.

The moment diagram for a simply supported, uniformly loaded beam is a parabola; and a concentrated load produces a triangular moment diagram. The following shows the area and distance to the centroid of these areas.

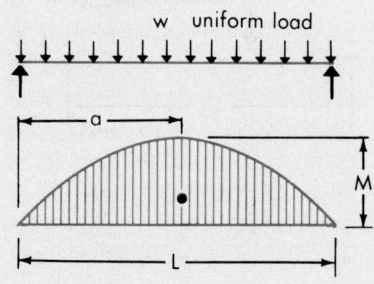
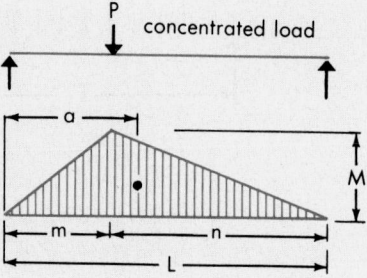

Area
$$A = 2/3 \, M \, L$$

Distance to centroid
$$a = L/2$$

Area
$$A = 1/2 \, M \, L$$

Distance to centroid
$$a = \frac{m + L}{3}$$

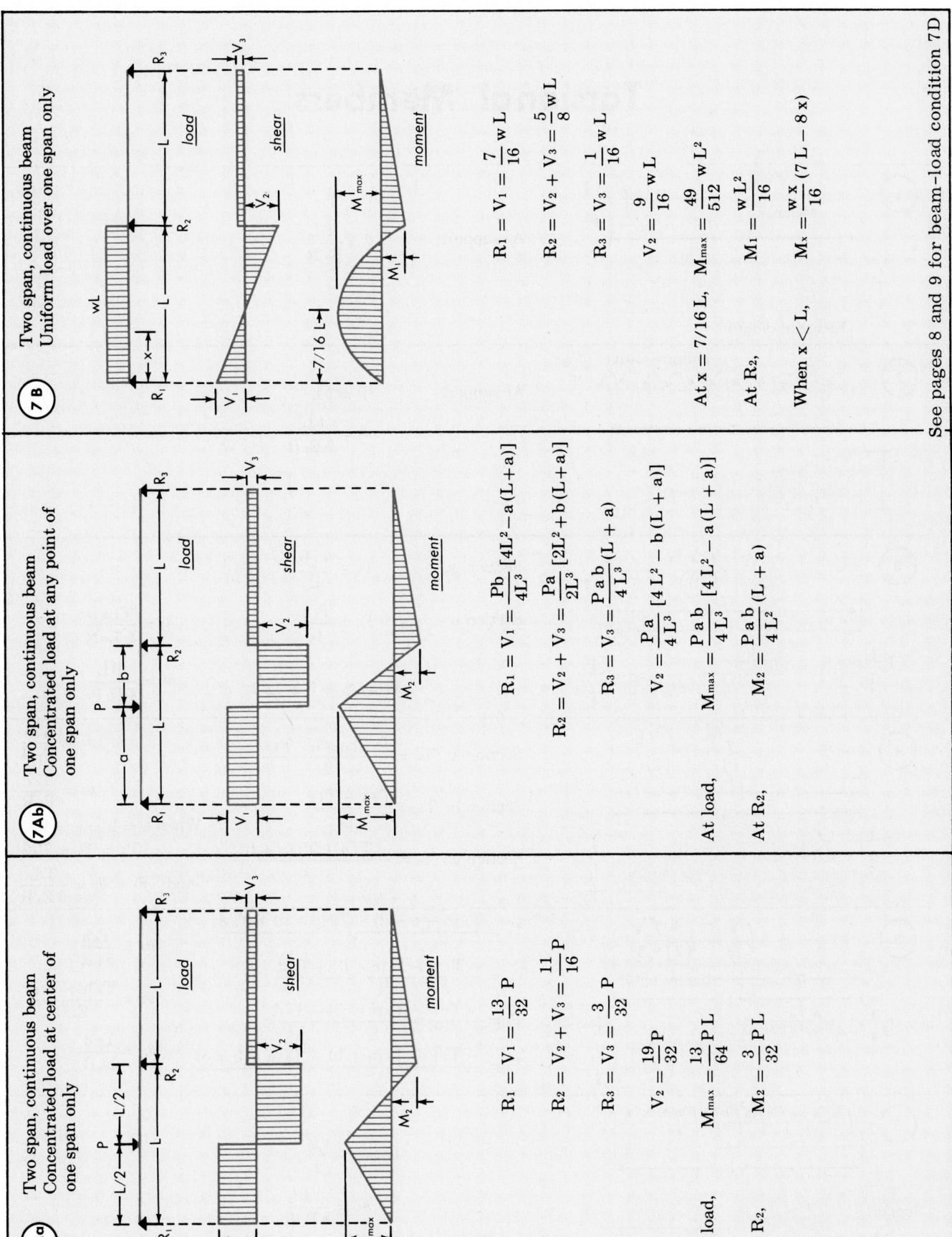

7Aa

Two span, continuous beam
Concentrated load at center of one span only

$$R_1 = V_1 = \frac{13}{32}\,P$$

$$R_2 = V_2 + V_3 = \frac{11}{16}\,P$$

$$R_3 = V_3 = \frac{3}{32}\,P$$

$$V_2 = \frac{19}{32}\,P$$

$$M_{max} = \frac{13}{64}\,P\,L$$

$$M_2 = \frac{3}{32}\,P\,L$$

At load,

At R_2,

7Ab

Two span, continuous beam
Concentrated load at any point of one span only

$$R_1 = V_1 = \frac{Pb}{4L^3}\,[4L^2 - a(L+a)]$$

$$R_2 = V_2 + V_3 = \frac{Pa}{2L^3}\,[2L^2 + b(L+a)]$$

$$R_3 = V_3 = \frac{Pab}{4L^3}\,(L+a)$$

$$V_2 = \frac{Pa}{4L^3}\,[4L^2 - b(L+a)]$$

$$M_{max} = \frac{Pab}{4L^3}\,[4L^2 - a(L+a)]$$

$$M_2 = \frac{Pab}{4L^2}\,(L+a)$$

At load,

At R_2,

7B

Two span, continuous beam
Uniform load over one span only

$$R_1 = V_1 = \frac{7}{16}\,w\,L$$

$$R_2 = V_2 + V_3 = \frac{5}{8}\,w\,L$$

$$R_3 = V_3 = \frac{1}{16}\,w\,L$$

$$V_2 = \frac{9}{16}\,w\,L$$

At $x = 7/16\,L$, $\quad M_{max} = \frac{49}{512}\,w\,L^2$

At R_2, $\quad M_1 = \frac{w\,L^2}{16}$

When $x < L$, $\quad M_x = \frac{w\,x}{16}\,(7\,L - 8\,x)$

See pages 8 and 9 for beam-load condition 7D

Torsional Members

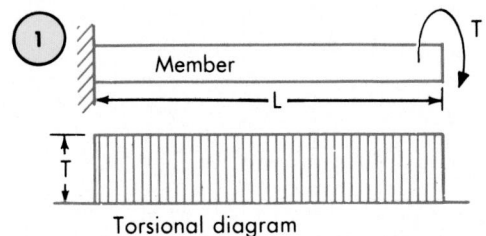

1

At support,

$$T = T$$

$$\theta = \frac{T L}{E_s R}$$

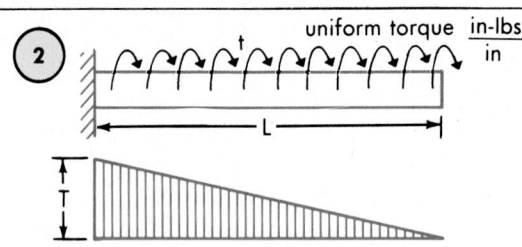

2

At support,

$$T = t L$$

$$\theta = \frac{t L^2}{2 E_s R}$$

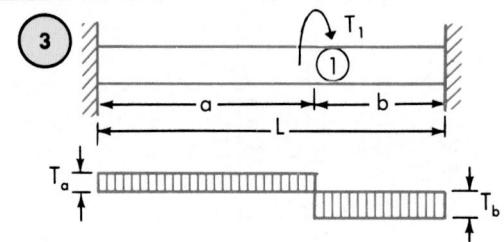

3

Section a:

$$T_a = \frac{T_1 b}{L}$$

Section b:

$$T_b = \frac{T_1 a}{L}$$

$$\theta_1 = \frac{T_1 a b}{L E_s R}$$

When $a = b = L/2$

$$\theta_{\text{L}} = \frac{T L}{4 E_s R}$$

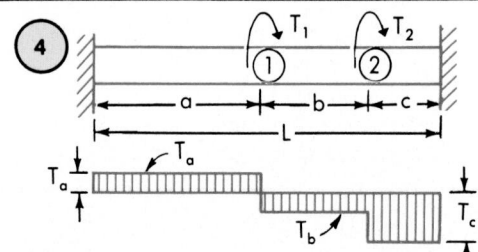

4

Section a: $T_a = \dfrac{T_1 (b + c) + T_2 c}{L}$

Section b: $T_b = \dfrac{T_2 c - T_1 a}{L}$

Section c: $T_c = -\dfrac{T_1 a + T_2 (a + b)}{L}$

$$\theta_1 = \frac{T_a a}{E_s R}$$

$$\theta_2 = \frac{T_c c}{E_s R}$$

When $a = b = c = L/3$

$$T_1 = T_2 = T/2$$

and $\theta_1 = \theta_2 = \dfrac{T L}{6 E_s R}$

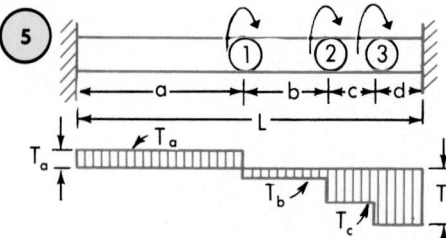

5

$$T_a = \frac{T_1 (b + c + d) + T_2 (c + d) + T_3 d}{L}$$

$$T_b = \frac{- T_1 a + T_2 (c + d) + T_3 d}{L}$$

$$T_c = \frac{- T_1 a - T_2 (a + b) + T_3 d}{L}$$

$$T_d = \frac{- T_1 a - T_2 (a + b) - T_3 (a + b + c)}{L}$$

$$\theta_1 = \frac{T_a a}{E_s R}$$

$$\theta_2 = \frac{T_b b + T_a a}{E_s R}$$

$$\theta_3 = \frac{T_d d}{E_s R}$$

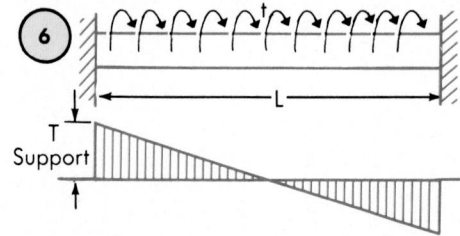

6

$$T_{\text{support}} = \frac{t L}{2}$$

$$\theta_{\text{L}} = \frac{t L^2}{8 E_s R}$$

CIRCULAR FLAT PLATES

The following table of formulas is for stress and deflection of circular flat steel plates. (Poisson's ratio = .3)

σ_r = tensile stress in radial direction (psi)

σ_t = tensile stress in tangential direction (psi)

t = thickness of plate (inches)

r = outer radius of plate (inches)

r_1 = inner radius of plate (inches)

E = modulus of elasticity (for steel = 30,000,000 psi)

W = total load on plate (pounds)

p = uniform load on plate (psi)

M = couple or moment applied to central portion (inch-lbs)

log to the base (e) (Natural or Naperian logarithms):

$\log_e x = 2.3026 \log_{10} x$

A positive sign for the stress indicates tension on the top surface and compression on the lower surface.

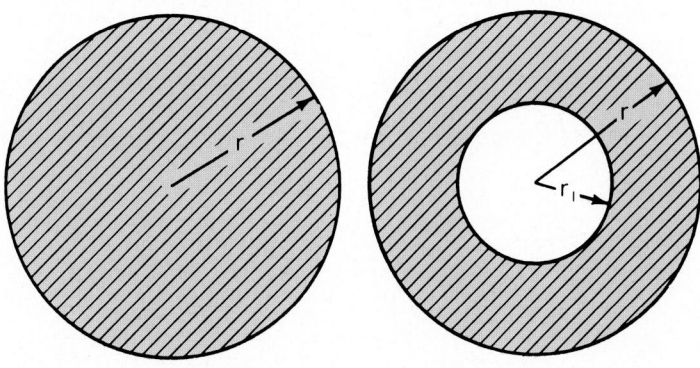

Adapted from Roark "Formulas for Stress and Strain", and Timoshenko "Theory of Plates and Shells".

1 — Outer edge fixed and supported
Uniform load over entire area

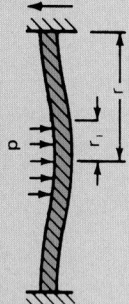

At center,

$$\sigma_r = \sigma_t = -\frac{39\,p}{80}\left(\frac{r}{t}\right)^2$$

At edge,

$$\text{Max } \sigma_r = \frac{3\,p}{4}\left(\frac{r}{t}\right)^2$$

At center,

$$\text{Max } \Delta = -\frac{273\,p\,r^4}{1600\,E\,t^3}$$

2 — Outer edge fixed and supported
Uniform load over concentric circular area of radius r_1

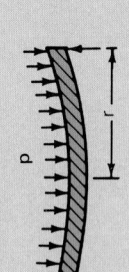

At center (max when $r_1 < .588r$),

$$\sigma_r = \sigma_t = -\frac{3\,p}{80}\left(\frac{r_1}{t}\right)^2\left[52\log\frac{r}{r_1}+13\left(\frac{r_1}{r}\right)^2\right]$$

At edge (max when $r_1 > .588\,r$),

$$\sigma_r = \frac{3\,p}{4}\left(\frac{r_1}{t\,r}\right)^2(2\,r^2 - r_1^2)$$

At edge,

$$\sigma_t = \frac{9\,p}{40}\left(\frac{r_1}{t\,r}\right)^2(2\,r^2 - r_1^2)$$

At center,

$$\text{Max } \Delta = -\frac{273\,p\,r_1^2}{1600\,E\,t^3}\left(4\,r^2 - 3\,r_1^2 - 4\,r_1^2\log\frac{r}{r_1}\right)$$

__When r_1 is very small (concentrated load)__

At center,

$$\text{Max } \Delta = -\frac{273\,W\,r^2}{400\,\pi\,E\,t^3}$$

For stress, Roark suggests using the following in which r_e is equal to either r_1 or the effective radius $\left(\sqrt{1.6\,r_1^2 + t^2} - .675\,t\right)$ whichever is largest:

At center,

$$\text{Max } \sigma_r = \sigma_t = -\frac{3\,W}{80\,\pi\,t^2}\left[52\log\frac{r}{r_e}+13\left(\frac{r_e}{r}\right)^2\right]$$

At edge,

$$\sigma_r = \frac{9\,W}{40\,\pi\,t^2\,r^2}(2\,r^2 - r_b^2)$$

3 — Outer edge supported
Uniform load over entire area

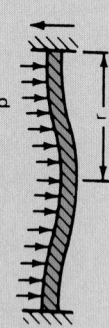

At center,

$$\text{Max } \sigma_r = \sigma_t = -\frac{99\,p}{80}\left(\frac{r}{t}\right)^2$$

At center,

$$\text{Max } \Delta = -\frac{1113\,p\,r^4}{1600\,E\,t^3}$$

At edge,

$$\theta = \frac{21\,p}{20\,E}\left(\frac{r}{t}\right)^3$$

4 Outer edge supported
Uniform load over concentric circular area of radius r_1

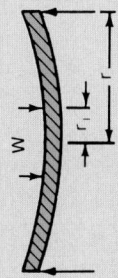

At center, $\text{Max } \sigma_r = \sigma_t = \dfrac{3\,p}{80}\left(\dfrac{r_1}{t}\right)\left[40 + 52\log\dfrac{r}{r_1} - 7\left(\dfrac{r_1}{r}\right)^2\right]$

At center, $\text{Max } \Delta = -\dfrac{21\,p\,r_1{}^2}{1600\,E\,t^3}\left(132\,r^2 - 52\,r_1{}^2\log\dfrac{r}{r_1} - 73\,r_1{}^2\right)$

When r_1 is very small (concentrated load)

At center, $\text{Max } \Delta = -\dfrac{693\,W\,r^2}{400\,\pi\,E\,t^3}$

At edge, $\theta = \dfrac{21\,W\,r}{10\,\pi\,E\,t^3}$

For stress, Roark suggests using the following in which r_e is equal to either r_1 or the effective radius $\left(\sqrt{1.6\,r_1{}^2 + t^2} - .675\,t\right)$ whichever is largest:

At center, $\text{Max } \sigma_r = \sigma_t = \dfrac{3\,W}{80\,\pi\,t^2}\left[40 + 52\log\dfrac{r}{r_e} - 7\left(\dfrac{r_e}{r}\right)^2\right]$

5 Outer edge supported
Uniform load on concentric circular ring of radius r_1

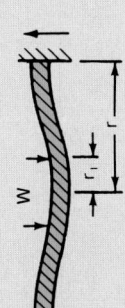

At $< r_1$, $\text{Max } \sigma_r = \sigma_t = -\dfrac{3\,W}{40\,\pi\,t^2}\left[7 + 26\log\dfrac{r}{r_1} - 7\left(\dfrac{r_1}{r}\right)^2\right]$

At center, $\text{Max } \Delta = -\dfrac{273\,W}{5200\,\pi\,E\,t^3}\left[33\,(r^2 - r_1{}^2) - 26\,r_1{}^2\log\dfrac{r}{r_1}\right]$

6 Outer edge fixed and supported
Uniform load on concentric circular ring of radius r_1

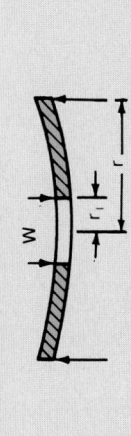

At $< r_1$ (max when $r_1 < .31\,r$),

$\sigma_r = \sigma_t = -\dfrac{39\,W}{40\,\pi\,t^2}\left[2\log\dfrac{r}{r_1} + \left(\dfrac{r_1}{r}\right)^2 - 1\right]$

At edge (max when $r_1 > .31\,r$),

At edge, $\sigma_t = \dfrac{3\,W}{2\,\pi\,t^3}\left[1 - \left(\dfrac{r_1}{r}\right)^2\right]$

At edge, $\sigma_t = \dfrac{9\,W}{20\,\pi\,t^2}\left[1 - \left(\dfrac{r_1}{r}\right)^2\right]$

At center, $\text{Max } \Delta = -\dfrac{273\,W}{400\,\pi\,E\,t^3}\left(r^2 - r_1{}^2 - 2\,r_1{}^2\log\dfrac{r}{r_1}\right)$

7 Outer edge supported
Uniform load around inner edge

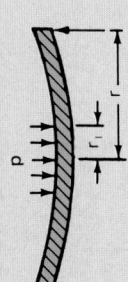

At inner edge, $\text{Max } \sigma_t = -\dfrac{3\,W}{20\,\pi\,t^2}\left[\dfrac{26\,r^2}{(r^2 - r_1{}^2)}\log\dfrac{r}{r_1} + 7\right]$

At inner edge, $\text{Max } \Delta = -\dfrac{273\,W}{36{,}400\,\pi\,E\,t^3}\left[231\,(r^2 - r_1{}^2) + \dfrac{676\,r^2\,r_1{}^2}{(r^2 - r_1{}^2)}\left(\log\dfrac{r}{r_1}\right)^2\right]$

8

Outer edge fixed and supported
Uniform load around inner edge

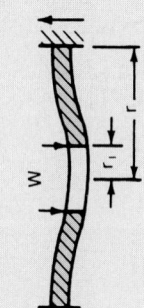

At outer edge (max when $r_1 > .416\, r$),

$$\sigma_r = \frac{3\,W}{2\,\pi\,t^2}\left[\,1 - \frac{20\,r_1{}^2 - 26\,r_1{}^2 \log\dfrac{r}{r_1}}{7\,r^2 + 13\,r_1{}^2}\,\right]$$

At inner edge (max when $r_1 < .416\, r$),

$$\sigma_r = \frac{9\,W}{20\,\pi\,t^2}\left[\,1 + \frac{70\,r^2 - 130\,r_1{}^2 - 182\,r^2 \log\dfrac{r}{r_1}}{21\,r^2 + 39\,r_1{}^2}\,\right]$$

At inner edge,

$$\text{Max } \Delta = -\frac{273\,W}{400\,\pi\,E\,t^3}\left[\,r^2 - r_1{}^2 + \frac{20\,r_1{}^2\,(r^2 - r_1{}^2) - 80\,r^2\,r_1{}^2 \log\dfrac{r}{r_1} + 52\,r^2\,r_1{}^2\left(\log\dfrac{r}{r_1}\right)^2}{7\,r^2 + 13\,r_1{}^2}\,\right]$$

9

Outer edge supported; inner edge fixed
Uniform load around inner edge

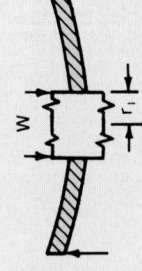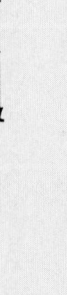

At inner edge,

$$\text{Max } \sigma_r = \frac{3\,W}{2\,\pi\,t^2}\left[\,\frac{7\,(r^2 - r_1{}^2) + 26\,r_1{}^2 \log\dfrac{r}{r_1}}{13\,r^2 + 7\,r_1{}^2}\,\right]$$

At inner edge,

$$\text{Max } \Delta = -\frac{273\,W}{400\,\pi\,E\,t^3}\left[\,\frac{33\,r^4 - 7\,r_1{}^4 - 26\,r^2\,r_1{}^2 \log\dfrac{r}{r_1} - 80\,r^2\,r_1{}^2 \log\dfrac{r}{r_1} - 52\,r^2\,r_1{}^2\left(\log\dfrac{r}{r_1}\right)^2}{13\,r^2 + 7\,r_1{}^2}\,\right]$$

10

Outer edge fixed and supported; inner edge fixed
Uniform load around inner edge

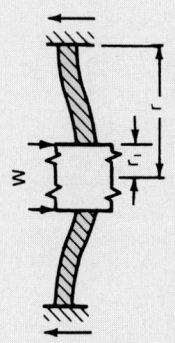

At inner edge,

$$\text{Max } \sigma_r = \frac{3\,W}{2\,\pi\,t^2}\left[\,1 - \frac{2\,r^2}{r^2 - r_1{}^2}\,\log\frac{r}{r_1}\,\right]$$

At outer edge,

$$\sigma_r = \frac{3\,W}{2\,\pi\,t^2}\left[\,1 - \frac{2\,r_1{}^2}{r^2 - r_1{}^2}\,\log\frac{r}{r_1}\,\right]$$

At inner edge,

$$\text{Max } \Delta = -\frac{273\,W}{400\,\pi\,E\,t^3}\left[\,r^2 - r_1{}^2 - \frac{4\,r^2\,r_1{}^2}{r^2 - r_1{}^2}\left(\log\frac{r}{r_1}\right)^2\,\right]$$

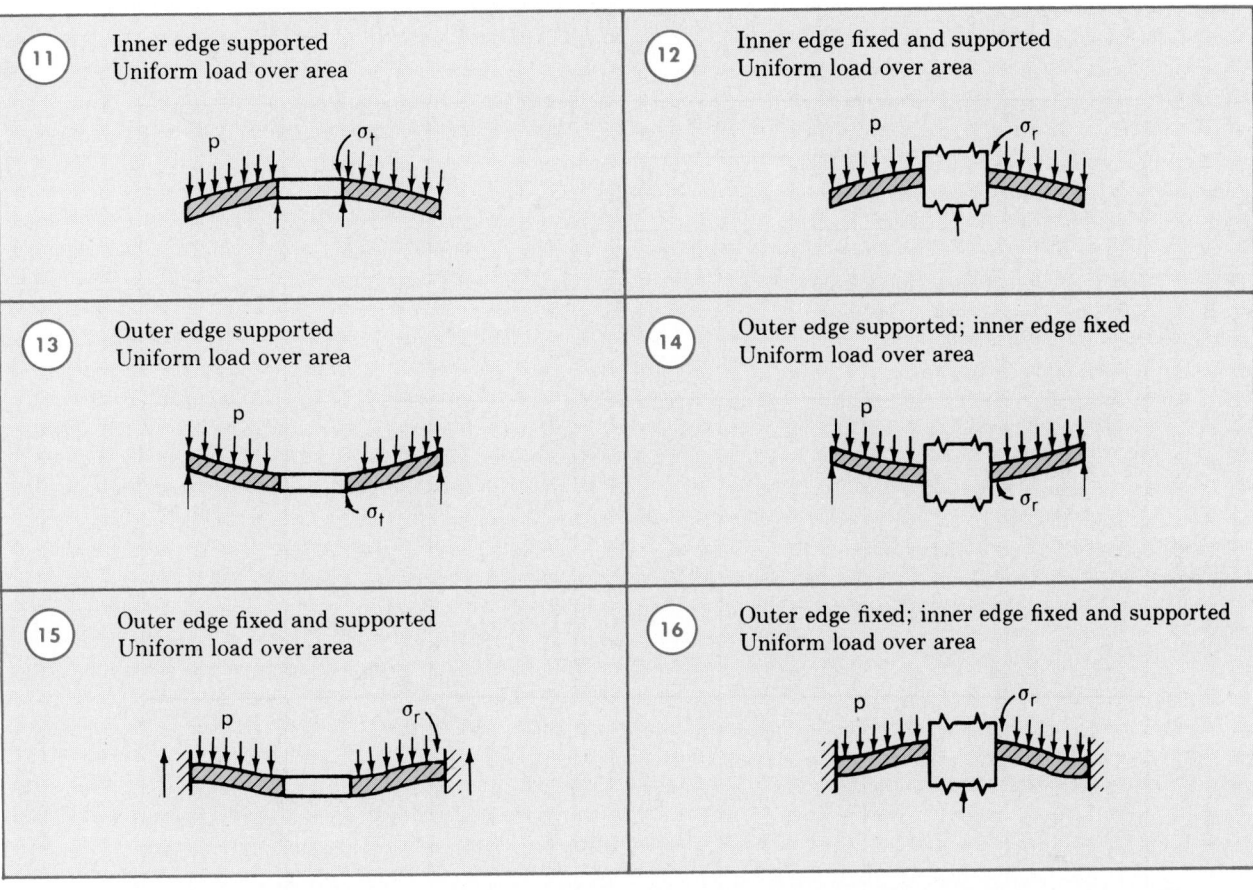

TABLE 1 – VALUES OF K FOR MAXIMUM STRESS AND DEFLECTION FORMULAS

$$\sigma_{max} = \frac{K_1 \, p \, r^2}{t^2} \qquad \sigma_{max} = \frac{K_1 \, W}{t^2} \qquad\qquad \Delta_{max} = \frac{K_2 \, p \, r^4}{Et^3} \qquad \Delta_{max} = \frac{K_2 \, Wr^2}{Et^3}$$

Type of disc	Type of load	$\frac{r}{r_1} = 1.25$		$\frac{r}{r_1} = 1.5$		$\frac{r}{r_1} = 2.0$		$\frac{r}{r_1} = 3.0$		$\frac{r}{r_1} = 4.0$		$\frac{r}{r_1} = 5.0$	
		K_1	K_2	K_1	K_2	K_1	K_2	K_1	K_2	K_1	K_2	K_1	K_2
5	W	.199	.136	.345	.226	.557	.338	.832	.437	1.02	.480	1.16	.501
7	W	1.10	.341	1.26	.519	1.48	.672	1.88	.734	2.17	.724	2.34	.704
8	W	.194	.00504	.320	.0242	.454	.0810	.673	.172	1.02	.217	1.305	.238
9	W	.227	.00510	.428	.0249	.753	.0877	1.205	.209	1.51	.293	1.745	.350
10	W	.115	.00129	.220	.0064	.405	.0237	.703	.062	.933	.092	1.13	.114
11	p	.660	.202	1.19	.491	2.04	.902	3.34	1.22	4.30	1.30	5.10	1.31
12	p	.135	.00231	.410	.0183	1.04	.0938	2.15	.293	2.99	.448	3.69	.564
13	p	.592	.184	.976	.414	1.44	.664	1.88	.824	2.08	.830	2.19	.813
14	p	.122	.00343	.336	.0313	.740	.1250	1.21	.291	1.45	.417	1.59	.492
15	p	.105	.00199	.259	.0139	.480	.0575	.657	.130	.710	.162	.730	.175
16	p	.090	.00077	.273	.0062	.710	.0329	1.54	.110	2.23	.179	2.80	.234

See related graphs on following pages

FIGURE 1 – K₁ CURVES FOR VARIOUS PLATE-LOAD CONDITIONS

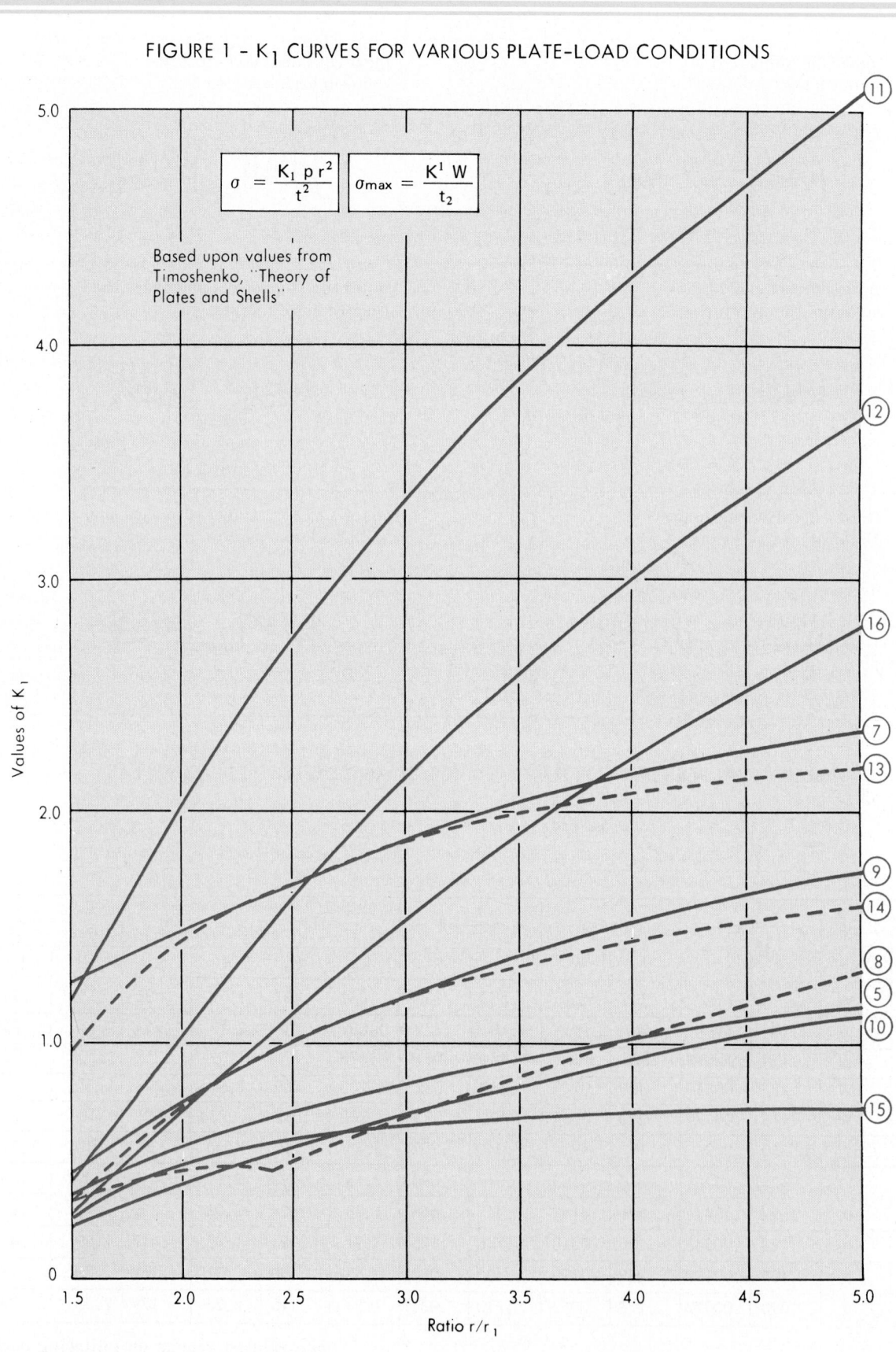

$$\sigma = \frac{K_1\, p\, r^2}{t^2} \qquad \sigma_{max} = \frac{K^1\, W}{t_2}$$

Based upon values from
Timoshenko, "Theory of
Plates and Shells"

Values of K₁

Ratio r/r₁

FIGURE 2 – K$_2$ CURVES FOR VARIOUS PLATE-LOAD CONDITIONS

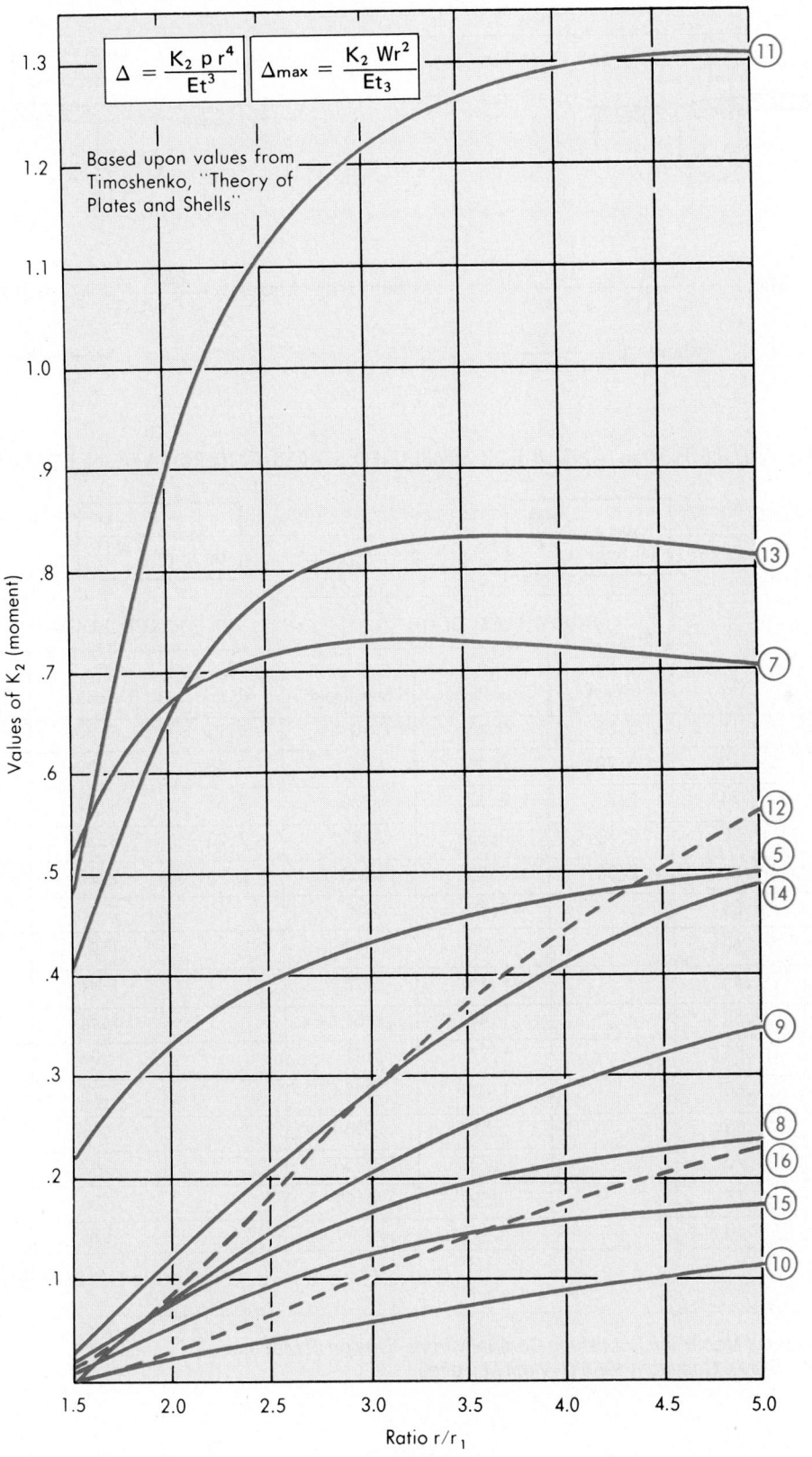

$$\Delta = \frac{K_2\, p\, r^4}{Et^3} \qquad \Delta_{max} = \frac{K_2\, Wr^2}{Et_3}$$

Based upon values from Timoshenko, "Theory of Plates and Shells"

Values of K$_2$ (moment)

Ratio r/r$_1$

17 Outer edge supported
Couple applied at hub

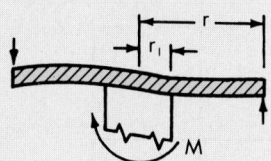

18 Outer edge fixed and supported
Couple applied at hub

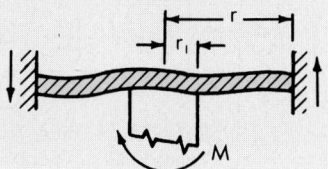

At hub (r₁),

$$\text{Max } \sigma_r = \frac{69\,M}{40\,\pi\,r_1\,t^2} \log \frac{2\,(r - r_1)}{k\,r}$$

$$\text{where} \quad k = \frac{.49\,r^2}{(.7\,r + r_1)^2}$$

At hub (r₁),

$$\text{Max } \sigma_r = \frac{3M}{4\,\pi\,r_1\,t^2} \left[1 + 1.3 \log \frac{2\,(.45\,r - r_1)}{.45\,k\,r} \right]$$

$$\text{where} \quad k = \frac{.1\,r^2}{(.28\,r + r_1)^2}$$

TABLE 2 – VALUES FOR α AND β FOR SIMPLIFIED STRESS AND ROTATION FORMULAS

$$\text{Max } \sigma_r = \frac{\beta\,M}{r\,t^2} \quad \text{(at hub)}$$

$$\text{Max } \theta = \frac{\alpha\,M}{E\,t^3} \quad \text{(at hub)}$$

$\frac{r}{r_1}$	$\frac{r_1}{r}$	SUPPORTED EDGE **17**			FIXED EDGE **18**		
		β Roark	β Timoshenko	α Timoshenko	β Roark	β Reissner	α Reissner
10.	.1	5.05	9.48	1.40	4.92	9.36	1.325
6.67	.15	3.70	6.26	1.06	3.60	6.09	.819
5.00	.20	2.75	4.62	.820	2.65	4.41	.597
4.00	.25	2.30	3.63	.643	2.20	3.37	.438
3.33	.30	2.00	2.95	.503	1.95	2.66	.321
2.86	.35		2.50	.391		2.13	.233
2.50	.40		2.06	.301		1.73	.167
2.22	.45		1.75	.228		1.41	.118
2.00	.50		1.49	.169		1.14	.081
1.82	.55		1.27	.121		.93	.0542
1.67	.60		1.07	.0844		.75	.035
1.54	.65		.89	.0560		.60	.0216
1.43	.70		.73	.0356		.47	.0125
1.33	.75		.59	.0199		.36	.0067
1.25	.80		.45	.0101		.26	.0032

Table from Roark "Formulas for Stress and Strain"

Reprinted by permission of Macmillan Publishing Company from "Design of Machine Elements" by Virgil M. Faires. Copyright 1965 by Virgil M. Faires

LVDT GLOSSARY
(CONDITIONERS)

Transducer Drive

The voltage used to power the transducer. This is quoted as rms voltage and frequency for ac transducers, and dc voltage for dc transducers.

Linearity

Linearity error is the deviation from the best fit straight line that passes through zero. Maximum linearity error is the maximum deviation of the calibration curve from this line, expressed as a percentage of total stroke. This error includes any error due to poor symmetry above and below zero.

Transducer Sensitivity Range

The range of transducer sensitivities that the unit can condition to provide the specified dc output.

Temperature Coefficient

As the ambient temperature changes, the output voltage of a conditioner will drift slightly, both in zero position, and gain. The temperature coefficient defines the amount of drift (in percent of full scale output) per degree centigrade rise.

Output Ripple

The amount of ac component in the dc output voltage. This is normally caused by the ac voltage used to excite the transducer.

Output Filter

Each conditioner has a low pass filter on the dc output to remove the ac voltage exciting the transducer.

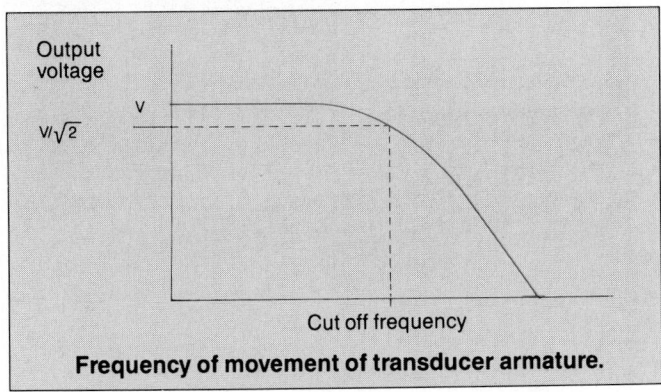

Frequency of movement of transducer armature.

The output voltage remains virtually constant at frequencies up to the cut off frequency, where it is reduced to $1/\sqrt{2}$ of its dc value. Above the cut off frequency, the output voltage halves for every doubling of frequency (for a first order filter), and quarters for a second order filter.

Eg. For a filter: second order, 500 Hz

Frequency	Output (fraction of dc)	Decibels
dc	1	0
250	1/1.03	−0.3
400	1/1.19	−1.5
500	$1/\sqrt{2}$	−3
1000	1/4.1	−12.3
2000	1/16.0	−24.1

Exact figures near the cut off frequency will vary slightly depending on the degree of damping built into the filter.

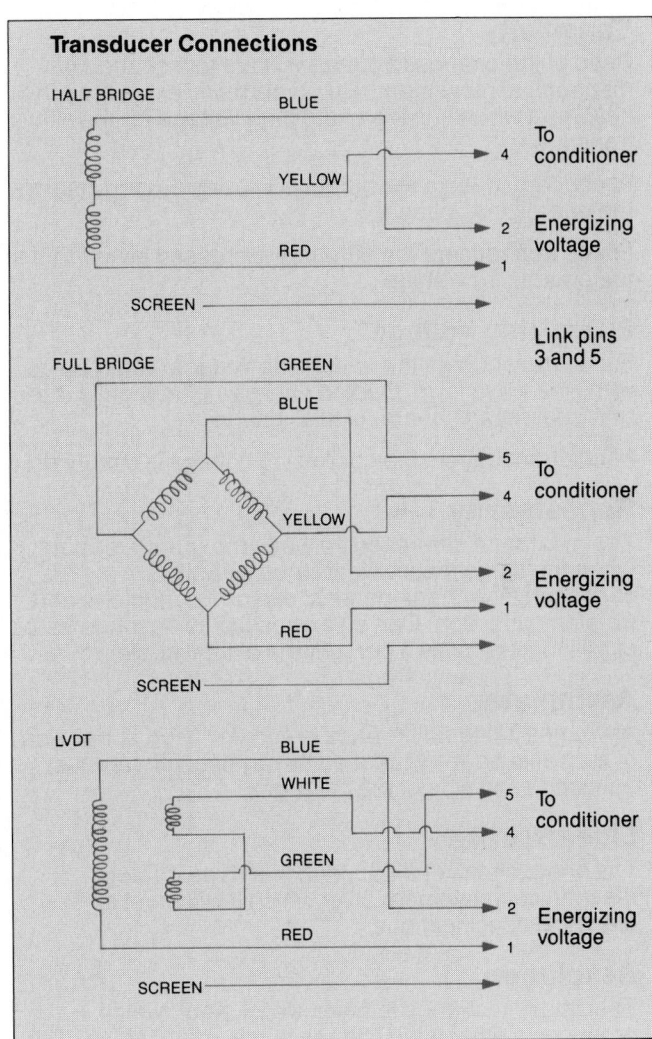

LVDT GLOSSARY
(TRANSDUCERS)

Non-Linearity
Non-linearity error is the deviation from the best fit straight line that passes through zero. Maximum linearity error is the maximum deviation of the calibration curve from this line, expressed as a percentage of total stroke. This includes any error due to poor symmetry above and below zero.

Total Stroke
The total stroke of a displacement transducer is its full mechanical calibrated movement, ie. an LD300-15 measures ±15mm giving a total stroke of 30mm.

Sensitivity
Ratio of the change in output voltage to a change in mechanical movement. This is normally expressed in mV/V/mm when V is the energizing voltage for the transducer.

For ac transducers the output is linearly proportional to the energizing voltage.

For dc transducers the output is expressed as mV/mm at the energizing voltage.

Energizing Voltage
For ac transducers the energizing voltage would be ac with sine wave form. Quoted energizing voltage is the rms (root mean square) of this voltage.

For dc transducers the energizing voltage is simply dc.

Repeatability
The maximum difference between the output readings, when the same mechanical input is applied consecutively, under identical external conditions and from any direction. Can be expressed as absolute value of millimeters, or as a percentage of total stroke.

Asymmetry
Asymmetry is the difference in sensitivity on either side of zero. It is normally caused by physical differences between each side of the LVDT coil.

Linear Stroke
The linear stroke of a transducer is its calibrated mechanical movement, over which it will meet all electrical specifications.

Resolution
The smallest change in mechanical input, which produces a detectable change in the output signal. For an LVDT the resolution is infinite and is usually only restricted by the resolution of the measuring instruments.

Phase Shift
The angle in degrees between the energizing voltage waveform and the output signal waveform at a positive mechanical input.

Residual Voltage at Zero
The minimum output voltage attainable by positioning the core (armature) of the displacement transducer. Usually quoted as a figure below which this value will be. This value is usually not relevant when a conditioning amplifier is used, only when measuring true ac output voltage.

Pretravel
That part of the stroke that exists between the outward travel stop and the start of the specified calibrated range.

Overtravel
That part of the stroke that exists between the end of the specified calibrated range and the inward travel stop.

Frequency Response
The frequency range within which the output follows a sinusoidally varying mechanical input.

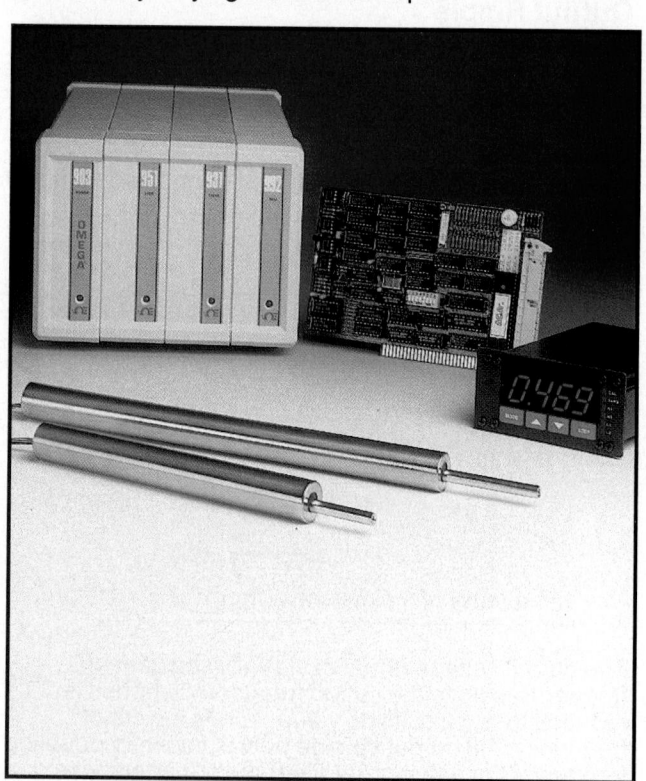

THE LD100, A FAST LINEAR DISPLACEMENT TRANSDUCER

Early in 1983, development of an electrically non-contacting linear displacement transducer (LDT) for use in reciprocating heat engine research began. LVDT's in this service were unsatisfactory for several reasons. They frequently failed under the severe combination of vibration, high temperature, and oscillating pressure that existed in their operating environment. Their relatively low bandwidth resulted in significant misleading phase shifts between motion and output. If they were mounted in close proximity to the AC generators that were the usual means of coupling power out of the research engines, fringing fields of the generator caused serious disturbance of the LVDT output. Each engine required two LVDT's, and the consequent necessity of bringing eight to 12 leadouts through a pressurized container always presented design problems, as did the relatively low range-to-length ratio of most LVDT's. Special-purpose LVDT's could avoid one or two of these problems, but not all of them.

PERFORMANCE SPECIFICATIONS

The LD100 is a precision variable inductor, essentially in the form of a helical coil with a slidable aluminum or copper tube core (see Figure 1).

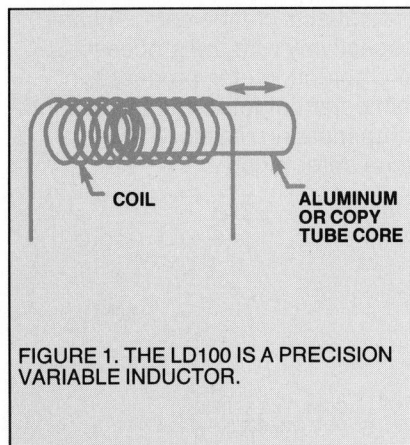

COIL

ALUMINUM OR COPY TUBE CORE

FIGURE 1. THE LD100 IS A PRECISION VARIABLE INDUCTOR.

The processor circuit drives the coil with a 112 kHz current source. At 112 kHz the skin depth in aluminum is about 0.25 mm. Typical core diameter, however, is about 10 mm. Therefore, 112 kHz magnetic fields are practically excluded from most of the core, and inductance is reduced as the core is inserted. Another effect of core insertion is an increase in resistance seen at the coil terminals, but resistance change is lower than reactance change by a factor of 10. Impedance at 112 kHz of even a simple helical coil is nearly a linear function of core insertion, provided the inside end of the core is several diameters away from the coil ends.

Thus, 112 kHz voltage appearing across the coil is nearly a linear function of core position. The processor rectifies this voltage, subtracts a rectified balance signal to produce a bipolar output, and filters the difference to generate a voltage output proportional to movement of the core from a zero position. Several means of reducing nonlinearity and of extending linear range have been incorporated in the improved LDT and its processor, so that it is feasible to guarantee 0.15 percent linearity in production units (0.1 percent optional), and to produce a transducer with length exceeding its linear range by only about 25 mm.

Null Stability

An important design goal was zero voltage (null) stability. To this end, circuitry for processing the balance signal is nominally identical to that which processes the transducer signal, and circuit elements performing the same function in each channel are located so they are at nearly the same temperature. The processor achieves typical zero voltage warm-up drift of 0.15 percent and, after warm-up, typical null stability of ±0.025 percent. Changes in processor ambient temperature typically produce ±60 ppm/°C zero voltage shift.

Changing the transducer temperature also influences null voltage, mainly because of an increase in skin depth in the core material as the temperature rises, which causes inductance to increase. This effect is reduced by increasing the core diameter and by

THE LD100, A FAST LINEAR DISPLACEMENT TRANSDUCER

using high conductivity core material. A 9.5 mm core tube typically has a 130 ppm/°C temperature coefficient of null voltage (relative to full range) if made of copper, and about 140 ppm,/°C if aluminum. Optional composite cores achieve less than 70 ppm/°C.

Gain Stability

Another major design goal was stability of gain factor (volts out per millimeter of core movement). Since gain is directly proportional to excitation frequency, a quartz crystal is used in the processor to practically eliminate frequency drift. Gain is also proportional to the magnitude of the 112 kHz current driving the transducer. The processor closely regulates this current, using a temperature compensated Zener diode as a reference. Gain is directly influenced by the transfer functions of the amplifier, detector, and filter, which all operate on the transducer signal. These are stabilized by using low temperature coefficient components and negative feedback circuitry. Typically, the processor's gain temperature coefficient is 80 ppm/°C.

Changing the transducer temperature influences gain, mostly because of increases in the core material's skin depth with increasing temperature, which effectively changes core diameter. Increasing core diameter and/or conductivity reduces this effect. Gain temperature coefficient of a 9.5 mm core tube is typically 90 ppm/°C if it is made of copper and 130 ppm/°C if aluminum.

Leadout Effects

Two conductors connect the transducer to the processor and constitute a transmission line with a loading effect that is summarized in Figure 2, provided the line is electrically short and the FLDT reactance is small compared to the reactance of C(line).

Both qualifications are met if a 50 or 75 ohm line, less than 100 m long, is used for leadout. Line loading shifts the null voltage, changes the gain, and introduces nonlinearity. For a fixed line, all three effects can be compensated, respectively with the processor's zero potentiometer, processor's gain potentiometer, and by a shunt compensating resistor R_C with a value determined

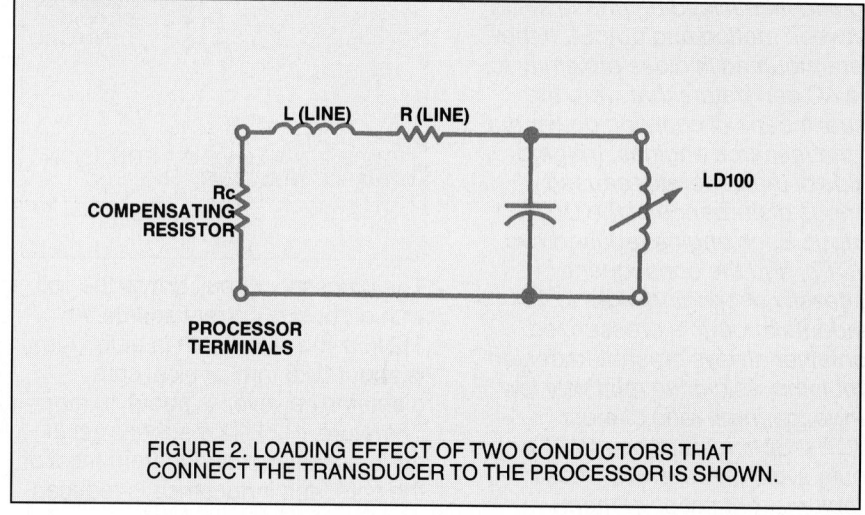

FIGURE 2. LOADING EFFECT OF TWO CONDUCTORS THAT CONNECT THE TRANSDUCER TO THE PROCESSOR IS SHOWN.

by C (line). Standard leadout is three meters of miniature 75 ohm coaxial cable. Correct R_C for this length is installed in the processor. Optional compensated extension cables are available or can readily be made.

Frequency Response

The transducer and its processor are a carrier system in which core displacement amplitude modulates the 112 kHz carrier voltage appearing across the transducer. Displacement information is recovered by filtering the half-wave rectified carrier. Filter bandwidth is determined by a trade-off between residual carrier in the output and information bandwidth, and is 12 kHz (-3 dB point) in the processor. This choice results in a maximum of 0.006 percent residual carrier and a delay of 30 μs between core motion and output (1.1 degree of phase shift per

100 Hz) for core motion having frequency components up to about 6 kHz.

By comparison, a typical LVDT using a 2500 Hz carrier and scaled filtering would introduce a 1370 μs time delay for core motion having frequency components up to about 0.14 kHz. Because it uses a high carrier frequency, the transducer is capable of accurately measuring much faster motion than a typical LVDT.

Noise and Resolution

Total noise in the new transducer's output is typically 0.01 percent (rms) of F.S. output. Resolution is determined by low-frequency output jitter, which is typically 0.0005 percent of full range. Displacements on the order of three times the low-frequency jitter can be resolved, which leads to the formula:

$$\text{resolution} = \frac{\text{range}}{60.000}$$

Life Expectancy

The core moves in a tube made of polyimide plastic, which is an extraordinarily tough bearing material and has nearly the same coefficient of expansion as aluminum or copper. Friction is low, and hundreds of hours at 60 Hz motion frequency have produced

no signs of wear. For these reasons, life expectancy is believed to be essentially infinite.

Stray EM Interference

The transducer is exceptionally resistant to interference from stray fields. One reason for this is the fact that predetection filtering of the transducer voltage need only pass signals in the range 112 kHz ±12 kHz in order to retain all sideband information generated by core motion in the frequency range 0 to 12 kHz. Signals outside the filter's range are attenuated at a rate of 40 dB/decade. Interference at 60 Hz, for example, is attenuated by 131 dB.

Another reason for high rejection of low-frequency interference is the low value of transducer impedance, which is on the order of 2 ohms at 60 Hz.

Others

Currently available linear ranges are 2.5 mm, 20 mm, 60 mm, 160 mm, and 400 mm. A spring-loaded gauging transducer is being developed.

It has been found that immersion in hydraulic fluid has no measurable electrical effect on operation. Development of a long-stroke transducer for installation within a hydraulic cylinder has therefore begun.

CONCLUSION

The transducer is a simple, compact, rugged device that offers significant advantages in measuring linear motion. The accuracy and resolution with which it will measure static displacements compare favorably with those of other transducers, and its ability to accurately measure dynamic displacement containing high-frequency motion components is exceptional. **ΩE**

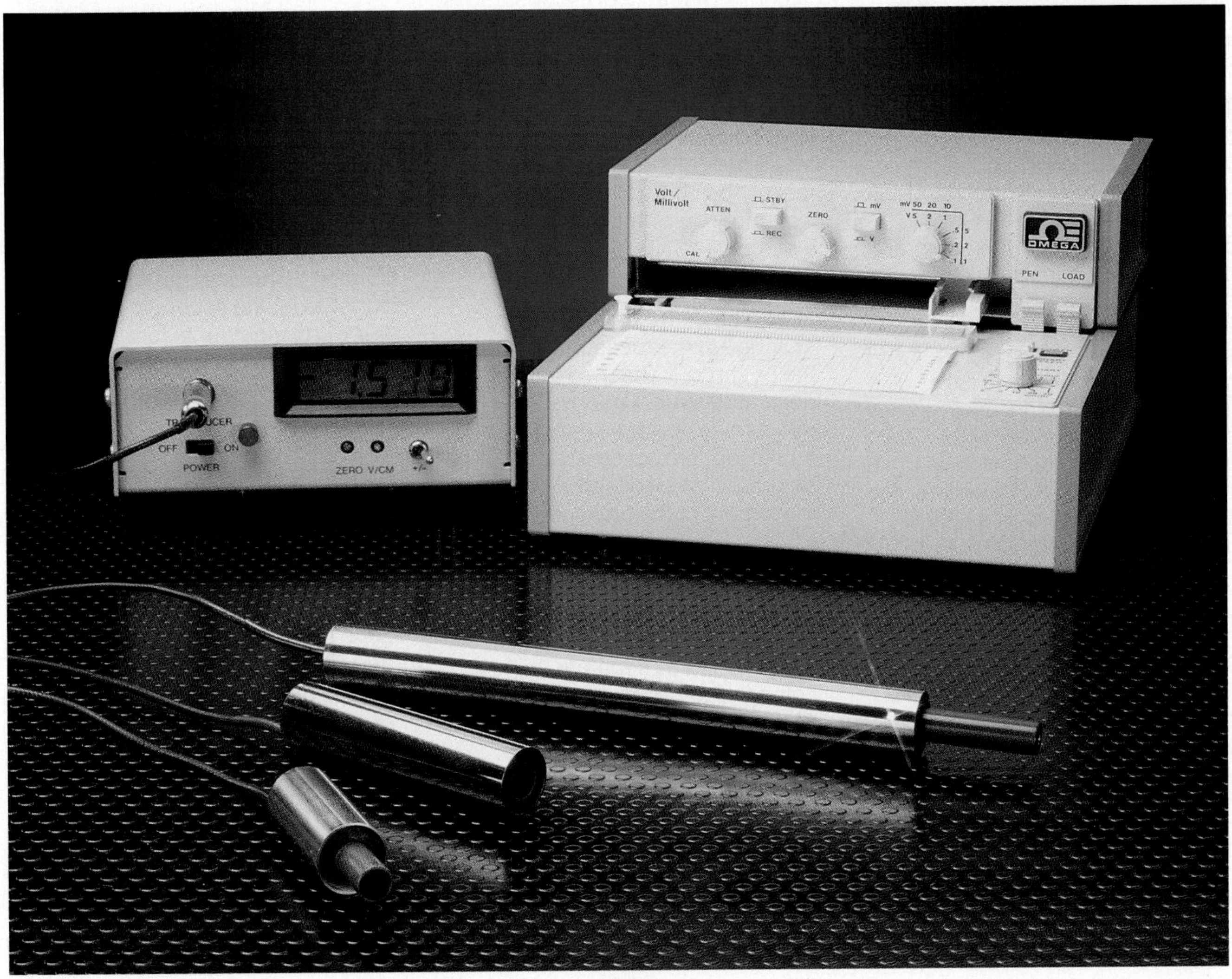

OMEGA'S SENSORS IN POSITION FEEDBACK
APPLICATION REFERENCE FOR THE DESIGN ENGINEER

INTRODUCTION

As automated control systems grow in complexity and scope, so does their appetite for information about the outside world.

The growth of CNC, servo, and micro-computer-controlled technologies has fueled increasing demand for accurate, cost-effective position feedback technologies.

This paper describes the OMEGA system for position feedback sensing. OMEGA employs LVDT (linear variable differential transformer) technology, which offers exceptional accuracy and stability plus infinite resolution. This technology is packaged with appropriate signal conditioning, ancillary electronics, physical suspension and mounting hardware as the designer requires for each OEM application.

The discussion is divided into two parts. The first part provides an introduction to LVDT technology and the principles which underlie its performance capabilities. The second part surveys contemporary design achievements which employ LVDT-based linear position feedback. While the majority of applications are for linear measurements, in many cases innovative engineering has enabled the user to enjoy the benefits of LVDT technologies in measurement applications which seem, at first glance, ill-suited to linear sensing systems.

LVDT BASICS

OMEGA position feedback technology is based on the LVDT, an infinitely variable transducer which outputs a voltage precisely proportional to the position of a measurand.

Physically, the LVDT is a hollow metallic cylinder in which a shaft of smaller diameter moves freely back and forth along the cylinder's long axis (see Figure 3).

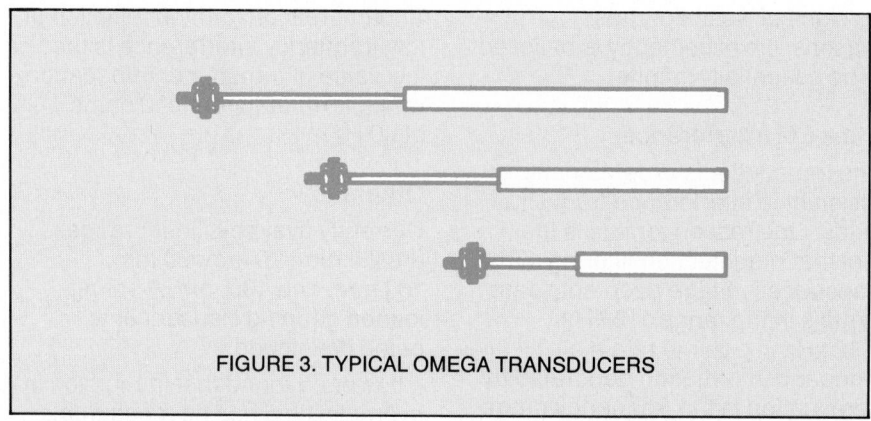

FIGURE 3. TYPICAL OMEGA TRANSDUCERS

The shaft, or pushrod, ends in a magnetically conductive core which must be within the cylinder, or coil assembly, when the device is operating (see Figure 4).

In common practice, the pushrod is physically attached to the moveable object whose position is to be determined (the measurand), while the coil assembly is attached to a fixed reference point. Movement of the measurand moves the core within the coil assembly; this motion is measured electrically.

Numerous installation options exist. The coil assembly can be attached to the measurand while the pushrod is attached to the fixed point, if desired. Various mechanical linkages can be employed, so that core motion may be greater or smaller than the movement of the measurand.

Finally, the transducers themselves are available in several physical configurations. In the free-armature design, the core and coil are supplied as separate components. This is the simplest and least costly configuration, but in using it the user assumes responsibility for providing physical suspension of device components. Captive guided armature transducers are supplied as fully-assembled, telescoping units; they are relatively quick and easy to install.

The core may be guided within the coil by simple O-rings, or by Delrin bearings for greater accuracy. When utmost accuracy is required, the user may consider gauging transducers. These exquisitely constructed devices use precision linear ball bearing mechanisms, springs and bushings to provide the highest possible linearity and repeatability.

Electrically, the LVDT is a mutual inductance device. Within the coil assembly are three transformer windings. A central primary is flanked by two secondaries, one on either side; the secondary outputs are wired together to form a series-opposing circuit. AC excitation is applied to the primary, giving rise to inductance currents in the secondaries as mediated by the magnetically conductive core. With the core at dead center (equidistant with respect to both secondary windings), no voltage appears at the secondary outputs. As soon as the core moves, by even the smallest amount, a differential voltage is induced at the secondary output. The phase of the voltage is determined by the direction of the core's displacement; the amplitude is determined more or less linearly by the magnitude of the core's excursion from the center.

This differential design gives the LVDT significant advantage over potentiometer-type devices, in that

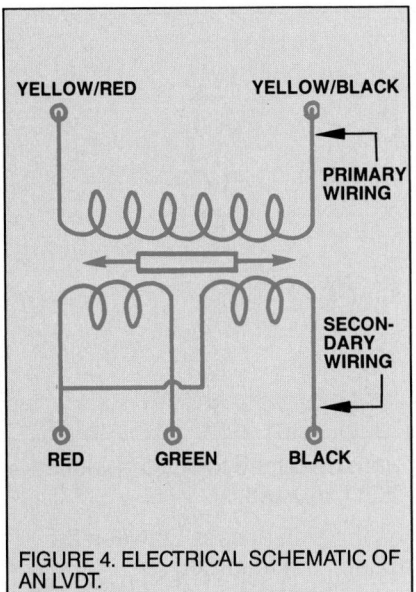

FIGURE 4. ELECTRICAL SCHEMATIC OF AN LVDT.

resolution is not limited by the spacing of coil windings. In an LVDT any movement of the core causes a proportional change in output. The LVDT thus has theoretically infinite resolution: in practice, resolution is limited only by the external output electronics and the physical suspensions.

Because it is a transformer, the LVDT requires an ac drive signal. A dedicated electronics package, or signal conditioner, is generally used to generate this drive signal, and also to convert the device's analog ac output to +5Vdc, 4-20mA or some other format compatible with downstream equipment. This circuitry may be external, or it may be housed within the transducer body. Internal electronics allow the user to feed the transducer a dc signal of only moderate quality, often a benefit in battery-powered and onboard vehicular applications. However, external electronics offer higher quality and may provide optional features such as calibration to enable direct readout in engineering units.

High accuracy, repeatability, stability and linearity are characteristic of the LVDT.

In addition to its infinite resolution, it offers one more advantage over potentiometer devices; since the core and coil are never in physical contact, the LVDT almost never wears out.

TYPICAL LVDT APPLICATIONS

LVDT Rig is Better For Tensile Test Measurements

When tensile testing a material to determine its modulus of elasticity it is necessary to know precisely the applied load and the distance that the material stretches under that load. Traditionally, these parameters are accurately measured using a load cell and LVDT displacement transducer respectively. In the latter case, an extensometer-incorporating the displacement transducer—is connected directly to the sample under test. This method has two distinct disadvantages: (1) the extensometer has to be set up for each sample and tends to restrict access to it; (2) if the sample is tested to breaking point, the sudden shock can damage the transducer. These disadvantages can be avoided by using instead a rig having an OMEGA LVDT gauging transducer moving in contact with a precision machined 'wedge' transfer mechanism (see Figure 5).

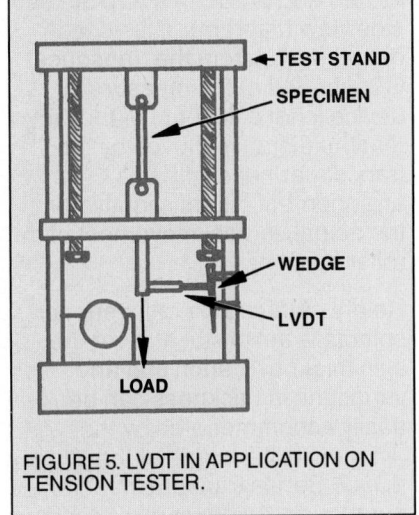

FIGURE 5. LVDT IN APPLICATION ON TENSION TESTER.

With this alternative method, the gauging transducer is fixed to the sample securing clamp which moves as the material stretches. As the gauging transducer sensing head travels up the inclined surface of the wedge, the vertical movement is transferred to a proportional horizontal movement of the transducer core. The linear voltage output signal from the transducer is fed to a digital voltmeter or similar measuring device, which can be calibrated with reference to the angle of the inclined surface to give a direct and precise measurement of the elongation of the material under load. Because the precision ball tip of the gauging transducer travels freely along the smooth machined surface of the incline, and because the transducer shaft runs in precision bearings, no sideways stressing of the transducer shaft occurs. This is further ensured by using a very shallow angle of incline relative to the direction of travel, which also enables the use of a small stroke transducer; the horizontal movement of the transducer core can be as much as 10 times smaller than the vertical distance moved. OMEGA gauging transducers have highly accurate linear outputs, even for small strokes, so that the calibrated measurement of the test sample's elongation is also very accurate.

For very small elongations, e.g. less than 1 mm under high applied loads, an extensometer using an OMEGA linear displacement transducer will be marginally more accurate. However, the gauging transducer device is preferable for most applications and it is especially suitable when testing materials such as soft metals, plastics and rubber that stretch by significant amounts without breaking.

Because the gauging transducer is fixed to the side of the clamp, it does not obstruct access to the test

sample. Also it does not require to be set up every time a new sample is placed in the testing machine. If the sample breaks, the transducer tip simply moves more quickly along the incline without risk of damage. The overall design is very compact.

OMEGA Transducers Shape up to Changing Material Thicknesses

Gauging transducers are commonly used in industry to check that the thickness of a manufactured sheet material such as paper or metal remains within the specified tolerances. Where the profile of the measured product involves several different thicknesses, such as a complex extrusion, a gauging rig can be devised incorporating a number of transducers to monitor the various dimensions. In a further variation on this idea, OMEGA LVDT type gauging transducers have been built into a rig designed to measure the varying thickness of a natural manufacturing material - processed animal skins. These profile measurements are then used to build up a picture of a complete skin, so that areas of uniform thickness can be cut from it and used to best advantage; the thinnest leather being selected perhaps for gloves, the somewhat thicker areas for handbags and so on.

As with sheet materials of uniform thickness, the skin is passed for thickness measurement between basically two rollers, which are both free to rotate about their axes. The lower roller is fixed in its vertical plane to provide a datum for measurement. The other can move vertically to follow the upper surface of the material, the distance that it moves away from the datum (i.e. the thickness of the material) being measured by gauging transducers.

To accommodate the varying thicknesses of the skin, however, the upper roller is divided in this instance across its width into

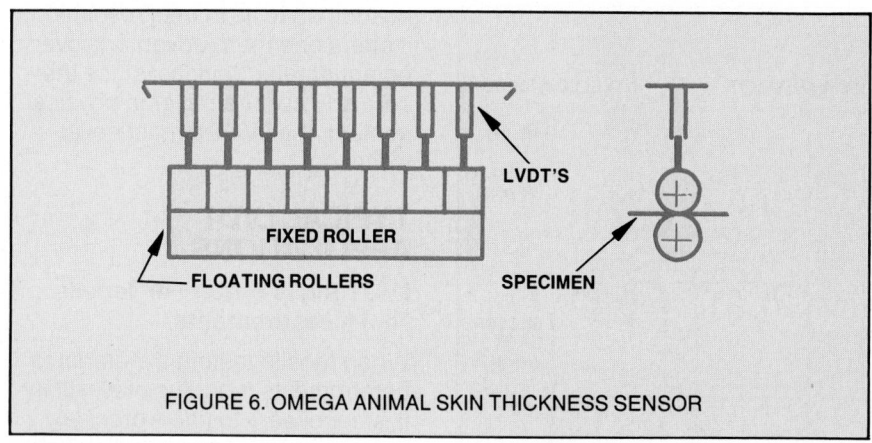

FIGURE 6. OMEGA ANIMAL SKIN THICKNESS SENSOR

sixteen separate sections (see Figure 6). Each section is spring loaded against a common supporting spindle, which is set at a fixed distance above the datum roller. As the skin passes between the rollers, the sections of the upper roller are held in positive contact with the material surface by the springs, yet they are able to move up and down as the skin thickness varies.

A separate gauging transducer is dedicated to each roller section and monitors the changing skin thickness at that point. To avoid any sideways straining of the transducer sensing head, that might be caused by direct contact with the rotating roller, the vertical displacement is transmitted mechanically to the transducer by a pivoted flat bar, which rests with its free end on top of the roller (see side view diagram). The voltage output signal from the transducer is calibrated at the measuring device to take account of the fact that the distance moved by the transducer head with this arrangement differs slightly from the actual vertical movement of the roller section.

Height of the upper roller support spindle is set to suit an average skin thickness, such that any variations in thickness can be easily accommodated by the ±5 mm stroke length of the chosen LD500 Series transducers. The number and width of roller sections

were designed to suit the widest skin expected.

As the skin passes between the rollers, the recorded measurements give a precise indication of the varying skin thickness along the line of each transducer. A "contour map" of the whole skin, showing the areas of different thickness, is generated by processing the transducer output signals in a computer and presenting the resulting data either as a VDU graphics display or as hard copy printout in chart form. Color codes or monochrome tones can be used to clarify the areas of different thicknesses, just as various land heights are denoted on a normal map.

Any section of the skin of a required thickness can be easily identified for manufacture of specific items, thus facilitating positioning of the patterns and making optimum use of the material with minimal wastage.

Using OMEGA Displacement Transducers to Measure Pressure and Load

Used in conjunction with a suitable force-sensitive device, such as a metallic diaphragm or proof ring, OMEGA linear displacement transducers can provide a highly accurate and stable but relatively low-cost means of measuring pressure and load. One application for the diaphragm system is the measurement of pressure inside a

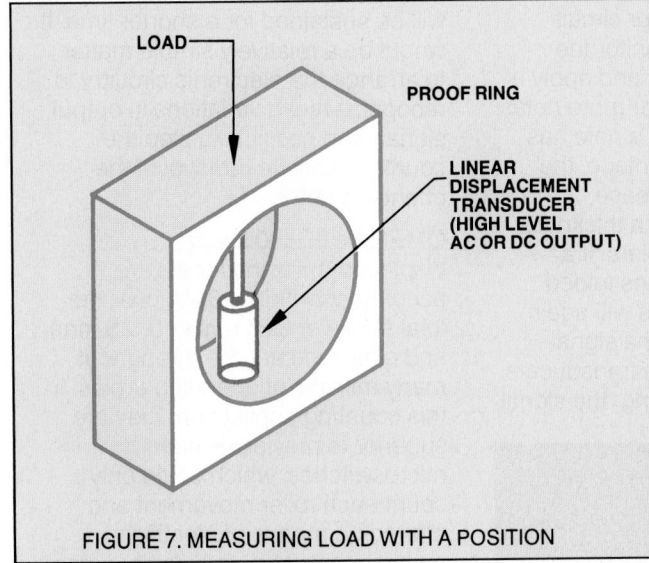

FIGURE 7. MEASURING LOAD WITH A POSITION

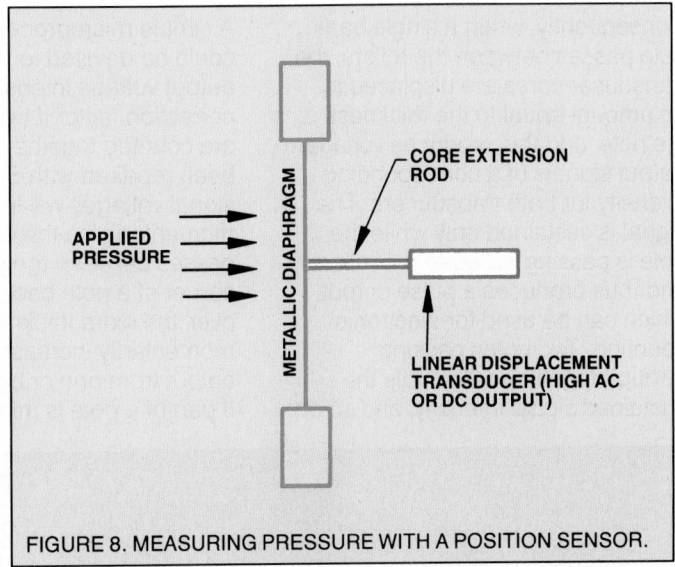

FIGURE 8. MEASURING PRESSURE WITH A POSITION SENSOR.

containment, such as engine cylinder block pressure during development and testing. Mounted inside a proof ring, the displacement transducer can offer advantages over the strain gage for measuring very small loads or if there is a possibility of shock loading (see Figures 7 and 8).

Typically, the convoluted metallic diaphragm is built into the wall of the pressurized vessel and deflects under pressure. Diaphragm thickness and sensitivity are designed to suit the pressure range.

The linear displacement transducer is mounted at right angles to the diaphragm (see Figure 3) with its core extension rod attached to the center of the disc. OMEGA linear displacement transducers are available for operating temperatures up to 600°C. Alternatively for high temperatures, a proximity transducers can be used, which does not make contact with the diaphragm. Any flexing of the diaphragm is reflected by the output voltage signal from the transducers. A simple microchip can be used to calibrated simply by pressurizing to one known high pressure and one low pressure,

since the disc movement is linear with pressure at the center. The resulting low-cost, simple pressure sensor is highly repeatable and reliable.

Incorporation of a linear displacement transducer into a proof ring (Figure 3) gives a load measuring system having significant advantages over the strain gage in some applications. Operating with very little actual movement, strain gages tend to be stiff and insensitive to very small loads. The proof ring, on the other hand, is a comparatively floppy beam capable of moving more freely under load—only relatively speaking, because the distance moved needs to be less than the overall stroke e.g., ±0.5 mm of the transducer. This system is therefore more sensitive to light loads.

Although the proof ring flexes, it is in fact more robust and resilient than the strain gage. Stiffness in a strain gage has an advantage when the load is applied and removed rapidly, since the stiff system gives a high frequency response. If the strain gage is subject to high shock loading, however, it can be easily overloaded. A proof ring on the

other hand, can move farther to absorb the shock load without detrimental effect.

Using a Linear Displacement Transducer for Counting

High speed counting of bank notes—or similar sheet items requiring absolute numerical accuracy—can be achieved by means of a simple design principle based on LD400 miniature linear displacement transducers available from OMEGA. The voltage signal output from these highly sensitive transducers can be used to: count the notes individually at high speed; detect when two or more notes are counted together; identify a taped repair; indicate when a note has become folded over; and alert the operator when part of a note is missing.

In a typical machine design, the notes are fed between two rotating rollers, one of which runs in fixed bearings while the other is able to move linearly to vary the gap between them. The latter roller is held in positive contact with the bank note by suitable loading. A miniature transducer is mounted at each end of this moveable roller to measure its linear displacement as the notes pass through the gap.

Consequently, when a single bank note passes between the rollers, the transducer cores are displaced by an amount equal to the thickness of the note, and this produces voltage output signals of a corresponding intensity for both transducers. The signal is sustained only while the note is passing between the rollers and thus produces a pulse output which can be used for electronic counting. Two notes passing through together will double the sustained signal intensity, and so on.

A simple microprocessor circuit could be devised to monitor the output voltage intensity and apply a correction factor if two or more notes are counted together. If a note has been repaired with Sellotape, the signal voltages will increase momentarily as the extra thickness passes between the rollers. If a corner of a note becomes folded over, the extra thickness will again momentarily increase the signal output from one or both transducers. If part of a note is missing, the signal

will be sustained for a shorter time. It would be a relatively simple matter to arrange the electronic circuitry to recognize these variations in output signal, and possibly to stop the count to facilitate removal of the offending notes.

OMEGA's LD400 linear displacement transducers are accurate to within $\pm 0.5\%$ over the total stroke of 0.25 mm (± 0.125 mm) and offer repeatability throughout many millions of operating cycles. In this counting application, they are superior to previously used microswitches, which could only count each roller movement and offered no means of identifying multiple throughputs or faulty notes. When ordered for large quantity production, these transducers are also extremely competitive on price.

CONCLUSION

For today's designer, there are few limits on the capacity of OMEGA's LVDT-based sensor technology to gather position data. With the properly-engineered interfaces and housings, these versatile linear transducers and their support technologies can provide accurate, stable, repeatable measurement of linear motion, thickness, rotary motion, pressure, load, temperature and other variables - and can simultaneously survive a variety of hostile environments if required. For information specific to your application, write or call OMEGA Engineering. ΩE

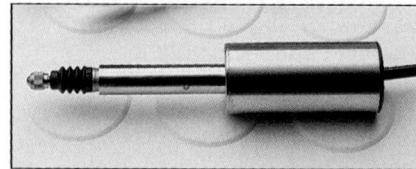

THE LINEAR VARIABLE DISPLACEMENT TRANSDUCER

INTRODUCTION

A linear variable displacement transducer is essentially a miniature transformer having one primary winding, two symmetrically wound secondary coils, and an armature core that is free to move along its linear axis in precision bearing guides. A push rod connects the monitored component to the armature core, such that the displacement of that component moves the core off-center.

A voltage is applied across the primary winding and the EMF induced in the magnetic circuit produces corresponding voltages in the secondary windings, which are connected differentially to produce a zero output signal when the armature core is in its central position. When the core is displaced off center in either direction, the efficiency of transformation in the secondary winding on that side is increased and decreases in the other secondary coil. This results in a positive (+ve) voltage output signal when the core moves off center in one direction and a negative (-ve) voltage output in the other direction. The intensity of the output signal is directly proportional to the linear displacement of the core and, hence, of the monitored component.

The LVDT is an ac device which means there is a need for electronics to translate its output into a useful dc signal. There are two hybrid modules that are the foundation for LVDT Signal Processing; an Oscillator and a Demodulator. The Oscillator is designed to provide a stable sine wave for driving the transducer, and a square wave reference for the Demodulator. The Demodulator is designed to amplify the output from the transducer, and convert it into a highly accurate dc voltage which is directly proportional to displacement. The Oscillator and Demodulator are the backbone for OMEGA's DP-LVDT, LDX-2, LDX-3 Signal Conditioners, and the dc powered transducers (the dc powered transducers have integral signal conditioning). See Figure 9.

To operate the transducer, it is necessary to drive the primary with a sine wave and the output from the secondaries consist of a sine wave with the position information contained in the amplitude and phase. The output at the center of the stroke is zero, rising to maximum amplitude at either end of the stroke. The output is in phase with the primary drive at one end of the stroke and out of phase at the other end.

In a high quality transducer, the relationship between position and phase/amplitude is linear. The Oscillator and Demodulator are what makes the transition between position and phase/amplitude easy. See Figure 10 for a graphical illustration.

DESCRIPTION OF OSCILLATOR

The function of the Oscillator is to provide an accurate sine wave voltage to drive the transducer, stable in both amplitude and frequency. It also provides a square wave phase reference to the

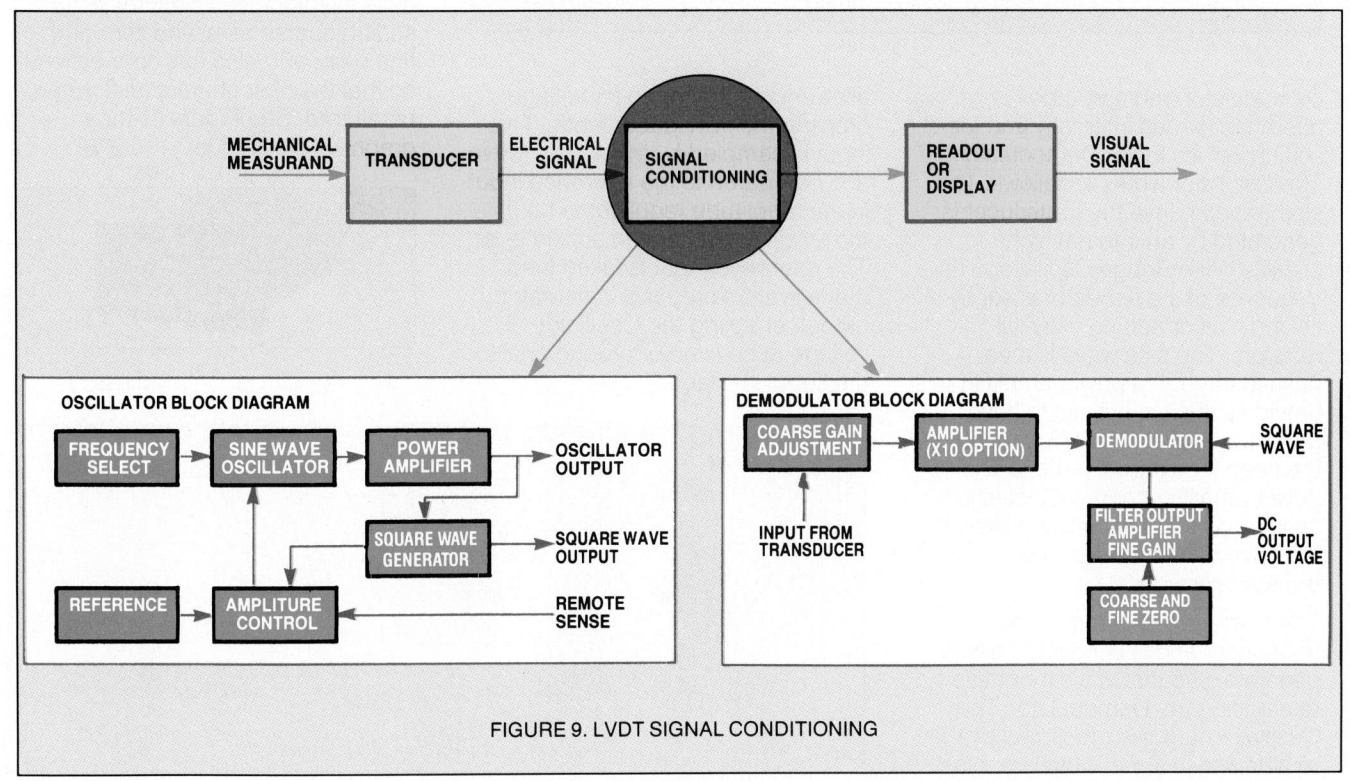

FIGURE 9. LVDT SIGNAL CONDITIONING

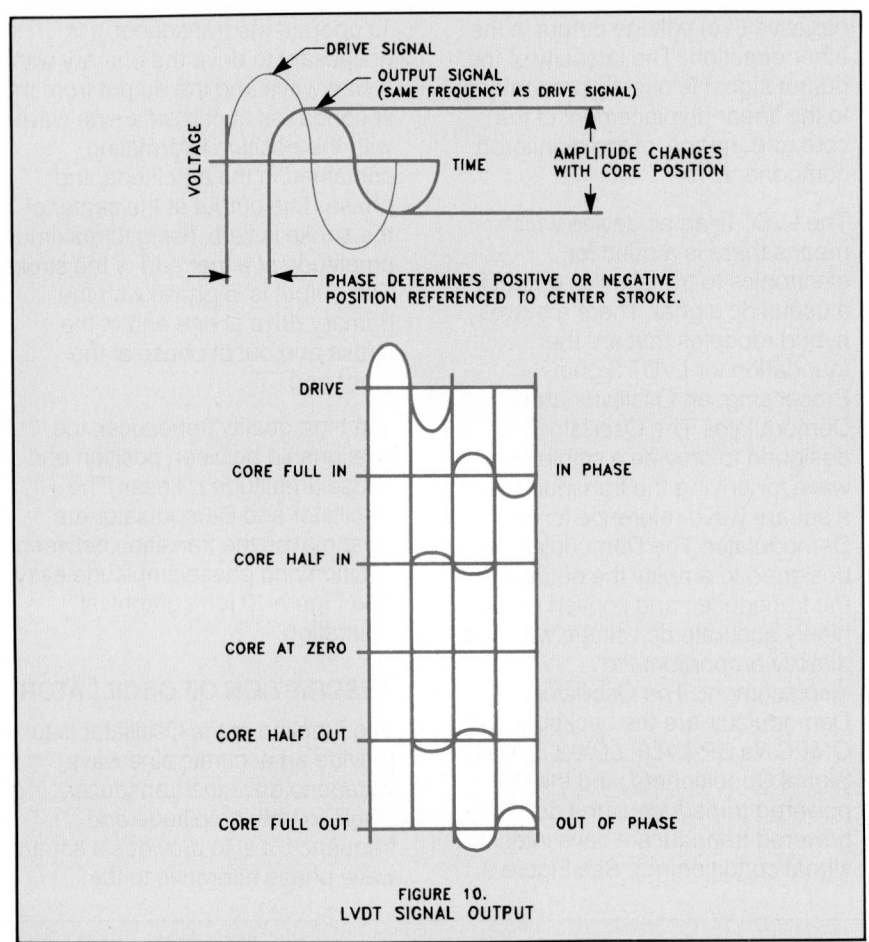

FIGURE 10.
LVDT SIGNAL OUTPUT

DESCRIPTION OF DEMODULATOR

The function of the Demodulator is to take the AC output of the transducer and convert it into a useful dc voltage proportional to displacement, load etc. It also contains circuitry to enable the adjustment of Gain and Zero to accommodate a wide range of transducers.

The Demodulator works as follows. The output from the transducer is fed into a coarse gain select circuit and is then amplified. This amplifier can have a gain of 25 or 250 if the x10 option is used, the extra gain allowing operation with low output transducers such as strain gages.

Doing the main amplification with the ac signal means that the drift of the circuit is reduced. The high level ac signal is then passed to a phase synchronous Demodulator, which uses the square wave from the Oscillator to convert it into a dc voltage with some superimposed ac. This is then fed through a low pass filter which removes the majority of the ac components leaving a steady dc voltage with slight ripple. The low pass filter includes circuitry for setting coarse zero, fine zero and fine gain, and also has connections so that the filter characteristics can be altered. See Figure 11 for a graphical illustration. **ΩE**

Demodulator and a voltage reference for use internally and for setting zeroes in the Demodulator. The Oscillator works as follows. The sine wave to drive the transducer is generated by an internal high stability Wien Bridge Oscillator. The frequency of the oscillator is set by linking pins or adding external resistors. The sine wave is then passed through a power amplifier to provide sufficient current to drive most transducers (50mA) without the need for external buffers. The power amplifier contains protection circuitry as short circuits are likely in the environment where most transducers work.

The sine wave is output to the transducer and is used internally to generate a square wave for phase referencing the Demodulator. The Oscillator output is monitored by the remote sense input, which enables

allowance to be made for voltage drops in the transducer leads. This input is sampled by the square wave and compared to the reference input in the amplitude regulator to hold the Oscillator voltage to a fixed level. The reference input is taken from the reference output or ratiometric output, enabling the Oscillator voltage to be fixed or proportional to the supply voltage.

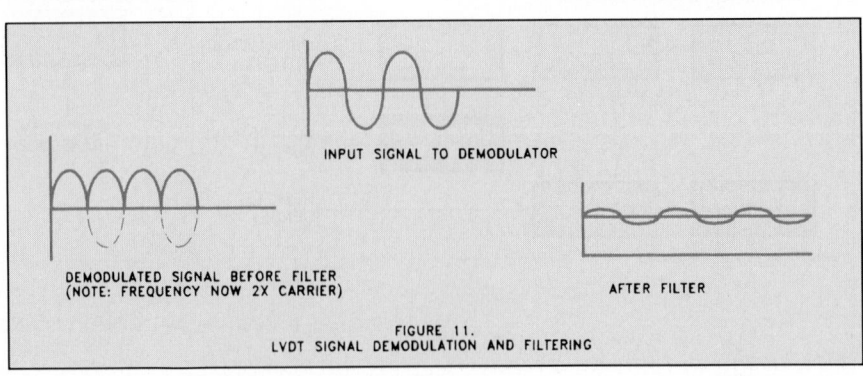

INPUT SIGNAL TO DEMODULATOR

DEMODULATED SIGNAL BEFORE FILTER
(NOTE: FREQUENCY NOW 2X CARRIER)

AFTER FILTER

FIGURE 11.
LVDT SIGNAL DEMODULATION AND FILTERING

CHEMICAL RESISTANCE CHART

CHEMICAL RESISTANCE DATA

These recommendations are based upon information from material suppliers and careful examination of available published information and are believed to be accurate. However, since the resistance of metals, plastics and elastomers can be affected by concentration, temperature, presence of other chemicals and other factors, this information should be considered as a general guide rather than an unqualified guarantee. Ultimately, the customer must determine the suitablility of the pump used in various solutions.

All recommendations assume ambient temperatures unless otherwise noted.

RATINGS — CHEMICAL EFFECT
A—No effect—Excellent
B—Minor effect—Good
C—Moderate effect—Fair
D—Severe effect—Not Recommended

FOOTNOTES
1. P.V.C.—Satisfactory to 72° F.
2. Polypropylene—Satisfactory to 72° F.
3. Polypropylene—Satisfactory to 120° F.
4. Buna-N—Satisfactory for "O" Rings
5. Polyacetal—Satisfactory to 72° F.
6. Ceramag—Satisfactory to 72° F.

The ratings for these materials are based upon the chemical resistance only. Added consideration must be given to pump selections when the chemical is abrasive, viscous in nature, or has a Specific Gravity greater than 1.1

	302 Stainless Steel	304 Stainless Steel	316 Stainless Steel	440 Stainless Steel	Aluminum	TITANIUM	HASTELLOY C	Cast Bronze	Brass	Cast Iron	Carbon Steel	KYNAR	PVC (Type 1)	Tygon (E-3606)	Teflon	Noryl	Polyacetal	Nylon	Cycolac (ABS)	Polyethylene	POLYPROPYLENE	RYTON	CARBON	CERAMIC	CERAMAGNET "A"	VITON	BUNA N (NITRILE)	Silicon	Neoprene	Ethylene Propylene (EPM)	Rubber (Natural)	Epoxy
Acetaldehyde[5]	A	A	A	-	B	A	A	D	-	-	C	-	D	D	A	-	A	A	D	C	B	A	A	A	-	D	B	B	B	D	B	C
Acetamide	-	B	A	-	-	-	-	-	-	-	C	-	-	-	-	-	B	-	-	-	-	-	-	-	-	A	-	A	A	-	A	A
Acetate Solv.[2]	A	B	A	B	B	-	-	A	C	B	A	-	B	D	A	-	-	A	-	B	D	-	A	A	-	D	D	-	D	-	-	A
Acetic Acid, Glacia[1]	-	B	A	A	B	A	A	C	C	D	A	-	C	B	A	C	D	D	D	B	B	A	A	A	-	D	D	B	C	B	C	B
Acetic Acid 20%	-	B	A	-	-	A	A	-	C	-	-	A	B	-	A	A	-	D	-	-	A	A	-	A	-	A	C	-	C	-	-	B
Acetic Acid 80%	-	B	A	-	-	A	A	-	C	-	-	A	D	-	A	B	-	D	-	-	B	-	-	A	-	A	C	-	D	-	-	B
Acetic Acid	-	B	A	B	B	A	A	C	C	D	C	B	A	B	A	A	D	D	C	B	A	A	A	A	-	C	C	-	C	B	C	A
Acetic Anhydride	B	A	A	B	B	A	A	C	D	B	D	D	D	D	A	D	D	D	D	A	A	A	A	A	-	D	A	C	B	B	C	A
Acetone[6]	A	A	A	B	A	A	A	A	A	A	A	D	D	D	A	D	B	A	D	C	B	A	A	A	A	D	D	B	C	A	D	B
Acetyl Chloride	-	C	A	-	-	-	-	D	-	-	-	-	-	-	-	A	-	-	-	-	-	-	A	-	-	A	-	-	-	-	A	A
Acetylene[2]	A	A	A	A	A	B	-	B	-	A	A	-	B	-	-	-	A	A	-	-	D	A	A	A	-	A	A	C	B	A	C	A
Acrylonitrile	A	A	C	-	B	B	B	A	-	C	-	-	-	-	-	-	B	-	D	-	B	A	A	A	-	C	D	-	D	D	-	A
Alcohols																																
Amyl	A	A	A	-	C	A	A	A	B	C	C	A	A	B	A	C	A	A	B	B	B	A	A	A	-	A	A	D	A	A	C	A
Benzyl	-	A	A	-	B	A	A	A	C	-	-	-	D	B	-	A	A	A	D	D	A	-	A	A	-	A	D	-	B	B	B	D	A
Butyl	A	A	A	-	B	B	A	B	C	C	C	A	A	B	A	A	A	A	-	B	B	A	A	A	-	A	A	D	A	A	A	A
Diacetone[2]	-	A	A	-	A	A	A	A	C	-	A	-	D	-	-	A	A	A	-	-	D	-	A	A	-	D	D	-	D	A	D	A
Ethyl	-	A	A	A	B	A	A	A	C	A	A	-	A	C	-	A	B	A	B	B	A	-	A	A	A	A	A	A	A	B	A	B	A
Hexyl	-	A	A	-	A	A	A	A	C	-	A	-	-	-	-	A	A	A	-	-	-	A	A	A	-	A	A	D	B	A	A	A
Isobutyl	-	A	A	-	B	A	A	A	C	-	A	-	-	-	-	A	A	A	B	-	-	A	A	A	-	A	C	B	A	A	A	A
Isopropyl	-	A	A	-	B	A	A	A	C	C	A	-	-	-	-	A	A	A	-	-	-	A	A	A	-	A	C	C	B	A	A	A
Methyl[6]	-	A	A	A	B	A	A	A	C	A	A	-	B	-	A	A	C	A	D	B	A	-	A	A	A	C	B	-	A	A	A	A
Octyl	-	A	A	-	A	A	A	A	C	-	A	-	-	-	-	A	A	A	-	-	-	A	A	A	-	A	A	B	-	B	A	C	A
Propyl	-	A	A	-	A	A	A	A	-	-	A	B	A	-	A	A	A	A	-	-	A	-	A	A	-	A	A	B	A	A	A	A

A—No effect—Excellent
B—Minor effect—Good
C—Moderate effect—Fair
D—Severe effect-Not Recommended

1. P.V.C.—Satisfactory to 72° F.
2. Polypropylene—Satisfactory to 72° F.
3. Polypropylene—Satisfactory to 120° F.
4. Buna-N—Satisfactory for "O" Rings
5. Polyacetal—Satisfactory to 72° F.
6. Ceramag—Satisfactory to 72° F.

Ceramagnet "A" is generically known as Barium Ferrite

Courtesy of Little Giant Pump Company.

CHEMICAL RESISTANCE CHART Cont'd.

	302 Stainless Steel	304 Stainless Steel	316 Stainless Steel	440 Stainless Steel	Aluminum	TITANIUM	HASTELLOY C	Cast Bronze	Brass	Cast Iron	Carbon Steel	KYNAR	PVC (Type 1)	Tygon (E-3606)	Teflon	Noryl	Polyacetal	Nylon	Cycolac (ABS)	Polyethylene	POLYPROPYLENE	RYTON	CARBON	CERAMIC	CERAMAGNET "A"	VITON	BUNA N (NITRILE)	Silicon	Neoprene	Ethylene Propylene (EPM)	Rubber (Natural)	Epoxy
Aluminum Chloride 20%	-	D	C	D	B	A	A	D	-	D	A	-	A	B	-	A	C	A	-	B	A	A	A	A	-	A	A	-	A	A	A	A
Aluminum Chloride	C	D	C	-	D	C	A	C	-	D	B	A	A	A	A	A	-	D	-	-	A	A	A	A	-	A	A	C	A	-	-	A
Aluminum Flouride	-	D	C	D	-	D	B	-	-	-	A	A	A	-	A	A	C	D	-	B	A	-	A	-	-	A	A	C	A	-	C	A
Aluminum Hydroxide6	-	A	A	A	A	-	-	A	-	D	A	-	A	-	A	A	B	A	-	A	-	A	A	A	A	A	-	A	-	A	A	A
Alum Potassium Sulfate (Alum), 10%	-	A	-	A	-	B	-	-	-	D	A	-	A	-	-	A	-	A	-	-	A	-	A	A	-	A	-	-	A	-	A	A
Alum Potassium Sulfate (Alum), 100%	-	D	A	B	B	-	B	C	-	A	-	A	B	A	A	C	D	-	B	A	-	A	A	A	-	A	-	A	-	A	A	A
Aluminum Sulfate	-	C	C	A	A	A	A	C	C	D	A	A	A	B	A	A	C	-	B	A	A	A	A	-	A	A	-	A	A	A	A	A
Amines	A	A	A	-	A	B	A	B	-	A	B	-	C	A	A	B	D	A	-	-	-	A	A	-	D	D	C	B	B	C	A	
Ammonia 10%	-	-	A	-	-	A	A	-	-	-	D	A	-	A	A	-	A	-	-	A	A	-	A	-	-	A	D	-	A	-	-	B
Ammonia, Anhydrous	A	B	A	A	B	B	A	D	-	D	B	D	A	B	A	A	D	A	-	B	A	B	C	A	-	D	B	B	A	A	D	A
Ammonia, Liquids	-	A	A	A	D	-	B	D	-	-	-	A	B	A	A	D	-	-	D	A	-	A	A	-	D	B	B	A	A	D	A	
Ammonia, Nitrate	-	A	A	A	C	-	-	-	D	-	-	A	B	B	-	A	C	-	-	-	A	A	-	-	A	-	C	-	-	-	A	
Ammonium Bifluoride	-	C	A	-	D	-	B	-	-	-	-	A	-	-	A	D	-	-	-	A	-	A	A	-	-	A	-	-	-	A		
Ammonium Carbonate	B	A	A	A	C	A	B	B	-	C	B	-	A	B	A	A	D	A	-	-	A	-	A	A	-	B	D	C	A	A	-	A
Ammonium Casenite	-	-	A	-	-	-	-	-	-	-	-	-	A	D	-	-	-	-	-	-	-	A	-	-	-	A	-	A				A
Ammonium Chloride	C	A	C	A	C	D	A	D	C	D	D	A	A	B	A	A	B	A	-	B	A	A	A	A	-	A	A	C	A	A	A	A
Ammonium Hydroxide	A	A	A	C	A	A	D	D	A	C	-	A	B	A	A	D	A	B	B	A	A	A	A	-	B	B	B	A	A	C	A	
Ammonium Nitrate	A	A	A	B	A	A	D	D	A	D	-	A	B	A	A	C	D	-	B	A	A	A	A	-	D	A	C	A	A	A	A	
Ammonium Oxalate	-	A	A	A	-	-	A	-	-	A	-	-	-	-	B	-	-	-	-	A	-	-	-	A	-	A	-	-	A			
Ammonium Persulfate	-	A	A	A	C	C	A	A	-	D	A	D	A	-	A	A	D	D	-	-	A	-	A	A	-	C	A	-	A	A	A	A
Ammonium Phosphate, Dibasic	B	A	A	A	B	A	A	C	-	-	D	-	A	-	A	A	B	A	-	B	A	-	A	A	-	A	A	B	A	A	A	A
Ammonium Phosphate, Monobasic	-	A	A	A	B	A	A	D	-	-	A	-	A	A	A	A	B	A	-	B	A	-	A	A	-	A	A	B	A	A	A	A
Ammonium Phosphate, Tribasic	B	A	A	A	B	A	A	C	-	C	D	-	A	-	A	A	B	A	-	B	A	-	A	A	-	A	A	B	A	A	A	A
Ammonium Sulfate	C	D	B	A	B	A	A	B	C	C	C	A	A	D	A	A	B	D	-	B	A	A	A	A	-	D	A	B	A	A	A	A
Ammonium Thio-Sulfate	-	-	A	-	-	A	-	-	D	A	-	-	-	-	-	B	-	-	-	A	A	-	-	A	-	A	-	-	A			A
Amyl-Acetate	B	A	A	C	B	A	A	C	-	-	C	C	D	D	A	D	A	B	-	D	D	A	A	A	-	D	D	D	D	A	D	A
Amyl Alcohol	-	A	A	-	B	A	A	A	-	-	A	A	A	B	A	C	A	A	-	B	A	-	A	A	-	B	B	B	D	A	A	C	A
Amyl Chloride	-	C	B	-	D	-	A	A	-	-	A	A	D	C	A	D	A	C	-	D	D	-	A	A	-	A	D	-	D	D	D	A
Aniline	B	A	A	A	C	A	B	C	-	-	C	C	D	D	A	D	D	C	D	C	B	A	A	A	-	C	D	C	D	B	D	A
Anti-Freeze	-	A	A	-	A	-	A	B	B	B	C	-	A	B	A	A	A	A	B	B	A	A	A	A	A	A	A	C	A	A	A	A
Antimony Trichloride	-	D	D	-	D	C	A	-	-	-	-	-	A	A	A	-	-	D	-	A	-	-	-	A	-	A	-	-	C	-	A	A
Aqua Regia (80%, HCl, 20%, HNO)	-	D	D	-	D	A	D	D	-	-	-	C	D	D	A	D	D	D	-	D	C	-	-	D	-	C	D	C	D	D	D	D
Arochlor 1248	-	-	-	-	-	-	-	-	-	A	-	-	-	D	-	-	-	-	-	A	-	-	A	D	-	D	B	D	A			
Aromatic Hydrocarbons	-	-	A	-	A	-	-	A	-	A	A	-	D	-	-	D	A	-	C	-	A	-	-	A	D	-	D	D	D	A		
Arsenic Acid	B	A	A	-	D	-	-	D	B	D	D	A	A	B	A	A	D	A	-	B	A	-	A	A	-	A	A	-	A	-	C	A
Asphalt	-	B	A	-	C	-	-	A	-	C	-	-	A	-	-	-	A	A	-	-	A	A	-	A	A	A	B	C	B	D	D	A
Barium Carbonate	B	A	A	A	B	A	A	B	-	B	B	-	A	A	A	A	A	A	-	B	A	-	A	A	A	A	A	-	A	-	A	A
Barium Chloride	C	D	A	A	D	A	A	B	-	-	C	A	A	B	A	A	A	B	-	B	A	-	A	A	-	A	A	B	A	A	A	A
Barium Cyanide	-	-	A	-	-	-	C	-	-	A	-	-	-	-	-	B	-	B	-	-	A	-	-	-	A	-	A	A	-	A	A	
Barium Hydroxide	B	C	A	A	D	B	B	B	-	C	C	A	A	-	A	A	D	A	-	B	A	-	A	A	-	A	A	B	A	A	A	A
Barium Nitrate	-	A	A	-	-	A	-	D	-	A	A	-	B	-	-	A	A	-	-	-	-	A	A	-	-	A	A	-	A	-	-	B
Barium Sulfate	B	A	A	A	D	A	A	C	-	C	C	A	A	-	A	A	A	A	-	B	A	A	A	A	B	-	A	A	D	A	A	-
Barium Sulfide	B	A	A	-	D	B	-	C	-	C	C	-	A	A	A	A	A	A	-	A	A	-	A	A	-	A	C	A	A	A	A	A
Beer2	A	A	A	-	A	A	A	A	B	D	D	A	A	-	A	A	B	D	B	B	D	-	A	A	-	A	D	C	A	A	A	A

A—No effect—Excellent
B—Minor effect—Good
C—Moderate effect—Fair
D—Severe effect—Not Recommended

1. P.V.C.—Satisfactory to 72° F.
2. Polypropylene—Satisfactory to 72° F.
3. Polypropylene—Satisfactory to 120° F.
4. Buna-N—Satisfactory for "O" Rings
5. Polyacetal—Satisfactory to 72° F.
6. Ceramag—Satisfactory to 72° F.

	302 Stainless Steel	304 Stainless Steel	316 Stainless Steel	440 Stainless Steel	Aluminum	TITANIUM	HASTELLOY C	Cast Bronze	Brass	Cast Iron	Carbon Steel	KYNAR	PVC (Type 1)	Tygon (E-3606)	Teflon	Noryl	Polyacetal	Nylon	Cycolac (ABS)	Polyethylene	POLYPROPYLENE	RYTON	CARBON	CERAMIC	CERAMAGNET "A"	VITON	BUNA N (NITRILE)	Silicon	Neoprene	Ethylene Propylene (EPM)	Rubber (Natural)	Epoxy
Beet Sugar Liquids	A	A	A	-	A	-	-	A	B	A	-	-	A	-	A	A	B	A	B	-	A	-	A	A	-	A	A	-	A	-	B	A	A
Benzaldehyde[3]	A	A	A	-	B	A	A	A	-	B	A	C	D	D	A	D	A	C	D	D	D	A	A	A	-	D	D	B	D	A	D	A
Benzene[2]	B	A	A	A	B	A	B	B	A	B	C	B	D	C	A	D	A	A	D	D	D	A	A	A	A	A	D	-	D	D	D	A
Benzoic Acid[2]	B	A	A	A	B	A	A	B	-	D	-	A	A	B	A	A	B	D	-	B	D	-	A	B	-	A	D	-	D	D	D	A
Benzol	-	A	A	-	B	A	A	B	A	-	-	-	D	-	A	D	A	A	-	-	A	-	A	A	A	D	D	-	D	-	-	A
Borax (Sodium Borate)	-	A	A	A	C	B	A	A	B	A	C	A	A	A	A	A	A	-	B	A	A	A	A	A	A	A	B	C	A	A	C	A
Boric Acid	B	A	A	A	B	A	A	B	C	D	-	A	A	B	A	A	A	-	B	A	-	A	A	A	A	A	-	A	A	A	A	A
Brewery Slop	-	-	A	-	-	-	A	-	A	-	-	-	-	-	-	A	-	-	-	-	A	A	-	A	A	-	A	-	-	-	A	A
Bromine[2] (wet)	D	D	D	D	D	A	A	C	-	D	D	A	B	B	A	D	D	D	D	D	D	D	D	A	D	A	D	D	D	D	D	C
Butadiene	A	A	A	-	A	-	-	C	A	C	C	A	A	-	A	-	A	A	-	-	B	A	A	-	A	A	-	-	B	A	-	A
Butane[2][1]	A	A	A	-	A	-	-	A	A	C	C	A	A	C	A	D	A	A	B	C	D	A	A	A	-	A	A	D	B	D	D	A
Butanol	-	A	A	-	A	-	A	A	-	-	-	-	-	-	-	A	-	-	-	-	-	-	-	-	-	-	-	-	-	-	-	-
Butter	-	B	A	-	A	-	-	D	-	D	-	-	-	B	-	B	A	-	B	-	-	-	A	A	-	A	A	-	-	B	A	D	A
Buttermilk	A	A	A	A	A	-	-	D	-	D	-	-	-	B	A	A	A	B	-	-	-	A	A	-	A	A	-	-	A	-	D	A
Butylene	A	B	A	-	A	-	-	A	A	A	A	-	B	-	A	-	A	-	-	-	A	A	A	-	A	B	-	-	-	D	D	A
Butyl Acetate[1]	-	-	C	-	A	-	A	A	-	-	A	C	D	D	A	D	A	-	-	C	D	A	A	A	-	D	B	D	D	B	D	A
Butyric Acid[1]	B	B	A	A	B	A	A	C	-	D	-	A	B	-	A	A	C	D	D	-	A	-	A	D	-	D	D	-	D	B	-	A
Calcium Bisulfate	C	D	A	-	D	-	-	D	D	D	-	-	A	A	A	-	-	A	-	-	-	-	-	-	-	A	A	C	C	-	A	A
Calcium Bisulfide	-	-	B	-	C	A	A	C	-	-	-	-	A	-	A	A	D	A	-	B	A	-	A	A	-	-	A	A	-	A	D	-	A
Calcium Bisulfite	-	B	A	-	C	A	A	C	-	-	-	-	A	A	-	A	-	-	A	-	-	A	-	-	A	A	-	A	-	A	-	-
Calcium Carbonate	B	A	A	A	C	A	A	C	-	D	-	A	A	A	A	A	A	-	B	A	-	A	A	-	A	A	-	A	-	A	A	A
Calcium Chlorate	-	B	A	-	-	B	B	C	-	-	-	-	A	A	A	-	A	-	A	-	-	A	-	-	A	-	-	A	-	A	A	A
Calcium Chloride	C	A	D	C	C	A	A	B	-	C	-	A	A	A	A	D	A	B	B	A	A	A	A	B	A	A	B	A	A	B	D	A	A
Calcium Hydroxide	B	A	A	-	C	A	A	B	-	C	-	A	A	A	A	A	B	A	-	B	A	-	A	A	A	A	C	A	A	A	A	A
Calcium Hypochlorite	D	D	C	C	C	A	B	D	-	C	-	A	-	D	D	-	A	A	D	D	-	A	A	A	B	C	D	A	C	A	-	A
Calcium Sulfate	B	A	A	A	B	A	B	B	-	-	-	-	A	A	A	A	A	C	B	A	A	A	A	-	A	A	-	A	-	D	-	C	A
Calgon	-	A	A	-	-	-	-	C	-	D	-	-	-	-	-	-	A	B	-	-	A	-	-	-	-	-	-	-	-	-	-	A
Cane Juice[2]	-	A	A	-	B	-	-	B	C	A	-	-	A	-	-	A	A	-	-	-	D	-	A	A	-	-	A	-	A	-	A	A
Carbolic Acid (See Phenol)	-	-	-	-	-	-	-	-	-	-	-	-	-	-	-	-	-	-	-	-	-	-	-	-	-	-	-	-	-	-	-	-
Carbon Bisulfide[2]	B	A	A	A	A	-	-	C	-	B	-	-	D	D	-	A	A	-	-	D	-	A	A	A	A	D	-	D	D	D	D	A
Carbon Dioxide (wet)	-	A	A	-	C	-	A	C	C	C	-	-	-	A	-	-	-	A	-	-	-	-	A	A	-	A	A	-	A	A	A	A
Carbon Disulfide[2]	-	B	A	-	C	-	-	C	C	B	C	-	D	C	A	D	A	A	-	-	D	D	A	A	B	-	A	D	-	D	D	D	A
Carbon Monoxide	-	A	A	-	A	-	-	-	-	-	-	-	A	-	-	B	A	A	-	B	A	-	A	A	-	A	A	B	B	B	A	C	A
Carbon Tetrachloride[2][1]	B	B	B	A	C	A	A	C	A	C	D	A	C	C	A	D	A	A	D	D	D	C	A	A	A	A	C	C	D	-	D	C
Carbonated Water	B	A	A	A	A	-	-	B	-	D	-	-	A	A	-	A	A	-	A	-	-	A	A	-	A	A	-	A	A	-	A	A
Carbonic Acid	B	A	B	A	A	-	A	B	-	D	-	A	A	-	A	A	B	A	-	A	A	-	A	B	B	A	A	A	A	A	A	A
Catsup	-	A	A	A	D	-	-	C	-	D	-	-	A	-	-	A	B	A	B	-	A	-	A	A	-	A	A	-	C	-	-	A
Chloracetic Acid[2]	D	D	D	D	C	A	A	D	-	D	-	D	A	D	A	-	D	D	-	D	D	-	A	A	-	D	D	-	D	B	D	B
Chloric Acid	-	D	D	-	-	-	-	-	-	-	-	-	D	-	A	-	-	-	-	-	-	-	-	-	-	D	-	D	-	-	-	D
Chlorinated Glue	-	A	A	-	D	-	-	C	-	D	-	-	-	C	-	C	D	-	-	-	-	-	A	A	C	-	D	B	D	A
Chlorine, Anhydrous Liquid	-	D	D	D	D	D	A	D	-	C	-	-	D	B	A	A	D	D	-	D	D	C	A	D	-	A	D	-	D	B	D	A
Chlorine (dry)	B	A	A	-	D	D	A	A	B	A	-	-	-	A	-	-	-	-	-	-	-	-	C	A	A	-	D	-	-	D	-	D	D
Chlorine Water	D	-	D	-	D	A	B	D	D	D	-	A	A	-	A	C	-	D	-	-	D	C	C	A	-	A	D	C	D	-	-	-
Chlorobenzene (Mono)	A	A	A	-	B	-	A	B	-	B	C	A	D	D	A	D	A	A	D	D	D	A	A	A	-	A	D	-	D	D	D	A

A—No effect—Excellent
B—Minor effect—Good
C—Moderate effect—Fair
D—Severe effect—Not Recommended

1. P.V.C.—Satisfactory to 72° F.
2. Polypropylene—Satisfactory to 72° F.
3. Polypropylene—Satisfactory to 120° F.
4. Buna-N—Satisfactory for "O" Rings
5. Polyacetal—Satisfactory to 72° F.
6. Ceramag—Satisfactory to 72° F.

CHEMICAL RESISTANCE CHART Cont'd.

	302 Stainless Steel	304 Stainless Steel	316 Stainless Steel	440 Stainless Steel	Aluminum	TITANIUM	HASTELLOY C	Cast Bronze	Brass	Cast Iron	Carbon Steel	KYNAR	PVC (Type 1)	Tygon (E-3606)	Teflon	Noryl	Polyacetal	Nylon	Cycolac (ABS)	Polyethylene	POLYPROPYLENE	RYTON	CARBON	CERAMIC	CERAMAGNET "A"	VITON	BUNA N (NITRILE)	Silicon	Neoprene	Ethylene Propylene (EPM)	Rubber (Natural)	Epoxy
Chloroform	A	A	A	A	D	A	A	B	-	D	C	C	C	D	C	A	D	A	C	D	D	D	A	A	A	A	A	D	D	D	D	A
Chlorosulfonic Acid[1]	D	D	-	D	D	A	B	D	-	-	D	D	C	C	A	D	D	D	-	D	D	D	-	C	-	D	D	D	D	D	D	C
Chlorox (Bleach)	-	A	A	-	C	-	A	A	-	D	C	-	A	B	A	A	D	D	B	-	D	C	A	A	-	A	C	-	B	B	D	A
Chocolate Syrup	-	A	A	-	A	-	-	D	-	-	-	-	A	A	A	-	A	-	A	-	A	A	-	A	A	-	A	-	D	A		
Chromic Acid 5%	-	A	A	B	C	A	A	D	D	D	-	-	A	B	-	C	D	D	B	B	A	A	D	C	-	A	D	C	D	A	B	B
Chromic Acid 10%	-	B	-	-	-	A	A	-	D	-	-	A	A	-	A	A	-	D	-	-	A	-	A	-	A	D	-	D	-	-	-	C
Chromic Acid 30%	-	B	-	-	-	A	A	-	D	-	-	B	A	-	A	D	-	D	-	-	A	-	A	-	A	D	-	D	-	-	-	D
Chromic Acid 50%	C	B	B	-	C	A	A	D	D	D	-	C	B	B	A	D	D	D	C	C	B	B	B	D	A	-	A	D	-	D	A	D
Cider	-	A	A	A	B	-	-	A	-	D	-	-	-	A	B	-	-	B	-	-	A	A	-	A	A	-	A	-	A	-	-	A
Citric Acid	-	A	A	A	C	A	A	D	C	D	—	A	A	-	A	A	B	C	C	B	B	-	A	A	B	A	D	C	A	A	A	A
Citric Oils	-	A	A	-	C	-	-	B	-	-	-	-	A	B	-	-	-	A	-	A	A	-	A	A	C	D	-	-	A			
Coffee	A	A	A	A	A	-	-	B	-	C	-	-	-	-	A	A	A	A	-	-	A	A	-	A	A	-	A	-	A	A		
Copper Chloride	C	D	D	B	D	A	A	D	-	D	-	A	A	B	A	A	B	D	-	B	A	A	-	A	-	A	A	-	A	A	A	A
Copper Cyanide	-	A	A	A	D	A	A	C	-	D	-	A	A	-	A	A	B	A	-	B	A	A	A	A	-	B	B	-	A	A	A	C
Copper Floborate	-	D	D	-	D	-	B	D	-	D	-	A	-	A	-	B	-	-	A	-	A	-	-	A	B	-	A	-	A	A		
Copper Nitrate	B	A	A	B	D	A	A	D	-	-	-	A	A	-	A	A	B	D	-	B	A	A	-	A	A	-	A	-	A	-	-	A
Copper Sulfate (5% Solution)	-	A	A	A	D	A	A	D	D	D	-	-	A	A	B	D	-	B	A	A	A	A	-	A	A	C	A	-	C	A		
Copper Sulfate	B	B	-	-	-	A	A	C	D	-	A	A	A	A	-	C	-	-	A	-	-	A	-	A	B	B	-	A	A	-	A	
Cream	-	A	A	-	A	-	-	C	-	D	-	-	-	-	A	A	A	-	-	A	-	A	A	-	A	A	-	C	-	A		
Cresols[2]	-	A	A	-	B	-	-	D	C	-	-	D	D	-	-	D	-	D	D	C	A	A	A	-	D	D	D	D	D	D	A	
Cresylic Acid	B	A	A	-	C	A	B	C	-	-	-	B	B	D	A	-	D	D	-	C	-	-	A	A	-	A	D	-	D	D	D	A
Cyclohexane	-	A	-	-	A	A	-	A	-	-	A	-	-	D	-	D	A	-	-	D	A	A	A	-	A	A	D	D	D	D	D	A
Cyanic Acid	-	A	-	-	-	-	-	-	-	-	-	-	-	-	D	-	-	-	-	-	-	-	-	-	-	C	-	D	-	-	A	
Detergents	-	A	A	-	A	-	A	-	-	A	-	A	-	A	B	A	B	B	A	A	A	A	-	A	A	-	B	A	C	A		
Dichlorethane	-	A	A	-	-	-	A	-	-	-	-	D	D	A	-	-	A	-	D	-	-	-	-	-	-	B	-	-	D	-	D	A
Diesel Fuel	A	A	A	-	A	-	-	A	-	C	A	-	-	-	-	D	A	-	-	D	A	A	A	-	A	A	-	-	D	D	D	A
Diethylamine	A	A	-	-	A	-	-	A	-	-	-	D	-	A	B	D	-	-	-	C	-	A	A	-	D	B	-	B	B	B	C	A
Diethylene Gycol	-	A	-	-	-	-	A	-	-	-	-	-	A	A	A	B	B	-	-	A	A	-	A	A	C	A	A	A	A	A		
Diphenyl Oxide	-	A	-	-	-	-	A	-	-	-	-	-	-	A	-	-	-	A	-	-	A	A	-	A	D	-	D	D	D	A		
Dyes	-	A	A	-	B	-	-	C	-	-	-	-	A	A	-	-	-	A	A	-	-	-	A	-	-	C	-	-	A			
Epsom Salts (Magnesium Sulfate)	B	A	A	A	A	A	B	B	-	-	-	A	-	-	A	A	-	-	A	-	A	A	-	A	A	-	A	-	C	A		
Ethane	A	A	-	-	A	-	-	A	-	-	-	-	-	D	A	-	-	A	A	-	A	A	-	B	D	D	A					
Ethanolamine	-	A	A	-	-	-	-	-	-	C	-	-	-	D	-	-	-	A	A	A	-	D	B	C	B	-	C	A				
Ether[3]	A	A	A	A	A	-	B	B	A	-	B	-	D	C	-	D	A	C	-	-	-	A	A	A	C	D	-	D	C	D	A	
Ethyl Acetate[2]	-	A	A	-	B	-	B	B	-	-	C	D	D	D	A	D	A	A	D	C	C	A	A	A	-	D	D	C	D	B	D	A
Ethyl Chloride	-	A	A	A	B	A	B	B	-	C	D	A	D	D	A	D	A	A	-	D	D	A	A	A	-	A	D	D	C	A	A	A
Ethyl Sulfate	-	D	-	-	-	-	-	-	-	-	-	-	-	B	-	-	-	-	A	-	-	-	-	-	-	-	-	-	A			
Ethylene Chloride[2]	-	A	A	-	C	B	B	A	-	C	C	-	D	-	A	D	A	-	D	-	D	A	A	A	-	A	D	D	D	C	D	A
Ethylene Dichloride	-	A	A	-	D	A	B	C	-	-	C	-	D	D	A	D	A	A	-	D	A	A	C	A	-	A	D	D	D	C	D	A
Ethylene Glycol[4]	-	A	A	-	A	-	A	B	B	B	C	A	A	B	A	A	B	B	A	A	A	A	-	A	A	A	C	A	A	A	A	A
Ethylene Oxide	-	A	-	A	-	A	-	A	-	-	-	-	D	-	A	A	A	-	-	A	-	-	D	D	D	D	C	D	A			
Fatty Acids	-	A	A	-	B	A	A	C	-	D	-	A	A	B	A	B	A	A	-	B	A	-	A	A	-	A	C	C	B	C	C	A
Ferric Chloride	-	D	D	D	D	A	B	D	D	D	-	A	A	B	A	A	B	D	-	B	A	A	A	-	A	D	C	B	A	A	A	
Ferric Nitrate	-	A	A	A	D	A	A	D	-	-	-	A	A	-	A	A	B	D	-	B	A	A	A	-	A	A	D	A	A	A	A	A
Ferric Sulfate	-	A	C	A	D	A	A	D	D	D	-	A	A	B	A	A	B	A	C	-	A	A	C	A	-	A	B	C	A	-	A	A
Ferrous Chloride	-	D	D	-	D	A	B	C	-	D	-	A	A	B	A	A	B	D	-	B	A	A	A	A	-	A	B	C	A	-	A	A

A—No effect—Excellent
B—Minor effect—Good
C—Moderate effect—Fair
D—Severe effect—Not Recommended

1. P.V.C.—Satisfactory to 72° F.
2. Polypropylene—Satisfactory to 72° F.
3. Polypropylene—Satisfactory to 120° F.
4. Buna-N—Satisfactory for "O" Rings
5. Polyacetal—Satisfactory to 72° F.
6. Ceramag—Satisfactory to 72° F.

CHEMICAL RESISTANCE CHART Cont'd.

	302 Stainless Steel	304 Stainless Steel	316 Stainless Steel	440 Stainless Steel	Aluminum	TITANIUM	HASTELLOY C	Cast Bronze	Brass	Cast Iron	Carbon Steel	KYNAR	PVC (Type 1)	Tygon (E-3606)	Teflon	Noryl	Polyacetal	Nylon	Cycolac (ABS)	Polyethylene	POLYPROPYLENE	RYTON	CARBON	CERAMIC	CERAMAGNET "A"	VITON	BUNA N (NITRILE)	Silicon	Neoprene	Ethylene Propylene (EPM)	Rubber (Natural)	Epoxy
Ferrous Sulfate	B	A	C	-	D	A	B	C	-	D	D	A	A	B	A	A	B	D	-	B	A	A	A	A	-	A	B	-	A	-	A	A
Fluoboric Acid	-	D	B	-	-	D	A	-	-	D	-	A	A	B	A	B	B	C	-	B	A	-	A	D	-	A	B	-	A	-	-	A
Fluorine	D	D	D	-	D	D	A	D	-	D	D	-	C	-	C	-	-	D	-	C	-	D	-	-	-	-	-	-	-	-	-	D
Fluosilicic Acid	-	-	B	-	D	D	B	-	-	D	-	A	A	B	A	A	B	D	-	B	A	-	A	D	-	B	A	-	A	-	-	C
Formaldehyde 40%	-	-	A	-	-	A	A	-	-	-	-	B	B	-	A	A	-	D	-	-	A	A	-	A	-	D	B	B	A	-	-	A
Formaldehyde	A	A	A	-	A	A	B	A	B	D	A	-	A	B	A	D	A	A	-	B	A	A	A	A	-	D	C	B	D	B	C	A
Formic Acid⁶	C	A	B	B	D	C	A	C	C	D	D	A	D	B	A	A	D	D	-	B	A	A	A	A	B	B	D	C	D	A	C	B
Freon 11¹	A	-	A	-	B	-	-	B	-	C	B	-	B	D	A	D	A	A	-	C	-	A	A	A	A	A	C	D	D	D	D	A
Freon 12 (wet)²	-	-	D	-	B	-	-	B	-	-	-	-	B	D	A	D	A	A	B	C	-	A	A	A	A	D	D	D	B	B	B	D
Freon 22	-	-	A	-	B	-	-	B	-	-	-	D	D	-	B	A	A	-	-	A	A	A	A	A	D	D	D	A	A	A	A	A
Freon 113	-	-	A	-	B	-	-	B	-	-	-	C	D	-	-	A	A	-	-	A	A	A	A	C	A	D	A	-	D	-	-	A
Freon T.F.⁴	-	-	A	-	B	-	-	B	-	-	-	B	D	-	D	A	A	-	-	A	A	A	A	B	A	D	A	D	A	D	D	A
Fruit Juice	A	A	A	A	B	-	-	B	-	D	D	-	A	-	D	A	B	A	-	B	A	-	A	A	A	A	A	-	A	-	-	A
Fuel Oils	A	A	A	-	A	A	A	B	-	C	B	A	A	-	A	A	A	A	-	D	B	A	A	A	-	A	A	C	B	D	D	A
Furan Resin	-	A	A	-	A	-	-	A	-	A	A	-	-	-	A	-	A	-	-	-	-	A	-	A	-	A	D	-	D	-	D	A
Furfural¹	A	A	A	-	A	-	B	A	-	-	A	D	D	-	A	D	B	A	D	D	D	A	A	A	-	D	D	D	D	B	D	A
Gallic Acid	B	A	A	-	A	-	A	A	-	D	D	-	A	A	A	-	-	A	-	-	-	-	-	-	-	B	A	-	-	-	-	-
Gasoline¹⁴	A	A	A	A	A	D	A	A	-	A	A	A	C	-	A	D	A	A	D	D	C	A	A	A	A	A	A	D	D	C	D	A
Gelatin	A	A	A	A	A	-	A	A	C	D	D	-	A	-	A	A	A	A	-	A	-	A	A	A	A	-	A	A	-	A	A	A
Glucose	A	-	A	-	A	-	-	A	A	B	B	-	A	B	A	B	A	A	B	B	A	-	A	-	A	A	B	A	A	A	A	A
Glue P.V.A.¹	B	B	A	-	B	A	-	A	-	-	A	-	A	B	A	-	A	-	-	A	-	A	A	A	A	-	A	A	-	A	-	A
Glycerine	A	A	A	A	A	A	A	A	B	B	B	A	A	B	A	A	A	A	C	-	A	-	A	A	A	B	A	A	A	A	A	A
Cycolic Acid	-	-	-	-	-	A	-	-	-	-	-	-	A	-	A	C	-	-	B	A	A	A	-	-	A	-	-	-	A	-	-	-
Gold Monocyanide	-	-	A	-	-	-	A	-	D	-	-	-	-	-	-	-	-	-	-	-	-	-	-	-	-	-	-	-	-	-	-	-
Grape Juice	-	A	A	-	B	-	-	B	-	D	-	A	-	-	-	A	B	-	B	B	-	-	-	-	-	-	A	-	-	A	-	-
Grease⁴	A	A	A	-	A	-	-	B	-	A	A	-	-	A	-	A	A	-	-	-	A	-	A	A	-	A	A	-	D	-	-	A
Heptane¹	A	-	A	-	A	-	A	A	-	-	B	A	A	-	A	D	A	A	C	D	D	A	A	A	-	A	A	-	B	D	-	A
Hexane¹	A	A	A	-	A	-	A	B	-	-	B	A	C	-	A	D	A	A	D	-	C	A	A	A	-	A	A	B	B	D	D	A
Honey	-	A	A	-	A	-	-	A	-	A	-	-	A	-	A	A	A	B	-	A	-	A	A	-	A	A	-	A	A	-	A	-
Hydraulic Oils (Petroleum)¹	A	A	A	-	A	-	-	B	-	A	A	-	-	A	-	A	A	-	-	D	-	A	A	-	A	A	A	-	B	D	D	A
Hydraulic Oils (Synthetic)¹	-	A	A	-	A	-	-	A	-	A	-	-	-	-	A	A	-	-	-	D	-	A	A	-	A	C	D	-	-	-	-	A
Hydrazine	-	A	A	-	-	-	-	-	-	C	-	-	-	-	-	D	-	-	-	-	A	-	-	A	-	A	B	D	B	A	C	A
Hydrobromic Acid 20%	-	-	D	-	-	A	A	-	-	-	A	A	-	A	A	-	D	-	-	A	-	-	B	-	A	D	-	C	-	-	-	B
Hydrobromic Acid⁴	D	D	D	D	D	A	A	D	-	D	D	A	A	B	A	C	D	D	-	B	B	-	A	A	-	A	D	D	D	A	A	A
Hydrochloric Acid (Dry gas)	D	C	A	-	D	-	A	-	-	D	-	A	-	A	-	-	-	-	-	-	-	-	A	-	-	A	-	-	-	A	A	A
Hydrochloric Acid (20%)⁴	-	D	D	D	D	C	B	D	-	D	-	A	A	B	A	A	D	D	B	A	A	D	A	A	D	A	C	-	C	A	C	A
Hydrochloric Acid (37%)⁴	-	D	D	D	D	C	B	D	-	D	-	A	A	B	A	A	D	D	C	A	A	D	A	C	D	A	C	C	C	C	D	A
Hydrochloric Acid 100%	-	D	D	-	D	D	C	D	-	D	-	A	A	A	-	-	D	A	-	-	A	C	-	C	D	-	C	-	A	A	A	A
Hydrocyanic Acid	A	A	A	C	A	A	A	D	D	-	C	-	A	B	A	A	B	A	-	B	A	-	A	A	-	A	C	-	B	-	A	A
Hydrocyanic Acid (Gas 10%)	-	D	D	-	-	-	-	-	-	-	A	-	A	-	-	-	-	-	-	-	-	-	-	-	-	-	-	-	C	A	C	A
Hydrofluoric Acid (20%)¹	-	D	D	D	D	B	D	-	D	-	-	D	B	A	A	D	D	-	C	A	C	B	C	D	A	D	-	C	A	C	B	B
Hydrofluoric Acid (75%)¹²	-	C	D	-	D	D	C	D	-	D	-	A	C	B	A	D	D	D	-	C	B	C	D	D	D	A	D	D	D	C	C	C
Hydrofluoric Acid 100%	D	D	D	-	D	D	B	D	-	D	D	-	C	D	A	-	-	-	-	C	D	D	-	-	D	-	D	-	D	-	D	A
Hydrofluosilicic Acid (20%)	-	D	D	-	D	D	B	A	-	D	-	-	D	-	A	B	D	D	-	-	A	A	D	-	A	B	-	-	B	A	A	C
Hydrofluosilicic Acid	-	D	D	-	C	-	C	D	-	-	-	-	C	A	-	-	-	-	-	-	-	A	-	-	-	-	-	D	A	-	-	-

A—No effect—Excellent
B—Minor effect—Good
C—Moderate effect—Fair
D—Severe effect—Not Recommended

1. P.V.C.—Satisfactory to 72° F.
2. Polypropylene—Satisfactory to 72° F.
3. Polypropylene—Satisfactory to 120° F.
4. Buna-N—Satisfactory for "O" Rings
5. Polyacetal—Satisfactory to 72° F.
6. Ceramag—Satisfactory to 72° F.

CHEMICAL RESISTANCE CHART Cont'd.

	302 Stainless Steel	304 Stainless Steel	316 Stainless Steel	440 Stainless Steel	Aluminum	TITANIUM	HASTELLOY C	Cast Bronze	Brass	Cast Iron	Carbon Steel	KYNAR	PVC (Type 1)	Tygon (E-3606)	Teflon	Noryl	Polyacetal	Nylon	Cycolac (ABS)	Polyethylene	POLYPROPYLENE	RYTON	CARBON	CERAMIC	CERAMAGNET "A"	VITON	BUNA N (NITRILE)	Silicon	Neoprene	Ethylene Propylene (EPM)	Rubber (Natural)	Epoxy
Hydrogen Gas	A	A	A	-	A	-	-	A	-	B	B	A	A	-	A	-	-	A	-	-	-	-	-	-	-	A	-	-	-	-	-	A
Hydrogen Peroxide 10%	-	C	C	-	A	C	A	D	D	D	-	-	A	A	A	-	-	D	-	A	-	B	A	A	-	A	-	D	-	C	D	
Hydrogen Peroxide 30%	-	-	B	-	-	B	A	-	D	-	-	-	A	-	A	-	-	D	-	-	A	C	-	-	-	A	D	-	C	-	-	B
Hydrogen Peroxide	-	A	B	A	A	B	A	D	D	D	D	C	A	C	A	B	D	D	-	B	A	C	-	A	A	A	D	C	D	C	C	A
Hydrogen Sulfide, Aqueous Solution	-	D	A	C	C	A	A	D	C	D	-	A	A	B	A	A	D	D	-	B	A	A	A	A	A	D	C	-	B	A	D	A
Hydrogen Sulfide (dry)	A	C	A	-	D	-	A	D	C	B	B	-	A	-	A	-	-	D	-	-	A	-	A	-	D	-	-	-	-	-	A	A
Hydroxyacetic Acid (70%)	-	-	-	-	D	B	-	-	-	-	-	A	-	-	-	D	-	-	-	-	-	A	A	-	A	A	-	A	A	-	A
Ink	A	A	A	-	C	-	-	C	-	D	D	-	-	-	-	B	A	A	-	B	-	-	A	A	A	A	A	-	A	-	-	A
Iodine	-	D	D	D	D	A	B	D	-	D	-	-	D	B	A	A	C	D	D	D	D	-	D	A	-	A	B	-	D	B	D	A
Iodine (In Alcohol)	-	-	B	-	-	D	A	-	-	-	-	-	D	-	A	C	-	D	-	-	B	-	-	A	-	A	D	-	D	-	-	-
Iodoform	B	C	A	-	A	-	-	C	-	C	B	-	-	A	-	-	A	-	-	-	-	-	-	-	-	A	-	-	-	-	-	-
Isotane[2]	-	-	-	-	A	-	-	-	-	-	-	-	-	D	A	-	-	-	D	-	-	A	-	A	A	-	-	-	D	A
Isopropyl Acetate	-	-	B	-	C	-	-	-	-	-	-	-	-	-	A	-	-	-	-	-	-	A	A	-	D	D	-	D	B	D	A
Isopropyl Ether[2]	A	-	A	-	-	A	-	-	A	-	-	-	A	D	A	-	-	D	-	A	A	D	B	-	D	D	D	-
Jet Fuel (JP#, JP4, JP5)	A	A	A	-	A	-	-	A	-	A	A	A	A	-	A	D	A	A	-	-	D	A	A	A	-	A	A	D	D	D	D	A
Kerosene[2]	A	A	A	A	A	A	A	A	A	A	A	B	A	A	D	A	D	A	A	A	B	D	D	A	A	A	A	A	A	D	D	A	D	A
Ketones	A	A	A	-	B	A	A	A	-	A	A	D	D	D	A	D	B	A	-	D	D	A	C	A	-	D	D	-	D	D	C	C
Lacquers	A	A	A	-	A	-	-	A	C	C	C	-	-	D	-	C	A	A	-	A	-	A	A	-	D	D	-	D	-	D	A
Lacquer Thinners	-	-	A	-	-	A	A	-	C	-	-	-	C	-	A	D	-	A	-	B	-	-	A	-	-	D	-	D	A	-	-
Lactic Acid	A	A	B	C	C	A	A	D	-	D	D	C	A	B	A	A	B	C	-	B	A	A	A	A	-	B	B	-	A	B	A	A
Lard	B	A	A	A	A	-	-	A	-	A	C	-	A	-	-	A	A	C	-	A	-	A	A	-	A	A	C	B	-	D	A
Latex	-	A	A	-	A	-	-	A	-	-	-	-	A	A	A	-	B	-	-	A	-	A	A	-	C	A	-	A
Lead Acetate	B	A	A	-	D	A	A	C	-	-	D	-	A	B	A	A	A	A	-	B	A	-	A	A	-	D	B	-	D	A	A	A
Lead Sulfamate	-	-	-	-	-	-	-	-	-	-	-	-	A	-	-	A	-	-	A	-	-	A	B	C	A	D	C	A
Ligroin[3]	-	-	A	-	-	A	-	-	A	-	-	-	-	D	A	-	-	D	-	A	A	-	A	A	-	B	A	D	A
Lime	-	A	A	-	C	A	-	A	-	-	-	-	A	-	A	D	-	C	-	-	A	A	-	A	A	C	B	D	-	A
Lubricants	-	A	A	-	A	A	A	B	-	-	-	-	A	-	A	A	B	-	A	A	A	A	-	A	A	C	D	-	D	A
Magnesium Carbonate	-	A	A	A	-	-	B	-	-	-	-	-	A	-	-	-	-	-	B	A	-	A	-	-	A	-	-	A	A	-	A
Magnesium Chloride	B	B	B	A	D	A	A	B	C	D	C	-	A	B	A	A	A	A	-	B	A	-	A	A	-	A	A	-	A	A	A	A
Magnesium Hydroxide	A	A	A	-	D	A	A	C	B	B	B	A	A	-	A	A	A	A	-	B	A	A	A	A	-	A	B	-	B	-	C	A
Magnesium Nitrate	-	A	A	A	-	A	A	-	-	-	-	-	A	-	-	A	-	-	B	A	-	A	-	-	A	A	-	A	-	A
Magnesium Oxide	-	A	A	-	-	-	-	-	-	-	-	-	-	-	A	-	-	A	-	-	A	A	-	A	A	-	A
Magnesium Sulfate	B	B	A	-	B	A	B	B	B	C	B	-	A	B	A	A	A	A	-	B	A	A	A	A	-	A	A	-	A	D	C	A
Maleic Acid	C	A	A	A	B	A	A	C	-	-	B	-	A	B	A	A	C	A	-	-	C	-	A	A	-	A	D	-	A	D	D	A
Maleic Anhydride	-	-	-	-	-	-	A	-	-	-	-	-	-	-	-	-	-	-	C	-	-	A	A	-	A	D	-	D	-	D	A
Malic Acid	B	A	A	-	C	-	A	D	-	-	D	-	A	-	A	-	-	A	-	-	-	-	A	B	-	A	-	A	-	A	-
Mash	-	A	A	-	-	-	A	-	-	-	-	-	-	A	A	-	-	A	-	-	A	A	-	A	-	A	-	A	-	-	A
Mayonnaise	A	A	A	-	D	-	-	D	-	D	D	-	-	-	A	A	A	A	B	S	-	A	A	-	A	A	-	A	-	-	A
Melamine	-	D	D	-	-	-	-	D	-	-	-	-	-	-	D	-	-	-	-	D	-	-	A	A	-	C	-	-	-	-	A
Mercuric Chloride (Dilute Solution)	D	D	D	D	D	A	B	D	D	D	D	-	A	A	A	A	A	A	-	B	A	-	A	A	-	A	A	-	A	A	A	A
Mercuric Cyanide	A	A	A	-	D	A	-	D	-	-	D	-	A	A	A	A	A	A	-	B	A	-	A	A	-	A	A	-	A	A	A	A
Mercury	A	A	A	A	C	C	A	D	D	A	A	-	A	-	A	A	A	A	-	B	A	-	A	A	-	A	A	-	A	A	A	A
Methanol (See Alcohol Methyl)	-	-	-	-	-	-	-	-	-	-	-	-	-	-	-	-	-	-	-	-	-	-	-	-	-	-	-	-	-	-	-	-
Methyl Acetate	A	-	A	-	A	-	A	A	-	-	B	-	-	-	A	-	A	-	D	-	-	A	A	-	D	D	D	B	B	D	-
Methyl Acrylate	-	-	-	-	-	-	-	-	-	-	-	-	-	-	A	-	-	-	-	-	-	A	A	-	D	D	-	B	B	D	A

A—No effect—Excellent
B—Minor effect—Good
C—Moderate effect—Fair
D—Severe effect—Not Recommended

1. P.V.C.—Satisfactory to 72° F.
2. Polypropylene—Satisfactory to 72° F.
3. Polypropylene—Satisfactory to 120° F.
4. Buna-N—Satisfactory for "O" Rings
5. Polyacetal—Satisfactory to 72° F.
6. Ceramag—Satisfactory to 72° F.

	302 Stainless Steel	304 Stainless Steel	316 Stainless Steel	440 Stainless Steel	Aluminum	TITANIUM	HASTELLOY C	Cast Bronze	Brass	Cast Iron	Carbon Steel	KYNAR	PVC (Type 1)	Tygon (E-3606)	Teflon	Noryl	Polyacetal	Nylon	Cycolac (ABS)	Polyethylene	POLYPROPYLENE	RYTON	CARBON	CERAMIC	CERAMAGNET "A"	VITON	BUNA N (NITRILE)	Silicon	Neoprene	Ethylene Propylene (EPM)	Rubber (Natural)	Epoxy
Methyl Acetone	A	-	A	-	A	-	A	-	A	A	-	-	A	D	A	-	-	-	-	-	-	-	A	-	-	D	D	-	D	-	-	C
Methyl Alcohol 10%	A	-	A	-	C	-	A	C	-	-	B	-	A	-	A	-	-	A	-	-	-	-	-	-	-	B	-	-	-	A	A	
Methyl Bromide	-	-	-	-	-	-	-	-	-	-	-	-	A	-	-	D	-	-	A	A	-	A	B	-	-	D	D	D	B			
Methyl Butyl Ketone	-	-	A	-	A	-	-	-	-	-	-	-	D	B	-	-	-	A	A	-	D	D	C	D	A	D	B					
Methyl Cellosolve	-	-	-	-	A	-	-	A	-	-	-	-	C	B	-	-	-	A	-	A	A	-	D	D	-	D	B	D	C			
Methyl Chloride	-	A	A	-	D	A	A	A	-	-	-	A	D	-	A	D	A	A	-	D	D	-	A	A	-	A	D	D	D	C	D	A
Methyl Dichloride	-	-	-	-	-	-	-	-	-	-	-	-	D	A	-	-	-	A	A	-	A	D	-	D	D	D	A					
Methyl Ethyl Ketone	-	A	A	-	A	A	A	A	-	-	-	D	D	-	A	D	B	A	D	D	A	A	A	A	-	D	D	C	D	A	D	B
Methyl Isobutyl Ketone[2]	-	-	A	-	-	A	A	-	-	-	-	D	D	-	A	D	B	A	D	-	C	A	A	A	-	D	D	C	D	C	D	B
Methyl Isopropyl Ketone	-	-	A	-	-	-	-	-	-	-	-	-	D	B	A	-	-	-	-	-	A	A	-	D	D	B	D	B	D	B		
Methyl Methacrylate	-	-	-	-	-	-	-	-	-	-	-	-	-	A	-	-	-	-	-	-	A	A	-	D	D	-	D	D	D	A		
Methylamine	A	-	A	-	A	-	-	D	-	B	B	-	-	-	-	B	D	-	-	-	-	-	A	A	-	-	B	-	-	-	-	A
Methylene Chloride	A	A	A	-	A	A	A	A	C	-	B	D	D	-	A	D	A	D	-	D	D	-	A	A	-	D	D	-	D	D	D	A
Milk	A	A	A	A	A	-	-	C	C	D	D	-	A	-	-	A	A	A	B	B	A	-	A	A	A	A	A	B	A	A	A	A
Molasses	A	A	A	A	A	-	-	A	B	A	A	-	A	-	-	B	A	A	-	B	A	-	A	A	A	A	A	-	A	-	-	A
Mustard	A	A	A	A	B	-	-	B	-	C	B	-	A	-	-	B	B	A	B	-	A	-	A	A	-	A	B	C	C	-	-	A
Naptha	A	A	A	A	A	A	A	B	-	B	B	A	A	C	A	D	A	D	A	A	C	D	A	A	A	A	-	A	B	D	D	D	D	A
Napthalene	B	A	B	-	B	A	A	C	-	B	A	A	D	-	A	D	A	-	-	D	B	A	A	A	-	B	D	-	D	D	D	A
Nickel Chloride	-	A	B	-	D	A	A	D	-	D	-	A	A	B	A	A	B	A	-	B	A	-	A	A	-	A	A	-	A	A	A	A
Nickel Sulfate	B	A	B	-	D	A	B	C	C	C	D	D	A	A	A	A	A	B	A	-	B	A	-	A	A	-	A	A	-	A	A	C	A
Nitric Acid (10% Solution)	A	A	A	D	A	A	D	-	D	D	A	A	B	A	A	D	D	C	B	A	D	C	B	D	A	D	-	D	B	D	A		
Nitric Acid (20% Solution)	-	A	A	A	D	A	A	D	-	D	-	B	A	B	A	A	D	D	D	B	A	C	D	C	D	A	D	-	D	D	D	B
Nitric Acid (50% Solution)	-	A	A	A	D	A	A	D	-	D	-	B	A	B	A	A	D	D	D	C	D	C	D	A	-	A	D	-	D	D	D	D
Nitric Acid (Concentrated Solution)	-	D	B	A	B	A	B	D	D	D	-	-	D	C	A	D	D	D	D	D	C	D	A	C	B	D	-	D	D	D	D
Nitrobenzene[2]	B	A	B	-	C	A	B	D	-	B	B	D	D	D	A	D	B	C	D	D	C	B	A	A	-	D	D	D	D	D	D	B
Oils																																
Aniline	-	A	A	-	C	A	D	A	-	-	D	-	A	D	D	C	D	-	A	-	A	A	-	A	D	-	D	B	D	A		
Anise	-	A	A	-	-	-	-	-	-	-	-	-	A	-	-	-	-	A	A	-	-	-	-	D	-	-	A					
Bay	-	A	A	-	-	-	-	-	-	-	-	-	A	-	-	-	-	A	A	-	-	-	-	D	-	-	A					
Bone	-	A	A	-	-	-	-	A	-	-	-	-	A	-	-	-	-	A	A	-	A	A	-	D	-	-	A					
Castor	-	A	A	-	A	-	A	-	A	-	-	-	A	-	-	A	-	-	A	A	A	A	-	A	A	-	A	B	A	A		
Cinnamon	-	A	A	-	-	-	-	-	-	-	-	A	-	-	A	-	-	A	A	-	A	A	-	D	-	-	D	-	-	A		
Citric	-	A	A	-	-	-	-	D	-	D	-	-	-	A	A	-	A	A	-	A	A	-	A	A	-	A	A	-	-	-	A	
Clove	-	A	A	-	-	-	-	-	-	-	-	-	A	A	-	B	A	-	A	A	-	A	-	-	-	A						
Coconut	-	A	A	-	B	-	A	-	A	-	-	-	A	A	-	A	A	A	A	-	A	A	A	A	D							
Cod Liver	-	A	A	-	B	-	-	-	-	-	-	A	A	C	-	A	A	-	A	A	-	A	A	B	A	D	A					
Corn	-	A	A	A	B	-	-	B	-	A	-	-	-	-	A	A	C	-	A	A	-	A	A	-	D	C	D	A				
Cotton Seed	B	A	A	A	B	-	-	B	-	A	C	-	A	-	A	A	A	C	-	A	A	A	A	A	A	-	D	C	D	A		
Cresote[2]	-	A	A	-	A	-	-	-	-	-	-	-	D	-	-	D	-	A	A	-	A	A	B	D	D	A						
Diesel Fuel (2D, 3D, 4D, 5D)	-	A	A	-	A	-	-	A	-	-	-	-	-	-	D	A	A	-	A	A	A	A	-	A	A	-	D	D	D	A		
Fuel (1, 2, 3, 5A, 5B, 6)	-	A	A	-	A	A	A	A	-	-	-	A	-	A	D	A	-	-	-	B	-	A	A	-	A	B	-	D	D	D	A	

A—No effect—Excellent
B—Minor effect—Good
C—Moderate effect—Fair
D—Severe effect—Not Recommended

1. P.V.C.—Satisfactory to 72° F.
2. Polypropylene—Satisfactory to 72° F.
3. Polypropylene—Satisfactory to 120° F.
4. Buna-N—Satisfactory for "O" Rings
5. Polyacetal—Satisfactory to 72° F.
6. Ceramag—Satisfactory to 72° F.

	302 Stainless Steel	304 Stainless Steel	316 Stainless Steel	440 Stainless Steel	Aluminum	TITANIUM	HASTELLOY C	Cast Bronze	Brass	Cast Iron	Carbon Steel	KYNAR	PVC (Type 1)	Tygon (E-3606)	Teflon	Noryl	Polyacetal	Nylon	Cycolac (ABS)	Polyethylene	POLYPROPYLENE	RYTON	CARBON	CERAMIC	CERAMAGNET "A"	VITON	BUNA N (NITRILE)	Silicon	Neoprene	Ethylene Propylene (EPM)	Rubber (Natural)	Epoxy
Oils (Cont.)																																
Ginger	-	A	A	-	-	-	-	-	-	-	-	-	-	-	-	-	A	-	-	-	-	A	A	-	A	A	-	A	A	-	-	A
Hydraulic (See Hydraulic)	-							-		-	-																		-		-	
Lemon	-	A	A	-	-	-	-	-	-	-	-	-	-	-	-	-	A	-	-	D	-	A	A	-	A	-	-	D	-	-	-	A
Linseed	-	A	A	A	A	-	-	A	-	A	-	-	A	B	-	-	A	A	C	-	A	-	A	A	A	A	A	-	D	D	D	A
Mineral	A	A	A	A	A	-	-	A	-	A	B	-	A	-	-	B	A	A	-	-	B	A	A	A	A	A	A	-	B	D	D	A
Olive	A	A	A	-	A	-	-	B	-	A	B	-	A	-	A	-	A	A	-	-	A	-	A	A	A	A	C	B	-	D	-	A
Orange	-	A	A	-	-	-	-	-	-	-	-	-	-	-	-	-	A	-	-	-	-	A	A	-	A	A	-	D	-	-	-	A
Palm	-	A	A	-	A	-	-	B	-	-	-	-	A	-	-	-	A	A	-	-	A	-	A	A	-	A	A	-	D	-	-	A
Peanut[3]	-	A	A	A	-	-	A	-	A	-	-	-	A	-	-	-	A	-	-	D	-	A	A	-	A	A	-	D	-	D	-	A
Peppermint[2]	-	A	A	-	-	-	A	-	-	-	-	-	-	-	-	-	A	-	-	D	-	A	A	-	A	D	-	D	-	-	-	A
Pine	A	A	A	-	A	-	-	D	-	C	B	-	A	-	A	-	A	-	-	-	A	-	A	A	-	A	A	-	D	-	D	A
Rape Seed	-	A	A	-	A	-	-	A	-	-	-	-	A	-	-	-	A	A	-	-	A	-	A	A	-	A	B	-	D	-	D	A
Rosin	-	A	A	-	A	-	-	-	-	-	-	-	-	-	-	-	A	A	-	-	A	-	A	A	-	A	A	-	-	-	-	A
Sesame Seed	-	A	A	-	A	-	-	A	-	A	-	-	A	-	-	-	A	A	-	-	A	-	A	A	-	A	A	-	D	-	-	A
Silicone	-	A	A	-	A	-	-	A	-	A	-	-	A	-	-	-	A	A	-	-	A	-	A	A	-	A	A	-	A	A	A	A
Soybean	-	A	A	-	A	-	-	B	-	A	-	-	A	-	-	-	A	A	-	-	A	-	A	A	-	A	A	-	D	-	-	A
Sperm	-	A	A	-	A	-	-	-	-	-	-	-	A	-	-	-	A	-	-	-	A	-	A	A	-	A	A	-	A	-	-	A
Tanning	-	A	A	-	-	-	-	-	-	-	-	-	-	-	-	-	A	-	-	-	A	-	A	A	-	A	A	-	D	-	-	A
Turbine	-	A	A	-	A	-	-	A	-	A	-	-	A	-	-	-	A	-	C	-	A	-	A	A	-	A	A	-	D	-	D	A
Oleic Acid	B	A	A	B	B	-	B	B	C	C	C	-	A	C	A	C	B	A	B	D	C	-	A	A	-	D	B	D	D	D	D	A
Oleum 25%	-	-	-	-	-	A	-	-	-	-	B	D	-	A	D	-	-	-	-	-	-	A	-	A	D	D	D	D	D	-	D	-
Oleum	B	-	A	-	B	-	-	C	C	-	B	D	D	-	A	-	D	-	-	-	D	-	A	-	A	C	D	D	D	D	D	A
Oxalic Acid (cold)	C	A	B	A	C	C	B	B	B	C	D	D	-	A	B	A	C	C	D	-	A	A	-	A	A	-	A	B	C	B	A	C
Paraffin	A	A	A	A	A	-	-	A	-	B	B	B	A	A	-	A	B	A	A	B	-	A	-	A	A	A	A	-	-	-	-	A
Pentane	A	C	C	-	A	-	B	A	-	B	B	-	-	A	D	A	A	D	-	A	A	-	A	A	-	A	A	-	B	D	D	A
Perchloroethylene[2]	B	A	A	-	A	-	-	C	-	B	B	A	-	A	D	A	-	D	-	D	A	A	A	A	A	-	A	C	D	D	D	D
Petrolatum	A	-	A	-	B	-	-	B	-	C	C	-	-	-	A	D	A	A	B	-	-	A	A	-	A	A	-	B	A	D	A	A
Phenol 10%	B	A	A	-	A	-	B	C	-	B	D	-	A	C	A	-	-	D	-	-	-	A	-	-	B	D	-	C	D	C	D	C
Phenol (Carbolic Acid)	B	A	A	A	B	C	A	B	D	D	D	A	A	C	A	C	D	D	-	D	B	A	A	D	A	A	D	-	D	D	D	B
Phosphoric Acid (to 40% Solution)	-	B	A	A	D	A	A	D	D	D	-	-	A	B	A	A	D	D	C	B	A	A	B	C	D	A	D	-	D	B	C	A
Phosphoric Acid (40%-100% Solution)	-	C	B	B	D	B	A	D	D	D	-	-	A	B	A	A	D	D	D	C	A	A	B	D	D	A	D	-	D	B	C	C
Phosphoric Acid (Crude)	-	D	C	C	D	C	A	D	D	D	D	A	-	-	A	-	D	D	D	C	-	A	C	D	-	A	D	-	D	B	-	A
Phosphoric Anhydride (Dry or Moist)	-	A	A	-	-	-	-	D	-	-	-	D	D	A	-	-	-	-	-	-	A	-	-	D	D	-	D	-	A	-
Phosphoric Anyhdride (Molten)	-	A	A	-	D	-	-	D	D	-	-	-	D	-	A	-	-	A	-	D	-	-	-	-	-	D	C	-	D	-	D	A
Photographic (Developer)	-	C	A	C	C	A	A	-	-	D	-	-	A	-	-	A	C	-	-	B	A	-	A	A	-	A	A	-	A	-	-	A
Phthalic Anhydride	B	A	B	-	B	-	A	B	-	C	C	-	-	-	A	-	-	-	-	-	-	A	-	-	A	C	-	-	-	-	-	-
Picric Acid	B	A	A	-	C	-	A	D	D	D	D	-	A	A	A	-	-	A	-	A	-	-	-	-	-	A	A	D	A	-	A	A
Plating Solutions																																
Antimony Plating 130°	-	-	A	-	A	A	-	-	-	-	-	A	-	A	A	-	D	-	-	A	-	-	A	-	A	A	A	D	A	-	-	B
Arsenic Plating 110° F	-	-	A	-	-	A	A	-	-	-	-	A	-	A	A	-	A	-	-	A	-	-	C	-	A	A	A	D	A	-	-	B
Brass Plating																																
Regular Brass Bath 100° F	-	-	A	-	-	A	A	-	-	-	-	A	-	A	A	-	A	-	-	A	-	-	C	-	A	A	A	D	A	-	-	B
High Speed Brass Bath 110° F	-	-	A	-	-	A	A	-	-	-	-	A	-	A	A	-	A	-	-	A	-	-	D	-	A	A	A	D	A	-	-	B
Bronze Plating																																
Copper-Cadmium Bronze Bath R.T.	-	-	A	-	-	A	A	-	-	-	-	A	-	A	A	-	A	-	-	A	-	-	C	-	A	A	A	D	A	-	-	B
Copper-Tin Bronze Bath 160° F	-	-	A	-	-	A	A	-	-	-	-	D	-	A	A	-	A	-	-	A	-	-	D	-	A	A	D	B	-	-	-	C

A—No effect—Excellent
B—Minor effect—Good
C—Moderate effect—Fair
D—Severe effect—Not Recommended

1. P.V.C.—Satisfactory to 72° F.
2. Polypropylene—Satisfactory to 72° F.
3. Polypropylene—Satisfactory to 120° F.
4. Buna-N—Satisfactory for "O" Rings
5. Polyacetal—Satisfactory to 72° F.
6. Ceramag—Satisfactory to 72° F.

CHEMICAL RESISTANCE CHART Cont'd.

	302 Stainless Steel	304 Stainless Steel	316 Stainless Steel	440 Stainless Steel	Aluminum	TITANIUM	HASTELLOY C	Cast Bronze	Brass	Cast Iron	Carbon Steel	KYNAR	PVC (Type 1)	Tygon (E-3606)	Teflon	Noryl	Polyacetal	Nylon	Cycolac (ABS)	Polyethylene	POLYPROPYLENE	RYTON	CARBON	CERAMIC	CERAMAGNET "A"	VITON	BUNA N (NITRILE)	Silicon	Neoprene	Ethylene Propylene (EPM)	Rubber (Natural)	Epoxy
Platings (Cont.)																																
Copper-Zinc Bronze Bath 100° F	-	-	A	-	-	A	A	-	-	-	-	-	A	-	A	A	-	A	-	-	A	-	-	C	-	A	A	-	A	-	-	B
Cadmium Plating																																
Cyanide Bath 90° F	-	-	A	-	-	A	A	-	-	-	-	-	A	-	A	A	-	A	-	-	A	-	-	C	-	A	A	-	A	-	-	B
Fluoborate Bath 100° F	-	-	A	-	-	D	A	-	-	-	-	-	A	-	A	A	-	D	-	-	A	-	-	D	-	A	B	-	C	-	-	B
Chromium Plating																																
Chromic-Sulfuric Bath 130° F	-	-	C	-	-	A	A	-	-	-	-	-	A	-	A	D	-	D	-	-	A	-	-	A	-	C	D	-	D	-	-	D
Fluosilicate Bath 95° F	-	-	C	-	-	C	A	-	-	-	-	-	A	-	A	D	-	D	-	-	A	-	-	B	-	C	D	-	D	-	D	D
Fluoride Bath 130° F	-	-	D	-	-	C	A	-	-	-	-	-	A	-	A	D	-	D	-	-	A	-	-	B	-	C	D	-	D	-	-	D
Black Chrome Bath 115° F	-	-	C	-	-	A	A	-	-	-	-	-	A	-	A	D	-	D	-	-	A	-	-	A	-	C	D	-	D	-	-	D
Barrel Chrome Bath 95° F	-	-	D	-	-	C	A	-	-	-	-	-	A	-	A	D	-	D	-	-	A	-	-	A	-	C	D	-	D	-	-	D
Copper Plating (Cyanide)																																
Copper Strike Bath 120° F				-	A	A	A	-	-	-	-	-	A	A	-				-	-		-	-	C	-	B	-	A	-	-	-	
Rochelle Salt Bath 150° F	-	-	A	-	-	A	A	-	-	-	-	-	D	-	A	A	-	A	-	-	A	-	-	D	-	A	A	-	B	-	-	C
High Speed Bath 180° F	-	-	A	-	-	A	A	-	-	-	-	-	D	-	A	A	-	A	-	-	A	-	-	D	-	A	A	-	B	-	-	C
Copper Plating (Acid)																																
Copper Sulfate Bath R.T.	-	-	D	-	-	A	A	-	-	-	-	-	A	-	A	A	-	D	-	-	A	-	-	D	-	A	A	-	A	-	-	D
Copper Fluoborate Bath 120° F	-	-	D	-	-	D	A	-	-	-	-	-	A	-	A	A	-	D	-	-	A	-	-	D	-	A	B	-	C	-	-	D
Copper (Misc.)																																
Copper Pyrophosphate 140° F	-	-	A	-	-	A	A	-	-	-	-	-	A	-	A	A	-	A	-	-	A	-	-	B	-	A	A	-	A	-	-	B
Copper (Electroless) 140° F	-	-	-	-	-	-	D	-	-	-	-	-	A	-	A	A	-	A	-	-	A	-	-	D	-	A	D	-	D	-	-	B
Gold Plating																																
Cyanide 150° F	-	-	A	-	-	A	A	C	-	-	-	-	D	-	A	A	-	A	-	-	A	-	-	B	-	A	A	-	A	-	-	D
Neutral 75° F	-	-	C	-	-	A	A	-	-	-	-	-	A	-	A	A	-	A	-	-	A	-	-	A	-	A	A	-	A	-	-	A
Acid 75° F	-	-	C	-	-	A	A	-	-	-	-	-	A	-	A	A	-	A	-	-	A	-	-	A	-	A	A	-	A	-	-	A
Indium Sulfamate Plating R.T.	-	-	C	-	-	A	A	-	-	-	-	-	A	-	A	A	-	D	-	-	A	-	-	A	-	A	A	-	A	-	-	A
Iron Plating																																
Ferrous Chloride Bath 190° F	-	-	D	-	-	A	D	-	-	-	-	-	D	-	A	A	-	D	-	-	C	-	-	A	-	A	B	-	D	-	-	D
Ferrous Sulfate Bath 150° F	-	-	C	-	-	A	A	-	-	-	-	-	D	-	A	A	-	D	-	-	A	-	-	A	-	A	A	-	B	-	-	D
Ferrous Am. Sulfate Bath 150° F	-	-	C	-	-	A	A	-	-	-	-	-	D	-	A	A	-	D	-	-	A	-	-	A	-	A	A	-	B	-	-	D
Sulfate-Chloride Bath 160° F	-	-	D	-	-	A	D	-	-	-	-	-	D	-	A	A	-	D	-	-	A	-	-	A	-	A	B	-	C	-	-	D
Fluoborate Bath 145° F	-	-	D	-	-	D	B	-	-	-	-	-	D	-	A	A	-	D	-	-	A	-	-	D	-	A	B	-	C	-	-	D
Sulfamate 140° F	-	-	D	-	-	A	B	-	-	-	-	-	D	-	A	A	-	D	-	-	A	-	-	A	-	A	A	-	A	-	-	D
Lead Fluoborate Plating	-	-	C	-	-	D	A	-	-	-	-	-	A	-	A	A	-	D	-	-	A	-	-	D	-	A	B	-	C	-	-	A
Nickel Plating																																
Watts Type 115-160° F	-	-	C	-	-	A	A	-	-	-	-	-	D	-	A	A	-	A	-	-	A	-	-	A	-	A	A	-	A	-	-	D
High Chloride 130-160° F	-	-	C	-	-	A	A	-	-	-	-	-	D	-	A	A	-	D	-	-	A	-	-	A	-	A	A	-	B	-	-	D
Fluoborate 100-170° F	-	-	C	-	-	D	A	D	-	-	-	-	D	-	A	A	-	D	-	-	A	-	-	D	-	A	B	-	C	-	-	D
Sulfamate 100-140° F	-	-	C	-	-	A	A	-	-	-	-	-	A	-	A	A	-	A	-	-	A	-	-	A	-	A	A	-	A	-	-	D
Electroless 200° F	-	-	-	-	-	-	-	-	-	-	-	-	D	-	A	D	-	D	-	-	D	-	-	A	-	A	D	-	D	-	-	B
Rhodium Plating 120° F	-	-	D	-	-	D	D	-	-	-	-	-	A	-	A	A	D	D	-	-	A	-	-	A	-	A	A	-	B	-	-	D
Silver Plating 80-120° F	-	-	A	-	-	A	A	-	-	-	-	-	A	-	A	A	-	A	-	-	A	-	-	B	-	A	A	-	A	-	-	A
Tin-Fluoborate Plating 100° F	-	-	C	-	-	D	A	-	-	-	-	-	A	-	A	A	-	D	-	-	A	-	-	D	-	A	B	-	C	-	-	A
Tine-Lead Plating 100° F	-	-	C	-	-	D	A	-	-	-	-	-	A	-	A	A	-	D	-	-	A	-	-	D	-	A	B	-	C	-	-	A
Zinc Plating																																
Acid Chloride 140° F	-	-	D	-	-	A	D	-	-	-	-	-	A	-	A	A	-	D	-	-	A	-	-	A	-	A	A	-	A	-	-	A
Acid Sulfate Bath 150° F	-	-	C	-	-	A	A	-	-	-	-	-	D	-	A	A	-	D	-	-	A	-	-	A	-	A	A	-	B	-	-	D

A—No effect—Excellent
B—Minor effect—Good
C—Moderate effect—Fair
D—Severe effect—Not Recommended

1. P.V.C.—Satisfactory to 72° F.
2. Polypropylene—Satisfactory to 72° F.
3. Polypropylene—Satisfactory to 120° F.
4. Buna-N—Satisfactory for "O" Rings
5. Polyacetal—Satisfactory to 72° F.
6. Ceramag—Satisfactory to 72° F.

	302 Stainless Steel	304 Stainless Steel	316 Stainless Steel	440 Stainless Steel	Aluminum	TITANIUM	HASTELLOY C	Cast Bronze	Brass	Cast Iron	Carbon Steel	KYNAR	PVC (Type 1)	Tygon (E-3606)	Teflon	Noryl	Polyacetal	Nylon	Cycolac (ABS)	Polyethylene	POLYPROPYLENE	RYTON	CARBON	CERAMIC	CERAMAGNET "A"	VITON	BUNA N (NITRILE)	Silicon	Neoprene	Ethylene Propylene (EPM)	Rubber (Natural)	Epoxy
Platings (Cont.)																																
Acid Fluoborate Bath R.T.	-	-	C	-	D	-	-	-	-	-	A	-	A	A	-	D	-	-	A	-	-	D	-	A	B	-	C	-	-	A	-	A
Alkaline Cyanide Bath R.T.	-	-	A	-	A	A	-	-	-	-	A	-	A	A	-	A	-	-	A	-	-	A	-	A	A	-	A	-	-	A	-	A
Potash	-	A	-	A	C	-	A	C	-	B	-	-	A	B	-	A	B	A	-	B	A	-	A	A	A	A	A	-	B	-	B	A
Potassium Bicarbonate	-	A	-	B	C	A	B	B	-	D	-	A	A	-	A	A	C	A	C	B	A	A	A	A	-	A	A	-	A	-	B	A
Potassium Bromide	A	A	-	B	C	A	B	C	-	D	D	A	A	-	A	A	A	C	-	B	A	C	A	A	-	A	A	-	-	A	B	A
Potassium Carbonate	B	A	-	A	C	A	A	C	-	B	B	A	B	A	A	B	A	-	B	A	-	B	A	A	A	A	B	-	A	-	B	A
Potassium Chlorate	B	A	A	A	B	A	B	B	-	B	B	A	A	B	A	A	B	D	-	B	A	A	A	A	A	A	A	-	A	-	B	A
Potassium Chloride	C	A	A	B	B	A	A	C	C	B	B	A	A	A	A	A	A	B	C	B	A	A	A	A	A	A	A	-	A	-	A	A
Potassium Chromate	-	-	B	B	A	-	B	A	-	A	-	-	A	-	-	A	C	-	-	B	-	A	A	-	D	-	A	A	-	-	B	C
Potassium Cyanide Solutions	B	A	B	A	D	A	A	D	-	B	B	A	A	-	A	A	C	A	-	B	A	A	C	A	-	B	A	-	A	A	A	A
Potassium Dichromate	B	A	A	A	A	B	C	-	B	C	A	A	-	A	A	C	D	-	B	A	A	A	A	-	B	A	-	A	A	A	A	A
Potassium Ferrocyanide	B	A	-	A	C	-	B	A	-	-	C	-	A	-	A	-	-	A	-	A	-	-	-	-	-	-	D	-	-	-	A	A
Potassium Hydroxide (50%)	A	B	B	B	D	C	A	D	D	C	A	D	A	B	A	A	D	A	C	B	A	A	-	D	A	D	B	C	A	A	C	A
Potassium Nitrate	B	A	B	A	B	A	B	B	-	-	B	A	A	C	A	A	B	C	-	B	A	C	A	A	-	B	A	-	A	A	A	A
Potassium Permanganate	B	A	B	B	B	B	B	B	-	B	B	A	A	-	A	A	C	D	C	B	B	A	A	A	-	B	A	-	A	-	B	B
Potassium Sulfate	B	A	B	B	A	A	A	B	B	B	B	A	A	A	A	A	B	C	-	B	A	A	A	A	-	A	A	C	A	A	C	A
Potassium Sulfide	A	A	-	A	B	-	B	B	-	B	B	-	A	-	A	-	-	-	-	-	-	-	-	-	-	A	-	-	-	-	-	-
Propane (Liquified)[1][2]	A	A	-	A	A	-	-	A	A	-	B	-	D	-	A	D	A	A	-	-	D	-	A	A	-	A	A	D	B	D	D	A
Propylene Glycol	B	B	-	A	A	-	-	B	-	B	B	-	-	-	A	-	B	B	B	B	-	-	A	A	-	A	A	-	C	-	-	A
Pyridine	-	C	-	B	B	-	-	-	-	B	A	D	-	D	A	D	D	-	-	C	B	A	A	A	-	D	D	-	D	B	D	A
Pyrogallic Acid	B	A	A	A	B	-	A	B	-	B	B	-	A	-	A	-	-	D	A	-	-	A	A	A	A	-	A	A	-	-	-	A
Rosins	A	A	A	A	A	-	B	A	C	-	C	-	-	A	-	B	A	-	A	-	-	A	A	-	-	A	-	-	A	-	-	A
Rum	-	A	-	A	-	-	-	-	-	-	-	-	A	-	A	A	A	-	-	A	A	-	-	A	A	-	A	A	-	A	-	A
Rust Inhibitors	-	A	-	A	-	-	-	A	-	A	-	-	-	A	-	-	A	-	A	A	-	-	A	A	-	A	A	-	C	-	-	A
Salad Dressing	-	A	-	A	B	-	-	B	-	D	-	-	A	-	-	A	A	A	A	-	-	A	A	-	-	A	A	-	D	D	-	A
Sea Water	A	A	C	A	C	A	-	C	-	-	D	-	A	A	A	A	A	-	B	A	A	A	A	A	A	A	A	B	B	A	A	A
Shellac (Bleached)	A	A	-	A	A	-	A	B	B	A	-	-	A	-	A	A	-	-	A	-	-	A	A	-	-	A	-	A	-	-	-	A
Shellac (Orange)	A	A	-	A	A	-	A	C	C	A	-	-	A	-	A	A	-	-	A	-	-	A	A	-	-	A	-	A	-	-	-	A
Silicone	-	B	-	A	B	-	A	-	-	-	-	A	A	A	-	-	A	A	A	-	-	A	A	A	A	A	A	B	A	A	A	A
Silver Bromide	-	C	C	B	D	-	-	-	-	-	-	-	-	-	-	A	C	-	-	-	-	-	-	A	-	-	-	-	-	-	-	A
Silver Nitrate	B	A	B	A	D	A	A	D	-	D	D	A	A	B	A	A	C	A	-	B	A	-	A	A	-	A	C	-	A	C	A	A
Soap Solutions[1]	A	A	A	A	C	A	B	B	-	B	A	-	B	B	A	A	A	A	-	B	A	A	A	A	A	A	A	B	B	-	C	A
Soda Ash (See Sodium Carbonate)							A																									
Sodium Acetate	B	A	A	B	B	A	-	B	-	C	C	A	A	-	A	A	B	A	-	B	A	-	A	A	-	D	D	-	C	-	A	A
Sodium Aluminate	B	-	-	A	C	B	B	B	-	-	C	-	-	A	A	B	A	-	A	A	A	-	A	A	-	A	A	-	-	A	B	A
Sodium Bicarbonate	B	A	A	A	A	A	-	B	A	C	C	A	A	B	A	B	B	A	B	A	A	A	A	A	-	A	C	A	A	A	A	A
Sodium Bisulfate	A	A	-	A	D	B	B	C	C	D	D	A	A	B	A	A	B	C	C	B	A	A	A	A	-	B	A	C	A	-	A	A
Sodium Bisulfite	-	A	-	A	A	A	B	C	-	D	-	A	A	B	A	A	B	D	B	B	A	A	A	A	-	A	A	C	A	-	A	A
Sodium Borate	B	A	-	A	C	-	A	A	-	C	C	-	C	-	A	-	-	A	-	A	-	-	-	-	-	A	-	B	A	-	-	A
Sodium Carbonate	B	A	B	B	C	A	A	B	B	B	B	A	A	B	A	A	A	A	C	B	A	A	B	A	A	-	A	A	-	A	A	A
Sodium Chlorate	B	A	-	A	B	B	B	-	-	C	A	A	B	A	D	A	-	B	A	A	A	A	-	A	D	-	A	A	-	-	A	A
Sodium Chloride	B	A	C	B	C	A	A	B	C	B	C	A	A	B	A	A	B	B	A	A	A	A	A	A	A	A	C	A	A	B	B	A
Sodium Chromate	A	A	A	-	D	-	B	B	-	B	B	-	-	A	A	D	A	-	-	A	A	A	B	-	B	A	-	A	-	-	-	C
Sodium Cyanide	B	A	-	A	D	A	-	D	D	B	B	A	A	-	A	A	D	C	-	B	A	A	A	A	-	A	A	D	A	A	A	A
Sodium Fluoride	B	C	-	C	C	A	A	C	-	D	D	-	D	D	A	-	-	A	-	C	-	-	-	-	-	B	D	-	D	-	D	A
Sodium Hydrosulfite	-	-	-	-	A	-	A	C	-	-	-	-	C	A	A	-	-	A	-	-	-	-	-	A	-	A	-	-	A	-	A	-

A—No effect—Excellent
B—Minor effect—Good
C—Moderate effect—Fair
D—Severe effect—Not Recommended

1. P.V.C.—Satisfactory to 72° F.
2. Polypropylene—Satisfactory to 72° F.
3. Polypropylene—Satisfactory to 120° F.
4. Buna-N—Satisfactory for "O" Rings
5. Polyacetal—Satisfactory to 72° F.
6. Ceramag—Satisfactory to 72° F.

	302 Stainless Steel	304 Stainless Steel	316 Stainless Steel	440 Stainless Steel	Aluminum	TITANIUM	HASTELLOY C	Cast Bronze	Brass	Cast Iron	Carbon Steel	KYNAR	PVC (Type 1)	Tygon (E-3606)	Teflon	Noryl	Polyacetal	Nylon	Cycolac (ABS)	Polyethylene	POLYPROPYLENE	RYTON	CARBON	CERAMIC	CERAMAGNET "A"	VITON	BUNA N (NITRILE)	Neoprene	Ethylene Propylene (EPM)	Rubber (Natural)	Epoxy
Sodium Hydroxide (20%)	-	A	A	A	D	A	A	C	D	A	-	A	A	B	A	A	D	C	C	B	A	A	C	D	A	A	A	D	B	A	A
Sodium Hydroxide (50% Solution)	-	A	B	-	D	A	A	C	D	B	-	D	A	B	A	A	D	C	C	C	A	B	C	D	A	D	D	D	C	-	A
Sodium Hydroxide (80% Solution)	-	A	D	-	D	A	B	C	D	C	-	-	A	B	A	A	D	C	C	C	A	B	C	D	A	B	D	D	C	B	A
Sodium Hypochlorite³ (to 20%)	-	C	C	C	A	A	D	D	D	-	-	A	B	A	-	A	D	A	-	B	D	C	D	A	B	A	C	D	D	B	B
Sodium Hypochlorite	D	-	A	-	D	A	A	D	-	D	D	A	A	-	A	A	-	A	-	-	A	C	-	D	-	B	B	C	A	-	A
Sodium Hyposulfate	-	A	A	-	D	-	-	D	-	-	-	-	-	A	-	-	-	-	-	-	-	-	-	-	-	-	-	C	-	C	C
Sodium Metaphosphate²	A	-	A	-	-	-	C	C	B	B	-	-	A	-	B	A	-	D	-	A	A	-	A	A	-	B	A	A	A		
Sodium Metasilicate	A	-	A	B	-	-	B	-	C	C	-	-	A	-	D	-	-	-	-	A	-	-	A	A	D	A	-	-	A		
Sodium Nitrate	B	A	A	A	A	A	B	B	C	A	B	A	A	B	A	A	B	A	-	B	A	A	A	A	D	C	D	B	A	C	A
Sodium Perborate	B	-	C	-	B	-	-	C	C	B	B	-	A	A	B	A	-	-	A	-	A	A	-	A	B	D	B	A	C	A	
Sodium Peroxide	B	A	A	-	C	-	B	C	C	D	C	-	A	-	A	-	D	D	-	-	-	A	A	-	A	C	D	B	A	C	A
Sodium Polyphosphate (Mono, Di, Tribasic)	-	A	A	-	D	A	A	C	-	-	-	-	-	-	A	A	B	-	-	-	-	A	A	-	A	A	-	D	A	A	A
Sodium Silicate	B	A	B	A	C	A	B	C	C	-	B	-	A	B	A	A	C	A	-	-	A	-	A	A	-	A	A	-	A	A	A
Sodium Sulfate	B	A	A	C	B	A	B	B	B	A	B	-	A	-	A	A	B	A	-	B	A	A	A	A	-	A	A	-	A	A	A
Sodium Sulfide	B	A	B	-	D	A	B	D	D	A	B	-	A	B	A	A	B	A	-	B	A	A	A	A	-	A	C	-	A	C	A
Sodium Sulfite	-	C	C	-	C	A	A	C	-	A	-	-	A	A	A	-	-	D	-	A	-	A	A	-	A	A	-	A	-	A	A
Sodium Tetraborate	-	-	A	-	-	-	-	-	-	-	-	A	-	-	A	B	-	-	A	-	A	A	-	A	A	-	-	-	A		
Sodium Thiosulphate ("Hypo")	A	A	A	-	B	A	-	D	D	C	B	-	A	-	A	A	C	A	-	A	A	A	A	-	A	B	-	A	A	C	A
Sorghum	-	A	A	-	-	-	-	-	A	-	-	-	-	A	A	-	-	-	-	-	A	A	-	A	A	-	A	-	-	A	
Soy Sauce	-	A	A	-	A	-	-	A	-	D	-	-	-	A	A	A	-	-	-	-	A	A	-	A	A	-	A	-	D	A	
Stannic Chloride	D	D	D	-	D	A	B	D	-	D	D	A	A	-	A	A	C	A	-	B	A	-	A	-	A	A	A	D	A	A	A
Stannic Fluoborate	-	-	A	-	-	-	-	D	-	-	A	C	-	-	-	-	-	-	A	-	A	A	-	A	-	-	A	A			
Stannous Chloride	D	D	C	-	D	A	A	D	-	D	D	-	A	A	A	-	D	-	A	-	-	B	C	D	-	A	A	A			
Starch	B	A	A	-	A	-	-	B	-	C	C	-	A	A	A	-	B	-	A	A	-	A	A	-	A	-	A	-	-	A	
Stearic Acid²	B	A	A	B	A	A	C	C	C	C	A	A	B	A	A	A	-	A	B	D	D	A	A	A	-	A	B	D	B	B	C	A
Stoddard Solvent	A	A	A	A	A	A	A	A	B	B	A	A	D	A	D	A	A	B	D	D	A	A	A	-	A	A	B	D	D	D	D	A
Styrene	A	A	A	-	A	-	A	-	A	-	-	A	-	-	-	A	A	A	-	-	-	A	A	-	A	A	A	B	D	D	D	A
Sugar (Liquids)	A	A	A	A	-	A	A	-	B	B	-	-	A	A	A	A	B	-	A	-	A	A	A	A	-	-	-	B	-	A	A
Sulfate Liquors	-	C	C	-	B	-	A	C	-	-	-	-	D	-	-	A	-	A	A	-	-	-	-	C	-	-	A				
Sulfur Chloride	-	D	D	D	D	-	-	C	D	-	-	-	A	C	A	A	D	A	-	A	D	-	A	C	-	A	D	-	D	D	D	C
Sulfur Dioxide²	-	A	A	C	A	A	B	B	-	-	-	B	D	B	A	D	B	D	D	C	D	A	A	A	-	D	D	C	B	A	D	A
Sulfur Dioxide (dry)	A	A	A	-	A	-	A	A	C	A	B	-	D	-	A	-	A	-	D	-	-	A	A	-	D	-	-	D	-	D	D	
Sulfur Trioxide (dry)	A	A	C	-	A	-	-	B	-	B	B	-	A	B	A	D	D	D	-	-	-	-	B	A	-	A	D	-	D	B	C	A
Sulfuric Acid (to 10%)	-	D	C	C	C	A	A	D	D	D	-	A	A	B	A	A	D	D	B	B	A	A	A	A	-	A	C	-	D	D	C	A
Sulfuric Acid (10%-75%)²	-	D	D	D	D	C	B	D	D	D	-	A	A	B	A	B	D	D	B	C	A	B	A	D	C	A	D	-	D	D	D	B
Sulfuric Acid 75%-100%	-	-	D	-	-	D	B	-	D	-	-	A	B	-	A	A	-	D	-	-	B	C	-	A	-	A	D	-	D	-	-	D
Sulfurous Acid	C	C	B	C	C	A	B	D	-	D	D	-	A	B	A	A	D	D	-	B	A	-	B	A	-	A	C	D	B	B	C	A
Sulfuryl Chloride	-	-	-	-	-	-	-	-	-	-	-	A	-	A	-	-	-	-	-	-	-	A	-	-	-	-	-	-	-	-	A
Syrup	-	A	A	A	A	-	-	D	-	-	-	-	-	A	A	A	B	-	A	-	A	A	A	A	A	-	B	-	A	A	
Tallow	-	A	A	A	-	A	-	-	-	-	-	-	-	A	A	A	-	C	-	-	A	A	-	A	-	-	-	-	-	A	
Tannic Acid	B	A	A	A	C	A	B	B	-	C	C	A	A	B	A	A	B	D	-	B	A	A	A	A	A	A	D	C	A	A	A	A
Tanning Liquors	-	A	A	-	C	A	A	A	-	-	-	A	B	A	-	B	-	-	-	-	A	A	-	A	A	-	A	C	-	-	-	A
Tartaric Acid	B	A	B	B	C	A	B	A	C	D	D	A	A	B	A	A	B	A	-	B	A	-	A	A	-	A	A	D	C	A	A	A

A—No effect—Excellent
B—Minor effect—Good
C—Moderate effect—Fair
D—Severe effect—Not Recommended

1. P.V.C.—Satisfactory to 72° F.
2. Polypropylene—Satisfactory to 72° F.
3. Polypropylene—Satisfactory to 120° F.
4. Buna-N—Satisfactory for "O" Rings
5. Polyacetal—Satisfactory to 72° F.
6. Ceramag—Satisfactory to 72° F.

	302 Stainless Steel	304 Stainless Steel	316 Stainless Steel	440 Stainless Steel	Aluminum	TITANIUM	HASTELLOY C	Cast Bronze	Brass	Cast Iron	Carbon Steel	KYNAR	PVC (Type 1)	Tygon (E-3606)	Teflon	Noryl	Polyacetal	Nylon	Cycolac (ABS)	Polyethylene	POLYPROPYLENE	RYTON	CARBON	CERAMIC	CERAMAGNET "A"	VITON	BUNA N (NITRILE)	Silicon	Neoprene	Ethylene Propylene (EPM)	Rubber (Natural)	Epoxy
Tetrachlorethane	-	-	A	-	-	A	A	-	-	-	-	-	D	-	A	D	A	A	-	-	A	-	A	A	-	A	D	-	-	D	D	A
Tetrahydrofuran	-	A	A	-	D	-	-	D	-	D	A	D	D	-	A	D	A	A	-	D	C	A	A	A	-	D	D	-	D	B	D	A
Toluene, Toluol[3]	A	A	A	-	A	A	A	A	A	A	A	A	D	D	A	D	A	A	D	D	A	A	A	A	A	C	D	D	D	D	D	A
Tomato Juice	A	A	A	-	A	-	-	C	-	C	C	-	-	-	A	A	B	A	B	-	A	A	A	A	-	A	A	-	A	-	-	A
Trichlorethane	-	C	A	-	C	A	A	C	-	C	-	-	-	-	A	D	A	-	-	-	-	A	A	-	A	D	D	D	D	D	D	A
Trichlorethylene[2]	B	A	A	-	B	A	A	B	A	C	B	A	D	-	A	D	A	C	D	D	D	C	A	A	C	A	D	D	D	D	D	A
Trichloropropane	-	-	A	-	-	-	A	-	-	-	-	-	-	D	A	-	D	-	-	-	-	A	A	-	A	A	-	A	-	-	-	A
Tricresylphosphate	-	-	A	-	B	A	-	-	-	-	-	-	D	-	A	A	C	-	-	-	-	-	-	-	A	A	-	B	D	-	D	A
Triethylamine	-	-	-	-	-	-	A	-	-	-	-	-	A	-	-	B	D	-	-	-	-	-	-	-	A	A	A	A	D	B	-	A
Turpentine[3]	B	A	A	-	C	-	A	B	C	B	B	A	A	B	A	D	A	A	-	D	B	A	A	A	-	A	D	-	D	D	D	A
Urine	-	A	A	-	B	-	-	C	-	B	-	-	A	-	-	A	A	A	-	B	A	-	A	A	-	A	A	-	A	D	A	A
Vegetable Juice	-	A	A	-	A	-	-	C	-	D	-	-	-	-	A	A	A	-	-	-	-	A	A	-	A	A	-	A	B	D	-	A
Vinegar	A	A	A	A	D	A	A	B	B	C	D	A	A	-	A	A	B	A	B	B	A	A	A	A	A	-	C	-	B	A	C	A
Varnish (Use Viton for Aromatic)	A	A	A	A	A	-	-	A	B	-	C	-	-	-	A	D	A	A	-	-	A	A	A	A	-	A	B	C	D	-	D	A
Water, Acid, Mine	-	A	A	-	C	-	-	C	D	C	-	-	A	B	-	A	D	A	B	-	A	B	A	A	-	A	A	-	B	-	B	A
Water, Distilled, Lab Grade 7	-	A	A	-	B	-	-	A	-	D	-	-	A	B	A	A	A	A	A	-	A	A	A	A	-	A	A	-	A	B	A	A
Water, Fresh	A	A	A	-	A	-	-	A	C	B	D	-	A	B	A	A	A	A	A	D	A	A	A	A	-	A	A	-	A	B	A	A
Water, Salt	-	A	A	-	B	-	-	B	C	D	-	-	A	B	-	A	A	A	-	-	A	A	A	A	-	A	A	-	A	B	A	A
Weed Killers	-	A	A	-	C	-	-	C	-	-	-	-	-	-	-	A	A	-	-	-	-	A	A	-	A	B	-	C	-	-	-	A
Whey	-	A	A	-	B	-	-	-	-	-	-	-	-	-	-	A	-	-	-	-	-	A	A	-	A	A	-	-	-	-	-	A
Whiskey and Wines	A	A	A	A	D	-	-	B	B	D	D	-	A	-	A	A	A	A	-	B	A	-	A	A	-	A	A	B	A	A	A	A
White Liquor (Pulp Mill)	-	A	A	-	-	-	A	D	-	C	-	-	A	-	A	A	D	A	-	-	A	A	-	A	A	-	A	A	-	A	-	A
White Water (Paper Mill)	-	A	A	-	-	-	-	A	-	-	-	-	-	-	B	A	-	A	-	-	A	A	-	A	A	-	A	-	-	A	-	A
Xylene[2]	A	A	A	-	A	-	A	A	A	A	B	A	D	-	A	D	A	A	D	D	D	A	A	A	A	A	D	D	D	D	D	A
Zinc Chloride	D	D	B	B	D	A	B	D	D	D	D	A	A	-	A	A	C	A	-	B	A	A	A	A	-	A	A	-	A	A	A	A
Zinc Hydrosulphite	-	-	A	-	D	-	-	D	-	D	-	-	-	-	A	C	-	-	-	-	-	A	A	-	A	A	-	A	A	-	-	A
Zinc Sulfate	B	A	A	A	D	A	B	B	C	C	D	A	C	B	A	A	C	A	-	B	A	A	A	A	-	A	A	-	A	A	C	A

A—No effect—Excellent
B—Minor effect—Good
C—Moderate effect—Fair
D—Severe effect—Not Recommended

1. P.V.C.—Satisfactory to 72° F.
2. Polypropylene—Satisfactory to 72° F.
3. Polypropylene—Satisfactory to 120° F.
4. Buna-N—Satisfactory for "O" Rings
5. Polyacetal—Satisfactory to 72° F.
6. Ceramag—Satisfactory to 72° F.

Carbon and Alloy Steel—Stainless Steel

Nominal Pipe Size Inches	Outside Diam. Inches	Identification Steel Iron Pipe Size	Sched. No.	Stainless Steel Sched. No.	Wall Thickness (t) Inches	Inside Diameter (d) Inches	Area of Metal Square Inches	Transverse Internal Area (a) Square Inches	(A) Square Feet	Moment of Inertia (I) Inches⁴	Weight Pipe Pounds per foot	Weight Water Pounds per foot of pipe	External Surface Sq. Ft. per foot of pipe	Section Modulus $\left(2\frac{I}{O.D.}\right)$
1/8	0.405	...	...	10S	.049	.307	.0548	.0740	.00051	.00088	.19	.032	.106	.00437
		STD	40	40S	.068	.269	.0720	.0568	.00040	.00106	.24	.025	.106	.00523
		XS	80	80S	.095	.215	.0925	.0364	.00025	.00122	.31	.016	.106	.00602
1/4	0.540	...	...	10S	.065	.410	.0970	.1320	.00091	.00279	.33	.057	.141	.01032
		STD	40	40S	.088	.364	.1250	.1041	.00072	.00331	.42	.045	.141	.01227
		XS	80	80S	.119	.302	.1574	.0716	.00050	.00377	.54	.031	.141	.01395
3/8	0.675	...	...	10S	.065	.545	.1246	.2333	.00162	.00586	.42	.101	.178	.01736
		STD	40	40S	.091	.493	.1670	.1910	.00133	.00729	.57	.083	.178	.02160
		XS	80	80S	.126	.423	.2173	.1405	.00098	.00862	.74	.061	.178	.02554
1/2	0.840	...	...	5S	.065	.710	.1583	.3959	.00275	.01197	.54	.172	.220	.02849
		...	...	10S	.083	.674	.1974	.3568	.00248	.01431	.67	.155	.220	.03407
		STD	40	40S	.109	.622	.2503	.3040	.00211	.01709	.85	.132	.220	.04069
		XS	80	80S	.147	.546	.3200	.2340	.00163	.02008	1.09	.102	.220	.04780
		...	160	...	.187	.466	.3836	.1706	.00118	.02212	1.31	.074	.220	.05267
		XXS	...	...	.294	.252	.5043	.050	.00035	.02424	1.71	.022	.220	.05772
3/4	1.050	...	...	5S	.065	.920	.2011	.6648	.00462	.02450	.69	.288	.275	.04667
		...	...	10S	.083	.884	.2521	.6138	.00426	.02969	.86	.266	.275	.05655
		STD	40	40S	.113	.824	.3326	.5330	.00371	.03704	1.13	.231	.275	.07055
		XS	80	80S	.154	.742	.4335	.4330	.00300	.04479	1.47	.188	.275	.08531
		...	160	...	.219	.612	.5698	.2961	.00206	.05269	1.94	.128	.275	.10036
		XXS	...	...	.308	.434	.7180	.148	.00103	.05792	2.44	.064	.275	.11032
1	1.315	...	...	5S	.065	1.185	.2553	1.1029	.00766	.04999	.87	.478	.344	.07603
		...	...	10S	.109	1.097	.4130	.9452	.00656	.07569	1.40	.409	.344	.11512
		STD	40	40S	.133	1.049	.4939	.8640	.00600	.08734	1.68	.375	.344	.1328
		XS	80	80S	.179	.957	.6388	.7190	.00499	.1056	2.17	.312	.344	.1606
		...	160	...	.250	.815	.8365	.5217	.00362	.1251	2.84	.230	.344	.1903
		XXS	...	...	.358	.599	1.0760	.282	.00196	.1405	3.66	.122	.344	.2136
1¼	1.660	...	...	5S	.065	1.530	.3257	1.839	.01277	.1038	1.11	.797	.435	.1250
		...	...	10S	.109	1.442	.4717	1.633	.01134	.1605	1.81	.708	.435	.1934
		STD	40	40S	.140	1.380	.6685	1.495	.01040	.1947	2.27	.649	.435	.2346
		XS	80	80S	.191	1.278	.8815	1.283	.00891	.2418	3.00	.555	.435	.2913
		...	160	...	.250	1.160	1.1070	1.057	.00734	.2839	3.76	.458	.435	.3421
		XXS	...	...	.382	.896	1.534	.630	.00438	.3411	5.21	.273	.435	.4110
1½	1.900	...	...	5S	.065	1.770	.3747	2.461	.01709	.1579	1.28	1.066	.497	.1662
		...	...	10S	.109	1.682	.6133	2.222	.01543	.2468	2.09	.963	.497	.2598
		STD	40	40S	.145	1.610	.7995	2.036	.01414	.3099	2.72	.882	.497	.3262
		XS	80	80S	.200	1.500	1.068	1.767	.01225	.3912	3.63	.765	.497	.4118
		...	160	...	.281	1.338	1.429	1.406	.00976	.4824	4.86	.608	.497	.5078
		XXS	...	...	.400	1.100	1.885	.950	.00660	.5678	6.41	.42	.497	.5977
2	2.375	...	...	5S	.065	2.245	.4717	3.958	.02749	.3149	1.61	1.72	.622	.2652
		...	...	10S	.109	2.157	.7760	3.654	.02538	.4992	2.64	1.58	.622	.4204
		STD	40	40S	.154	2.067	1.075	3.355	.02330	.6657	3.65	1.45	.622	.5606
		XS	80	80S	.218	1.939	1.477	2.953	.02050	.8679	5.02	1.28	.622	.7309
		...	160	...	.344	1.687	2.190	2.241	.01556	1.162	7.46	.97	.622	.979
		XXS	...	...	.436	1.503	2.656	1.774	.01232	1.311	9.03	.77	.622	1.104
2½	2.875	...	...	5S	.083	2.709	.7280	5.764	.04002	.7100	2.48	2.50	.753	.4939
		...	...	10S	.120	2.635	1.039	5.453	.03787	.9873	3.53	2.36	.753	.6868
		STD	40	40S	.203	2.469	1.704	4.788	.03322	1.530	5.79	2.07	.753	1.064
		XS	80	80S	.276	2.323	2.254	4.238	.02942	1.924	7.66	1.87	.753	1.339
		...	160	...	.375	2.125	2.945	3.546	.02463	2.353	10.01	1.54	.753	1.638
		XXS	...	...	.552	1.771	4.028	2.464	.01710	2.871	13.69	1.07	.753	1.997
3	3.500	...	...	5S	.083	3.334	.8910	8.730	.06063	1.301	3.03	3.78	.916	.7435
		...	...	10S	.120	3.260	1.274	8.347	.05796	1.822	4.33	3.62	.916	1.041
		STD	40	40S	.216	3.068	2.228	7.393	.05130	3.017	7.58	3.20	.916	1.724
		XS	80	80S	.300	2.900	3.016	6.605	.04587	3.894	10.25	2.86	.916	2.225
		...	160	...	.438	2.624	4.205	5.408	.03755	5.032	14.32	2.35	.916	2.876
		XXS	...	...	.600	2.300	5.466	4.155	.02885	5.993	18.58	1.80	.916	3.424

Identification, wall thickness and weights are extracted from ANSI B36.10 and B36.19. The notations STD, XS, and XXS indicate Standard, Extra Strong, and Double Extra Strong pipe respectively

Transverse internal area values listed in "square feet" also represent volume in cubic feet per foot of pipe length.

Tubing Working Pressures

INSIDE DIAMETER Inches	OUTSIDE DIAMETER Inches	WALL THICKNESS Inches	MAXIMUM SUGGESTED WORKING PRESSURE AT ROOM TEMPERATURE psi	kPa
1/16	1/8		70	483
1/8	3/16	1/32	45	310
3/16	1/4		34	234
1/4	5/16		28	193
1/16	3/16		108	744
3/32	7/32		78	537
1/8	1/4		62	427
5/32	9/32		52	358
3/16	5/16	1/16	45	310
1/4	3/8		36	248
5/16	7/16		30	207
3/8	1/2		26	179
7/16	9/16		23	158
1/2	5/8		20	138
5/8	3/4		24	165
3/16	3/8		62	427
1/4	7/16		49	338
5/16	1/2		41	282
3/8	9/16	3/32	36	248
7/16	5/8		31	214
1/2	11/16		28	193
9/16	3/4		26	179
5/8	13/16		24	165
11/16	7/8		22	152
3/4	7/8		22	152
1/8	3/8		34	237
3/16	7/16		78	537
1/4	1/2		62	427
5/16	9/16		52	358
3/8	5/8		45	310
7/16	11/16		39	269
1/2	3/4	1/8	36	248
9/16	13/16		32	220
5/8	7/8		30	207
11/16	15/16		28	193
3/4	1		26	179
7/8	1-1/8		23	158
1	1-1/4		20	138
1-1/8	1-3/8		19	131
1-1/4	1-1/2		17	117

INSIDE DIAMETER Inches	OUTSIDE DIAMETER Inches	WALL THICKNESS Inches	MAXIMUM SUGGESTED WORKING PRESSURE AT ROOM TEMPERATURE psi	kPa
1/2	13/16		42	289
9/16	7/8		39	269
5/8	15/16		36	248
11/16	1	5/32	33	227
3/4	1-1/16		31	214
7/8	1-3/16		27	186
1	1-5/16		24	165
3/16	9/16		108	744
1/4	5/8		85	586
3/4	1-1/8		36	248
1	1-3/8	3/16	28	193
1-1/8	1-1/2		26	179
1-1/4	1-5/8		24	165
1-1/2	1-7/8		20	138
5/16	13/16		28	197
3/4	1-1/4		45	310
1	1-1/2		36	248
1-1/4	1-3/4		30	207
1-1/2	2	1/4	26	179
1-3/4	2-1/4		23	158
2	2-1/2		20	138
2-1/4	2-3/4		19	131
2-1/2	3		17	117
3	3-1/2		15	103
3/8	1	5/16	29	200
5/8	1-3/8		22	152
2	2-3/4	3/8	28	193
2-1/2	3-1/4		24	165
3	3-3/4		20	138
2	3		36	248
3	4	1/2	26	179
4	5		20	138

This chart contains Maximum Suggested Working Pressures, at room temperature, for various sizes of Tygon B-44-3 tubing. To obtain this figure for the other tubing formulations offered by OMEGA, multiply the "Maximum Suggested Working Pressure" shown in the chart by the appropriate factor:

Courtesy of Norton Performance Products

Tygon R-3603
(OMEGA Type TYTY)
value shown times: 0.70

Norprene A-60-G
(OMEGA Type TYNT)
value shown times: 0.30

Working pressures are calculated at a conservative 1:5 ratio relative to burst pressure.

NATIONAL PIPE TAPER AND STRAIGHT THREAD DIMENSIONS

NPT DIMENSIONS

NPT SIZE	THREADS PER INCH	DIM "A" (IN.)	DIM "B" (IN.)
$1/16$	27	.312	.261
$1/8$	27	.405	.264
$1/4$	18	.540	.402
$3/8$	18	.675	.408
$1/2$	14	.840	.534
$3/4$	14	1.050	.546
1	11½	1.315	.683
$1\frac{1}{4}$	11½	1.660	.707

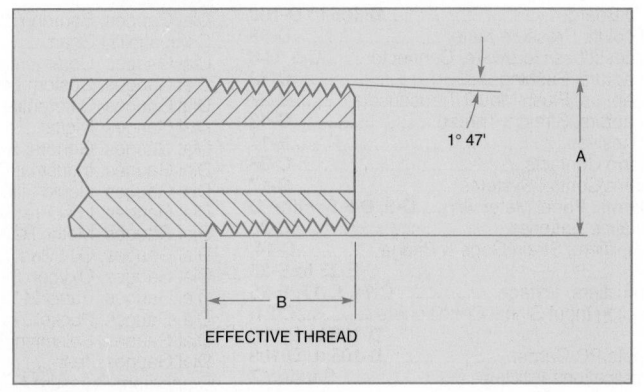

STRAIGHT THREAD DIMENSIONS

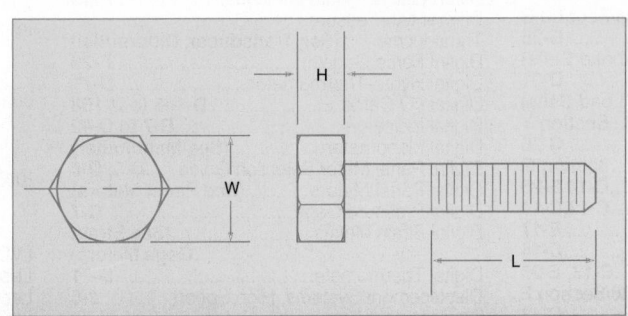

NOMINAL THREAD SIZE	THREADS PER INCH		MAJOR DIA.	W	H	L
	COARSE (UNC)	FINE (UNF)				
0	—	80	0.0600			
1	64	72	0.0730			
2	56	64	0.0860			
3	48	56	0.0990			
4	40	48	0.1120			
5	40	44	0.1250			
6	32	40	0.1380			
8	32	36	0.1640			
10	24	32	0.1900			
12	24	28	0.2160			
$1/4$	20	28	0.2500	$7/16$	$11/64$	0.750
$5/16$	18	24	0.3125	$1/2$	$7/32$	0.875
$3/8$	16	24	0.3750	$9/16$	$1/4$	1.000
$7/16$	14	20	0.4375	$5/8$	$19/64$	1.125
$1/2$	13	20	0.5000	$3/4$	$11/32$	1.250
$9/16$	12	18	0.5625	$13/16$	$3/8$	1.375
$5/8$	11	18	0.6250	$15/16$	$27/64$	1500
$3/4$	10	16	0.7500	$1\frac{1}{8}$	$1/2$	1.750
$7/8$	9	14	0.8750	$1\frac{5}{16}$	$37/64$	2.000
1	8	12	1.0000	$1\frac{1}{2}$	$43/64$	2.250
$1\frac{1}{8}$	7	12	1.1250	$1\frac{11}{16}$	$3/4$	2.500
$1\frac{1}{4}$	7	12	1.2500	$1\frac{7}{8}$	$27/32$	2.750
$1\frac{3}{8}$	6	12	1.3750	$2\frac{1}{16}$	$29/32$	3.000
$1\frac{1}{2}$	6	12	1.5000	$2\frac{1}{4}$	1	3.250

PRODUCT INDEX

A

A/D Boards ....D-105 to D-108
Absolute Pressure Meter D-58
Accessories/Hardware, Connector C-5, C-6
Adaptors, Bushing......................................C-43
Adaptors, Flush Mount Transducers B-27
Adaptors, Straight Thread..........................C-43
Adhesives E-17
Alarm Contacts...C-36
Alarm/Control Systems C-17
Alarms, Panel Meter with .....D-5, D-6/Section D
Alkaline Batteries C-26
Amplifiers, Strain Gage & Bridge C-14,
                                            E-23 to E-25
Amplifiers, Voltage C-14, C-17, E-25
Analog Input Signal Conditioners C-21,
                                            D-105 to D-108
Apple PC Cards.........................D-105 to D-108
Applications Articles ....Section Z

B

Barometer, Electronic ......B-46, B-98/Section B
Batteries C-26
Beam Load Cells ....(See Load Cells)
Benchtop Indicators D-31
Bending Beam Load Cells ......(See Load Cells)
Books ....Section Y
Borden Tube Compatibility Chart G-26
Bourdon Tube Dial Gauges...............Section G
Bridge Amplifier C-14,E-25
Bridge Excitation C-12,C-14
Bridge Resistors E-17
Bridge Signal Conditioner C-14
Bridge Transmitter...............................C-13, E-25
Bridge-Type Transducers..B-8 to B-30/Section F
Bushings...C-43

C

Cables B-94, C-21
Calibrators..................................D-43 to D-71
Calibrators, Current ....D-43 to D-45, D-47,
                                            D-60 ,D-61
Calibrators, Frequency................................D-46
Calibrators, Loop D-43, D-44
Calibrators, NIST Traceable............D-61 to D-65
Calibrators, Pneumatic...............................D-61
Calibrators, Portable D-43, D-47, D-51, D-52,
                                            D-59 to D-64
Calibrators, Pressure Standard..D-55, D-56, D-58
Calibrators, Temperature D-47
Cement for Strain Gages E-17
Clamps, Hose/Tubing C-41
Coatings, Protective E-18
Compression Fittings C-43, C-44
Computer Cards ....D-105 to D-108
Computer Interface Equipment....D-93 to D-120
Connector Accessories/Hardware........C-5, C-6
Connector Pins C-6, C-47
Connectors ....B-94, C-3 to C-5
Connectors, Thermocouple..C-6, C-47, C-48, C-49
Controllers ....D-14, D-32, D-37 to D-42
Conversion Charts, Pressure.....................Z-27
Converter, 3-15 PSIG to Current .B-50, B-57, B-73
Converter, Current to Pressure...................C-29
Converter, Pressure to Current.........C-49, B-87
Crimp Tools C-6, C-50
Current Input Meter...........................Section D
Current Output Transducers...(See Transducers)
Current to Pressure (I/P) Converter ..C-29, C-30
Custom Pressure Products...................B-5, B-6

D

Data Acquisition Equipment........D-72 to D-120,
                                            C-21, E-27 to E-29
Dataloggers...D-93
Data, Technical ....Section Z

Deadweight Testers D-65, D-66
Dial Gauges ....Section G
Dial Gauges, Bourdon Tube
Compatibility Chart....................................G-26
Dial Gauges, Commercial...............G-5 to G-12
Dial Gauges, Custom Dial Faces ...G-8 to G-10
Dial Gauges, Differential Pressure....G-17, G-18
Dial Gauges, Digital....................................C-7
Dial Gauges, General Service ....G-13 to G-15
Dial Gauges, Industrial Process........G-19, G-20
Dial Gauges, Liquid Filled G-15, G-16
Dial Gauges, Low Pressure Diaphragm G-21
Dial Gauges, Metric Ranges G-25
Dial Gauges, Oil Filled.....................G-15, G-16
Dial Gauges, Oxygen Service ....G-13 to G-23
Dial Gauges, Panel Mount................G-11, G12
Dial Gauges, Pocket Test G-21
Dial Gauges, Selection Guide G-3, G-4
Dial Gauges, Test ....G-21 to G-24
Diaphragm Pressure Seals G-27, G-28
Differential Pressure Gauges G-17, G-18
Differential Pressure Switches..........H-17, H-18
Differential Pressure
Transducers .....(See Transducer, Differential)
Digital Force Gage......................................F-29
Digital Hygro-Thermometer D-71
Digital I/O Cards ....D-105 to D-108
Digital Indicators ....D-7 to D-42
Digital Manometer .... (See Manometer)
Digital Panel Meter Selection Guide......D-5, D-6
Digital Panel Meters .... (See Panel Meters)
Digital Pressure Gage C-7
Digital Strain Meters ....(See Strain
                                            Gage Meters)
Digital Thermometer D-71
Displacement Systems, High Speed...........J-5
Displacement Transducer Meter J-20
Displacement Transducers................Section J
Displacement Transducers,
AC Long Stroke J-9
Displacement Transducers, AC Powered J-9
Displacement Transducers, DC Long Stroke..J-15
Displacement Transducers, Loop-Powered ..J-17
Displacement Transducers, Miniature DC J-11
Displacement Transducers, Miniature DC J-11
Displacement Transducers, Precision
DC Gauging J-13
Displacement Transmitter, Loop-Powered J-17
Displays, Large Digital D-17,D-18
Displays...Section D

E

Epoxy Adhesives for Strain Gages E-17, E-18
Excitation, Bridge ....(See Power Supply)
Explosion-Resistant Housing......................C-13

F

FM (Factory Mutual) Rated
Transducers ....B-73 to B-88
Feedthroughs ....C-44 to C-48
Ferrules C-43
Fittings, Tubing..................................C-41, C-43
Flush Diaphragm Transducers ..(See Transducer,
                                    Flush Mount Diaphragm)
Force Gage...F-29
Frequency Indicating Meter D-13,D-14
Frequency Output Pressure
Transducer B-97
Frequency Simulator...................................D-46
Function Recorder.........................D-77 to D-79

G

Gage Adapter...C-30
Gage Calibrators ....(See Calibrators)
Gage Pressure Transducer ..(See Transducer)
Gauges ....(See Dial Gauges)
Glossary..Z-3 to Z-6

Glues for Strain Gages................................E-17

H

Half-Bridge Complementary Resistors E-17
Hand Pump D-59
Handheld Hygro-Thermometer D-71
Handheld Pressure Meter..................D-25,D-50
Hazardous Location Switches........H-19 to H-24
Hazardous Location Pressure
Transducers ....B-73 to B-88
Hermetic Seals................................C-45 to C-47
Hose Clamps..C-41
Humidity Meter ....D-71, D-89 to D-92

I

I/P Converter...............................C-27 to C-30
IBM PC Cards............................D-105 to D-108
Indicator, Melt Pressure B-95
Indicators ....(See Panel Meters) Section D
Indicators, Portable....................D-48 to D-52
Interface Equipment ....D-105 to D-120
Interface Systems, Plug-In ....D-105 to D-108
Intrinsic Safety...C-51

J

Junction Boxes for Load Cells F-22

K

Kits, Strain Gage Equipment E-31

L

LVDT's..Section J
Labels, Temperature Indicating...................E-30
Lacquers..E-17
Latching Relays..C-36
Load Bolts F-11
Load Cell Selection/Applications Guide ...F-5, F-6
Load Cells ....Section F
Load Cells, Accessories..............................F-24
Load Cells, Beam F-17
Load Cells, Compression F-7, F-8, F-12
Load Cells, Junction Boxes.........................F-22
Load Cells, Load Buttons for.......................F-24
Load Cells, NIST Traceable ....Section F
Load Cells, OEM...F-25
Load Cells, Platform F-23
Load Cells, Rod Ends for F-24
Load Cells, S-Shaped.........................F-13, F-14
Load Cells, Thin Beam................................F-25
Load Cells, Washer.....................................F-12
Load Washers...F-12
Loop Calibrators D-43, D-44
Loop Powered Indicator......................D-33, D-34

M

Macintosh PC Cards ....D-105 to D-108
Manometer, Electronic Transducer ....Section B
Manometer, Handheld.........................D-51, D-52
Manometers...........................Sections B and D
Melt Pressure Indicators B-95
Melt Pressure Transducers ....B-91 to B-94
Meter Selection Guide.........................D-5, D-6
Meters, Digital Panel .... D-5 to D-24
Meters, Panel....................................D-5 to D-24
Modular Signal Conditioners C-21
Multi-Channel Meter...........................D-5, D-6
Multi-Channel Recorders ....D-73 to D-92
Multi-Conductor Cable C-38
Multi-Conductor Feedthroughs ....C-44 to C-48
Multi-Pin Connector C-47, C-49
Multi-Wire Connection.................................C-49

N

NEMA Ratings B-50, D-76
NEMA Ratings, Solenoid Valves C-22,C-24

NEMA-4 and NEMA-4X Explanation............H-4
NPT Adaptors & Bushings......................C-43
NPT Feedthroughs C-46,C-48
NPT Plug/Couple..............................C-46
New Product Showcase ....**Section A**

O

O-Rings...B-27,B-29
O-Rings, Buna-N...................................B-34

P

Panel Meter for Displacement Transducers J-20
Panel Meters, Digital ....D-5 to D-24
Panel Meters, Frequency Indicating..D-13, D-14
Panel Meters, Large Display D-17, D-18
Panel Meters, Selection Guide D-5, D-6
Panel Meters, Strain Gage....D-7 to D-10, D-20,
E-21, E-22
Panel Meters, Transducer Indicating....D-5, D-6,
D-11 to D-16, D-19
Panel Mount Dial Gauges G-11, G-12
Passthroughs.....................................C-48
Photo-Optic ....**(See Optical)**
Photo-Optic Pressure Meter D-57
Pins, Thermocouple...............................C-50
Plastic Melt Transducers ....B-91 to B-96
Plastic Tubing...................................C-41
Platform Load Cells ....**(See Load Cells)**
Plug-In Boards..........................D-105 to D-108
Plugs..C-42
Pneumatic Instrumentation.....B-50, C-29, C-30,
D-59, D-61
Pneumatic Pressure Transducers .....**Section B**
Portable Calibrators.................**(See Calibrator)**
Portable Pressure Meter, Benchtop D-31
Power Cord......................................C-8
Power Supplies..........................C-8 to C-12
Pressure Calibrators.................D-43 to D-66
Pressure Controllers....................D-38 to D-42
Pressure Dial Gauges ....**(See Dial Gauges)**
Pressure Feedthroughs.................C-45 to C-47
Pressure Gage Adapter...........................C-42
Pressure Gage, Digital.............................C-7
Pressure Gage, Portable ....**Section D**
Pressure Gauges.................**(See Dial Gauges)**
Pressure Indicators ....**Section D**
Pressure Measurement Instrumentation,
Introduction to....................................D-3
Pressure Meter, Handheld D-25, D-50
Pressure Pump...................................D-59
Pressure Recorders ....D-68, D-85 to D-92
Pressure Reference ....**Section Z**
Pressure Sensors ....**(See Transducer)**
Pressure Snubbers...............................C-7
Pressure Standards, Digital.....D-55, D-56, D-58
Pressure Switches ....**Section H**
Pressure Switches, General
Purpose..................H-10, H-13, H-14 , H-18
Pressure Switches, Miniature H-7, H-11
Pressure Test Gages ....G-21 to G-24
Pressure Test Plugs.............................C-42
Pressure Transducers...................**Section B**
Pressure Transmitters ....B-49 to B-88
Pressure Transmitters, Smart ......B-79 to B-82
Printed Circuit Boards ....D-105 to D-108
Process Controller..............................D-37
Process Loop Analyzer...........................D-45
Process Loop Indicator ....D-33 to D-36
Process Meters D-5, D-6
Process Scanner D-24
Protective Coatings..............................E-18
Putty for Strain Gages...........................E-18

R

RS-232 Communications, Meters .....**Section D**
RS-232 Output C-15, C-16,C-58
Recorders ....D-72 to D-92
Reducing Adaptors C-43

Reducing Bushings C-43
Reference, Pressure ....**Section Z**
Relays..C-36
Resistors for Strain Gages.......................E-17
Ribbon Cable C-38

S

Scanners, Process................................D-26
Selection Guide, Dial Gauges G-3, G-4
Selection Guide, Digital Panel Meter.....D-5, D-6
Selection Guide, Linear Displacement
Measurement J-3, J-4
Selection Guide, Load Cells F-5, F-6
Selection Guide, Pressure Dial Gauges...G-3, G-4
Selection Guide, Pressure Switches H-5, H-6
Signal Analyzer D-45
Signal Conditioners C-13, C-17, C-21,E-25
Signal Conditioners for Displacement
Transducers J-6, J-18, J-19
Silicone Resin...................................E-18
Slip Ring Assembly C-37
Smart Pressure Transmitter ....B-79 to B-82
Snubbers, Pressure C-7
Software ....D-105 to D-108
Solenoid Valves ....C-22 to C-25
Solenoid Valves Selection Guideline C-23
Solid State Time C-31
Square Root Transducer B-82, B-87, B-88
Strain Gage ....**Section E**
Strain Gage Adhesives E-17
Strain Gage Amplifiers.........C-14, E-23 to E-25
Strain Gage Bridge Resistors E-17
Strain Gage Coverings...........................E-18
Strain Gage Kits...................................E-31
Strain Gage Meters......D-7, D-9, D-10, E-21, E-22
Strain Gage Monitoring System E-21, E-22
Strain Gage Terminal Pads......................E-17
Strain Gages, Accessories........................E-17
Strain Gages, Axial Strains E-11
Strain Gages, Bending Strains E-12
Strain Gages, Crack Propagation E-16
Strain Gages, Full Bridge Diaphragm.........E-16
Strain Gages, General Purpose E-8
Strain Gages, Long Grid E-9
Strain Gages, Perpendicular Grid Type E-11
Strain Gages, Pre-Wired Gages E-10
Strain Gages, Rosettes E-13, E-14
Strain Gages, Rosettes, Corner..................E-15
Strain Gages, Rosettes, Pre-Wired E-14
Strain Gages, Specifications.....................E-7
Strain Gages, Stress Relief.......................E-15
Strain Gages, Torque E-12
Strain Sensors F-27, F-28
Submersible Pressure Transducer ...B-89, B-90
Summing Box F-22
Switches, Pressure ....**Section H**

T

Tank Weighing F-20, F-21
Tape...C-44
Technical Article: Basic Load Cell
Principles......................................F-3, F-4
Technical Article: Installing Thin
Beam Load Cells F-26
Technical Articles ....**Section Z**
Technical Books ....**Section Y**
Technical Data Section.........................Z-27
Technical Information: Intro to Pressure
Measurement Systems.............................B-3
Technical Information: Introduction to Pressure
Measurement Instrumentation...................D-3
Technical Information: NEMA
Enclosure Ratings..................................H-4
Technical Information: Positioning
Strain Gages..................................E-5, E-6
Technical Information: Practical
Strain Gage Measurements ....E-31 to E-58
Technical Information: Pressure Control H-3

Technical Information: Solenoid
Valve Selection Guidelines C-23
Technical Information: Strain Gage Data.....E-3, E-4
Teflon Tape.....................................C-44
Temperature Labels E-30
Temperature Measurement
Meters D-17, D-18, D-71
Temperature Sensors E-30
Temperature Test Plugs...........................C-42
Terminal Pads for Strain Gages...................E-17
Test Dial Gauges ....G-21 to G-24
Test Instrumentation.........D-58, D-65, D-66
Thermocouple Connectors C-47, C-48, C-49
Thermocouple Feedthroughs.........C-45 to C-48
Thermocouple Gage Controller B-88
Thermocouple Meters....D-17, D-18, D-26, D-71
Thermocouple Pins C-6, C-50
Thermocouple Recorder...........................D-76
Thermocouple Slip Ring Assembly C-37
Thermocouples, Self Adhesive E-30
Thermometer....................................D-71
Timer..C-31
Tools C-6, C-50, E-19
Torque Reaction.............................F-30, F-31
Torque Sensors ....F-30 to F-32
Torque, Rotary In-Line.............................F-32
Transducer, Pressure, Amplified
Voltage Output ....B-31 to B-48
Transducer, Pressure, Bi-Directional B-67
Transducer, Pressure, Bridge-Type.....B-8 to B-30
Transducer, Current Output............B-49 to B-88
Transducer, Load Cells
Pressure ....B-55, B-75 to B-88
Transducer, Pressure, European Style
Threads...............................B-100 to B-102
Transducer, Pressure, Flush
Mount Adaptors B-27
Transducer, Pressure, Frequency Output ...B-97
Transducer, Pressure, Hazardous
Location ....B-73 to B-88
Transducer, High Temperature..........B-63, B-91
to B-94,B-99
Transducer, Indicators D-25
Transducer, Load Cells ....**(See Load Cells)**
Transducer, Low Pressure......B-10, B-32, B-34,
B-51, B-52, B-89
Transducer, Melt Pressure ....B-91 to B-94
Transducer, Millivolt Output ....B-9 to B-30
Transducer, Panel Meters.. **(See Panel Meters)**
Transducer, Printed Circuit Board
Mount...........B-10 to B-13, B-31 to B-33, B-49
Transducer, Selection Guide...................B-7, B-8
Transducer, Snubber.............................B-9
Transducer, Pressure, Square Root...........B-83
Transducer, Pressure, Submersible...B-89, B-90
Transducer, Voltage Output ....B-31 to B-48
Transducers, Displacement ..**(See Displacement)**
Transmitter D-35
Tube Clamps C-41
Tubing...C-41

V

Vacuum Dial Gauges........................G-19, G-22
Vacuum Feedthroughs ....C-44 to C-48
Vacuum Monitoring System B-88
Vacuum Pressure Switches H-7
Vacuum , Sensors.............................**Section B**
Valves, Solenoid ....C-22 to C-25
Voltage Analyzer D-45

W

Weighing Systems, Industrial F-20, F-21
Weight Measurement Products ....**Section F**
White Box Cards ....D-105 to D-108
Wire C-38

Z

X-Y Recorder D-75

PART NUMBER INDEX

A

100 Series	G-27
102 Series	G-27
2-013-P	B-27
2-013-V	B-27
2-018-P	B-27
2-018-V	B-27
302 Series	G-27
555	D-82
585	D-82
595	D-82
70-A	H-20
790	D-75
791	D-75
ABM 75	E-1
AD-1N	B-27
AD-1SF	B-27
AD-1SS	B-27
AD-2SS	B-27
AD-3SS	B-27
AD-4N	B-27
AD-5SS	B-27
AD-6SS	B-27
AK-22	E-31

B

B-FER	C-43
BRLK	C-43
BRLK	C-43

C

C-1800	D-111
CL300 Series	D-45
CL424	D-47
CN-2000	D-37
CN4400	D-39
CN4500	D-39
CN4600	D-39
CN4700	D-39
CP (CLAMP)	C-41
CT-485	D-89
CT585	D-68
CT1000A Series	D-85
CT-1100A	D-85
CT-1200A	D-85
CT-1300A	D-85
CX-105	C-3
CX-106	C-3
CX-136	C-3
CX-340	B-94

D

D1000 Series	D-95
D2000 Series	D-95
D3000 Series	D-98
D4000 Series	D-98
DAS-8	D-111
DAS-16	D-113
DFG51	F-29
DMD-21	E-21
DMD-22	E-22
DMD-465	C-14
DMD-519	E-23
DMD-520	E-24
DP40	D-7
DP41	D-7
DP-87	D-10
DP-88	D-10
DP100 Series	D-23
DP205	D-21
DP302	D-19
DP-350	D-15
DP-352	D-15
DP-352-KIT	D-15
DP-354	D-16
DP-409	B-95
DP-434	B-95
DP460	D-22
DP461	D-22
DP462	D-22
DP-760	D-20
DP-770	D-20
DP914	B-88
DP-2000	D-14
DP-2000H	D-13
DP-2000P	D-12
DP-2000S	D-11
DP3002	D-19
DP-3400	D-27
DP3600	D-28
DP3700	D-28
DP3800	D-28
DPF-50	D-30
DPF-64	D-29
DPG-500	C-7
DPI601	D-59
DP-LVDT	J-20
DPS-3100	D-26
DPS-3200	D-26
DS-41	D-31
DS-205	D-31
DS-350	D-31
DWT-1305D	D-65
DWT-1327D	D-66

E

E-00	D-75
E-02	D-75
E-06	D-75

E (cont.)

EXP-16	D-111
EXP-GP	D-116

F

FLCK	D-67
FMK	G-13
FVL Series	C-27

G

GZ10	F-27

H

HHM1	D-69
HHP100	D-48
HHP-520	D-50
HHP-5100	D-50
HHP-SG	D-25

I

IP210	C-27
IP310	C-29
IP311	C-311

J

JBOX	F-22

K

KFG-C1	E-10
KFG-D16	E-11
KFG-D17	E-14

L

LBC	F-24
LCAA	F-23
LCCA	F-13
LCCB	F-14
LCDA	F-18
LCDB	F-17
LCF	F-9
LCG	F-8
LCH	F-10
LCJA	F-15
LCJB	F-16
LCK	F-7
LCL	F-25
LCS	F-11
LCTB	F-19
LCW	F-12
LD100	J-5
LD200	J-7
LD300	J-9
LD400	J-11
LD500	J-13
LD600	J-15
LDP2	D-17

LDP4 ....D-17	PSS C-9	PX243 ....B-34
LDX-2.................................J-17	PST C-12	PX271 ....B-50
LDX-3.................................J-18	PST4130 ....C-8	PX272 ....B-51
LDX-4.................................J-19	PSW-100 ....H-13	PX273 ....B-55
	PSW-150 ....H-18	PX300 ....B-17

———— M ————

MFT C-44	PSW-170 ....H-11	PX302 ....B-18
MN (BATTERIES) C-26	PSW-180 ....H-11	PX303 ....B-41
MOD D-93	PSW-190 ....H-9	PX305 ....B-60
MTC C-49	PSW-200 ....H-19	PX330 ....B-91
	PSW-300 ....H-15	PX335 ....B-91

———— O ————

OM-3 ....C-17	PSW-350 ....H-17	PX340 ....B-91
OM-5 ....C-21	PSW-370 ....H-21	PX341 ....B-91
OM-6 ....D-101	PSW-400 ....H-23	PX350 ....B-91
OM-160.............................D-93	PSW-520 ....H-7	PX351 ....B-91
OM-1050 ....D-103	PSW-560 ....H-8	PX360 ....B-91
OMD-5508 ....E-27	PSW-570 ....H-8	PX361 ....B-91
OPNE C-30	PSW-580 ....H-12	PX370 ....B-91
OPNO C-30	PSW-700 ....H-22	PX371 ....B-91
	PSW-800 ....H-10	PX380 ....B-91

———— P ————

	PTO1F C-4	PX381 ....B-91
PC-5300 ....D-32	PTO 6F C-4	PX390 ....B-91
PCL41 ....D-55	PTM C-48	PX391 ....B-91
PCL-200 ....D-51	PTS C-48	PX410 ....B-58
PCL-401 ....D-44	PU 100 ....E-18	PX418 ....B-89
PCL-402 ....D-44	PX102 ....B-38	PX425 ....B-22
PCL-420 ....D-43	PX105 ....B-36	PX428 ....B-90
PCL-422 ....D-43	PX106 ....B-97	PX440 ....B-64
PCL423.............................D-47	PX120 ....B-16	PX510 ....B-48
PCL425.............................D-60	PX126 ....B-12	PX540 ....B-62
PCL-2500 ....D-57	PX136 ....B-11	PX541 ....B-67
PCL-3000 ....D-58	PX141 ....B-31	PX542 ....B-63
PCL-5000 ....D-63	PX142 ....B-31	PX543 ....B-63
PCL-5100 ....D-63	PX143 ....B-31	PX600 ....B-29
PCL-701 ....D-49	PX149 ....B-49	PX602 ....B-20
PCL-730 ....D-54	PX154 ....B-52	PX603 ....B-43
PFT2 ....C-46	PX155 ....B-52	PX605 ....B-61
PFTCC C-47	PX160 ....B-13	PX610 ....B-30
PFTFS C-45	PX161 ....B-32	PX612 ....B-20
PGC G-5	PX162 ....B-32	PX613 ....B-43
PGC G-5	PX163 ....B-32	PX615 ....B-61
PGD G-17	PX170 ....B-10	PX621-G10V B-45
PGF G-16	PX176 ....B-37	PX621-GI B-65
PGH G-19	PX180 ....B-15	PX623-G10V B-45
PGJ G-19	PX181 ....B-35	PX623-GI B-65
PGL G-21	PX182 ....B-56	PX633 ....B-38
PGP G-11	PX184 ....B-33	PX635 ....B-57
PGS G-13	PX185 ....B-33	PX643 ....B-38
PGT-25 ....G-21	PX212 ....B-19	PX645 ....B-57
PGT-35 ....G-21	PX213 ....B-42	PX653 ....B-39
PGT-45 ....G-27	PX215 ....B-59	PX654 ....B-40
PGT-60 ....G-27	PX216 ....B-71	PX655 ....B-53
PS-2 ....C-7	PX222 ....B-100	PX656 ....B-54
PS-4 ....C-7	PX223 ....B-101	PX725 ....B-72
PS-8 ....C-7	PX225 ....B-102	PX750-DI B-84
PSC C-10	PX236 ....B-14	PX750-GI B-79
	PX241 ....B-34	PX750-SQ B-86
	PX242 ....B-34	PX761 ....B-75

PX763	B-79	
PX800	B-24	
PX811	B-25	
PX880	B-73	
PX903	B-47	
PX905	B-69	
PX906	B-21	
PX931	B-23	
PX941	B-68	
PX945	B-70	
PX951	B-44	
PX960	B-98	
PXTX-703	C-13	

——— R ———

RA (ADAPTORS)	C-43
RB (BUSHINGS)	C-43
RC (CABLE)	C-38
RD100	D-83
RD101	D-83
RD102	D-83
RD103	D-83
RD106	D-83
RD255	D-72
RD288	D-72
RD292	D-72
RD-790	D-75
RD-1201	D-81
RD1202	D-81
RD-2010	D-77
RD2020	D-77
RD2030	D-77
RD-2081	D-80
RD6110	D-73
RD6111	D-73
RD-I	D-77
RD-MV	D-77
RD-PH	D-77
RD-SG	D-77
RD-TC	D-77
RDX6110	D-73
RDX6111	D-73
REC	F-24
RES-120	E-17
RES-250	E-17
RES-350	E-17
RH411	D-71

——— S ———

SA1	E-30
SDX	D-69
SG 250	E-18
SG401	E-17
SG496	E-17
SG-CP1	E-16
SG-DG11	E-16
SG-DY11	E-12

SG-DY13	E-12
SG-DY41	E-12
SG-DY43	E-12
SG-KIT	E-19
SG-LY11	E-8
SG-LY13	E-8
SG-LY40	E-9
SG-LY41	E-9
SG-LY43	E-9
SG-RY11	E-13
SG-RY13	E-13
SG-RY21	E-15
SG-RY23	E-15
SG-RY31	E-13
SG-RY33	E-13
SG-RY41	E-13
SG-RY43	E-13
SG-RY71	E-13
SG-RY73	E-13
SG-RY91	E-15
SG-RY93	E-15
SG-SR11	E-15
SG-SR13	E-15
SG-SR41	E-15
SG-SR43	E-15
SG-XY11	E-11
SG-XY13	E-11
SG-XY21	E-12
SG-XY23	E-12
SG-XY41	E-11
SG-XY43	E-11
SL-301	D-73
SL-650	D-72
SL-651	D-72
SL-652	D-72
SL-653	D-72
SMTC	C-5
SP100	J-5
SP150	J-5
SP200A	J-5
SP300A	J-5
SR-2	C-37
SS-FER	C-43
SSLK	C-43
SSR	C-32
SSRL	C-36
STA-08	D-111
STA-16	D-113
STS	D-69
SV Series	C-22

——— T ———

T-FER	C-43
TFCP	C-38
THERMCOAT	E-31
TL-E	E-30
TL-F	E-30
TP-1	E-17
TP-2	E-17
TP-3	E-17

TQ101	F-30
TQ102	F-31
TQ501	F-32
TWA1	F-20
TWA2	F-20
TWA3	F-21
TWA4	F-21
TX (WIRE)	C-38
TX-21	D-34
TX-81	D-33
TX-82	D-35
TX-83	D-35
TX-84	D-35
TY (TUBING)	C-41

——— U ———

U24Y101	C-11
U48Y40	C-11
UBK	G-13

——— W ———

WB-AAI-B	D-105
WB-AAI-M2	D-117
WB-AAI-SE	D-117
WB-AIO	D-105
WB-ASC	D-105
WB-AVO	D-109
WB-FAI-B	D-105
WB-FAI-M2	D-117
WB-FAI-SE	D-117
WK6-21C	B-94

——— Z ———

ZB-440	B-64
ZB-510	B-48

Can't find what you're looking for? Call our toll-free Engineering Hotline for assistance! Dial: 1-800-872-9436™ 1-800-USA-WHEN™

Always from OMEGA: Unbeatable Service, Support and Selection!

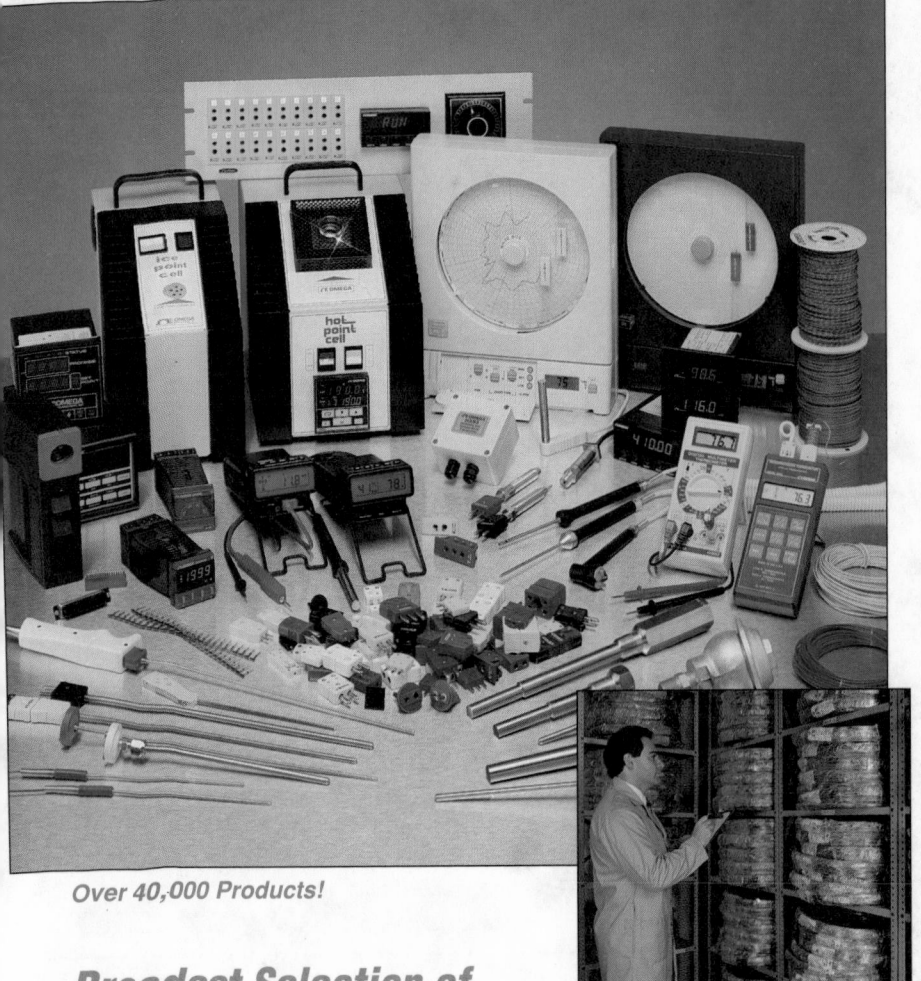

Over 40,000 Products!

Custom Engineering and Special Calibrations

- ✔ OMEGA can modify almost any type of sensor to your specification. Sensors may be bent or given special coatings, terminations, or fittings.
- ✔ Custom designs of all sorts are easily accommodated. We'll even give you the CAD drawing!
- ✔ Material certifications, NIST traceable calibrations and other support documentation may be supplied for individual products or entire systems.
- ✔ Instruments may be specially calibrated to your specifications.
- ✔ Total system design, from process sensors to data acquisition and control hardware and software.

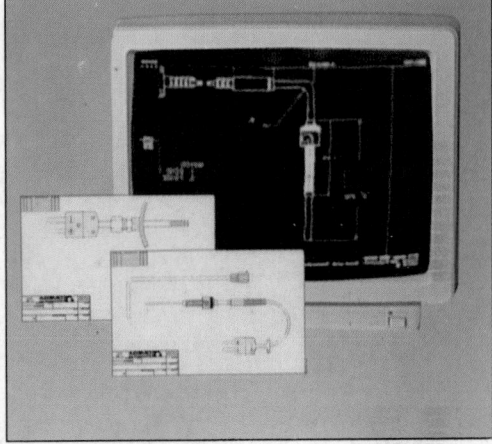

State-of-the-Art Computer-Aided Design and Manufacturing

Broadest Selection of Quality Instrumentation Available

- ✔ Each year OMEGA manufactures millions of feet of thermocouple wire, hundreds of thousands of sensors, and a multitude of instrumentation.
- ✔ Thousands of items available off-the-shelf for fast delivery.
- ✔ Wide selection of instruments from our Temperature, Pressure and Strain, Flow and Level, pH and Conductivity, Electric Heaters and Data Acquisition handbooks. Over 4,500 full color pages!
- ✔ Full operations in the United Kingdom including Technical Sales, Customer Service, Repair/Calibration and Stocking Center.

Comprehensive Customer Service and Support

- ✔ Remember those convenient loaner cars? OMEGA maintains a stock of loaner equipment (at no charge) for customer emergencies. We do everything possible to keep your system running!
- ✔ OMEGACARE™ extended warranties of an additional one, two, and three years are available for many products.
- ✔ Repairs and recalibrations are made simple by our efficient Customer Service group.
- ✔ Calibrate your probes and equipment to NIST standards.
- ✔ Ask about our new 4-point thermocouple calibration services.

Our new Volume 28 Handbooks are loaded with hundreds of exciting new products! There's sure to be something of interest to you!

OMEGA: The Company Behind the Handbooks!

Expert Technical Support

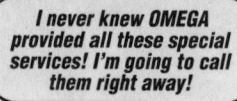

> *I never knew OMEGA provided all these special services! I'm going to call them right away!*

- ✔ Free unlimited expert assistance from our staff of degreed engineers via a toll-free call. Let us be your off-site engineer!
- ✔ We make "house calls!" Our technical experts will do on-site visits to help set up and troubleshoot equipment.
- ✔ We'll walk you through product setup, or set up your system in advance.
- ✔ OMEGA can assemble complete systems, from sensor to software, for total process measurement and control.
- ✔ Let us recommend the right equipment for your application.

Unlimited Technical Assistance - Toll Free!

Comprehensive Technical Training Programs

- ✔ OMEGA's training professionals provide expert "hands-on" application training.
- ✔ OMEGA's exclusive complimentary Customer Days training programs are tailored to the needs of your organization in two-day sessions for groups up to 140.
- ✔ Individual courses cover topics of your choice, including basic overviews, refresher courses, or in-depth training.
- ✔ The OMEGA Technical Center, at OMEGA's Stamford, Connecticut, headquarters, features a fully equipped auditorium plus complete training laboratory—an ideal learning environment.

OMEGAfax™

OMEGA's 24 Hour-a-Day On-Demand Information System

OMEGAFax numbers are listed in all of our magazine advertising. To receive information on any item, call **1-800-848-4271** from any Touch-Tone phone and enter the *OMEGAfax* numbers for the products of interest. Information will be faxed to you automatically!

Building 3 of OMEGA's Stamford, Connecticut, Corporate Headquarters